Symbols of Common Elements

Ag	silver	Cu	copper	O	oxygen
Al	aluminum	F	fluorine	P	phosphorus
As	arsenic	Fe	iron	Pb	lead
Au	gold	H	hydrogen	Pt	platinum
Ba	barium	Hg	mercury	S	sulfur
Bi	bismuth	I	iodine	Sb	antimony
Br	bromine	K	potassium	Sn	tin
C	carbon	Mg	magnesium	Sr	strontium
Ca	calcium	Mn	manganese	Ti	titanium
Cl	chlorine	N	nitrogen	U	uranium
Co	cobalt	Na	sodium	W	tungsten
Cr	chromium	Ni	nickel	Zn	zinc

Symbols of Common Polyatomic Ions

$C_2H_3O_2^-$	acetate	$Cr_2O_7^{2-}$	dichromate	NH_4^-	ammonium
ClO^-	hypochlorite	HCO_3^-	hydrogen carbonate	NO_3^-	nitrate
ClO_2^-	chlorite		bicarbonate	NO_2^-	nitrite
ClO_3^-	chlorate	H_3O^+	hydronium	O_2^{2-}	peroxide
ClO_4^-	perchlorate	HPO_4^{2-}	hydrogen phosphate	OH^-	hydroxide
CN^-	cyanide	HSO_3^-	hydrogen sulfite	PO_4^{3-}	phosphate
CO_3^{2-}	carbonate	HSO_4^-	hydrogen sulfate	SO_3^{2-}	sulfite
CrO_4^{2-}	chromate	MnO_4^-	permanganate	SO_4^{2-}	sulfate

Other Symbols and Abbreviations

α	alpha rays	gmm	gram molecular mass	m	mass
β	beta rays	H	enthalpy	m	molality
γ	gamma rays	H_f	heat of formation	mL	milliliter (*volume*)
Δ	change in	hr	hour	mm	millimeter (*length*)
δ^-, δ^+	partial atomic charge	h	Planck's constant	mol	mole (*amount*)
λ	wavelength	Hz	hertz (*frequency*)	mp	melting point
π	pi bond	J	joule (*energy*)	N	normality
σ	sigma bond	K	Kelvin (*temperature*)	n	neutron
ν	frequency	K_a	acid dissociation constant	n	number of moles
amu	atomic mass unit	K_b	base dissociation constant	n	principal quantum number
aq	aqueous solution	K_b	molal boiling point	P	pressure
atm	atmosphere (*pressure*)		elevation constant	p^+	proton
bp	boiling point	K_{eq}	equilibrium constant	Pa	pascal (*pressure*)
°C	degree Celsius (*temperature*)	K_f	molal freezing point	R	ideal gas constant
c	speed of light in a vacuum		depression constant	S	entropy
cm	centimeter (*length*)	K_w	ion product constant	s	second
D	density		for water	s	solid
E	energy	K_{sp}	solubility product constant	SI	International System
e^-	electron	kcal	kilocalorie (*energy*)		of Units
fp	freezing point	kg	kilogram (*mass*)	STP	standard temperature
G	Gibb's free energy	kPa	kilopascal (*pressure*)		and pressure
g	gram (*mass*)	L	liter (*volume*)	T	temperature
g	gas	*l*	liquid	$t_{1/2}$	half-life
gam	gram atomic mass	M	molarity	V	volume
gfm	gram formula mass	m	meter (*length*)	v	velocity

Addison-Wesley

Chemistry

Teacher's Edition

Antony C. Wilbraham

Dennis D. Staley

Candace J. Simpson

Michael S. Matta

Addison-Wesley Publishing Company

Menlo Park, California ▪ Reading, Massachusetts ▪ Don Mills, Ontario
Wokingham, England ▪ Amsterdam ▪ Sydney ▪ Singapore
Tokyo ▪ Madrid ▪ Bogota ▪ Santiago ▪ San Juan

Contributing Authors

William S. Frazer, Santa Teresa High School, San Jose, CA

David M. Olsen, Merced Union High School District, Merced, CA

Reviewers and Consultants

Roy J. Arlotto, Louis E. Dieruff High School, Allentown, PA

E. Patricia Buchanan, Menlo-Atherton High School, Menlo Park, CA

Carolyn Csongradi, Sequoia High School, Redwood City, CA

Marilyn Linner, Fulton High School, Fulton, IL

Samuel M. Meyer, Southwest Miami High School, Miami, FL

John Moore, John F. Kennedy High School, Richmond, CA

Margaret Nicholson, Lawrence Hall of Science, Berkeley, CA

Lee Carollo Pforsich, Oak Grove High School, San Jose, CA

Robert Sund, Wichita Falls High School, Wichita Falls, TX

Costella Watson, Tennyson High School, Hayward, CA

Bonnie Williams, Delany High School, Timonium, MD

Addison-Wesley Staff

Editor: Cathy Robertson

Designer: Linda S. Stinchfield

Photo Editor: Margee H. Huntzicker

Cover Photo:
A yellow precipitate of cadmium sulfide, CdS, forms spontaneously when clear aqueous solutions of sodium sulfide, Na_2S, and cadmium nitrate, $Cd(NO_3)_2$ are mixed. **Caution:** *Sodium sulfide is an irritant. Avoid skin or eye contact with this and all other chemicals.* Photo taken expressly for Addison-Wesley by Stephen Frisch.

ISBN 0-201-21094-0   ISBN 0-201-20874-1T

BCDEFGHIJKL–VH–89876

A Comprehensive Text
To Match Your Curriculum

All core concepts and supplementary topics are presented in a clear and well-organized format. Each chapter follows a logical sequence so that as you build ideas, you build understanding.

Turn to page T16 for a course planning guide that lists chapter sections for regular and honors classes.

A Stimulating Program

That Motivates Students

Student Edition

- Clear, readable text in a well-organized, easy-to-follow format allows students with diverse abilities to understand chemistry.

- More coverage of the basics with frequent review of fundamentals, builds student understanding of principles and processes.

- More exercises develop students' problem-solving abilities and provide examples of applications.

- Chemical principles are tied to real life applications, current technologies, and future developments.

Laboratory Manuals

- Budget-saving ideas allow you to tailor the laboratory exercises to your school's needs and resources.

- One core lab exercise for each chapter and additional lab exercises for enrichment provide a flexible laboratory program.

- Consumable and nonconsumable editions allow you to choose the best package for your school.

- The informative teacher's edition contains answers, organizational tips, and detailed directions for preparing all the laboratory exrcises.

A Flexible Program
That Meets Your Teaching Needs

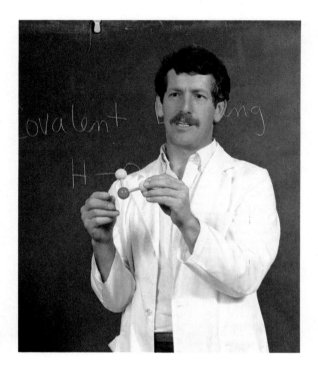

Teacher's Edition

- Easy-to-implement ideas and suggestions support your need for flexible lesson planning and effective delivery.

- Safe and stimulating demonstrations are designed to bring chemical properties and principles to life for your students.

- Success-oriented teaching tips and classroom-tested suggestions promote student understanding and interest in chemistry.

Teacher's Resource Books

- **Tests and Quizzes** are on blackline masters for effective evaluation.

- **Teaching Diagrams** for overhead transparencies support your daily lectures and discussions.

- The **Skills Practice Book** provides strong reinforcement materials and includes Chapter Objective Worksheets, Skillsheets, Pre Lab Assignments, and Reviewsheets.

- **Issues in Chemical Technology** provide enrichment that broadens the curriculum.

- A **Solutions Manual** provides complete solutions to Student Text questions and problems to allow for easy grading and/or self-checking.

Software

- **Information Laboratory** teaches students research skills, provides additional problem solving practice, and helps students to conceptually establish relationships between data.

- **Test Generator** saves you time as you custom prepare tests for your students.

A Clearly Written Text

With a Focus on Understanding

With **Addison-Wesley Chemistry** your students will learn more easily and thoroughly. Text material relates chemical processes and principles to everyday experiences.

These **Addison-Wesley Chemistry** features make the text easy to read and understand.

- Appropriate chemical terminology is used in short, understandable sentences to maintain a high school reading level.

- Key terms appear in boldface type.

- Definitions of key terms are given in context when each of the terms is first introduced.

- Main ideas for each section are annotated in the Student Text.

- Safety notes encourage careful laboratory practices and raise student awareness of possible hazards.

- Questions within the captions invite students to apply their knowledge and reasoning skills.

2·13 Specific Heat Capacity

The quantity of heat required to change an object's temperature by exactly 1°C is the **heat capacity** *of that object.* Heat capacity depends partly on mass. The greater the mass of the object, the greater its heat capacity. A massive steel girder, for example, has a much larger heat capacity than a small steel nail. Likewise, the heat capacity of a cup of water is much greater than a drop of water. Besides varying with mass, the heat capacity of an object also depends on the kind of substance from which it is made. For this reason, different substances of the same mass may have different heat capacities.

The **specific heat capacity,** *or simply the* **specific heat,** *of a substance is the quantity of heat required to raise the temperature of 1 g of the substance 1°C.* Water has a high specific heat, and metals have low specific heats (Table 2·9). One calorie of heat raises the temperature of 1 g of water by 1°C. The same amount of heat raises the temperature of 1 g of iron by 9°C. Therefore iron has a specific heat only one-ninth that of water. Specific heat is important because it can be used to calculate how many calories are required to heat a known mass of substance from one temperature to another.

$$\text{Specific heat} \left(\frac{J}{g \times °C} \right) = \frac{\text{heat (J)}}{\text{mass (g)} \times \text{change in temperature (°C)}}$$

Using the unit calories, the equation is as follows.

$$\text{Specific heat} \left(\frac{cal}{g \times °C} \right) = \frac{\text{heat (cal)}}{\text{mass (g)} \times \text{change in temperature (°C)}}$$

■ Specific heat measures the ability of a substance to store heat energy.

Safety

Because of its high heat capacity, hot water can cause very serious burns. Use care when heating water in the laboratory.

Warm soup warms a person more than hot toast because soup has a higher heat capacity.

Figure 2·25
Which food will warm you up most when you are cold: warm soup or hot toast? Why?

Table 2·9	Specific Heat Capacities of Some Common Substances	
	Specific heat capacity	
Substance	[cal/(g × °C)]	[J/(g × °C)]
Water	1.00	4.18
Grain alcohol	0.58	2.4
Ice	0.50	2.1
Wood	0.42	1.8
Steam	0.40	1.7
Chloroform	0.23	0.96
Aluminum	0.21	0.88
Glass	0.12	0.50
Iron	0.11	0.46
Silver	0.057	0.24
Mercury	0.033	0.14

42   Chapter 2   Scientific Measurement

A Well Organized Text

That Makes Learning Easier

The central topics of chemistry are introduced in early chapters and later discussed in greater depth as students' basic knowledge and understanding grows.

- Diagrams clarify abstract concepts.

- Concepts are fully explained, reviewed, and reinforced.

- Enrichment topics are clearly identified so that the student knows they are of lesser importance.

- Numerous photographs help acquaint students with unfamiliar materials and processes.

- Annotations that review, reinforce, and enrich appear throughout the Student Text.

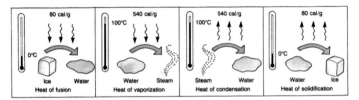

Figure 9·26
The heat of fusion equals the heat of solidification. The heat of vaporization equals the heat of condensation.

Since vaporization and condensation are reverse processes, the heat of vaporization of a substance must be equal in magnitude to its heat of condensation. As you might expect, various liquids have different heats of vaporization and boiling points. This is because their intermolecular attractive forces vary.

9·C Plasma: The Fourth State of Matter

What happens if you heat a gas to a very high temperature? First the kinetic energy of the molecules becomes great enough to separate molecules into atoms. Then at even higher temperatures, electrons are stripped off the gaseous atoms. The substance now consists of a mixture of electrons and positive ions. This new substance behaves like ordinary gases in some ways. It also has some very peculiar properties. It is really a fourth state of matter, called *plasma*.

A gas can be ionized at low temperatures by common events. Partial plasmas are created in fluorescent lights, neon signs, lightning bolts, and even in flames. In all of these examples, only a few of the atoms present are ionized at any moment. Even these will not remain ionized. A free electron will lose energy when it collides with anything, including other particles or the walls of its container. When it has lost enough energy, it can be recaptured by a gas ion. Because of this, plasmas in the atmosphere or those created in lights and flames are only weakly ionized.

A tremendous amount of energy is required to create highly ionized plasmas. Some materials can be mostly converted into plasmas at temperatures of 50 000 K–100 000 K. These are called "cold plasmas." In contrast, some plasmas require temperatures of 10 000 000 K–100 000 000 K and more. These "hot plasmas" are the material of the stars. Scientists are trying to create hot plasmas to produce energy by nuclear fusion, the same process that produces energy in our sun. No material can contain matter at these temperatures. In the sun the hot plasmas are held together by gravity due to the huge mass of the sun. In the laboratory, of course, the mass of plasma is much too small to be held together by gravity.

Figure 9·27
The aurora borealis is caused by the presence of low density plasma in the upper atmosphere.

The fusion process and the problems faced in producing and containing hot plasma are described in Section 24·7.

9·C Plasma: The Fourth State of Matter **215**

Problem-Solving Skills

You Can Teach With Confidence

Problem-solving skills will become second nature for your students as they progress through the text.

- Chapter 3 introduces problem-solving techniques with a thorough presentation of how to use dimensional analysis.

- Numerous examples throughout the text demonstrate how to approach each type of problem.

- Problem-solving exercises encourage the students to practice using concepts as soon as the ideas are introduced.

- Students can refresh important math skills with the Math Review in Appendix B.

Appendix C of the Student Text contains complete solutions to all in-text exercises in the Student Text. (Answers and solutions to chapter-end problems are available in the Teacher's Edition and Solutions Manual only.)

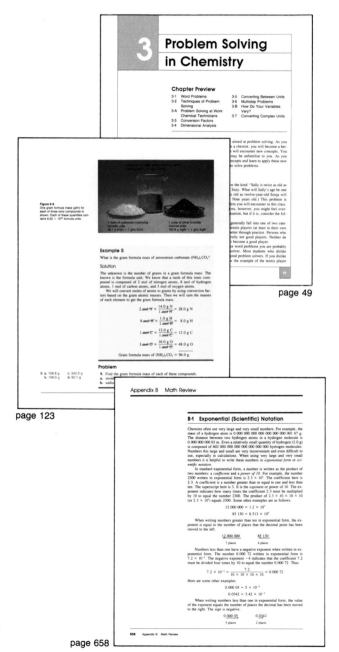

page 49

page 123

page 658

Plenty of Practice

For Every Student

Addison-Wesley Chemistry offers an extensive variety of problem-solving exercises to challenge and develop student skills. Four problem-solving sets and a list of research projects for further study appear at the end of each chapter. You can tailor assignments to challenge the interest and ability of each student.

Practice Questions and Problems

14. A metal cylinder contains 1 mol of nitrogen gas at STP. What will happen to the pressure if another mole of gas is added to the cylinder but the temperature and volume do not change? *10·1*

Mastery Questions and Problems

41. If 4.50 g of methane gas (CH_4) is introduced into an evacuated 2.00-L container at 35°C, what is the pressure in the container, in atmospheres? *10·10*

Review Questions and Problems

51. Calculate the gram formula mass of each of ___ances.
___H$_3$O$_2$)$_2$ **c.** $C_{12}H_{22}O_{11}$

Challenging Questions and Problems

61. Oxygen is produced in the laboratory by heating potassium nitrate.

$$2KNO_3 \longrightarrow 2KNO_2 + O_2$$

Research Projects

1. How did early hot air balloonists such as the Montgolfier brothers influence the work of Charles and Gay-Lussac?

Practice Questions and Problems

- These questions and problems review concepts in the order in which they are presented in each chapter. Section numbers tell students where to find help when needed.

Mastery Questions and Problems

- These questions and problems appear in random order to encourage students to come up with solutions on their own without referring to the text.

Review Questions and Problems

- Key concepts and skills from previous chapters are reviewed at appropriate intervals as students progress through the text.

Challenging Questions and Problems

- Questions requiring higher reasoning abilities and the integration of information are included to challenge students with above-average skills.

Research Projects

- Special research projects offer students stimulating opportunities to expand problem-solving and research skills in the laboratory and library.

New Ideas

For Teaching Chemistry

From the most complex concepts to examples of how chemistry impacts daily life, **Addison-Wesley Chemistry** helps you create a course that's stimulating and relevant. The Teacher's Edition is organized for efficient lesson planning and effective delivery. Whether presenting chemistry fundamentals or cutting edge applications, you can successfully teach **Addison-Wesley Chemistry** for maximum student understanding and retention.

Chapter Planning Guides

- All the teaching resources are listed in a single place for easy lesson planning.

- The importance and role of each text section is indicated so that you can choose those topics which are best suited for your classes.

Demonstrations

- A list of materials for each demonstration saves you time and guess-work.

- A numbered step-wise procedure makes the directions easy to follow.

- Safety notes are included whenever necessary.

Teaching Suggestions

The Teaching Notes appear where you need them—at the beginning of each chapter.

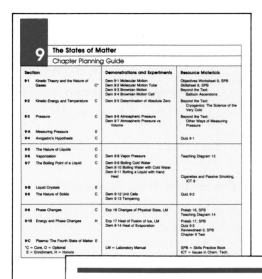

Demonstrations

17·1 Temperature and Reaction Rate

Concept: Increasing temperature increases reaction rate.

Materials: 3 effervescent antacid tablets, 3 flasks, ice, hot water, safety goggles, timer with second hand.

Procedure: 1. Put ice, room temperature water, and hot water in three different flasks. 2. Add a tablet to each flask. 3. Record the time for each reaction to go to completion. Ice is the slowest and hot water the fastest.

Teaching Suggestions

2·1 The Importance of Measurement

To open this section, ask the students to describe some common but interesting object which you have placed before them. (Use something which involves energy, such as a burning candle, or an electrically driven or wind-up toy, to illustrate that measurement involves more that just material objects.) Ask them to make their descriptions as complete as possible. Depending on the time available, a list of

Full Teaching Support

Right at Your Fingertips

All the supplements that will save you time are available in an easy-to-use format.

Tests and Quizzes

These blackline masters provide you with a quick and easy way to evaluate student progress.

Skills Practice Book

This workbook provides all the additional drill and practice some students need to master chemical concepts and problem-solving skills. Four types of worksheets provide diversity: Chapter Objective Worksheets, Skillsheets, PreLab Assignments, and Reviewsheets. Three formats are available for you to choose from: a student workbook, a teacher's edition, and a book of blackline masters.

Teaching Diagrams

These transparencies and blackline masters save you lecture preparation time and explain the content graphically for students.

Solutions Manual

Complete solutions to student text questions and problems are provided in this easy-to-use guide for grading assignments or student self-checking.

Issues in Chemical Technology

These essays make it easy for your students to relate the basics of chemistry to social and political issues. Topics for student discussion and research are included along with short-answer questions. Both student workbooks and a teacher's edition are available.

A Choice of Laboratory Manuals

To Match Your Needs and Budget

Nonconsumable Edition

This complete laboratory manual teaches students how to make their own data tables and prepare written reports.

Consumable Edition

This complete laboratory manual and record book guides students as they record data, do calculations, and report conclusions.

Teacher's Edition

Complete directions help you plan, supervise, and evaluate the students' laboratory experiences. An overview, organizational tips, sample data, and answers are provided for each laboratory exercise.

Additional Features

- 26 budget-saving core laboratory exercises: one for every chapter of the student text.

- 27 optional experiments for an in-depth supplement to your laboratory program.

- Going Further directions for advanced students to do additional work on their own.

- Clear, safe instructions for disposing of chemicals.

- Complete directions in the Teacher's Edition for preparing all the reagents.

- Easy-to-follow instructions in the Teacher's Edition for reclaiming expensive chemicals.

Plenty of Experiments

For a Complete Laboratory Program

![bar]

Correlation with the Student Text

Ch.		Laboratory Exercise	Ch.		Laboratory Exercise
1		1. The Scientific Method	15		28. Distillation
1	C*	2. Physical and Chemical Properties	15		29. Water of Hydration
1		3. Observing a Chemical Reaction	15		30. Electrolytes and Nonelectrolytes
2	C	4. Mass, Volume, and Density	16	C	31. Factors Affecting Solution Formation
3	C	5. The Specific Heat of a Metal	16		32. Supersaturation
4	C	6. Atomic Structure: Rutherford's Experiment	16		33. Introduction to Chromatography
			16		34. Freezing Point Changes
5	C	7. Identification of Anions and Cations in Solution	17	C	35. Factors Affecting Chemical Reaction Rate
5		8. Precipitation Reactions	17		36. The Clock Reaction
6		9. The Masses of Equal Volumes of Gases	17		37. Disturbing Equilibrium: LeChâtelier's Principle
6	C	10. Empirical Formula Determination	18		38. Acids and Bases: Determination of pH
7		11. Qualitative Analysis	18	C	39. Characteristic Reactions of Acids
7	C	12. Types of Chemical Reactions	19		40. Neutralization Reactions
8	C	13. Quantitative Analysis	19	C	41. Acid–Base Titrations
8		14. Balanced Chemical Equations	19		42. Salt Hydrolysis
8		15. Heat of Reaction	19		43. Buffers
9	C	16. Changes of Physical State	19		44. A Solubility Product Constant
9		17. Heat of Fusion of Ice	20	C	45. Oxidation–Reduction Reactions
10		18. Boyle's Law	20		46. Corrosion
10	C	19. Charles' Law	21	C	47. Electrochemistry
10		20. Graham's Law	22	C	48. Reactivity of Metals
11	C	21. Identification of Metals: Flame Tests	23	C	49. Allotropic Forms of Sulfur
11		22. Introduction to the Spectrophotometer	24	C	50. Radioactivity and Radiation
11		23. Energies of Electrons	25	C	51. Hydrocarbons: A Structural Study
12	C	24. The Periodic Law	26	C	52. Esters of Carboxylic Acids
13	C	25. Crystal Structures	26		53. Preparation of Soap
14	C	26. Model Building			
15	C	27. The Solvent Properties of Water			

*C = Core laboratory exercise

Software Support

To Enhance Student Learning

Test Generator

Evaluation questions are grouped by chapter, so that you can easily design your own tests. You can use as many or as few items as you wish, plus you can make multiple forms of the same exam.

Information Laboratory

This instructional program teaches students how to use a database of chemical principles and facts. Students can obtain research data and observe the interrelationships of chemical concepts and processes.

Companion Software

Distributor: Compress
P.O. Box 102
Wentworth, NH 03282

Compatible Hardware: Apple II, IIe
Subject Areas: The Elements, Inorganic Nomenclature, General Formulas and Equations, Atomic Weights, Percent Composition, Chemaze (game), Gas Laws, pH
Type of Program: Tutorial, Drill and Practice
Documentation: Not needed. Sample disk available.

Distributor: Conduit
University of Iowa Oakdale Campus
Iowa City, IA 52242

Compatible Hardware: Apple, some Tandy, and Commodore
Subject Areas: Chem Lab Simulations: Acid–Base Titration, Ideal Gas Law, Hess' Law, Thermodynamics, Ammonia Synthesis, ID Game, Reaction Kinetics
Type of Program: Simulation, Game
Documentation: User's notes

Distributor: Carolina Biological Supply
2700 York Road
Burlington, NC 27215

Compatible Hardware: Apple II, IIe, TRS 80
Subject Areas: Periodic Table, Moles and Formulas, Chemical Equations, Oxidation, Reduction, Acid–Base Theories, Acid–Base Problems, Solutions, Electron Structure, Bonding in Molecules, Bonding Between Molecules, Gas Relationships, Kinematics, Reaction Kinematics, Equilibrium, Electrochemical Cells, Organic Chemistry
Type of Program: Question/Informational, Interactive
Documentation: User's notes

Distributor: Knowledge Factory, Inc.
2358 Gianera St.
Santa Clara, CA 95054

Compatible Hardware: Apple II, IIe
Subject Area: Atomic Theory and Structure, Stoichiometry, Periodic Table, Chemical Bonding, Molecular Geometry, Properties of Solids and Liquids, Change of State, Solutions and Colligative Properties, Chemical Properties of Selected Elements
Type of Program: Knowledge Base, Tutorial
Documentation: Teacher's Manuals

Distributor: Programs for Learning (PFL)
30 Elm St. (P.O. Box 954)
New Milford, CT 06776

Compatible Hardware: Apple II, IIe, TRS 80, PET-CBM
Subject Areas: Balancing Equations, Metric/English Conversions, Density, Elements, Exponential Notation, Ions, SI Units, Formula Weights, Names and Formulas of Conversion Compounds, Temperature Conversions, Significant Figures.
Type of Program: Drill and Practice
Documentation: Instructor's Guide

Distributor: Project Seraphim
Department of Chemistry
Eastern Michigan University
Ypsilanti, MI 48197

Compatible Hardware: Apple II and IIe, IBM PC, Atari 800, Commodore 14, TRS 80
Subject Areas: All areas of General Chemistry including honors level material
Type of Program: Drill and Practice, Tutorial, Computer Experiments
Documentation: Supplied on disk.

Audiovisual Supplies

To Enhance Student Understanding

The Teaching Notes at the beginning of each chapter include a list of films, filmstrips, and videotapes. It is always a good idea to preview these before showing them to the class.

Addresses of film distributors are given below. Before ordering from a distributor, check local film libraries for the film. It is wise to order films about three months before they are to be used.

Film Distributors

Arthur Makin Productions, Inc.
17 W. 60 St.
New York, NY 10023

Atomic Industrial Forum
7101 Wisconsin Ave.
Bethesda, MD 20814

Audio Visual Narrative Arts, Inc.
Box 9
Pleasantville, NY 10570

Berguall Productions, Inc.
839 Stewart Avenue
Garden City, NY 11530

BFA Educational Media
468 Park Avenue South
New York, NY 10016

Carolina Biological Supply Co.
Burlington, NC 27215

Centron Films
1621 W. 9th St.
Lawrence, KS 66044

Chem Study Films
Wards Natural Science
  Establishment
P.O. Box 92912
Rochester, NY 14692-9012
800-962-2660

Churchill Films
662 N. Robertson Blvd.
Los Angeles, Ca 60069

Charles W. Clark Co. Inc.
168 Express Dr. S.
Brentwood, NY 11717

Coronet Films
65 E. South Water St.
Chicago, IL 60601

EME: Educational Materials &
  Equipment Co.
P.O. Box 17
Pelham, NY 10803

Educational Dimensions Corp.
Box 126
Stamford, CT 06904

Encyclopaedia Brittanica Educ. Corp.
425 W. Michigan Avenue
Chicago, IL 60611

ERDA: Energy Research &
  Development Administration
P.O. Box 62
Oak Ridge, TN 37830

Eye Gate Media Inc.
146-01 Archer Avenue
Jamaica, NY 11435

Films, Inc.
1144 Wilmette Avenue
Wilmette, IL 60091

Focus Media
135 Nassau Blvd.
Garden City, NY 11530

Human Relations Media
175 Tomkins Avenue
Pleasantville, NY 10570

Indiana University
Audio Visual Center
Bloomington, IN 47401

International Film Bureau, Inc.
332 S. Michigan Avenue
Chicago, IL 60604

Kalmia Co.
Dept. C6
Concord, MA 01742

Knowledge Unlimited
Box 52
Madison, WI 53701-0052

Lead Industries Association, Inc.
292 Madison Avenue
New York, NY 10017

McGraw Hill Films
Dept. 4SS
1221 Avenue of the Americas
New York, NY 10020

The Media Guild
11526 Sorrento Valley Road, Suite J
San Diego, CA 92121

Modern Talking Picture Service, Inc.
5000 Park St., N.
St. Peterburg, FL 33709

National Audio Visual Center
National Archives & Records
  Service
Washington, DC 20409

National Film Board of Canada
16th Floor
1251 Avenue of the Americas
New York, NY 10020

National Geographic Society
Educational Services
17th & M Streets, NW
Washington, DC 20036

Prentice-Hall Media, Inc.
150 White Plains Road
Tarrytown, NY 10591

Pyramid Films
P.O. Box 1048
Santa Monica, CA 90406

Random House, Inc.
400 Hahn Road
Westminster, MD 21157

Science & Mankind
Communications Park
Box 200
White Plains, NY 10602

Shell Oil Film Library
433 Sadlier Creek, W. Drive
Indianapolis, IN 46232

Sterling Educational Films
241 East 34th St.
New York, NY 10016·

Stewart-Finley, Inc.
3428 Mansfield Road
Falls Church, VA 22041

Time-Life Video
Time & Life Building
New York, NY 10020

Master Planning Guide

For Addison-Wesley Chemistry

Built-in flexibility makes **Addison-Wesley Chemistry** easy for you to use with your particular classes. The text includes more than enough material for a full-year course. Thus you can choose the topics that best meet the needs and abilities of your students.

This master planning guide gives much of the information you need to develop a yearly plan for your classes. The function of each topic is identified so that you can decide whether or not to include it in your course.

For regular level students we recommend that you plan to teach only the core topics along with any others that are required by your state, county, or local school system. By completing about three chapters every four weeks, the students will cover the entire range of introductory topics in their first year of chemistry.

■ **Core topics** are essential for a complete first year course in chemistry.

■ **Optional topics** are appropriate for regular level chemistry classes that have sufficient time to cover additional material.

■ **Enrichment topics** stimulate student interest in chemistry by means of historical discoveries, laboratory techniques, careers, applications, and technologies. *These topics are not covered by the chapter review or by the evaluation materials.*

■ **Honors topics** are appropriate for fast-moving honors classes which can handle more complex topics.

■ Core   ■ Optional   ■ Enrichment   ■ Honors

■ Core   ■ Optional   ■ Enrichment   ■ Honors

■ Core ■ Optional ▓ Enrichment ░ Honors

Addison-Wesley

Chemistry

Antony C. Wilbraham

Dennis D. Staley

Candace J. Simpson

Michael S. Matta

Addison-Wesley Publishing Company

Menlo Park, California ▪ Reading, Massachusetts ▪ Don Mills, Ontario
Wokingham, England ▪ Amsterdam ▪ Sydney ▪ Singapore
Tokyo ▪ Madrid ▪ Bogota ▪ Santiago ▪ San Juan

Reviewers and Consultants

Roy J. Arlotto, Lewis E. Dieruss High School, Allentown, PA

E. Patricia Buchanan, Menlo-Atherton High School, Menlo Park, CA

Carolyn Csongradi, Sequoia High School, Redwood City, CA

Marilyn Linner, Fulton High School, Fulton, IL

Samuel M. Meyer, Southwest Miami High School, Miami, FL

John Moore, John F. Kennedy High School, Richmond, CA

Margaret Nicholson, Lawrence Hall of Science, Berkeley, CA

Lee Carollo Pforsich, Oak Grove High School, San Jose, CA

Roberta Sund, Wichita Falls High School, Wichita Falls, TX

Costella Watson, Tennyson High School, Hayward, CA

Bonnie Williams, Delany High School, Timonium, MD

ISBN 0-201-21093-2

ABCDEFGHIJKL–VH–89876

Contents

Matter, Change, and Energy

Chapter Planning Guide

Section			Demonstrations and Experiments	Resource Materials
1·1	Chemistry	C*	Dem 1·1 Painted Signs	Objectives Worksheet 1, SPB
			Dem 1·2 Cornstarch Paste	Skillsheet 1, SPB
			Dem 1·3 Luminol	
			Dem 1·4 Fire Writing	
			Dem 1·5 Secret Writing	
			Dem 1·6 Freezing Flowers	
			Dem 1·7 Boiling Water in a Paper Cup	
1·A	Chemical Technology	E		
1·2	The Scientific Method	C	Exp 1 The Scientific Method, LM	Prelab 1, SPB
				Quiz 1·1
1·B	Alchemy and the Birth of Chemistry	E		
1·3	Properties of Matter	C	Dem 1·8 Mass	
1·4	The States of Matter	C	Dem 1·9 Solids, Liquids, and Gases	
			Dem 1·10 Compressibility of Gases and Liquids	
1·5	Physical Changes	C	Dem 23·6 Sublimation of Iodine	Quiz 1·2
			Dem 1·11 Chemical vs Physical Changes	
			Exp 2 Physical and Chemical Properties, LM	Prelab 2, SPB
1·6	Mixtures	C	Dem 1·12 Mixtures vs Pure Substances	Desalination, ICT 1
			Dem 1·13 Mixtures and Compounds	
1·7	Elements and Compounds	C	Dem 1·14 Elements and Compounds	Beyond the Text: Berzelius and the Search for Pure Substances
			Dem 21·6 Electrolysis of Water	
			Dem 7·4 Mercury and Oxygen from Mercury Oxide	
			Dem 1·15 The Decomposition of Sugar	
1·8	Chemical Symbols	C		Quiz 1·3
1·9	Energy	C	Dem 21·5 The Lead Cell	
1·10	Conservation of Energy	C		Teaching Diagram 1
1·11	Chemical Reactions	C	Dem 1·16 An Exothermic Reaction	Beyond the Text: Origin of the Names of Some Elements
			Dem 1·17 Magician's Flash Powder	
			Dem 26·1 A Burning Kerchief	
			Dem 1·18 Copper in Acid	
			Dem 22·6 Silver Chloride and Silver Chromate	
			Exp 3 Observing a Chemical Reaction, LM	Prelab 3, SPB
1·12	Conservation of Mass	C	Dem 1·19 Conservation of Mass	Quiz 1·4
			Dem 1·20 Conservation of Flashbulb Mass	Reviewsheet 1, SPB
				Chapter 1 Test

*C = Core, O = Optional	LM = Laboratory Manual	SPB = Skills Practice Book
E = Enrichment, H = Honors		ICT = Issues in Chem. Tech.

Chapter Objectives

Having studied this chapter and done the problems, the student should be able to:

1. Define chemistry. *1·1*

2. Show how the terms experiment, hypothesis, theory, and law fit into the scientific method. *1·2*

3. Distinguish between matter and a substance. *1·3*

4. Name and characterize the three states of matter. *1·4*

5. Identify physical changes of matter. *1·5*

6. Classify a sample of matter as a substance or a mixture. *1·6*

7. Further classify a sample of matter as homogeneous or heterogeneous. *1·6*

8. State the difference between an element and a compound. *1·7*

9. Write the symbols of common elements, and write the names of common elements given their symbols. *1·8*

10. Distinguish between potential and kinetic energy. *1·9*

11. Give an example of the conversion of one form of energy into another. *1·9*

12. State the law of conservation of energy. *1·10*

13. Classify changes in matter as physical or chemical changes. *1·11*

14. Define a chemical reaction. *1·11*

15. State the law of conservation of mass. *1·12*

Teaching Suggestions

You may want to start the school year with some interesting demonstrations, such as **Demonstrations 1·1** *Painted Signs*, **1·2** *Cornstarch Paste*, **1·3** *Luminol*, **1·4** *Fire Writing*, **1·5** *Secret Writing*, **1·6** *Freezing Flowers*, and **1·7** *Boiling Water in a Paper Cup*.

You can place an emphasis on observation and analysis through these and the other demonstrations noted in the Planning Guide. From five to eight demonstrations may be performed on the first day, with only general and humorous comments. You may quote from Louis Pasteur:

"Chance favors the prepared mind." These demonstrations and an emphasis on personal observation and analysis may help each student to become more open to, and less apprehensive about, chemistry.

1·1 Chemistry

Emphasize that chemistry is an *activity* of human beings and not just a collection of facts. Not only do chemists share a knowledge of chemistry, but they are also doing something with that knowledge. Whether they are teaching, doing research, performing analyses, or finding practical applications and products, they are doing something with their knowledge of chemistry. Point out that the purpose of this course is to help the students gain some understanding of the facts and principles of chemistry so that they can better deal with their world.

To underline just how much all of us are dependent upon chemistry, ask the students to consider their activities during a single day. Ask them to give examples of anything they do which does not in some way involve chemical processes, or contact with chemical products. They will have considerable difficulty! Here you could state how much all forms of industry depend on chemistry.

You could also note that knowledge of chemistry is necessary for good citizenship. Chemistry is involved in issues such as toxic and radioactive wastes, acid rain, drug and alcohol abuse, air and water pollution, and scarcity of resources.

You might also mention the applications of the major branches of chemistry: biochemistry, inorganic chemistry, organic chemistry, analytical chemistry, and physical chemistry. You should also note the careers associated with chemistry, and that men and women have contributed to chemical knowledge and been successful in this field.

1·2 The Scientific Method

Many students think of the scientific method as something they have had to memorize for previous science classes which applies only to science. Point out that it is a common sense approach to solving problems of all kinds. It is an approach which involves proposing a tentative explanation, a solution based on that explanation, a test of the solution, and a revision of the proposal based on the results of the test.

You might wish to propose an everyday type of problem which the students would be likely to encounter and then go through the steps of the scientific method with them, to illustrate how logical it is to use in solving the problem. Typical problems might be:

1. "Your car won't start."

2. "Every time you buy a new fish for your aquarium, it dies."

3. "Whenever you take pictures with your new camera, they come out blurry."

4. "Your grades in a particular course are not as high as you think they should be."

5. "You are invited to a party. When you show up, nobody is there."

Once the students have become familiar with the scientific method in this way, have them do **Experiment 1** *The Scientific Method* in the laboratory manual.

You can discuss the difference between fact and opinion, or how we can know something is true. You can also discuss the different means used to obtain "knowledge": scientific method, insight, authority, tradition, revelation, logical deduction, and personal observation.

The scientific method can be related to modeling. Scale models can be used to learn about large or dangerous systems, such as in the design of ships and airplanes. Computer programs and mathematical equations also model physical systems. The scientific method is used for design, analysis, testing, and quality control.

1·3 Properties of Matter

We define matter in terms of an object occupying space and having mass. However, the amount of space an object takes up is an unreliable measure of the amount of matter it contains. Mass is much more useful for this purpose since it does not depend upon the conditions under which we observe a material (excluding relativistic effects). To illustrate this you might wish to use samples of different materials of equal volume, as in **Demonstration 1·8** *Mass.* Ask the students how we can decide how much matter each contains. The discussion inevitably leads to the conclusion that we must somehow compare their masses to answer the question. (An alternative arrangement would be to bring in samples of substances which have equal masses and note how much their volumes vary.)

It is likely that the students will be thinking in terms of weight instead of mass during this discussion. It is probably not worthwhile to make the distinction at this point except, perhaps, to point out that weight is the result of the interaction of a gravitational field with the mass of an object and can vary from place to place. Mass on the other hand is unchanging. Since the weight of an object in a given location is proportional to the mass of an object, we can use them interchangeably, even if we are technically incorrect. The relation between mass and weight is illustrated by the experiences of astronauts in free fall or on the moon.

The knowledge of matter through the five senses can also be discussed. The smell, taste, sound when struck, texture, heaviness, color, and shininess are some points to note.

For advanced students, you might define matter in relation to inertia. The mass measures how much an object

tries to keep its state of motion: it is harder to start motion and harder to stop it the more massive an object is.

1·4 The States of Matter

Students will have little trouble in grasping the basic differences between gases, liquids, and solids. **Demonstration 1·9** *Solids, Liquids, and Gases* can be done to show them. However, you may wish to contrast the differences in compressibility between gases and liquids, as in **Demonstration 1·10** *Compressibility of Gases and Liquids.*

You may also note the ways the three phases occupy space. Gases act to fill up any space they are in. Liquids take the shape of their container. Solids have a definite shape and volume already.

Also you can ask if the mass differs when one substance is in different states.

1·5 Physical Changes

It is important to emphasize in this section that physical changes only change the *form* of a material. The appearance of the material undergoing a physical change may be altered considerably, but no new substance has been formed. You can point out the properties of common substances as they change physical states. Point out as each change occurs that although some properties may have changed (such as phase), there are still some properties remaining which allow us to tell that the original substance is still there. **Demonstration 23·6** *Sublimation of Iodine* shows a change of state. **Demonstration 1·11** *Chemical vs Physical Changes* shows the differences. **Experiment 2** *Physical and Chemical Properties* covers ideas discussed in Sections 1·3 to 1·11.

1·6 Mixtures

There are two key points to be made when discussing mixtures. One is that mixtures are variable in composition. They can be made with different ratios of substances. The other point is that the substances which make up a mixture retain enough of their original properties that they can still be detected. **Demonstration 1·12** *Mixtures vs Pure Substances* helps to show these points. Point out that the making of a mixture is always a physical change. No new substances are produced.

The terms in this section are difficult for students to keep straight. After you have introduced these terms, take some time to help the students tie them together by letting them identify heterogenous and homogenous mixtures, the phases in mixtures, and the components in each phase. You can use a three-phase system with one substance and

layers of substances with different densities, as in **Demonstration 1·12** above. **Demonstration 1·13** *Mixtures and Compounds* compares mixtures with compounds.

1·7 Elements and Compounds

Students always learn better if they can deal with concrete examples rather than with abstract words. Introduce this topic by making a raid on your chemical storeroom to find as many examples as you can of pure elements and compounds containing these elements. **Demonstration 1·14** *Elements and Compounds* is about this. Ask the students to describe the physical appearance of each element and to list the formulas of the compounds which contain them. Be sure to note that a single physical property does not usually suffice to identify a chemical.

After they have done this, point out how much the physical properties of the compounds differ from the physical properties of the elements which make them up. This will help set the stage for your discussion of chemical reactions in Section 1·11. You may also wish to demonstrate how a compound can be broken down into its elements, as in **Demonstration 21·6** *Electrolysis of Water,* **Demonstration 7·4** *Mercury and Oxygen from Mercury Oxide,* and **Demonstration 1·15** *The Decomposition of Sugar.*

1·8 Chemical Symbols

You might mention that the names of the elements are based on Latin and Greek words, geographic locations, or names of famous scientists. The fact that these symbols are a sort of international language can be contrasted to the secrecy of the alchemists. The chemical symbols used by alchemists, or those of Berzelius or Dalton, can also be illustrated.

1·9 Energy

Make the point in these sections that energy is found in many forms, but that each of these forms can be classified into one of two types: active (kinetic) and stored (potential). Ask your students to give all the examples they can of the forms of energy with which they are familiar. List these on the board under the headings kinetic and potential. Some of these, such as electrical energy, may take some discussion before they can be classified. **Demonstration 21·5** *The Lead Cell* makes a working battery to aid you. Such a discussion will be helpful in getting the students to understand the concept of energy rather than just memorizing definitions.

After the lists have been made on the board, have the students help you come up with examples of how the various forms can be converted successively from one to another. (A good challenge problem would be to ask the students to start with one form of energy and find the greatest number of changes they can put it through.) Once you have discussed the forms of energy and their changes, the students will grasp the concept of the conservation of energy much more readily.

You may wish to discuss the sources of energy for our society: petroleum, natural gas, falling water, nuclear fuel, geothermal springs, solar collectors, ocean waves, batteries, and animal muscle. Articles from newspapers and magazines can be used for a discussion on energy conservation, alternative energy sources, and the economic and political factors involved in decision-making about these issues.

1·10 Conservation of Energy

Use a fuel such as gasoline to illustrate the transformations of its energy from chemical potential energy into mechanical kinetic energy for moving an automobile, electrical energy to charge the battery, heat energy to warm the occupants of the car, and chemical energy in the waste gases. Use the radiant energy of light in the room to find its origins: electrical, chemical, or mechanical energy, and ultimately the energy from the sun. Remind the students that although the form of the energy changes, the total amount of energy remains the same.

1·11 Chemical Reactions

The chemical and physical properties of substances change during a chemical reaction. Chemical reactions may show a change of color, change of smell, formation of a new state, change of temperature, or other change. You can mention the chemical properties of materials: reaction with acid or base, reaction with oxygen, decomposition upon heating, and other reactivities of substances. **Demonstration 1·16** *An Exothermic Reaction* and **1·17** *Magician's Flash Powder* are examples of exothermic and spectacular chemical reactions. **Demonstration 26·1** *Burning Kerchief* shows a burning fuel. **Experiment 3** *Observing a Chemical Reaction* shows changes in chemical and physical properties after reaction. Other colorful reactions are shown in **Demonstrations 1·18** *Copper in Acid* and **22·6** *Silver Chloride and Silver Chromate.*

1·12 Conservation of Mass

You can illustrate the conservation of mass by weighing the container before and after a reaction. **Demonstration 1·19** *Conservation of Mass* or **1·20** *Conservation of Flashbulb Mass* can be used.

You might discuss how a fact comes to be accepted as a law of nature, through repeated observations and an underlying theory to support them.

Demonstrations

1·1 Painted Signs

Concept: Colorful signs can be made from chemicals.

Materials: small paintbrushes, small beakers, porous paper, spray can or bottle, 1% aqueous (use alcohol for phenolphthalein) solutions of the following:

Solution to Paint With	Solution to Spray With	Color
phenolphthalein (in alcohol)	ammonium hydroxide	pink
lead(II) chloride (in hot water)	ammonium sulfide	black
potassium thiocyanate	iron(III) chloride	red
potassium ferrocyanide	iron(III) chloride	blue

Procedure: 1. The day before class, use the brush to write with the "paint" solution. Use two coats, and allow to dry overnight. 2. To reveal the colored message, spray with the second solution.

1·2 Cornstarch Paste

Concept: Under pressure, a mixture may be a solid. With no pressure, it becomes a liquid.

Materials: pie tin, water, cornstarch.

Procedure: 1. Mix the water and cornstarch in the pie tin to get a lump-free, barely flowing mixture. 2. Roll a handful of the mixture into a ball, keeping it under pressure. 3. Hand it to a student. 4. The mixture flows out of the student's hand. 5. Hit the mixture with a hammer; it does not splash.

1·3 Luminol

Concept: Chemical reactions can generate light without heat.

Materials: Soln. A: 0.02 g of luminol (5-amino-2,3-dihydrophthalazine-1,4-dione) and 1 mL of 5% sodium hydroxide (NaOH) in 200 mL water; Soln. B: 2 mL of 3% hydrogen peroxide (H_2O_2) and 0.05 g potassium ferricyanide ($K_3Fe(CN)_6$) in 200 mL water, 100 mL of 5% sodium hydroxide, large funnel in a ring attached to a ring stand, 1-L Erlenmeyer flask, safety goggles.

Procedure: 1. Set up the funnel and ring stand with the large flask under the funnel. 2. Pour solutions A and B simultaneously into the funnel in a darkened room. 3. The flowing liquid glows, as does the liquid in the flask. 4. If the glow fades, add more 5% sodium hydroxide. **Caution:** *Sodium hydroxide is corrosive.*

1·4 Fire Writing

Concept: Invisible ink makes a fiery message when lit.

Materials: wood splints, matches, porous paper, 100 mL of saturated potassium nitrate (KNO_3), tape.

Procedure: 1. Use wood splint to write a continuous message with the solution on the paper. Trace it three times. 2. Let the paper dry thoroughly. 3. Suspend it from the blackboard with the tape. 4. Touch a glowing splint to the start of the message. 5. The message glows.

1·5 Secret Writing

Concept: Invisible ink turns brown when heated.

Materials: 25 mL of lemon juice, index cards, wooden splints, gas/matches, burner, safety goggles.

Procedure: 1. Use the wooden splint to write on the card with the juice. 2. Let the card dry thoroughly. 3. Hold the card about 7–8 cm above the burner flame, taking care that it doesn't burn. 4. The writing turns brown.

1·6 Freezing Flowers

Concept: Frozen flowers shatter if hit.

Materials: fresh flowers, rubber hose, tomato, a slurry of dry ice and acetone in a large beaker, tongs, hammer, safety goggles.

Procedure: 1. Drop the flowers, hose, or tomato, into the slurry. 2. The slurry boils and the objects become hard. 3. Remove with tongs and hit with a hammer. **Caution:** *Do not touch dry ice; use tongs. Dry ice can cause frostbite. Acetone is flammable, keep flames away.*

1·7 Boiling Water in a Paper Cup

Concept: Liquid water cannot exceed 100° C.

Materials: paper cup, water, gas burner, matches, gauze, ring stand, ring.

Procedure: 1. Fill the cup with water. 2. Heat the cup but do not let the flame touch the parts of the cup not in contact with water. 3. When the water boils, note that the cup is not burning.

1·8 Mass

Concept: Equal volumes of different materials will differ in mass.

Materials: water, oil, alcohol, sawdust, styrofoam, colored liquids, small beakers.

Procedure: 1. Prepare beakers of equal volumes of the materials before class. 2. Ask the students how we could rank them according to the amount of matter they contain. 3. The discussion leads to the conclusion that the concept of mass is needed.

1·9 Solids, Liquids, and Gases

Concept: The states of matter have different properties.

Materials: wooden block or other solid object, water, beaker, bottle of perfume.

Procedure: 1. Hold up the block and point out its fixed shape. 2. Try to put your hand through it. State that its particles are tightly packed, with strong attractions that maintain the shape. 3. Pour water into a beaker and mention that it takes the shape of the container. 4. Place your fingers in it and state that its particles are not as tightly packed as in a solid. 5. Open a bottle of perfume. 6. Ask the students to signal at what moment they can smell it. 7. Mention that gases are free to move around because they have negligible attractions between particles and the gas particles are far apart. 8. Wave your hand in the air and state that you can feel the molecules of the air hitting your hand.

1·10 Compressibility of Gases and Liquids

Concept: Gases are compressible, but liquids are not.

Materials: 2 large syringes with caps or rubber stoppers.

Procedure: 1. Fill one syringe with water and the other with air and seal. 2. As you push the air piston in and out, point out how easily the volume of the sample can be changed, and that the volume of the gas is *always* that of the syringe. Show that you cannot push the piston of the water syringe in or pull it out.

1·11 Chemical vs Physical Changes

Concept: Changes in physical properties reveal whether a physical or chemical change has occurred.

Materials: paper, stick, candle, matches, safety goggles.

Procedure: 1. Tear the paper and break the stick to show a physical change. 2. Melt the candle wax to show another physical change. 3. Ignite the candle to show another chemical change. 4. Explain that in a physical change, the composition of the material is unchanged: the stick is still recognizably a stick. In a chemical change, there is a change in composition, even though it is not always easy to determine exactly how it has changed. The lighted candle shows both physical and chemical changes. The wax melts to a liquid, then vaporizes; both are physical changes. When the wax burns, the chemical composition of the material changes.

1·12 Mixtures vs Pure Substances

Concept: Mixtures and pure substances have different properties.

Materials: household mixtures such as milk, colored gum balls, mixed nuts or mixed candies; ice, water, 500-mL flask, stopper, 500-mL graduated cylinder, mercury, nail or washer, paint thinner, colored water, glycerine, cork, oil, vegetable pieces.

Procedure: 1. Place several mixtures in front of the class. 2. Have them classify the mixtures as heterogeneous or homogeneous, identify the phases, and identify the components of each phase. 3. Make a three-phase system with floating ice on water in a sealed container, with room for water vapor on top of the ice. Ask the same questions as in step *2*. 4. Devise a system with multiple layers of substances of varying densities in a graduated cylinder: mercury, a nail or washer, paint thinner, colored water, glycerine, and a cork can be used. Ask the same questions as in step *2*. 5. Layer mercury, water, and oil in a graduated cylinder. Ask the questions of step *2*. 6. Add solid pieces of nail, cork, tomato, grape, etc., and ask again. **Caution:** *Paint thinner is flammable and an irritant. Mercury is highly toxic. Use a mercury clean-up sponge for mercury spills.*

1·13 Mixtures and Compounds

Concept: Mixtures can be separated into their components by physical means, but compounds cannot.

Materials: 5 g of iron filings (Fe), 5 g of sulfur (S), glass plate, spatula, magnet, crucible, ring stand, triangle, ring, gas burner, matches, safety goggles.

Procedure: 1. Mix the iron and sulfur on the glass plate. 2. Use the magnet to separate the iron from the sulfur. 3. Place the iron filings from the magnet and the sulfur from the pile into a crucible. 4. Heat until the reaction is complete. **Caution:** *Heat the sulfur and iron in a fume hood.* 5. Use the magnet to try to remove the iron and to test for magnetism. 6. State that two substances can be combined in any ratio to make a mixture. Physical means, such as magnetism and solubility, can be used to separate the two. After a compound is formed, the new substance has a new set of properties and cannot be broken down by physical means.

1·14 Elements and Compounds

Concept: The unique properties of an element are lost when it forms a compound.

Materials: various elements, and compounds containing the same elements.

Procedure: 1. Display the elements and compounds on a large table. 2. The students can view these in an informal manner or study them as part of a structured assignment. 3. A typical assignment might ask them to describe the physical appearance of each element and to list the formulas of the compounds which contain them. 4. Stress the extent to which the physical properties of the compounds differ from the physical properties of the elements from which they are formed.

1·15 The Decomposition of Sugar

Concept: Compounds can decompose into elements or other compounds.

Materials: 10 g of sugar, 3 mL of concentrated sulfuric acid (H_2SO_4), 50-mL beaker, safety goggles.

Procedure: 1. Place the granulated sugar in the beaker. 2. Pour concentrated sulfuric acid onto the sugar. 3. The mixture gradually darkens. A tall column of carbon rises out of the beaker, and large amounts of steam are produced. **Caution:** *The carbon column still contains unreacted sulfuric acid, and the steam contains sulfur dioxide. Do this demonstration in a fume hood. Sulfuric acid is corrosive. Sulfur dioxide is an irritant.*

1·16 An Exothermic Reaction

Concept: Some reactions give off heat and light.

Materials: steel wool, oxygen gas from a cylinder, gas burner, matches, beaker, forceps, safety goggles.

Procedure: 1. Heat the steel wool to glowing. 2. Drop it into a beaker of oxygen gas. 3. The wool bursts into flames.

1·17 Magician's Flash Powder

Concept: Chemical reactions can be explosive.

Materials: 5 g of lycopodium powder, explosion can or metal can with lid and aspirator bulb (with room inside the can for a candle), matches, candle, candle holder, safety goggles.

Procedure: 1. Place some powder in the aspirator tray inside the can. 2. Place the lighted candle in the can away

bulb to blow the powder to the candle. An explosion will occur. 4. With the lid resting on the top, repeat step *3*. The lid flies off. 5. Note that the reaction is rapid since the particles are small and burn easily. **Caution:** *Lycopodium powder is explosive. Make sure students stand back during the demonstration. Keep your face and hands away from the mouth of the can. Wear safety goggles.*

1·18 Copper in Acid

Concept: Compounds are made from elements.

Materials: 2 cm × 7 cm strip of copper metal, 50 mL of $6M$ nitric acid (HNO_3) in a 150-mL beaker, safety goggles.

Procedure: 1. Set up the beaker with the acid. **Caution:** *Do this in a fume hood. The nitrogen dioxide (NO_2) gas is toxic. Nitric acid is corrosive.* 2. Put the strip in it, asking the students to observe carefully. 3. The copper dissolves; the solution is blue. A red-brown gas is evolved.

1·19 Conservation of Mass

Concept: Mass is conserved in reactions.

Materials: 50 mL of $1M$ lead(II) nitrate ($Pb(NO_3)_2$), 100 mL of $1M$ sodium iodide (NaI), two 250-mL flasks, large balance, safety goggles.

Procedure: 1. Weigh both flasks together, each containing one of the solutions. 2. Mix the contents of the flasks. 3. Weigh both flasks again to show that the mass has not changed in the reaction. **Caution:** *Lead salts are toxic.*

1·20 Conservation of Flashbulb Mass

Concept: Mass is conserved in reactions.

Materials: new flashbulb, 6 V DC power supply, 2 wires with clips on both ends, triple-beam balance.

Procedure: 1. Weigh a new flashbulb. 2. Fire it with the power supply. 3. Weigh it again. The masses are the same.

Audiovisual Resources

(Symbols: F Film, FS Filmstrip, V Videotape)

All About Matter (4 FS) Focus Media, 1980, 20–30 min. each. (Use with Sections 1·5, 1·6, 1·7, 1·8, or 1·11.) Discusses elements, compounds, and mixtures, compares physical and chemical changes, and explains chemical symbols and formulas.

Chemistry in Nature (F) Centron, 1974, 16 min. (Use with Section 1·11.) Investigates two examples of chemical change in nature; filmed in Japan.

Chemistry: The Ins and Outs of Energy (8 FS) Charles Clark, 1979, 12–21 min. each. (Use with Section 1·9.) Discusses potential and kinetic energy. Also covers topics in Chapter 8.

Elements Discovered (F, V) Media Guild, 1980, 25 min. (Use with Section 1·2.) Describes experiments leading to the discovery of chemical elements throughout history. Also covers topics in Chapter 5.

Elements of Change (F, V) Films Inc., 1976, 30 min. (Use with Section 1·1.) Introduces the concepts of physical and chemical change, atomic structure, the periodic table and chemical reactivity, and describes the role of chemistry in today's world.

Explaining Matter: Chemical Change (F, V) Encyclopaedia Brittanica, 1982, 13 min. (Use with Section 1·11.) Introduces the relationships between atomic structure, chemical bonding, and chemical change.

Introducing Chemistry: Formulas and Equations (F) Coronet, 1966, 10 min. (Use with Section 1·8.) Explains and demonstrates the use of symbols in chemistry. Also covers topics in Chapter 5.

Introduction to Chemistry (4 FS) Educational Dimensions, (Use with Sections 1·1, 1·7, or 1·11.) Illustrates the scope of chemistry and its importance in everyday life.

Introduction to Energy and Heat (FS, V) Arthur Mokin, 1982, 25 min. each. (Use with Sections 1·9 and 1·10.) Presents the various forms of energy and examines energy changes.

The Forms of Energy (2 FS) Focus Media, 1980, 13–17 min. each. (Use with Section 1·9.) Shows differences between kinetic and potential energy and relates them to specific energy forms.

The States of Matter (F) McGraw Hill, 1973, 18 min. (Use with Section 1·4.) Discusses the three states of matter including the atomic and molecular movements within each state.

What is Chemistry? (FS) Prentice-Hall, Media, 1977. (Use with Section 1·1.) Uses theories and industrial applications to illustrate the many of the different aspects of chemistry.

The Earth: Resources in Its Crust (F, V) Coronet, 1982, 9 min. (Use with Section 1·7.) Presents a brief overview of important elements and compounds, their chemistry, mining, and uses. Also covers topics in Chapter 23.

Beyond the Text

Berzelius and the Search for Pure Substances

The definitions of an element and compound may seem simple and obvious. How would you prove beyond any doubt though, that a particular substance could not be broken down to give simpler substances? You might try heating the substance, or reacting it with other chemicals. If you observe a change in the substance, could you tell whether the new material was simpler or more complex than the original? Imagine the difficulty faced by the early chemists! They were just beginning to understand combustion. No wonder they were still puzzling over the behavior of even the most common materials.

Jons Jacob Berzelius was a Swedish physician and chemist. He made great contributions to the work of categorizing substances in the later eighteenth and early nineteenth centuries. Using the standard methods of mineral analysis and the very new techniques of electrochemistry, Berzelius was able to decompose compounds. He and his students discovered cerium, selenium, lithium, vanadium, and some of the rare earth elements. Using equipment that he designed and built himself, he found the atomic masses of 45 of the 49 elements known in 1818. He also determined the composition of more than 2000 compounds.

Berzelius recognized the need for simple symbols to represent the growing list of elements and compounds. He proposed a system of using the first letter of the Latin name to represent an element. To represent compounds he used a combination of element symbols with numerical superscripts. His system is still used today, although the superscripts have been replaced by subscripts.

As Berzelius grew older, he often refused to accept new ideas. In spite of compelling evidence to the contrary, he insisted that the substances made by living organisms could never be synthesized. He did not accept chlorine as an element until 1818, even though it had been discovered more than 40 years earlier. In spite of these errors, Berzelius is recognized as the greatest chemist of his day, and one of the greatest of all time.

Origin of the Names of Some Elements

Element	Origin of Name
Arsenic (As)	Greek: *arsenikos,* male; based on the belief that metals were of different sexes
Berkelium (Bk)	First isolated at the University of California, Berkeley
Beryllium (Be)	Discovered as the oxide in beryl
Bismuth (Bi)	German: *weisse masse,* white mass; later changed to *wismuth*

Bromine (Br)	Greek: *bromos*, stench; named for its strong odor
Calcium (Ca)	Latin: *calx*, lime; found abundantly in limestone
Californium (Cf)	Discovered at the University of California
Carbon (C)	Latin: *carbo*, charcoal
Cerium (Ce)	Named for the planetoid Ceres, discovered two years before the element
Chlorine (Cl)	Greek: *chloros*, greenish-yellow
Cobalt (Co)	German: *kobold*, goblin or evil spirit
Copper (Cu)	Latin: *cuprum*, from the island of Cyprus
Curium (Cm)	Named after Pierre and Marie Currie
Gold (Au)	Symbol from Latin: *aurum*, shining down
Helium (He)	Greek: *helius*, the sun; first detected in the solar spectrum
Hydrogen (H)	Greek: *hydro*, water, and *genes*, forming
Iodine (I)	Greek: *iodes*, violet
Iridium (Ir)	Latin: *iris*, rainbow; named for its colorful salts
Krypton (Kr)	Greek: *kryptos*, hidden; discovered in the residue after liquid air had boiled away
Lithium (Li)	Greek: *lithos*, stone; traces found in nearly all igneous rocks
Nobelium (No)	Discovered at the Nobel Institute in Stockholm, Sweden
Phosphorus (F)	Greek: *phosphorus*, bringer of light; certain forms give off light
Polonium (Po)	Named after Poland, native land of Marie Curie
Potassium (K)	English: *potash*
Promethium (Pm)	In mythology, Promethius stole fire from heaven
Radium (Ra)	Latin: *radius*, ray; the element emits radiation
Selenium (Se)	Greek: *Selene*, moon; when discovered, it was associated with tellurium, named for the earth
Silicon (Si)	Latin: *silex*, flint
Tantalum (Ta)	Greek: *Tantalos*, mythological character

Technetium (Te)	Greek: *technetos*, artificial; does not occur in nature
Tellurium (Te)	Latin: *tellus*, earth
Titanium (T)	Latin: *Titans*, the first sons of the earth
Uranium (U)	Latin: *Uranus*, heaven, named for the planet

Answers to End of Chapter Questions and Problems

Practice Questions and Problems

9. Chemistry is the study of the composition of substances and the changes that substances undergo.

10. Organic, inorganic, analytical, physical, biochemistry.

11. A law is a concise statement that summarizes the results of a broad variety of observations and experiments. A theory is a tested (by experiments) hypothesis.

12. Experiments are used to test hypotheses.

13. Matter includes **a.** concrete, **b.** acetone vapor, and **e.** air. Heat and sound are forms of energy.

14. Solid, metallic luster, malleable, definite melting point, gray color.

15. a. 2,3 **b.** 1,2 **c.** 2,3 **d.** 1,2

16. Solid: wood, bar soap. Liquid: diesel fuel, milk. Gas: carbon monoxide, helium.

17. a. solid **b.** gas **c.** liquid **d.** liquid **e.** solid **f.** gas

18. a. Iron is magnetic; salt is not. Salt will dissolve in water; iron will not. **b.** Water has a much lower boiling point than salt. It can be evaporated, leaving the solid.

19. Physical properties: **a, c, e, f.** The others are chemical properties.

20. a. odor, boiling point, rate of evaporation, density **b.** color, malleability, melting point, density **c.** density, solubility in water, boiling point

21. Heterogeneous mixtures have two or more phases. Homogeneous mixtures have a uniform composition.

22. Components of a mixture are physically separable.

23. Homogeneous: **b, c, d, e, f, h, j.** Heterogeneous: **a, g, i.**

24. Compounds are chemically separable into elements. Elements cannot be separated into simpler substances.

25. Element: **b, f, j.** Compound: **e.** Mixture: **a, c, d, g, h, i.**

26. a. Cu **b.** O **c.** P **d.** Ag **e.** Na **f.** He

27. a. nitrogen, hydrogen, chlorine **b.** potassium, manganese, oxygen **c.** carbon, hydrogen, oxygen **d.** calcium, iodine

28. Potential energy is the energy of position or composition. Kinetic energy is the energy of motion.

29. Radiant, chemical, thermal, mechanical, electrical, nuclear.

30. Energy is neither created nor destroyed.

31. Physical property: no change in composition (color and odor). Chemical property: change in composition (burning and rusting).

32. a. physical **b.** chemical **c.** chemical **d.** physical **e.** chemical **f.** physical **g.** physical **h.** physical

33. a. color, melting point, malleability, reaction with acid **b.** color, odor, flammability, vapor pressure **c.** boiling point, freezing point, taste, density

Mastery Questions and Problems

34. Dissolve the sugar in water; filter out charcoal and sand; separate large charcoal pieces; burn small charcoal pieces.

35. a. solar calculator **b.** lawn mower engine **c.** rechargable battery **d.** drill bit

36. a. color and odor change **b.** gas production **c.** formation of precipitate, not easily reversed **d.** color change, not easily reversed **e.** energy change, not easily reversed

37. It is a compound because it is broken down chemically by heating. A new substance with new properties is formed. The shiny liquid is probably an element, but this has not yet been proven.

38. a. physical **b.** physical **c.** physical **d.** physical **e.** chemical **f.** physical

39. a. homogenous mixture **b.** homogeneous mixture **c.** heterogenous mixture **d.** most are homogeneous mixtures **e.** heterogenous mixture **f.** compound **g.** heterogenous mixture **h.** homogeneous mixture

40. A chemical change results in a change in composition. There is no change in composition in a physical change.

Challenging Questions and Problems

41. a. radiant energy of the sun → water vapor carried aloft by winds → raindrops **b.** radiant energy of the sun → chemical energy of plants (millions of years ago) → oil **c.** radiant energy of the sun → chemical energy of plants → cows

42. Heat "flows". To warm a substance, "caloric" must be taken from another. "Atoms of caloric" cause expansion on heating.

1 Matter, Change, and Energy

Chapter Preview

1·1   Chemistry

Chemists work at an amazing variety of jobs. Some develop new products such as textiles, paints, medicines, or cosmetics. Others may find methods to reduce pollution or to clean up the environment. A specialized chemist may be called on to identify and interpret the evidence found at the scene of a crime. Many chemists teach. Others do analyses of substances or check the quality of manufactured products. What all of these people have in common is a knowledge of chemistry.

■ Chemistry is a natural science.

Chemistry *is the study of the composition of substances and the changes that substances undergo.* Our world is complex. Chemistry reflects this complexity in the broad areas of interest that it covers. It contributes to other natural sciences including biology, geology, and physics. Chemistry overlaps with agriculture, medicine, and many manufacturing industries as well.

Most of the careers just mentioned apply a knowledge of chemistry to attain specific goals. These are examples of applied chemistry, or chemical technology. Pure chemistry, like other pure sciences, accumulates knowledge for its own sake. Pure science is neither good nor bad. Applied chemistry focuses on the uses of chemical knowledge. Technology can use scientific knowledge in ways that benefit or harm people or the environment. The political and social debates about the uses of scientific knowledge are really debates about technology.

Because chemistry is so diverse, it is usually considered to have five major divisions. With a few exceptions, **organic chemistry** *is the study of*

Figure 1·1
Chemical changes are responsible for many of the spectacular events around us. Here molten lava is being ejected from the Hawaiian volcano Kilauea.

Figure 1·2
Glassware is used extensively in a "wet chemistry" laboratory. Most laboratories now use many automated electronic instruments to do chemical analyses.

essentially all substances containing carbon. It was originally the study of substances from living organisms. **Inorganic chemistry** *specializes in substances without carbon.* These are mainly substances from nonliving things. **Analytical chemistry** *is concerned primarily with the composition of substances.* Finding the amount of silver in an ore or minute quantities of a substance in a blood sample requires the practice of analytical chemistry. **Physical chemistry** *specializes in the discovery and description of the theoretical basis of the behavior of chemical substances.* Usually it relies heavily on mathematics. **Biochemistry** *is the study of the composition and changes in composition of living organisms.* Obviously, these five subdivisions of chemistry overlap. For example, one cannot measure a change in an organic or inorganic substance without some proficiency in analytical chemistry.

Figure 1·3
After designing a chemical processing system, a chemical engineer must be able to explain the system's features.

1·A   Chemical Technology

To meet the needs of our modern world, enormous quantities of chemicals are manufactured every year. These include fertilizers, fuels, pesticides, textiles, plastics, and other materials. Working with ordinary laboratory glassware, chemists develop the processes for producing small amounts of these chemicals. It is the job of the chemical engineer to plan and carry out the same reactions on a large scale.

Chemical engineers are employed by many industries. They work for companies that produce fuels, metals, rubber, cosmetics, drugs, paper, paints, and foods. Chemical engineers must determine whether a reaction can be used for mass production. They plan the layout of a plant, design equipment for it, and supervise its construction and operation. Often they are asked to redesign an existing plant to increase productivity. They may add new safety or pollution control features. Because they are responsible for the efficient operation of the plant, they must always be aware of costs.

Many engineering and technical schools offer degrees in chemical engineering. The course of study emphasizes chemistry, physics, mathematics, economics, writing, and the use of computers. Specialized engineering courses are also required.

1·2   The Scientific Method

The scientific method helps scientists answer questions about the physical universe.

Like most fields of human endeavor, science has evolved formal and time-tested methods to solve problems. The scientific method is one important approach. It was through the scientific method that many of the chemical elements were first discovered. *The* **scientific method** *incorporates observations, hypotheses, experiments, theories, and laws. Scientists make* **observations** *when they note and record facts about natural phenomena.* They try to explain their observations by devising hypotheses. **Hypotheses** *are descriptive models for observations.* A hypothesis is useful if it accounts for what scientists observe in many situations.

In order to learn more, *scientists often perform* **experiments** *in which one or more of the conditions are controlled.* An important principle of an experiment is that it can be repeated numerous times. *The observations, which are recorded from an experiment, constitute* **data.** When observations or experimental data do not fit the hypothesis, it must be scrapped or adjusted. The new or refined hypothesis is then subjected to further experimental testing. An important interplay takes place between hypotheses and experiments. The hypothesis guides the design of new experiments. At the same time, experiments guide the rejection or refinement of the hypothesis.

When viewing the world, a scientist is interested in both what is happening and why it is happening.

Once a hypothesis meets the test of repeated experimentation, it may be elevated to a theory. *A* **theory** *is a thoroughly tested model that explains why experiments give certain results.* A theory can never be proved. Nevertheless, theories are very useful because they help us to form mental pictures of objects or processes that cannot be seen. Moreover they give us the power to predict the behavior of natural systems under circumstances that are different from those of the original observations.

Another product of scientific research is a law. *A* **scientific law** *is a concise statement that summarizes the results of a broad variety of observations and experiments.* A scientific law is different from a theory in that it only describes a natural phenomenon. It does not attempt to explain it. Scientific laws can often be expressed by simple mathematical relationships. They usually concern natural behaviors that are not immediately obvious. For most people a statement like Boyle's law: "The volume of a gas is inversely proportional to the pressure exerted on it" meets these criteria.

Occasionally a widely held scientific theory must be modified to agree with new experimental evidence. This is usually the cause of much excitement in the scientific community.

Figure 1·4
This outline of the scientific method shows how experimental observations lead to the development of hypotheses and theories. A scientific law summarizes the results of many experiments, but it does not explain why a behavior is observed; that is the role of the hypothesis and the theory.

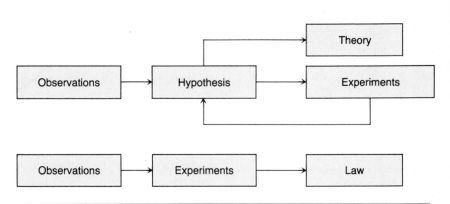

Problem

1. a. hypothesis
b. law
c. experiment
d. theory

1. Classify each of the following statements as an example of experiment, hypothesis, theory, or law.
   a. The ashes from a campfire weigh less than the wood that was burned. Therefore mass is destroyed (or lost) when wood is burned.
   b. A body at rest tends to remain at rest.
   c. Water boils at 100°C on your kitchen stove and in the laboratory.
   d. All matter is composed of atoms, which themselves are composed of protons, electrons, and neutrons.

1·B Alchemy and the Birth of Chemistry

Long before the science of chemistry existed, people made use of chemical reactions to dye cloth, tan leather, and prepare foods. Eventually people began to search for explanations for the structure and behavior of matter. Greek philosophers 2500 years ago believed that knowledge of the natural world could be achieved through pure reasoning. One group, the "Atomists," proposed that matter was made of tiny indivisible particles called atoms. The famous philosopher Aristotle disagreed. He said that matter was composed of four elements: fire, air, water, and earth. Because of Aristotle's fame and reputation, much of the world agreed with his ideas. As a result, the idea of atoms was not discussed seriously for more than 2000 years.

With the destruction of Greek civilization, European science fell into disrepair and did not reappear until the Middle Ages. This period saw the rise of the alchemists. Their goal was to change common metals into gold. Although the alchemists were unable to succeed in their quest, they did spur the development of science. They developed many experimental procedures and laboratory apparatus. Through trial and error they also developed a wealth of knowledge about the characteristics of substances.

During the thirteenth century, an English Franciscan monk named Roger Bacon introduced a new idea. He held that an understanding of the natural world could be gained through observation and experiment rather than by pure logic. Bacon's ideas were not immediately popular. They were finally put into practice, however, by scientists of the sixteenth and seventeenth centuries. The Englishman Robert Boyle (1627–1691) emphasized the necessity of using experiments to test ideas that were obtained by reason. In his book, *The Sceptical Chymist,* he challenged Aristotle's four "elements." He also advanced a definition of an element very similar to that used today.

Figure 1·5
Alchemists mixed materials together in hundreds of different ways. For this purpose they designed various types of balances, crucibles, and glassware. Chemists later used this equipment for chemical research.

Figure 1·6
This nineteenth century chemical laboratory was named after Lavoisier, the great eighteenth century chemist.

Every substance has a unique set of physical properties.

Antoine Lavoisier (1743–1794) took an important new step in the process of experimentation. This was to make precise measurements of the mass changes in chemical reactions. His experiments transformed chemistry from a science of observation to the science of measurement that it is today. For this reason, Lavoisier is often called the founder of modern chemistry.

1·3 Properties of Matter

The material things around us are all various types of matter. **Matter** *is anything that takes up space and has mass.* Aluminum, water, air, glass, and you are different kinds of matter. Ideas, light, and heat are not matter. They do not take up space or have mass. *The amount of matter that an object contains is its* **mass.** A golf ball has more mass than a table tennis ball. It contains more matter.

Some materials are composed of numerous types of matter; others consist of a single kind. *A* **substance** *is a particular kind of matter that has a uniform and definite composition.* Table sugar is a substance. It is 100% sucrose. Substances are often called pure substances. Lemonade is not a substance. It contains different amounts of sugar and lemon juice in water.

All samples of a substance have identical properties. A **physical property** *is a quality or condition of a substance that can be observed or measured without changing the substance's composition.* It can be specified without reference to any other substance. Some physical properties of matter include color, solubility, mass, odor, hardness, density, electrical conductivity, magnetism, melting point, and boiling point. Physical properties help chemists identify substances (Table 1·1). A colorless odorless liquid in which both salt and sugar dissolve and that boils at 100°C is probably water. Another colorless liquid that has a distinctive odor, that evaporates quickly when placed on your skin, and in which salt will not dissolve is most certainly not water.

Table 1·1	Physical Properties of Some Common Substances			
Substance	State (at normal conditions)	Color	Melting point (°C)	Boiling point (°C)
Oxygen	Gas	Colorless	−218	−183
Bromine	Liquid	Red-brown	−7	59
Water	Liquid	Colorless	0	100
Sulfur	Solid	Yellow	113	445
Sodium chloride (table salt)	Solid	White	801	1413
Iron	Solid	Silver-white (freshly cut)	1535	2750

1·4   The States of Matter

Under normal laboratory conditions matter can exist in three physical states.

Matter can exist in three different physical states: solid, liquid, and gas. The physical state of a substance is a physical property of that substance. Certain characteristics summarized in Table 1·2 distinguish each state of matter.

A **solid** *is matter that has a definite shape and volume*. The shape of a solid does not depend on the shape of the container (Figure 1·7). Solids usually have a high density, and they expand only slightly when heated. They are almost incompressible. Coal, sugar, bone, ice, and iron are examples of solids.

A **liquid** *is a form of matter that flows, has a fixed volume, and takes the shape of its container*. Liquids are generally less dense than solids. They expand slightly when heated and are almost incompressible. Examples of liquids are water, milk, and blood.

A **gas** *is matter that takes both the shape and the volume of its container*. Gases expand without limit to fill any space and are easily compressed. The term *gas* is limited to those substances that exist in the gaseous state at room temperature. For example, air is a mixture of gases including oxygen and nitrogen. *The word* **vapor** *describes a substance that, although in the gaseous state, is generally a liquid or solid at room temperature*. Steam, the gaseous form of water, is a vapor. Moist air contains water vapor. The words *gas* and *vapor* should not be used interchangeably; there is a difference.

Safety

Gases expand dramatically when heated. Never heat a tightly closed vessel, as the build-up in gas pressure may cause an explosion.

A fourth state of matter, plasma, exists only at very high temperatures. Most of the universe is plasma because stars are in a plasma state.

Problem

2. **a.** solid   **d.** solid
   b. liquid   **e.** liquid
   c. gas

2. What is the physical state of each of the following at room temperature?   **a.** silver   **b.** gasoline   **c.** helium   **d.** paraffin wax   **e.** rubbing alcohol

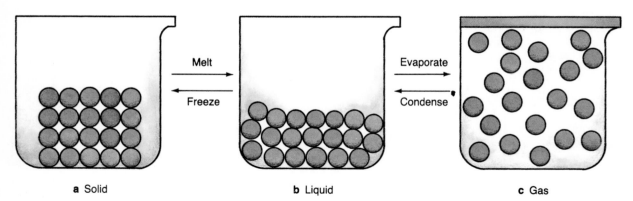

a Solid   **b** Liquid   **c** Gas

Figure 1·7
The three states of matter differ because of the arrangement of their particles.
a A solid has its own shape and volume. **b** A liquid conforms to the shape but not the volume of its container. **c** A gas will occupy all the volume of its container.

Table 1·2	Important Properties of the States of Matter		
Property	Solid	Liquid	Gas or vapor
Mass	Definite	Definite	Definite
Shape	Rigid	Indefinite	Indefinite
Volume	Definite	Definite	Indefinite
Temperature increase	Very small expansion	Moderate expansion	Large expansion
Compressibility	Almost incompressible	Almost incompressible	Compressible

1·5   Physical Changes

Physical changes in the state of matter can result from changes in temperature.

Matter can be changed in many ways. *A **physical change** will alter a substance without changing its composition.* Cutting, grinding, or bending a material will cause a physical change. The substance remains the same. A change in temperature may also bring about a physical change. The melting of ice, the freezing of water, the conversion of water to steam, and the condensation of steam to water are all examples of physical changes. We know that these physical transformations do not change the identity of the water. The physical properties of water are the same for water that has been frozen and melted as they are for water that has been converted to steam and then condensed.

Words like boil, freeze, melt, condense, break, split, crack, grind, cut, crush, and bend usually signify a physical change. Table salt (sodium chloride) is a white solid at room temperature. It can also exist in each of the three physical states. However, the temperatures at which the changes of state occur in sodium chloride are much higher than for the corresponding changes in water. Sodium chloride melts at 801°C and boils at 1413°C.

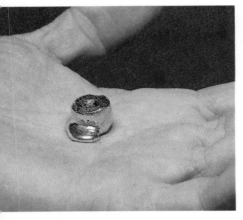

Figure 1·8
Physical changes can take place as a result of temperature changes. The melting point of the metal gallium is 30°C. Body temperature is about 37°C.

1·6   Mixtures

Most matter consists of mixtures of substances.

Mixtures *consist of a physical blend of two or more substances.* They differ from pure substances because they have a variable composition. Most materials found in nature are mixtures. We all recognize beef stew as a mixture of meat, vegetables, and gravy. On the other hand, the identification of air or brine as mixtures is much less obvious. (Air is a mixture of gases. Brine is a mixture of salt and water.) The component parts of these mixtures cannot be distinguished even under a microscope.

Greek: *heteros* = different
genos = kind
homo = the same

Mixtures can be heterogeneous or homogeneous. *A **heterogeneous mixture** is not uniform in composition.* If we were to sample one portion of the mixture, its composition would be different from another sample. Soil is a heterogeneous mixture. It contains bits of decayed material along with sand, silt, and/or clay. By contrast, *a **homogeneous mixture**

Figure 1·9
All these items are mixtures. The toothpaste is a homogeneous mixture. It has a uniform composition. The sand in water, fruit salad, granite, and soil are heterogeneous mixtures. They consist of a number of phases that are not evenly distributed.

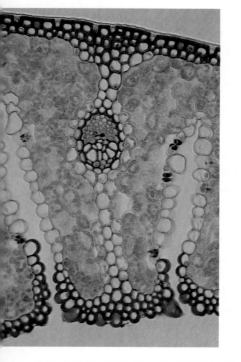

Figure 1·10
This is a microscopic view of the cross section of a leaf. Like most foods and all living things, a leaf is a complex heterogeneous mixture of substances.

has a completely uniform composition. Its components are evenly distributed throughout the sample. Salt water from the ocean is a homogeneous mixture. It is the same throughout a sample.

One important characteristic of both heterogeneous and homogeneous mixtures is that their compositions may vary. The composition of air in a forest differs from that near an industrial city, particularly in the amounts and kinds of pollutants it contains. Blood is a mixture of water, various chemicals, and cells. Blood composition varies somewhat from one individual to another. Moreover, each person's blood composition varies with health, nutrition, and activity.

Homogeneous mixtures are so important in chemistry that chemists give them the special name of solutions. *A* **solution** *is a homogeneous mixture.* As shown in Table 1·3, solutions may be gases, liquids, or solids. If we were to sample any portion of a sugar solution, we would find that it has the same composition as any other portion. *Any part of a system with uniform composition and properties is called a* **phase.** Thus a homogeneous mixture consists of a single phase, and a heterogeneous mixture consists of two or more phases. Vinegar and oil dressing is a heterogeneous mixture with two phases.

Some mixtures can be separated into their various components by simple physical methods. We could use a spoon to separate beef stew into meat, vegetables, and gravy. As a slightly more sophisticated example, consider the gray-colored heterogenous mixture of powdered yellow

Table 1·3	Some Common Types of Solutions
System	Examples
Gas–gas	Carbon dioxide and oxygen in nitrogen (air)
Liquid–gas	Water vapor in air (moist air)
Gas–liquid	Carbon dioxide in water (soda water)
Liquid–liquid	Acetic acid in water (vinegar)
Solid–liquid	Sodium chloride in water (brine)
Solid–solid	Copper in silver (sterling silver, an alloy)

Figure 1·11
Physical methods can be used to separate a mixture. The iron filings are attracted to a magnet, but the powdered sulfur is not.

sulfur and black iron filings. The individual particles of sulfur and iron can be readily distinguished from one another under a microscope. The mixture is easy to separate. The iron filings can be removed from the mixture with a magnet, leaving the sulfur behind (Figure 1·11). Both the sulfur and the iron are unchanged in composition.

Tap water is a homogeneous mixture of water plus other substances that are dissolved in it. One method used to purify water is distillation. *During **distillation** a liquid is boiled to produce a vapor that is then condensed again to a liquid.* When water is distilled it is heated to form steam, which is then condensed to give water (Figure 1·12). The water is collected in a receiver. The solid substances originally dissolved in the water remain in the distillation flask. Distilled water is pure except for the dissolved gases it contains. Water from which even the dissolved gases are removed is a pure substance. Water has a unique set of properties: It freezes at 0°C and boils at 100°C.

Example 1

How would you separate the following mixtures?   **a.** iron filings from aluminum filings   **b.** sawdust from sand   **c.** sand from salt

Solution

a. Use a magnet to attract the iron filings.
b. Add water to the mixture. The sawdust floats, and sand sinks.
c. Add water to dissolve the salt. Pour the mixture onto a piece of cloth. The sand remains on the cloth, and the salt solution goes through. Use evaporation to remove the water and leave solid salt.

3. a. heterogeneous
 b. heterogeneous
 c. homogeneous
 d. homogeneous
 e. homogeneous

Problem

3. Classify each of the following as homogeneous or heterogeneous mixtures.   **a.** blood   **b.** chocolate-chip ice cream   **c.** brass (copper and zinc)   **d.** homogenized milk   **e.** a cup of coffee

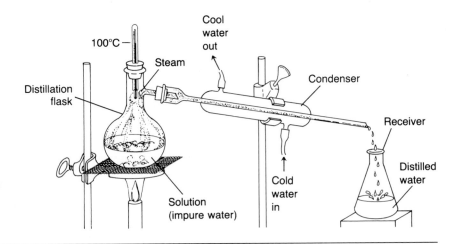

Figure 1·12
A solution of impure water is being distilled. The water is boiled to steam that is passed through a water-cooled condenser. The steam condenses to distilled water that is collected in a receiver.

1·7 Elements and Compounds

Every substance is either an element or a compound.

No two substances have identical physical and chemical properties.

By separating mixtures into their component parts we obtain pure substances. As you remember, a substance has a uniform and definite composition. Substances are divided into two groups, elements and compounds. Because you will work with elements and compounds in the laboratory, you should know how to distinguish between them. **Elements** *are the simplest forms of matter that can exist under normal laboratory conditions.* They cannot be separated into simpler substances by chemical reactions. Elements are the building blocks for all other substances. Two or more elements can combine with one another to form compounds. **Compounds** *are substances that can be separated into simpler substances only by chemical reactions.* The constituent elements in a compound are always present in the same proportions. Every element and every compound has its own unique set of properties.

The difference between elements and compounds can be demonstrated by heating refined cane sugar, a compound. Upon heating, the sugar undergoes a chemical reaction. It decomposes to carbon and water vapor. This experiment shows that cane sugar is a compound, not an element. It is separated by a chemical reaction into two substances, carbon and water. Now, what about the carbon and water? The water that comes from the breakdown of the sugar can be broken down into hydrogen and oxygen by another chemical reaction. Thus water too is a compound. Carbon, hydrogen, and oxygen cannot be broken down into simpler substances. They are elements.

Figure 1·13
Some elements and compounds are common household items. The elements shown here are aluminum, gold (in the ring), and mercury (in the thermometer). The compounds are sodium chloride (table salt) and sodium bicarbonate (baking soda).

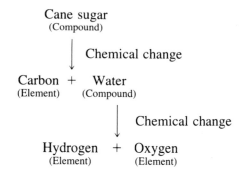

In general, the chemical and physical properties of compounds are quite different from those of their component elements. For example, sugar is a white sweet solid, but carbon is a black tasteless solid. Water is a colorless liquid, but oxygen and hydrogen are colorless gases. Table salt (or sodium chloride, to use its chemical name) is a harmless compound in most instances. It is composed of the elements sodium and chlorine. Sodium is a soft metal that reacts explosively with water. Chlorine is a pale green poisonous gas (Figure 1·14).

Much of what we have said about elements, compounds, and mixtures is summarized in Figure 1·15. Deciding whether a sample of matter is a pure substance or a homogeneous mixture can be difficult. After all, a homogeneous mixture looks like a pure substance. As a help, ask

Safety

Never taste any chemical in the laboratory, even if you are sure that it is safe.

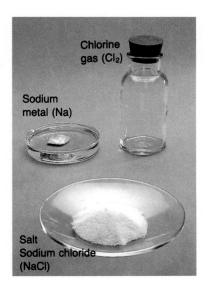

Chlorine gas (Cl₂)

Sodium metal (Na)

Salt Sodium chloride (NaCl)

Figure 1·14
The compound sodium chloride is common table salt. It is composed of the elements sodium (a solid) and chlorine (a gas). As a safety precaution, sodium is stored under oil to prevent it from reacting explosively with moisture in the air.

yourself: "Is there more than one kind of this material?" For example, how would you classify gasoline? Based on its physical appearance you might conclude that gasoline is a compound. It must be a homogenous mixture, however, since there are so many different grades of gasoline (at so many different prices).

Example 2

When a blue solid is heated in the absence of air a colorless gas and a white solid are formed. Which of these substances are elements and which are compounds? Explain.

Solution

The blue solid was separated into two substances by heating. Therefore it must be a compound. The two resulting substances may be elements or compounds.

Problem   4. A mixture

4. A clear liquid in an open container is allowed to evaporate. After three days a solid residue is left. Was the original liquid an element, compound, or mixture? How do you know?

Figure 1·15
Any sample of matter can be classified as an element, compound, or mixture.

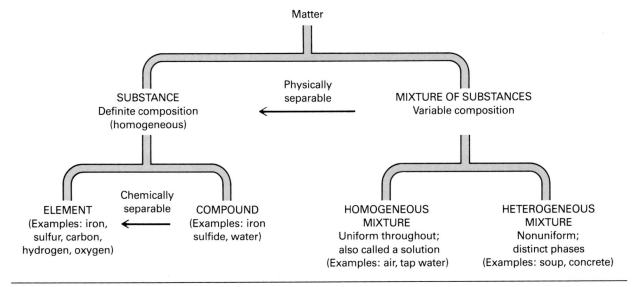

Matter

Physically separable

SUBSTANCE
Definite composition
(homogeneous)

MIXTURE OF SUBSTANCES
Variable composition

Chemically separable

ELEMENT
(Examples: iron, sulfur, carbon, hydrogen, oxygen)

COMPOUND
(Examples: iron sulfide, water)

HOMOGENEOUS MIXTURE
Uniform throughout; also called a solution
(Examples: air, tap water)

HETEROGENEOUS MIXTURE
Nonuniform; distinct phases
(Examples: soup, concrete)

1·8   Chemical Symbols

Elements are represented by chemical symbols.

Table A·4 is in Appendix A.

Only about 90 of the elements are known to occur naturally on earth. The other known elements have been created in the laboratory.

Only about one-third of the naturally occurring elements are known to be essential for some form of life.

Figure 1·16
Berzelius was not the first chemist to devise symbols to represent the elements. Dalton's symbols are shown in this reproduction of one of his lecture diagrams.

Carbon, hydrogen, oxygen, sodium, and chlorine are only a few of the approximately 100 known elements. All matter in the universe is composed of these elements. *Each element is represented by a* **chemical symbol.** The symbols for most elements consist of the first one or two letters of the name of the element (Table A·4). The first letter is always capitalized. If a second letter is needed, it must be lowercase. Some element symbols are derived from older Latin names. In those cases, the symbol is not always consistent with the common name. Table 1·4 lists these exceptions.

Each element has properties in some way different from those of every other element. For example, helium (He) is a chemically inert gas that is lighter than air. Iron (Fe) is a silver-gray solid that conducts electricity and rusts in moist air.

Chemical symbols are used to write chemical formulas of compounds. The familiar compound water is composed of the elements hydrogen and oxygen. The formula for water is H_2O. The formula for sucrose (table sugar) is $C_{12}H_{22}O_{11}$. Sucrose is composed of the elements carbon, hydrogen, and oxygen. Baking soda, sodium bicarbonate, has the formula $NaHCO_3$. Baking soda is made of four elements: sodium, hydrogen, carbon, and oxygen. The numbers in chemical formulas represent the proportions of the various elements in the compound. Every compound is always made-up of the same elements in the same proportions. Thus the formula for each of these compounds is always the same.

Example 3

Write the chemical symbol for each of these elements.   **a.** mercury   **b.** gold   **c.** iodine   **d.** magnesium   **e.** calcium   **f.** barium

Table 1·4	Symbols and Latin Names for Some Elements	
Element	Symbol	Latin name
Sodium	Na	*Natrium*
Potassium	K	*Kalium*
Antimony	Sb	*Stibium*
Copper	Cu	*Cuprum*
Gold	Au	*Aurum*
Silver	Ag	*Argentum*
Iron	Fe	*Ferum*
Lead	Pb	*Plumbum*
Mercury	Hg	*Hydrargyrum*
Tin	Sn	*Stannum*
Tungsten	W	From wolfram (not Latin)

Problems

5. **a.** tin
   b. copper
   c. nitrogen
   d. cadmium
   e. phosphorus
   f. chlorine

6. **a.** element
   b. compound
   c. mixture
   d. mixture
   e. element

5. What chemical elements are represented by the following symbols?
   a. Sn **b.** Cu **c.** N **d.** Cd **e.** P **f.** Cl

6. Classify each of the following as an element, compound, or mixture.
   a. argon **b.** ethyl alcohol (C_2H_5OH) **c.** grape juice
   d. cheese **e.** zinc

1·9 Energy

Energy is needed to bring about changes in matter.

Figure 1·17
Describe the energy in a tomato by using terms introduced in Section 1·9. What is the source of its energy?

Chemical potential energy that was converted from the radiant energy of the sun.

7. Radiant energy (sun), to chemical energy (plants), to kinetic energy (person), to mechanical energy (bike), to kinetic energy (moving wheel), to mechanical energy (generator), to electrical energy (generator), to light energy (light bulb).

Energy *is the capacity for doing work*. All chemical and physical changes in nature involve the absorption or emission of energy. Energy may exist in any one of several forms. It includes chemical, nuclear, electrical, radiant, mechanical, and thermal energies.

Light is *radiant energy*. The use of light by plants is an example of how one form of energy may be converted to another. Green plants use the radiant energy of sunlight to do the work of making carbon dioxide and water into complex chemicals. This process is called photosynthesis. The chemicals store *chemical energy* that can be used by plants for life processes. Green plants therefore survive by acquiring energy in one form and using it in another. Stored chemical energy is a form of **potential energy,** *the energy of position*. Chemical energy depends on the composition of a substance. When we buy gasoline to power our cars, we are buying chemical potential energy. When the gasoline is burned in the car's engine, this potential energy is converted into **kinetic energy,** *the energy of motion*.

As a second example of the interconvertibility of forms of energy, consider what can happen when natural gas is burned in air. This chemical process releases the chemical energy stored in the chemical structure of the gas. This chemical energy could be lost as **heat,** *which is energy that is transferred from one body to another because of a temperature difference*. The heat could also be used to raise the *thermal energy* of water, changing it to steam. The steam can drive a turbine (*mechanical energy*), and the turbine can generate *electrical energy* (Figure 1·18). The electrical energy can then be used to power an electric drill (mechanical energy).

Problem

7. One type of bicycle light is powered by a generator located on the rear wheel of the bicycle. Trace the interconversion of energy from the sun to the light produced by this bicycle light.

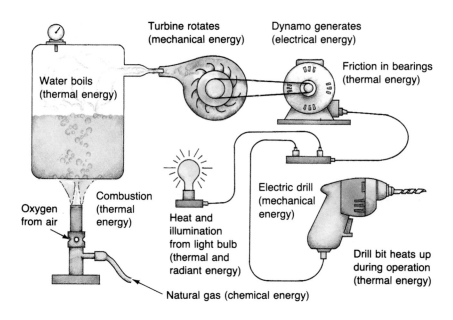

Turbine rotates (mechanical energy)

Dynamo generates (electrical energy)

Friction in bearings (thermal energy)

Water boils (thermal energy)

Combustion (thermal energy)

Oxygen from air

Electric drill (mechanical energy)

Heat and illumination from light bulb (thermal and radiant energy)

Drill bit heats up during operation (thermal energy)

Natural gas (chemical energy)

1·10   Conservation of Energy

The forms of energy can be interconverted, but energy is neither created nor destroyed in ordinary physical and chemical changes.

It is not hard to see that various forms of energy may be interconverted. An important question is: What happens to the amount of energy as it is changed from one form to another? When steam is used to drive a turbine, the kinetic energy of the moving turbine will be less than the energy used to heat the water to steam. Does this mean that some of the energy is destroyed? No, because some of the energy escapes as heat. The connections between moving parts of the turbine become hot from friction. The air surrounding the turbine becomes warm. When this thermal energy is taken into account, then the energy input equals the energy output.

Thermonuclear reactions at first appear to be an exception to this law, since energy is created in great quantities. The energy is produced by the conversion of matter into energy. It is not really appearing from nowhere.

The **law of conservation of energy** *states that in any chemical or physical process, energy is neither created nor destroyed.* The energy may be converted from one form to another. Often it is converted to a form that is not useful. In any chemical or physical process, however, energy is conserved. All of the energy involved can be accounted for as work, stored energy, or heat.

1·11   Chemical Reactions

Chemical changes in matter are called chemical reactions.

Energy changes occur whenever a chemical reaction takes place. *In a* **chemical reaction** *one or more substances are changed into new substances.* For example, when refined cane sugar is heated it undergoes a process called caramelization. The sugar melts to a colorless liquid that soon develops a brown color and a caramel odor as the temperature is raised. At this point the sugar is breaking down, and a chemical change is taking place. The important point is that when the hot liquid is allowed to cool, the sugar has lost its identity. It does not turn back into sugar, because the sugar has been changed to other substances. The change in

Mixture of
iron and sulfur

Iron sulfide

Figure 1·19
A chemical change occurs when a mixture of powdered sulfur and iron filings is heated. The reactants are converted into a product that has different chemical and physical properties than the reactants do.

composition of the sugar is the result of a chemical reaction. *In a chemical reaction, the starting substances are called* **reactants,** *and the new substances are the* **products.** Chemists use an arrow as a shorthand form of the phrase "are changed into."

$$\text{Reactants} \longrightarrow \text{products}$$

To help distinguish between physical and chemical changes, recall how sulfur and iron filings may be separated unchanged from a mixture. This separation is an example of a physical change. If the mixture of these two substances is heated, however, a chemical change takes place. The sulfur and iron are changed into a nonmagnetic substance, iron sulfide (Figure 1·19). Using the shorthand expression, this change can be written as follows.

$$\underset{\text{Reactants}}{\text{Iron + sulfur}} \xrightarrow{\text{heat}} \underset{\text{Product}}{\text{iron sulfide}}$$

Several occurrences are common indicators of a chemical change. Energy is always absorbed or evolved in chemical reactions. Burning coal evolves heat; cooking food absorbs heat. Energy is also absorbed or evolved, however, in physical changes of state. A color change, as in leaves turning in the fall, or an odor change, as in meat rotting, often accompanies a chemical change. The production of a gas or a solid (a precipitate) during a change can be the result of a chemical change. Gas bubbles rising from the bottom of a stagnant lake are formed by the chemical decay of plant matter on the lake floor. Note though that gas or vapor formation can also be the result of a change of state. Boiling water is an example. Finally, it is sometimes most helpful to consider whether the change can be easily reversed. Physical changes, especially those involving a change of state, are usually reversible. Ice can be melted and then the water refrozen. In contrast, most chemical changes are not easily reversed. Once iron has reacted with oxygen to form rust, as it often does on a car, you cannot easily reverse the process.

Figure 1·20
The formation of a gas or of a solid precipitate is a common indication that a chemical change may be taking place.

Just as every substance has physical properties, it also has chemical properties. *The ability of a substance to undergo chemical reactions and to form new substances constitutes its* **chemical properties.** Chemical properties describe chemical changes. For example, when iron is exposed to water and oxygen it corrodes and produces a new substance called iron oxide (rust). Rusting is a chemical property of iron. Chemical properties are observed only when a substance is undergoing a change in composition. Words like rot, rust, decompose, ferment, grow, decay, and sprout usually signify a chemical change.

Problem

8. Classify the following changes as physical or chemical.
   - **a.** Food spoils.
   - **b.** Water boils.
   - **c.** A nail rusts.
   - **d.** A firefly emits light.
   - **e.** Oil is pumped out of a well.
   - **f.** Bread is baked.
   - **g.** Sugar dissolves in water.
   - **h.** A snowflake melts.

8. a. chemical   **e.** physical
    b. physical   **f.** chemical
    c. chemical   **g.** physical
    d. chemical   **h.** physical

1·12   Conservation of Mass

The total mass of substances involved in a physical or chemical change is conserved.

Combustion, or burning, is an example of one of the most familiar chemical changes. When we burn a piece of coal, atmospheric oxygen combines with the carbon in the coal. The products are carbon dioxide gas, water vapor, and a large residue of ash. With careful measurements we find that the mass of the reactants (the coal and oxygen consumed) equals the mass of the products (the carbon dioxide, water vapor, and ash). During the chemical reaction, the quantity of matter is unchanged. Similarly, when 10 grams of ice melt, 10 grams of water is obtained. Again, in this physical process, mass is conserved. Similar observations have been made for millions of chemical and physical changes. Thus the **law of conservation of mass** *states that in any physical or chemical reaction, mass is neither created nor destroyed; it is conserved.* In every case, the mass of the products is equal to the mass of the reactants.

The law of conservation of mass does not hold in nuclear reactions. In these reactions matter and energy are interconverted.

Figure 1·21
This experiment demonstrates the law of conservation of mass. On the left a candle is being burned in a sealed flask of oxygen. As the candle burns it combines with the oxygen within the flask. At the same time, it produces water and carbon dioxide. Throughout this process the mass of the flask does not change.

Key Terms

analytical chemistry	1·1	law of conservation	
biochemistry	1·1	of mass	1·12
chemical property	1·11	liquid	1·4
chemical reaction	1·11	mass	1·3
chemical symbol	1·8	matter	1·3
chemistry	1·1	mixture	1·6
compound	1·7	observation	1·2
data	1·2	organic chemistry	1·1
distillation	1·6	phase	1·6
element	1·7	physical change	1·5
energy	1·9	physical chemistry	1·1
experiment	1·2	physical property	1·3
gas	1·4	potential energy	1·9
heat	1·9	product	1·11
heterogeneous		reactant	1·11
mixture	1·6	scientific law	1·2
homogeneous		scientific method	1·2
mixture	1·6	solid	1·4
hypothesis	1·2	solution	1·6
inorganic chemistry	1·1	substance	1·3
kinetic energy	1·9	theory	1·2
law of conservation		vapor	1·4
of energy	1·10		

Chapter Summary

Chemistry is a natural science that deals with the composition of matter and the changes it undergoes. Matter is anything that has mass and occupies space. Matter exists in three states: solid, liquid, and gas. Chemists use the scientific method to learn how matter can be changed and how energy is involved in these changes.

A physical combination of two or more substances is a mixture. A mixture has a variable composition and may be identified as heterogeneous or homogeneous. A mixture can be separated into its components by physical methods. Homogeneous mixtures (solutions) have uniform properties throughout. Solutions may be gases, liquids, or solids. Like all other mixtures, solutions have variable composition.

A pure substance is either an element or a compound. A pure substance is identified by its physical properties. Elements are the building blocks for all compounds. Elements are always present in the same ratio in a given compound. The properties of a compound are usually quite different from those of the elements of which it is composed. Chemical methods are required to separate compounds into their constituent elements.

A change in the properties of a substance without a change in composition is a physical change. If there is a change in the composition of a substance, however, a chemical change is indicated. In a chemical change (chemical reaction) reactants are converted to products. In any physical or chemical change, both mass and energy are conserved.

Practice Questions and Problems

9. Define chemistry.   *1·1*

10. List the five major divisions of chemistry.   *1·1*

11. Distinguish between a theory, hypothesis, and law.   *1·2*

12. What is the purpose of an experiment as part of the scientific method?   *1·2*

13. Which of the following are examples of matter?
a. concrete   **b.** acetone vapor   **c.** heat   *1·3*
d. sound   **e.** air

14. List four physical properties of an iron nail. *1·3*

15. Match each state of matter with the terms on the left. More than one state can match each term.   *1·4*
a. incompressible   **1.** gas
b. indefinite shape   **2.** liquid
c. definite volume   **3.** solid
d. flows

16. Give two examples, different from those in your text, for each state of matter. *1·4*

17. In which state of matter do the following exist at room temperature and atmospheric pressure? *1·4*
a. diamond
b. oxygen
c. cooking oil
d. mercury
e. clay
f. neon

18. What physical properties would you use to separate these mixtures? *1·5*
a. iron filings and salt   b. salt and water

19. Which of the following are physical properties of water? *1·5*
a. colorless
b. produces a gas when sodium metal is dropped on it
c. changes from a liquid to solid at 0°C
d. decomposed by electricity into the elements hydrogen and oxygen
e. condenses at 100°C
f. liquid at room temperature
g. produces acetylene gas when dropped on calcium carbide

20. Name two physical properties that could be used to distinguish between these substances. *1·5*
a. water and rubbing alcohol
b. gold and aluminum
c. helium gas and oxygen gas

21. What is the difference between a heterogeneous and a homogeneous mixture? *1·6*

22. How can the various components of a mixture be separated? *1·6*

23. Identify each of the following samples of matter as homogeneous or heterogeneous. *1·6*
a. soil
b. iron
c. milk
d. glass
e. table sugar
f. sulfur
g. river water
h. cough syrup
i. grape juice
j. nitrogen

24. What are two ways to distinguish between an element and a compound? *1·7*

25. Classify each of the samples of matter in Problem 23 as an element, compound, or mixture. *1·7*

26. Write the chemical symbols for each of the following elements. *1·8*
a. copper
b. oxygen
c. phosphorus
d. silver
e. sodium
f. helium

27. Name the elements found in each compound.
a. ammonium chloride, NH_4Cl *1·8*
b. potassium permanganate, $KMnO_4$
c. isopropyl alcohol, C_3H_7OH
d. calcium iodide, CaI_2

28. Distinguish between potential energy and kinetic energy. *1·9*

29. List five forms of energy. *1·9*

30. State the law of conservation of energy. *1·10*

31. Distinguish between physical and chemical properties. Give two examples of each for iron. *1·11*

32. Classify each of the following as a physical or chemical change. *1·11*
a. bending a piece of wire
b. burning of coal
c. cooking a steak
d. dissolving sugar in water
e. souring of milk
f. stretching an elastic band
g. cutting grass
h. dissolving aspirin in water

33. State several physical or chemical properties that could be used to distinguish between these substances and mixtures. *1·11*
a. copper and silver
b. water and gasoline
c. water and a solution of table salt in water

Mastery Questions and Problems

34. Devise a way to separate sand from a mixture of charcoal, sand, sugar, and water. *1·6*

35. Give an example of conversions between these forms of energy. Do not use the examples given in your text. *1·10*
a. light to electrical
b. chemical to mechanical
c. electrical to chemical
d. mechanical to thermal

36. How do you know that each of these is a chemical change? *1·11*
a. Food spoils.
b. A foaming antacid table fizzes in water.
c. A ring of scum forms around your bathtub.
d. Iron rusts.
e. A firecracker explodes.

37. When a small amount of a red powder is heated, it darkens and then changes into a shiny silvery liquid. Is the red powder an element or a compound? Explain. Can you classify the shiny liquid with certainty? Explain. *1·7*

38. Classify the following properties of the element silicon as chemical or physical properties. *1·11*
  a. blue-gray color
  b. brittle
  c. insoluble in water
  d. melts at 1410°C
  e. reacts vigorously with fluorine
  f. shiny

39. Identify each of the following as a mixture or a compound. For the mixtures, classify as homogeneous or heterogeneous. *1·7*
  a. soda
  b. candle wax
  c. fog
  d. ink
  e. an egg
  f. ice
  g. blood
  h. gasoline

40. What is the difference between a physical or chemical change? *1·11*

Challenging Questions and Problems

41. Energy is conserved. It cannot be created or destroyed. Trace the origin of the energy in these bodies.
  a. a falling raindrop
  b. a gallon of gasoline
  c. a piece of steak

42. We now know that heat is a form of energy. In the not-too-distant past (the late 1700s), however, it was widely thought by scientists that heat was a weightless invisible fluid called caloric. In defense of these early scientists, can you think of some simple observations or experiments that would seem to support the *incorrect* theory that heat was a fluid?

Research Projects

1. What did the ancients know about the chemical elements?

2. What chemical processes were used by people in primitive cultures or in early societies?

3. Trace the history of alchemy. What did the alchemists contribute to the growth of chemistry? In your opinion, were the alchemists scientists? Why or why not?

4. What are some assumptions of the scientific method? What limitations of science result from these assumptions?

5. How are personal bias and error minimized by the use of the scientific method?

6. How is scientific research carried out on phenomena which cannot be manipulated or controlled? A few examples are tidal waves, weightlessness in space, volcanic eruptions, solar fusion, and "the greenhouse effect."

7. Describe the use of the scientific method by a famous chemist of your choice.

8. Devise a "system" for separating one of these mixtures into its components: garden soil, ocean water, "natural" (cloudy) apple juice, a carbonated soft drink.

9. What are the components of gasoline? How do the various grades and types of gasoline differ?

10. Discuss the efficiency of the interconversion of energy in various "alternative" energy sources, such as solar, wind, geothermal, and tidal.

Readings and References

Fine, Leonard W. *Chemistry Decoded*. New York: Oxford U Pr, 1976.

Jorpes, J. Erik. *Jac Berzelius, His Life and Work*. Berkeley, CA: University of California, 1971.

Kieffer, William F. *Chemistry: A Cultural Approach*. New York: Harper & Row, 1971.

Moravcsik, Michael J. *How to Grow Science*. New York: Universe, 1980.

Rossotti, Hazel. *Introducing Chemistry*. New York: Penguin, 1975.

Smith, Richard Furnald. *Chemistry for the Millions*. New York: Scribner, 1972.

2 Scientific Measurement

Chapter Planning Guide

Section	Demonstrations and Experiments	Resource Materials
2·1 The Importance of Measurement C*		Objectives Worksheet 2, SPB Skillsheet 2, SPB
2·A Lavoisier: The Founder of Modern Chemistry E		
2·2 Accuracy and Precision C	Dem 2·1 Accuracy vs Precision	
2·3 Significant Figures in Measurement C		
2·4 Significant Figures in Calculations C		
2·5 The Metric System C		Quiz 2·1 Beyond the Text: The Metric Story
2·6 Units of Length C		
2·7 Units of Volume C		
2·8 Units of Mass C	Dem 2·2 The Mass/Weight Relationship	
2·9 Measuring Density C	Exp 4 Mass, Volume, and Density, LM Dem 2·3 The Density of Liquids	Prelab 4, SPB
2·10 Specific Gravity O		Quiz 2·2
2·11 Measuring Temperature C		The Fluoridation of Water Supplies, ICT 2
2·B Choosing a Thermometer E		
2·12 Measuring Heat C		
2·13 Specific Heat Capacity C		Quiz 2·3 Reviewsheet 2, SPB Chapter 2 Test

*C = Core, O = Optional, E = Enrichment, H = Honors	LM = Laboratory Manual	SPB = Skills Practice Book, ICT = Issues in Chem. Tech.

Chapter Objectives

Having studied this chapter and done the problems, the student should be able to:

1. Distinguish between quantitative and qualitative measurements.　　　　　　　　　　*2·1*

2. Distinguish between the accuracy and precision of a measurement.　　　　　　　　　　*2·2*

3. Identify the number of significant figures in a measurement.　　　　　　　　　　*2·3*

4. Use the rules for significant figures in calculations to correctly round off numbers.　　　　*2·4*

5. State the advantages of the metric system.　　*2·5*

6. Name the metric units of length, mass, and volume.　　　　　　　　　　*2·5*

7. List and define the common metric prefixes.　　*2·6*

8. Use a decimeter cube to explain why the milliliter and cubic centimeter have the same volume.　　*2·7*

9. State the difference between the mass and weight of an object.　　　　　　　　　　*2·8*

10. Calculate the density of an object from experimental data.   *2·9*

11. State some useful applications of the measurement of specific gravity.   *2·10*

12. Convert between the Celsius and Kelvin temperature scales.   *2·11*

13. Name and define the units of heat energy.   *2·13*

14. Identify two factors that determine the heat capacity of an object.   *2·13*

Teaching Suggestions

2·1 The Importance of Measurement

To open this section, ask the students to describe some common but interesting object which you have placed before them. (Use something which involves energy, such as a burning candle, or an electrically driven or wind-up toy, to illustrate that measurement involves more that just material objects.) Ask them to make their descriptions as complete as possible. Depending on the time available, a list of 30-50 statements is a reasonable goal for your sharper students.

When the students have gone as far with this as they can, discuss the kinds of descriptions they have made. Most students will have had little experience in describing anything quantitatively, and their descriptions will likely have few measurements.

Point out that the qualitative descriptions which they have just given are useful, but are just not enough when dealing with the topics in this course. In chemistry we need to be able to state *quantities* in answer to questions like "What is the rate of the reaction?", "How much heat was given off?", or "What is the concentration of the solution?" To answer such questions meaningfully, we must be able to make a measurement precisely and accurately, to state its value properly, and to use this value in calculations. Point out that the purpose of this chapter is to help them develop these skills.

Measuring requires a unit of measurement and a method of comparing the object to be measured with this unit. The physical quantities always have a number and a unit, and each is as important as the other.

2·2 Accuracy and Precision

Emphasize that any time we perform measurements we are trying to find out the "true" value of the property which we are measuring. That is, we are trying to be *accurate*. We have a higher probability of being accurate when we make the measurement as *precisely* as possible. However, one does not guarantee the other. You may wish to do **Demonstration 2·1** *Accuracy vs Precision* to get across the idea that these terms cannot be used interchangeably.

After seeing you go through the steps in this demonstration, your students will probably be convinced that there is a difference between precision and accuracy. Then you can discuss the means by which we can obtain the greatest accuracy when making measurements. These would include zeroing a balance each time it is used, checking a thermometer against others, not using the end of a meter stick or ruler (use the 1 cm mark as the beginning of the ruler and then subtract 1 cm from the measurement), and most importantly, choosing a measuring instrument which has the smallest divisions (within the limits of practicality).

Students can judge measured results as being accurate or not and precise or not. You can also calculate the absolute and percentage errors of measured results compared to accepted values. You can use the results of the students' own experiments.

2·3 Significant Figures in Measurements

Several ideas should be emphasized in this section:

1. All measurements should use the measuring instrument to the limit of its precision. To obtain the last digit of a measurement, we must estimate between the finest gradations of the measuring device. Regardless of whether we are measuring mass, volume, or length, we *always* end up with an estimated digit which is slightly doubtful. The uncertainty of the estimated digit affects the certainty of the other digits in any calculation.

2. The measured value which has the most significant figures is likely to be the most certain, since the relative error is less. Consider two measurements with the same precision, for example, 2.1 cm and 132.1 cm. If the uncertainty in the measurement is plus or minus 0.1 cm, then the uncertainty in the first value is 0.1 cm out of 2.1 cm or nearly 5%, while the uncertainty of the second measurement is 0.1 cm out of 132.1 cm or only 0.08%.

3. We are concerned with significant figures only when we are dealing with measured quantities. Mathematical quantities, such as the 1/2 in $1/2 \ mv^2$, have an unlimited number of significant figures.

Most students have a great deal of difficulty in mastering the use of significant figures. In particular, they have the most trouble with the uses of zeros. Emphasize that it is extremely important for them to memorize the rules for determining the number of significant figures as soon as possible. You will very likely need to present the students with many examples before they will feel comfortable with significant figures. Students can make their own measurements and state the correct number of significant figures found for various instruments.

2·4 Significant Figures in Calculations

A calculated answer can never be any better than the weakest piece of information used in calculating that answer. Ask your students to find the answer to the following problem on their calculators: What is the mass of one gram of aluminum if 15 grams have a volume of 41 cm^3? Their answer will be 2.7333333 grams. Then ask them if they really think they know this mass to the nearest ten-millionth of a gram as their answer indicates. This shows how important it is to have some rules to decide just which digits we should keep in an answer. This section acquaints the students with these rules.

A major point of confusion is the fact that we have an entirely different rule for multiplication and division than we have for addition and subtraction. Emphasize that in addition and subtraction the number of digits in the answer is determined *solely by the precision* of the quantities being combined and *has nothing to do with significant figures*. In contrast, the number of digits in the answer found by multiplying or dividing quantities *has nothing to do with the number of decimal places but is determined solely by the number of significant figures* in the numbers which are being combined.

Expect that even after going over examples and discussing the problems in this chapter, many of your average and below average students will still be struggling with significant figures. A little drill and repetition at the beginning of the period each day could be extremely helpful. Many students become upset by an overemphasis on the correct number of significant figures in a calculation. Emphasize that the truth of a measurement depends on following the rules for significant figures. Make most problems have numbers with no more than 3 significant figures to keep the emphasis on the problem and not on the number of significant figures.

2·5 The Metric System

It is tempting when introducing the metric system or the SI units to try to cover the whole system and all of its units. This can only lead to confusion for the students. Try to limit your presentation only to those basic units, derived units, and prefixes which will be used in this course.

Point out that the prefixes listed in Table 2·3 can be used with all measured quantities. It is very helpful to the students if they can relate actual objects to these abstract terms. Bring in examples of familiar objects with approximate mass, length, and volume known to the students. After stating these quantities in the fundamental units, ask the students to express them with different prefixes. For example, if an object has a volume of 5.0 L, what is its volume in mL, cm^3, and microliters?

You can ask students to bring in examples of products that have metric system measurements on them. This provides an opportunity to note the metric system units.

2·6 Units of Length

Measure the dimensions of different objects using rulers or calipers of different units. Take this opportunity to practice significant figures.

2·7 Units of Volume

Measure the volumes of different objects using rulers, graduated cylinders, flasks, and beakers with different units of measurement. Practice significant figures.

2·8 Units of Mass

You may want to treat Sections 2·5 to 2·8 all at once. Should you decide to do this, then you probably would want to present these sections to the students, have them work the in-text problems, have them work the end of chapter problems, and then have them do **Experiment 4** *Mass, Volume, and Density* which includes mass, volume, and density. If you have students with strong backgrounds, you may wish to select only certain activities from each of the experiments.

Remind them that mass and weight are not synonymous. The weight of an object varies with the strength of the gravitational field in a particular location. Mass does not. When using a balance we are determining the mass of an object by comparing it to a set of known masses. This procedure works regardless of the force of gravity in our location. **Demonstration 2·2** *The Mass/Weight Relationship* is helpful.

2·9 Measuring Density

It is important that the students realize that density is a property which does not depend upon how much of a substance is present. You can illustrate this by showing different quantities of the same material and asking if they have the same density. A glance at Table 2·8 shows that different substances have different densities. Thus density can be used to identify and distinguish substances.

Often when students calculate densities they write the units, g/cm^3, without any understanding of what they mean. Point out that a density of 2.7 g/cm^3 means that regardless of the volume a particular sample has, one cubic centimeter of it has a mass of 2.7 grams. Thus density is really answering the question "What is the mass of a one cubic centimeter of a substance?"

If you have not done so already, you might wish to repeat **Demonstration 1·12** in which you make layers of substances of varying densities. **Demonstration 2·3** *The Density of Liquids* suggests other sets of substances of varying density.

You can ask students to think of ways to measure the densities of irregularly-shaped solids, liquids, and gases.

2·10 Specific Gravity

Students will have some difficulty with the concept of specific gravity since it is one step more abstract than density. One possible approach is to consider specific gravity as a means by which the mass of a cubic centimeter of any substance is compared to the mass of a cubic centimeter of some other substance, usually water. Thus a specific gravity of 2.7 for a particular substance means that 1 cm^3 of it has a mass which is 2.7 times that of 1 cm^3 of water. Point out that when specific gravity is calculated, the units cancel out. *Specific gravity is dimensionless.*

2·11 Measuring Temperature

The Celsius temperature scale is a relative scale. It is partially based on the behavior of water. There is no particular advantage to either one. Inform the students that in most of our work in chemistry we will be using the Celsius scale.

Point out that one disadvantage to both scales is that zero degrees does not represent the lowest possible value of temperature. Thus we must deal with negative numbers for temperature values at times. The advantage of the Kelvin scale is that it is based on a true, "absolute" zero. The lowest possible temperature is 0 K. Why this is true can be better explained after the concepts of molecular motion and kinetic energy are covered.

2·12 Measuring Heat

While most students catch onto the concept of temperature quite readily, many will have great difficulty in mastering the concept of heat. In their minds something which has a very high temperature has a large amount of heat as well. You will need to convince them that the amount of heat a body contains has to do with the total amount of energy it contains, not how hot it is.

A given amount of heat energy may or may not cause a significant temperature change when put into a substance. As an example you might suggest a large coin heated in a bunsen burner flame. There is no doubt that this coin has a very high temperature. If this hot coin were placed in a milliliter of water, it would probably raise the temperature of the water to the boiling point. On the other hand, the same coin put into a bathtub full of water would produce a change that would be barely detectable. In both cases the amount of heat transferred to the water is the same, yet the effect on temperature is quite different.

Point out that we have no way to measure heat directly. To find out how much heat is transferred, we must know the amount of temperature change, the amount of substance into which it was transferred, and the identity of the substance. Thus the calorie is defined in terms of raising the temperature of 1 g of water 1°C.

2·13 Specific Heat Capacity

Make it clear to the students that not all substances respond in the same way to the input of heat. A given amount of heat raises the temperature of some substances (such as metals) far more than others (such as nonmetals). The ability of a substance to absorb or release heat energy is measured by its specific heat capacity.

Water is the standard substance with which the calorie is defined; it has one of the highest heat capacities. Thus it can absorb or release relatively large amounts of energy without undergoing a large temperature change.

Demonstrations

2·1 Accuracy vs Precision

Concept: A very precise measurement can still be very inaccurate.

Materials: shortened meter stick, regular meter stick.

Procedure: 1. Saw a centimeter off of a meter stick. Inform your class that you are going to illustrate precision in measurement using this meter stick (but take care no one notices that the meter stick is defective). 2. Emphasize how you are measuring the table or some long object to the nearest millimeter (0.001 m) and estimating between the lines to the nearest 0.0001 m. For a measurement of the depth of your demonstration table you can use a six digit number. 3. Mention that you could repeat this measurement. The estimate of the last digit might vary, but the precision of the measurement is reproducible. 4. State that you have a high degree of precision, but what about the accuracy? 5. The measurement is inaccurate. Reveal an actual meter stick and compare the two. State that the numbers you have obtained do not represent the true value, since the measuring instrument is defective.

2·2 The Mass/Weight Relationship

Concept: Mass and weight differ.

Materials: two-pan balance, desk, piece of aluminum, copper or zinc, string, set of standard weights, beaker, water, alcohol.

Procedure: 1. Hang the piece of metal from the underside of one pan of a two-pan balance on the edge of the desk. 2. Find its weight by balancing it with standard weights. 3. Immerse the metal in a beaker of water as it hangs and note that the balance is no longer balanced. Find its new weight. 4. Immerse it in alcohol, and then find its weight again. 5. Note that it is the same object and has the same amount of mass, but its weight changes.

2·3 The Density of Liquids

Concept: Liquids of different densities will separate to form layers.

Materials: copper coin, oak block, cork, mercury, water, hydrometer jar, glass plate, piece of steel, rubber stopper, plastic, corn oil.

Procedure: 1. Put all the materials into the hydrometer jar. 2. Seal the top with the glass plate and epoxy if you want to store it. 3. The liquids separate into layers. The solids are suspended between the layers; the cork is on top. 4. Shake the system and invert it to remix materials to repeat the demonstration. **Caution:** *Mercury is highly toxic. Use a mercury clean-up sponge for any spills.*

Audiovisual Resources

Density (V) EME, 1982, 25 min. (Use with Section 2·7, 2·8, and 2·9.) Explains the measurement of mass and volume and examines the densities of solids, liquids, and gases.

Make Mine Metric (F) Pyramid Films, 1975, 13 min. (Use with Sections 2·5, 2·6, 2·7, and 2·8.) Introduces the metric system, using real-life situations to compare metric units to English.

Beyond the Text

The Metric Story

Cubits, furlongs, fathoms, and drams evoke the long and colorful past of measurement. The cubit, used in constructing the Egyptian pyramids, is the earliest recorded unit of measurement. Like many early units of measure, it was defined in terms of the human body. A cubit was the distance from a man's elbow to the tip of his middle finger. A yard was defined by King Henry I of England as the distance from the tip of his nose to the end of his fingers. An inch was the width of an English soldier's thumb, a foot the length of his boot.

The difficulty with such units is obvious. Human anatomy is not uniform. The Egyptian cubit was $20\frac{1}{2}$ inches; the Roman cubit was $17\frac{1}{2}$ inches; and the English cubit is 18 inches.

The rise of science and the increase in international commerce created a need for the establishment of a standard system of measurement. In 1791 French scientists proposed the metric system. Antoine Lavoisier described this system in glowing terms: "Never has anything more grand and simple, more coherent in all its parts, issued from the hand of man."

The system that earned this lavish praise was indeed simple. Its basic unit of length was the meter. It was defined as one ten-millionth of the distance along a line at sea level, from the earth's equator to its north pole. The unit of volume, the liter, was the volume of a cube measuring one-tenth of a meter on a side. The unit of mass, the gram, was defined as the mass of one thousandth of a liter of water. These basic units were multiplied by powers of ten to obtain smaller and larger units. Thus all units were ultimately defined in terms of something that was assumed to be invariable (the dimension of the earth). The surveying of the earth was later found to be in error. The meter was redefined as the length of a particular metal bar made of a platinum-iridium alloy. Later the kilogram was represented by a cylinder made of the same metal. This prototype kilogram is still used as the standard for measuring mass. In 1983 the meter was redefined, however, for greater accuracy. A meter is now the distance traveled by light in a vacuum in 0.000 000 033 56 second.

Answers to End of Chapter Questions and Problems

Practice Questions and Problems

14. a. qualitative **b.** qualitative **c.** quantitative **d.** qualitative **e.** quantitative **f.** quantitative

15. Accuracy is concerned with the "correctness" of a measurement. Precision is concerned with the reproducibility of a series of measurements.

16. a. accurate and precise **b.** inaccurate and precise **c.** inaccurate and imprecise

17. Jim: inaccurate and imprecise. Leigh Anne: accurate and precise. Bob: inaccurate and precise.

18. a. 3 **b.** 2 **c.** 4 **d.** 4 **e.** 3 **f.** 3 **g.** 5 **h.** 5

19. a. 2 **b.** 3 **c.** 3 **d.** 3 **e.** 2 **f.** 5

20. a. 98.5 L **b.** 0.000 763 cg **c.** 57.0 m **d.** 9.50×10^3 s **e.** 12.2°C **f.** $0.007\ 50 \times 10^4$ mm **g.** 1760 mL **h.** 8.86 km

21. a. 9.85×10^1 L **b.** 7.63×10^{-4} cg **c.** 5.70×10^1 m **d.** 9.50×10^3 s **e.** 1.22×10^1 °C **f.** 7.50×10^1 mm **g.** 1.76×10^3 mL **h.** 8.86×10^0 km

22. a. 43 g **b.** 7.3 cm² **c.** 225.8 L **d.** 92.0 kg **e.** 32.4 m³ **f.** 104 cm³

23. a. 4.3×10^1 g **b.** 7.3×10^0 cm^2
c. 2.258×10^2 L **d.** 9.20×10^1 kg
e. 3.24×10^1 m^3 **f.** 1.04×10^2 cm^3

24. 23.9 g

25. a. 6.6×10^4 **b.** 4.0×10^{-7} **c.** 10^{+7}
d. 8.65×10^{-1} **e.** 4.0×10^{-7} **f.** 1.9×10^{14}

26. Units are based on multiples of ten. Prefixes have the same meaning when attached to different units of measure.

27. a. second **b.** meter **c.** mole **d.** kelvin **e.** kilogram

28. a. liter **b.** gram **c.** meter

29. a. m, 10^{-3} of **b.** n, 10^{-9} of **c.** k, 10^3 times **d.** d, 10^{-1} of **e.** c, 10^{-2} of

30. c, d, a, e, f, b.

31. a. 2 **b.** 3 **c.** 1 **d.** 4

32. a. and **d, f, e, c, b.**

33. The mass of an object is constant. The weight of an object varies with location.

34. a. 1 **b.** 4 **c.** 2 **d.** 3

35. Density is independent of sample size.

36. No. Density of the metal bar is 12 g/cm^3, but density of gold is 19 g/cm^3.

37. 1.7×10^{-2} g/L

38. Specific gravity has no unit. It is a ratio of two densities.

39. Mercury has the highest specific gravity. Wood has the lowest.

40. Melting point: 1234 K. Boiling point: 2485 K.

41. -196

42. The calorie (cal) and the joule (J).

43. 2.8×10^3 cal or 1.2×10^4 J

44. $\dfrac{0.13 \text{ J}}{\text{g} \times {}^\circ\text{C}}$

45. Substance with the higher heat capacity absorbs more energy.

Mastery Questions and Problems

46. Improper calibration or improper use of the measuring device.

47. f, e, c, g, d, a, b, h.

48. Significant figures in the answer of an addition problem depend on the least number of decimal places.

49. 1.6×10^5 cm^3 = 1.6×10^2 L

50. a. cg **b.** L **c.** kcal **d.** cs **e.** mL **f.** dm^3

51. The digit to the right of the last significant figure is dropped if it is less than five.

52. Water has a high specific heat.

Review Questions and Problems

53. a. Na **b.** Al **c.** Cl **d.** Cu **e.** S **f.** Sr

54. a. chemical **b.** physical **c.** physical
d. chemical **e.** chemical **f.** physical

55. Add water to dissolve all the salt. Then decant or filter.

56. Radiant, heat, sound, chemical, mechanical, electrical, nuclear.

57. A homogeneous mixture can be separated by physical means. A compound can be chemically separated into its elements.

58. To understand the world around us.

59. 116.7 g

Challenging Questions and Problems

60. Hot and cold are relative terms and depend on our perceptions.

61. 510 g Pb

62. 1.3×10^7 kcal

63. $2.1 \dfrac{\text{g}}{\text{cm}^3}$

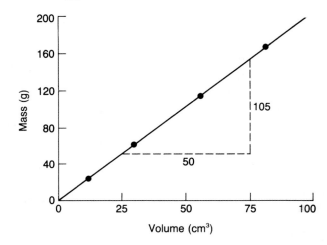

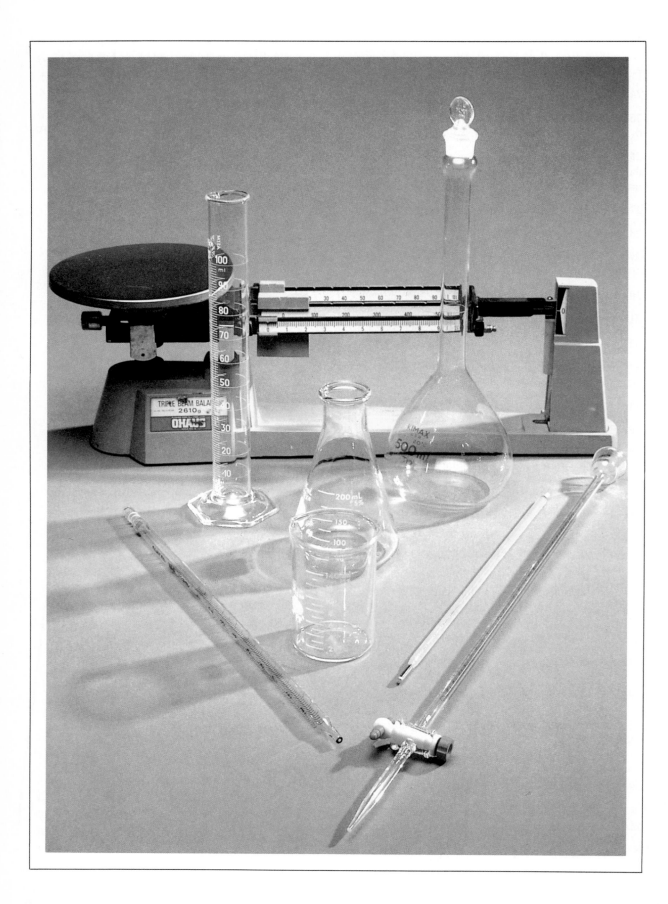

2 Scientific Measurement

Chapter Preview

Figure 2·1
Chemists use a wide variety of measuring devices. Balances are used to measure mass and thermometers are used to measure temperature. Glassware is used to measure volume.

Everyone makes and uses measurements. You decide how to dress in the morning based on the measured outside temperature. You measure out the ingredients for your favorite cookie recipe. If you were building a cabinet for your stereo system, you would carefully measure each piece of wood.

Measurements are also fundamental to the experimental sciences. The reference standards used by scientists are those of the metric system. This is a system based on multiples of 10. The understanding of scientific concepts is often based on measurements. It is important to be able to make measurements and to decide whether a measurement is good or bad.

2·1 The Importance of Measurement

■ Measuring is a fundamental skill.

One of your most important skills for chemistry is making measurements. **Quantitative measurements** *give results in a definite form, usually as numbers.* **Qualitative measurements** *give results in a descriptive nonnumeric form.* Some measurements can be made either qualitatively or quantitatively. Consider, for example, a sick person with a fever. If we touch a person's forehead we might decide, "Yes! This person does feel feverish." This is a qualitative and subjective evaluation. If we need to be objective, we can use a thermometer. It will give us a numerical, or

Figure 2·2
By lifting the watermelon, the child finds it is heavy. This is a qualitative observation. The weight of the watermelon can also be determined with a spring scale. This is a quantitative observation.

quantitative, measurement. We get a specific number, the temperature, that can be recorded for future reference.

If several people touch the person's forehead, they might or might not agree with the original observer. Personal biases, as well as people's own temperatures could influence their decisions. By using a thermometer we can eliminate personal bias. Then everyone will report the same number. Remember, we have not questioned whether the thermometer gives us the correct temperature. Any instrument whose calibration is in doubt must be checked or discarded. A measurement can be no more reliable than the measuring instrument. Before looking at some common types of measurement, we will discuss the accuracy and precision of measurements.

Figure 2·3
When Lavoisier heated mercury in the container at left, some red oxide of mercury formed. At the same time, the volume of air in the bell jar at the right decreased.

2·A Lavoisier: The Founder of Modern Chemistry

Antoine-Laurent Lavoisier (1743–1794) was a brilliant French scientist and dedicated public servant. He is most famous for his work on combustion, which brought about the overthrow of the phlogiston theory. This erroneous theory had dominated chemistry for nearly 300 years.

Scientists before Lavoisier believed that all burnable substances contained phlogiston ("fire stuff"). When a substance burned, it was thought to have lost phlogiston. The ash, of course, was the substance minus its phlogiston. Lavoisier performed many experiments in which he made extremely careful measurements of the mass of a substance before and after combustion. He proved that many ashes weigh more than their original substance. This fact could not be explained by the phlogiston theory.

In 1772 Lavoisier began his experiments on combustion. In one of these experiments, he sealed mercury in a glass vessel and carefully determined the mass of the vessel with its contents. He then heated the vessel in a furnace. After 4 days of heating, flecks of red

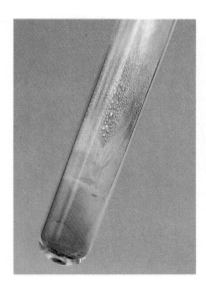

Figure 2·4
The red compound shown here is mercury(II) oxide. When heated, it decomposes into mercury and oxygen. You can see tiny drops of liquid mercury that have condensed on the inner surface of the test tube.

Safety

Mercury and its compounds are toxic. Heating any form of mercury should be avoided in the school laboratory. Mercury compounds should not be flushed down the drain.

Scientific measurements should be both accurate and precise.

powder appeared on the surface of the mercury. After 12 days of continuous heating, most of the mercury had been converted to the red powder. Lavoisier again weighed the sealed vessel and found the mass unchanged. When the seal was broken, however, he heard the sound of air rushing into the vessel. He reasoned that during the change of mercury to its red powder, the mercury metal must have used up some component of the air sealed in the vessel. This created a partial vacuum. When the vessel was opened air rushed in to fill it. After this air had entered, Lavoisier weighed the vessel again and found it heavier. He deduced that the gain in mass was the mass of the component of air used up.

By 1777 Lavoisier had completed a series of experiments with the red powder of mercury. When this powder was heated to higher temperatures, it gave off a gas that proved to be oxygen. This gas had been discovered in 1773 by Carl Scheele and again in 1774 by Joseph Priestly. (They were working independently.) In many tests, Lavoisier found that nothing could be burned in the absence of oxygen. He concluded that *combustion is the combination of a burnable substance with oxygen.* Younger chemists accepted his conclusions, and the mysterious phlogiston theory soon passed into history.

During the eighteenth century, very few women were involved in scientific work. Nevertheless, Marie Ann Lavoisier actively assisted her husband in scientific research. She recorded measurements and took notes in the laboratory. She learned both Latin and English, which her husband did not know. This allowed her to write translations and condensations of scientific articles. Marie Ann Lavoisier also learned to draw. She illustrated several books which Antoine-Laurent authored.

Like many other scientists of this time, Antoine-Laurent was an aristocrat. He was also a member of the despised royal taxation commission, a position he took to finance his scientific work. Although he had dedicated much of his time and money to improving the lives of the common people, Lavoisier was hated during the French Revolution. He refused to flee France even though he knew his life was in danger. In 1794 he was arrested, tried, and beheaded. A Frenchman has written, "Until it is realized that the gravest crime of the French Revolution was not the execution of the King, but of Lavoisier, there is no right measure of values, for Lavoisier was one the greatest three or four men France had produced."

2·2 Accuracy and Precision

The words *accuracy* and *precision* mean the same thing to many people. To scientists, however, their meanings are different. **Accuracy** *is how close a measurement comes to the actual dimension or true value of whatever is measured.* **Precision** *is concerned with the reproducibility of the measurement.* Darts stuck in a dart board can be used to illustrate

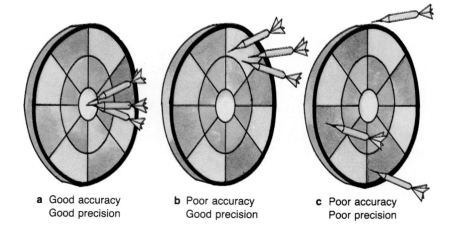

a Good accuracy
Good precision

b Poor accuracy
Good precision

c Poor accuracy
Poor precision

accuracy and precision in making measurements. Let the bull's-eye of the dart board represent the true value of what we are measuring. Then, the closeness of a dart to the bull's-eye is a measure of our accuracy. It represents how close we come to the true value. Let's consider three possible outcomes of tossing three darts at the board (Figure 2·5).

1. All the darts stick in the bull's-eye. Each dart in the bull's eye represents an accurate measurement of the true value. Thus, our measurements are very accurate. All the measurements are also closely grouped together. Therefore our measurements are very reproducible and very precise.

2. All the darts are closely grouped, but they are not in the bull's-eye. Our precision is excellent because our tosses are very reproducible. The tosses are inaccurate, though, because they do not reflect the true value.

3. The darts are spread randomly around the target. Our shots are neither accurate nor precise. We have missed the target, and we have failed to toss the darts reproducibly.

Note that the precision of a measurement depends on more than one measurement. By contrast, an individual measurement might be accurate or inaccurate. The accuracy of real measurements often depends on the quality of the measuring device. Precision often depends on the skill of the person making the measurement. We must usually assume that the measuring devices we use in the laboratory are as accurate as their manufacturers specify. Our job is to use these devices with enough care to obtain good precision.

Every measuring device should be periodically checked against a standard to ensure its accuracy.

Before reading this section you should review your knowledge of exponential notation by doing Section B·1 of the Math Review in Appendix B.

2·3 Significant Figures in Measurements

Scientists report measurements in significant figures. *The **significant figures** in a measurement include all the digits that can be known accurately plus a last digit that must be estimated.* When you are taking a temperature using a thermometer calibrated in 1° intervals, it is easy to report the temperature to the nearest degree. With this thermometer you can also estimate the temperature to the nearest tenth of a degree. Suppose you estimate a temperature that lies between 35° and 36° to be 35.8°. This number has three significant figures. The first two digits

■ Significant figures are digits in a measurement that have meaning.

Figure 2·6

Three different meter sticks could be used to measure the length of a board. What measurement do you get in each case? Is there a difference in the number of significant figures in the three measurements? Why or why not?

a 0.6 m **b** 0.65 m **c** 0.647 m Yes. The greater the number of divisions on the meter stick, the greater the number of significant figures in the measurement.

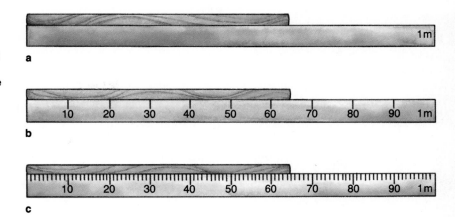

Because of the uncertainty in the estimated digit in a measurement, we must use the calculation rules given in the next section.

In scientific writing, commas are not used to separate groups of digits. This is because a comma is used as a decimal point in many countries.

(3 and 5) are known with certainty. The last digit (8) has been estimated. It involves some uncertainty.

By estimating the last digit in a measurement, scientists are able to get additional information. The digits retained in a measurement are all significant figures, but the last digit is uncertain. Suppose you have a thermometer that is calibrated in 0.1° intervals. You can easily report the temperature to the nearest 0.1° and estimate it to the nearest 0.01°. You might report the temperature as 35.82°. This measurement has four significant figures, and the last digit (2) is uncertain.

The rules for determining which digits in a measurement are significant are as follows.

1. Every nonzero digit in a recorded measurement is significant. The measurements 24.7 m, 0.743 m, and 714 m all express a measure of length to three significant figures. The abbreviation, *m*, stands for the unit of length, meter.

2. Zeros appearing between nonzero digits are significant. The measurements 7003 m, 40.79 m, and 1.503 m all have four significant figures.

3. Zeros appearing in front of all nonzero digits are not significant. They are acting as place holders. The measurements 0.0071 m, 0.42 m, and 0.000 099 m all have two significant figures.

4. Zeros at the end of a number and to the right of a decimal point are significant. The measurements 43.00 m, 1.010 m, and 9.000 m all have four significant figures.

5. Zeros at the end of a measurement and to the left of the decimal point can be confusing. They are not significant if they just serve as place markers to show the magnitude of the number. The zeros in the measurements 300 m, 7000 m, and 27 210 m are probably not significant, but some of them may be. We cannot tell any difference. *If these zeros were measured then they are significant.* To avoid ambiguity, the measurements should then be written in standard exponential form: 3.00×10^2 m, 7.000×10^3 m, and 2.7210×10^4 m. In these examples the number of significant figures is three, four, and five, respectively.

Figure 2·7
Quality control chemists determine the range of characteristics that indicate whether the quality of a product is acceptable.

Significant figures in measurements are used to correctly round off calculated answers.

Example 1

How many significant figures are in each of these measurements?

a. 123 m
b. 0.123 m
c. 40 506 m
d. 9.8000×10^4 m

e. 4.5600 m
f. 0.078 m
g. 0.070 80 m
h. 98 000 m

Solution

All nonzero digits are significant. Use rules 2–5 to decide about zeros.

a. 3 (rule 1)
b. 3 (rule 3)
c. 5 (rule 2)
d. 5 (rules 4 and 5)

e. 5 (rule 4)
f. 2 (rule 3)
g. 4 (rules 2, 3, 4)
h. 2 (rule 5)

Problem

1. Determine the number of significant figures in each of the following measurements.

a. 5.730×10^{-2} m
b. 8765 m
c. 0.000 73 m
d. 40.007 m

e. 3000 m
f. 0.010 m
g. 50 700 m
h. 0.070 020 m

1. a. 4
b. 4
c. 2
d. 5

e. 1
f. 2
g. 3
h. 5

2·4   Significant Figures in Calculations

When calculations are done with scientific measurements, we sometimes end up with an answer with more digits than can be justified as significant. Such numbers must be rounded off to make them consistent with the data they represent. *An answer cannot be more precise than the least precise measurement.* To round off a number, we must first decide how many significant figures it should have. Our decision will depend on the given measurements and on the arithmetic operation used. Once we know the number of significant figures our answer should have, we count that many digits starting on the left. *If the digit immediately following the last significant digit is less than 5, all the digits after the last significant place are dropped. If the digit is 5 or greater, the value of the digit in the last significant place is increased by 1.* Rounding off 56.212 m to four significant figures gives us 56.21 m, and 56.216 m becomes 56.22 m.

Example 2

Round off each of these measurements to the number of significant figures shown in parentheses. Write the answer in standard exponential form.

a. 314.721 m (4)
b. 0.001 775 m (2)

c. 64.32×10^{-1} m (1)
d. 8792 m (2)

Solution

The arrow points to the digit immediately following the last significant digit. (Significant figures are shown in parentheses.)

a. 314.721 m; 2 is less than 5; 314.7 m (4) = 3.147×10^2 m

b. 0.001 775 m; 7 is greater than 5; 0.0018 m (2) = 1.8×10^{-3} m

c. 64.32×10^{-1} m; 4 is less than 5; 60×10^{-1} m (1) = 6 m

d. 8792 m; 9 is greater than 5; 8800 m (2) = 8.8×10^3 m

Problem

2. a. 87.1 m, 9×10^1 m
b. 4.36×10^8 m, 4×10^8 m
c. 1.55×10^{-2} m, 2×10^{-2} m
d. 9.01×10^3 m, 9×10^3 m
e. 1.78×10^{-3} m, 2×10^{-3} m
f. 6.30×10^2 m, 6×10^2 m

2. Round off each measurement to three significant figures and then to one significant figure. Write your answers in standard form.

a. 87.073 m   **c.** 0.01552 m   **e.** 1.7777×10^{-3} m

b. 4.3621×10^8 m   **d.** 9009 m   **f.** 629.55 m

Addition and Subtraction. The answer of an addition or subtraction can have no more digits to the right of the decimal point than are contained in the measurement with the least number of digits to the right of the decimal point.

Example 3

Do the following operations and give the answer to the correct number of significant figures.

a. 12.52 m + 349.0 m + 8.24 m   **b.** 74.626 m − 28.34 m

Solution

a. Align the decimal points and add the numbers.

$$
\begin{array}{r}
12.52 \text{ m} \\
349.0 \text{\ \ m} \\
8.24 \text{ m} \\
\hline
369.76 \text{ m}
\end{array}
$$

The answer must be rounded off to one digit after the decimal point. The answer is 369.8 m or 3.698×10^2 m.

b. Align the decimal points and subtract the numbers.

$$
\begin{array}{r}
74.626 \text{ m} \\
-28.34 \text{\ \ m} \\
\hline
46.286 \text{ m}
\end{array}
$$

The answer must be rounded off to two digits after the decimal point. The answer is 46.29 m or 4.629×10^1 m.

3. a. 79.2 m   c. 11.53 m
   b. 7.33 m   d. 17.3 m

Problem

3. Do the following operations and give your answer to the correct number of significant figures.
   a. 61.2 m + 9.35 m + 8.6 m   **c.** 1.36 m + 10.17 m
   b. 9.44 m − 2.111 m   **d.** 34.61 m − 17.3 m

Multiplication and Division.   In calculations involving multiplication and division, the answer must contain no more significant figures than the measurement with the least number of significant figures. The position of the decimal point has nothing to do with the number of significant figures.

Figure 2·8
This calculator was used to multiply the measurements 3.24 cm and 1.78 cm. When correctly rounded off, the product is 5.77 cm². The answer to a multiplication or division problem should not contain more significant digits than the least precise measurement in the problem.

Example 4

Do the following operations and give the answer to the correct number of significant figures.
   a. 7.55 m × 0.34 m   **c.** 2.4526 m ÷ 8.4
   b. 2.10 m × 0.70 m   **d.** 0.365 m ÷ 0.0200

Solution

The calculated answer is given, then rounded off.
   a. 2.567 m² = 2.6 m² (0.34 m has two significant figures)
   b. 1.47 m² = 1.5 m² (0.70 m has two significant figures)
   c. 0.291 976 m = 0.29 m (8.4 has two significant figures)
   d. 18.25 m = 18.3 m (both numbers have three significant figures)

Problem

4. Do the following problems and give your answer to the correct number of significant figures.
   a. 8.3 m × 1.22 m
   b. $(1.8 \times 10^{-3}$ m$) \times (2.9 \times 10^{-2}$ m$)$
   c. 8432 m ÷ 12.5
   d. 5.3×10^{-2} m ÷ 0.255

4. a. 1.0×10^1
   b. 5.2×10^{-5} m²
   c. 6.75×10^2 m
   d. 0.21 m

Calculations are often easier with measurements in the metric system because the use of fractions is nearly eliminated.

◼ The metric system, or the SI, is the preferred system of scientific measurement.

2·5 The Metric System

A measurement depends on a standard for reference. *The standards of measurement used by scientists are those of the* **metric system.** Other systems of measurement are still in use, but they are gradually being phased out. They are less useful because there is no systematic digital relationship among the units. The metric system is important because of its simplicity and convenience. All the units are based on 10 or multiples of 10. As a result, conversions between units are easy to do. The metric

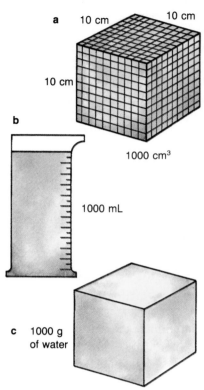

Table 2·1   SI Base Units of Measurement

Quantity measured	Unit	SI symbol
Length	meter	m
Mass	kilogram	kg
Time	second	s
Electric current	ampere	A
Thermodynamic temperature	kelvin	K
Amount of substance	mole	mol
Luminous intensity	candela	cd

Figure 2·9
The metric units of mass, length, and volume are related by definition. **a** The volume of a 10 cm cube is 1000 cm³. **b** The cube can hold 1000 ml of water. **c** This volume of water has a mass of 1000 grams.

system was originally established in France in 1790. *The* **International System of Units** (abbreviated **SI,** after the French name Le Système International d'Unités) *is a revised version of the metric system.* It was adopted by international agreement in 1960. The SI has seven base units (Table 2·1). From these, other SI units of measurement such as volume, density, and pressure are derived.

It is possible to report all measured quantities in SI units. Sometimes, however, non-SI units are preferred for convenience or practical reasons. Table 2·2 lists some SI and non-SI units of measurement that are used in this text.

When a measurement is made, the numerical value must be assigned the correct units. Without the correct units it is not possible to communicate the resulting measurement. Imagine the confusion that would ensue if you were instructed to "heat the solution for 20." Your immediate response would be "Twenty what? Seconds, minutes, hours, or days?" The units of length, volume, and mass will be discussed in the three sections that follow.

Table 2·2   Some Units of Measurement Used in This Text

Quantity	SI base unit or SI derived unit	Non-SI unit
Length	meter (m)	
Volume	cubic meter (m³)	liter
Mass	kilogram (kg)	
Density	grams per cubic centimeter (g/cm³) grams per milliliter (g/mL)	
Temperature	kelvin (K)	degree Celsius (°C)
Time	second (s)	
Pressure	pascal (pa)	atmosphere (atm) millimeter of mercury (mm Hg)
Energy	joule (J)	calorie (cal)

2·6 Units of Length

The meter is the basic metric unit of length.

A meter is defined as the distance that light travels in a vacuum in 1/299 792 458 of a second.

Size is an important property of matter. *In the metric system the basic unit of length, or linear measure, is the* **meter** *(m)*. All measurements of length can be expressed in meters. (The length of a page in this book is about one-fifth of a meter.) For very large and very small lengths, however, it is more convenient to use the appropriate metric prefix with the base unit meter. Table 2·3 lists the prefixes in common use in the metric system. As an example, this dash - is about 0.001 m long. Compare the length of this dash with the section of meter stick reproduced in Figure 2·10. The dash measures about 1 millimeter (mm), or 1/1000 of a meter. Both 1 mm and 0.001 m measure the same length.

For large distances, it is most appropriate to express a measurement in kilometers (km). The prefix *kilo-* means 1000 times larger; 1 km is equal to 1000 m. The marathon distance race of about 42 000 m is more conveniently expressed as 42 km (42 × 1000 m). Table 2·4 summarizes the relationships among units of length in the metric system.

Figure 2·10
A meter stick is divided into 100 divisions. Each division is a centimeter. Each centimeter is divided into 10 millimeters. How many millimeters are in a meter?
1000.

Table 2·3	Prefixes in Common Use in the Metric System	
Prefix	Symbol	Meaning
kilo	k	1000 times larger than the unit it precedes (1000 or 10^3)
deci	d	10 times smaller than the unit it precedes (1/10 or 10^{-1})
centi	c	100 times smaller than the unit it precedes (1/100 or 10^{-2}
milli	m	1000 times smaller than the unit it precedes (1/1000 or 10^{-3})
micro	μ	1 million times smaller than the unit it precedes (1/1 000 000 or 10^{-6}) (μ is the lowercase Greek letter "mu")
nano	n	1000 million times smaller than the unit it precedes (1/1 000 000 000 or 10^{-9})

Table 2·4	Metric Units for Length		
Unit	Symbol	Relationship	Examples (approximate values)
Kilometer	km	$1 \text{ km} = 10^3 \text{ m}$	Length of about five city blocks ≈ 1 km
Meter (base unit)	m		Height of door knob from the floor ≈ 1 m
Decimeter	dm	$10^1 \text{ dm} = 1 \text{ m}$	Diameter of large orange ≈ 1 dm
Centimeter	cm	$10^2 \text{ cm} = 1 \text{ m}$	Width of shirt button ≈ 1 cm
Millimeter	mm	$10^3 \text{ mm} = 1 \text{ m}$	Thickness of dime ≈ 1 mm
Micrometer	μm	$10^6 \text{ } \mu\text{m} = 1 \text{ m}$	Diameter of bacterial cell ≈ 1 μm
Nanometer	nm	$10^9 \text{ nm} = 1 \text{ m}$	Thickness of RNA molecule ≈ 1 nm

5. **a.** 2 mm
   b. 16.4 cm
   c. 25.3 cm
   d. 1.9 cm

Problem

5. Measure the following dimensions using metric units with the appropriate metric prefix.   **a.** the height of this letter I   **b.** the width of Table 2·4   **c.** the height of this page   **d.** the distance between these brackets [   ]

2·7   Units of Volume

The space occupied by matter is called **volume.** It is a derived unit. Volume is calculated from linear measures of length, width, and height. The SI unit of volume is the cubic meter (m^3). This is the amount of space occupied by a cube that is 1 m on each side. A more convenient metric unit of volume is the liter (L) (Figure 2·11). A **liter** *is the volume of a cube*

Figure 2·11
The volume of a cube 10 cm on each edge is 1000 cubic centimeters (cm^3). This is a liter. One liter contains 1000 milliliters (mL). Thus 1 mL and 1 cm^3 have the same volume. The face of the cube is shown actual size.

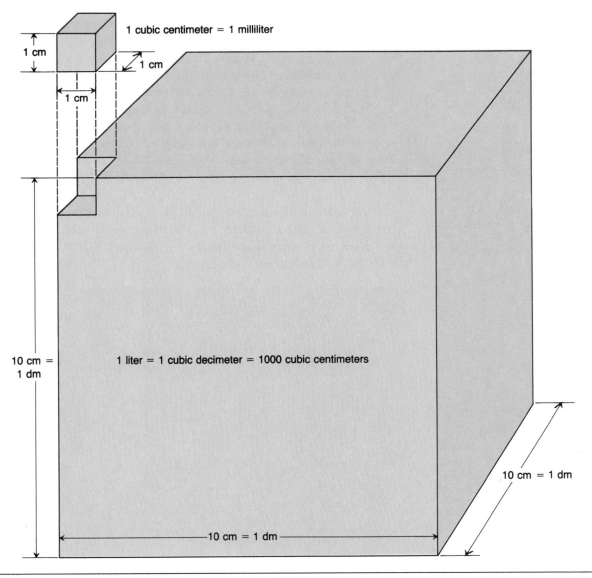

1 cubic centimeter = 1 milliliter

1 cm

1 cm

1 cm

10 cm = 1 dm

1 liter = 1 cubic decimeter = 1000 cubic centimeters

10 cm = 1 dm

10 cm = 1 dm

Table 2·5	Metric Units for Volume		
Unit	Symbol	Relationship	Examples
Liter (base unit)	L		Quart of milk ≈ 1 L
Milliliter	mL	10^3 mL = 1 L	20 drops of water ≈ 1 mL
Cubic centimeter	cm^3	$1\ cm^3 = 1$ mL	Cube of sugar $\approx 1\ cm^3$
Microliter	μL	$10^6\ \mu$L = 1 L	Crystal of table salt $\approx 1\ \mu$L

The liter is the most commonly used metric unit of volume.

Figure 2·12
One cubic centimeter of water is shown actual size. This much water has a mass of 1 g at 4°C. Twenty drops of water equals approximately 1 mL.

that is 10 centimeters (cm) on each edge (10 cm × 10 cm × 10 cm = 1000 cm^3 = 1 L). A smaller unit of volume is the milliliter (mL), which is 1/1000 part of a liter. Because a liter is defined as 1000 cm^3, the milliliter and cubic centimeter must have the same volume. These two units are used interchangeably. Table 2·5 summarizes the most commonly used relationships among units of volume.

Note that the prefixes *milli-* and *micro-* are used with both the unit of volume, a liter, and with the unit of length, a meter. This is one of the advantages of the metric system. Each prefix retains its same meaning regardless of the unit of measurement to which it is attached.

There are many devices for measuring the volume of a liquid (Figure 2·13). A graduated cylinder is useful for dispensing approximate volumes. A pipet or buret must be used, however, when accuracy is important. A volumetric flask contains a specified volume of liquid when it is filled to the calibration mark. Volumetric flasks are available in many sizes. A syringe is used to measure small volumes of liquids for injection.

The volume of any solid, liquid, or gas will change with temperature. For this reason, accurate volume-measuring devices are calibrated at a given temperature. Usually they are calibrated at 20 degrees Celsius (20°C). This is about room temperature.

Figure 2·13
These five types of glassware are used for measuring liquid volumes. The four beakers at the left and the two Erlenmeyer flasks and tall graduated cylinder at the right are used to measure approximate volumes. Small volumes are measured accurately with a pipet (on the left). Larger volumes are measured accurately with a volumetric flask (in the center).

2·8 Units of Mass

Figure 2·14
An astronaut's weight on the moon is 1/6th as much as it is on earth. How does his mass on the moon compare with his mass on the earth?
It is the same.

Mass is the quantity of matter an object contains. Mass is not weight. **Weight** *is a force*. It is a measure of the pull on a given mass by the earth's gravity. Although the weight of an object can change with its location, its mass remains constant regardless of its location. A block of wood on earth has a weight that is six times its weight on the moon. This is because the force of gravity on earth is about six times that on the moon. On a passage from the earth to the moon, the wood has no weight. Whether on earth, on the moon, or in space, however, the mass of the wood does not change.

The mass of an object is measured by comparing it to a standard mass of 1 kilogram (kg), the basic SI unit of mass. *A* **kilogram** *is defined as the mass of 1 L of water at 4°C.* (Water freezes at 0°C.) Imagine a cube of water at 4°C measuring 10 cm on each edge. This cube would have a volume of 1 L and a mass of 1000 grams (g), or a kilogram. *A* **gram** *is defined as the mass of 1 cm³ of water at 4°C* (Figure 2·12).

The relationships among units of mass are shown in Table 2·6. The mass of an object is measured with a balance. An object of unknown mass is placed on one side, and standard masses are added to the other side until the beam is in a position of balance (Figure 2·15). When the

Figure 2·15
A beam balance compares an unknown mass to a known mass. **a** The pans are empty, and the beam is balanced. **b** An object of unknown mass is placed on the left-hand pan. The balance is disturbed. **c** Standard masses are placed on the right-hand pan to restore the balance. The mass of the unknown object is the same as the sum of the standard masses added to the right-hand pan. In this case the mass is 150 g.

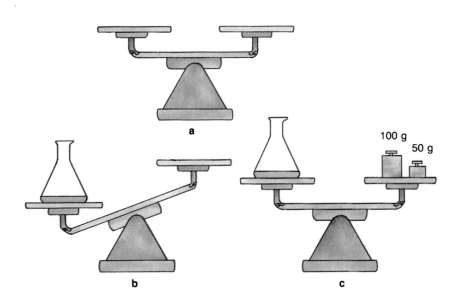

Table 2·6	Metric Units for Mass		
Unit	Symbol	Relationship	Examples
Kilogram (base unit)	kg	$1 \text{ kg} = 10^3 \text{ g}$	Small textbook ≈ 1 kg
Gram	g		Dollar bill ≈ 1 g
Milligram	mg	$10^3 \text{ mg} = 1 \text{ g}$	Ten grains of salt ≈ 1 mg
Microgram	μg	$10^6 \text{ μg} = 1 \text{ g}$	Particle of baking powder ≈ 1 μg

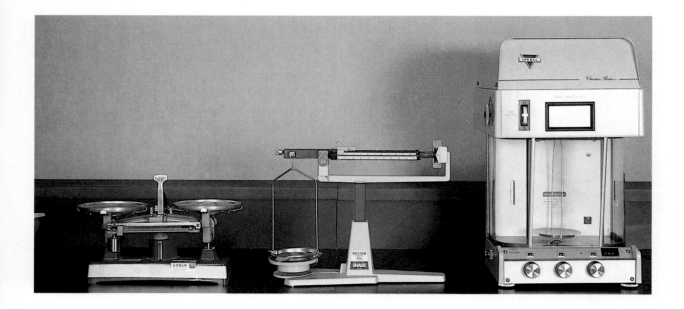

Figure 2·16
It is possible to determine mass to the nearest 0.1 g on a platform balance (left) and to the nearest 0.01 g on a triple beam balance (center). Even greater precision is possible with an analytical balance (right).

Before reading this section you should review your knowledge of algebraic equations by doing Section B·2 of the Math Review in Appendix B.

The relationship between mass and volume is called density.

beam is balanced, the unknown mass is equal to the sum of the standard masses. Several balances are commonly used in laboratories (Figure 2·16). They range from very sensitive instruments with a maximum capacity of only a few milligrams to devices for measuring quantities in kilograms. The analytical balance is used to measure masses of less than 100 g.

2·9 Measuring Density

The statement "Lead is heavier than wood" has no precise meaning. Most people take it to mean that if pieces of lead and wood of the same volume are weighed, the lead has a greater mass than the wood. It would take a much larger volume of wood to equal the mass of the lead. What all this brings us to is the idea that there is an important relationship between an object's mass and its volume. This relationship is called density.

Density *is the ratio of the mass of an object to its volume.*

$$\text{Density} = \frac{\text{mass}}{\text{volume}}$$

When mass is measured in grams, and volume in cubic centimeters, density has units of grams per cubic centimeter. As the density of a substance increases, the volume of a given mass of that substance decreases (Table 2·7). The densities of materials are extremely important. If bones were as dense as lead, for example, you would collapse under your own weight. Table 2·8 gives the densities of some common substances.

The density of a substance usually decreases as its temperature increases. This is because its volume usually increases as the temperature is increased. Meanwhile, its mass remains the same. As we will see in Chapter 15, water is an important exception. Ice floats because it is less dense than water.

Substance	Cube of substance (face shown actual size)	Mass (g)	Volume (cm³)	Density (g/cm³)

Table 2·7   Relationship Between Volume and Density for Identical Masses of Common Substances

Substance	Cube of substance (face shown actual size)	Mass (g)	Volume (cm³)	Density (g/cm³)
Wood		10	20	0.5
Water		10	10	1.0
Aluminum		10	3.7	2.7
Lead		10	0.88	11.3

Figure 2·17
Solid paraffin (left) sinks in liquid paraffin, but solid water (ice) floats in water. What does this tell you about the density of these substances? Solid paraffin, like most solids, is more dense than its liquid. Ice, however, is less dense than water and floats.

Table 2·8	Densities of Some Common Substances		
Substance	Density at 25°C (g/cm³)	Substance	Density at 25°C (g/cm³)
Gold	19.3	Water	0.997
Mercury	13.5	Water	1.00 (4°C)
Lead	11.4	Ice	0.917 (0°C)
Iron	7.87	Gasoline	0.66–0.69
Aluminum	2.70	Wood	0.11–0.75
Bone	1.7–2.0	Air (dry)	0.00119 (1 atm)

Example 5

A copper penny has a mass of 3.1 g and a volume of 0.35 cm³. What is the density of copper?

Solution

We can calculate the density of a substance if we know the mass and volume of a sample of the substance.

$$\text{Density} = \frac{\text{mass}}{\text{volume}} = \frac{3.1 \text{ g}}{0.35 \text{ cm}^3} = 8.8571$$
$$= 8.9 \text{ g/cm}^3 \text{ (two significant figures)}$$

Problems

6. Density = 2.50 g/cm³; no.
7. Density = .802 g/cm³; sink.
8. Yes, density does not change with location.

6. A student finds a shiny piece of metal that she thinks is aluminum. In the lab she determines that the metal has a volume of 245 cm³ and a mass of 612 g. Is the metal aluminum?

7. A plastic ball with a volume of 19.7 cm³ has a mass of 15.8 g. Would this ball sink or float in a container of gasoline?

8. Would the density of a person be the same on the surface of the earth and on the surface of the moon? Explain.

2·10 Specific Gravity

Specific gravity is the ratio of two densities.

Specific gravity *is a comparison of the density of a substance to the density of a reference substance, usually at the same temperature.* Water at 4°C, which has a density of 1 g/cm³, is a convenient reference and is commonly used for this measurement.

A substance will float on top of another substance if its specific gravity is lower than that of the other.

$$\text{Specific gravity} = \frac{\text{density of substance (g/cm}^3)}{\text{density of water (g/cm}^3)}$$

The units in the equation cancel. Thus specific gravity has no units.

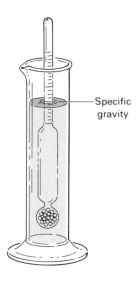

Figure 2·18
A hydrometer is a sealed tube with a weight in the bottom. It is used to measure the specific gravity of a liquid. A hydrometer can be used to check the antifreeze solution in an automobile radiator or the amount of acid in a storage battery. For these purposes, it is enclosed in a glass tube fitted with a rubber bulb. The liquid to be tested is drawn up into the tube and the hydrometer reading is taken.

9. **a.** 2.70 **b.** 13.5 **c.** 0.917

The specific gravity of a liquid can be measured with a **hydrometer** (Figure 2·18). The depth to which the hydrometer sinks depends on the specific gravity of the liquid. The calibration mark on the hydrometer stem at the surface of the liquid indicates the specific gravity.

The use of measurements of specific gravity is fairly common. A physician uses the measured specific gravity of a patient's urine to help diagnose certain diseases, such as diabetes. A service station attendant checks the condition of the antifreeze of your car by measuring the specific gravity of the solution in the radiator.

Problem

9. Use the values in Table 2·8 to calculate the specific gravity of the following substances at 25°C. **a.** aluminum **b.** mercury **c.** ice

2·11 Measuring Temperature

Temperature *is the degree of hotness or coldness of an object.* Our bodies are sensitive to temperature differences but not to specific temperatures. When we hold a glass of hot water, we feel hot because heat transfers from the hot glass to our hand. If we hold a piece of ice, however, heat transfers from our hand to the ice. Temperature determines the direction of heat transfer. **Heat transfer** *occurs when two objects at different temperatures contact each other.* Heat transfers from the object at the high temperature to the object at the low temperature.

Almost all substances expand with an increase in temperature. They also contract as the temperature decreases (a very important exception is water). These properties are the basis for the common mercury-in-glass thermometer. Until recently this was the only type of thermometer in

general use. The mercury in the thermometer expands and contracts more than the volume of the bulb that holds it.

Several temperature scales have been devised. Two readily determined temperatures, the freezing and boiling points of water, are used as reference temperature values. The Celsius scale of the metric system is named after the Swedish astronomer Anders Celsius (1701–1744). *The* **Celsius scale** *takes the freezing point of water as 0°C and boiling point as 100°C.* The space between these two fixed points is divided into 100 equal intervals, or degrees.

Another temperature scale used in the physical sciences is the Kelvin scale, or absolute scale. It is named after Lord Kelvin (1824–1907), a Scottish physicist and mathematician. *On the* **Kelvin scale,** *the freezing point of water is 273 K, and the boiling point is 373 K.* Notice that with the Kelvin scale the degree sign is not used. A change of 1° on the Kelvin scale is the same as that on the Celsius scale. *The zero point on the Kelvin scale, 0 K or* **absolute zero,** *is −273°C.* The relationship between a temperature on the Celsius scale and one on the Kelvin scale is given by these equations.

$$K = °C + 273 \text{ or } °C = K − 273$$

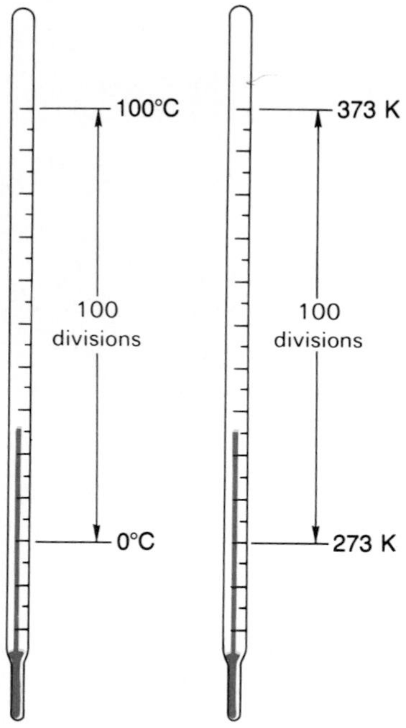

Celsius   **Kelvin**

Figure 2·19
These thermometers show a comparison of the Celsius and Kelvin temperature scales.

Example 6

Normal human body temperature is 37°C. What is your temperature in K?

Solution

$$K = °C + 273$$
$$= 37°C + 273$$
$$= 310 \text{ K}$$

Problems

10. 443 K
11. −186°C

10. Surgical instruments may be sterilized by heating at 170°C for 1.5 hr. Convert 170°C to K.

11. The boiling point of the element argon is 87 K. What is the boiling point of argon in °C?

Figure 2·20
Liquid-in-glass thermometers commonly contain mercury or colored alcohol. The bulb contains a large amount of liquid which expands and contracts with temperature changes.

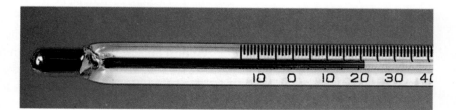

2·B Choosing a Thermometer

A teaspoon of sugar dissolves easily in a cup of hot tea, but lies undissolved in the bottom of a glass of iced tea. A tightly closed container explodes when it is heated. Food stays fresh for days or weeks in a cold refrigerator. By contrast, it spoils rapidly at room temperature. The solubility of solids, the pressure of a gas, and the rate of chemical reactions are just a few of the properties of matter that change with a change in temperature. In fact, all thermometers work because of the change of some property of matter with a change in temperature.

The thermometers used in a school laboratory are usually sealed glass tubes filled with either mercury or alcohol. Both the glass and the liquid inside of it expand when the thermometer is heated, but the liquid expands more. The scale on the thermometer translates the height of the liquid column into a temperature reading. Most mercury thermometers measure temperatures between $-20°C$ and $150°C$, with an accuracy of $0.2°C$. One type, the Beckmann thermometer, has an accuracy of $0.001°C$. The chief disadvantage of mercury thermometers is that they are easily broken. This could expose people in the laboratory to toxic mercury metal.

The thermometer in your home thermostat is probably a bimetallic thermometer. Narrow ribbons of two different metals are laid on top of each other to make a layered metal strip. Different metals expand different amounts when heated. Thus the metal strip will curl as the temperature changes. The amount of curvature is translated into a temperature reading. The range of a bimetallic thermometer depends on what metals are used in the strip. Thermometers of this type are available to cover temperatures from $-180°C$ to $425°C$.

Bimetallic strips consist of two strips of different metals fastened together. The metals expand by different amounts when heated, causing the strip to curl as its temperature rises.

Figure 2·21
Bimetallic strips are often used in home thermostats. When warmed, the strip bends. Why?

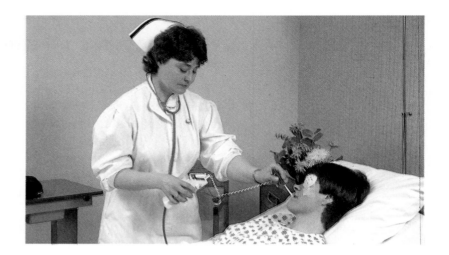

Figure 2·22
The electronic thermometer used in hospitals senses temperature with a thermistor. A thermistor is a metal oxide chip whose resistance to current flow changes with temperature.

Figure 2·23
The liquid crystals in the plastic strip change color at different temperatures. Different strips must be used to measure room temperature and body temperature.

Electronic thermometers are commonly used in hospitals and laboratories. They make use of another temperature measuring device, the thermistor. The thermistor is a bead, rod, or disc made of a mixture of metal oxides. These compounds are semiconductors. Their ability to conduct electricity increases as the temperature increases. The thermistor is connected to an electric current. When the temperature of the thermistor changes, the amount of current that can pass through it changes. This change is translated into a temperature reading. Thermistors are very fast and accurate. Some can record a change as small as 0.0005°C.

Perhaps you have seen plastic strips or blocks that display the temperature in numbers that change color as the temperature changes. These thermometers contain a liquid crystal. Such a substance flows like a liquid, but has an orderly arrangement of its molecules, like a solid crystal. The flexible strips used to take a person's temperature contain a liquid crystal that changes color dramatically at different temperatures. As the strip heats up, the color of the liquid crystal changes. At each temperature, a different reading is visible on the scale. These devices are used mainly to measure body temperature or room temperature. This is because they are only useful over a small range of temperatures. The liquid crystal remains in its special "in-between" state only when it is very close to its melting point. It will turn into a solid at lower temperatures, and into a true liquid at higher ones. A liquid crystal thermometer is not as accurate as the common mercury thermometer. The former is very easy to use, however, and it is virtually unbreakable.

Very high temperatures, like those encountered in steel making, can be measured very accurately by a thermocouple. This device contains two wires of different metals, joined at two points. One point, called the cold or reference junction, is kept at a known temperature. It may, for example, be cooled in ice water to keep it at 0°C. The other point, called the sensing junction, is located where the temperature measurement is to be taken. If the temperature at the

Figure 2·24
Temperatures as high as 1400°C
are measured accurately by a
thermocouple.

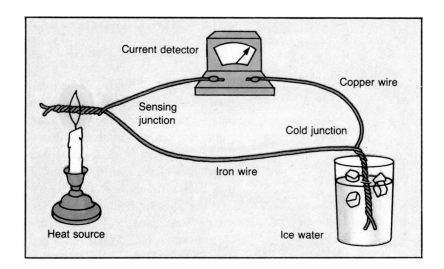

two junctions is different, an electric current is generated in the wires. The amount of current generated depends on the size of the temperature difference. The current is measured, and translated into a temperature reading. The cold junction and the current detector can be located at a considerable distance from the sensing junction with no loss of accuracy. This is very important because this device is used to measure temperatures as high as 1400°C.

2·12 Measuring Heat

Chemical and physical changes involve a change in heat energy.

Heat is a form of energy. It can be measured in units such as the joule (J) or the calorie (cal). The **joule** *is the SI unit of energy*. It is named after the English physicist James Prescott Joule (1818–1889). *One **calorie** is the quantity of heat that raises the temperature of 1 g of pure water 1°C*. The kilocalorie (kcal) is used to measure large amounts of heat; 1 kcal = 1000 cal. Conversions between calories and joules can be carried out by using the following relationships.

A joule is a rather small unit of energy. A television set might use a million joules of energy in one hour.

$$1J = 0.239 \text{ cal} \quad and \quad 1 \text{ cal} = 4.18 \text{ J}$$

The term *Calorie* used in nutrition is actually the kilocalorie. Notice that the dietary Calorie is written with a capital C. The statement "10 g of sugar has 41 Calories" means that 10 g of sugar will release 41 kcal of heat if it is burned completely to carbon dioxide and water by fire. The same amount of heat is also released when 10 g of sugar is "burned" to carbon dioxide and water by your body.

Since heat cannot be measured directly, heat flow must be calculated from its *effect* on the temperature of a given quantity of substance.

Problem

12. 1.76 × 10³ cal

12. Using the definition of a calorie, how much heat energy does 32.0 g of water absorb when it is heated from 25°C to 80°C?

2·13 Specific Heat Capacity

The quantity of heat required to change an object's temperature by exactly 1°C is the **heat capacity** *of that object*. Heat capacity depends partly on mass. The greater the mass of the object, the greater its heat capacity. A massive steel girder, for example, has a much larger heat capacity than a small steel nail. Likewise, the heat capacity of a cup of water is much greater than a drop of water. Besides varying with mass, the heat capacity of an object also depends on the kind of substance from which it is made. For this reason, different substances of the same mass may have different heat capacities.

The **specific heat capacity,** *or simply the* **specific heat,** *of a substance is the quantity of heat required to raise the temperature of 1 g of the substance 1°C*. Water has a high specific heat, and metals have low specific heats (Table 2·9). One calorie of heat raises the temperature of of 1 g of water by 1°C. The same amount of heat raises the temperature of 1 g of iron by 9°C. Therefore iron has a specific heat only one-ninth that of water. Specific heat is important because it can be used to calculate how many calories are required to heat a known mass of substance from one temperature to another.

$$\text{Specific heat} \left(\frac{J}{g \times °C}\right) = \frac{\text{heat (J)}}{\text{mass (g)} \times \text{change in temperature (°C)}}$$

Using the unit calories, the equation is as follows.

$$\text{Specific heat} \left(\frac{cal}{g \times °C}\right) = \frac{\text{heat (cal)}}{\text{mass (g)} \times \text{change in temperature (°C)}}$$

■ Specific heat measures the ability of a substance to store heat energy.

Safety

Because of its high heat capacity, hot water can cause very serious burns. Use care when heating water in the laboratory.

Warm soup warms a person more than hot toast because soup has a higher heat capacity.

Figure 2·25
Which food will warm you up most when you are cold: warm soup or hot toast? Why?

Table 2·9	Specific Heat Capacities of Some Common Substances	
	Specific heat capacity	
Substance	[cal/(g × °C)]	[J/(g × °C)]
Water	1.00	4.18
Grain alcohol	0.58	2.4
Ice	0.50	2.1
Wood	0.42	1.8
Steam	0.40	1.7
Chloroform	0.23	0.96
Aluminum	0.21	0.88
Glass	0.12	0.50
Iron	0.11	0.46
Silver	0.057	0.24
Mercury	0.033	0.14

Figure 2·26
Water must give off a lot of heat in order to freeze. The high specific heat of water makes the climate warmer in the winter and cooler in the summer near large bodies of water.

Example 7

The temperature of a piece of copper with a mass of 95.4 grams changes from 25.0°C to 48.0° when the metal absorbs 849 J of energy. What is the specific heat of copper?

Solution

Use the equation for specific heat and substitute in the given values. The change in temperature is 48.0°C − 25.0°C = 23.0°C.

$$\text{Specific heat} = \frac{J}{g \times °C} = \frac{\text{heat (J)}}{\text{mass (g)} \times \text{change in temperature (°C)}}$$

$$= \frac{849 \text{ J}}{95.4 \text{ g} \times 23.0°C}$$

$$= 0.387 \frac{J}{g \times °C}$$

Problem

13. When 435 J of heat energy is added to 3.4 g of olive oil at 21°C, the temperature increases to 85°C. What is the specific heat of olive oil?

13. $2.0 \dfrac{J}{g \times °C}$

2 Scientific Measurement

Chapter Review

Key terms

absolute zero	2·11	kilogram (kg)	2·8
accuracy	2·2	liter (L)	2·7
calorie	2·12	meter (m)	2·6
Celsius temperature		metric system	2·5
scale	2·11	precision	2·2
density	2·9	qualitative	
gram (g)	2·8	measurement	2·1
heat capacity	2·13	quantitative	
heat transfer	2·11	measurement	2·1
hydrometer	2·10	significant figures	2·3
International System of		specific gravity	2·10
Units (SI)	2·5	specific heat	2·13
joule (j)	2·12	temperature	2·11
Kelvin temperature		volume	2·7
scale	2·11	weight	2·8

Chapter Summary

Measurements can be qualitative or quantitative. The accuracy of a measurement describes how close a measurement comes to the true value. By contrast, the precision of a measurement depends on its reproducibility.

The metric system or International System of Units (SI) is a system of measurement used by scientists. The SI has seven base units from which all other SI units of measurement are derived.

In the metric system the basic unit of length is the meter. The space occupied by matter is called volume. A cubic decimeter (liter) has a volume of 1000 cm^3. One cubic centimeter has the same volume as 1 mL.

The quantity of matter an object contains is its mass. The mass of an object is constant and independent of gravity. A balance is used to measure mass. Weight is not the same as mass. Weight is the measure of the pull of gravity on an object of given mass.

The ratio of the mass of an object to its volume is its density. The unit of density is grams per cubic centimeter. Specific gravity is the ratio of the density of a substance to the density of water. Specific gravity has no units. It is commonly measured with a hydrometer.

Temperature determines the direction of heat flow between two bodies. Heat flows from a hot body to a cold body. Two temperature scales are used: Celsius and Kelvin.

Heat is a form of energy. Heat is measured in joules or calories. One calorie is the quantity of heat required to raise the temperature of 1 g of pure water 1°C.

Heat capacity is the quantity of heat required to raise the temperature of a substance 1°C. For any given substance, the greater the mass of an object, the larger its heat capacity. The heat capacity of 1 g of a substance is the specific heat capacity, or specific heat, of that substance.

Practice Questions and Problems

14. Identify the following as quantitative or qualitative measurements.   *2·1*
  a. A flame is hot.
  b. A candle is blue.
  c. A candle weighs 90 g.
  d. Wax is soft.
  e. A candle burns for 3.5 hr.
  f. A candle's height decreases 4.2 cm per hr.

15. Distinguish between the accuracy and precision of a measurement.   *2·2*

16. Comment on the accuracy and precision of these basketball free-throw shooters.   *2·2*
  a. 99 of 100 shots are made.
  b. 99 of 100 shots hit the front of the rim and bounce off.
  c. 33 of 100 shots are made; the rest either miss the rim completely or rebound off the backboard.

17. Three students made multiple weighings of a copper cylinder, each using a different balance. The correct mass of the cylinder had been previously determined to be 47.432 g. Describe the accuracy and precision of each student's measurements. *2·2*

	Mass of cylinder		
	Jim	*Leigh Anne*	*Bob*
Weighing 1	47.13	47.45	47.95
Weighing 2	47.94	47.39	47.91
Weighing 3	46.83	47.42	47.89
Weighing 4	47.47	47.41	47.93

18. How many significant figures are in each of these measurements? *2·3*
a. 143 g   **e.** 10 800 cal
b. 0.074 cm   **f.** 5.00 dm^3
c. 8.750×10^{-2} ng   **g.** 9.9000×10^8 m
d. 1.072 km   **h.** 55.330 kJ

19. Which of these measurements have two or more significant figures? *2·3*
a. 0.000 72 kcal   **d.** 6.00×10^{-3} L
b. 8.07×10^4 cm   **e.** 8700 kg
c. 155 dg   **f.** 1.0003 mm

20. Round off each of these measurements to three significant figures. *2·4*
a. 98.473 L   **e.** 12.17°C
b. 0.000 763 21 cg   **f.** $0.007\ 498\ 3 \times 10^4$ mm
c. 57.048 m   **g.** 1764.9 mL
d. 9500 sec   **h.** 8.859 km

21. Write each of the rounded-off measurements in Problem 20 in standard exponential form. *2·4*

22. Round off each of the answers correctly. *2·4*
a. 8.7 g + 15.43 g + 19 g = 43.13 g
b. 4.32 cm $\times$ 1.7 cm = 7.344 cm^2
c. 853.2 L $-$ 627.443 L = 225.757 L
d. 38.742 kg $\div$ 0.421 = 92.023 75 kg
e. 5.40 m $\times$ 3.21 m $\times$ 1.871m = 32.431 914 m^3
f. 5.47 m^3 + 11 m^3 + 87.300 m^3 = 103.770 m^3

23. Express each of the rounded-off answers in Problem 22 in standard exponential form. *2·4*

24. Water with a mass of 35.4 g is added to an empty flask with a mass of 87.432 g. The mass of the flask with the water is 146.72 g after a rubber stopper is added. Express the mass of the stopper to the correct number of significant figures. *2·4*

25. Express the answer to each problem in standard exponential form. *2·4*
a. $5.3 \times 10^{+4} + 1.3 \times 10^{+4} =$
b. $\dfrac{7.2 \times 10^{-4}}{1.8 \times 10^3} =$
c. $10^{+4} \times 10^{-3} \times 10^{+6} =$
d. $9.12 \times 10^{-1} - 4.7 \times 10^{-2} =$
e. $\dfrac{4.8 \times 10^{-5}}{(2.0 \times 10^{-2}) \times (6.0 \times 10^3)} =$
f. $(5.4 \times 10^{+4}) \times (3.5 \times 10^{+9}) =$

26. List at least two advantages to using the metric system (or SI). *2·5*

27. List the SI base unit of measurement for these quantities. *2·5*
a. time   **d.** temperature
b. length   **e.** mass
c. amount of substance

28. State the common, nonprefixed metric unit of these quantities. *2·5*
a. volume   **b.** mass   **c.** length

29. What is the symbol and meaning of these common metric prefixes? *2·6*
a. milli   **d.** deci
b. nano   **e.** centi
c. kilo

30. List these units in order from smallest to largest. *2·6*
a. centimeter   **d.** millimeter
b. kilometer   **e.** decimeter
c. micrometer   **f.** meter

31. Match the approximate volume with each item.
a. an orange   **(1)** 30 m^3 *2·7*
b. a basketball   **(2)** 200 cm^3
c. a van   **(3)** 20 L
d. an aspirin tablet   **(4)** 200 mm^3

32. List these units in order from largest to smallest. *2·7*
a. 1 dm^3 **c.** 1 mL   **e.** 1 cL
b. 1 μL   **d.** 1 L   **f.** 1 dL

33. Astronauts in space are said to be weightless. Explain why it is incorrect to say that they are massless. *2·8*

34. Match the approximate mass with each item.
a. a peanut   **(1)** 400 cg   *2·8*
b. a pear   **(2)** 50 mg
c. a stamp   **(3)** 60 kg
d. a person   **(4)** 150 g

35. Does the density of an object depend upon its size? Explain. *2·9*

36. A shiny, gold-colored bar of metal weighing 57.3 g has a volume of 4.7 cm^3. Is the metal bar pure gold? *2·9*

37. A weather balloon is inflated to a volume of 2.2×10^3 L with 37.4 g of helium. What is the density of helium in grams per liter? *2·9*

38. What is the unit of measure of specific gravity? Explain. *2·10*

39. Which of these substances has the highest specific gravity? Which has the lowest specific gravity? *2·10*
  a. mercury   **d.** iron
  b. wood   **e.** lead
  c. ice   **f.** aluminum

40. The element silver melts at 960.8°C and boils at 2212°C. Express these temperatures in Kelvin. *2·11*

41. Liquid nitrogen boils at 77.2 K. What is this temperature in Celsius? *2·11*

42. What are the two common units of heat energy? *2·12*

43. How much heat energy is absorbed when 88.0 g of water is heated from 5°C to 37°C? *2·13*

44. A piece of gold weighing 35.0 g absorbs 185 J of heat energy when its temperature increases by 41°C. What is the specific heat of gold? *2·13*

45. The temperature of two substances with the same mass increases by 20°C when heated. Which absorbs the most energy, the substance with the higher or lower specific heat? Explain. *2·13*

Mastery Questions and Problems

46. List two possible reasons for precise, but inaccurate, measurements. *2·2*

47. Rank these numbers from smallest to largest. *2·3*
  a. 5.3×10^4 **e.** 0.0057
  b. 57×10^3 **f.** 5.1×10^{-3}
  c. 4.9×10^{-2} **g.** 0.0072×10^2
  d. 6230   **h.** 2×10^6

48. Criticize this statement: "When two measurements are added together, the answer can have no more significant figures than the measurement with the least number of significant figures." *2·4*

49. A rectangular fish tank measures 87 cm long, 45.3 cm wide, and 41 cm high. What is the volume of the tank in cubic centimeters and in liters? *2·4*

50. Which is larger? *2·8*
  a. a centigram or a milligram
  b. a liter or a centiliter
  c. a calorie or a kilocalorie
  d. a millisecond or a centisecond
  e. a microliter or milliliter
  f. a mm^3 or a dm^3

51. Criticize this statement: "When a number is rounded off, the last significant figure is dropped if it is less than 5." *2·4*

52. The human body is approximately 60% water. Explain how this high percentage of water helps the body handle rapid changes in outside temperatures. *2·13*

Review Questions and Problems

53. What are the correct symbols for each element?
  a. sodium   **d.** copper
  b. aluminum   **e.** sulfur
  c. chlorine   **f.** strontium

54. Classify each of the following as a chemical or physical change.
  a. grass growing
  b. sugar dissolving in water
  c. crushing a rock
  d. cooking potatoes
  e. bleaching clothes
  f. boiling water

55. How would you separate a mixture of ground glass and salt?

56. Name four forms of energy.

57. How can you distinguish between a homogeneous mixture and a compound?

58. What is a general goal of the scientific method?

59. How many grams of salt (NaCl) will be formed if 45.8 g of sodium reacts completely with 70.9 g of chlorine?

Challenging Questions and Problems

60. You have been introduced to the concepts of heat and temperature in this chapter. Are the ideas of hot and cold more closely associated with heat or with temperature? Do you think it is possible for something to be hot and cold at the same time?

61. The mass of a cube of iron is 355 g. What is the mass of a cube of lead that has the same dimensions?

62. A swimming pool measures 10 m by 25 m by 3.5 m. Assuming the pool is full of water, how many kcal of heat energy are needed to raise the temperature of the water from 18°C to 33°C?

63. Plot this data that shows how the mass of sulfur increases with an increase in the volume. Determine the density of sulfur from the slope of the line.

Mass of sulfur (g)	Volume of sulfur (cm^3)
23.5	11.4
60.8	29.2
115	55.5
168	81.1

Research Projects

1. How did Lavoisier's work benefit people during his lifetime?

2. Describe the history and the use of the various kinds of balances used by chemists.

3. Trace the development of the liquid-in-glass thermometer.

4. Heat was once thought to be an invisible fluid, called *caloric*. Trace the history of this concept.

5. Discuss the history of this country's conversion from English customary units to metric units.

6. Write an account of your daily routine. Use metric units to describe the objects and processes in this part of your life.

7. Compile a pictorial dictionary of objects to demonstrate metric units. (The objects should be easily recognized as having a standard size.)

8. What does the standard deviation of a set of measurements represent? How is it used in research?

9. What are the toxic effects of mercury? Would the mercury in a broken thermometer be enough to contaminate the air in a classroom above acceptable levels?

10. Discuss other methods (besides significant figures) for showing uncertainty in measurements and calculations.

Readings and References

Diagram Group. *Comparisons of Distance, Size, Area, Volume, Mass, Weight, Density, Energy, Temperature, Time, Speed and Number Throughout the Universe*. New York: St. Martin, 1980.

Grey, Vivian. *The Chemist Who Lost His Head: The Story of Antoine Laurent Lavoisier*. New York: Coward, McCann & Geoghegan, 1982.

Morrison, Philip and Phylis, and The Office of Charles and Ray Eames. *Powers of Ten: A Book about the Relative Size of Things in the Universe and the Effect of Adding Another Zero*. New York: Scientific American (dist. by Freeman), 1982.

Smith, Richard Furnald. *Chemistry for the Millions*. New York: Scribner, 1972.

3

Problem Solving in Chemistry

Chapter Planning Guide

Section			Demonstrations and Experiments	Resource Materials
3·1	Word Problems	C*		Objectives Worksheet 3, SPB Skillsheet 3, SPB
3·2	Techniques of Problem Solving	C		
3·A	Problem Solving at Work	E		
3·3	Conversion Factors	C	Dem 3·1 Seconds/Year	Quiz 3·1
3·4	Dimensional Analysis	C	Dem 3·2 Factor-label Flash Cards	Beyond the Text: Calculating
3·5	Converting Between Units	C	Exp 5 The Specific Heat of a Metal, LM	Prelab 5, SPB Quiz 3·2
3·6	Multistep Problems	C		Kerosene Heaters, ICT 3
3·B	How Do Your Variables Vary?	E		
3·7	Converting Complex Units	H		Quiz 3·3 Reviewsheet 3, SPB Chapter 3 Test
*C = Core, O = Optional E = Enrichment, H = Honors			LM = Laboratory Manual	SPB = Skills Practice Book ICT = Issues in Chem. Tech.

Chapter Objectives

Having studied this chapter and done the problems, the student should be able to:

1. State how to become a better problem solver. *3·1*

2. List five steps that can be used in solving problems. *3·2*

3. Find the mass, volume, or density of a substance when any two of these values are known. *3·2*

4. Construct conversion factors from equivalent measurements. *3·3*

5. Find the mass, heat change, temperature change, or specific heat when any three of these values are given. *3·4*

6. Apply the techniques of dimensional analysis to a variety of conversion problems. *3·4*

7. Convert measurements within the metric system. *3·5*

8. Use dimensional analysis to solve multistep problems. *3·6*

9. Solve rate conversion problems using dimensional analysis. *3·7*

Teaching Suggestions

3·1 Word Problems

Chemistry not only attempts to describe phenomena but to quantify them as well. The application of the quantitative relationships usually involves a statement of the type "How many grams of sulfur are needed to react completely with 50.0 grams of iron to produce the compound, iron sulfide?" Thus, in this course the student will continually be encountering word problems.

The purpose of this chapter is to help the student gain the skills necessary for successfully attacking and solving word problems.

3·2 Techniques of Problem Solving

Many students approach problem solving with the attitude that they will just keep trying combinations of numbers until something works. This approach is poor at best. Try to emphasize that an orderly approach to problem solving

is much better. Such an approach takes time and practice to develop.

The five-step technique in this section is a common-sense way by which word problems can be successfully solved. The first reaction of many students will be that it is too time-consuming or cumbersome. Students should force themselves to follow each step of the method every time. It helps to have them write down and number the steps as they do them. It will eventually become a habit.

Emphasize that in Step 5 an investment of just a minute or two in looking over the results of a calculation can pick up inadvertent errors. If the units have not worked out correctly, the answer cannot possibly be correct. Mention that it is worthwhile to round the numbers in the problem to simple whole numbers and then mentally estimate the answer. If the calculated answer is very different from the estimated, then an error should be suspected.

3·3 Conversion Factors

It is fairly typical for measurements to be obtained in one unit and calculations to be done in another. For example, we might measure volume in cubic decimeters in the laboratory, but our calculations might be done in liters instead. Students can get confused when making these conversions and forget how to do them. A common example is forgetting whether to multiply or divide by 1000 when changing back and forth from milliliters to liters. The use of conversion factors helps them to change from one unit to another in an orderly fashion. This can be shown by **Demonstration 3·1** *Seconds/Year*.

It might be helpful to give a "quiz" consisting of a few simple conversions before you start this section. After seeing their scores, most students will realize the importance of having a systematic approach.

Conversion factors always follow the same pattern:

$$1 \text{ L} = 1000 \text{ mL}$$

(small number)(large unit) = (large number)(small unit)

3·4 Dimensional Analysis

Dimensional analysis requires an extra effort on the part of the students. Many will resist having to write down and manipulate the units *in addition to* working with the numbers. There is a major benefit which makes it all worthwhile, however. The advantage of using dimensional analysis is that arranging the units so they work out properly helps in the solution of the problem. That is, the way the units must combine is the way in which the numbers must be combined.

Try the following example with the class. "If three teaspoons are equal to one tablespoon and one cup is equal to 16 tablespoons, how many cups are 100 teaspoons?" In solving this, first list the possible conversion factors.

3 t = 1 T   1 T = 3 t   1 c = 16 T   16 T = 1 c

Then discuss how these factors could be arranged to give a conversion from teaspoons to cups. This arrangement then dictates how to manipulate the numbers.

$$\text{Solution: } 100 \, t \times \frac{1 \, T}{3 \, t} \times \frac{1 \, c}{16 \, T} = 2.1 \text{ c}$$

Once the students have caught on, try a problem which uses imaginary units, like the following example. "If four densos equal 10 waps, and 7 greems equal 20 densos, how many waps are there in 50 greems?"

$$\text{Solution: } \frac{10 \text{ w}}{4 \, d} \times \frac{20 \, d}{7 \, g} \times 50 \, g = 360 \text{ w}$$

This problem gets them to focus on the manipulation of the conversion factors, and not take memorized shortcuts.

Dimensional analysis (or the factor-label method) is an extremely powerful tool. As logical as this system may seem, many students still have difficulty with it. The secret to the factor-label method is that each conversion factor must be used so that when multiplied by the next factor a cancellation of units will result, and a new, desired unit will be obtained. Often students do not know whether to use a given conversion factor "right-side up" or "upside down". An activity which would be appropriate here is **Demonstration 3·2** *Factor-label Flash Cards*.

3·5 Converting Between Units

3·6 Multistep Problems

3·7 Converting Complex Units

Encourage the students to design a "plan of attack" for the solution of each of the problems in these sections. This plan should include the known (given), all of the intermediate units, and the unknown (to be found). Insist that they write down each step in the plan. Once the steps are in place, it is merely a matter of properly arranging the conversion factors to obtain the desired answer.

Examples of multistep and complex units conversions:

1. The conversion: yd ————→ cm
   The steps: yd → ft → m → cm

2. The conversion: gal ————→ mL
   The steps: gal → qt → L → mL

Point out that the units in the path (yd → cm) always appear as the units in the *numerators of the fractions*. For the above examples this appears as follows.

1. $yd \times \dfrac{ft}{yd} \times \dfrac{m}{ft} \times \dfrac{cm}{m} \rightarrow$ cm

2. $gal \times \dfrac{qt}{gal} \times \dfrac{L}{qt} \times \dfrac{mL}{L} \rightarrow$ mL

Experiment 5 *The Specific Heat of a Metal* is appropriate to do now for practice in the conversion of units and in problem solving.

Demonstrations

3·1 Seconds/Year

Concept: Dimensional analysis uses conversion factors to solve problems.

Materials: sets of large cards with ratios of seconds/minute, minutes/hour, hours/day, days/year on one side, and minute/seconds, hour/minutes, day/hours, and year/days on the other side.

Procedure: 1. Ask how the number of seconds per year can be found. 2. Note that it is necessary to know the relationship between days and years, hours and days, etc. 3. Have the students suggest an arrangement of the cards that can give the answer. 4. Arrange the cards to check their suggestions. 5. Point out that the final units must be seconds/year, and that each card cancels one of the units of the preceding card. Stress that dimensional analysis makes problem solving easier by eliminating the need for memorization.

3·2 Factor-label Flash Cards

Concept: Dimensional analysis can be demonstrated with cards.

Materials: a set of large-size cards, each of which has two symbols separated by a horizontal line. Symbols could be circles, squares, triangles, stars, diamonds, hexagons, or even large letters. Another set of cards with metric units should also be made. An inverse set in which the upper and lower symbols are exchanged should be made for both of the sets.

Procedure: 1. Ask the class how you should arrange the cards so that a final "unit" could be obtained by multiplying the "conversion factors" on the cards when an initial unit is given. 2. A typical problem could be "Given *A,* find *B.*" 3. Point out the importance of the proper order and the need for the inverted cards. 4. After the class has mastered a few of these, have a few students stand in front of the class, each holding a different card, and have *them* arrange the cards. 5. Practice with the metric unit cards as well. 6. Use the cards for drills and quizzes. Students could profit by using them in small groups, in pairs, or individually for practice and review.

Beyond The Text

Calculating

The growth of commerce inspired the invention of devices to help calculate. The abacus probably originated more than five thousand years ago, but it is still widely used today in many parts of Japan and China. An abacus consists of groups of beads strung on wires in a frame. The beads in one row represent 1s, those in the next 10s, the next 100s, and so on. By sliding the beads along the wires, an experienced operator can add, subtract, multiply, and divide faster than a person operating a modern adding machine.

A Scottish inventor, John Napier, conceived the idea of logarithms more than four hundred years ago. This led to the nineteenth century invention of the slide rule. This device consists of two rulers marked in logarithmic scales. By properly aligning the two rulers, the operator can multiply and divide, or find square roots and other functions. Before the invention of small, inexpensive, electronic calculators, the slide rule was the constant companion of any student of science.

Modern computers are able to do calculations with tremendous speed and accuracy. In 1946 at the University of Pennsylvania in Philadelphia, the first computer, called the ENIAC (short for *E*lectronic *N*umerical *I*ntegrator *A*nd *C*alculator), was assembled. It impressed its audience by performing 1500 additions in 0.3 seconds. Computers in the 1970s could complete *five million* additions in that same 0.3 seconds. Today the speed of a computer is limited only by the need to get rid of the heat generated during its operation.

Although computers are extremely fast at calculating, they can only perform tasks that they have been programmed to do. A person must give the computer the problem, the background information necessary to do it, and the logic by which it should be solved. Of course, once programmed, the computer can do any number of similar problems very quickly. Chemists today face mathematics problems that would take a lifetime to do "by hand." Fortunately, they can be done by the computer in a matter of minutes or hours.

Pocket calculators are a great convenience when properly used. A calculator, however, cannot decide how to do a problem. It will not automatically round off an answer to the proper number of significant figures. Neither will it notice that a student is dividing instead of multiplying, or has hit the wrong key!

A professor of mathematics education once programmed a group of calculators to give wrong answers. He then asked students to do a set of problems, first estimating their answers, then using the calculators to get exact answers. Most of the students (93%) made good estimates. Only 20% of them suspected that the calculator was at fault, however, when the estimated answer and the calculated answer did not agree. In fact, 36% of the students worked through all the problems still thinking that they were at fault. This occurred when the calculator's answer was off by 50%! A calculator is a useful tool, but it should not become a security blanket. Remind your students to always estimate answers so that a calculator error can be detected and corrected.

Answers to End of Chapter Questions and Problems

Practice Questions and Problems

15. **c**, **f**, and **g**, correct; **a**, correct if "productive" work; **d**, correct if facts not needed are ignored.

16. A ratio of equivalent measurements.

17. **a.** 1 min/60 s **b.** 4.18 J/1 cal
c. 1 cm^3 H_2O/1 g H_2O **d.** 1 g/10^9 ng **e.** 10^3 mL/1 dm^3

18. 35 students

19. 42.5 kg ash

20. **a.** 7.4×10^{-1} m **b.** 8.32 g **c.** 5.55×10^5 cm^3
d. 5.27×10^{-6} kcal **e.** 8.6×10^6 μg **f.** 9.62×10^3 J
g. 9.52×10^1 dm

21. **b.** 4×10^2 m

22. 1.68×10^4 L

23. 3.06×10^{21} atoms gold

24. **a.** 5.0×10^{-2} km **b.** 7.4×10^1 μg
c. 3.3×10^{-1} mg **d.** 7.86×10^4 J **e.** 6.29×10^{-1} μL
f. 2.34×10^{-8} cm

25. 4.35×10^3 cg $= 4.35 \times 10^{-2}$ kg $= 4.35 \times 10^1$ g
$\qquad\qquad\qquad\qquad\qquad = 4.35 \times 10^7$ μg
1.2×10^2 cg $= 1.2 \times 10^{-3}$ kg $= 1.2$ g
$\qquad\qquad\qquad\qquad\qquad = 1.2 \times 10^6$ μg
4.4×10^3 cg $= 4.4 \times 10^{-2}$ kg $= 4.4 \times 10^1$ g
$\qquad\qquad\qquad\qquad\qquad = 4.4 \times 10^7$ μg

26. 11 L

27. 180 vum

28. 2.3×10^1 cal/s

29. 31 m/s

30. 1.08×10^9 km/hr

31. 8.3 min

Mastery Questions and Problems

32. 1.1 kg/L

33. 1.2×10^{-1} $\dfrac{cal}{g^\circ C}$

34. 2.3×10^1 g

35. 3.6 min lost

36. 1.1×10^3 g

37. 3.5×10^2 cm^3

38. 50°C

39. 9.60×10^1 kg water

40. 0.804 g/cm^3

41. 14 kJ

Review Questions and Problems

42. 1337 K

43. **a.** mixture **b.** element **c.** mixture **d.** element
e. compound **f.** element

44. Shiny (has a luster), silvery color, malleable, ductile.

45. **a.** μg **b.** cal **c.** dm^3 **d.** cm **e.** kg

46. **a.** 4 **b.** 3 **c.** 2 **d.** 3 **e.** 4 **f.** 5

47. **a.** 5.4 g **b.** 9.0×10^6 cal **c.** 4.5×10^{-4} dm^3
d. 3.0×10^{-3} mm **e.** 1.5×10^2 K **f.** 35 s

48. The mass of fuel plus the mass of oxygen must equal the mass of ash plus gaseous products. The chemical energy of the fuel equals the heat and light energy given off.

49. Answers will vary.

Challenging Questions and Problems

50. 1.19

51. 54 cm

52. 8.0 g Sr

53. 26°C

54. **a.** 2.47×10^{-11} μm^3 **b.** 1.81×10^{-1} nm

55.

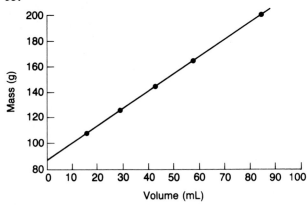

a. The mass is the y-intercept = 83 g.
b. The density is the slope of the line = 1.3 g/mL.

3 Problem Solving in Chemistry

Chapter Preview

Chemistry is an experimental science aimed at problem solving. As you study chemistry and learn to think like a chemist, you will become a better problem solver. In this course you will encounter new concepts. You will be asked to develop skills that may be unfamiliar to you. As you gain an understanding of these new concepts and learn to apply these new skills, you will improve your ability to solve problems.

3·1 Word Problems

Do you like word problems? You know the kind: "Sally is twice as old as Sara, who is three years younger than Suzy. What will Sally's age be one year from now if Suzy is one-third as old as twelve-year-old Sonja will be nine years from now?" (Answer: Nine years old.) This problem is probably more difficult than any problem you will encounter in this class. Even with much simpler word problems, however, you might feel overwhelmed. We hope this is not your situation, but if it is, consider the following analogy.

Persons who like playing tennis generally fall into one of two categories. Either they are already good tennis players (at least in their own minds), or they feel they are getting better through practice. Persons who try tennis and then give up are generally not good players. Neither do they want to put in the time needed to become a good player.

In much the same way, if you like word problems you are probably already a fairly proficient problem solver. Most students who dislike word problems have not yet become good problem solvers. If you dislike word problems you should not follow the example of the tennis player

Real world problems are word problems. We deal not with numbers, but with measurements and the relationships between measurements.

Figure 3·1
The day to day work of chemists involves solving many different types of problems.

Figure 3·2
Developing a skill takes practice.

who quits. You can become a better problem solver. Like the tennis player who gets better with practice, *you can become a better problem solver by doing problems*.

3·2 Techniques of Problem Solving

After you have read a lengthy, complex word problem, the first thought that is likely to cross your mind is "Where do I begin?" Often there are several ways to solve a problem. No one method will work in every situation. Nevertheless, most word problems can be solved by using the following guidelines.

Approaching problem solving in an organized consistent fashion will ensure your success at problem solving.

1. **Identify the unknown.** Be certain that you know what the problem is asking. Read the problem carefully. If the problem is long you might need to read it a number of times. If the problem will have a numerical answer, be aware of the unit of the answer.

2. **Identify what is known or given.** This usually includes a measurement and one or more relationships between measurements. Facts might also be given in a problem that are not needed to solve the problem. Learn to recognize extra information as such, and do not be misled.

3. **Plan a solution.** This is obviously the "heart" of problem solving: getting from the known to the unknown. Sketching a picture of the problem often helps you see a relationship between the given and the unknown. It might also suggest a way to break down a complex problem into two or more simpler problems. At this point you might need to use resources such as tables or figures to find other facts or relationships. For example, you might need to look up a constant or an equation that relates a known measurement to an unknown measurement. The solutions to the simpler problems can then be combined to form the solution to the more complex problem.

4. **Do the calculations.** This is usually a straightforward step if you have done a good job on Step 3. It may involve solving an equation for the unknown, substituting in known quantities, and doing the arithmetic.

In some problems you might be asked to express a measurement in a different form. In such a case, you must use relationships correctly to move from the given quantity to the unknown.

5. **Finish up.** The answer to a problem should always be expressed to the correct number of significant figures. Where appropriate the answer should be written in standard exponential form. Most importantly, **you must check your work.** Have you found what was asked for? Reread the problem. Did you copy down the given facts correctly? Check your math and check the units. Does your answer make sense? Is it reasonable? You can often estimate an approximate answer as a quick check.

Example 1

What is the volume, in cubic centimeters, of a sample of cough syrup that has a mass of 50.0 g? The density of cough syrup is 0.950 g/cm³.

Solution

Step 1. The unknown is the volume, in cubic centimeters.

Step 2. The knowns are the mass and density.
   a) mass = 50.0 g
   b) density = 0.950 g/cm³

Step 3. An equation that relates mass, density, and volume is this.

$$\text{Density} = \frac{\text{mass}}{\text{volume}}$$

This equation can be solved for the unknown, the volume.

Step 4. Solve for volume.

$$\left(\frac{\text{volume}}{\text{density}}\right) \text{density} = \frac{\text{mass}}{\text{volume}} \left(\frac{\text{volume}}{\text{density}}\right)$$

$$\text{Volume} = \frac{\text{mass}}{\text{density}}$$

Substitute values for the knowns.

$$\text{Volume} = \frac{50.0 \text{ g}}{0.950 \text{ g/cm}^3} = 52.632 \text{ cm}^3$$

Step 5. Volume = 52.6 cm³ (three significant figures)

Figure 3·3
The problem solving steps in this section are also helpful for solving everyday problems. When fixing a car you need to know how the car should work and what is currently wrong. Then you need to plan how to fix it, do the work, and check that it is fixed, before you drive away.

Problems

1. A small piece of gold has a volume of 0.87 cm³.   **a.** What is the mass if the density of gold is 19.3 g/cm³?   **b.** What is the value of this piece of gold if the market value of gold is $12 per gram?

1. a. 17 g   **b.** $204
2. 6.27 × 10² J

2. How many joules are required to raise the temperature of 10.0 g of water from 10.0°C to 25.0°C?

3. 72°C
4. 2.60 × 10² g
5. 27.0 cm³

3. What is the final temperature of a 140-g piece of glass at 21°C that absorbs 8.5 × 10² cal of heat when exposed to sunlight?

4. A volume of 15.0 mL of mercury is added to a beaker that has a mass of 56.7 g. What is the mass of the beaker with the added mercury?

5. The density of silicon is 2.33 g/cm³. What is the volume of a piece of silicon that weighs 62.9 g?

3·A Problem Solving at Work: Chemical Technicians

Behind every successful chemist there is probably a well-trained chemical technician. While chemists invent new chemical procedures to produce a desired product, chemical technicians have the job of carrying out the chemists' ideas. Their job is generally practical rather than theoretical. They must have a good understanding of the procedures they are expected to follow. By contrast, the chemist must understand the theory behind the procedure.

Chemical technicians work in every type of chemical laboratory and factory. They may be part of a team that is engaged in research, design, development, production, analysis, or testing. Some technicians work with standard laboratory glassware. Others work with very sophisticated instruments. Technicians are expected to maintain accurate records of their work. They compute and analyze results and make reports. Some technicians may supervise other employees.

Preparation for a chemical technician position includes considerable on-the-job training. The technician must become familiar with the particular procedures, apparatus, and instruments used. For some

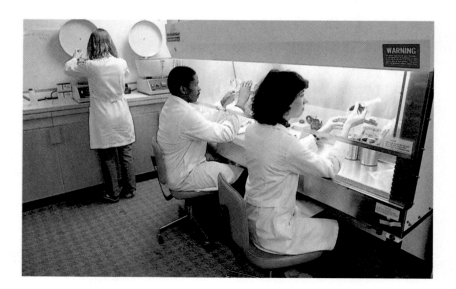

Figure 3·4
A successful year of chemistry in high school can qualify you for a summer job as a chemical technician.

jobs, a strong background in high school science and mathematics may be sufficient education. Many other jobs require some training beyond high school. Community colleges, technical schools, and some universities offer two-year programs for chemical technicians. In general, a person who is willing to continue his or her education will find more opportunities for promotion and challenging work.

3·3 Conversion Factors

The same quantity can usually be measured or expressed in many different ways. One dollar = 4 quarters = 10 dimes = 20 nickels = 100 pennies. These are all expressions, or measurements, of the same amount of money. One meter = 10 decimeters = 100 centimeters = 1000 millimeters. These are different ways to express the same length. Whenever two measurements are equal, or equivalent, a ratio of these two measurements will equal unity, or one.

$$\frac{100 \text{ cm}}{1 \text{ m}} = 1 \quad and \quad \frac{1 \text{ m}}{100 \text{ cm}} = 1$$

Each of these ratios of equivalent measurements is called a **conversion factor.** In a conversion factor, the measurement in the numerator (on the top) is equivalent to the measurement in the denominator (on the bottom). The conversion factors above are read "one-hundred centimeters per one meter" and "one meter per one-hundred centimeters." As we shall see in the next section, conversion factors are very useful in solving problems in which a given measurement must be expressed in some other unit of measure. When a measurement is multiplied by a conversion factor, the value of the measurement remains the same. Although the *numerical value* of the measurement is changed, the change in the unit compensates for this. Consider, for example, 1 g and 10 dg. Even though the numbers in these two measurements differ, both represent the same mass. Conversion factors are defined quantities. Therefore they generally have an unlimited number of significant figures.

■ Conversion factors show the relationship between two measurements.

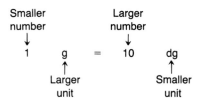

Figure 3·5
The two parts of a conversion factor are equal. The smaller number is part of the quantity with the larger unit. The larger number is part of the quantity with the smaller unit.

Example 2

Write the two possible conversion factors for each pair of units.
a. kilograms and grams   **b.** liters and milliliters

Solution

a. Since 1000 g = 1 kg, the conversion factors are: $\frac{1000 \text{ g}}{1 \text{ kg}}$ and $\frac{1 \text{ kg}}{1000 \text{ g}}$.

b. Since 1 L = 10^3 mL, the conversion factors are: $\frac{1 \text{ L}}{10^3 \text{ mL}}$ and $\frac{10^3 \text{ mL}}{1 \text{ L}}$.

6. a. $\dfrac{1 \text{ m}}{10^6 \mu m}$ and $\dfrac{10^6 \mu m}{1 \text{ m}}$

b. $\dfrac{1 \text{ g}}{10^2 \text{ cg}}$ and $\dfrac{10^2 \text{ cg}}{1 \text{ g}}$

c. $\dfrac{1 \text{ g}}{1 \text{ mL}}$ and $\dfrac{1 \text{ mL}}{1 \text{ g}}$

d. $\dfrac{10^3 \text{ J}}{1 \text{ kJ}}$ and $\dfrac{1 \text{ kJ}}{10^3 \text{ J}}$

7. $\dfrac{1 \text{ g}}{10^2 \text{ cg}} \quad \dfrac{100 \text{ cg}}{1 \text{ g}} \quad \dfrac{1 \text{ g}}{10^6 \mu g}$

$\dfrac{10^6 \mu g}{1 \text{ g}} \quad \dfrac{10^2 \text{ cg}}{10^6 \mu g} \quad \dfrac{10^6 \mu g}{10^2 \text{ cg}}$

The use of units of measurements is a key factor in solving problems by dimensional analysis.

Problems

6. What are the two conversion factors for each pair of units?
   a. meters and micrometers   **b.** grams and centigrams   **c.** grams of water and milliliters of water   **d.** joules and kilojoules

7. Write six possible conversion factors involving these units of measure: $1 \text{ g} = 100 \text{ cg} = 10^6 \ \mu g$.

3·4 Dimensional Analysis

No one method is best for solving every type of problem. Several good approaches are available, however, and one of the best is dimensional analysis (also called the factor-label, or unit factor method). As the name implies, *in **dimensional analysis** we use the units (dimensions) that are a part of measurements to help solve (analyze) the problem.* The best way to explain this problem-solving technique is to use it to solve an everyday-type problem and then apply it to chemistry.

Your school club has sold 600 tickets to a chili supper fund-raising event. You, unfortunately, volunteered to make the chili. You have a very large pot and a chili recipe serving ten persons that calls for two teaspoons of chili powder. How much chili powder do you need for this pot of chili?

Let's work this problem using dimensional analysis and the problem-solving techniques we discussed in Section 3·2.

Step 1. The unknown is the number of teaspoons of chili powder.

Step 2. The knowns are as follows.
   a) 600 servings of chili must be made.
   b) 10 servings require two teaspoons (2 t.) of chili powder.

Step 3. To solve the problem we start with the known measurement, 600 servings of chili. We can use the relationship between servings of chili and teaspoons of chili powder from the recipe to write two conversion factors.

$$\frac{10 \text{ servings}}{2 \text{ t. chili powder}} \quad and \quad \frac{2 \text{ t. chili powder}}{10 \text{ servings}}$$

We always use the form of the conversion factor that has the unit of the known in the denominator. This allows us to cancel the known unit. It also gives us an answer that has the units of the unknown. Our plan then is to change the unit "servings" into the unit "teaspoons of chili powder": servings → teaspoons of chili powder.

Step 4. The solution can now be calculated.

$$\frac{600 \text{ servings}}{1} \times \frac{2 \text{ t. chili powder}}{10 \text{ servings}} = \frac{(600)\,(2)}{10} = 120 \text{ t. chili powder}$$

Notice that the unit of the known has cancelled and that we are left with the correct unit for the answer.

Step 5. What have we done in solving this problem? We have taken a known measurement, 600 servings, and multiplied it by a conversion factor (which equals unity). This gives us another measurement: 120 teaspoons of chili powder. According to this recipe, 120 teaspoons of chili powder is needed to make 600 servings of chili.

Now you have a problem of a different sort. Do you really take the time to measure out 120 teaspoons of chili powder or do you just estimate and dump in the whole can? The first option would be tedious; the second could be dangerous! Why not measure out the chili powder by the cup? This should be much quicker and still give a good-tasting product. The question then becomes, how many cups are 120 teaspoons of chili powder?

Step 1. The unknown is the number of cups of chili powder.

Step 2. The known is 120 t. chili powder.

Step 3. We start with the known, 120 t. chili powder. To solve this problem we need to know how many teaspoonsful of chili powder are in a cup of chili powder. A cookbook gives us this information.

$$3 \text{ teaspoons (t.)} = 1 \text{ tablespoon (T.)}$$

$$16 \text{ tablespoons} = 1 \text{ cup}$$

We can use the first relationship to write a conversion factor that allows us to express 120 t. as tablespoons. The conversion factor must be written with the unit teaspoons in the denominator so the known unit will cancel. We can then use the second conversion factor to change the unit tablespoons into the unit cups. This conversion factor must be written with the unit tablespoons in the denominator.

The overall plan then is to change the unit teaspoons into the unit tablespoons; then change the unit tablespoons into the unit cups: teaspoons → tablespoons → cups.

Figure 3·7
Metric measuring cups hold 250 mL. A metric tablespoon is 15 mL and a metric teaspoon is 5 mL.

Step 4. The solution can now be calculated.

$$\frac{120\ \cancel{t.}}{1} \times \frac{1\ \cancel{T.}}{3\ \cancel{t.}} \times \frac{1\ \text{cup}}{16\ \cancel{T.}} = \frac{120 \times 1 \times 1}{1 \times 3 \times 16} = 2.5\ \text{cups}$$

The process of arranging the units of conversion factors is a great help in setting up problems correctly. The cancellation of units serves as a check as to whether or not the method was correct.

Notice that the units in the numerator of the solution are the same as the units in the plan: t. → T. → cups. *In every problem it is important to check to make sure that the units cancel and that the numerator and denominator of each conversion factor are equal to one another.* You should probably do this *before* you do the actual arithmetic to get an answer.

Step 5. We have shown that 2.5 cups of chili powder is the same amount as 120 teaspoons of chili powder. We have found the answer by multiplying the known measurement by two conversion factors, each of which is equal to unity. In doing this we have calculated a new measurement that is equivalent to the known measurement. The solution to this problem could have been shortened by combining the two relationships given in Step 3 into one: 48 teaspoons = 1 cup. We in effect did this in our solution in Step 4. Look at the product of the two conversion factors in the solution in Step 4.

At the beginning of this section we said that there is usually more than one way to solve a problem. As you read through the examples, you may have been thinking about a different way to approach some of the problems. For instance, the example in this section could also be worked using the ratio-and-proportion method. Some problems are most easily worked with simple algebra. You may already be able to use these other methods of problem solving. If so, you should learn how to use dimensional analysis as well. It will broaden your problem-solving skills. Then you will be able to choose the best way to solve each problem.

Of course you will work to get the correct answer to a problem. At the same time though you should try to explain the reasoning behind the steps to your solution. A negative aspect of solving problems by dimensional analysis is that, for some students, it becomes an almost mechanical procedure. Use the units to help you set up the solution to the problem. More importantly though, *think* the solution through. Try to understand why you are using particular conversion factors in progressing from the *known* to the *unknown*. Consider every problem to be unique. Becoming proficient at a particular method of problem solving will be helpful. It will never, however, replace your ability to read and interpret a problem. With perseverance you can learn to apply all your problem-solving skills toward the solution of problems.

Example 3

The directions of an experiment ask each student to weigh out 1.84 g of copper (Cu) wire. The only copper wire available is a spool weighing 50.0 g. How many students can do the experiment before the copper runs out?

Solution

Step 1. The unknown is the number of students.

Step 2. The knowns are as follows.
a) the mass of copper, 50.0 g
b) each student uses 1.84 g of copper

Step 3. The conversion factor is 1 student/1.84 g Cu.

Step 4. The solution can now be calculated.

$$\frac{50.0 \text{ g Cu}}{1} \times \frac{1 \text{ student}}{1.84 \text{ g Cu}} = \frac{50.0}{1.84} = 27.174 \text{ students}$$

Step 5. The answer is 27 students. The rules for rounding off would allow us to give the answer as 27.2 students, but this does not make any sense.

Problems

8. 47.4°C
9. 9.75 g silver

8. A 1° increase on the Celsius scale is equivalent to a 1.8° increase on the Fahrenheit scale. If the temperature decreased 85.4°F, what is the corresponding temperature drop on the Celsius scale?

9. One of the first dental amalgams, used for tooth fillings, consisted of 26.0 g of silver, 10.8 g of tin, 2.4 g of copper, and 0.8 g of zinc. How much silver is in a 15.0-g sample of this amalgam?

3·5 Converting Between Units

Dimensional analysis is one approach used to convert a given measurement to a different measurement with a different unit.

When doing chemistry it is often necessary to express a measurement in a different unit. The directions for a laboratory experiment may ask you to measure out 145 cg of magnesium metal. The balance in the laboratory is calibrated in grams. How many grams of magnesium do you want? This

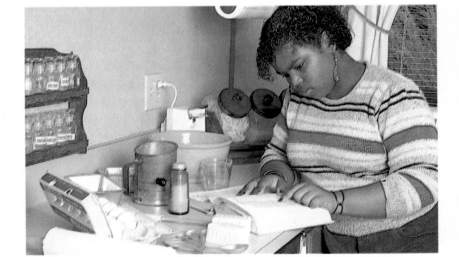

Figure 3·8
Understanding how to use conversion factors can make cooking easier. Some recipes call for ingredients by weight. You can look up the volume for a given weight in a table. Then you can measure the ingredient by volume.

is an example of a typical *conversion problem*. The need here is to express a given measurement in a different unit. As we have seen, conversion problems are easily solved using dimensional analysis.

In working the examples we will use the problem solving steps discussed in Section 3·2.

Figure 3·9
Architects use conversion factors to accurately scale a building.

Example 4

Express 145 cg in grams.

Solution

Step 1. The unknown is the number of grams.

Step 2. The known is 145 cg.

Step 3. The desired conversion is: centigrams → grams. The expression relating the units is 100 cg = 1 g. The conversion factor is 1 g/100 cg. (We want to cancel the centigram unit and be left with the unit grams.)

Step 4. The solution is as follows.

$$\frac{145 \ \cancel{cg}}{1} \times \frac{1 \ g}{100 \ \cancel{cg}} = \frac{145}{100} = 1.45 \ g$$

Step 5. We see that the known unit (cg) cancels, and the answer has the correct unit, grams.

Example 5

What is the volume of a silver coin that has a mass of 14.0 g? The density of silver (Ag) is 10.5 g/cm³.

Solution

Step 1. The unknown is the volume of the coin.

Step 2. The knowns are as follows.
a) the mass of the coin = 14.0 g
b) the density of silver = 10.5 g/cm³

Step 3. This problem can be solved algebraically, but it can also be solved as a conversion problem. We need to convert the given mass of the coin into an equivalent volume. A density measurement gives a relationship between mass and volume: 1 cm³ Ag = 10.5 g Ag.

Step 4. The solution can now be calculated.

$$\frac{14.0 \ \cancel{g \ Ag}}{1} \times \frac{1 \ cm^3 \ Ag}{10.5 \ \cancel{g \ Ag}} = \frac{14.0}{10.5} = 1.33333 \ cm^3$$

Step 5. The answer is 1.33 cm³.

10. a. 7.3×10^2 m
   b. 1.75×10^3 mg
   c. 4.7×10^{-9} m
   d. 7.2 cm
   e. 5.3×10^{-2} dm^3
   f. 8.34×10^{-3} kJ
   g. 6.7×10^{-3} s
   h. 4.53×10^4 cal
11. a. 10.1 cm^3 B **b.** 2.5 g Ar
   c. 0.664 cm^3 Hg

Problems

10. Using tables from Chapter 2, make the following conversions.
   a. 0.73 km to meters
   b. 1.75 g to milligrams
   c. 4.7 nm to meters
   d. 0.072 m to centimeters
   e. 53 cm^3 to cubic decimeters
   f. 8.34 J to kilojoules
   g. 6.7 ms to seconds
   h. 45.3 kcal to calories

11. Use the given densities to make the following conversions.
   a. 23.6 g of boron to cm^3 of boron (density of boron = 2.34 g/cm^3)
   b. 1.4 L of argon to g of argon (density of argon = 1.78 g/L)
   c. 8.96 g of mercury to cm^3 of mercury (density of mercury = 13.5 g/cm^3)

Figure 3·10
When playing a complex piece of music for the first time, a pianist may play only the upper or lower portion of the music. In a similar way, you should break down a complex problem into simpler parts.

Combining the solutions to two or more simple one-step conversions will give the solution to a multistep conversion problem.

3·6 Multistep Problems

When converting between units it is often necessary to use more than one conversion factor. For example, you probably don't know how many seconds are in a day. This is something that you can easily calculate using dimensional analysis.

Example 6

How many seconds are in one day?

Solution

Step 1. The unknown is the number of seconds.

Step 2. The known is one day.

Step 3. The desired conversion is: day → seconds. This conversion can be carried out by the following sequence of conversions: day → hours → minutes → seconds. The expressions relating the units are: 1 day = 24 hr, 1 hr = 60 min, and 1 min = 60 s.

Step 4. The solution can now be calculated.

$$\frac{1 \text{ day}}{1} \times \frac{24 \text{ hr}}{1 \text{ day}} \times \frac{60 \text{ min}}{1 \text{ hr}} \times \frac{60 \text{ s}}{1 \text{ min}} = 1 \times 24 \times 60 \times 60 \text{ s}$$

$$1 \text{ day} = 86\ 400 \text{ s}$$

Each conversion factor is written so that the unit in the denominator cancels the unit in the numerator of the previous factor.

Step 5. The answer in standard exponential form is 8.64×10^4 s. *Remember to check that the numerator and denominator of each conversion factor are equivalent. When the units cancel you should be left with the unit of the unknown.*

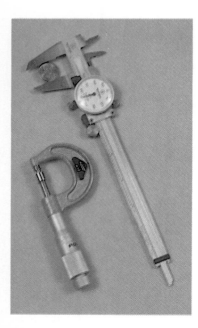

Figure 3·11
Micrometers are tools that are used to measure small distances very accurately. What units might be used for such measurements?

Millimeters and micrometers.

12. **a.** 5.7×10^{-5} cg
   b. 2.76×10^{-2} mL
   c. 5.83×10^{-4} mm
   d. 23 dcal
   e. 6.78×10^{-3} kJ
   f. 5.75×10^{12} ng
13. **a.** 3.0×10^2 g
   b. 0.30 kg

Example 7

How many micrometers is 0.073 cm?

Solution

Step 1. The unknown is the number of micrometers.

Step 2. The known is 0.073 cm.

Step 3. The desired conversion is: centimeters → micrometers. We do not have an expression that relates centimeters to micrometers. However, we know that 100 cm = 1 m and 1 m = 10^6 μm. The problem can be solved in two steps. Change centimeters to meters, then change meters to micrometers: centimeters → meters → micrometers.

Step 4. The solution is as follows.

$$\frac{0.073 \;\text{cm}}{1} \times \frac{1 \;\text{m}}{100 \;\text{cm}} \times \frac{10^6 \;\mu\text{m}}{1 \;\text{m}} = \frac{7.3 \times 10^{-2} \times 10^6}{10^2} = 7.3 \times 10^2 \;\mu\text{m}$$

Step 5. Check to make sure that units cancel, that conversion factors are correct, and that the correct unit remains on the answer.

Problems

12. Make the following conversions.
   a. 0.57 μg to centigrams
   b. 27.6 μL to milliliters
   c. 583 nm to millimeters
   d. 0.0023 kcal to decicalories
   e. 678 cJ to kilojoules
   f. 5.75×10^5 cg to nanograms

13. To raise the temperature of a mass of water from 25°C to 50°C requires 7.5 kcal. Calculate the mass of the water. **a.** grams **b.** kilograms.

3·B   How Do Your Variables Vary?

Imagine you are on a cross-country automobile trip. You decide to do an experiment to see whether your driving speed has any effect on how much gas your car uses. You fill up the gas tank, and get on the highway. Holding the car's speed as nearly as you can at 80 kilometers per hour, you drive for 3 hours before refueling. Back on the highway, you now drive at 100 kilometers per hour for a similar time period. You can now calculate the number of kilometers driven per liter of gas consumed at each speed. The results are 12 kilometers per liter at 80 kph and 14 kilometers per liter at 100 kph.

In this experiment, there are two variables. The speed of the car is changing because you are manipulating it, that is, you are deliberately making it change. The speed is called the independent (or manipulated) variable. Your fuel consumption per liter also changes,

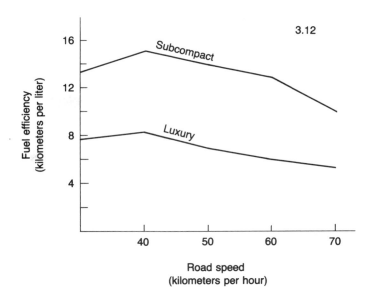

Figure 3·12
On a graph, the independent variable is shown on the horizontal axis. The dependent variable is shown on the vertical axis. Controlled variables are not generally shown. As this graph shows, the lighter-mass subcompact cars are more fuel efficient at all road speeds than the more massive luxury-size car. The best fuel efficiencies are obtained at intermediate speeds.

because it depends on the speed. The fuel consumption is called the dependent (or responding) variable. Any other possible variables should not have been allowed to change during the experiment. For example, the terrain the car is passing through will affect the fuel consumption. You could not tell how much of the mileage change was due to different terrains, and how much was due to the change in speed. You should guard against this problem by driving the same route for each of the two speeds. In this way the terrain would become one of the controlled variables. All other variables should also be controlled. Some of these are the type of gasoline used, the presence of winds, and the use of an air conditioner.

The conclusion that the fuel economy is greater at the higher speed is not supported by other experiments. This should lead you to think that some other variable must account for the unexpected results. The experiment must be repeated, with better control over the variables.

In a similar way, chemistry experiments involve manipulated (independent) variables, responding (dependent) variables, and controlled variables. Some examples of variables that must be controlled in sensitive chemical experiments are temperature, pressure, and acidity. The concentration of reactants, degree of mixing, and purity of chemicals must also be controlled.

3·7 Converting Complex Units

Many common measurements are expressed as a ratio of two units. We measure how fast we drive our car in kilometers per hour. We measure the densities of solids and liquids in grams per cm^3. If we use dimensional analysis, converting these types of measurements is just as easy as converting measurements with a single unit.

Figure 3·13
Different units of density would be used in these two situations. In an industrial setting the density is often stated in kg/m³. In the laboratory, it is often stated in g/cm³.

Example 8

The density of manganese is 7.21 g/cm³. What is the density of manganese expressed in units kg/m³?

Solution

Step 1. The unknown is the density in kg/m³.

Step 2. The known is a density of 7.21 g/cm³.

Step 3. The desired conversion is $\dfrac{g}{cm^3} \longrightarrow \dfrac{kg}{m^3}$

We have two conversions to carry out. In the numerator, the mass unit must be changed from grams to kilograms. The relationship is 10^3 g = 1 kg. In the denominator, the volume unit must be changed from cm³ to m³. Since 10^2 cm = 1 m, then $(10^2 \text{ cm})^3 = (1 \text{ m})^3$, or 10^6 cm³ = 1 m³.

Step 4. The calculations can now be done.

$$\frac{7.21\,\cancel{g}}{1\,\cancel{cm^3}} \times \frac{1\,kg}{10^3\,\cancel{g}} \times \frac{10^6\,\cancel{cm^3}}{1\,m^3} = 7.21 \times 10^3\ kg/m^3$$

(mass conversion)   (volume conversion)

Step 5. Check that the units cancel, the conversion factors are correct, and the answer has the correct ratio of units.

Conversions of measurements with ratios of units are conveniently accomplished by converting each unit of the ratio in sequence.

Problem

14. **a.** 4.65 g/cm³
    b. 12 cal/s
    c. 14.2 mg/mm²

14. Make the following conversions.
   a. 4.65 kg/L to grams per cubic centimeter
   b. 0.74 kcal/min to calories per second
   c. 1.42 g/cm² to milligrams per square millimeter

Problem Solving in Chemistry
Chapter Review

Key Terms

conversion factor   *3·3*
dimensional analysis   *3·4*

Chapter Summary

Problem solving is a skill learned through practice. To solve a word problem you should identify both the known and the unknown. A solution is then planned and calculations are done. An answer to any problem should always be properly rounded off and checked.

Any two measurements that are equal to one another can be written as a ratio. This ratio of equivalent measurements is equal to unity and is called a conversion factor. Conversion factors are used in the problem-solving technique of dimensional analysis. Problems in which you are asked to express a measurement in some other unit (conversion problems) are easily solved using dimensional analysis. In this technique, the units are used to help write the solution to the problem.

No problem-solving method can replace the need for you to *read carefully* and to *think* as you work problems.

Practice Questions and Problems

15. Which of these statements correctly complete this sentence? Good problem solvers . . .   *3·2*
 a. will always work at a problem until they get an answer.
 b. read a problem only once.
 c. check their work.
 d. use every fact given in the problem.
 e. do as much of the work as possible in their head.

 f. break complex problems down into one or more simpler problems.
 g. look for relationships between pieces of information.

16. What is a conversion factor?   *3·3*

17. What conversion factor would you use to convert between these pairs of units?   *3·3*
 a. seconds and minutes
 b. calories and joules
 c. grams of water and cm^3 of water
 d. nanograms and grams
 e. cubic decimeters and milliliters

18. The directions for an experiment are to weigh out 28 g of sodium carbonate. There is a 1000-g bottle of sodium carbonate in the laboratory. How many students can do the experiment?   *3·4*

19. A 5.00-kg sample of bituminous coal is composed of 3.20 kg of carbon, 0.500 kg of ash, 0.150 kg of moisture, and 1.15 kg of volatile (gas-forming) material. How many kilograms of ash are in 425 kg of this coal?   *3·4*

20. Make the following conversions. Express your answers in standard exponential form.   *3·5*
 a. 74 cm to meters
 b. 8.32×10^{-3} kg to grams
 c. 555 L to cubic centimeters
 d. 0.00527 cal to kilocalories
 e. 8.6 g to micrograms
 f. 9.62 kJ to joules
 g. 9.52 m to decimeters

21. Which of the following linear measures is the longest?   *3·5*
 a. 4×10^3 cm   d. 0.04 km
 b. 4×10^5 mm   e. 4×10^8 nm
 c. 4 m   f. 4×10^7 μm

22. The density of dry air at 25°C is 1.19×10^{-3} g/cm^3. What is the volume of 20.0 g of air?   *3·5*

23. An atom of gold weighs 3.271×10^{-22} g. How many atoms of gold are in 1.00 g of gold?   *3·5*

24. Make the following conversions. Express your answers in standard exponential form.   *3·6*
  a. 5.0×10^4 mm to kilometers
  b. 0.0074 cg to micrograms
  c. 3.3×10^5 ng to milligrams
  d. 18.8 kcal to joules
  e. 6.29×10^{-6} dL to microliters
  f. 0.234 nm to centimeters

25. Complete this table so that the measurements in each horizontal line have the same value.   *3·6*

cg	kg	g	μg
——	——	43.5	——
1.2×10^2	——	——	——
——	4.4×10^{-2}	——	——

26. How large a container, in liters, would you need to hold 7.2 kg of gasoline? (Take the density of gasoline to be 0.68 g/cm^3.)   *3·6*

27. In a primitive barter society the following rates of exchange exist: 1 fot = 5 vum, 2 sop = 3 tuz, 4 bef = 3 tuz, and 9 fot = 2 bef. A man has 4 sop and wants to convert all his possessions into vum. How many vum can he trade for?   *3·6*

28. The food that the average American consumes in a day provides 2.0×10^3 kcal of energy. How many calories/second is this?   *3·7*

29. A cheetah has been clocked at 112 km/hr over a 100-m distance. What is this speed in m/s?   *3·7*

30. Light travels at a speed of 3.00×10^{10} cm/sec. What is the speed of light in kilometers/hour?   *3·7*

31. The earth is approximately 1.5×10^8 km from the sun. How many minutes does it take light to travel from the sun to the earth?   *3·7*

Mastery Questions and Problems

32. A tank measuring 14.3 cm $\times$ 73.0 mm $\times$ 0.72 m is filled with olive oil that weighs 8.2×10^3 g. What is the density of olive oil in kg/L?   *3·7*

33. The specific heat of diamond (carbon) is 5.0×10^{-4} kJ/g°C. Express the specific heat in units cal/g°C.   *3·7*

34. What is the mass of a silver ring if its temperature changes from 20°C to 320°C when it absorbs 4.00×10^2 cal of heat energy?   *3·2*

35. A watch loses 0.15 s every minute. How many minutes will the watch lose in 1 day?   *3·7*

36. An apple can provide 110 kcal of energy. What mass of water could this same amount of energy raise from the freezing point to the boiling point?   *3·6*

37. What is the mass of a cube of aluminum that is 5.0 cm on each edge if the density of aluminum is 2.7 g/cm^3?   *3·4*

38. A quantity of heat equal to 4.44 cal is added to 5.40 g of mercury at 25.0°C. What is the final temperature of the mercury?   *3·2*

39. How many kilograms of water (at 4°C) are needed to fill an aquarium that measures 80.0 cm $\times$ 40.0 cm $\times$ 30.0 cm?   *3·2*

40. A flask that can hold 158 g of water at 4°C can hold only 127 g of ethyl alcohol. What is the density of ethyl alcohol?   *3·4*

41. How many kilojoules are required to raise the temperature of 170.0 g of grain alcohol from 10.0°C to 45.0°C?   *3·4*

Review Questions and Problems

42. The melting point of gold is 1064°C. Express this temperature in Kelvin.

43. Classify each of the following as an element, compound, or mixture.
  a. milk shake
  b. copper wire
  c. lipstick
  d. neon
  e. dry ice (CO_2)
  f. iron powder

44. List three physical properties of silver.

45. Identify the larger quantity in each of these pairs of measurements.
  a. nanogram and microgram
  b. calorie and joule
  c. cubic decimeter and milliliter
  d. centimeter and millimeter
  e. decigram and kilogram

46. How many significant figures are in each of these measurements?

a. 5.432 g

b. 9.00×10^6 cal

c. 0.00045 dm^3

d. 0.00304 mm

e. 145.6 K

f. 34.563 s

47. Round each of the measurements in Problem 46 to two significant figures.

48. Describe how the law of conservation of mass and the law of conservation of energy apply to a burning campfire.

49. Name three physical and three chemical changes that you have seen today.

Challenging Questions and Problems

50. When 121 g of sulfuric acid was added to 400 mL of water, the resulting solution's volume was 437 mL. What is the specific gravity of the resulting solution?

51. How tall is a rectangular block of balsa wood measuring 3.2 cm wide and 2.5 cm deep that has a mass of 85.0 g? The specific gravity of balsa wood is 0.20.

52. Seawater contains 8.0×10^{-1} cg of the element strontium per kilogram of seawater. Assuming that all the strontium could be recovered, how many grams of strontium could be recovered from a cubic meter of seawater? Assume the density of seawater is 1.0 g/mL.

53. If 50.0 g of iron at 75°C is placed in 250 g water at 25°C in an insulated container and both are allowed to come to the same temperature, what will the temperature be? The specific heat of iron is 0.106 cal/g°C.

54. There are 6.02×10^{23} atoms of mercury in 201 g of mercury. The density of mercury is 13.5 g/mL. **a.** What is the volume, in μm^3, occupied by one mercury atom? **b.** Assuming the atom is a sphere, what is the radius of the mercury atom in nanometers?

55. Different volumes of the same liquid were added to a flask on a balance. After each addition of liquid the mass of the flask with the liquid was measured.

Graph the data using mass as the independent variable. Use the graph to answer these questions.

a. What is the mass of the flask?

b. What is the density of the liquid?

volume (mL)	14	27	41	55	82
mass (g)	103.0	120.4	139.1	157.9	194.1

Research Projects

1. Find out more about the job of a chemical technician. To do this, contact the personnel offices of local industries that manufacture products such as plastics, paints, cosmetics, pharmaceuticals, or other chemicals.

2. Design an experiment to investigate how one of the physical properties of a substance varies under different conditions. Identify the variables that are manipulated, controlled, and responding.

3. Program a programmable calculator to do a calculation, such as to calculate the heat released for a substance with a known specific heat when a given mass undergoes an observed temperature change.

4. Write a computer program to do a routine calculation such as to calculate density given the mass and volume.

5. Find out what kind of mathematical problems are common in one of the five major divisions of chemistry listed in Chapter 1.

Readings and References

Easton, Thomas A. *Careers in Science*. Homewood, Il: Dow Jones-Irwin, 1984.

Loebel, Arnold B. *Chemical Problem-Solving by Dimensional Analysis: A Self-instructional Program*. Boston: Houghton Mifflin, 1978.

Pierce, Conway, and R. Nelson Smith. *General Chemistry Workbook: How to Solve Chemistry Problems,* 4th ed. San Francisco: Freeman, 1980.

4 Atomic Structure

Chapter Planning Guide

Section			Demonstrations and Experiments	Resource Materials
4·1	Atoms	C*		Objectives Worksheet 4, SPB
4·A	John Dalton and the Role of Theories	E		Skillsheet 4, SPB
4·2	Electrons, Protons, and Neutrons	C	Dem 4·1 Cathode Rays	Teaching Diagram 2
4·B	The Discovery of the Nucleus	E		
4·3	The Structure of the Atom	C	Dem 4·2 Space Within the Atom Exp 6 Atomic Structure: Rutherford's Experiment, LM	Teaching Diagram 3 Prelab 6, SPB Quiz 4·1
4·C	New Discoveries of Subatomic Particles	E		
4·4	Atomic Number	C	Dem 4·3 Atomic Number	
4·5	Mass Number	C		
4·6	Isotopes	C		Nuclear Power Plants, ICT 4
4·7	Atomic Mass	C	Dem 4·4 Isotopes and Atomic Mass	Quiz 4·2 Reviewsheet 4, SPB Chapter 4 Test
4·D	The Mass Spectrometer	E		

*C = Core, O = Optional
E = Enrichment, H = Honors

LM = Laboratory Manual

SPB = Skills Practice Book
ICT = Issues in Chem. Tech.

Chapter Objectives

Having studied this chapter and done the problems, the student should be able to:

1. Define an atom.   *4·1*

2. Summarize Dalton's atomic theory.   *4·1*

3. Distinguish between protons, electrons, and neutrons in terms of their relative masses and charges.   *4·2*

4. Discuss the structure of an atom including the location of the proton, electron, and neutron with respect to the nucleus.   *4·3*

5. Use the atomic number and mass number of an element to find the number of protons, electrons, and neutrons.   *4·4, 4·5*

6. Define an atomic mass unit.   *4·5*

7. State how isotopes of an atom differ.   *4·6*

8. Use the concept of isotopes to explain why the atomic masses of elements are not whole numbers.   *4·7*

9. Calculate the average atomic mass of an element from isotope data.   *4·7*

Teaching Suggestions

4·1 Atoms

Most beginning chemistry students already have been convinced of the existence of atoms. Some still question whether we really know they exist when we cannot even "see" them. It is impossible to cite any single piece of evidence that "proves" the existence of atoms. The development of atomic theory has taken place over a long period of time and has occurred in a step-by-step fashion. This chapter presents the atom in a historical context. It is not necessary for this course that the history be emphasized. Nevertheless, it is important that the students come to

appreciate the process by which a theory in *any* field of science is developed.

Emphasize that a sample of an element cannot be infinitely subdivided. Eventually we reach a point where the pieces suddenly no longer have the properties of the element. It is at this point where we encounter the atom.

4·A John Dalton and the Role of Theories

This section illustrates how Dalton developed a theory of atoms even though he had no *direct* knowledge of their existence. A possible approach is to list the facts Dalton knew about matter and its behavior. Then propose different explanations for this behavior.

4·2 Electrons, Protons, and Neutrons

Emphasize that the discovery of subatomic particles started in the middle of the nineteenth century and is still going on! (See Section 4·C.) If the equipment is available, you may wish to do **Demonstration 4·1** *Cathode Rays* to illustrate one of the early experiments with electrons.

4·B The Discovery of the Nucleus

One of the major steps in atomic theory was the abandonment of the idea that the atom was a ball of uniform density. The principles of Rutherford's experiment are easily followed by most students.

4·3 The Structure of the Atom

Sketch on the board a rough picture of an atom. Draw a tiny nucleus surrounded by a very large round cloud. Avoid drawing the erroneous planetary Bohr model. Point out that the drawing you have just made is erroneous, since the scale is entirely wrong. It would be very difficult to make a drawing where the nucleus and outer edge of the atom could be seen at the same time.

A sample calculation will help drive home the idea that although it contains nearly all the mass, the nucleus occupies only a tiny fraction of the volume. For example, if you drew a circle 1 mm in diameter to represent the nucleus, you would have to draw a circle 150 meters in diameter to represent the outer edge of the aluminum atom!

A calculation of the density of the nucleus is perhaps even more surprising:

$$\text{Mass} = 27 \text{ g/mole} \div 6.02 \times 10^{23} \text{ atoms/mole}$$
$$= 4.5 \times 10^{-23} \text{ g/atom}$$
$$\text{Volume} = 4/3 \; \pi r^3$$
$$= 4/3 \; \pi (2.0 \times 10^{-15} \text{ m})^3$$
$$= 3.4 \times 10^{-44} \text{ m}^3$$
$$\text{Density} = \text{mass/volume} = 1.3 \times 10^{21} \text{ g/m}^3$$

If the students follow these calculations, they will conclude that the atom is mostly empty space.

4·C New Discoveries of Subatomic Particles

This section points out that the search for the understanding of atomic structure is still continuing. Use it only as background, since the internal structure of the atom (beyond electrons, protons, and neutrons) has little to do with our understanding of chemistry until Chapter 24.

4·4 Atomic Number

Students will have little trouble grasping the definition of atomic number. Most will not see its significance, however. Emphasize that the atomic number "decides" the kind of atom. All atoms with an atomic number of 6 are carbon atoms, regardless of what state they may be in. All atoms with an atomic number of 7 are entirely different and are nitrogen atoms. **Demonstration 4·3** *Atomic Number* shows these ideas.

4·5 Mass Number

It may help to use the classic symbols for atomic number and mass number: Atomic number = Z; mass number = A; number of neutrons = $A - Z$.

4·6 Isotopes
4·7 Atomic Mass

Up until now we have been using the false assumption that all atoms of an element are identical. It is important that the students understand that there can be slight differences in the masses of the atoms of a given element, but *those differences in no way affect their chemical behavior.*

The fact that the atoms do not have the same masses does not affect the *total* mass of a sample which contains these atoms and so we must deal with the concept of the average mass of the atoms in an element.

For those students who have a difficult time with mathematics, they might try visualizing a fixed number of atoms and then finding their total masses and average masses. Do the problem given in the text as follows.

Assume there are 100 atoms of element X.

If 20% of the atoms have mass number 10, then there are 20 atoms with that mass number present.

If 80% of the atoms have mass number 11, then there are 80 atoms with that mass number present.

To get the average mass, find the total mass of all of these atoms and divide by 100.

$$\left(20 \; \cancel{\text{atoms}} \times \frac{10 \text{ amu}}{\cancel{\text{atom}}}\right) + \left(80 \; \cancel{\text{atoms}} \times \frac{11 \text{ amu}}{\cancel{\text{atom}}}\right)$$
$$= 1080 \text{ amu}$$

Atomic mass = 10.8 amu/atom

Demonstration 4·4 *Isotopes and Atomic Mass* illustrates these ideas.

Demonstrations

4·1 Cathode Rays

Concept: A cathode ray tube or oscilloscope can be used to demonstrate electron behavior.

Materials: cathode ray demonstration apparatus or oscilloscope, high voltage power source, vinyl strip, wool, acetate strip, cotton, magnet.

Procedure: 1. Apply a high voltage to the terminals of the cathode ray demonstration apparatus. 2. A straight beam moves across the tube. 3. Demonstrate that the beam behaves differently than a beam of light by bringing electrically charged strips or rods near the beam. It deflects toward the positively charged strip and away from the negatively charged strip. A strong negative charge can be obtained by rubbing a vinyl strip with wool. A strong positive charge can be obtained by rubbing an acetate strip with cotton. 4. If a magnet is brought near, a deflection of the beam is observed. 5. A similar demonstration can be done with an oscilloscope. Set the horizontal and vertical gain controls so that a spot of light appears on the screen. This spot can be moved with electrically charged strips or with magnets. 6. Point out that the behavior of a cathode ray is consistent with that of a stream of electrons.

4·2 Space Within the Atom

Concept: Atoms are mostly empty space with a relatively tiny nucleus at the center (Rutherford's experiment).

Materials: blackboard, chalk, 3 or more ping pong balls.

Procedure: 1. Draw a dot on one side of the blackboard, and label it the nucleus of a hydrogen atom. 2. Draw an arc 5 m from the dot, calling it the orbit of the electron. 3. Move to 5 m in front of the dot, noting the size of the whole orbit compared to the size of nucleus. 4. Move to 10 m in front of the dot, showing the location of the nucleus of an adjacent hydrogen atom. 5. Throw balls at the dot. Note that very few of the balls hit the dot. Compare to the alpha particles Rutherford used to bombard metal atoms.

4·3 Atomic Number

Concept: The atomic number is the number of protons in the nucleus.

Materials: 20 marbles (10 each of 2 different colors), 125-mL Florence flask.

Procedure: 1. Write on the blackboard: The number of protons in the nucleus determines the identity of an atom. This number is called the atomic number. 2. Roll one marble into the tilted flask, noting that this is the single proton of a hydrogen atom. 3. Roll marbles of the same color into the flask one at a time. Have the class state the atomic numbers and the names of the elements represented. 4. Marbles of the second color can be included to represent neutrons in each of the depicted elements. 5. Continue for the first ten elements (through neon).

4·4 Isotopes and Atomic Mass

Concept: Isotopes have the same atomic number but different atomic masses.

Materials: 20 marbles (10 each of 2 different colors), 125-mL Florence flask.

Procedure: 1. Place 6 marbles of one color and 6 marbles of another color in the flask, noting which are protons and which are neutrons. Also note the total atomic mass. 2. Add 2 marbles of the neutron's color, noting the atomic mass of carbon-14 and that it is still carbon because of the 6 protons. 3. Change the number of proton and neutron marbles for other elements and their isotopes.

Audiovisual Resources

An Introduction to the Atom (F) National Geographic, 1982, 15 min. (Use with Sections 4·1, 4·2, and 4·3.) Presents the historical development of the present concept of the atom.

The Atom (2 FS) Hawkhill, 1984, 18–20 min. each. (Use with Sections 4·1, 4·2, and 4·3.) Presents information about atomic theory from ancient times to the present, emphasizing the people involved in the development of the theory.

Answers to End of Chapter Questions and Problems

Practice Questions and Problems

7. The smallest particle of an element that retains the properties of that element.

8. An element is composed of identical atoms. Atoms of different elements differ. Atoms combine to form molecules of compounds. Chemical reactions involve a rearrangement of the way in which atoms are joined.

9. They are composed of electrons and can be deflected by a magnetic field.

10. See Figures 4·6 and 4·7. Cathode rays are deflected by magnetic fields.

11. Proton and neutron, masses of about 1 amu; electron, essentially "massless". Neutron, no charge; proton, +1 charge; electron, −1 charge.

12. It is composed of protons and neutrons and is very dense.

13. The number of protons in the nucleus.

14. The number of positively charged protons is balanced by an equal number of negatively charged electrons.

15. a. 8 **b.** 2 **c.** 26 **d.** 7

16. a. 16 **b.** 1 **c.** 15 **d.** 48 **e.** 20

17. A unit of mass equaling one-twelfth the mass of a carbon-12 atom.

18. 18, 40, Ar

19. a. 5, 6, 5 **b.** 36, 48, 36 **c.** 21, 24, 21 **d.** 19, 20, 19

20.

Element	Number of protons	Mass number	Number of electrons	Atomic number	Number of neutrons
Se	34	79	34	34	45
O	8	16	8	8	8
Si	14	28	14	14	14
H	1	1	1	1	0

21. Mass number, number of neutrons, atomic mass.

22. Oxygen-17, $^{17}_{8}$O.

23. Cobalt-60, $^{60}_{27}$Co.

24.

Isotope	Symbol	Atomic number	Mass number	Number of protons	Number of neutrons
Hydrogen-2	$^{2}_{1}$H	1	2	1	1
Strontium-83	$^{83}_{38}$Sr	38	83	38	45
Uranium-238	$^{238}_{92}$U	92	238	92	146
Carbon-14	$^{14}_{6}$C	6	14	6	8
Mercury-201	$^{201}_{80}$Hg	80	201	80	121

25. a. 18, 18, 18 **b.** 29, 32, 29 **c.** 1, 2, 1 **d.** 8, 9, 8 **e.** 35, 44, 35

26. The weighted average of the masses of the isotopes of that element.

27. 238 amu

28. 107.4 amu

Mastery Questions and Problems

29. The atomic mass is the weighted average of the masses of the isotopes of an element.

30. Yes. Atoms were rearranged in chemical reactions, but not changed.

31. The volume of an atom is large in relation to the volume of the nucleus. The density of the nucleus is high relative to the density of the atom.

32. +29

33. All have one proton and one electron; they have 0, 1, or 2 neutrons.

34. 28.2 amu

35. Atoms of the same element are not identical (isotopes). The atom is not the smallest particle of matter.

36. 207 amu

Review Questions and Problems

37. a. 5 **b.** 2 **c.** 4 **d.** 4

38. a. 57 cg **b.** 0.0045 km **c.** 5.2 × 10⁻³ mL **d.** 1.0 × 10¹ kJ

39. 55.6 g

40. 5.86 × 10⁴ cal

41. 32 g O₂

42. Answers will vary; heterogeneous.

43. 6.66 × 10³ cal

44. a. element **b.** mixture **c.** mixture **d.** compound **e.** mixture **f.** mixture

45. 297 dm³

Challenging Questions and Problems

46. Lithium-7, 92.5%; lithium-6, 7.5%.

47. The density of diamond is greater than that of graphite. Graphite atoms need to be forced closer together.

48. 4 × 10⁻²⁵ g

4 Atomic Structure

Chapter Preview

By the late 1800s scientists were convinced that atoms are the fundamental units of which all matter is composed. They soon discovered, however, that the atom is not indivisible. It is composed of smaller particles: electrons, protons, and neutrons. In this chapter we will begin with Dalton's atomic theory and see how our present knowledge of atomic structure was developed.

4·1   Atoms

A typical atom has a diameter of 10^{-8} cm and a mass of 10^{-23} g.

Greek: *atomos* = indivisible

Suppose we take a small cube of the element lead (Pb) and cut it into the smallest pieces we can. As the soft, gray, metallic pieces get smaller and smaller, they still retain the properties of lead. A point would finally come, however, when the particle of lead can no longer be divided and still retain its properties. This particle is an **atom,** *the smallest particle of an element that retains the properties of that element*. Fortunately this problem is only theoretical. Lead atoms are very small, and no cutting tool would be fine enough to isolate a single atom. One gram of lead, a cube less than 0.5 cm on a side, contains 2.9×10^{21} atoms. By comparison, the earth's population is only about 4×10^9 people.

The idea of atoms was first suggested by Democritus of Abdera, an ancient Greek who lived in the fourth century BC. However, Democritus' ideas were not useful in explaining chemical phenomena because they were not based on experimental evidence. It was not until the late 1700s that chemists were able to relate chemical changes to events at the level of individual atoms. At that time the English chemist and physicist John

Figure 4.1
These tracks record the movement of subatomic particles through a bubble chamber.

Figure 4·2
Clusters of uranium atoms appear in this photograph taken with a scanning transmission electron microscope. The individual uranium atoms are the white dots on the dark carbon surface. The magnification is ×500 000.

Dalton (1766–1844) first stated his atomic theory. **Dalton's atomic theory** included the following ideas.

1. All elements are composed of tiny indivisible particles called atoms.
2. Atoms of the same element are identical. The atoms of any one element are different from those of any other element.
3. Atoms of different elements can combine with one another in simple whole number ratios to form compounds.
4. Chemical reactions occur when atoms are separated, joined, or rearranged. However, atoms of one element are not changed into atoms of another by a chemical reaction.

■ An element is composed of many atoms that behave alike.

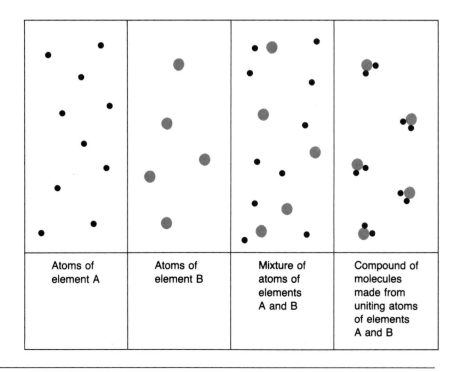

Atoms of element A	Atoms of element B	Mixture of atoms of elements A and B	Compound of molecules made from uniting atoms of elements A and B

Figure 4·3
According to Dalton's atomic theory, an element is a large collection of atoms and a compound is a large collection of molecules.

Figure 4·4
John Dalton is known for his interpretation of the experimental results of other chemists. His atomic theory helped chemists understand why many chemicals behave in certain ways.

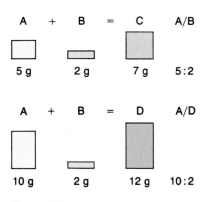

Figure 4·5
Dalton's law of multiple proportions says that atoms of different elements always combine in simple whole number ratios. In this example, the ratio of the mass of A in B to the mass of A in D is 5:10 or 1:2.

4·A John Dalton and the Role of Theories

Two thousand years of error and oversight ended with Dalton's proposal of an atomic theory to explain chemical behavior. Dalton was only twelve years old when he took his first job as a school teacher in his own village in England. Throughout his life he earned his living as a teacher, first in high schools, later in a college, and finally as a private tutor. His real love and his real genius, however, were for science. During his lifetime he studied many different topics, including the aurora borealis, the tradewinds, and color blindness.

Dalton was particularly curious about how substances combined. He discovered that when two substances, A and B, combined to make a new substance, C, they seemed to do so in a fixed proportion by mass. Furthermore, if A and B could also combine to make a second new substance, D, the ratio of the masses of A and B in D would be a simple multiple of the ratio of their masses in C. For example, if substance C consisted of 5 grams of A for every 2 grams of B, substance D might consist of 10 grams of A for every 2 grams of B. Dalton demonstrated this "law of multiple proportions" and proposed an explanation for it in 1803.

Dalton concluded that all matter was made of atoms, which were indivisible, indestructible particles. They could be separated from each other or combined to form new substances. The atoms of different substances had different masses and were packed closely together even in a gas. This explained the differing densities of gases. Dalton assumed that if two elements combined to make only one compound, that compound consisted of one atom of each element. If two compounds were possible, one would consist of one atom of one element and two of the other. Because of this simple ratio of atoms, the masses of the combining elements were in simple ratios to each other.

We now know that some of Dalton's assumptions were not correct. The particles of a gas are not close together. There is no guarantee that the simplest compound formed from A and B will be made of one atom of A and one of B. Water, for example, is made of 2 atoms of hydrogen to one of oxygen. Finally, in the last century, science has shown that the atom is far from indivisible.

Dalton was not known as a great experimenter. He based most of his conclusions on the work of other chemists. He was, however, a brilliant theoretician. His atomic theory was a historic step in the understanding of chemical behavior. It is also an excellent example of the way in which theories bring about progress in scientific work. In spite of its flaws, Dalton's theory inspired a generation of chemists to conduct experiments. These clarified and refined our picture of the fundamental particles of matter.

4·2 Electrons, Protons, and Neutrons

Most of Dalton's atomic theory is still accepted. One revision concerns his idea that atoms are indivisible. This belief was held until about a century ago. Today we know that matter can be broken down into particles more fundamental than atoms. With the help of increasingly powerful atom smashers, physicists have found dozens of subatomic particles. In fact, so many particles have been found that no single theory of atomic structure can account for all of them. In chemistry we concern ourselves with only three of these particles: electrons, protons, and neutrons.

Electrons *are negatively charged subatomic particles.* They were discovered by scientists whose main interests were in electricity rather than chemistry. These scientists studied the flow of electric current through gases at low pressure. They contained the gases using a closed glass tube with metal disks called electrodes at each end (Figure 4·6). When connected to a source of high-voltage, the tube glows. One electrode, the anode, becomes positively charged. The other electrode, the cathode, becomes negatively charged. *The glowing beam, which travels from the cathode to the anode, is called a* **cathode ray.**

Atoms are divisible into electrons, protons, and neutrons.

Safety

Under some conditions, cathode tubes emit x-rays. Care should be used in operating this equipment.

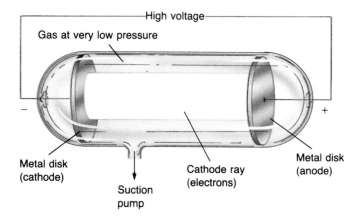

Figure 4·6
In a cathode ray tube, electrons travel as a ray from the cathode (−) to the anode (+). A television tube is a specialized type of cathode ray tube.

The English physicist Sir Joseph J. Thomson (1856–1940) experimented with cathode rays. In 1897 he found that cathode rays could be deflected either by magnets or by electrically charged plates (Figure 4·7). Thomson showed that a cathode ray is a collection of very small negatively charged particles, all alike, moving at high speed. He named these particles electrons. Thomson determined the mass of the newly discovered electron. He found that is was almost 2000 times lighter than a hydrogen atom, which was thought to be the lightest component of matter. Moreover, he observed that cathode rays are always composed of electrons. This was true regardless of the gas in the cathode ray tube or the type of metal used for the electrodes. Thomson reasoned that electrons must be a part of the atoms of all the elements.

Shortly after electrons were discovered, scientists began to think about the particles left over when a hydrogen atom loses an electron. Since atoms are electrically neutral, researchers reasoned that the leftover

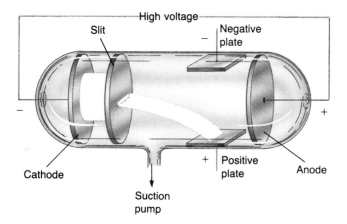

Figure 4·7
Cathode rays are attracted by a positively charged plate. This deflection shows the negatively charged character of the particles.

Greek: protos = first

particle should have a positive charge. Experimental evidence for such particles, protons, was soon found. *Researchers named this positively charged subatomic particle a* **proton.** It carries a single unit of positive charge and is 1840 times heavier than an electron. A proton is what remains when a hydrogen atom is stripped of an electron.

In 1932 the English physicist Sir James Chadwick (1891–1974) confirmed the existence of yet another subatomic particle: the neutron. **Neutrons** *are subatomic particles with no charge,* but their mass nearly equals that of the proton. Thus the fundamental building blocks of all atoms are the electron, the proton, and the neutron. Table 4·1 summarizes the properties of these subatomic particles.

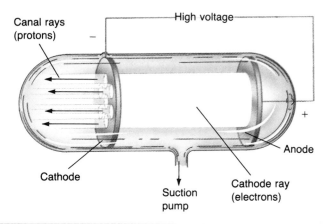

Figure 4·8
In 1886, Goldstein observed rays traveling in the opposite direction of the cathode ray. This occurred when he used a cathode with holes in it. He called these rays "canal rays". Later, the canal rays were found to be made up of positively charged particles called protons.

Table 4·1	Properties of Subatomic Particles			
Particle	Symbol	Relative electrical charge	Approximate relative mass (amu)*	Actual mass (g)
Electron	e^-	1−	1/1840	9.11×10^{-28}
Proton	p^+	1+	1	1.67×10^{-24}
Neutron	n^0	0	1	1.67×10^{-24}

*1 amu = 1.66×10^{-24} g.

4·B The Discovery of the Nucleus

In 1911 Ernest Rutherford (1871–1937) decided to test the prevailing theory of atomic structure. In the process of doing so, he and his co-workers at the University of Manchester, England, were able to develop a more refined picture of the atom. The current theory was that the protons and electrons were evenly distributed throughout the volume of an atom. To test this theory, they directed a beam of particles at a very thin sheet of gold. The particles they chose for this were alpha particles, which are positively charged helium atoms that each lack two electrons. The expectation was that the alpha particles would pass through the thin sheet of metal unhindered.

To everyone's surprise, a very small fraction of the alpha particles bounced back (Figure 4·9). From these results, Rutherford proposed that the mass of the atom and the positive charge are concentrated in a small region. He called this region the nucleus. He thought of the rest of the atom as more or less empty space. The electrons were in that area, but they were so small that they did not interfere with the movement of the alpha particles. Rutherford later recollected: "It was quite the most incredible event that has ever happened to me in my life. It was almost as if you fired a 15-inch shell into a piece of tissue paper and it came back and hit you."

Safety

Proper shielding should always be used with radioactive emissions such as alpha particles.

An atom has a dense nucleus but is mostly empty space.

Figure 4·9
a To learn more about the nature of the atom, Rutherford and Marsden aimed a beam of alpha particles at a piece of gold foil surrounded by a fluorescent screen. They found that most of the particles passed through the foil. A few particles were deflected.
b Rutherford concluded that most of the alpha particles pass through the gold foil because the nucleus is a small region of the atom. Particles that pass near or approach the nucleus directly are deflected.

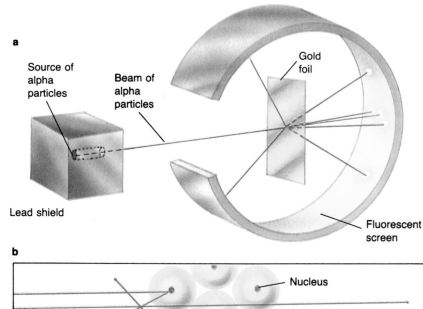

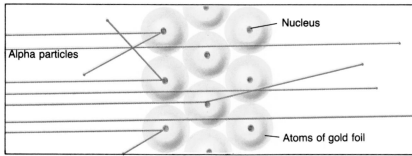

4·3 The Structure of the Atom

Typically, the diameter of the nucleus is only 1/10,000 the diameter of the atom, yet nearly all of the mass of the atom is contained in the nucleus.

Even before neutrons were discovered, scientists were wondering how electrons and protons were positioned within an atom. This was difficult to determine since atoms are such small particles. Using a rather ingenious experiment, Rutherford discovered the nucleus, a basic feature of atomic structure. *The **nucleus** of an atom is composed of protons and neutrons.* The nucleus has a positive charge, and it occupies a very small part of the volume of an atom. By contrast, the negatively charged electrons occupy most of the volume of the atom. They exist outside the nucleus. Since protons and neutrons have a much greater mass than electrons, the nucleus of an atom has a very high density.

■ In an atom, negatively charged electrons move about the positively charged nucleus.

All atoms are composed of electrons, protons, and neutrons. How then are atoms of one element different from those of another element?

Figure 4·10
If an atom were the size of this stadium, then its nucleus would be the size of a tennis ball.

Table 4·2	Atoms of the First Ten Elements					
			Composition of the nucleus			Number of
Name	Symbol	Atomic Number	Protons	Neutrons	Mass number	electrons
Hydrogen	H	1	1	0	1	1
Helium	He	2	2	2	4	2
Lithium	Li	3	3	4	7	3
Beryllium	Be	4	4	5	9	4
Boron	B	5	5	6	11	5
Carbon	C	6	6	6	12	6
Nitrogen	N	7	7	7	14	7
Oxygen	O	8	8	8	16	8
Fluorine	F	9	9	10	19	9
Neon	Ne	10	10	10	20	10

The answer is simple. Differences among the elements result from different numbers of subatomic particles in their atoms. For example, atoms of gold (Au) have 79 protons, 118 neutrons, and 79 electrons, whereas silver (Ag) atoms have 47 protons, 61 neutrons, and 47 electrons.

Cyclotrons, synchrotrons, and linear accelerators are discussed in Section 24·B.

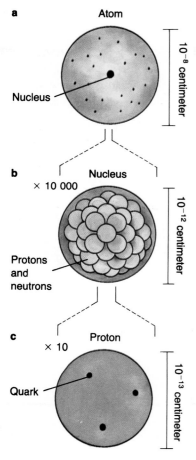

Figure 4·11
a The atom consists of a nucleus surrounded by electrons.
b The nucleus is composed of protons and neutrons.
c Each proton and neutron is composed of three quarks. Notice the large size difference between the atom and the nucleus compared to the size difference between the nucleus and the proton.

4·C New Discoveries of Subatomic Particles

The discovery that all atoms were made of just three types of particles showed a great simplicity in the structure of matter. Unfortunately, this simplicity was soon proven false. In the decades following the discovery of the neutron, scientists discovered more subatomic particles. These particles were not stable; they did not exist in ordinary matter. Instead they turned up when atomic nuclei were struck by high-energy particles or radiation. A target nucleus would shatter, giving rise to one or more new particles. Such collisions happened very infrequently in nature.

In order to have more collisions to study, scientists built cyclotrons, synchrotrons, and linear accelerators. These machines differ in the manner by which the particle "bullets" are accelerated. As a result of these new tools, however, hundreds of new subatomic particles have been discovered. This huge family of particles can now be explained in terms of more truly elementary particles.

Physicists now refer to two families of particles. The first, the leptons, includes the electron, the mu-meson (or muon), the tau-meson, and three types of neutrino. Each neutrino is matched to each of the three particles mentioned. Neutrinos have no charge and no detectable mass. These six particles are grouped as a family because they are affected only by the electroweak force. This is a force that affects charged particles and is also involved in certain kinds of radioactive decay. Leptons seem to be truly elementary. No evidence yet exists that leptons are made of smaller particles.

The second family of particles is called the hadrons. These particles are affected by the strong force that holds the nucleus of an atom together. Hundreds of hadrons are known, including the familiar proton and neutron. These particles are not elementary. Physicists have discovered tht hadrons consist of smaller particles called quarks. The six types, or "flavors," of quarks are called up and down, top and bottom (or truth and beauty), and strange and charm. Each type of quark can have one of three "colors." These are not colors in the normal sense but they are more like a kind of charge. Up, top, and charm quarks have a charge of $+2/3$. The remaining three quarks have a charge of $-1/3$. The proton is made of two up quarks and one down quark; thus its charge is $+1$. The neutron is made of two down quarks and one up; its charge is 0.

Each lepton and quark also has a corresponding "antiparticle." For example, the antielectron is called the positron. It has the same mass as the electron but a charge of +1. The antidown quark has the same mass as a down quark but the opposite charge and color. When a particle collides with its antiparticle, both are annihilated. A burst of energy is released, and new particles are formed.

The study of the forces within atoms is equally important and fascinating. Physicists have identified the particles that carry the atomic forces. The photon, which has no charge and no mass, carries the electromagnetic force. Other particles, called bosons, carry the strong and weak forces mentioned earlier. The massless particles that carry the strong force, holding quarks together, are called gluons. Those that carry the weak force are known as the W+, W-, and Z particles. Unlike photons and gluons, these particles are very heavy. Their mass is as much as 100 times the mass of the proton.

Again the number of "elementary particles" has grown. They now include 6 types of quarks, 6 leptons, 24 antiparticles, 8 gluons, the W and Z bosons, and the photon. The physicists' hope for simplicity is not satisfied by these numerous subatomic particles. Hence, the search for truly fundamental particles continues.

4·4 Atomic Number

In Table 4·2 an atomic number is listed for each element. *The* **atomic number** *of an element is the number of protons in the nucleus of the atom of that element.* Hydrogen (atomic number 1) contains one proton in its nucleus. Oxygen (atomic number 8) contains eight protons in its nucleus. Atoms are electrically neutral. Thus the number of protons in the nucleus of an atom must equal the number of electrons around its nucleus. An atom of hydrogen has one electron around its nucleus, and an oxygen atom has eight electrons.

The number of protons in an atomic nucleus identifies the element.

The atomic number of each element is given in the periodic table (Figure 12·4). The atomic number is the whole number that increases as you read across each row of the periodic table from left to right.

Problems

1. Element carbon is atomic number 6. How many protons and electrons are in a carbon atom?

2. The atomic number of an element is 11. What is the element?

1. Six protons and six electrons
2. Sodium

4·5 Mass Number

A glance at Table 4·1 shows that the actual mass of protons and neutrons is very small: 1.67×10^{-24} g. Even compared with this small mass, the mass of an electron is negligible: 9.11×10^{-28} g. These values are useful information, but they are inconvenient for us to work with. In most

instances chemists use relative comparisons of the masses of atoms. The unit of comparison is the **atomic mass unit** (amu), *which is defined as one-twelfth the mass of a carbon atom that contains six protons and six neutrons*. For all practical purposes we can consider the mass of a single proton or a single neutron as 1 amu.

Most of the mass of an atom is concentrated in its nucleus. *Thus the total number of protons and neutrons in the nucleus is the* **mass number** *of an atom*. Table 4·2 gives the composition of atoms of the first 10 elements. Hydrogen (atomic number 1) has a mass number of 1. Helium (atomic number 2) has a mass number of 4. From these data we can conclude that an atom of helium is four times heavier than an atom of hydrogen. Likewise, we can see that an atom of neon (mass number 20) is five times heavier than an atom of helium.

■ The mass number is the approximate mass of an atom.

With the exception of hydrogen, the mass number is always equal to or greater than twice the atomic number. This means that the number of neutrons is always equal to or greater than twice the number of protons (except for hydrogen).

The composition of the nucleus of an atom is calculated from the atomic number and the mass number.

Example 1

How many protons, electrons, and neutrons are in the following atoms?

	Atomic number	Mass number
a. Beryllium (Be)	4	9
b. Neon (Ne)	10	20
c. Sodium (Na)	11	23

Solution

a. For an atom, the number of electrons equals the number of protons and is given by the atomic number. Be has 4 protons and 4 electrons. We get the number of neutrons by subtracting the atomic number from the mass number. Be has $9 - 4 = 5$ neutrons.

b. Ne has 10 protons, 10 electrons, and $20 - 10 = 10$ neutrons.

c. Na has 11 protons, 11 electrons, and $23 - 11 = 12$ neutrons.

Problem

3. Complete this table.

Atomic number	Mass number	Number of protons	Number of neutrons	Number of electrons	Symbol of element
7	____	____	7	____	____
____	____	9	10	____	____
____	39	____	____	19	____
____	59	27	____	____	____

3.

	Atomic number	Mass number	Number of protons
a.	7	14	7
b.	9	19	9
c.	19	39	19
d.	27	59	27

	Number of neutrons	Number of electrons	Symbol
a.	7	7	N
b.	10	9	F
c.	20	19	K
d.	32	27	Co

4·6   Isotopes

Most of Dalton's atomic theory (Section 4·1) is still accepted today. We now know, however, that all atoms of the same element are not identical. The nuclei of the atoms of a given element must all contain the same

■ Most elements in nature are a mixture of two or more isotopes.

76   Chapter 4   Atomic Structure

number of protons, but the number of neutrons may vary. *Atoms that have the same number of protons but different numbers of neutrons are called* **isotopes.** Since isotopes of an element have different numbers of neutrons, they also have different mass numbers and different atomic masses. Despite these differences, isotopes are chemically alike. This is because they have identical numbers of protons and electrons. These subatomic particles are responsible for the characteristic behavior of each element.

To symbolize the composition of an isotope we use the chemical symbol with two additional numbers written to the left of it. The mass number is written as a superscript (a number slightly above). The atomic number is written as a subscript (a number slightly below). Atoms of hydrogen with a mass number of 1 are designated hydrogen-1. Atoms of helium with a mass number of 4 are designated helium-4. They are represented as shown.

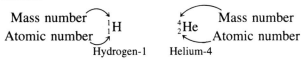

Mass number $\quad {}^{1}_{1}\text{H}$
Atomic number
Hydrogen-1

${}^{4}_{2}\text{He}\quad$ Mass number
Atomic number
Helium-4

Greek: *isotopos* = the same place

The number of neutrons in an atom does not affect its chemical behavior. It only affects the mass of the atom.

Carbon-12
6 protons
6 neutrons
6 electrons

Carbon-13
6 protons
7 neutrons
6 electrons

Carbon-14
6 protons
8 neutrons
6 electrons

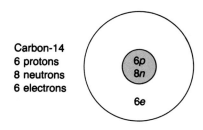

Figure 4·12
Carbon-12, carbon-13, and carbon-14 are three isotopes of carbon. Do they differ in the number of protons, the number of neutrons, or the number of electrons? Number of neutrons.

Example 2

Two of the isotopes of carbon are carbon-12 and carbon-14. Give the chemical symbol for each.

Solution

Carbon is atomic number 6. All atoms of carbon have six protons.

$$\text{Carbon-12, } {}^{12}_{6}\text{C} \qquad \text{Carbon-14, } {}^{14}_{6}\text{C}$$

Example 3

How many neutrons are in the following atoms?
a. ${}^{18}_{8}\text{O}$ **b.** ${}^{32}_{16}\text{S}$ **c.** ${}^{108}_{47}\text{Ag}$ **d.** ${}^{80}_{35}\text{Br}$ **e.** ${}^{207}_{82}\text{Pb}$

Solution

Recall that the superscript is the mass number and the subscript is the atomic number. The mass number minus the atomic number equals the number of neutrons.
a. 10 **b.** 16 **c.** 61 **d.** 45 **e.** 125

Problems
4. ${}^{16}_{8}\text{O}$ and ${}^{18}_{8}\text{O}$
5. **a.** 6 **b.** 8 **c.** 138

4. Two isotopes of oxygen are oxygen-16 and oxygen-18. Write the chemical symbol for each.

5. Using the periodic table, determine the number of neutrons in these atoms. **a.** ${}^{12}\text{C}$ **b.** ${}^{15}\text{N}$ **c.** ${}^{226}\text{Ra}$

Table 4·3 Natural Isotopes of Some Familiar Elements

Name	Symbol	Mass (amu)	Natural percent abundance	"Average" atomic mass
Hydrogen	^1_1H	1.0078	99.985	
	^2_1H	2.0141	0.015	1.0079
	^3_1H	3.0160	negligible	
Helium	^3_2He	3.0160	0.0001	
	^4_2He	4.0026	99.9999	4.0026
Carbon	$^{12}_6C$	12.000	98.89	
	$^{13}_6C$	13.003	1.11	12.011
Nitrogen	$^{14}_7N$	14.003	99.63	
	$^{15}_7N$	15.000	0.37	14.007
Oxygen	$^{16}_8O$	15.995	99.759	
	$^{17}_8O$	16.995	0.037	15.999
	$^{18}_8O$	17.999	0.204	
Sulfur	$^{32}_{16}S$	31.972	95.00	
	$^{33}_{16}S$	32.971	0.76	
	$^{34}_{16}S$	33.967	4.22	32.064
	$^{36}_{16}S$	35.967	0.014	
Zinc	$^{64}_{30}Zn$	63.929	48.89	
	$^{66}_{30}Zn$	65.926	27.81	
	$^{67}_{30}Zn$	66.927	4.11	65.37
	$^{68}_{30}Zn$	67.925	18.57	
	$^{70}_{30}Zn$	69.925	0.62	

Before reading this section you should review your knowledge of percents by doing Section B·3 of the Math Review in Appendix B.

The atomic mass of an element is not always a whole number.

Your grade in a class is often calculated as a weighted average. Major exams, quizzes, homework assignments, and laboratory work may all have a different "weight" (or degree of importance) when your grade is averaged.

4·7 Atomic Mass

The mass of an atom is concentrated in the nucleus. You know that the mass of a proton is 1 amu as is the mass of a neutron. Thus it is reasonable to expect that the mass of an atom expressed in atomic mass units should be a whole number. This view, however, ignores the existence of isotopes. *The atomic mass of an element is the weighted average of the masses of the isotopes of that element.* A weighted average reflects both the mass and the relative abundance of the isotopes as they occur in nature.

The percent abundances of the natural isotopes of some familiar elements are listed in Table 4·3 along with their atomic masses. How is the atomic mass of an element calculated? *Most elements occur as two or more isotopes in nature.* For example, chlorine has two isotopes, both of which have 17 protons in their atomic nuclei. One isotope has 18 neutrons and an atomic mass of 35 amu. This isotope is chlorine-35. The

Ratio of chlorine atoms in natural abundance: three $^{35}_{17}$Cl to one $^{37}_{17}$Cl

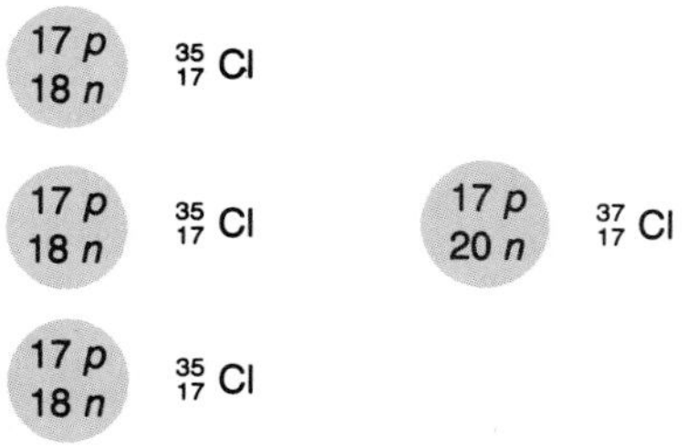

17 p
18 n $^{35}_{17}$Cl

17 p
18 n $^{35}_{17}$Cl   17 p
20 n $^{37}_{17}$Cl

17 p
18 n $^{35}_{17}$Cl

Total number of protons in three $^{35}_{17}$Cl atoms and one $^{37}_{17}$Cl atom = 68

Total number of neutrons in three $^{35}_{17}$Cl atoms and one $^{37}_{17}$Cl atom = 74

Total mass (amu) of all the protons and neutrons = 142 amu

Average mass (amu) of one atom = $\frac{142}{4}$ = 35.5 amu

Figure 4·13
The average atomic mass of an element is calculated as a weighted average of the masses of its naturally occurring isotopes.

other isotope is chlorine-37. It has 20 neutrons. In nature the isotopes of chlorine occur in a nearly 3 : 1 ratio. What is their average atomic mass? Figure 4·13 shows how the calculation is made. The average atomic mass that is calculated by this method is 35.5 amu. In the periodic table the atomic mass is 35.453 amu. The difference between these numbers is that the ratio of the isotopes is not exactly 3 : 1. In addition, the masses of a proton and a neutron are not exactly 1 amu. In calculating average atomic masses, we must remember to take into account the relative abundance of each isotope.

Example 4

Element X has two natural isotopes. The isotope with a mass number of 10 has a relative abundance of 20%. The isotope with a mass number of 11 has a relative abundance of 80%. Estimate the average atomic mass for the element from these figures. What is the true identity and atomic number of element X?

Solution

The mass that each isotope contributes toward the average atomic mass is equal to the product of its mass multiplied by its relative abundance. Remember to express percent as so many parts per 100 parts: 20% = 20/100 = 0.20.

$$^{10}X \quad 10 \text{ amu} \times 0.20 = \quad 2.0 \text{ amu}$$
$$^{11}X \quad 11 \text{ amu} \times 0.80 = \quad \underline{8.8 \text{ amu}}$$
$$\text{Total } 10.8 \text{ amu}$$

The average atomic mass of element X is 10.8 amu. Element X is boron, atomic number 5.

Problem   6. 63.6 amu

6. The element copper is found to contain the naturally occurring isotopes $^{63}_{29}$Cu and $^{65}_{29}$Cu. The relative abundances are 69.1% and 30.9%, respectively. Calculate the average atomic mass of copper.

Each of the three known isotopes of hydrogen has one proton in the nucleus. The most common hydrogen isotope has no neutrons. It has an atomic mass of 1 amu and is called hydrogen-1 ($^1_1$H), or hydrogen. The second isotope has one neutron and an atomic mass of 2 amu. It is called either hydrogen-2 ($^2_1$H), or deuterium. The third isotope has two neutrons and an atomic mass of 3 amu. This isotope is hydrogen-3 ($^3_1$H), or tritium. Tritium nuclei are unstable and slowly disintegrate. Almost all hydrogen in nature is hydrogen-1. The other two isotopes are present in only trace amounts. Thus the average atomic mass for hydrogen is 1.0079 amu. You will see in Chapter 24 that many isotopes with unstable nuclei such as iodine-131 and cobalt-60 are useful in the diagnosis and treatment of disease.

4·D The Mass Spectrometer

One of the most useful and versatile instruments found in the modern chemistry laboratory is the mass spectrometer. This device was invented early in the twentieth century by F. W. Aston, an English physicist. Aston was interested in the newly proposed theory of isotopes. In the process of his research he created an instrument that could separate atoms of slightly different masses. In this way he proved that many samples of naturally occurring elements were really mixtures of isotopes. For his work he was awarded the Nobel Prize in Physics in 1922.

In a mass spectrometer the sample is placed in a vacuum chamber. The vaporizing sample leaks through a very small hole into the instrument. There the vaporized sample is bombarded by high-energy electrons coming from a heated filament. When a particle in the sample is hit by one of these electrons, it may lose an electron of its own and become positively charged. The charged particles are passed through a slit to give a narrow beam of particles. Then they are accelerated to a high speed by an electric field. Because of their charge, the particles can be deflected by electric and magnetic fields. The amount of deflection depends on the size of the fields and the speed, charge, and mass of the particles.

An analogy may help to explain how this deflection takes place. Imagine an electric fan set up to blow *across* a table top. Now imagine that you are rolling table tennis balls *along* the table top, across the path of the fan. The balls will roll in a straight line until they feel the effect of the breeze from the fan. Then they will be deflected from their path. If you roll the balls faster, the deflection will not be so much. If you increase the speed of the fan, the deflection will be more. If you were to use golf balls instead of table tennis balls, the deflection would be less. Because the golf balls have a greater mass, they are harder to deflect.

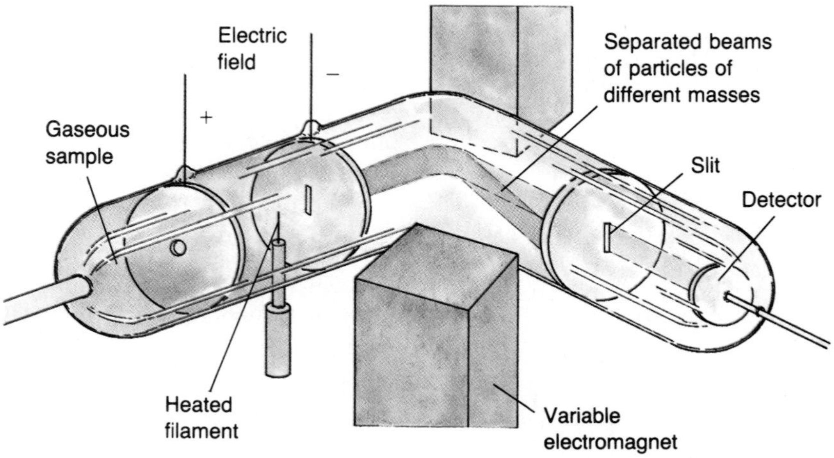

In a mass spectrometer, the beams of deflected particles are detected electrically. In a mass spectroscope, the beams are detected by being focused on a photographic plate.

Figure 4·14
In a mass spectrometer, the ionized sample is deflected by variable electric and magnetic fields. High mass ions are deflected less than lower mass ions. The detector measures how many particles are present when the beam is deflected by a given amount.

By measuring the deflection of the particles in the mass spectrometer, their mass can be determined. If a sample contains particles of several different masses, each different mass corresponds to a different deflection. Using his invention, Aston was able to determine atomic masses to the fourth decimal place.

4 Atomic Structure

Chapter Review

Key Terms

atom	4·1	electron	4·2
atomic mass	4·7	isotope	4·6
atomic mass unit	4·5	mass number	4·5
atomic number	4·4	neutron	4·2
cathode ray	4·2	nucleus	4·3
Dalton's atomic theory	4·1	proton	4·2

Chapter Summary

The basic building blocks of matter are elements. More than 100 elements exist, and each is composed of atoms. The atoms of a given element are different from the atoms of all other elements.

Atoms are exceedingly small. Dalton theorized that atoms were indivisible, but the discovery of the electron changed this theory. Besides negatively charged electrons, atoms contain positively charged protons and electrically neutral neutrons. The proton has a mass nearly 2000 times the mass of an electron. A proton and a neutron are nearly identical in mass.

The nucleus of the atom is composed of protons and neutrons. The nucleus contains most of the mass of the atom in a very small volume. The electrons surround the nucleus and occupy most of the volume of the atom.

The number of protons in the nucleus of the atom is the atomic number of that element. Atoms are electrically neutral. Thus an atom has the same number of protons and electrons. The sum of the protons and neutrons is the mass number. The atoms of a given element all contain the same number of protons, but the number of neutrons may vary. Atoms with the same number of protons but different numbers of neutrons are isotopes.

The atomic mass of an element is expressed in atomic mass units (amu). An atom of any element has an atomic mass that is approximately a whole number. This is because protons and neutrons each have a mass of about 1 amu. The atomic mass in the periodic table is a weighted average of all the naturally occurring isotopes of that element. For this reason, the atomic mass of most elements is generally not a whole number.

Practice Questions and Problems

7. What is an atom? 4·1

8. State the main ideas of Dalton's atomic theory. 4·1

9. What are the properties of cathode rays? 4·2

10. Sketch and label a typical cathode ray tube. What forces can deflect or bend a cathode ray? 4·2

11. What are the charges and relative masses of the three subatomic particles that are of most interest to chemists? 4·2

12. Describe the composition of the nucleus of the atom. 4·3

13. What does the atomic number of each atom represent? 4·4

14. What is meant by the statement: "Atoms are electrically neutral"? 4·4

15. What are the atomic numbers of the following elements? *4·4*
  a. oxygen   **c.** iron
  b. helium   **d.** nitrogen

16. How many protons are in the nuclei of the following atoms? *4·4*
  a. sulfur   **c.** phosphorus   **e.** calcium
  b. hydrogen   **d.** cadmium

17. What is an atomic mass unit? *4·5*

18. An atom has 22 neutrons and 18 protons in its nucleus. What is the atomic number, mass number, and symbol of this element? *4·5*

19. How many protons, neutrons, and electrons are in an atom of the following elements? *4·5*
  a. boron, mass number 11
  b. krypton, mass number 84
  c. scandium, mass number 45
  d. potassium, mass number 39

20. Complete this table. *4·5*

Elements	Number of protons	Mass number	Number of electrons	Atomic number	Number of neutrons
Se	—	—	—	—	45
—	—	16	8	—	—
—	14	28	—	—	—
—	—	1	—	—	—

21. Name three ways that isotopes of an element differ. *4·6*

22. The mass number of an isotope of oxygen is 17. Write the name and symbol for this isotope. *4·6*

23. Cobalt-60 is used in the treatment of cancer. Write the symbol for this isotope. *4·6*

24. Complete this table. *4·6*

Isotope	Symbol	Atomic number	Mass number	Number of protons	Number of neutrons
hydrogen-2	$^{2}_{1}$H	—	—	—	—
—	$^{83}_{38}$Sr	—	—	—	—
—	—	92	—	—	146
—	C	—	—	—	8
—	—	—	201	80	—

25. List the number of protons, neutrons, and electrons in each of the following atoms. *4·6*
  a. $^{36}_{18}$Ar **b.** $^{61}_{29}$Cu **c.** $^{3}_{1}$H **d.** $^{17}_{8}$O **e.** $^{79}_{35}$Br

26. What is the atomic mass of an element? *4·7*

27. Uranium has three isotopes with the following percent abundances: $^{234}_{92}$U (0.0058%), $^{235}_{92}$U (0.71%), $^{238}_{92}$U (99.23%). What do you expect the atomic mass of uranium to be in whole numbers? Why? *4·7*

28. A sample of silver as it occurs in nature is 52.0% of isotope $^{107}_{47}$Ag and 48.0% of isotope $^{108}_{47}$Ag. What is the average atomic mass of silver? (Compare your result with the value given in the periodic table.) *4·7*

Mastery Questions and Problems

29. Explain why the atomic masses for most elements are not whole numbers. *4·7*

30. Did Dalton's ideas support the law of conservation of mass (Section 1·12)? Explain. *4·1*

31. Compare the relative size and relative density of an atom to its nucleus. *4·3*

32. What is the charge of a copper nucleus? *4·4*

33. How are the three isotopes of hydrogen alike? How are they different? *4·6*

34. Ninety-two percent of the atoms of an element have a mass of 28.0 amu, 5.0% of the atoms have a mass of 29.0 amu, and the remaining atoms have a mass of 30.0 amu. Calculate the average atomic mass and identify the element. *4·7*

35. What parts of Dalton's atomic theory no longer agree with our current picture of the atom? *4·6*

36. Use the following isotope data for lead to show that its atomic mass is 207 amu. $^{204}_{82}$Pb (1.37%) $^{206}_{82}$Pb (26.26%) $^{207}_{82}$Pb (20.82%) $^{208}_{82}$Pb (51.55%) *4·7*

Review Questions and Problems

37. How many significant figures are in each of these measurements?
  a. 56.902 cg   **c.** 5.200×10^{-3} mL
  b. 0.0045 km   **d.** 10.04 kJ

38. Round each of the measurements in Problem 37 to two significant figures.

39. What is the mass of 2.47 cm^3 of platinum? The density of platinum is 22.5 g/cm^3.

40. A piece of coal was burned and emitted 245 kJ of heat energy. How many calories is this?

41. Oxygen and hydrogen react explosively to form water. In one reaction 4 g of hydrogen combines with oxygen to form 36 g of water. How much oxygen was used?

42. Give examples of two mixtures that have two phases. Are these homogeneous or heterogeneous mixtures?

43. Calculate the number of calories needed to raise the temperature of 88.8 g of water from 14.0°C to 89.0°C.

44. Classify each of the following as an element, compound, or mixture.
   a. silver
   b. salad oil
   c. apple
   d. water
   e. cardboard
   f. perfume

45. An aquarium measures 45.0 cm × 1.10 m × 60.0 cm. How many dm^3 of water will this aquarium hold?

Challenging Questions and Problems

46. Lithium has two naturally occurring isotopes. Lithium-6 has an atomic mass of 6.015 amu; lithium-7 has an atomic mass of 7.016 amu. The atomic mass of lithium is 6.941 amu. What is the percentage of lithium-7 in nature?

47. Diamond and graphite are both composed of carbon atoms. The density of diamond is 3.51 g/cm^3 and graphite is 2.25 g/cm^3. In 1955 scientists successfully made diamond from graphite. Try to imagine what happens at the atomic level when this change occurs. Then suggest how this synthesis may have been accomplished.

48. When the masses of the particles that make up an atom are added together, the sum is always larger than the actual mass of the atom. The "missing" mass, called the mass defect, represents the amount of matter converted into energy when the nucleus was formed from its component protons and neutrons. Calculate the mass defect of a chlorine-35 atom by using the data in Table 4·1. The actual mass of a chlorine-35 atom is 5.81×10^{-23} g.

Research Projects

1. Dalton studied many scientific topics besides chemistry. Report on some of his findings.

2. How was the proton discovered?

3. How was the neutron discovered?

4. Measure the effect of distance on the attraction between oppositely charged particles.

5. How are radioactive isotopes isolated? How are they created?

6. What is a cloud chamber? How was it invented, and what discoveries did it make possible?

7. Report on the experiments that are being done to try to find a "free quark" or to record the decay of a proton. Why are these experiments important?

8. Visit a laboratory that has a mass spectrometer. Report on the instrument and its applications.

Readings and References

Boslough, John. "Worlds Within the Atom." *National Geographic,* (May 1985), pp. 634–663.

Ellis, R. Hobart, Jr. *Knowing the Atomic Nucleus.* New York: Lothrop, Lee & Shepard, 1973.

Janos, Leo. "Timekeepers of the Solar System." *Science 80,* (May/June 1980), pp. 44–55.

Shropshire, Walter, Jr., ed. *The Joys of Research.* Washington, DC: Smithsonian Institution, 1981.

Taubes, Gary. "Detecting Next to Nothing." *Science 85,* (May 1985), pp. 58–66.

Taubes, Gary. "The Ultimate Theory of Everything." *Discover,* (April 1985), pp. 52–59.

Trefil, James S. *From Atoms to Quarks: An Introduction to the Strange World of Particle Physics.* New York: Scribner, 1980.

Trefil, James. "Matter vs Antimatter." *Science 81,* (September 1981), pp. 66–69.

5 Chemical Names and Formulas

Chapter Planning Guide

Section			Demonstrations and Experiments	Resource Materials
5·1	The Periodic Table	C*		Objectives Worksheet 5, SPB Skillsheet 5, SPB Teaching Diagram 4
5·2	Atoms and Ions	C	Dem 5·1 Ionization of Sodium Metal	
5·3	Compounds	C	Dem 5·2 Formation of Sodium Chloride	
5·4	Chemical Formulas	C	Dem 13·2 Formation of Cubic Crystals	
5·5	Law of Multiple Proportions	O	Dem 5·3 Multiple Proportions	Quiz 5·1
5·6	Ionic Charges of the Elements	C		
5·7	Polyatomic Ions	C	Dem 5·4 Molecular Models	
5·8	Common and Systematic Names	O		Quiz 5·2 Teaching Diagram 5
5·A	Pharmacy from Scheele to the Present	E		
5·9	Writing Formulas for Binary Ionic Compounds	C		
5·10	Naming Binary Ionic Compounds	C	Dem 7·1 Combination of Sulfur and Zinc Dem 7·2 Combination of Iodine and Zinc	
5·11	Ternary Ionic Compounds	C	Exp 7 Identification of Anions and Cations in Solution Exp 8 Precipitation Reactions, LM Dem 7·7 Double Replacement Reactions	Prelab 7, SPB Prelab 8, SPB
5·12	Binary Molecular Compounds	C		Radon Pollution, ICT
5·13	Acids			
5·14	Summary of Naming and Formula Writing	C		Quiz 5·3 Reviewsheet 5, SPB Chapter 5 Test
5·B	Chemical Data Banks	E		
*C = Core, O = Optional E = Enrichment, H = Honors			LM = Laboratory Manual	SPB = Skills Practice Book ICT = Issues in Chem. Tech.

Chapter Objectives

Having studied this chapter and done the problems, the student should be able to:

1. Relate these terms to the periodic table: group, period, representative element, transition element, metal, nonmetal, and metalloid. *5·1*

2. Define the terms cation and anion and show how they are related to the terms metal and nonmetal. *5·2*

3. Using experimental data, show that different samples of the same compound obey the law of definite proportions. *5·3*

4. Differentiate between ionic compounds and molecular compounds, and between formula units and molecules. *5·3, 5·4*

5. Using experimental data, show that two different compounds composed of the same two elements obey the law of multiple proportions. *5·5*

6. Use the periodic table to determine the charge on an ion. *5·6*

7. Distinguish between a polyatomic ion and a monatomic ion. *5·7*

8. Explain why a systematic method of naming chemical compounds is necessary. *5·8*

9. Write the chemical formula of an ionic compound, either binary or ternary, when given the name of the compound. *5·9, 5·11*

10. Name an ionic compound, either binary or ternary, when given the formula of the compound. *5·10, 5·11*

11. Name a binary molecular compound when given the formula of a compound. *5·12*

12. Write the chemical formula of a binary molecular compound when given the name of the compound. *5·12*

13. Name an acid when given the formula of the acid. *5·13*

14. Write the chemical formula of an acid when given the name of the acid. *5·13*

15. Use the flowchart in Figure 5·21 to correctly name a compound. *5·14*

Teaching Suggestions

5·1 The Periodic Table

In this chapter an emphasis is placed on how the grouping of the elements determines the naming of their compounds. Time should be spent in discussing the major groups found on the periodic table. Point out where the metals, nonmetals, and metalloids are to be found. Show examples of each of these types of elements. Point out some of the more obvious similarities in physical properties which exist within each type. You can easily show the high luster and high electrical conductivity of the metals and the color and low electrical conductivity of the non-metals. To demonstrate electrical conductivity you can borrow an ohmmeter or similar device from your physics teacher or set up a simple series circuit with a light bulb and battery.

You may wish to present the idea of classification. You can illustrate it with the metals, nonmetals, and metalloids, or by an example from biology (kingdom, phylum, order, species).

5·2 Atoms and Ions

At this point students are familiar with only the basic structure of atoms. They know little or nothing about electron configurations. They can successfully learn to name and identify ions, however, by using the periodic table as their guide. Initially this will be a relatively rote process. Its advantage though is that students can begin to use chemical names and formulas early in the course.

Section 5·2 introduces the concept of ions. The students should learn to identify positive and negative ions and to associate ionic charges with the gain and loss of electrons. They should not yet be expected to understand why ions form nor should they be expected to predict the ionic charge that is characteristic of an element when it forms an ion. The latter will be covered in Section 5·6.

You may wish to spend some time describing how atoms go through the process of gaining or losing various numbers of electrons to form ions. For the slower students, you may need to count the number of protons and electrons present in the atom before and after it becomes an ion and then add up the positive and negative charges to obtain the charge of the ion. Emphasize repeatedly that negative ions are formed by the gain of electrons and that positive ions are formed by the loss of electrons, never by the gain of protons. Emphasize as well that there is a striking difference in chemical and physical properties between the original atom and its ion. **Demonstration 5·1** *Ionization of Sodium Metal* will help clarify this difference.

5·3 Compounds

Demonstration 5·2 *Formation of Sodium Chloride* shows a compound made from elements.

5·4 Chemical Formulas

Students may have difficulty with the distinction between a molecular formula and a formula unit. There is no difference in appearance between "H_2O" and "Li_2O", yet one is a molecular formula and one is a formula unit. To help them, go back to the process (mentioned in Section 4·1) of repeatedly dividing a substance into smaller and smaller parts until a final unit is reached. Point out that, in the case of a molecular compound like water, the smallest particle which has the properties of water is a group of atoms composed of two hydrogen atoms and one oxygen atom. If any further division is attempted, the particle with the properties of water will no longer exist. This smallest unit is the *molecule*. We represent the composition of this particle with the *molecular formula*.

On the other hand, when the same division process is applied to an ionic compound, a very different result is

obtained. There is no smallest single particle which represents the substance as a whole. Instead, we find that an ionic compound is a collection of individual ions. The positive and negative ions are there in an exact ratio. The formula Li_2O is not suggesting that there are two lithium atoms attached to an oxygen atom. It is instead representing the fact that there are two Li^+ ions for every one O^{-2} ion. The formula unit is only a statement of a ratio, not of an arrangement.

To help keep this from being so abstract for them, refer to Figures $5 \cdot 9$ and $5 \cdot 10$. Better yet, use models of molecules and ionic lattices if they are available. **Demonstration 13·2** *Formation of Cubic Crystals* might be done here to help the students visualize ionic crystals.

5·5 Law of Multiple Proportions

This law is significant in that it is an important part of the history of the development of atomic theory. Many students fail to see the importance of the fact that the ratios of the *masses* are simple whole numbers. They may understand this better if they are shown a few representative examples of the formulas of compounds which have multiple proportions. Good examples are CO and CO_2; SO_2 and SO_3; NO and NO_2; FeO, Fe_2O_3, and Fe_3O_4.

When they see that the combining ratios in these compounds compare as simple whole numbers, they should have no trouble in seeing that the masses should have the same relationship.

A dramatic way to show that elements can combine in more than one ratio, and that the products are *different* is to do **Demonstration 5·3** *Multiple Proportions*.

5·6 Ionic Charges of the Elements

In this section, students learn to use the periodic table as a tool to predict the ionic charges of various elements. This will allow them to recognize and write names and formulas early in the course. A thorough understanding of why atoms form the particular ions that they do is developed later in Chapters 11 through 13. (Electron configurations are presented in Chapter 11. They are related to the properties of the elements and to the periodic table in Chapter 12. With this foundation, Chapter 13 shows how ionic charges depend on both the electron configuration of an atom and the stable electron configurations of the noble gases.) To try to develop such an understanding for regular level students at this point, however, would be difficult and premature. Instead, you should consider the students' learning in this section to simply be skill-building. The understanding will come later when they have an in-depth grasp of atomic structure.

If you teach an honors class, some of those students may want an explanation of why ions form as they do. In this case you may wish to cover Chapter 11 and Sections $12 \cdot 1$ through $12 \cdot 3$ before teaching Sections $5 \cdot 6$ through $5 \cdot 14$.

5·7 Polyatomic Ions

The students are presented with a great many names and formulas in these two sections. Except for honors students the task of memorizing them could be quite formidable. You may wish to consider two possible approaches.

1. Requiring the students to memorize these names and formulas as soon as possible. In this case daily drills and quizzes would be important.

2. Letting the students use the charts in the textbook in an open-book format at first. After having worked through the problems of this chapter, many will have learned formulas and names through sheer usage. At the end of the chapter you could then push for the memorization of remaining ones.

In any case, the students may find it helpful to prepare their own sets of flash cards, each with the name of an ion on the front and its formula on the back. There are also sets of chemical bingo or similar games commercially available which could add some fun to the memorization process.

Demonstration 5·4 *Molecular Models* will help the students visualize the structure of polyatomic atoms. The models can later be used for review or a quiz.

5·8 Common and Systematic Names

Students should have no trouble realizing that common names usually give no clue as to the composition of the substance each represents, and that there simply cannot be enough common names available to name all of the compounds now known. They very likely will be receptive to the systematic nomenclature which follows.

5·9 Writing Formulas for Binary Ionic Compounds

5·10 Naming Binary Ionic Compounds

5·11 Ternary Ionic Compounds

5·12 Binary Molecular Compounds

5·13 Acids

5·14 Summary of Naming and Formula Writing

The classroom approach used in each of these sections could follow the same pattern.

1. Introduce the applicable rule and the reason(s) for it.
2. Show examples of applications of the rule.
3. Give the students experience in applying the rule.
4. Drill on and review of previous rules. (Games will help here.)
5. Quiz the students to make sure they are up-to-date and on the right track.

Once the students have mastered the individual rules for naming compounds, spend some time going over the use of Figure 5·21 Flowchart for Naming Compounds. Depending on the level of the class you may wish to have the students memorize the flowchart for use on tests or you could supply a copy for an "open-note" type of test. In either case, the use of the flowchart will eliminate most of the problems students will have with nomenclature.

Do **Demonstration 7·1** *Combination of Sulfur and Zinc* or **7·2** *Combination of Iodine and Zinc,* which show combination reactions, to add a little variation to the routine of this chapter. Tell the students which elements you are reacting together, do the demonstration, and then ask them to predict the formula of the compound formed, and to give its name.

Experiment 7 *Identification of Anions and Cations in Solution* can be done as soon as Section 5·11 is completed. This experiment provides an enjoyable change of pace as well as a review and application of the rules the students have just learned. **Experiment 8** *Precipitation Reactions* is similar to **Demonstration 7·7** *Double-Replacement Reactions.*

Demonstrations

5·1 Ionization of Sodium Metal

Concept: Sodium metal reacts with water to produce sodium ions.

Materials: 1 g of sodium metal (Na), water, 5 mL of 0.1% phenolphthalein, 500-mL beaker or large flat tray, forceps, knife, safety goggles.

Procedure: 1. Half-fill the beaker or tray with water. Add 3 drops of phenolphthalein to test for alkalinity. 2. Cut a pea-size piece of sodium. 3. Using forceps, add the sodium to the water. 4. Observe the fizz, heat, and light. The gas is hydrogen, which occasionally ignites. The sodium melts into a ball which rapidly darts over the water. 5. The sodium atom loses one electron to become a sodium ion. It attains the electron configuration of neon. Remind the class that electron structure determines chemical behavior. All sodium in nature is in the ionic state, in the form of salts. **Caution:** *Sodium metal is corrosive. Wear goggles and keep students back. Wash off splashes immediately. Store sodium under kerosene.*

5·2 Formation of Sodium Chloride

Concept: Sodium metal and chlorine gas react to make a salt, sodium chloride.

Materials: 1 g of sodium metal (Na), dry chlorine gas (Cl_2) from a cylinder, 1-L flask with stopper, deflagrating spoon, dry sand, dropper, spatula, 10x magnifying glass or dissecting microscope, safety goggles.

Procedure: 1. Before class, fill the flask with chlorine gas and stopper it. 2. Fill the spoon with sand. 3. Put a pea-size piece of sodium on the sand. 4. Loosen the stopper of the flask. 5. Add a drop of water on the sodium and immediately lower the spoon into the flask. 6. The reaction has a bright yellow flame, and white billows of sodium chloride condense on the sides of the flask. 7. When the reaction is complete, remove the spoon and stopper the flask. 8. Note that these two reactive materials combine to make edible salt. 9. Examine the crystals on the sides of the flask with the magnifying glass. **Caution:** *Chlorine is highly toxic and an irritant. Sodium metal is corrosive. Wear goggles and use a fume hood.*

5·3 Multiple Proportions

Concept: Two elements can combine in different reacting proportions. The compounds formed in each case have different properties.

Materials: 7.5 g of mercury (Hg), 10 g of iodine (I_2), mortar and pestle, safety goggles.

Procedure: 1. Place the mercury in the mortar. 2. Add 5 g of the iodine crystals, a little at a time, to the mortar. 3. With the pestle, grind after each addition of crystals. 4. The amounts added contain roughly the same number of mercury and iodine. They react in a one-to-one ratio to form mercury(I) iodide, Hg_2I_2. Note the appearance of the product. 5. Add another 5 g of iodine, grinding after the addition of each small quantity. 6. Point out that there are now twice as many iodine atoms as mercury atoms. The compound, mercury(II) iodide, HgI_2, forms. Note its appearance. This demonstration is best done for small groups. **Caution:** *Mercury, iodine, mercury(I) iodide, and mercury(II) iodide are all extremely toxic. Use a fume hood. Use a mercury sponge to clean up spills.*

5·4 Molecular Models

Concept: Molecules can be modeled by using balls and sticks.

Materials: Polystyrene balls of many sizes and colors, toothpicks, commercial kits for making molecular models.

Procedure: 1. Use the balls and toothpicks to make models of polyatomic ions and ion complexes. 2. More realistic models emphasizing different molecular features can be made from commercial kits.

Molecular: 1. composed of two or more nonmetals
2. are solids, liquids, or gases at room temperature
3. have relatively low melting points.

Audiovisual Resources

Atoms and Molecules: Building Blocks of Matter (6 FS) Science and Mankind, 1981, 12–18 min. each. (Use with Sections 5·2 and 5·3.) Discusses the structure of atoms and molecules. Also covers topics in Chapters 13, 14, and 26.

Chemical Symbols: Formulas and Equations (4 FS) Charles Clark, 1973, 11–20 min. each. (Use with Sections 5·4, 5·9, and 5·11.) Discusses chemical symbols and formula writing. Also covers topics in Chapter 7.

Elements Discovered (F, V) Media Guild, 1980, 25 min. (Use with Section 5·1.) Examines experiments leading to the discovery of the chemical elements throughout history.

Introducing Chemistry: Formulas and Equations (F) Coronet, 1966, 10 min. (Use with Section 5·4.) Explains and demonstrates the use of symbols in formulas and balanced equations.

Answers to End of Chapter Questions and Problems

Practice Questions and Problems

18. a. metal **b.** metal **c.** metalloid **d.** nonmetal **e.** metal

19. a. 3A **b.** 1B **c.** 4A **d.** 0 **e.** 2B

20. An ion is a charged particle formed by the loss or gain of one or more electrons. A cation is a positively charged ion formed by the loss of one or more electrons. An anion is a negatively charged ion formed by the gain of one or more electrons.

21. a. two electrons gained **b.** one electron lost **c.** one electron gained. **d.** two electrons lost **e.** one electron lost **f.** one electron gained

22. a. sulfide ion **b.** potassium ion **c.** chloride ion **d.** barium ion **e.** lithium ion **f.** hydride ion

23. a. molecular **b.** ionic **c.** ionic **d.** molecular **e.** molecular **f.** ionic

24. Atoms combine in simple whole-number ratios. Their proportion by mass must be the same.

25. Ionic: 1. formed by an anion and a cation 2. usually exist in the solid state 3. have relatively high melting points.

26. a. molecule **b.** formula unit **c.** formula unit **d.** molecule **e.** molecule **f.** formula unit

27. When atoms of elements combine in more than one way, they do so in the ratio of small whole numbers.

28. a. lithium ion, Li^+ **b.** oxide ion, O^{2-} **c.** barium ion Ba^{2+} **d.** nitride ion, N^{3-} **e.** fluoride ion, F^- **f.** potassium ion, K^+ **g.** no ion formed **h.** beryllium ion, Be^{2+}

29. a. nitrate ion **b.** hydrogen ion **c.** cyanide ion **d.** chromium(III) ion or chromic ion **e.** dichromate ion **f.** dihydrogen phosphate ion **g.** tin(IV) or stannic ion **h.** permanganate ion **i.** sulfite ion **j.** selenide ion

30. a. Mg^{2+} **b.** Pb^{4+} **c.** CrO_4^{2-} **d.** NO_2^- **e.** I^- **f.** ClO_3^- **g.** OH^- **h.** Fe^{2+} **i.** NH_4^+ **j.** Cu^+

31. A metal and a nonmetal.

32. -ide

33. The sum of the ionic charges must equal zero.

34. a. SrSe **b.** K_2O **c.** Ca_3N_2 **d.** CoI_3

35. a. Ag_2S **b.** $SnCl_4$ **c.** Na_3N **d.** SrI_2

36. When the cation has more than one common ionic charge.

37. a. zinc oxide **b.** sodium iodide **c.** copper(I) oxide or cuprous oxide **d.** calcium bromide

38. -ite or -ate

39. Parentheses are used to indicate more than one of a polyatomic ion.

40. a. $HgBr_2$ **b.** $(NH_4)_2Cr_2O_7$ **c.** $LiHSO_4$ **d.** $Cr(NO_2)_3$

41.

$CaSO_4$ calcium sulfate	$Ca(OH)_2$ calcium hydroxide	$Ca_3(PO_4)_2$ calcium phosphate	CaS calcium sulfide
$(NH_4)_2SO_4$ ammonium sulfate	NH_4OH ammonium hydroxide	$(NH_4)_3PO_4$ ammonium phosphate	$(NH_4)_2S$ ammonium sulfide
$Al_2(SO_4)_3$ aluminum sulfate	$Al(OH)_3$ aluminum hydroxide	$AlPO_4$ aluminum phosphate	Al_2S_3 aluminum sulfide
$Pb(SO_4)_2$ lead(IV) sulfate	$Pb(OH)_4$ lead(IV) hydroxide	$Pb_3(PO_4)_4$ lead(IV) phosphate	PbS_2 lead(IV) sulfide

42. Two nonmetals.

43. a. tri **b.** mono **c.** hexa **d.** tetra **e.** di **f.** hepta
g. deca **h.** octa **i.** penta **j.** nona

44. a. oxygen difluoride **b.** dichlorine octoxide
c. sulfur trioxide **d.** tetraphosphorus decoxide

45. a. N_2O_4 **c.** NF_3
       b. PCl_5 **d.** S_2Cl_2

46. a. oxalic acid **b.** hydrofluoric acid **c.** chlorous acid
d. carbonic acid

47. a. HNO_2 **c.** H_3PO_4
       b. H_2Se **d.** $HC_2H_3O_2$

Mastery Questions and Problems

48. $\dfrac{1.29 \text{ g O}}{0.774 \text{ g O}} = \dfrac{1.67}{1}$ $\begin{array}{l} 1.67 \times 3 = 5 \\ 1 \times 3 = 3 \end{array}$

P_2O_3 and P_2O_5

49. a. polyatomic **b.** monatomic **c.** polyatomic
d. monatomic **e.** polyatomic **f.** polyatomic
g. monatomic **h.** polyatomic **i.** polyatomic
j. monatomic

50. a. cation **b.** cation **c.** anion **d.** anion **e.** anion
f. anion **g.** anion **h.** cation **i.** cation **j.** cation

51. a. calcium oxide **b.** barium phosphate **c.** iodine
d. barium sulfate **e.** magnesium hydroxide **f.** nitrogen
dioxide **g.** copper(I) acetate or cuprous acetate
h. perchloric acid **i.** dichlorine monoxide **j.** mercury(II)
fluoride or mercuric fluoride **k.** ammonium oxalate
l. nitrite ion

52. a. $CaCO_3$ **b.** NaBr **c.** $Fe_2(SO_4)_3$ **d.** MgS **e.** H_2SO_4
f. SO_3 **g.** N_2 **h.** $Ba(OH)_2$ **i.** HBr **j.** SO_3^{2-} **k.** CuI_2
l. ZnC_2O_4

53. a. ammonium hydroxide **b.** hydrogen fluoride or
hydrofluoric acid **c.** phosphorus triiodide **d.** beryllium
nitrate **e.** hydrogen permanganate or permanganic acid
f. carbon monoxide **g.** potassium carbonate
h. dinitrogen tetrahydride **i.** zinc oxide **j.** magnesium
permanganate **k.** lithium hydrogen phosphate **l.** lithium
carbonate

54. a. AgCl **b.** Al_4C_3 **c.** LiH **d.** $HC_2H_3O_2$ **e.** $FeCO_3$
f. HClO **g.** Na_2SiO_3 **h.** CaO **i.** HCN **j.** $Sn(CN)_4$ **k.** HBr
l. KI

55. a. sodium dichromate **b.** aluminum iodide
c. tin(IV) oxide or stannic oxide **d.** iron(III) acetate or
ferric acetate **e.** potassium hydrogen sulfate **f.** cobalt(II)
nitrite or cobaltous nitrite **g.** calcium hydride
h. hydrogen chlorate or chloric acid **i.** mercury(I)
bromide or mercurous bromide **j.** aluminum phosphide
k. iron(II) carbonate or ferrous carbonate **l.** hydrogen
chromate or chromic acid

56. a. PBr_5 **b.** CCl_4 **c.** $KMnO_4$ **d.** NH_4ClO_4
e. $Ca(HCO_3)_2$ **f.** CuOH **g.** NH_4NO_3 **h.** Cl_2O_7 **i.** Si_3N_4
j. NaH_2PO_4

Review Questions and Problems

57. a. 54.6 mg
     b. 2.34×10^2 mL
     c. 0.790 kJ
     d. K = 248

58. 2.50 g/mL

59. Answers will vary.

60. a. Br^-, $35p^+$ and $36e^-$
     b. Al^{3+}, $13p^+$ and $10e^-$
     c. Ca^{2+}, $20p^+$ and $18e^-$
     d. O^{2-}, $8p^+$ and $10e^-$

Challenging Questions and Problems

62. a. Potassium carbonate has a much greater water
solubility than $CaCO_3$.
b. The copper compound is blue; the iron
compound is white.
c. Water could be added to dissolve the NH_4Cl.
The resulting solution could be filtered, leaving the
insoluble $BaSO_4$.
d. chlorine (nonmetal), sulfur (nonmetal), bromine
(nonmetal), barium (metal), iodine (nonmetal),
mercury (metal)
e. barium sulfate, calcium carbonate, potassium
carbonate, copper(II) sulfate pentahydrate, iron(II)
sulfate pentahydrate, and ammonium chloride
f. 1.79×10^3 g Hg
g. 27 cm^3 S
h. color, density, melting point, boiling point

63. a. carbon **b.** hafnium **c.** iridium **d.** antimony
e. silicon **f.** barium **g.** boron **h.** germanium **i.** helium or
curium

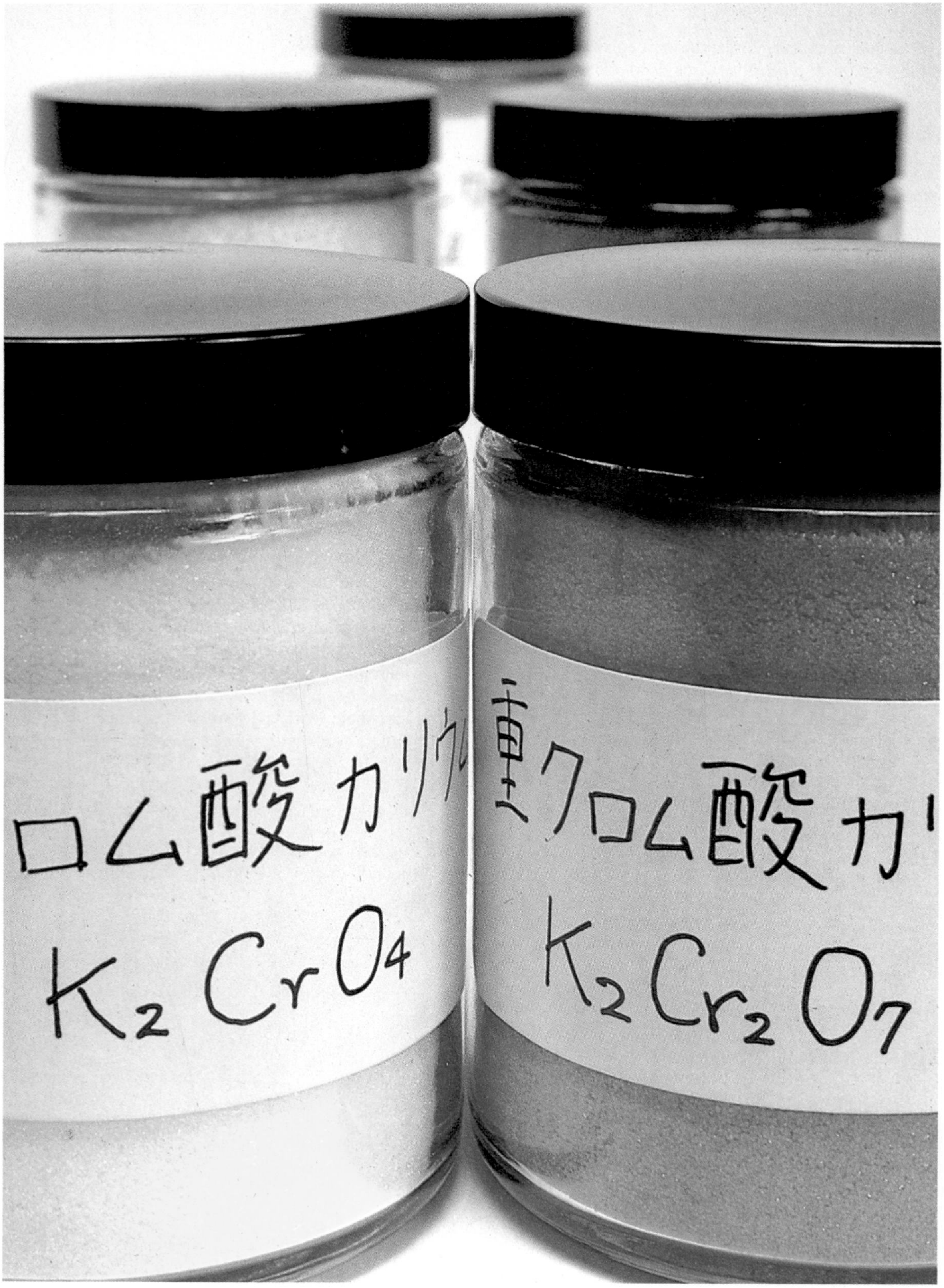
ロム酸カリウ
K_2CrO_4
重クロム酸カ
$K_2Cr_2O_7$

5 Chemical Names and Formulas

Chapter Preview

Only about 100 types of atoms, the elements, exist. Even so, a tremendous variety of combinations of atoms can be formed. With such a diversity of substances, we need an orderly way in which to communicate chemistry. We could identify a particular substance by listing its physical and chemical properties. However, this would be very time-consuming at best. Instead, each substance is identified by its own unique name and chemical formula. This identification is the language of chemistry and the topic of this chapter.

5·1 The Periodic Table

The periodic table groups the elements according to similarities in their properties.

The elements are arranged in rows and columns on the **periodic table,** *according to similarities in their properties.* On the next page you can see that the elements are listed in order of increasing atomic number (Figure 5·2). Hydrogen, the smallest lightest element, is in the top left corner. Helium, He, is atomic number 2 at the top right. Lithium, Li, is atomic number 3 at the left side of row two.

A column of elements in the periodic table is known as a **group.** Each group is designated by a number–letter combination. For example, the first vertical column on the left is Group 1A. It is composed of the elements H, Li, Na, K, Rb, and Cs. The next vertical column to the right,

Figure 5·1
The language of chemistry, which you will learn in this chapter, is an international language.

Figure 5·2

The short form of the periodic table shows three major divisions. In what area are the nonmetals grouped?

In the upper right section of the representative elements.

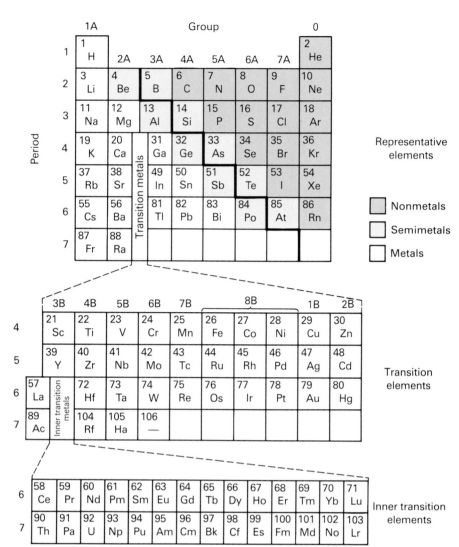

Representative elements

☒ Nonmetals

☐ Semimetals

☐ Metals

Transition elements

Inner transition elements

Figure 5·3

Mercury, a transition metal, is the only metallic element that is a liquid at room temperature. It is used in thermometers and barometers.

Figure 5·4

Sulfur is a nonmetallic element that occurs as a crystalline solid or in the amorphous state. Sulfur is used primarily in the manufacture of sulfuric acid.

starting with Be, is Group 2A, and so forth. *The Group A elements in the periodic table are known as the* **representative elements.** They are called this because they illustrate the entire range of chemical properties. The representative elements include both metals and nonmetals. They do not include the transition metals or the inner transition metals.

The metallic elements are grouped on the left side of the periodic table. **Metals** *are elements that have a high luster when clean and a high electrical conductivity.* They are ductile (can be drawn into wires) and malleable (can be beaten into thin sheets). Most of the elements are metals. They include the **transition metals,** *which are the B group elements,* and the inner transition metals, which are called the rare earths.

The nonmetallic elements are grouped on the right side of the periodic table. **Nonmetals** *are elements that are nonlustrous and are poor conductors of electricity.* Some of these elements are gases, others are brittle solids, and one, bromine, is a liquid at room temperature. Notice that hydrogen is a special case. It is a nonmetal in Group 1A.

The **semimetals,** *or* **metalloids,** *are elements with the properties of both metals and nonmetals.* Silicon is a basic component of transistors and chips because it is a semiconductor. It conducts electricity in a special way.

Problems

1. **a.** metal **b.** nonmetal **c.** metal **d.** nonmetal **e.** metal
2. potassium, boron, and iodine

1. Identify the following elements as metals or nonmetals.
   a. potassium **b.** boron **c.** molybdenum **d.** iodine **e.** uranium

2. Which of the above elements are part of the representative elements?

5·2 Atoms and Ions

We know that elements are composed of atoms of the same kind. An atom is electrically neutral because it has an equal number of protons and electrons. Sodium is atomic number 11. A sodium atom has 11 positively charged protons, 12 neutrons, and 11 negatively charged electrons. Because neutrons have no charge, the net charge on a sodium atom is zero $[+11 + (-11) = 0]$. In forming a chemical compound, an atom of an element can gain or lose one or more electrons. When the number of electrons is no longer equal to the number of protons, then the atom becomes an ion. **Ions** *are atoms or groups of atoms that have a positive or negative charge.* An ion is formed when an atom or group of atoms gains or loses electrons.

Atoms of the metallic elements tend to form positive ions by losing one or more electrons. *A* **cation** *is any atom or group of atoms with a positive charge.* Compared with an electrically neutral atom, a cation has fewer electrons. For example, a *sodium ion* is formed by the loss of one electron from a sodium atom. Since a sodium ion has 11 protons but only 10 electrons, it has a charge of 1+ (Figure 5·6). An ionic charge is written with a number followed by a sign. If the number is 1, it can be omitted; Na^{1+} and Na^+ are equivalent. Similarly, a magnesium atom forms a magnesium ion by the loss of two electrons. A magnesium ion therefore has a charge of 2+ because it has 12 protons but only 10 electrons.

There are many important chemical differences between metals and their ions. Sodium metal, for example, reacts explosively with water. By

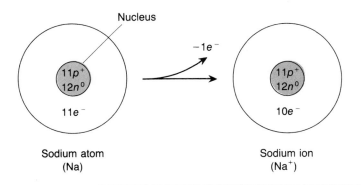

Nucleus

$-1e^-$

$11p^+$
$12n^0$

$11e^-$

Sodium atom
(Na)

$11p^+$
$12n^0$

$10e^-$

Sodium ion
(Na^+)

Figure 5·6
A sodium atom loses an electron to become a positively charged sodium ion.

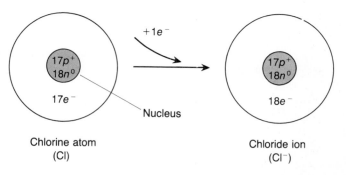

Figure 5·7
A chlorine atom gains an electron to become a negatively charged chloride ion.

Chlorine atom
(Cl)

Chloride ion
(Cl⁻)

$+1e^-$

$17p^+$
$18n^0$

$17e^-$

Nucleus

$17p^+$
$18n^0$

$18e^-$

Safety

All the alkali metals (lithium, sodium, potassium, rubidium, and cesium) are stored under oil to prevent them from contacting air or water. Their reactions can be very violent. They should be used only with extreme caution and under direct supervision of the teacher.

The names of some common anions are fluoride, chloride, bromide, iodide, oxide, sulfide, nitride, and phosphide.

contrast sodium ions are a component of table salt, a compound that we know is stable in water.

When forming ions, atoms of the nonmetallic elements tend to gain one or more electrons. In this way they form **anions,** *which are atoms or groups of atoms with a negative charge.* In comparison to an electrically neutral atom, an anion has more electrons. For example, when a chlorine atom gains one electron, it forms a *chloride ion.* A chloride ion has 17 protons and 18 electrons. It is therefore an anion with an ionic charge of $1-$ (Figure 5·7). Another common anion is the oxide ion, O^{2-}. The ionic charge of the oxide ion is $2-$ because an oxygen atom gains two electrons in forming its common ion.

Example 1

Write the symbol and name of the ion formed.   **a.** A strontium atom loses two electrons.   **b.** An iodine atom gains one electron.   **c.** A nitrogen atom gains three electrons.   **d.** A hydrogen atom loses one electron.

Solution

An atom that loses electrons forms a positively charged ion (cation). The numerical value of the charge equals the number of electrons lost.

An atom that gains electrons forms a negatively charged ion (anion). The numerical value of the charge is the number of electrons gained. The names of anions of nonmetallic elements end in *-ide*.
a. Sr^{2+}, strontium ion   **b.** I^{1-} or I^-, iodide ion   **c.** N^{3-}, nitride ion
d. H^{1+} or H^+, hydrogen ion

Problem

3. a. Ca^{2+}, calcium ion
  b. 1 electron gained, fluoride ion
  c. Al, 3 electrons lost, aluminum ion
  d. Se^{2-}, selenide ion

3. Complete this table.

	Symbol of element	Change in electrons	Formula of ion	Name of ion
a.	Ca	2 electrons lost	_____	_____
b.	F	_____	F^-	_____
c.	_____	_____	Al^{3+}	_____
d.	Se	2 electrons gained	_____	_____

5·3 Compounds

Compounds, which may be molecular or ionic, are formed from elements.

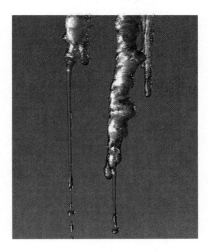

Figure 5·8
Molecular compounds can be solids, liquids, or gases. Water commonly exists in all three phases.

Atoms in a compound are held together by forces called chemical bonds (Chapters 13 and 14).

Compounds are pure substances that differ from elements because they contain more than one kind of atom. Compounds are formed when atoms of two or more different elements combine. Compounds obey the **law of definite proportions.** *In any chemical compound the elements are always combined in the same proportion by mass*. Magnesium sulfide is a compound. It is produced by the combination of two kinds of atoms, magnesium atoms and sulfur atoms. If we take 100.00 g of magnesium sulfide and break it down into its elements, we always obtain 43.13 g of magnesium and 56.87 g of sulfur. How the magnesium sulfide was formed, or the size of the sample, will not change this mass ratio. For example, 10.000 g of magnesium sulfide will be composed of 4.313 g of magnesium and 5.687 g of sulfur. The law of definite proportions is explained by Dalton's atomic theory. If atoms combine in simple whole number ratios as Dalton postulated, then their proportions by mass must always be the same.

In many compounds, the atoms are bound together in molecules. *A* **molecule** *is a neutral group of atoms that act as a unit*. All the molecules of any given compound are identical. The molecules of one compound are different, however, from those of any other compound.

Compounds that are composed of molecules are **molecular compounds.** They tend to have relatively low melting and boiling points. Many molecular compounds exist as gases or liquids at room temperature. Most are composed of two or more nonmetallic elements. Water and carbon dioxide are examples of molecular compounds (Figure 5·9).

Not all compounds are composed of molecules. **Ionic compounds** *are composed of positive and negative ions*. The ions are arranged in an orderly three-dimensional pattern. Each positive ion is between two or more negative ions. At the same time, each negative ion is between two or more positive ions. Ionic compounds are electrically neutral although they are composed of ions. Most ionic compounds are crystalline solids at room temperature. They are usually formed from a metallic and a nonmetallic element. A familiar example of an ionic compound is table salt, or sodium chloride.

5·4 Chemical Formulas

Chemists have identified more than four million chemical compounds. Some are molecular compounds, others are ionic compounds. No two of these compounds have identical properties. Fortunately, the composition of each of these chemical substances can be represented by a chemical formula. *A* **chemical formula** *shows the kinds and numbers of atoms in the smallest representative unit of the substance*.

The chemical formula of a molecular compound is called a molecular formula. *A* **molecular formula** *shows the number and kinds of atoms present in a molecule of a compound*. The number of atoms of each kind is indicated by a subscript written after the symbol. Water is a molecular

The formula of a molecular compound represents a molecule. The formula of an ionic compound represents a formula unit.

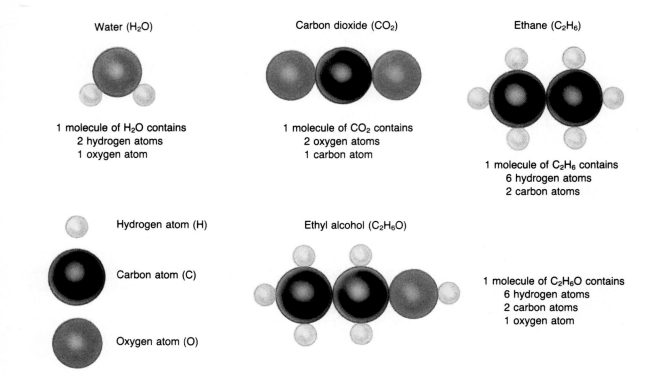

Water (H_2O)

1 molecule of H_2O contains
2 hydrogen atoms
1 oxygen atom

Carbon dioxide (CO_2)

1 molecule of CO_2 contains
2 oxygen atoms
1 carbon atom

Ethane (C_2H_6)

1 molecule of C_2H_6 contains
6 hydrogen atoms
2 carbon atoms

Hydrogen atom (H)

Carbon atom (C)

Oxygen atom (O)

Ethyl alcohol (C_2H_6O)

1 molecule of C_2H_6O contains
6 hydrogen atoms
2 carbon atoms
1 oxygen atom

Figure 5·9
The formula of a molecular compound indicates the numbers and kinds of atoms in a molecule of the compound. The arrangement of the atoms within a molecule is called the molecular structure.

Safety

Ethyl alcohol is extremely flammable. Never use a flame when others are working nearby with flammable liquids.

compound. A water molecule is a tightly bound unit of two hydrogen atoms and one oxygen atom. Its molecular formula is H_2O. The molecular formula for the molecular compound carbon dioxide is CO_2. This formula represents a molecule containing two oxygen atoms and one carbon atom. Ethane, a component of natural gas, is also a molecular compound. Its molecular formula is C_2H_6. This tells us that a molecule of ethane is composed of two carbon atoms and six hydrogen atoms. Another molecular compound is ethyl alcohol, C_2H_6O. What do you know about its composition?

Although a molecular formula gives us the composition of a molecule, it tells us nothing about the molecular structure. We need a diagram to show the arrangement of the atoms within the molecule. Figure 5·9 shows chemical formulas and molecular structures of some molecular compounds.

Chemical formulas can also be written for ionic compounds. In this case, though, the formula does not represent a molecule. Sodium chloride, table salt, is an ionic compound. It is composed of equal numbers of sodium ions, Na^+, and chloride ions, Cl^-. They are arranged in an orderly pattern. In order to represent this compound, should the formula be Na_2Cl_2, Na_3Cl_3, or $NaCl$? Chemists use the simplest of these formulas, a formula unit, to represent an ionic compound. *A* **formula unit** *is the lowest whole-number ratio of ions in an ionic compound.* For sodium chloride, the lowest whole-number ratio of the ions is 1:1 (1 Na^+ to 1 Cl^-). Thus the formula unit is $NaCl$. (Once we have determined the correct ratio of ions, we ignore the charges in writing the formula unit.) Another ionic compound is magnesium chloride. It contains magnesium ions,

Table 5·1 Characteristics of Ionic and Molecular Compounds		
Characteristic	Ionic compound	Molecular compound
Representative unit	Formula unit (balance of oppositely charged ions)	Molecule
Type of element	Metallic combined with nonmetallic	Nonmetallic
Physical state	Solid	Solid, liquid, or gas
Melting point	High (usually above 300°C)	Low (usually below 300°C)

Mg^{2+}, and chloride ions, Cl^-. In magnesium chloride the ratio of magnesium ions to chloride ions is 1:2 (one Mg^{2+} to two Cl^-). Thus the formula unit is $MgCl_2$. Notice that there are twice as many chloride ions (with a $1-$ charge) as magnesium ions (with a $2+$ charge). Thus the grouping is electrically neutral. There is no such thing as a molecule of sodium chloride or magnesium chloride. Instead, sodium chloride consists of a collection of positively and negatively charged ions. As in ionic compounds in general, the ions are arranged in repeating three-dimensional patterns (Figure 5·10).

Much of your success at naming compounds and writing formulas of compounds will hinge on your ability to recognize compounds as either ionic or molecular. Table 5·1 summarizes some of the differences between ionic and molecular substances.

Sodium chloride
NaCl

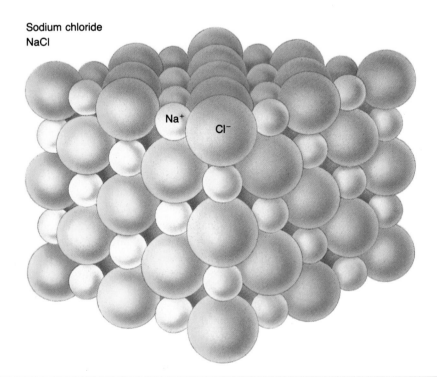

Figure 5·10
Sodium ions and chloride ions form a three-dimensional array in sodium chloride, NaCl. How many ions are part of a single formula unit for this compound?
Two: one chloride ion and one sodium ion.

a
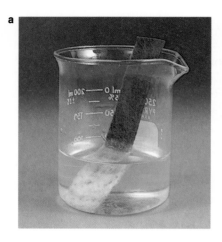

b
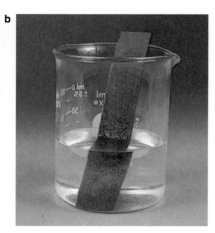

5·5 The Law of Multiple Proportions

■ The law of multiple proportions is explained by atomic theory.

Atoms of two elements can often combine in more than one way. For example, the elements hydrogen and oxygen combine to form the familiar compound water, H_2O. These same two elements can also form the compound hydrogen peroxide, H_2O_2. The compound water and the compound hydrogen peroxide each obey the law of definite proportions. In every sample of water the mass ratio of oxygen to hydrogen is 8 to 1. That is, 8.0 g of oxygen are present for each 1.0 g of hydrogen. In hydrogen peroxide the mass ratio of oxygen to hydrogen is always 16 to 1. For a given mass of hydrogen (1.0 g), the ratio of the masses of oxygen in these two compounds is a simple whole-number ratio.

Safety

Concentrated solutions of hydrogen peroxide enhance the combustion of other materials, and can cause explosions. They also cause burns. Handle with extreme care.

$$\frac{16 \text{ g O (in } H_2O_2)}{8 \text{ g O (in } H_2O)} = \frac{2}{1}$$

In the early 1800s Dalton and his contemporaries studied similar pairs of compounds. In each case, the two compounds were composed of the same two elements. Using the results from these experiments, Dalton put forth the **law of multiple proportions.** *Whenever two elements form more than one compound, the different masses of one element that combine with the same mass of the other element are in the ratio of small whole numbers.*

The law of multiple proportions is an offshoot of the law of definite proportions.

Example 2

Carbon reacts with oxygen to form two compounds. Compound A contains 2.41 g carbon for each 3.22 g oxygen. Compound B contains 6.71 g carbon for each 17.9 g oxygen. What is the lowest whole-number mass ratio of carbon that combines with a given mass of oxygen?

Solution

For each compound find the grams of carbon that combine per 1.00 g of oxygen.

$$\text{Compound A} \quad \frac{2.41 \text{ g C}}{3.22 \text{ g O}} = \frac{0.748 \text{ g C}}{1.00 \text{ g O}}$$

$$\text{Compound B} \quad \frac{6.71 \text{ g C}}{17.9 \text{ g O}} = \frac{0.375 \text{ g C}}{1.00 \text{ g O}}$$

The mass ratio of carbon per gram of oxygen in the compounds is 2:1.

$$\frac{0.748 \text{ g C (in compound A)}}{0.375 \text{ g C (in compound B)}} = \frac{2}{1}$$

Problem

4. 2:1

4. Lead forms two compounds with oxygen. One compound contains 2.98 g of lead combined with 0.461 g of oxygen. The other compound contains 9.89 g of lead combined with 0.763 g of oxygen. What is the lowest whole-number mass ratio of lead that combines with a given mass of oxygen?

5·6   Ionic Charges of the Elements

■ The periodic table can be used to determine the charge on the ions of many elements.

By using the periodic table, students can predict the ionic charges of many elements. After they have learned about electron configurations (Ch. 12), the students will be able to understand *why* the ions form as they do.

In order to write chemical formulas, we need to know the types of ions that atoms tend to form. In other words, we need to know the ionic charges of the elements. For the representative elements (those in Group A), the ionic charges can easily be determined using the periodic table.

The metals in Groups 1A, 2A, and 3A lose electrons when they form ions. The ionic charge is positive and is numerically equal to the group number. Hydrogen, lithium, and potassium in Group 1A form cations. They have a 1+ charge (H^+, Li^+, and K^+), as do all the other Group 1A ions. Magnesium and calcium are Group 2A metals. They form cations with a 2+ charge (Mg^{2+} and Ca^{2+}), as do all the other Group 2A metals. Aluminum is the only common Group 3A metal. As expected, it forms a 3+ cation (Al^{3+}).

The numerical charge of an ion of a Group A nonmetal is determined by subtracting the group number from 8. The sign of the charge is minus because nonmetals gain electrons and form anions. For example,

Table 5·2	Ionic Charges of Representative Elements						
1A	2A	3A	4A	5A	6A	7A	0
H^+						H^-	
Li^+	Be^{2+}			N^{3-}	O^{2-}	F^-	
Na^+	Mg^{2+}	Al^{3+}		P^{3-}	S^{2-}	Cl^-	
K^+	Ca^{2+}				Se^{2-}	Br^-	
Rb^+	Sr^{2+}					I^-	
Cs^+	Ba^{2+}						

the elements in Group 7A form ions with a 1− charge: fluoride, $F^−$, chloride, $Cl^−$, and so forth. When hydrogen reacts with Group 1A metals, it also forms an anion with a 1− charge, the hydride ion, $H^−$. Anions of nonmetals in Group 6A have a 2− charge (8 − 6 = 2), for example, oxide, $O^{2−}$. The three nonmetals in Group 5A can form ions with a 3− charge (8 − 5 = 3), for example, nitride, $N^{3−}$.

The elements in the two remaining representative groups, 4A and 0, do not commonly form ions. The elements in Group 0 are uncharged. The two nonmetals in Group 4A, carbon and silicon, rarely form ions. They are ordinarily found in molecular compounds. The ionic charges of representative elements that can be obtained from the periodic table are summarized in Table 5·2.

Unlike the Group A representative metals, many of the transition metals have more than one common ionic charge. This is also a characteristic of metals in Groups 4A and 5A. For example, the transition metal iron has two common ions, Fe^{2+} and Fe^{3+}. Two methods of naming such ions are used. The preferred method is called the Stock system. A roman numeral in parentheses is used after the name of the element to indicate the numerical value of the charge. For example, the cation Fe^{2+} is the iron(II) ion. This is read as the "iron two" ion.

An older, less preferred, method of naming these ions uses a root word and suffixes. The classical name of the element is used as the root word. An -ous ending is used for the name of the ion with the lower of the two ionic charges. An -ic ending is used with the higher of the two ionic charges. In the example of iron, Fe^{2+} is the ferrous ion, and Fe^{3+} is the ferric ion. Table 5·3 lists some of the elements that have two common ionic charges. Note that you can usually identify what may be unfamiliar classical names by looking for the symbol of the element in the name. *Fe*rrous (Fe) is iron; *Cu*prous (Cu) is copper; and *S tan*nous (Sn) is tin. A major disadvantage of using classical names is that the name does not indicate the charge of the ion. The name only tells you that the ion is either the smaller (-ous) or the larger (-ic) charge of the pair.

A few transition metals have only one ionic charge. The names of these cations will not have a roman numeral. You should know about three of these "exceptions." Silver ions always have a 1+ charge (Ag^+). Cadmium and zinc ions always have a 2+ charge (Cd^{2+} and Zn^{2+}).

You need to be able to recognize ions named with the older system. You will find these names on containers of old chemicals and in the older scientific literature.

Safety

Many transition metals are toxic. Make a habit of washing your hands thoroughly after handling any chemicals.

Example 3

What is the charge of the ion of the following elements? (For transition metals with more than one common ionic charge, the number of electrons lost is indicated.)   **a.** sulfur   **b.** lead, four electrons lost   **c.** zinc   **d.** argon   **e.** bromine   **f.** copper, one electron lost

Solution

a. 2− (in Group 6A)   **b.** 4+   **c.** 2+   **d.** 0 (in Group 0)
e. 1− (in Group 7A)   **f.** 1+

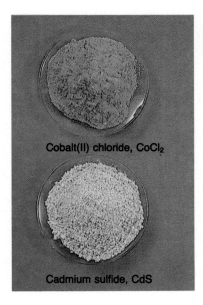

Cobalt(II) chloride, CoCl₂

Cadmium sulfide, CdS

Figure 5·12
Many transition metals form brightly colored compounds. Cobalt(II) chloride and cadmium sulfide are shown here. Some artists' pigments are named after the metals involved, for example: cobalt blue and cadmium yellow.

Table 5·3	Formulas and Names of Common Metal Ions with More than One Ionic Charge	
Formula	**Stock name**	**Classical name**
Cu^{1+}	Copper(I) ion	Cuprous ion
Cu^{2+}	Copper(II) ion	Cupric ion
Fe^{2+}	Iron(II) ion	Ferrous ion
Fe^{3+}	Iron(III) ion	Ferric ion
$*Hg_2^{2+}$	Mercury(I) ion	Mercurous ion
Hg^{2+}	Mercury(II) ion	Mercuric ion
Pb^{2+}	Lead(II) ion	Plumbous ion
Pb^{4+}	Lead(IV) ion	Plumbic ion
Sn^{2+}	Tin(II) ion	Stannous ion
Sn^{4+}	Tin(IV) ion	Stannic ion
Cr^{2+}	Chromium(II) ion	Chromous ion
Cr^{3+}	Chromium(III) ion	Chromic ion
Mn^{2+}	Manganese(II) ion	Manganous ion
Mn^{3+}	Manganese(III) ion	Manganic ion
Co^{2+}	Cobalt(II) ion	Cobaltous ion
Co^{3+}	Cobalt(III) ion	Cobaltic ion

*A diatomic elemental ion.

Example 4

Name the ions in Example 3. Classify each as a cation or an anion.

Solution

The names of nonmetallic anions end in *-ide*. Metallic ions take the name of the metal. If the metal has more than one common ionic charge, a roman numeral is used.   **a.** sulfide ion, anion   **b.** lead(IV) or plumbic ion, cation   **c.** zinc ion, cation   **d.** no ion formed   **e.** bromide ion, anion   **f.** copper(I) or cuprous ion, cation

Problems

5. Write the symbol for each ion. Be sure to include the charge.
   a. iodide ion
   b. mercury(II) ion
   c. phosphide ion
   d. barium ion
   e. stannic ion
   f. silver ion

6. Name the following ions. Use Table 5·3 if necessary.
   a. Cu^{2+}
   b. O^{2-}
   c. Li^+
   d. Pb^{2+}
   e. F^-
   f. H^+

5. **a.** I⁻   **d.** Ba^{2+}
   b. Hg^{2+} **e.** Sn^{4+}
   c. P^{3-} **f.** Ag^+

6. **a.** copper(II) or cupric ion
   b. oxide ion
   c. lithium ion
   d. lead(II) or plumbous ion
   e. fluoride ion
   f. hydrogen ion

5·7 Polyatomic Ions

■ Recognizing polyatomic ions is a key in naming chemical compounds and writing chemical formulas.

In the past, polyatomic ions were called radicals.

As the name implies, **polyatomic ions** *are tightly bound groups of atoms that behave as a unit and carry a charge*. An example of a polyatomic ion is the sulfate ion, SO_4^{2-}. A sulfate polyatomic ion is composed of one sulfur atom and four oxygen atoms. These five atoms together form a unit. This ion has a 2− charge.

You should memorize the names and formulas of the common polyatomic ions listed in Table 5·4. There are others, of course, and your teacher may wish to expand this list. Observe that the names of most polyatomic ions end in *-ite* or *-ate*. You should note three important exceptions to this. The ammonium ion (NH_4^+) is the one common polyatomic ion that is postively charged. The two anions that end in *-ide* are the cyanide (CN^-) and the hydroxide (OH^-) ions. *Compounds that give off OH^- ions when dissolved in water are known as* **bases.**

It is important to be able to recognize polyatomic ions. The bicarbonate (HCO_3^-), monohydrogen phosphate (HPO_4^{2-}), and the dihydrogen phosphate ($H_2PO_4^-$) ions are essential components of living systems. The cyanide ion (CN^-) is extremely poisonous to living systems because it blocks the cell's means of producing energy. Most laundry bleaches contain the hypochlorite ion (ClO^-).

Notice the relationship among the polyatomic ions for which there is an *-ite*/*-ate* pair. The *-ite* ending will always indicate one less oxygen atom than the *-ate*. The charge on each ion in the pair is the same. Notice that the ending does not tell you how many oxygen atoms are in the ion.

$$\textit{-ite} \quad SO_3^{2-} \quad NO_2^- \quad ClO_2^-$$

$$\textit{-ate} \quad SO_4^{2-} \quad NO_3^- \quad ClO_3^-$$

A polyatomic ion whose formula begins with H (hydrogen) can be viewed as a hydrogen ion (H^+) combined with another polyatomic ion. For example, HCO_3^- is a combination of H^+ and CO_3^{2-}. The charge on the new ion is just the algebraic sum of the ionic charges.

$$\underset{\text{carbonate}}{H^+ + CO_3^{2-}} \longrightarrow \underset{\text{hydrogen carbonate}}{HCO_3^-}$$

$$\underset{\text{phosphate}}{H^+ + PO_4^{3-}} \longrightarrow \underset{\text{hydrogen phosphate}}{HPO_4^{2-}}$$

$$\underset{\text{hydrogen phosphate}}{H^+ + HPO_4^{2-}} \longrightarrow \underset{\text{dihydrogen phosphate}}{H_2PO_4^-}$$

Safety

Very poisonous ions like the cyanide ion should be made into a chemically safe form before being disposed of.

Figure 5·13
These models show the arrangement of atoms in four common polyatomic ions.

NO_3^-

SO_4^{2-}

PO_4^{3-}

NH_4^+

Nitrate ion

Sulfate ion

Phosphate ion

Ammonium ion

Table 5·4 Common Polyatomic Ions

1− charge		2− charge		3− charge	
Formula	Name	Formula	Name	Formula	Name
$H_2PO_4^-$	Dihydrogen phosphate	HPO_4^{2-}	Hydrogen phosphate	PO_4^{3-}	Phosphate
$C_2H_3O_2^-$	Acetate	$C_2O_4^{2-}$	Oxalate	PO_3^{3-}	Phosphite
HSO_3^-	Hydrogen sulfite (bisulfite)	SO_3^{2-}	Sulfite		
HSO_4^-	Hydrogen sulfate (bisulfate)	SO_4^{2-}	Sulfate		
HCO_3^-	Hydrogen carbonate (bicarbonate)	CO_3^{2-}	Carbonate		
NO_2^-	Nitrite				
NO_3^-	Nitrate	CrO_4^{2-}	Chromate		
CN^-	Cyanide				
OH^-	Hydroxide	$Cr_2O_7^{2-}$	Dichromate		
MnO_4^-	Permanganate	SiO_3^{2-}	Silicate		
ClO^-	Hypochlorite				
ClO_2^-	Chlorite				
ClO_3^-	Chlorate				
ClO_4^-	Perchlorate				

1+ charge

Formula	Name
NH_4^+	Ammonium

5·8 Common and Systematic Names

The large number of known compounds requires that we use a systematic method of naming.

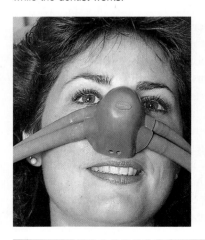

As the science of chemistry developed, it became apparent that some systematic method of naming chemical compounds was needed. In the early days of chemistry, the discoverer of a new compound often named the compound. It was not uncommon for the name to describe some physical or chemical property of the substance or the source of the compound. A common name for potassium carbonate, K_2CO_3, is potash. The name evolved because the compound was separated by boiling wood *ash*es in iron *pots*. Laughing gas is the common name for a gaseous compound, dinitrogen monoxide (N_2O). It causes people to laugh when they inhale it. These and other common names are very descriptive. Unfortunately, they do not tell us anything about the chemical composition of the compound. What are the components of baking soda, plaster of paris, quicksilver, or lye? Table 5·5 gives the formulas and systematic names for some substances with common names that you might recognize.

A few common names are used even by scientists. Water (for H_2O) is preferred to the systematic name dihydrogen monoxide. It is important, however, that we use a systematic method of naming compounds. The rest of this chapter is devoted to learning about this system for inorganic compounds. These are compounds that are not carbon-based. We will look first at binary ionic compounds.

Table 5·5	Common and Systematic Names Plus Formulas for Some Familiar Substances	
Common name	Formula	Systematic name
Water	H_2O	Dihydrogen monoxide
Lime	CaO	Calcium oxide
Slaked lime	$Ca(OH)_2$	Calcium hydroxide
Lye	NaOH	Sodium hydroxide
Potash	K_2CO_3	Potassium carbonate
Table salt	NaCl	Sodium chloride
Laughing gas	N_2O	Dinitrogen monoxide
Baking soda (bicarbonate soda)	$NaHCO_3$	Sodium hydrogen carbonate
Muriatic acid	$HCl(aq)$	Hydrochloric acid
Hypo	$Na_2S_2O_3$	Sodium thiosulfate

Figure 5·15
In the eighteenth century, pharmacists both prescribed and prepared remedies.

5·A Pharmacy from Scheele to the Present

Over 5000 years ago, Chinese physicians treated respiratory diseases with a tea brewed from a common herb *Ephedra sinica*. In the seventh and eighth centuries AD Arabian alchemists extracted and purified the essential ingredients in such herbs. Today millions of allergy patients find relief by taking ephedrine. The Chinese herb contained this chemical which is now used in prescription and over-the-counter drugs.

One pharmacist who dramatically changed his profession was the Swedish scientist Carl Wilhelm Scheele. In 1756 when he was barely 15 years old, Scheele was apprenticed to a pharmacist. At that time pharmacists both prepared remedies and prescribed them for patients. Scheele and others were constantly making new remedies. He used new combinations of materials and reacted them to form novel substances. As a result, Sheele conducted thousands of experiments and made important chemical discoveries.

In Scheele's era, air, fire, water, and earth were considered the elements of which all matter was composed. Even as a teenager, Scheele opposed this view. Later his discoveries directly or indirectly led to the isolation of many true elements. These included chlorine, manganese, molybdenum, and oxygen. The names that Scheele used for several common chemicals reveal some of the mystery faced by pioneer chemists. Oxygen and nitrogen were called fire air and foul air. Carbon dioxide was known as aerial acid, and calcium oxalate was called rhubarb earth.

Perhaps the last item represents Scheele's greatest contribution to pharmacy and chemistry. By combining sugar and nitric acid he

Figure 5·16
Today's pharmacists must have a broad and thorough knowledge of how various medications affect the body. This requires an understanding of the chemistry of drugs.

produced a substance that was identical to an acid obtained from the rhubarb plant. Until this work, scientists were sure that substances produced by plants and animals could not be produced in the laboratory. Scheele's experiment disproved this. He opened the door to the field of pharmaceutical chemistry, which is the study of the analysis, synthesis, and description of drugs. Today most drugs, including ephedrine, are partially or wholly synthesized.

Many specialists now contribute to the work of controlling disease. Pharmaceutical chemists work toward the synthesis of effective new drugs. Pharmacologists focus on the effects of drugs on various parts of the body. This information is used by physicians and pharmacists in deciding which drugs to prescribe. A major responsibility of hospital and drugstore pharmacists is to dispense drugs. Physicians and patients also rely on pharmacists to have a thorough understanding of the effects of medications. Thus a degree program in pharmacy includes five or six years of course work. Chemistry, physiology, microbiology, and pharmacy courses are emphasized.

5·9 Writing Formulas for Binary Ionic Compounds

■ Metals combine with nonmetals to form binary ionic compounds.

Monatomic ions are formed from individual atoms.

Although composed of positively and negatively charged ions, ionic compounds themselves are electrically neutral.

Binary compounds *are composed of two elements.* The components of a binary ionic compound are a monatomic cation and a monatomic anion. Monatomic cations such as Na^+, Fe^{3+}, and Ca^{2+} are formed from metallic elements. The name of a monatomic cation is just the name of the element followed by the word ion. Monatomic anions such as O^{2-} and F^- are formed from nonmetallic elements. The name of a monatomic anion ends in *-ide*.

Ionic compounds are electrically neutral. In writing a formula for an ionic compound, we must exactly balance the positive charge of the cation by the negative charge of the anion. Stated another way, the net ionic charge of the formula must be zero. The binary ionic compound potassium chloride is composed of potassium ions, K^+, and chloride ions, Cl^-. In this compound, potassium and chloride ions must combine in a $1:1$ ratio. For each K^+ there is one Cl^-. The formula for potassium chloride then is KCl. The net ionic charge of the formula is zero. In the formula of an ionic compound, the cation is always written first.

Calcium bromide is composed of calcium ions, Ca^{2+}, and bromide ions, Br^-. In this compound the ions must combine in a $1:2$ ratio. Each calcium ion with its $2+$ charge must combine with (or be balanced by) two bromide ions, each with a $1-$ charge. The formula for calcium bromide is $CaBr_2$.

What is the formula of iron(III) oxide? The roman numeral tells us the charge of the metal ion. Thus this compound consists of Fe^{3+} ions combined with O^{2-} ions. Writing a balanced formula for this compound may not seem as obvious as in the previous two examples. One way to reason through the problem is on the next page.

Action	Result	Observation
1. Start with the ions.	Fe^{3+} O^{2-}	More minus charge is needed.
2. Add an additional O^{2-}.	Fe^{3+} O^{2-} O^{2-}	More positive charge is needed.
3. Add an additional Fe^{3+}.	Fe^{3+} O^{2-} Fe^{3+} O^{2-}	More negative charge is needed.
4. Add another O^{2-}.	Fe^{3+} O^{2-} Fe^{3+} O^{2-} O^{2-}	The charges now balance.
5. Sum the ions.	$2Fe^{3+}$ $3O^{2-}$	
6. Write the balanced formula.	Fe_2O_3	Check that the net ionic charges balance. $2(3+) + 3(2-) = 0$

This is a rather lengthy process. A much quicker way to the same answer is to use what can be called the crisscross method. In this method, the numerical charge of each ion is crossed over and used as a subscript for the other ion. The signs of the numbers are dropped.

$$Fe^{3+} \quad O^{2-}$$
$$Fe_2O_3$$
$$2(3+) + 3(2-) = 0$$

This method can also be used with the previous examples.

$$K^{1+} \quad Cl^{1-} \qquad Ca^{2+} \quad Br^{1-}$$
$$KCl \qquad\qquad CaBr_2$$

Do not forget that formulas for ionic compounds are the lowest whole-number ratio of ions. The formula for calcium sulfide is CaS, not Ca_2S_2.

$$Ca^{2+} \quad S^{2-}$$
$$Ca_2S_2 \text{ reduces to CaS}$$

Of course, if the magnitudes of the charges of the cation and anion are the same, there is no reason to use the crisscross method. The ions will combine in a 1 : 1 ratio because the charges will balance.

Example 5

Write formulas for these binary ionic compounds.
a. copper(II) sulfide   **b.** potassium nitride

Solution

Write down the formula (symbol and charge) of each ion. Balance the formula with appropriate subscripts.

a. Cu^{2+} ⤬ S^{2-} **b.** K^{1+} ⤬ N^{3-}

CuS K_3N

$(2+) + (2-) = 0$ $3(1+) + (3-) = 0$

Problem

7. a. Li_2S **b.** SnO_2 **c.** HCl
d. Mg_3N_2

7. Write formulas for compounds composed of these pairs of ions.
   a. Li^+, S^{2-} **b.** Sn^{4+}, O^{2-} **c.** H^+, Cl^- **d.** Mg^{2+}, N^{3-}

■ The names of binary ionic compounds have this form: (cation name) (anion name).

5·10 Naming Binary Ionic Compounds

Binary ionic compounds are named by writing the name of the cation followed by the name of the anion (*-ide* ending). When a cation has more than one common ionic charge, it is important to use a roman numeral in the name. Giving the compound CuO the name "copper oxide" is not correct. This is because copper commonly forms two ions: Cu^{1+} and Cu^{2+}. The correct cation name of a transition metal can be determined by effectively working the formula backwards. The oxide ion always has a 2− charge. What must the charge of the copper ion be if the copper ion and oxide ion combine in a 1:1 ratio? Obviously it must be copper(II) oxide. Cu_2O is copper(I) oxide.

You need to know which transition metals have two common ionic charges. It should be apparent from this discussion, however, that there is not much advantage to memorizing the charges of the transition metals in Table 5·3. You may know, for example, that tin forms ions with 2+

Figure 5·18
Some transition metals can exist in more than one ionic state. When combining with another element, these metals can form more than one type of compound. Two pairs of examples for iron compounds are shown here.

Iron(II) sulfate, $FeSO_4$ Iron(III) sulfate, $Fe_2(SO_4)_3$

Iron(II) chloride, $FeCl_2$ Iron(III) chloride, $FeCl_3$

and 4+ charges. It will still be necessary, however, to determine which of these charges tin has in a particular compound. The name of SnO_2 is tin(IV) oxide. The tin(IV) ion, Sn^{4+}, will balance two oxide ions, each with a 2− charge.

Roman numerals are used on an "as needed" basis only. It is incorrect to use roman numerals with the name of a representative (Group A) metal. This is because these metals form ions with only one common ionic charge. For example, we would never write sodium(I) chloride or magnesium(II) oxide.

Example 6

Name these binary ionic compounds.   **a.** CoI_3 **b.** Cs_2O

Solution

Name the cation followed by the name of the anion.

a. cobalt(III) iodide, or cobaltic iodide

b. cesium oxide

Problem

8. Write names for these binary ionic compounds.
    a. AiI_3 **b.** FeO **c.** Cu_2S **d.** $CaSe$

8. a. aluminum iodide
  b. iron(II) oxide or ferrous oxide
  c. copper(I) sulfide or cuprous sulfide
  d. calcium selenide

5·11 Ternary Ionic Compounds

Ternary ionic compounds are easily named if we recognize the common polyatomic ions.

Figure 5·19
Calcium carbonate ($CaCO_3$) is a ternary ionic compound that oysters produce to form both their shells and pearls.

Ternary compounds *contain atoms of three different elements.* Ternary ionic compounds usually contain one or more polyatomic ions (Table 5·4). The procedure for writing the formula of a ternary ionic compound is the same as that for binary ionic compounds. This same procedure is also used for ionic compounds that have more than three different elements. First write down the formulas (symbol and charge) of the ions. Then balance the charges. An *-ate* or *-ite* ending on the name of a compound indicates that the compound contains a polyatomic anion. The two common exceptions are the hydroxide and cyanide polyatomic ions.

What is the formula of calcium nitrate? This compound is composed of calcium ions, Ca^{2+}, and nitrate ions, NO_3^-. To balance the formula, two nitrate ions, each a minus one, are needed to balance each calcium ion. Parentheses are used around the nitrate ion in the formula because two nitrate ions, NO_3^{1-}, are needed.

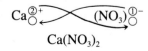

Whenever more than a single polyatomic ion is needed to balance a formula, parentheses must be used. This is the only time they are used.

Example 7

Write formulas for these compounds. **a.** potassium sulfate
b. magnesium hydroxide **c.** ammonium sulfide

Solution

a. K^{1+} $(SO_4)^{2-}$ → K_2SO_4

b. Mg^{2+} $(OH)^{1-}$ → $Mg(OH)_2$

The formula for magnesium hydroxide must have the parentheses. $MgOH_2$ would be incorrect because there would not be two hydroxide ions (only one oxygen atom).

c. $(NH_4)^{1+}$ S^{2-} → $(NH_4)_2S$

Problem

9. Write the formulas for these compounds. **a.** barium sulfate
b. aluminum hydrogen carbonate **c.** sodium hypochlorite
d. lead(IV) chromate

When naming a ternary ionic compound, be sure to note the polyatomic ion in the formula. Like a binary ionic compound, this compound is named by naming the ions, cation first. The compound $NaC_2H_3O_2$ is composed of sodium and acetate ions. Its name is sodium acetate. The compound $K_2Cr_2O_7$ is potassium dichromate (two K^+ combined with one $Cr_2O_7^{2-}$).

Example 8

Name these compounds.
a. LiCN
b. Sr(H$_2$PO$_4$)$_2$
c. (NH$_4$)$_2$C$_2$O$_4$
d. Fe(ClO$_3$)$_3$

Solution

a. lithium cyanide
b. strontium dihydrogen phosphate
c. ammonium oxalate
d. iron(III) chlorate

Problems

10. Write names for these compounds. **a.** Cr(NO$_3$)$_2$ **b.** Mg$_3$(PO$_4$)$_2$
c. Cu$_2$HPO$_4$ **d.** Li$_2$CrO$_4$

11. Write the name or formula, as appropriate. **a.** aluminum hydroxide **b.** K$_2$SiO$_3$ **c.** LiF **d.** potassium chlorite **e.** Sn$_3$(PO$_4$)$_2$
f. zinc hydrogen sulfate

5·12   Binary Molecular Compounds

When two nonmetals combine they form a binary molecular compound.

Binary molecular compounds are composed of two nonmetallic elements. Two characteristics of binary molecular compounds affect naming and writing formulas for these compounds. First, because these compounds are composed of molecules, the ionic charges of the representative elements are *not* used in writing formulas for the compounds. Second, when two nonmetallic elements combine, they often do so in more than one way. For example, the elements carbon and oxygen combine to form two different gaseous compounds and an ion, CO, CO_2, and CO_3^{2-}. They each have different physical and chemical properties.

At first glance it might seem satisfactory to give the name "carbon oxide" to a binary compound formed by the combination of carbon and oxygen atoms. This could have some severe consequences, however. Sitting in a room with moderate amounts of "carbon oxide" (CO_2) in the air would not present any problems. We exhale CO_2 as a product of our metabolism. Thus it is normally present in the air we breathe. If, however, the "carbon oxide" were the same amount of CO, we could die of asphyxiation. CO is a poisonous gas that interferes with our blood's ability to transport oxygen to body cells. Obviously, we need to distinguish between these two compounds when naming them.

The names of binary molecular compounds have this form:
(prefix + element name)
(prefix + element root + *-ide*).

Prefixes are used to show how many atoms of each element are present in each molecule (and formula) of a binary molecular compound. These prefixes are listed in Table 5·6. The two compounds of carbon and oxygen then are named carbon monoxide (CO) and carbon dioxide (CO_2). Note that the second element in the name is written with an *-ide* ending. *Thus all binary compounds, both ionic and molecular, end in -ide*. Note also that the vowel at the end of the prefix *mono-* is dropped when the name of the element begins with a vowel: monoxide, not monooxide. This prefix is normally omitted if there is just a single atom of the *first* element in the name.

Remember, prefixes are used in naming compounds composed of two nonmetals.

a

b

Figure 5·20
The binary molecular compounds of carbon and oxygen have very different properties. **a** Carbon monoxide (CO) is a poisonous gas found in automobile exhaust. **b** Carbon dioxide (CO_2) is used to put bubbles into soft drinks.

Table 5·6 Prefixes Used in Naming Binary Molecular Compounds	
Prefix	Number
mono-	1
di-	2
tri-	3
tetra-	4
penta-	5
hexa-	6
hepta-	7
octa-	8
nona-	9
deca-	10

Example 9

Name the compounds. **a.** N_2O **b.** PCl_3 **c.** $AlCl_3$ **d.** SF_6

Solution

When both elements are nonmetals, the compound is molecular, and prefixes are used to indicate the number of each atom. **a.** dinitrogen monoxide **b.** phosphorus trichloride **c.** aluminum chloride (not trichloride! This is an ionic compound formed between a metal and a nonmetal) **d.** sulfur hexafluoride

Formulas of binary molecular compounds should be among the easiest to write. The prefixes tell you the subscript of each element in the formula. You only need to write down the correct symbols for the two elements with the appropriate subscripts. For example, the formula for tetraiodine nonoxide is I_4O_9; for sulfur trioxide, SO_3; for phosphorus pentafluoride, PF_5.

12. **a.** carbon tetrabromide
b. dichlorine heptoxide
c. dinitrogen pentoxide
d. boron trichloride
e. chromium(III) chloride

13. **a.** CS_2 **b.** N_2H_4 **c.** CCl_4
d. P_2O_3

Problems

12. Name these compounds. **a.** CBr_4 **b.** Cl_2O_7 **c.** N_2O_5
d. BCl_3 **e.** $CrCl_3$

13. Write formulas for these compounds. **a.** carbon disulfide
b. dinitrogen tetrahydride **c.** carbon tetrachloride
d. diphosphorus trioxide

5·13 Acids

Acids are identified by formulas in which the element hydrogen appears first.

Acids are a group of compounds that are given special treatment in naming. You will see that acids are defined in several different ways when you look at the chemistry of acids in more detail in Chapter 18. For now it is sufficient to know that **acids** *are compounds that give off hydrogen ions when dissolved in water*.

The formulas of acids are of a general form HX, where X is a monatomic or polyatomic anion. We have previously named the compound HCl, hydrogen chloride. When the compound HCl is dissolved in water, it is named as an acid. Other compounds, such as HNO_3, exist only in water solution. They are always named as acids.

Consider the acid HX as dissolving in water. The acid can be named using three rules that focus on the ending of the anion of the acid (Table 5·7).

1. When the anion (X) ends in *-ide,* the acid name begins with the prefix *hydro-*. The stem of the anion has the suffix *-ic* and it is followed by the word *acid*. Thus HCl (X = chloride), dissolved in water, is named *hydro*chlor*ic acid*. H_2S (X = sulfide) is *hydro*sulfur*ic acid*.

Safety

Acids can cause serious burns. Acid should be washed from the skin or eyes by flushing with a stream of water for five minutes. Acid spills should be neutralized with sodium bicarbonate (baking soda) before being wiped up.

Table 5·7 Naming Acids

Anion ending	Example	Acid name	Example
-ide	Cl^- chlor*ide*	*hydro-*(stem)*-ic acid*	*hydro*chlor*ic acid*
-ite	SO_3^{2-} sulf*ite*	(stem)*-ous acid*	sulfur*ous acid*
-ate	NO_3^- nitr*ate*	(stem)*-ic acid*	nitr*ic acid*

2. When the anion ends in *-ite,* the acid name is the stem of the anion with the suffix *-ous,* followed by the word *acid.* H_2SO_3 (X = sulfite) is sulfur*ous acid.*

3. If the anion ends in *-ate,* the acid name is the stem of the anion with the suffix *-ic,* followed by the word *acid.* Thus HNO_3 (X = nitrate) is nitr*ic acid.*

Example 10

Name these compounds as acids. **a.** HClO **b.** HCN **c.** H_3PO_4

Solution

a. hypochlor*ous acid* (rule 2) **b.** *hydro*cyan*ic acid* (rule 1)
c. phosphor*ic acid* (rule 3)

Not all compounds which contain hydrogen are acids. For example methane, CH_4, is not an acid.

Formulas of acids are most easily written by using the preceding three rules in a reverse fashion. For example, what is the formula of chloric acid? As rule 3 shows, chloric acid (*-ic* ending) must be a combination of hydrogen ion (H^+) and chlor*ate* ion (ClO_3^-). The formula of chloric acid is $HClO_3$. Hydrobromic acid (*hydro-* prefix and *-ic* suffix), according to rule 1, must be a combination of hydrogen ion and bromide ion (Br^-). The formula of hydrobromic acid is HBr. Hydrogen ion and phosphite ion (PO_3^{3-}) must be the components of phosphorous acid (rule 2). The formula of phosphorous acid is H_3PO_3.

Problems

14. Name these compounds as acids. **a.** HF **b.** $HC_2H_3O_2$ **c.** H_2SO_4 **d.** HNO_2

15. Write formulas for the following acids. **a.** chromic acid **b.** hydroiodic acid **c.** chlorous acid **d.** perchloric acid

14. a. hydrofluoric acid **b.** acetic acid **c.** sulfuric acid **d.** nitrous acid

15. a. H_2CrO_4 **b.** HI **c.** $HClO_2$ **d.** $HClO_4$

5·14 Summary of Naming and Formula Writing

A systematic approach will lead to success in naming compounds and writing formulas.

In this chapter we have discussed two skills: writing chemical formulas and naming chemical compounds. If this is your first exposure to these concepts, you may feel a little overwhelmed at this point. When do you use prefixes or roman numerals in a name and when should you not use them? Should a compound's name end in *-ate*, *-ide*, or *-ite*? For example, what is the name of each of these compounds: $FeCl_3$, PCl_3, and $AlCl_3$? Each compound is composed of one element combined with the nonmetal chlorine in a $1:3$ ratio. On first glance, then, it may look as if these compounds should be named the same way. But the names differ.

$FeCl_3$ is iron(III) chloride. The name must include a roman numeral because iron is a transition metal.

PCl_3 is phosphorus trichloride. The compound is named with prefixes because phosphorus is a nonmetal.

$AlCl_3$ is aluminum chloride. Neither a roman numeral nor prefixes are needed in the name since aluminum is a Group A metal.

Figure 5·21 is a flowchart designed to help you name compounds correctly. By following the flowchart, you are led to the directions for

Figure 5·21
This flowchart will help you to name chemical compounds. P and Q in the general formula, P_xQ_y, can be atoms, monatomic ions, or polyatomic ions.

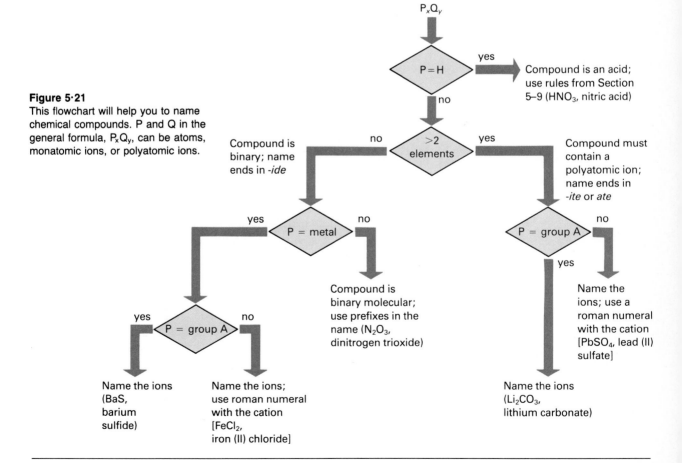

naming a particular compound. Use the flowchart while working exercises to increase your skill at naming compounds. With practice you will be able to mentally ask yourself the questions that will lead you to the correct name without having the flowchart in front of you.

In writing a chemical formula from a chemical name, it is helpful to remember the following.

1. In an ionic compound, the net ionic charge is zero.
2. An *-ide* ending indicates a binary compound.
3. An *-ite* or *-ate* ending means the formula has a polyatomic ion.
4. Prefixes in the name indicate a molecular compound. They show the number of each atom in the formula.
5. A roman numeral shows the ionic charge of the cation.

Problems

16. Name these compounds, using Figure 5·21 as an aid if necessary.

a. $CaCO_3$ **f.** Mg_3P_2
b. $KMnO_4$ **g.** $(NH_4)_2SO_4$
c. $PbCrO_4$ **h.** I_2Cl_2
d. $CaHPO_4$ **i.** HNO_2
e. $SnCr_2O_7$ **j.** $SrBr_2$

17. Write formulas for these compounds.

a. tin(II) hydroxide   **f.** aluminum hydrogen carbonate
b. barium fluoride   **g.** sodium phosphate
c. tetraiodine nonoxide   **h.** potassium perchlorate
d. iron(III) oxalate   **i.** disulfur trioxide
e. hydrosulfuric acid   **j.** magnesium nitrate

16. a. calcium carbonate
b. potassium permanganate
c. lead(II) chromate
d. calcium hydrogen phosphate
e. tin(II) dichromate
f. magnesium phosphide
g. ammonium sulfate
h. diiodine dichloride
i. nitrous acid
j. strontium bromide

17. a. $Sn(OH)_2$ **f.** $Al(HCO_3)_3$
b. BaF_2 **g.** Na_3PO_4
c. I_4O_9 **h.** $KClO_4$
d. $Fe_2(C_2O_4)_3$ **i.** S_2O_3
e. H_2S **j.** $Mg(NO_3)_2$

5·B Chemical Data Banks

The job of naming chemical compounds and recognizing formulas may seem like an overwhelming task. What you have seen so far, however, is much less than the tip of the iceberg. There are 217 different compounds that have the simple formula C_6H_6. Each of these has a unique name. In the field of organic chemistry, hundreds of thousands of new compounds are made, and named, every year. Recognizing the names of all these compounds is a tremendous challenge. Being able to look up the chemical, biochemical, and physical properties of all these substances is important as well.

Chemists today are using computers to manage this evergrowing body of data. This allows them to answer questions that would otherwise take weeks of library and laboratory work. Some systems store information on the names, properties, and reactions of compounds.

Others can draw all the possible structures of a given formula, such as all 217 versions of C_6H_6. One program will "look at" a molecule or part of a molecule drawn by a chemist and then search for it among all the compounds in its memory. A similar program can search for all reactions involving the molecule that has been drawn.

One of the largest chemical data banks is the Chemical Information System. This system, known as CIS, was developed in 1971. It contains data on hundreds of thousands of chemicals. It also is connected to other computer systems that can give bibliographies relevant to each substance. The system is used by government agencies, universities, and industries throughout Canada, the United States, and in many other countries. These customers pay a fee and can gain access to the system by telephone.

A user can type in the name or formula of a chemical and get information on its structure and properties. If the properties of an unknown substance are provided, the computer will list the compounds it might be. If an unknown chemical is released into the environment, an emergency team equipped with a portable computer can determine what the chemical is. Information may also be available on how to clean up the site, how to control any resulting fires, and how to treat any people or animals exposed to the chemical.

CIS also includes most of the specialized programs described earlier and is used in research. Hospitals and poison control centers use the system to identify poisons and choose proper medical treatment. Pollution control agencies can identify and manage pollutants in water supplies. It is an important tool for today's chemists.

Chemical Names and Formulas

Chapter Review

Key Terms

acid	5·13	metal	5·1
anion	5·2	metalloid	5·1
base	5·7	molecule	5·3
binary compound	5·9	molecular	
cation	5·2	compound	5·3
chemical formula	5·4	molecular formula	5·4
formula unit	5·4	nonmetal	5·1
group	5·1	periodic table	5·1
ion	5·2	polyatomic ion	5·7
ionic compound	5·3	representative	
law of definite		element	5·1
proportions	5·3	semimetal	5·1
law of multiple		ternary compound	5·11
proportions	5·5	transition metal	5·1

Chapter Summary

The elements in the periodic table are arranged in vertical columns called groups. Groups 1A through 7A and Group 0 make up the representative elements. Metals are on the left and lower sides of the periodic table. Nonmetals are on the right and upper sides.

Every substance is either an element or a compound. An element consists of one kind of atom. A compound consists of more than one kind of atom. A compound is either molecular or ionic in nature.

Molecular compounds are composed of two or more nonmetals. The representative particle of a molecular compound is a molecule. A molecular formula shows the number and kinds of atoms present in a molecule of a compound.

Ionic compounds are composed of oppositely charged ions (cations and anions) combined in electrically neutral groupings. The chemical formula of an ionic compound is a formula unit. A formula unit gives the lowest whole-number ratio of ions in the compound.

The charges of the ions of the representative elements can be determined by the position of these elements in the periodic table. Most transition metals have more than one common ionic charge. A polyatomic ion is a group of atoms that behave as a unit and has a charge.

As the number of known chemical compounds increased, a systematic naming method was devised. Binary (two-element) ionic compounds are named by writing the name of the cation followed by the name of the anion. Binary compounds end in -ide. For example, KBr is potassium bromide.

When a cation has more than one ionic charge, a roman numeral is used in the name. The compound FeO is named iron(II) oxide. Ternary ionic compounds contain a least one polyatomic ion. The names of these compounds generally end in -ite or -ate. The compound KNO_3 is potassium nitrate.

Binary molecular compounds are composed of two nonmetallic elements. The name of a binary molecular compound ends in -ide. Prefixes are used to show how many atoms of each element are present in a molecule of the compound. For example, N_2O_4 is named dinitrogen tetroxide.

Compounds with the formula HX, where X represents an anion, are named as acids when they are dissolved in water.

Practice Questions and Problems

18. Classify each element as a metal, nonmetal, or metalloid. **a.** aluminum **b.** silver **c.** silicon **d.** helium **e.** zinc   5·1

19. In which groups are the elements in Problem 18 found?   5·1

20. What is an ion? Describe the formation of a cation and an anion.   5·2

21. State the number of electrons either lost or gained in forming each ion. **a.** S^{2-} **b.** K^+ **c.** Cl^- **d.** Ba^{2+} **e.** Li^+ **f.** H^- 5·2

---

22. Name each of the ions in Problem 21. Identify them as anions and cations. 5·2

23. Would you expect the following compounds to be ionic or molecular? 5·3
a. CO
b. KBr
c. Li_2O
d. C_3H_8
e. SO_3
f. $AlCl_3$

24. How is the law of definite proportions explained by Dalton's atomic theory? 5·3

25. List three characteristics each for ionic compounds and molecular compounds. 5·3

26. State whether each formula in Problem 23 represents a molecule or a formula unit. 5·4

27. How is the law of multiple proportions explained by Dalton's atomic theory? 5·5

28. Using only the periodic table, name and write the formulas of the ions of these representative elements. 5·6
a. lithium
b. oxygen
c. barium
d. nitrogen
e. fluorine
f. potassium
g. neon
h. beryllium

29. Without consulting Table 5·4, name the following ions. 5·7
a. NO_3^-
b. H^+
c. CN^-
d. Cr^{3+}
e. $Cr_2O_7^{2-}$
f. $H_2PO_4^-$
g. Sn^{4+}
h. MnO_4^-
i. SO_3^{2-}
j. Se^{2-}

30. Write the formula and charge of each of the following ions. 5·7
a. magnesium ion
b. lead(IV) ion
c. chromate ion
d. nitrite ion
e. iodide ion
f. chlorate ion
g. hydroxide ion
h. iron(II) ion
i. ammonium ion
j. copper(I) ion

31. What are the components of a binary ionic compound? 5·9

32. What is the ending of the name of a binary ionic compound? 5·9

33. What condition must be met in writing a "balanced" formula of an ionic compound? 5·9

34. Write formulas for compounds formed from these pairs of ions. 5·9
a. Sr^{2+}, Se^{2-}
b. K^+, O^{2-}
c. Ca^{2+}, N^{3-}
d. Co^{3+}, I^-

35. Write formulas for these compounds. 5·9
a. silver sulfide
b. stannic chloride
c. sodium nitride
d. strontium iodide

36. When is a roman numeral used in the name of a compound? 5·10

37. Name these binary ionic compounds. 5·10
a. ZnO
b. NaI
c. Cu_2O
d. $CaBr_2$

38. The names of most ternary ionic compounds end in one of two suffixes. What are they? 5·11

39. When are parentheses used in writing a chemical formula? 5·11

40. Write formulas for these compounds. 5·11
a. mercury(II) bromide
b. ammonium dichromate
c. lithium hydrogen sulfate
d. chromium(III) nitrite

41. Complete this table by writing correct formulas for the compounds formed by combining positive and negative ions. Then name each compound. 5·11

	SO_4^{2-}	OH^-	PO_4^{3-}	S^{2-}
Ca^{2+}	___	___	___	___
NH_4^+	___	___	___	___
Al^{3+}	___	___	___	___
Pb^{4+}	___	___	___	___

42. What are the components of a binary molecular compound? 5·12

43. What prefix is used to indicate each of the following number of atoms in a formula of a molecular compound? 5·12
a. 3
b. 1
c. 6
d. 4
e. 2
f. 7
g. 10
h. 8
i. 5
j. 9

44. Name these binary molecular compounds.
a. OF_2 **b.** Cl_2O_8 **c.** SO_3 **d.** P_4O_{10} 5·12

45. Write formulas for the following binary molecular compounds. 5·12
a. dinitrogen tetroxide
b. phosphorus pentachloride
c. nitrogen trifluoride
d. disulfur dichloride

46. Assume that each of these is dissolved in water, and name each as an acid. 5·13
a. $H_2C_2O_4$
b. HF
c. $HClO_2$
d. H_2CO_3

47. Write formulas for these compounds.   *5·13*
  a. nitrous acid   **c.** phosphoric acid
  b. hydroselenic acid   **d.** acetic acid

Mastery Questions and Problems

48. Two compounds can be formed when phosphorus reacts with oxygen. One compound is prepared by reacting 8.29 g of oxygen with 6.43 g of phosphorus. The other can be prepared by reacting 2.64 g of oxygen and 3.41 g of phosphorus. Does this pair of compounds confirm the law of multiple proportions?   *5·5*

49. Classify each of the ions in Problem 29 as a monatomic or a polyatomic ion.   *5·7*

50. Classify each of the ions in Problem 30 as an anion or a cation.   *5·2*

51. Name each of the following substances. Use Figure 5·21 if necessary.   *5·14*
  a. CaO **g.** $CuC_2H_3O_2$
  b. $Ba_3(PO_4)_2$ **h.** $HClO_4$
  c. I_2 **i.** Cl_2O
  d. $BaSO_4$ **j.** HgF_2
  e. $Mg(OH)_2$ **k.** $(NH_4)_2C_2O_4$
  f. NO_2 **l.** NO_2^-

52. Write formulas for these compounds.   *5·14*
  a. calcium carbonate   **g.** nitrogen
  b. sodium bromide   **h.** barium hydroxide
  c. ferric sulfate   **i.** hydrobromic acid
  d. magnesium sulfide   **j.** sulfite ion
  e. sulfuric acid   **k.** copper(II) iodide
  f. sulfur trioxide   **l.** zinc oxalate

53. Name each compound.   *5·14*
  a. NH_4OH **g.** K_2CO_3
  b. HF **h.** N_2H_4
  c. PI_3 **i.** ZnO
  d. $Be(NO_3)_2$ **j.** $Mg(MnO_4)_2$
  e. $HMnO_4$ **k.** Li_2HPO_4
  f. CO **l.** Li_2CO_3

54. Write formulas for these compounds.   *5·14*
  a. silver chloride   **g.** sodium silicate
  b. aluminum carbide   **h.** calcium oxide
  c. lithium hydride   **i.** hydrocyanic acid
  d. acetic acid   **j.** tin(IV) cyanide
  e. ferrous carbonate   **k.** hydrogen bromide
  f. hypochlorous acid   **l.** potassium iodide

55. Name these compounds.   *5·14*
  a. $Na_2Cr_2O_7$ **g.** CaH_2
  b. AlI_3 **h.** $HClO_3$
  c. SnO_2 **i.** Hg_2Br_2
  d. $Fe(C_2H_3O_2)_3$ **j.** AlP
  e. $KHSO_4$ **k.** $FeCO_3$
  f. $Co(NO_2)_2$ **l.** H_2CrO_4

56. Write formulas for these compounds.   *5·14*
  a. phosphorus pentabromide
  b. carbon tetrachloride
  c. potassium permanganate
  d. ammonium perchlorate
  e. calcium hydrogen carbonate
  f. cuprous hydroxide
  g. ammonium nitrate
  h. dichlorine heptoxide
  i. trisilicon tetranitride
  j. sodium dihydrogen phosphate

Review Questions and Problems

57. Make the following conversions.
  a. 5.46 cg of Ag to milligrams of silver
  b. 0.234 dm³ of CCl_4 to milliliters of carbon tetrachloride
  c. 189 cal to kilojoules
  d. $-25°C$ to K

58. A student finds that 2.62 g of a substance occupies a volume of 1.05 mL. What is the density of the substance?

59. List ten properties of the chair you are sitting in. Classify the properties as physical or chemical.

60. How many protons and electrons are in each of these ions?
  a. bromide ion   **c.** calcium ion
  b. aluminum ion   **d.** oxide ion

Challenging Questions and Problems

61. The *Handbook of Chemistry and Physics* is a reference work that contains a wealth of information about elements and compounds. Two sections of this book that students often use are the "Physical Constants of Inorganic Compounds" and the "Physical Constants of Organic Compounds."

To familiarize yourself with this work, make a table with these headings: Name, Formula, Crystalline form or color, Density, Melting point (°C), Boiling point (°C), and Solubility in water. Enter these substances in the body of the table: ammonium chloride, barium, barium sulfate, bromine, calcium carbonate, chlorine, copper(II) sulfate pentahydrate, iodine, iron(II) sulfate pentahydrate, mercury, potassium carbonate, and sulfur. Use the *Handbook* to complete the table.

62. Use the table you prepared for Problem 61 to answer the following questions.

  a. You have two unlabeled bottles, each containing a white powder. You are told that one of the substances is calcium carbonate and the other is potassium carbonate. Describe a simple physical test you would carry out to distinguish between these two compounds.

  b. How would you distinguish between samples of copper(II) sulfate pentahydrate and iron(II) sulfate pentahydrate?

  c. A bottle contains a mixture of ammonium chloride and barium sulfate. What method could you use to separate these two compounds?

  d. List the *elements* in the preceding table in order of increasing density. Identify the elements as metals or nonmetals.

  e. List the *compounds* in the table in order of decreasing density.

  f. Calculate the mass of 132 cm³ of mercury.

  g. Calculate the volume of 56 g of sulfur.

  h. How would you distinguish among the halogens listed in this table?

63. Are you a creative thinker? Do you like puns? Even if you do not, you might enjoy groaning at these *elemental puns*. Each of the blanks can be completed with the name of an element. So *cesium* your pencil and try your luck.

  a. A large building for automobiles. A _____ .

  b. 0.5 times holmium = _____ .

  c. What the criminal said about his adversary: "Get _____ ."

  d. Funds from your mother's sister: _____ .

  e. A comical prisoner. A _____ .

  f. What you do with dead cats. You _____ .

  g. Well-driller's chant."_____ ."

  h. If it's pertinent to the issue, it's _____ .

  i. What a doctor can do to his patient: _____ or _____ .

Think of other puns that play on the names of elements or compounds. Work these into a short story.

Research Projects

1. Describe the function of various ions in our blood. Some of the most important ones are Na^+ K^+, Ca^{2+}, Mg^+, HCO_3^-, and Cl^-.

2. Interview a pharmacist in your area. Find out about his or her training and job responsibilities.

3. How do pharmaceutical chemists develop new drugs?

4. How do pharmacologists test new drugs for effectiveness and safety?

5. Compare and contrast the chemical composition of the planets.

6. What is a computer data bank and how is one constructed or maintained? Use chemical examples in explaining how a data bank works.

7. Construct a chemical data bank for one group of elements. Include information on how to identify them, toxicity, common reactions, etc.

8. Scheele's early death is sometimes attributed to his exposure to toxic chemicals. What other famous scientists died as a result of the unknown hazards they faced in their work?

9. Compare the chemical and physical properties of iron(II) and iron(III) compounds. Do the same for other transition metals that form more than one ion. Do you see any pattern in your information?

Readings and References

Hawley, Gessner G., ed. *The Condensed Chemical Dictionary*. 10th ed. New York: Van Nostrand Reinhold, 1981.

Neubauer, Alfred. *Chemistry Today: The Portrait of a Science*. New York: Arco, 1983.

Parker, Sybil P. *McGraw-Hill Encyclopedia of Chemistry*. New York: McGraw-Hill, 1983.

Weast, Robert C., ed. *CRC Handbook of Chemistry and Physics: A Ready Reference Book of Chemical and Physical Data*, 67th ed. Boca Raton, FL: Chemical Rubber Co., 1986.

6 Chemical Quantities

Chapter Planning Guide

Section		Demonstrations and Experiments	Resource Materials
6·1 Measuring Matter	C*		Objectives Worksheet 6, SPB Skillsheet 6, SPB
6·2 The Mole	C	Dem 6·1 Moles of Substances	
6·A The Size of a Mole	E		
6·3 The Gram Formula Mass	C		
6·4 The Molar Mass of a Substance	C		
6·5 Mole–Mass Conversions	C		Quiz 6·1 Teaching Diagram 6
6·6 The Volume of a Mole of Gas	C	Dem 6·2 Molar Volumes Exp 9 The Masses of Equal Volumes of Gases, LM	Prelab 9, SPB
6·7 Gas Density and the Gram Molecular Mass	O		Quiz 6·2
6·8 Converting Between Units with Moles	C		
6·B Who Was Avogadro?	E		
6·9 Calculating Percent Composition	C	Dem 6·3 Percent Composition	Quiz 6·3
6·10 Calculating Empirical Formulas	C	Exp 10 Empirical Formula Determination, LM	Prelab 10, SPB
6·11 Calculating Molecular Formulas	C		Quiz 6·4 Reviewsheet 6, SPB Chapter 6 Test
6·C Knowing Your Product: Chemical Sales	E		Hazardous Household Wastes, ICT 6
*C = Core, O = Optional E = Enrichment, H = Honors		LM = Laboratory Manual	SPB = Skills Practice Book ICT = Issues in Chem. Tech.

Chapter Objectives

Having studied this chapter and done the problems, the student should be able to:

1. Name the basic SI unit for measuring the amount of a substance. *6·1*

2. Identify the mole as the SI unit that measures the "amount of substance." *6·2*

3. Define a mole as Avogadro's number (6.02×10^{23}) of representative particles of a substance. *6·2*

4. Identify the representative particle of elements and compounds. *6·2*

5. Calculate the number of representative particles in a given number of moles of any substance. *6·2*

6. Calculate the number of moles in a given number of representative particles of any substance. *6·2*

7. Distinguish between the terms gram atomic mass, gram molecular mass, gram formula mass, and molar mass. *6·3, 6·4*

8. Calculate the mass of one mole of any substance. *6·5*

9. Calculate the mass of a given number of moles of a substance. *6·5*

10. Calculate the number of moles in a given mass of a substance. *6·5*

11. Use the volume of one mole of a gas at STP (22.4 L) to work mole–volume problems. *6·6*

12. Calculate the gram molecular mass of a gas from density measurements of gases at STP. *6·7*

13. Use the mole to convert among measurements of mass, volume, and number of particles. *6·8*

14. Calculate the percentage composition of a substance from its chemical formula or experimental data. *6·9*

15. Distinguish between an empirical and a molecular formula. *6·10, 6·11*

16. Derive empirical and molecular formulas from appropriate experimental data. *6·10, 6·11*

Teaching Suggestions

6·1 Measuring Matter

6·2 The Mole

There are few concepts in chemistry which are more fundamental than the mole. It is easy to define and to explain. It is simple and logical. Yet, many students will struggle and struggle with it. It is important that you go over this concept slowly and carefully, with plenty of review and drill. **Demonstration 6·1** *Moles of Substances* will help.

The students will often object that it is convenient to deal with more familiar quantities like grams, liters, and milliliters. But atoms and molecules react with each other in a manner which is based on the *number* of atoms and molecules, not how massive or voluminous they are. We must use a unit which counts numbers. This is the mole.

Frequently students get bogged down on problems which ask for the number of atoms in a compound, such as: "How many atoms of fluorine are in 3 moles of the compound, MoF_6?" Many have trouble with the idea that there are six times as many fluorine atoms as there are MoF_6 molecules. Analogies can help. Ask questions like: "How many legs are on an insect? How many legs are on a dozen insects? How many legs are on 3 dozen insects?" Then ask: "How many legs are on a mole of insects? How many legs are on 3 moles of insects? How many fluorine atoms are there in 3 moles of MoF_6 molecules?"

Once they go through the reasoning steps with familiar objects (insects) and familiar counting units (dozens), they will be much more successful with the mole. You may also refer to hands, fingers, noses, or toes to get the point across.

6·3 The Gram Formula Mass

6·4 The Molar Mass of a Substance

The students may be confused after the terms gram atomic mass, gram molecular mass, and gram formula mass are given, particularly when they are told that they can all be replaced with just gram formula mass or molar mass. Point out that the secret to all of these is that each "mass" in this case contains exactly one mole of representative particles, and that the terms atomic, molecular, and formula refer to the kind of representative particle being discussed.

An effective way to show this idea is to make a display which contains one gram formula mass of each of various elements and compounds. Place them in glass containers and point out the tremendous variety in mass, volume, and appearance among these samples. Yet, they have one feature in common: *they all contain exactly one mole of representative units*.

6·5 Mole–Mass Conversions

The approach used in this section is that grams can be changed to moles and vice versa through the use of conversion factors. If you find that your students try this and still have trouble, it may be easier just to give them a formula to use. The relationship is often stated:

Moles = Mass of sample/gram formula mass

or: Moles = Mass/gfm

This relationship can be rearranged to give:

Mass = Moles × gfm

6·6 The Volume of a Mole of Gas

6·7 Gas Density and the Gram Molecular Mass

The molar volumes of solids and liquids vary considerably. Students are surprised to find that the molar volume of a gas is so much *larger* than the liquid from which it came. They are often more surprised that the molar volume is the *same for all gases* (at the same temperature and pressure). **Demonstration 6·2** *Molar Volumes* will help them visualize the concept of molar volume. **Experiment 9** *The Masses of Equal Volumes of Gases* applies the concepts of molar volume and molar mass.

6·8 Converting Between Units with Moles

This section and Figure 6·10 drive home the idea that the mole is our basic unit for quantities of particles.

6·9 Calculating Percent Composition

Point out the difference between mass relationships and mole relationships. Percent composition deals strictly with

the part of the total mass that an element represents. It does not tell the number of atoms. Thus, in a compound like H_2O, hydrogen makes up 2/18 or 11% of the total mass. Yet it makes up 2/3 or 67% of the total number of atoms. Be sure the students see the difference. **Demonstration 6·3** *Percent Composition* may be helpful.

6·10 Calculating Empirical Formulas

Students may question the use of empirical formulas since several compounds may have the same empirical formula, yet be quite different from each other. Point out that the empirical formula is the *easiest to obtain* experimentally since it only involves the relative amounts of the atoms and not their order. When coupled with other experimental information such as molar volume (see Section 6·11), the empirical formula can provide us with enough information to determine the molecular formula of a substance.

Experiment 10 *Empirical Formula Determination* can be done here to give the students practical experience with percent composition and empirical formulas.

6·11 Calculating Molecular Formulas

We must know the empirical formula *and* its gram formula mass to be able to find the molecular formula. Remind the students that any information given to them in grams or percent *must* be converted to moles before it can be used to determine empirical or molecular formulas.

Demonstrations

6·1 Moles of Substances

Concept: A mole is used to count large quantities of small particles.

Materials: one mole of many elements and compounds, such as iron filings, lead shot, carbon, sucrose, table salt, water, naphthalene, etc., assorted bottles and beakers with stoppers or tops, five gallon pail.

Procedure: 1. Put one mole of each substance in a container and label it "one mole," with its formula. 2. Label the pail "one mole of air." 3. Display the substances. 4. Note their volume, mass, and appearance, and identify which are elements and which are compounds. State that each container has one mole, or Avogadro's number, of particles. The masses are different because the masses of each particle are different. Use the periodic table to identify the mass of each element and calculate the masses of the compounds. 5. State that a mole is a measure of a quantity of material. Mention others such as couple,

dozen, score, and gross. Each of these also identifies a certain number of objects. The mole is used when the objects are very small and numerous. It contains 6.02×10^{23} particles.

6·2 Molar Volumes

Concept: Molar volume is different for gases, liquids, and solids.

Materials: models of painted wood or from heavy paper or light cardboard showing the molar volumes of these materials: solid nitrogen (27.2 cm^3, a cube 3.0 cm on a side), liquid nitrogen (34.6 cm^3, a cube 3.26 cm on a side), nitrogen gas ($22\,400 \text{ cm}^3$, a cube 28.2 cm on a side), liquid water (18 cm^3, a cube 2.6 cm on a side).

Procedure: 1. Pass the models among your students. 2. The molar volume generally increases slightly from a solid to a liquid. The molar volume increases drastically as a liquid changes to a gas.

6·3 Percent Composition

Concept: Combination reactions help visualize percent composition problems.

Materials: same as in Demonstrations 5·2, 5·3, and 7·1.

Procedure: 1. Choose one of the combination reactions of Demonstrations 5·2, 5·3, and 7·1. Note especially the ratios of the masses of the reactants. 2. Calculate the percent composition using these mass ratios. 3. Calculate the percent composition of the product from its formula mass. 4. Note that this is the same percent composition as in step 2.

Audiovisual Resources

Atomic Weights, Molecular Weights and the Mole Concept (FS) Prentice-Hall Media, 1973. (Use with Sections 6·2, 6·3, and 6·4.) Discusses the mole concept and the relationship between moles and mass.

Formulas and Composition Calculations (FS) Prentice-Hall Media, 1973. (Use with Section 6·9.) Describes the calculation of percent composition from the gram formula mass of a compound.

Formulas from Analysis of Composition of Compounds (F) Prentice-Hall Media, 1973. (Use with Sections 6·10 and 6·11.) Illustrates the calculation of empirical formulas from percent composition data and the determination of the molecular formula from the empirical formula.

Answers to End of Chapter Questions and Problems

Practice Questions and Problems

24. Number, mass, or volume. Examples will vary.

25. The mole.

26. a, d, e. molecule **b, f.** formula unit **c.** atom

27. a. 2 **b.** 8 **c.** 9 **d.** 4

28. a. 3 **b.** 3 **c.** 3 **d.** 4

29. a. 3.01×10^{24} atoms Fe **b.** 7.46×10^{23} molecules Cl_2 **c.** 1.20×10^{23} formula units NaI **d.** 2.53×10^{21} atoms Al **e.** 2.05×10^{25} molecules SO_3 **f.** 3.16×10^{20} formula units K_2S

30. a. 1.00×10^{-1} mol Br_2 **b.** 7.99 mol Li **c.** 2.49×10^{-1} mol NH_3 **d.** 1.66×10^{-15} mol O_2 **e.** 6.00 mol $Ca(OH)_2$ **f.** 1.66×10^{-4} mol C_3H_8

31. a. 2.0 g **b.** 106.8 g **c.** 63.5 g **d.** 58.9 g **e.** 60.1 g **f.** 102.0 g

32. a. 100.1 g **b.** 132.1 g **c.** 58.0 g **d.** 253.8 g **e.** 98.0 g **f.** 108.0 g

33. a. 96.0 g NaOH **b.** 1.88×10^{-1} g Ni **c.** 7.18×10^{1} g $Ca(CN)_2$ **d.** 2.38×10^{2} g H_2O_2

34. a. 2.00×10^{-2} mol Ca **b.** 1.12 mol Cl_2 **c.** 1.06×10^{-1} mol KOH **d.** 5.93 mol $Ca(C_2H_3O_2)_2$

35. a. 2.2×10^{2} L He **b.** 1.1×10^{2} L N_2 **c.** 72 L CO_2

36. a. 2.50 mol N_2O **b.** 1.00×10^{-2} mol O_2 **c.** 0.571 mol CO

37. a. N_2O. The largest volume (largest number of moles) contains the largest number of molecules.

38. a. 1.25 g/L **b.** 1.78 g/L **c.** 1.34 g/L

39. 44.0 g/mol

40. a. 7.85×10^{23} molecules NO_2 **b.** 1.21 L **c.** 12.9 g CH_4 **d.** 234 L SO_3 **e.** 2.99×10^{-22} g $C_9H_8O_4$ **f.** 3.13×10^{25} atoms

41. a. 42.1% Na, 18.9% P, 39.0% O **b.** 5.9% H, 94.1% S **c.** 45.5% Sn, 54.5% Cl **d.** 22.6% N, 6.5% H, 19.4% C, 51.6% O **e.** 41.7% Mg, 54.9% O, 3.4% H **f.** 1.0% H, 35.3% Cl, 63.7% O

42. a. 152 g P **b.** 3.33 g S **c.** 116 g Sn **d.** 5.65 g N **e.** 40.6 g Mg **f.** 221 g Cl

43. e. %Fe in FeO = 81.9%

44. a. NaH **b.** Cu_2S **c.** AlI_3

45. a. CO **b.** Cl_2OC **c.** $C_2O_2NH_5$

46. a, c, d. empirical **b, e, f.** molecular

47. a. $C_4H_8O_4$ **b.** Hg_2Cl_2 **c.** $C_6H_{10}O_4$

48. a. $C_4O_4H_8$ **b.** H_2O_2 **c.** $C_4H_{12}N_2$ **d.** B_2H_6

Mastery Questions and Problems

49. 5.00 g H_2

50. 24.49 g

51. 3.76 mol

52. a. Fe_3O_4 **b.** Sc_2O_3 **c.** $Sn_2FeC_6N_6$

53. 15.7 mol atoms

54. 3.01×10^{13} km

55. a. and **c**: A molecule may be composed of more than one atom. **b**: A compound has a gram molecular mass, not a gram atomic mass.

56. 20

57. 11.8 g H_2O_2

58. a. $FeCl_2$ **b.** CH_3 **c.** C_2H_4O **d.** $C_3H_8O_3$ **e.** Fe_3O_4

Review Questions and Problems

59. 4.21 mol Cu

60. A molecule is composed of two or more atoms.

61. a. 0.235 kJ **b.** 2.1×10^{4} km/hr **c.** 3.4×10^{-3} dg

62. a. 1, 1, 1 **b.** 80, 80, 121 **c.** 35, 35, 44 **d.** 51, 51, 62

63. a. Na_2CO_3 **b.** CCl_4 **c.** $Fe(OH)_3$ **d.** NH_4I

64. Grams of O/1 gram of N: N_2O, .571/1; NO, 1.14/1; N_2O_3, 1.71/1; N_2O_5, 2.85/1. The ratio of grams of oxygen that combine with nitrogen is 1 : 2 : 3 : 5.

65. a. potassium nitrate **b.** copper(II) oxide **c.** magnesium nitride **d.** silver fluoride **e.** aluminum sulfate **f.** phosphoric acid

Challenging Questions and Problems

66. 8.26×10^{24} molecules H_2O

67. $C_3H_5O_9N_3$

68. 1.52×10^{2} cm^3

69. 1.89×10^{23} O_2 molecules

70. 2.4×10^{9} kg Au; 2×10^{11} L H_2O; not feasible.

71. 6.025×10^{23} formula units/mol

6 Chemical Quantities

Chapter Preview

Many scientists spend their time answering the question "How much?" How many grams of iron are in a kilogram of iron(II) oxide? How many grams of the elements hydrogen and oxygen must be combined to make 20 g of water? Both these typical chemistry questions emphasize that chemistry is a quantitative science. Chemists, and chemistry students, analyze the composition of samples of matter. They must also do chemical calculations relating quanties of reactants and products to chemical equations. To do any of these problems, you must be able to measure the amount of matter you have.

6·1   Measuring Matter

Counting is one way to measure how much of something we have. For example, we count how many students are in a class or how many pins we knock down when bowling. Another way to measure the amount of substance is by weighing. We buy potatoes by the pound or kilogram and silver and gold by the ounce or gram. We also measure matter by volume. We buy gasoline by the gallon or liter, and we take cough medicine by the teaspoon or milliliter. Some items are sold by all three of these ways: a count, a mass, and a volume. For example, strawberries may be sold for 10¢ each. A basket of strawberries may be sold by the quart or by the pound. Chemists also measure the amount of matter in these three

Figure 6·1
Do you recognize these elements? They are (clockwise from the bottom) sulfur, carbon, cobalt, aluminum, bromine, mercury, and copper (center). Although they have different masses, all the quantities shown here contain an equal number of particles.

A mole is an amount of substance.

Figure 6·2
Matter is counted in convenient quantities: 12 eggs equal a dozen; 144 pencils equal one gross; and 500 sheets of paper equal one ream.

Latin: *moles* = heap or pile

A mole is Avogadro's number of representative particles of a substance.

Mole is a word which is used to stand for an exact quantity, just as dozen stands for 12, ream stands for 500, score stands for 20, and gross stands for 144.

ways. In fact, each of these units of measurement is related by chemists to a single quantity called the mole. The mole, which is one of the seven base SI units, measures the "amount of substance."

6·2 The Mole

We know that matter is made up of different kinds of particles. *The term* **representative particle** *refers to whether a substance commonly exists as atoms, ions, or molecules*. The representative particle of most elements is the atom. Iron is composed of iron atoms. Helium is composed of helium atoms. Seven elements, however, normally exist as diatomic molecules (H_2, N_2, O_2, F_2, Cl_2, Br_2, and I_2). The representative particle of these elements and of molecular compounds is the molecule. The molecular compounds water and sulfur dioxide are composed of H_2O and SO_2 molecules respectively. The formula unit is the representative particle of ionic compounds. Calcium chloride, an ionic compound, has the formula unit $CaCl_2$. Calcium and chloride ions are present in a one to two ratio in this formula unit.

Because substances are composed of particles, one way to measure the amount of a substance is to count the number of representative particles of that substance. Atoms, molecules, and ions are very small. Thus the number of particles in even a relatively small sample of any substance is very large. Counting the particles is not practical or even possible. We can "count" particles, however, if we introduce a term that represents a certain number of particles. Just as a dozen eggs represents 12 eggs, *a* **mole** *of a substance represents* 6.02×10^{23} *representative particles of that substance*. This experimentally determined number, 6.02×10^{23}, is *called* **Avogadro's number.** It is named in honor of Amedeo Avogadro di Quarenga (1776–1856) who was a nineteenth-century Italian scientist and lawyer. His work (Section 6·B) made the calculation of this number possible. We usually talk about moles of elements or compounds. There is nothing wrong, however, with calling 6.02×10^{23} pencils a mole (1 mol) of pencils. The relationship between representative particles and moles of substances is summarized in Table 6·1.

Example 1

How many moles of magnesium is 3.01×10^{22} atoms of magnesium?

Solution

Step 1. The unknown is the number of moles.

Step 2. The known is the number of atoms: 3.01×10^{22} atoms.

Step 3. The desired conversion is: atoms $\longrightarrow$ moles. The expression relating the units is 1 mol Mg = 6.02×10^{23} atoms Mg. The conversion factor is 1 mol Mg/6.02×10^{23} atoms Mg. (We want to cancel the unit atoms and be left with the unit moles.)

Step 4. The solution is as follows.

$$3.01 \times 10^{22} \text{ atoms Mg} \times \frac{1 \text{ mol Mg}}{6.02 \times 10^{23} \text{ atoms Mg}}$$

$$= 0.500 \times 10^{-1} \text{ mol Mg}$$

Step 5. In standard form the answer is 5.00×10^{-2} mol Mg. The answer should have three significant figures. Since the given number of atoms was less than Avogadro's number, we would expect to have less than 1 mol of atoms.

Problems

1. **19.9 mol P**
2. **4.52×10^{23} atoms Zn**

1. How many moles are 1.20×10^{25} atoms of phosphorus?

2. How many atoms are in 0.750 mol of zinc?

The number of particles in a mole does not depend on the kind of particles being counted.

A mole refers to Avogadro's number of representative particles of any substance. A mole of a diatomic element such as nitrogen contains 6.02×10^{23} *molecules* of nitrogen. A mole of any molecular compound is composed of Avogadro's number of *molecules* regardless of the size of the molecule. A mole of dinitrogen tetroxide, N_2O_4, and a mole of sucrose, $C_{12}H_{22}O_{11}$, both contain 6.02×10^{23} molecules of these compounds. In a similar fashion, a mole of any ionic compound is composed of Avogadro's number of *formula units*. A mole of NaI and a mole of $(NH_4)_3PO_4$ each contains 6.02×10^{23} formula units.

Example 2

How many molecules are there in 4.00 mol of glucose, $C_6H_{12}O_6$?

Solution

Step 1. The unknown is the number of molecules of $C_6H_{12}O_6$.

Step 2. The known is the number of moles: 4.00 mol of $C_6H_{12}O_6$.

Step 3. The desired conversion is: moles $\longrightarrow$ molecules. Thus we need a conversion factor that gives molecules/mole. Glucose is a molecular compound. We know that 6.02×10^{23} molecules of $C_6H_{12}O_6$ is 1 mol of $C_6H_{12}O_6$.

Step 4. In doing the calculation, make sure that the units cancel.

$$4.00 \text{ mol } C_6H_{12}O_6 \times \frac{6.02 \times 10^{23} \text{ molecules } C_6H_{12}O_6}{1 \text{ mol } C_6H_{12}O_6}$$

$$= 24.08 \times 10^{23} \text{ molecules}$$

Step 5. The answer must be rounded to three significant figures and put in standard form: 2.41×10^{24} molecules glucose.

Table 6·1	Representative Particles and Moles		
Substance	Representative particle	Chemical formula	Representative particles in 1.00 mol
Atomic nitrogen	Atom	N	6.02×10^{23}
Nitrogen gas	Molecule	N_2	6.02×10^{23}
Water	Molecule	H_2O	6.02×10^{23}
Calcium ion	Ion	Ca^{2+}	6.02×10^{23}
Calcium fluoride	Formula unit	CaF_2	6.02×10^{23}
Sucrose	Molecule	$C_{12}H_{22}O_{11}$	6.02×10^{23}

Problems

3. 2.41×10^{23} molecules N_2O_5
4. 1.99 mol CO_2

3. How many molecules are in 0.400 mol N_2O_5?

4. How many moles are contained in 1.20×10^{24} molecules CO_2?

How many atoms are in a mole of a compound? We cannot answer this question unless we know how many atoms are in a representative particle of the compound. Consider this analogy. A dozen packages of pencils may contain four, eight, or twelve *dozen* pencils depending on the size of the package. If each package contains eight pencils, a dozen packages will contain 96 (8 × 12) pencils. Similarly, a mole of carbon dioxide, CO_2, contains Avogadro's number of CO_2 molecules. Each CO_2 molecule is composed of three atoms. Hence, a mole of carbon dioxide contains three times Avogadro's number of atoms. *To find the number of atoms in a mole of a compound, we must determine the number of atoms in a representative formula of that compound.*

Figure 6·3
A dozen packages of marbles contain more than a dozen marbles. Similarly, a mole of molecules contains more than a mole of atoms. If each molecule consists of 6 atoms, how many atoms will be in a mole of molecules?
$6 \times 6.02 \times 10^{23}$
or 3.61×10^{24} atoms.

Example 3

How many fluoride ions are in 1.46 mol of aluminum fluoride?

Solution

Step 1. The unknown is the number of F^- ions.

Step 2. The known is 1.46 mol of aluminum fluoride.

Step 3. The desired conversion is moles ⟶ formula units ⟶ ions. We know that 1 mol = 6.02×10^{23} formula units. The first conversion factor will be formula units/mole. To convert formula units to ions we need to know how many F^- ions are part of each formula unit. Thus we need to write the formula for aluminum fluoride: AlF_3. We find that this compound has three F^- ions per formula unit. The second conversion factor will be: three F^- ions/one formula unit AlF_3.

Problems

5. 6.50 × 10²² NH₄⁺ ions
6. 4.03 × 10²⁴ atoms C

5. How many ammonium ions are in 0.036 mol ammonium phosphate, $(NH_4)_3PO_4$?

6. How many carbon atoms are in a mixture of 3.00 mol acetylene (C_2H_2) and 0.700 mol carbon monoxide?

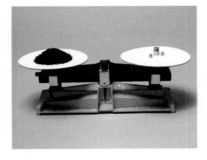

Figure 6·4
Twelve grams of charcoal is a mole of carbon. It contains 6.02×10^{23} atoms.

It would take over a billion (10^9) years to spend Avogadro's number of dollars if you spent a billion dollars each minute.

6·A   The Size of a Mole

Just how large is Avogadro's number? Twelve grams of charcoal contains a mole of carbon, or 6.02×10^{23} atoms of carbon. Of course, these atoms are very, very small, but what if each atom were as large as the period at the end of this paragraph? How big would a mole of carbon atoms be? Would it fill up the room you are in, the building you are in, the Superdome, Lake Erie? Let's assume that the effective volume of a spherical period (carbon atom) is 0.333 mm³. Now we can calculate the volume of Avogadro's number of carbon atoms in cubic meters.

$$6.02 \times 10^{23} \text{ atoms} \times \frac{0.333 \text{ mm}^3}{1 \text{ atom}} \times \frac{(1 \text{ m})^3}{(10^3 \text{ mm})^3} = 2.00 \times 10^{14} \text{ m}^3$$

Lake Erie has a volume of 4.55×10^{11} m³. Thus our pile of carbon atoms is much larger than Lake Erie. In fact, we would need the volume of 440 Lake Eries to hold a mole of our period-sized carbon atoms!

6·3   The Gram Formula Mass

You learned in Section 4·7 that the atomic mass of an element (the mass of a single atom) is given in atomic mass units (amu). The atomic masses can be found in the periodic table. Remember that atomic masses of atoms are relative values. A carbon atom with an atomic mass of 12.0 amu is 12 times heavier than a hydrogen atom with a mass of 1.0 amu. One hundred carbon atoms are 12 times heavier than 100 hydrogen atoms (Figure 6·5). In fact, any group of carbon atoms is 12 times heavier than

the same number of hydrogen atoms. Therefore we can be confident that 12.0 g of carbon atoms and 1.0 g of hydrogen atoms contain the same number of atoms.

Chemists always work with large numbers of atoms. One hundred atoms would be a very small amount of a substance. Several grams of atoms would be a much easier amount to measure. *Chemists have defined* **the gram atomic mass** *as the number of grams of an element that is numerically equal to the atomic mass in amu.* For carbon the gram atomic mass (gam) is 12.0 g. For hydrogen the gram atomic mass is 1.0 g. By checking the periodic table you can see that for oxygen, the gram atomic mass is 16.0 g.

You will remember that 12.0 g of carbon atoms and 1.0 g of hydrogen atoms contain the same number of atoms. In a similar way, *the gram atomic masses of any two elements contain the same number of atoms.* If we were to compare 12.0 g of carbon atoms with 16.0 g of oxygen atoms, we would find they contain the same number of atoms. How many atoms are contained in the gram atomic mass of an element? This is a quantity with which you are already familiar. The gram atomic mass of a monatomic element contains one mole of atoms $(6.02 \times 10^{23}$ atoms).

The size of a mole is defined as the quantity of substance that contains as many representative particles as the number of atoms in 12.0 g of carbon-12. As you remember, 12.0 g is the gram atomic mass of carbon-12. Thus the size of a mole is the number of atoms in the gram atomic mass of a monatomic element. Stated another way, *the gram atomic mass is the mass of one mole of atoms of a monatomic element.* Since 24.3 g is the gram atomic mass for magnesium, we know that 24.3 g is also 1 mol of magnesium. This is a quantity that contains 6.02×10^{23} atoms of magnesium.

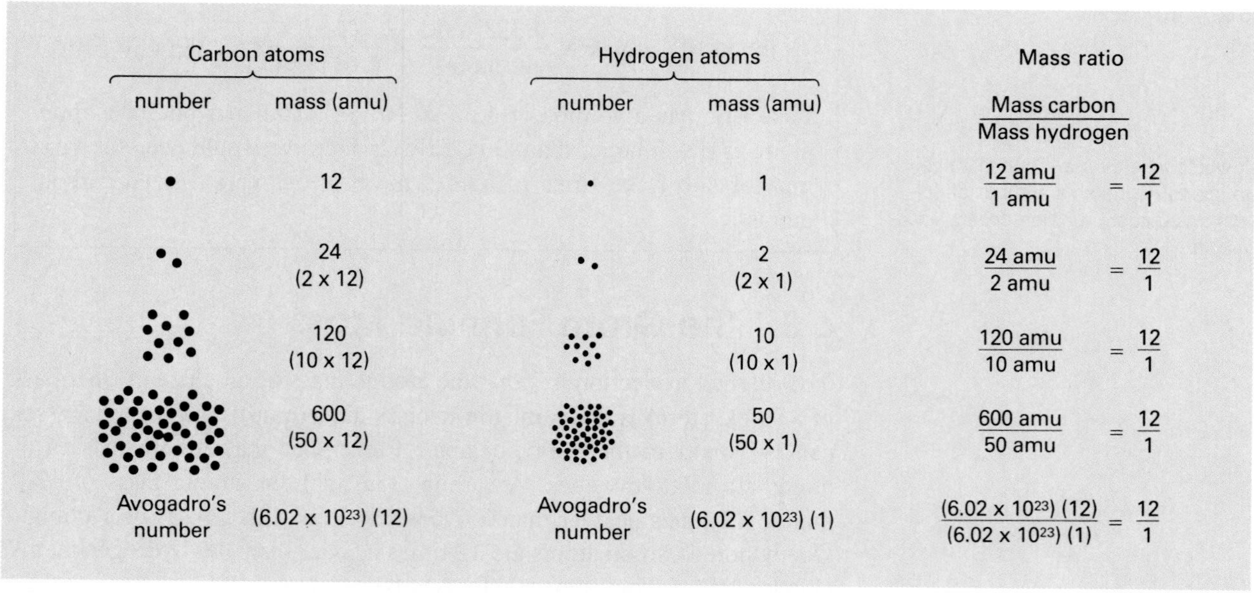

Figure 6·5
The mass ratio of equal numbers of carbon atoms to hydrogen atoms is always 12 to 1.

Carbon atoms		Hydrogen atoms		Mass ratio	
number	mass (amu)	number	mass (amu)	$\dfrac{\text{Mass carbon}}{\text{Mass hydrogen}}$	
•	12	•	1	$\dfrac{12 \text{ amu}}{1 \text{ amu}}$	$= \dfrac{12}{1}$
••	24 (2 x 12)	••	2 (2 x 1)	$\dfrac{24 \text{ amu}}{2 \text{ amu}}$	$= \dfrac{12}{1}$
(10 atoms)	120 (10 x 12)	(10 atoms)	10 (10 x 1)	$\dfrac{120 \text{ amu}}{10 \text{ amu}}$	$= \dfrac{12}{1}$
(50 atoms)	600 (50 x 12)	(50 atoms)	50 (50 x 1)	$\dfrac{600 \text{ amu}}{50 \text{ amu}}$	$= \dfrac{12}{1}$
Avogadro's number	$(6.02 \times 10^{23})(12)$	Avogadro's number	$(6.02 \times 10^{23})(1)$	$\dfrac{(6.02 \times 10^{23})(12)}{(6.02 \times 10^{23})(1)}$	$= \dfrac{12}{1}$

Figure 6·6
One gram atomic mass (gam) for each of three elements is shown. Each of these quantities contains 6.02×10^{23} atoms.

1 mole of mercury atoms
200.6 g Hg = 1 gam Hg

1 mole of iron atoms
55.8 g Fe = 1 gam Fe

1 mole of sulfur atoms
32.1 g S = 1 gam S

Problem

7. a. 23.0 g
b. 74.9 g
c. 238.0 g

7. What is the mass of 1 mol of each of these monatomic elements?
a. sodium   **b.** arsenic   **c.** uranium

What is the mass of a mole of a compound? The formula of a compound tells us the number of atoms of each element in a representative particle of that compound. For example, the formula of the molecular compound sulfur trioxide is SO_3. This shows us that a molecule of SO_3 is composed of one atom of sulfur and three atoms of oxygen. We can calculate the molecular mass of a molecule of SO_3 by adding together the atomic masses of the atoms making up a molecule of SO_3. The atomic mass of sulfur (S) is 32.1 amu. The mass of three atoms of oxygen is three times the atomic mass of oxygen (O): 3×16.0 amu $= 48.0$ amu. Thus, the molecular mass of SO_3 is 32.1 amu $+ 48.0$ amu $= 80.1$ amu.

1 mole of paradichlorobenzene molecules (moth crystals)
147.0 g $C_6H_4Cl_2$ = 1 gmm $C_6H_4Cl_2$

1 mole of sucrose molecules (table sugar)
342.0 g $C_{12}H_{22}O_{11}$ = 1 gmm $C_{12}H_{22}O_{11}$

1 mole of water molecules
18.0 g H_2O = 1 gmm H_2O

Figure 6·7
One gram molecular mass (gmm) for each of three molecular compounds is shown. Each of these quantities contains 6.02×10^{23} molecules.

Now if we substitute the unit, grams, for atomic mass units, we obtain the gram molecular mass of SO_3. *The **gram molecular mass** (gmm) of any molecular compound is the mass of one mole of that compound*. It is equal to the molecular mass expressed in grams. Thus 1 mol of SO_3 has a mass of 80.1 g. Gram molecular masses may be calculated directly from gram atomic masses. For each element in the compound we find the number of grams of that element per mole of the compound. Then we sum the masses of the elements in the compound.

Example 4

What is the gram molecular mass of hydrogen peroxide, H_2O_2?

Solution

The unknown is the number of grams in the gram molecular mass. The known is the molecular formula: H_2O_2. This tells us the number of moles of each element in a mole of compound: 2 mol of hydrogen atoms and 2 mol of oxygen atoms.

We can convert moles of atoms to grams by using conversion factors (g/mol) based on the gram atomic mass of each element: 1 mol H = 1.0 g H and 1 mol O = 16.0 g O. We will sum the mass of each element to get the gram molecular mass.

$$2 \text{ mol H} \times \frac{1.0 \text{ g H}}{1 \text{ mol H}} = 2.0 \text{ g H}$$

$$2 \text{ mol O} \times \frac{16.0 \text{ g O}}{1 \text{ mol O}} = 32.0 \text{ g O}$$

$$\text{Gram molecular mass of } H_2O_2 = 34.0 \text{ g}$$

Problem

8. Find the gram molecular mass of each compound.   **a.** CCl_4
b. PCl_3 **c.** C_8H_{18} **d.** N_2O_5

It is inappropriate to calculate the gram molecular mass of potassium iodide, KI, because it is an ionic compound. The representative particle of an ionic compound is a formula unit, not a molecule. *The mass of 1 mol of an ionic compound is the **gram formula mass** (gfm)*. It is equal to the formula mass expressed in grams. A gram formula mass is calculated the same way as a gram molecular mass. Simply sum the atomic masses of the atoms that are in the formula of the compound. The atoms are actually present as ions. For example, the gram formula mass of potassium iodide, KI, is the gram atomic mass of potassium plus the gram atomic mass of iodine.

$$39.1 \text{ g K} + 126.9 \text{ g I} = 166.0 \text{ g KI}$$

There are 166.0 g of KI in 1 gfm or 1 mol of KI.

Figure 6·8
One gram formula mass (gfm) for each of three ionic compounds is shown. Each of these quantities contains 6.02×10^{23} formula units.

1 mole of cobalt(II) chloride formula units
129.9 g $CoCl_2$ = 1 gfm $CoCl_2$

1 mole of potassium hydroxide formula units
56.1 g KOH = 1 gfm KOH

1 mole of silver bromide formula units
187.8 g AgBr = 1 gfm AgBr

Example 5

What is the gram formula mass of ammonium carbonate $(NH_4)_2CO_3$?

Solution

The unknown is the number of grams in a gram formula mass. The known is the formula unit. We know that a mole of this ionic compound is composed of 2 mol of nitrogen atoms, 8 mol of hydrogen atoms, 1 mol of carbon atoms, and 3 mol of oxygen atoms.

We will convert moles of atoms to grams by using conversion factors based on the gram atomic masses. Then we will sum the masses of each element to get the gram formula mass.

$$2 \text{ mol N} \times \frac{14.0 \text{ g N}}{1 \text{ mol N}} = 28.0 \text{ g N}$$

$$8 \text{ mol H} \times \frac{1.0 \text{ g H}}{1 \text{ mol H}} = 8.0 \text{ g H}$$

$$1 \text{ mol C} \times \frac{12.0 \text{ g C}}{1 \text{ mol C}} = 12.0 \text{ g C}$$

$$3 \text{ mol O} \times \frac{16.0 \text{ g O}}{1 \text{ mol O}} = 48.0 \text{ g O}$$

Gram formula mass of $(NH_4)_2CO_3$ = 96.0 g

Problem

9. **a.** 158.6 g   **c.** 342.3 g
    b. 106.0 g   **d.** 92.1 g

9. Find the gram formula mass of each of these compounds.
a. strontium chloride, $SrCl_2$
b. sodium carbonate, Na_2CO_3
c. aluminum sulfate, $Al_2(SO_4)_3$
d. calcium cyanide, $Ca(CN)_2$

6·4   The Molar Mass of a Substance

In the last section we introduced three terms: gram atomic mass (gam), gram molecular mass (gmm), and gram formula mass (gfm). Each term is used to represent a mole of a particular kind of substance. The gram *atomic* mass of an element contains a mole of *atoms*. The gram *molecular* mass of a molecular compound contains a mole of *molecules*. The gram *formula* mass of an ionic compound contains a mole of *formula units*. There is nothing wrong, however, with using the term *gram formula mass* to refer to a mole of an element, molecular compound, or ionic compound. In a broad sense, the gram formula mass is the mass in grams of the formula of the substance. *Some people use the term* **molar mass** *in place of gram formula mass to refer to the mass of a mole of any element or compound.*

Can you see the one advantage to using one of the three specific terms instead of the general term? What is the gram *formula* mass of oxygen? Is it any different from the gram *molecular* mass of oxygen? In the latter question, we have a reminder that oxygen is diatomic and is composed of molecules. The gram molecular mass of oxygen is 32.0 g (2×16.0 g). The gram formula mass of oxygen is 16.0 g *or* 32.0 g. This depends on whether we are talking about a mole of oxygen atoms (16.0 g/mol) or a mole of oxygen molecules (32.0 g/mol). We will use the three specific terms when necessary. Where there is no danger of ambiguity, we will use the term *gram formula mass* in its broadest sense.

■ The gram formula mass, or molar mass, is a mole of any substance.

When we refer to a mole of an element or compound we really mean a mole of atoms of the element or a mole of molecules of the compound.

6·5   Mole–Mass Conversions

The gram formula mass of an element or compound is used to convert grams of a substance into moles. It can also be used to convert moles of a substance into grams.

■ Conversions between moles and mass of a substance are done using the gram formula mass.

Example 6

How many grams are in 7.20 mol of dinitrogen trioxide?

Solution

From a known number of moles of a compound we want to calculate the unknown number of grams of the compound: mol → grams. First we need to write the formula: N_2O_3. If we calculate the gram formula mass we will know the number of grams in 1 mol of the compound.

$$2 \text{ mol N} \times \frac{14.0 \text{ g N}}{1 \text{ mol N}} = 28.0 \text{ g N}$$

$$3 \text{ mol O} \times \frac{16.0 \text{ g O}}{1 \text{ mol O}} = 48.0 \text{ g O}$$

$$1 \text{ mol } N_2O_3 = 1 \text{ gfm } N_2O_3 = 76.0 \text{ g}$$

Now we can use the gram formula mass to write a conversion factor. We will convert moles of N_2O_3 to grams of N_2O_3.

$$7.20 \text{ mol } N_2O_3 \times \frac{76.0 \text{ g } N_2O_3}{1.00 \text{ mol } N_2O_3} = 547.2$$

$$= 5.47 \times 10^2 \text{ g } N_2O_3$$

Problem

10. Find the mass in grams of each quantity.
    a. 10.0 mol Cr
    b. 3.32 mol K
    c. 2.20×10^{-3} mol Sn
    d. 0.720 mol Be
    e. 2.40 mol N_2
    f. 0.160 mol H_2O_2
    g. 5.08 mol $Ca(NO_3)_2$
    h. 15.0 mol H_2SO_4
    i. 4.52×10^{-3} mol $C_{20}H_{42}$
    j. 0.0112 mol K_2CO_3

10. a. 5.20×10^2 g Cr
    b. 1.30×10^2 g K
    c. 0.261 g Sn
    d. 6.49 g Be
    e. 67.2 g N_2
    f. 5.44 g H_2O_2
    g. 8.34×10^2 g $Ca(NO_3)_2$
    h. 1.47×10^3 g H_2SO_4
    i. 1.27 g $C_{20}H_{42}$
    j. 1.55 g K_2CO_3

You must know the chemical formula of a compound to calculate the number of moles in a given mass.

Example 7

Find the number of moles in 922 g of iron(III) oxide, Fe_2O_3.

Solution

From a known number of grams of a compound we want to calculate the unknown number of moles of the same compound: grams $\longrightarrow$ moles.

First we calculate the gram formula mass (to get a conversion factor).

$$2 \text{ mol Fe} \times \frac{55.8 \text{ g Fe}}{1 \text{ mol Fe}} = 111.6 \text{ g Fe}$$

$$3 \text{ mol O} \times \frac{16.0 \text{ g O}}{1 \text{ mol O}} = \underline{48.0 \text{ g O}}$$

$$\text{gfm } Fe_2O_3 = 159.6 \text{ g}$$

The number of grams can now be converted to moles of Fe_2O_3 by using the gfm as a conversion factor.

$$922 \text{ g } Fe_2O_3 \times \frac{1.00 \text{ mol } Fe_2O_3}{159.6 \text{ g } Fe_2O_3} = 5.776$$

$$= 5.78 \text{ mol } Fe_2O_3$$

Problem

11. Find the number of moles in each quantity.
    a. 72.0 g Ar
    b. 3.70×10^{-1} g B
    c. 187 g Al
    d. 333 g SnF_2
    e. 7.21×10^{-2} g He
    f. 27.4 g TiO_2
    g. 5.00 g hydrogen molecules
    h. 0.000 264 g Li_2HPO_4
    i. 11.0 g CH_4
    j. 847 g $(NH_4)_2CO_3$

11. a. 1.80 mol Ar
    b. 3.43×10^{-2} mol B
    c. 6.93 mol Al
    d. 2.13 mol SnF_2
    e. 1.80×10^{-2} mol He
    f. 0.343 mol TiO_2
    g. 2.5 mol H_2
    h. 2.40×10^{-6} mol Li_2HPO_4
    i. 0.688 mol CH_4
    j. 8.82 mol $(NH_4)_2CO_3$

6·6 The Volume of a Mole of Gas

Molar volumes vary greatly from substance to substance for solids and liquids. It is important to note that, in contrast, molar volumes are identical for all gases: 22.4 L at STP.

A mole of any gas at STP occupies a volume of 22.4 L.

The molar volume (22.4 L) is about the size of a neat stack of 13 of these chemistry books.

You may have noticed in Figure 6·7 that the volumes of moles of different substances can be different. For example, a mole of table sugar is much larger than a mole of water. The volume of a mole of gas is more predictable than the volume of a mole of a liquid or solid.

The volume of a gas is usually measured at a **standard temperature and pressure** (STP). *Standard temperature is 0°C. Standard pressure is 1 atmosphere (atm).* At STP, 1 mol of any gas occupies a volume of 22.4 L. *This quantity, 22.4 L, is known as the* **molar volume** *of a gas.* A mole of any substance contains Avogadro's number of particles. Thus 22.4 L of any gas at STP contains 6.02×10^{23} representative particles of that gas.

Would 22.4 L of one gas also have the same mass as 22.4 L of another gas at STP? Probably not. A mole of a gas (22.4 L at STP) has a mass equal to the gram formula mass. Only gases with equal gram formula masses would have equal masses for equal volumes.

Example 8

Determine the volume, in liters, of 0.600 mol of SO_2 gas at STP.

Solution

The known is the number of moles and the unknown is the number of liters of SO_2. We know that 1.00 mol SO_2 = 22.4 L of SO_2. We can express this equality as a conversion factor and use it to convert moles to liters (mol ⟶ L).

$$0.600\,\cancel{\text{mol SO}_2} \times \frac{22.4\ \text{L SO}_2}{1.00\,\cancel{\text{mol SO}_2}} = 13.4\ \text{L SO}_2$$

Example 9

Determine the number of moles in 33.6 L of He gas.

Solution

Here we want to convert liters to moles of He gas: L ⟶ mol. Again, we use a conversion factor based on the molar volume.

$$33.6\,\cancel{\text{L He}} \times \frac{1.00\ \text{mol He}}{22.4\,\cancel{\text{L He}}} = 1.50\ \text{mol He}$$

Problems

12. What is the volume at STP of these gases?
    a. 5.40 mol O_2 **b.** 3.20×10^{-2} mol CO_2? **c.** 0.960 mol CH_4?

13. Assuming STP, how many moles are in these volumes?
    a. 89.6 L SO_2 **b.** 1.00×10^3 L C_2H_6 **c.** 5.42×10^{-1} mL Ne

12. a. 1.21×10^2 L O_2
    b. 0.717 L CO_2
    c. 21.5 L CH_4

13. a. 4.00 mol SO_2
    b. 44.6 mol C_2H_6
    c. 2.42×10^{-5} mol Ne

Figure 6·9
Balloons this size at 0°C would each contain a mole of gas. At STP, a mole of any gas occupies 22.4 L and contains Avogadro's number of representative particles. Note however that moles of different gases have different masses.

6·7 Gas Density and the Gram Molecular Mass

The density of a gas is usually measured in the units g/L. The experimentally determined density of a gas at STP is used to calculate the gram formula mass of that gas. The gas can be an element or a compound.

■ The gram formula mass of a gas can be determined experimentally by measuring the density of the gas.

Example 10

The density of a gaseous compound of carbon and oxygen is 1.964 g/L at STP. Determine the gram formula mass of the compound. Is the compound carbon dioxide or carbon monoxide?

Solution

At STP the gram formula mass of any gas occupies a volume of 22.4 L. The density is used as a conversion factor to convert liters to mass: L $\longrightarrow$ g.

$$22.4 \ \cancel{L} \times \frac{1.964 \ g}{1 \ \cancel{L}} = 44.0 \ g$$

A volume of 22.4 L of this gas has a mass of 44.0 g. This mass must be compared with the gram formula masses of carbon monoxide and carbon dioxide.

gfm CO: 12 g/mol (C) + 16 g/mol (O) = 28 g/mol

gfm CO_2: 12 g/mol (C) + 2(16 g/mol)(O) = 44 g/mol

The compound is carbon dioxide.

Problem

14. gas A: 28.0 g, nitrogen
gas B: 64.1 g, sulfur dioxide
gas C: 16.0 g, methane

14. The densities of gases A, B, and C are 1.25 g/L, 2.86 g/L, and 0.714 g/L respectively. Calculate the gram formula mass of each of these substances. Identify each substance as ammonia (NH_3), sulfur dioxide, chlorine, nitrogen, or methane (CH_4).

6·8 Converting Between Units with Moles

■ The mole is the most useful way for chemists to express the amount of matter.

We have now defined a mole in terms of particles, mass, and volume (the last for gases at STP). These relationships are summarized in Figure 6·10. This diagram shows the importance of the mole. To change from one unit to another, the mole is used as an intermediate step. The form of the conversion factor will depend on whether you are going *from* moles or *to* moles.

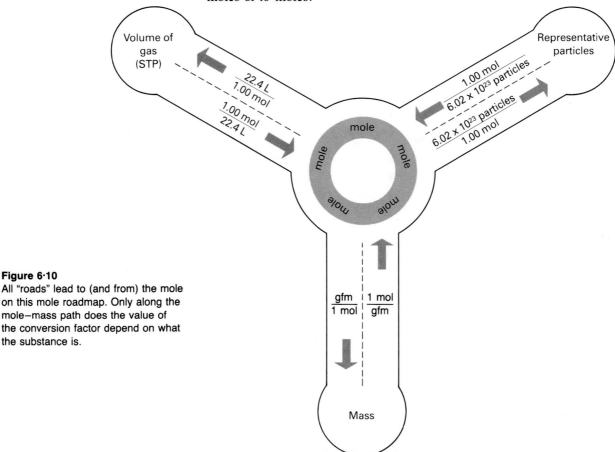

Figure 6·10
All "roads" lead to (and from) the mole on this mole roadmap. Only along the mole–mass path does the value of the conversion factor depend on what the substance is.

Example 11

How many carbon atoms are in a 50.0-carat diamond that is pure carbon? Fifty carats is the same as 10.0 g.

Solution

We want to convert from a known mass to an unknown number of atoms. Figure 6·10 shows that we will need to use moles in this process: grams $\longrightarrow$ moles $\longrightarrow$ atoms. Starting with a given mass, we can use the gram formula mass to find the number of moles.

$$10.0 \; \cancel{g \, C} \times \frac{1.00 \; \text{mol C}}{12.0 \; \cancel{g \, C}} = 0.833 \; \text{mol C}$$

Then we can use Avogadro's number to find the number of particles.

$$0.833 \text{ mol C} \times \frac{6.02 \times 10^{23} \text{ atoms C}}{1.00 \text{ mol C}} = 5.02 \times 10^{23} \text{ atoms C}$$

We can also set up the problem in "one solution."

$$50.0 \text{ carats C} \times \frac{10.0 \text{ gram C}}{50.0 \text{ carats C}} \times \frac{1.00 \text{ mol C}}{12.0 \text{ grams C}}$$

$$\times \frac{6.02 \times 10^{23} \text{ atoms C}}{1 \text{ mol C}} = 5.02 \times 10^{23} \text{ atoms C}$$

Problems

15. 9.75×10^{-23} g Ni
16. 1.61×10^{23} molecules, CO_2, no.

15. What is the mass in grams of an atom of nickel (Ni)?

16. How many molecules are in a 6.00-L balloon (at STP) filled with carbon dioxide? Would your answer change if the gas was carbon monoxide?

6·B Who Was Avogadro?

The first determination of Avogadro's number was made by a German physicist in 1865, nine years after Avogadro's death. Avogadro himself had never made any attempt to calculate it. This important number was given his name, however, to honor him for contributions that were not recognized until after his death.

Count Amedeo Avogadro was a lawyer who turned to the study of mathematics and physics. He soon became a professor of these subjects. His most famous work was his explanation of experiments done by the French chemist Joseph Gay-Lussac. Gay-Lussac had discovered that when two gases combine to give a new substance, they do so in a simple volume ratio. For example, one liter of oxygen combines with two liters of hydrogen to form two liters of gaseous water. One liter of nitrogen combines with three liters of hydrogen to form two liters of ammonia gas. Gay-Lussac called his discovery the law of combining volumes.

Gay-Lussac's results did not seem to be compatible with Dalton's recently published atomic theory. Dalton thought that when any two gases combined to make a single new substance, one atom of each was used. He also thought that atoms of a gas were packed closely together. If these two ideas were correct, it seemed that one liter of oxygen should react with one liter of hydrogen, not two. Even if one atom of oxygen reacted with two of hydrogen, it would seem that together they should form three liters of water, not two.

Avogadro was able to reconcile Gay-Lussac's data with Dalton's atomic theory. In the process he introduced an essential new concept

Figure 6·11
One hundred years after Avogadro published his hypothesis, the Italian Academy of Science had a coin minted to commemorate the occasion. The back of the coin reads: "Amedeo Avogadro. This commemorates the centennial of his molecular theory. September 24, 1911."

to chemistry, the concept of molecules. He disagreed with Dalton on two important points. He said that the particles of a gas were not atoms at all, but molecules. These were clusters of atoms that could be divided or created during chemical reactions. Second, these molecules were not packed closely together in the gas. They were separated by enough distance that they were not much affected by each other. Thus each gas, no matter what its composition, contained the same number of molecules per liter, if the temperature and pressure were the same. This theory, first published in 1811, is still known as Avogadro's hypothesis. It can be stated as follows: *Equal volumes of different gases, at the same temperature and pressure, contain an equal number of molecules.*

Gay-Lussac's data could now be easily explained. Take the case where one liter of oxygen reacts with two liters of hydrogen to give two liters of gaseous water. It follows from Avogadro's hypothesis that *one molecule* of oxygen reacts with *two molecules* of hydrogen to give *two molecules* of water. If one molecule of oxygen can give two of water, the molecule of oxygen must be dividing into halves. Since atoms are indivisible, the molecule must consist of two atoms of oxygen. Based on other experiments, Avogadro was able to demonstrate that hydrogen molecules were also diatomic. Therefore, since two molecules of hydrogen made two molecules of water, each molecule of water must contain one molecule (two atoms) of hydrogen. Thus the formula of water was H_2O, not HO as Dalton had assumed. Using similar reasoning Avogadro established correct formulas for many compounds. These included nitrous oxide, ammonia, carbon monoxide, carbon dioxide, sulfur dioxide, ethyl alcohol, ether, and others.

Avogadro's ideas were a breakthrough in understanding chemical reactions. Unfortunately, however, his work was generally ignored for several reasons. Avogadro did not correspond with other chemists, and his hypothesis was not supported by much experimental work. In addition, the most influential chemist of the day, Berzelius, did not accept Avogadro's conclusions. As a result, progress in chemistry was greatly handicapped for half a century.

Avogadro's hypothesis has some powerful applications. For instance, we can use it to compare the masses of the individual molecules of two different gases simply by comparing the masses of equal volumes of these gases (at the same temperature and pressure).

Figure 6·12
Avogadro's hypothesis explains why one liter of oxygen and two liters of hydrogen combine to make two liters of gaseous water. Since equal volumes of different gases at STP contain the same number of molecules, then the oxygen molecules must split into two parts. This suggests that oxygen and hydrogen molecules are diatomic and that the molecular formula for water is H_2O.

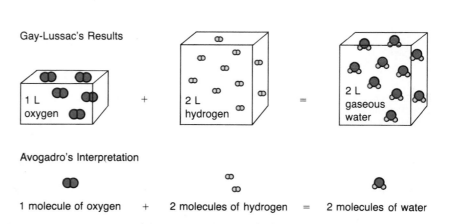

Gay-Lussac's Results

1 L oxygen + 2 L hydrogen = 2 L gaseous water

Avogadro's Interpretation

1 molecule of oxygen + 2 molecules of hydrogen = 2 molecules of water

Before reading this section you should review your knowledge of percents by doing section B·3 of the Math Review in Appendix B.

Safety

Potassium chromate is a common laboratory reagent. It has been shown to cause mutations in animals. Always handle all chemicals with caution.

■ The percent by mass of each element in a compound is the percent composition of the compound.

6·9 Calculating Percent Composition

When a new compound is made in the laboratory, we need to determine its formula. One of the first steps in doing this is to determine the **percent composition,** *the percent by mass of each element in a compound.* The percent composition includes as many percents as there are elements in the compound. For example, the percent composition of K_2CrO_4 is 40.3% K, 26.8% Cr, and 32.9% O. These percents must add up to 100% (40.3% + 26.8% + 32.9% = 100%).

The percent by mass of an element in a compound is the number of grams of the element per 100 grams of the compound, multiplied by 100%.

$$\% \text{ mass} = \frac{\text{grams of element}}{100 \text{ g of compound}} \times 100\%$$

To calculate the percent by mass we need to know the mass of each element that combined to form the compound.

Example 12

An 8.20-g piece of magnesium combines completely with 5.40 g of oxygen to form a compound. What is the percent composition of this compound?

Solution

Since we know the mass of each element, we can add them to find the mass of the compound.

$$8.20 \text{ g} + 5.40 \text{ g} = 13.60 \text{ g}$$

Now the percent mass of each element can be calculated. The mass of each element is divided by the mass of the compound.

$$\% \text{ Mg} = \frac{\text{mass of Mg}}{\text{mass of compound}} \times 100\% = \frac{8.20 \text{ g}}{13.60 \text{ g}} \times 100\%$$
$$= 60.3\%$$

$$\% \text{ O} = \frac{\text{mass of O}}{\text{mass of compound}} \times 100\% = \frac{5.40 \text{ g}}{13.60 \text{ g}} \times 100\%$$
$$= 39.7\%$$

As a check, the percents of the elements must add up to 100%: 60.3% + 39.7% = 100%.

Problem

17. Calculate the percent composition of the compounds that are formed from these reactions.

a. 29.0 g of Ag combines completely with 4.30 g of S.
b. 9.03 g of Mg combines completely with 3.48 g of N.
c. 222.6 g of Na combines completely with 77.4 g of O.

17. a. 87.1% Ag, 12.9% S
b. 72.2% Mg, 27.8% N
c. 74.2% Na, 25.8% O

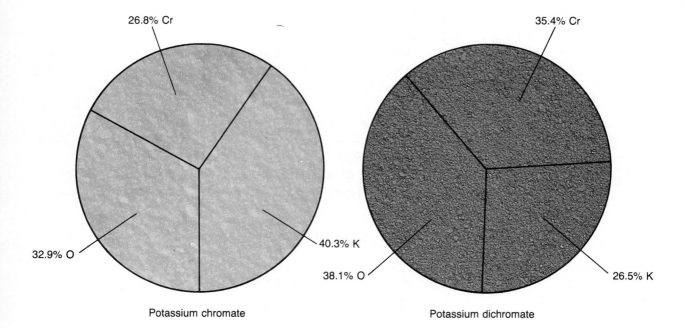

26.8% Cr

32.9% O

40.3% K

Potassium chromate

35.4% Cr

38.1% O

26.5% K

Potassium dichromate

Figure 6·13
Potassium chromate, K_2CrO_4, is composed of 40.3% potassium, 26.8% chromium, and 32.9% oxygen. How does this differ from the percent composition of potassium dichromate, $K_2Cr_2O_7$?
Potassium chromate has proportionately more potassium and less chromium and oxygen than potassium dichromate.

Occasionally we may want to calculate the percent composition of a known compound. To do this, we use the chemical formula to calculate the gram formula mass. This gives us the mass of one mole of the compound. Then for each element, we calculate the percent by mass in one mole of the compound. To calculate the percent by mass we divide the mass of the element in one mole by the gram formula mass and multiply this by 100%.

$$\% \text{ mass} = \frac{\text{grams of element in 1 mol of compound}}{\text{gfm of compound}} \times 100\%$$

Example 13

Calculate the percent composition of ethane, C_2H_6.

Solution

Given the formula, we can calculate the percent composition by using the gram formula mass: formula $\longrightarrow$ gfm $\longrightarrow$ % composition. First calculate the gram formula mass of ethane.

$$2 \text{ mol C} \times \frac{12.0 \text{ g C}}{1 \text{ mol C}} = 24.0 \text{ g C}$$

$$6 \text{ mol H} \times \frac{1.0 \text{ g H}}{1 \text{ mol H}} = \underline{6.0 \text{ g H}}$$

$$\text{gram formula mass of } C_2H_6 = 30.0 \text{ g}$$

Now the percent mass for each element can be calculated. The mass of each element is divided by the mass of the compound.

$$\% \text{ C} = \frac{\text{grams of C}}{\text{gfm of } C_2H_6} \times 100\% = \frac{24.0 \text{ g}}{30.0 \text{ g}} \times 100\% = 80.0\% \text{ C}$$

$$\% \text{ H} = \frac{\text{grams of H}}{\text{gfm of } C_2H_6} \times 100\% = \frac{6.0 \text{ g}}{30.0 \text{ g}} \times 100\% = 20.0\% \text{ H}$$

As a check, we can see that $80.0\% + 20.0\% = 100\%$.

Problem

18. Calculate the percent composition of each of these compounds.
    a. propane, C_3H_8 **b.** sodium bisulfate, $NaHSO_4$ **c.** calcium acetate, $Ca(C_2H_3O_2)_2$ **d.** hydrogen cyanide, HCN

Percent composition can be used to calculate the number of grams of an element in a specific amount of a compound. The mass of the compound is multiplied by a conversion factor that is based on the percent composition.

Example 14

Calculate the mass of carbon in 82 g of ethane, C_2H_6.

Solution

Given the number of grams of ethane, C_2H_6, we want to calculate the number of grams of carbon, C: grams $C_2H_6 \longrightarrow$ grams C. To do this, we use a conversion factor based on the percent mass of carbon in ethane. From Example 13 we know the percent composition is 80% C and 20% H.

$$82 \text{ g } C_2H_6 \times \frac{80 \text{ g C}}{100 \text{ g } C_2H_6} = 66 \text{ g C}$$

Problem

19. Using the results of Problem 18, calculate the amount of hydrogen in the following amounts of these compounds.
    a. 350 g C_3H_8 **b.** 20.2 g $NaHSO_4$ **c.** 124 g $Ca(C_2H_3O_2)_2$
    d. 378 g HCN

18. a. 81.8% C, 18.2% H
  b. 19.2% Na, 0.83% H, 26.7% S, 53.3% O
  c. 25.4% Ca, 30.4% C, 3.8% H, 40.5% O
  d. 3.7% H, 44.4% C, 51.9% N

Figure 6·14
Lawn and garden fertilizers are labeled with a series of three numbers. These numbers represent the mass percent of the elements nitrogen, phosphorus, and potassium respectively. One hundred kilograms of a 15-10-5 fertilizer would contain 15 kg of nitrogen, 10 kg of phosphorus, and 5 kg of potassium.

19. a. 63.7 g H **c.** 4.71 g H
  b. 0.17 g H **d.** 14 g H

Empirical formulas can be determined by chemical analysis.

6·10 Calculating Empirical Formulas

Once a new compound has been made in the laboratory, we can usually determine its percent composition experimentally. From the percent composition data, we can calculate the empirical formula of the compound. *The* **empirical formula** *gives the lowest whole-number ratio of the elements in a compound.* If we use the mole interpretation, an empirical

formula is the lowest whole-number ratio of moles of atoms in a compound. An empirical formula may or may not be the same as a molecular formula. For carbon dioxide, the empirical and molecular formulas are the same, CO_2. Dinitrogen tetrahydride (molecular formula, N_2H_4) has an empirical formula of NH_2 because this is the simplest ratio of nitrogen to hydrogen.

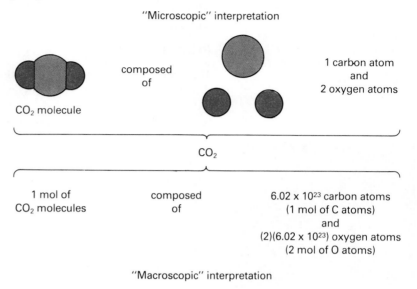

"Microscopic" interpretation

CO_2 molecule · composed of · 1 carbon atom and 2 oxygen atoms

CO_2

1 mol of CO_2 molecules · composed of · 6.02×10^{23} carbon atoms (1 mol of C atoms) and $(2)(6.02 \times 10^{23})$ oxygen atoms (2 mol of O atoms)

"Macroscopic" interpretation

Figure 6·15
A formula can be interpreted on a microscopic level in terms of atoms or on a macroscopic level in terms of moles of atoms.

Example 15

What is the empirical formula of a compound that is 25.9% nitrogen and 74.1% oxygen?

Solution

The unknown is the empirical formula. Thus we want to calculate the lowest whole-number ratio of moles of nitrogen atoms to oxygen atoms. The known is the percent composition. This tells us the ratio of masses of nitrogen to oxygen atoms in the compound. In 100.0 g of the compound there are 25.9 g N and 74.1 g O.

We can change the ratio of *masses* to a ratio of *moles* by using conversion factors based on the gram atomic mass of each element. (The gram atomic mass tells us the number of grams per mole.)

$$25.9 \text{ g N} \times \frac{1 \text{ mol N}}{14.0 \text{ g N}} = 1.85 \text{ mol N}$$

$$74.1 \text{ g O} \times \frac{1 \text{ mol O}}{16.0 \text{ g O}} = 4.63 \text{ mol O}$$

We now know the mole ratio of nitrogen to oxygen: $N_{1.85}O_{4.63}$. This is not the correct empirical formula because it is not the lowest whole-number ratio. We can reduce the ratio by dividing through by the smallest number of moles. This will give us a "1" for the smallest number of moles. It may not give us whole numbers for the others.

$$\frac{1.85 \text{ mol N}}{1.85} = 1 \text{ mol N}$$

$$\frac{4.63 \text{ mol O}}{1.85} = 2.50 \text{ mol O}$$

Is the final answer $N_1O_{2.5}$? No, because this is not the lowest *whole-*number ratio. We must now multiply each part of the ratio by a number (in this case 2) to convert the fraction to a whole number.

$$1 \text{ mol N} \times 2 = 2 \text{ mol N}$$

$$2.5 \text{ mol O} \times 2 = 5 \text{ mol O}$$

The empirical formula is N_2O_5.

Problems

20. a. CH_3
b. $HgSO_4$
c. OH
d. $Na_2Cr_2O_7$
e. C_2HNO_3
21. a. Ag_2S
b. Mg_3N_2
c. Na_2O

20. Calculate the empirical formula of each compound with the following percent composition.
a. 79.8% C, 20.2% H
b. 67.6% Hg, 10.8% S, 21.6% O
c. 94.1% O, 5.9% H
d. 17.6% Na, 39.7% Cr, 42.7% O
e. 27.59% C, 1.15% H, 16.09% N, 55.17% O

21. Calculate the empirical formula for each compound in Problem 17 without using the percent composition.

6·11 Calculating Molecular Formulas

Safety

Benzene, once commonly used in high school laboratories, has shown substantial evidence of causing cancer in humans. It is no longer recommended for use in schools. Formaldehyde is known to cause cancer and mutations in animals.

The molecular formula of a compound is either the same as its experimentally determined empirical formula, or it is some whole-number multiple of it. Consider the two series of compounds in Table 6·2. Acetylene and benzene have the same empirical formula, CH. Glucose, acetic acid, and formaldehyde all have the same empirical formula, CH_2O. This formula is also the molecular formula of formaldehyde. Each of the compounds in these series has a different gram formula mass.

Table 6·2 Comparison of Empirical and Molecular Formulas

Formula (name)	Classification of formula	Gram formula mass
CH	Empirical	13
C_2H_2 (acetylene)	Molecular	26 (2 × 13)
C_6H_6 (benzene)	Molecular	78 (6 × 13)
CH_2O (formaldehyde)	Empirical and molecular	30
$C_2H_4O_2$ (acetic acid)	Molecular	60 (2 × 30)
$C_6H_{12}O_6$ (glucose)	Molecular	180 (6 × 30)

We can determine the molecular formula of a compound if we know its empirical formula and its gram formula mass. From the empirical formula we calculate the empirical formula mass. This is simply the gram formula mass of the empirical formula. The known gram formula mass is then divided by the empirical formula mass. This gives the number of empirical formula units in a molecule of the compound.

■ An empirical formula and a molecular mass determine the molecular formula of a compound.

Example 16

Calculate the molecular formulas of the following compounds.

	Gram formula mass	Empirical formula
a.	60 g	CH_4N
b.	78 g	NaO
c.	181.5 g	C_2HCl

Solution

First calculate the empirical formula mass (efm). Then divide the empirical formula mass (efm) into the gram formula mass (gfm). It takes this many of the empirical formula units to make up the molecular formula of the compound.

	Empirical formula	efm	$\frac{gfm}{efm}$	Molecular formula
a.	CH_4N	30	$\frac{60}{30} = 2$	$C_2H_8N_2$
b.	NaO	39	$\frac{78}{39} = 2$	Na_2O_2
c.	C_2HCl	60.5	$\frac{181.5}{60.5} = 3$	$C_6H_3Cl_3$

Figure 6·16
Acetylene, C_2H_2, is a gas used in welder's torches. Benzene, C_6H_6, is a flammable liquid. These two compounds have the same empirical formula.

You may wonder how the gram formula mass could be determined without knowing the molecular formula. If the compound is a gas, then we can measure the mass of 22.4 L of the compound at STP. This is the molar volume. The mass of one mole of any compound is the gram formula mass.

Other methods to determine the gram formula mass must be used if the substance is not a gas. One such method involves measuring the freezing-point depression (Section 16·10).

Problems

22. The compound methyl butanoate smells like apples. Its percent composition is 58.8% C, 9.8% H, and 31.4% O. If its gram molecular mass is 102 g/mol, what is its molecular formula?

23. You find that 7.36 g of a compound has decomposed to give 6.93 g of oxygen. The rest of the compound is hydrogen. If the molecular mass of the compound is 34.0 g/mol, what is its molecular formula?

22. $C_5H_{10}O_2$
23. H_2O_2

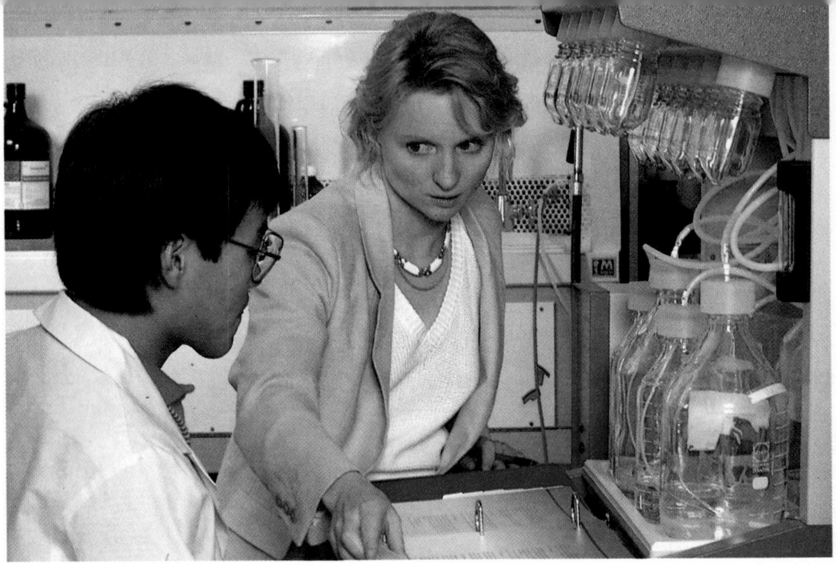

Figure 6·17
A salesperson for a chemical company must have a good knowledge of the language of chemistry.

6·C Knowing Your Product: Chemical Sales

A college degree in chemistry can be the basis of a rewarding career on the road or in an office as well as in a laboratory. The field of chemical marketing and sales includes many positions from field sales representative to marketing executive.

A chemical company generally sells chemicals that are used in the manufacture of other products. In addition to needing raw materials, manufacturing companies often need special chemicals for specific purposes. A cosmetics manufacturer may need a preservative that is safe for use in hand lotions. A paint manufacturer may need an additive to improve the spreading quality of paint. An agricultural chemicals company may need an anticaking agent for fertilizers. The job of a sales representative is to find customers that have a need for his or her product and to provide information about it. If the salesperson has accurately assessed the need of the customer, the product will sell itself.

To succeed at this task, a salesperson must know the properties, limitations, and applications of his or her product. He or she must be able to communicate this information to potential customers. Often sales representatives will be asked to train customers in the use of the product. A college degree in chemistry, courses in business, and skill in oral and written communication are important qualifications for someone considering a career in chemical sales.

A sales engineer's job is to help customers solve technical problems that involve the use of the company's products. He or she may also provide technical data to a salesperson and participate in determining prices. Sales representatives and sales engineers who are willing to continue their education often advance to management positions.

Key Terms

Chapter Summary

The SI unit that measures the amount of substance is the mole. A mole of any substance is composed of Avogadro's number (6.02×10^{23}) of representative particles. The representative particle of most elements is the atom. A molecule is the representative particle of diatomic elements and molecular compounds. The representative particle of ionic compounds is a formula unit.

   The formula mass of an atom, ion, molecule, or formula unit expressed in grams is its gram formula mass. One gram formula mass of any substance is a mole. One mole of any substance contains the same number of representative particles as one mole of any other substance. Thus one gfm of any substance contains 6.02×10^{23} representative particles of that substance.

   If we want to determine the number of moles of a gas, it is easier to measure its volume than its mass. One mole of any gas at STP (1 atm pressure and 0°C) occupies a volume of 22.4 L.

   The percent composition is the percent by mass of each element in a compound. An empirical formula is the simplest whole-number ratio of atoms of the elements in the compound. An empirical formula can be calculated from a compound's percent composition. A molecular formula will be the same as, or some simple multiple of, an empirical formula. For example, dinitrogen tetroxide has the empirical formula NO_2 and the molecular formula N_2O_4.

Practice Questions and Problems

24. List three common ways that matter is measured, giving examples of each.   6·1

25. Name the basic SI unit that measures the "amount of substance."   6·1

26. Name the representative particle (atom, molecule, or formula unit) of each of the following substances.   6·2
   a. hydrogen
   b. iron(II) hydroxide
   c. copper
   d. carbon monoxide
   e. silicon dioxide
   f. aluminum oxide

27. How many hydrogen atoms are in a representative particle of each of these substances?   6·2
   a. $Ca(OH)_2$ **c.** $(NH_4)_2HPO_4$
   b. C_3H_8O **d.** $C_2H_4O_2$

28. What is the total number of *ions* in a formula unit of each of these substances?   6·2
   a. $BaCl_2$ **c.** Na_2CO_3
   b. $(NH_4)_2SO_4$ **d.** $FeCl_3$

29. Find the number of representative particles in each of these substances.   6·2
   a. 5.00 mol Fe
   b. 1.24 mol Cl_2
   c. 0.200 mol NaI
   d. 4.20×10^{-3} mol Al
   e. 34.0 mol SO_3
   f. 5.25×10^{-4} mol K_2S

30. How many moles is each of the following? *6·2*
a. 6.02×10^{22} molecules Br_2
b. 4.81×10^{24} atoms Li
c. 1.50×10^{23} molecules NH_3
d. 1 billion (10^9) molecules O_2
e. 3.61×10^{24} formula units $Ca(OH)_2$
f. 1.00×10^{20} molecules propane, C_3H_8

31. Calculate the mass of 1.00 mol of each of these substances. *6·3*
a. H_2 **d.** Co
b. $Fe(OH)_3$ **e.** SiO_2
c. Cu   **f.** Al_2O_3

32. Calculate the gram formula mass of each of these substances. *6·3*
a. $CaCO_3$ **d.** I_2
b. $(NH_4)_2SO_4$ **e.** H_3PO_4
c. C_3H_6O **f.** N_2O_5

33. Find the mass of each of these substances. *6·5*
a. 2.40 mol NaOH
b. 3.21×10^{-3} mol Ni
c. 0.780 mol $Ca(CN)_2$
d. 7.00 mol H_2O_2

34. How many moles is each of the following? *6·5*
a. 0.800 g Ca
b. 79.3 g Cl_2
c. 5.96 g KOH
d. 937 g $Ca(C_2H_3O_2)_2$

35. Calculate the volume of each of these gases at STP. *6·6*
a. 9.6 mol He   **b.** 4.8 mol N_2 **c.** 3.2 mol CO_2

36. How many moles is each of the following, assuming STP? *6·6*
a. 56.0 L N_2O **b.** 0.224 L O_2 **c.** 12.8 L CO

37. Which of the volumes in Problem 36 would contain the most molecules? Explain. *6·6*

38. What is the density of each of these gases at STP?   **a.** NO   **b.** Ar   **c.** C_2H_6 *6·7*

39. The density of propane at STP is 1.964 g/L. What is the gram formula mass of propane?   *6·7*

40. Find each of the following quantities.   *6·8*
a. the number of molecules in 60.0 g of NO_2
b. the volume, in liters, of 3.24×10^{22} molecules (STP)
c. the mass of 18.0 L of CH_4 (STP)
d. the volume, in liters, of 835 g of SO_3 (STP)
e. the mass of a molecule of aspirin, $C_9H_8O_4$
f. the number of atoms in 5.78 mol of NH_4NO_3

41. Calculate the percent composition of each of these compounds.   *6·9*
a. Na_3PO_4 **d.** $(NH_4)_2C_2O_4$
b. H_2S **e.** $Mg(OH)_2$
c. $SnCl_4$ **f.** $HClO_4$

42. Using your answers from Problem 41, calculate the number of grams of these elements.   *6·9*
a. phosphorus in 804 g of Na_3PO_4
b. sulfur in 3.54 g of H_2S
c. tin in 256 g of $SnCl_4$
d. nitrogen in 25.0 g of $(NH_4)_2C_2O_4$
e. magnesium in 97.4 g of $Mg(OH)_2$
f. chlorine in 625 g of $HClO_4$

43. Which of the following compounds has the highest iron content?   *6·9*
a. Fe_2O_3 **d.** $Fe(C_2H_3O_2)_2$
b. $Fe(OH)_3$ **e.** FeO
c. $FeCl_3$ **f.** Fe_3O_4

44. Calculate the empirical formula of each compound formed.   *6·10*
a. 0.923 g of Na combines with H_2 to produce 0.963 g of the compound.
b. 1.58 g of Cu combines with S to give 1.98 g of the compound.
c. 0.274 g of Al combines with I_2 to give 4.14 g of the compound.

45. Determine the empirical formula of each of these compounds.   *6·10*
a. 42.9% C, and 57.1% O
b. 71.72% Cl, 16.16% O, and 12.12% C
c. 32.00% C, 42.66% O, 18.67% N, and 6.67% H

46. Classify each of these formulas as an empirical or a molecular formula.   *6·11*
a. K_2SO_4 **d.** $(NH_4)_2CO_3$
b. $C_6H_{12}O_6$ **e.** S_2Cl_2
c. $C_{17}H_{19}NO_3$ **f.** $C_6H_{10}O_4$

47. What is the molecular formula for each of these compounds? Each compound's empirical formula and gram formula mass is given.   *6·11*
a. CH_2O, 120 g/mol
b. HgCl, 472.2 g/mol
c. $C_3H_5O_2$, 146 g/mol

48. Determine the molecular formula for each of these compounds.   *6·11*
a. 40.0% C, 53.4% O, and 6.6% H; gfm = 120 g
b. 94.1% O and 5.9% H; gfm = 34 g
c. 54.5% C, 13.6% H, and 31.8% N; gfm = 88 g

Mastery Questions and Problems

49. Which of the following contains the largest number of atoms? *6·8*
  a. 82.0 g Ar
  b. 0.420 mol C_3H_8
  c. 5.00 g H_2

50. What is the total mass of a mixture of 3.5×10^{22} formula units of Na_2SO_4, 0.500 mol of H_2O, and 7.23 g of AgCl? *6·8*

51. How many moles of carbon would contain the same number of atoms as 3.76 mol of copper? *6·2*

52. Find the empirical formula for each compound from its percent composition. *6·10*
  a. 72.4% Fe and 27.6% O
  b. 65.2% Sc and 34.8% O
  c. 52.8% Sn, 12.4% Fe, 16.0% C, and 18.8% N

53. What is the total number of moles of atoms in a mixture of 20.0 g of H_2O_2, 1.20×10^{24} molecules of SiO_2, and 3.70 mol of I_2? *6·8*

54. A typical virus particle is 5×10^{-6} cm in diameter. If Avogadro's number of these virus particles were laid in a row, how many kilometers long would the line be? *6·2*

55. Explain what is wrong with each of the following statements. *6·2*
  a. One mole of any substance contains the same number of atoms.
  b. The gram atomic mass of a compound is the atomic mass expressed in grams.
  c. One gram molecular mass of CO_2 contains Avogadro's number of atoms.

56. How many formula units of magnesium nitride, Mg_3N_2, can be made from 60 magnesium ions and 60 nitride ions? *6·2*

57. How many grams of H_2O_2 would contain the same number of molecules as 9.70 g of C_2H_4? *6·8*

58. Calculate the empirical formula for each of these compounds. *6·10*
  a. The compound consists of 0.25 mol of Fe per 0.50 mol of Cl.
  b. The compound has 4 atoms of carbon for each 12 atoms of hydrogen.
  c. The compound has twice as many hydrogen atoms as carbon atoms, but only half as many oxygen atoms as carbon atoms.

Review Questions and Problems

59. How many moles is 30.0 cm³ of copper? The density of copper is 8.92 cm³.

60. How does an atom differ from a molecule?

61. Do each of these conversions.
  a. 56.3 cal to kilojoules
  b. 5.9×10^5 cm/sec to km/hr
  c. 0.34 mg to decigrams

62. How many protons, electrons, and neutrons are in each of these isotopes?
  a. hydrogen-2   **c.** bromine-79
  b. mercury-201   **d.** antimony-113

63. Write formulas for these compounds.
  a. sodium carbonate   **c.** iron(III) hydroxide
  b. carbon tetrachloride   **d.** ammonium iodide

64. Show that this series of the oxides of nitrogen obeys the law of multiple proportions: N_2O, NO, N_2O_3, and N_2O_5.

65. Name these compounds.
  a. KNO_3 **d.** AgF
  b. CuO   **e.** $Al_2(SO_4)_3$
  c. Mg_3N_2 **f.** H_3PO_4

Challenging Questions and Problems

66. How many molecules are in a sample of water that requires 8.40 kcal of heat energy to raise the temperature by 34°C?

67. Nitroglycerine contains 60% as many carbon atoms as hydrogen atoms; three times as many oxygen atoms as nitrogen atoms; and the same number of carbon and nitrogen atoms. The number of moles in a gram of nitroglycerine is 0.00441. What is the molecular formula?

68. The specific gravity of lead is 11.3. How large a cube, in cm³, would contain 5.00×10^{24} atoms of lead?

69. Dry air is about 20.95 percent oxygen by volume. Assuming STP, how many oxygen molecules are in a 40.0-g sample of air? The density of air is 1.19 g/L.

70. The element gold has properties that have made it much sought after through the ages. A cubic meter of ocean water contains 6×10^{-6} g gold. If the total mass of the water in the oceans of the world is 4×10^{20} kg, how many kilograms of gold are distributed throughout the oceans? (Assume that the density of seawater is 1 g/cm^3.) How many liters of seawater would have to be processed to recover a kilogram of gold (which had a value of about $11 000 at 1985 prices)? Do you think this recovery operation is feasible?

71. Have you ever wondered how Avogadro's number was determined? Actually, Avogadro's number has been independently determined by about 20 different methods. In one approach Avogadro's number is calculated from the volume of a film of a fatty acid floating on water. In another method it is determined by comparing the electric charge of an electron to the electric charge of a mole of electrons. In a third method the spacing between ions in an ionic substance can be determined by using a technique called X-ray diffraction. In the X-ray diffraction of sodium chloride it has been determined that the distance between adjacent Na^+ and Cl^- ions is 2.819×10^{-8} cm (Figure 5·10). The density of solid sodium chloride is 2.165 g/cm^3. Thus by calculating the gram formula mass to four significant figures, you can determine Avogadro's number. What value do you obtain?

Research Projects

1. Develop an illustration or a model to make clear to fellow students the magnitude of Avogadro's number.

2. Look up the fertilizer requirements for several kinds of plants. Record the price and percent composition of various brands of fertilizers. Calculate which ones would be the most economical for specific plant types.

3. Make data tables that list various properties of several compounds with identical empirical formulas. Can you find any patterns that hold true for several series of empirical formulas? How would you explain these patterns?

4. Describe one method of determining Avogadro's number using enough detail so that one of your classmates could reproduce the determination.

Readings and References

Dean, J. A. *Lange's Handbook of Chemistry,* 12th ed. New York: McGraw-Hill, 1978.

O'Connor, Rod, and Charles Mickey. *Solving Problems in Chemistry: With Emphasis on Stoichiometry and Equilibrium.* New York: Harper & Row, 1974.

Pierce, Conway, and R. Nelson Smith. *General Chemistry Workbook: How to Solve Chemistry Problems,* 5th ed. San Francisco: Freeman, 1980.

Taylor, L. B., Jr. *Chemistry Careers.* New York: Watts, 1978.

7 Chemical Reactions

Chapter Planning Guide

Section			Demonstrations and Experiments	Resource Materials
7·1	Writing Chemical Equations	C*		Objectives Worksheet 7, SPB
				Skillsheet 7, SPB
7·2	Balancing Chemical Equations	C		Quiz 7·1
				Teaching Diagram 7
7·A	Passing the Torch for Chemistry: St. Elmo Brady	E		
7·3	Combination Reactions	C	Dem 7·1 Combination of Sulfur and Zinc	
			Dem 7·2 Combination of Iodine and Zinc	
7·4	Decomposition Reactions	C	Dem 7·3 Decomposition of Calcium Carbonate	Teaching Diagram 8
			Dem 7·4 Mercury and Oxygen from Mercury Oxide	
			Dem 21·6 Electrolysis of Water	
7·5	Single-Replacement Reactions	C	Dem 7·5 Single-Replacement Reactions	
			Dem 7·6 Complex Single-Replacement Reactions	
7·6	Double-Replacement Reactions	C	Dem 7·7 Double-Replacement Reactions	Teaching Diagram 9
			Exp 11 Qualitative Analysis, LM	Prelab 11, SPB
			Dem 7·8 Potassium Iodide and Mercury(II) Bromide	
7·B	Qualitative and Quantitative Analysis	E		
7·7	Combustion Reactions	C	Dem 25·1 Methane Bubbles	Toxic Industrial Wastes, ICT 7
7·C	What's in a Flame?	E		
7·8	Summary of the Types of Reactions	C	Exp 12 Types of Chemical Reactions, LM	Prelab 12, SPB
				Quiz 7·2
				Reviewsheet 7, SPB
				Chapter 7 Test
7·D	The Chemistry of Firefighting	E		

*C = Core, O = Optional
E = Enrichment, H = Honors

LM = Laboratory Manual

SPB = Skills Practice Book
ICT = Issues in Chem. Tech.

Chapter Objectives

Having studied this chapter and done the problems, the student should be able to:

1. Identify the reactants and products in a chemical equation.   *7·1*

2. Use appropriate symbols when writing an equation to accurately describe the chemical reaction.   *7·1*

3. Write a balanced chemical equation when given the names or formulas of all the reactants and products in a chemical reaction.   *7·2*

4. Classify a reaction as combination, decomposition, single-replacement, double-replacement, or combustion.   *7·3-7·7*

5. Predict the products of simple combination and decomposition reactions.   *7·3, 7·4*

6. Use the activity series of metals to predict the products of single-replacement reactions.   *7·5*

7. Write the products of the double-replacement reaction between two ionic compounds.   *7·6*

8. Write the products for complete and incomplete combustion reactions.   *7·7*

9. State the method used to positively determine the products of a reaction.   *7·8*

Teaching Suggestions

7·1 Writing Chemical Equations

7·2 Balancing Chemical Equations

When students first encounter the concept of chemical equations, they often take them too literally. That is, they think the equation is just stating that the "things" on the left are equal in a mathematical sense to the "things" on the right. It is important to get across the idea that the substances on the left side of the equation *are not the same* as the substances on the right. Instead of being a statement of equality, the equation is a statement of *process*. In reading the equation from left to right we are told of a change of substances taking place. We are told what the substances are and what their reacting relationship is.

Of course, there is a quantity which is equal in the equation. In any reaction atoms are conserved. That is, the number of atoms of each element is the same on each side of the equation.

Illustrate the six rules for balancing equations by working through several examples with the class. Point out

as you are doing so that you are only changing the coefficients, never the subscripts. Point out also that there is an element of trial and error in balancing equations. Often it is not apparent at first which numbers are going to be right. Urge the students to "jump in" and keep trying numbers until they get a combination that works. With experience they will soon get a feeling for how to start the balancing process. Finally, they should realize that there is no quick and easy way to balance equations. They *must* go through the process of counting atoms, first on one side of the equation, then on the other, then back on the original side, and so on until a balanced equation is achieved.

It is helpful to illustrate the balancing of equations by holding up molecular models and arranging them to show conservation of atoms in simple reactions, such as $2H_2 + O_2 \rightarrow 2H_2O$. You can then represent the arrangement by writing the corresponding equation. If models are not available, try simple drawings. Be sure to get them to *visualize* what equations are trying to represent and what the balancing process is.

7·3 Combination Reactions

Demonstrations 7·1 *Combination of Sulfur and Zinc* and **7·2** *Combination of Iodine and Zinc* show combination reactions. Combination reactions are also shown in **Demonstrations 5·2** and **5·3**.

7·4 Decomposition Reactions

Demonstrations 7·3 *Decomposition of Calcium Carbonate* and **7·4** *Mercury and Oxygen from Mercury Oxide* are decomposition reactions. Decomposition reactions are also shown in **Demonstrations 1·15** and **21·6** *Electrolysis of Water*.

7·5 Single-Replacement Reactions

Demonstrations 7·5 *Single-Replacement Reactions* and **7·6** *Complex Single-Replacement Reactions* are some single-replacement reactions.

7·6 Double-Replacement Reactions

Demonstration 7·7 *Double-Replacement Reactions* and **Demonstration 7·8** *Potassium Iodine and Mercury(II) Bromide* both show double-replacement reactions. **Experiment 11** *Qualitative Analysis* is also appropriate here.

7·7 Combustion Reactions

Demonstration 25·1 *Methane Bubbles* is an example of combustion. **Demonstrations 1·16** and **1·17** also show combustion.

7·8 Summary of the Types of Reactions

The five general types of chemical reactions should all be presented at the same time so that they can be compared and contrasted. A good approach is to: 1. introduce the type of reaction, 2. demonstrate the reaction, 3. present more examples, and 4. give the students opportunity for practice and drill.

The timing of the demonstrations could take three forms: 1. Before the material in Sections 7·3 through 7·7 is presented. You can then refer back to them as illustrative examples. 2. One at a time as you present the material in the chapter. 3. At the end of the chapter as a summary. Have the students predict the products and write balanced equations for the reactions.

With upper-level students you may wish to do problems in which the formulas of the reactants and the type of reaction are given, and then let the students predict the products and balance the equations.

Once the students have become familiar with the types of reactions, have them do **Experiment 12** *Types of Chemical Reactions*. It covers the reactions discussed in Sections 7·3–7·7.

Demonstrations

7·1 Combination of Sulfur and Zinc

Concept: Two elements can combine to form a binary compound.

Materials: 5 g of powdered zinc (Zn), 5 g of powdered sulfur (S), 3 cm of magnesium (Mg) ribbon, ceramic plate, spatula, gas burner, matches, safety goggles, dark glasses.

Procedure: 1. Mix the zinc and sulfur in the middle of the wire gauze and shape into a cone. 3. Place the magnesium ribbon in the top of the cone as a fuse. 3. Ignite the ribbon with the burner. **Caution:** *Do not look at the burning ribbon without dark glasses. Use a fume hood. Sulfur dioxide is an irritant. Stand back during the reaction.* 4. The mixture ignites violently with a flash of light. Pale yellow flakes of zinc sulfide and acrid smoke are produced. Zinc oxide and sulfur dioxide are also formed. 5. State that combination reactions occur when two elements join together. Write this reaction on the board: $Zn + S \rightarrow ZnS$. 6. Have the students identify another combination reaction, the burning of the magnesium ribbon, and have them write out the reaction: $2Mg + O_2 \rightarrow 2MgO$. 7. In each case, discuss the properties of the reacting elements: physical state, color, luster, electrical conductivity, brittleness, etc. Point out that the properties of the individual elements are no longer present and that the product has a new set of properties. Ask the students to predict the formulas and names of the products formed.

7·2 Combination of Iodine and Zinc

Concept: Two elements combine to form a binary compound.

Materials: 1 g of powdered zinc (Zn), 4 g of iodine (I_2), watch glass, 8 mL of water, dropper, safety goggles.

Procedure: 1. Mix the zinc powder and iodine crystals in the watch glass. 2. Add the water with the dropper, one drop at a time. **Caution:** *Do this demonstration in a fume hood. Iodine is an irritant.*

7·3 Decomposition of Calcium Carbonate

Concept: Compounds can be the products of a decomposition reaction.

Materials: 10 g of calcium carbonate ($CaCO_3$), 100 mL of saturated calcium hydroxide (limewater, $Ca(OH)_2$), large test tube, one-hole stopper with glass tube and rubber tubing attached, mortar and pestle, gas burner, matches, test tube holder, safety goggles.

Procedure: 1. Arrange a test tube with a one-hole stopper and delivery tube so that gas produced in the tube can be bubbled through limewater. 2. Fill the test tube 1/4 full with powdered calcium carbonate. (Grind it with a mortar and pestle first, if necessary.) 3. When heated, the calcium carbonate decomposes into calcium oxide, CaO, and carbon dioxide, CO_2. 4. Carbon dioxide is present if the limewater turns cloudy.

7·4 Mercury and Oxygen from Mercury Oxide

Concept: Compounds can decompose into their elements.

Materials: 5 g of mercury(II) oxide (HgO), test tube, gas burner, matches, wood splint.

Procedure: 1. If a small sample of mercury(II) oxide is heated in a Pyrex test tube, it decomposes. 2. Liquid mercury collects at the cooler upper end of the test tube. 3. A glowing-splint thrust into the tube during heating bursts into flames, indicating that oxygen is present. **Caution:** *Do this demonstration in a fume hood. Mercury vapor and mercury(II) oxide are highly toxic.*

7·5 Single-Replacement Reactions

Concept: An element and a compound can react to form another element and another compound.

Materials: 200 mL of $0.1M$ copper(II) chloride ($CuCl_2$), 5 cm. square piece of aluminum foil (Al), 400-mL beaker, safety goggles.

Procedure: 1. Place the beaker of copper(II) chloride in front of the class. 2. Crumple the aluminum foil and throw it in the beaker. 3. Soon the solution starts to bubble as

hydrogen gas is produced. 4. A red-brown precipitate of copper falls to the bottom of the beaker, and the aluminum foil dissolves completely. 5. Aluminum would react spontaneously with water without its protective oxide coating. The aluminum–copper(II) chloride reaction removes this protection. **Caution:** *Copper (II) chloride is an irritant.*

7·6 Complex Single-Replacement Reactions

Concept: An element and a compound can react to form another element and another compound.

Materials: 300 mL of 10% tin(II) chloride ($SnCl_2$), 50 mL of 6M hydrochloric acid (HCl), 3 g of granular zinc (Zn), stirring rod, 2 600-mL beakers, water, safety goggles.

Procedure: 1. Pour the tin(II) chloride solution into the beaker and add the hydrochloric acid. 2. Add the zinc, spreading it evenly over the bottom of the beaker. 3. After the tin floats to the top, remove it with a spoon. 4. Rinse it with water. 5. Note that single-replacement reactions occur when an element and a compound react. The element replaces one portion of the compound molecule, liberating another element. Two reactions are taking place:

$$Zn + 2HCl \rightarrow H_2 + ZnCl_2$$
$$Zn + SnCl_2 \rightarrow ZnCl_2 + Sn$$

The tin floats to the surface on the hydrogen gas bubbles, giving the tin a spongy texture. **Caution:** *Tin(II) chloride and hydrochloric acid are corrosive.*

7·7 Double-Replacement Reactions

Concept: Two compounds can react to form two other compounds.

Materials: 50 mL each of 0.1M solutions of any of the following pairs of reactants:

Silver nitrate ($AgNO_3$) + sodium chloride (NaCl) → silver chloride (AgCl)(white precipitate)

Silver nitrate + sodium iodide (NaI) → silver iodide (AgI) (yellow precipitate)

Silver nitrate + sodium chromate (Na_2CrO_4) → silver chromate (Ag_2CrO_4)(red-brown precipitate)

Lead nitrate ($Pb(NO_3)_2$) + sodium iodide → lead iodide (PbI_2)(yellow precipitate)

Lead nitrate + sodium chloride → lead chloride ($PbCl_2$)(white precipitate)

Lead nitrate + sodium sulfide (Na_2S) → lead sulfide (PbS)(black precipitate)

Lead nitrate + sodium carbonate (Na_2CO_3) → lead carbonate ($PbCO_3$)(white precipitate)

Magnesium carbonate ($MgCO_3$) + sulfuric acid (H_2SO_4) → carbon dioxide (CO_2)(colorless gas)

eight 250-mL beakers, 8 stirring rods, safety goggles.

Procedure: 1. Mix the two solutions. 2. One of the reactions given above will occur. 3. Have the students suggest other double-replacement reactions and predict the products. **Caution:** *Silver nitrate is a suspected mutagen. Sodium sulfide is an irritant. Sulfuric acid is corrosive. Lead nitrate is toxic.*

7·8 Potassium Iodide and Mercury(II) Bromide

Concept: A double-replacement reaction occurs.

Materials: 3 g of potassium iodide (KI), 3 g of mercury(II) bromide ($HgBr_2$), mortar and pestle, safety goggles.

Procedure: 1. Grind the two solids in the mortar. 2. An orange product, mercury(II) iodide, HgI_2, appears. **Caution:** *Mercury(II) bromide and mercury(II) iodide are highly toxic.*

Audiovisual Resources

Chemical Reactions (2 FS) Focus Media, 1982, 13–18 min. each. (Use with Sections 7·1 and 7·2.) Introduces writing and balancing chemical equations. Also covers topics in Chapter 8.

Chemical Symbols: Formulas and Equations (4 FS) Charles Clark, 1973. (Use with Sections 7·1 and 7·2.) Introduces balancing chemical equations.

Chemistry: Atomic Weight, Molecular Weight; Moles; Equations (6 FS) Charles Clark, 1974, 10–15 min. each. (Use with Sections 7·1 and 7·2.) Discusses writing and balancing chemical equations.

Combustion: An Introduction to Chemical Change (F, V) BFA Educational Films, 1967, 16 min. (Use with Section 7·7.) Illustrates how substances are changed in chemical reactions, using combustion as an example.

Formulas and Equations (F, V) Coronet, 1966, 11 min. (Use with Sections 7·1 and 7·2.) Explains and illustrates the language and symbols used in chemical formulas and equations. Also discusses balancing equations.

Types of Chemical Change (F, V) Coronet, 1966, 13 min. (Use with Sections 7·3–7·6.) Includes combination, decomposition, single-replacement, and double-replacement reactions.

Answers to End of Chapter Questions and Problems

Practice Questions and Problems

11. a. K(s) **b.** NaCl(aq) **c.** $\xrightarrow{\Delta}$ **d.** Hg(l) **e.** $\xrightarrow{ZnCl_2}$ **f.** $CO_2(g)$

12. Speeds up a chemical reaction.

13. a. When solid potassium is dropped in water, hydrogen gas and aqueous potassium hydroxide are produced. **b.** Mixing aqueous sodium hydroxide and aqueous nitric acid results in the formation of water and aqueous sodium nitrate. **c.** Heating a mixture of solid iron(II) oxide and carbon produces iron and carbon monoxide gas.

14. Matter (in atoms) is neither created nor destroyed in a chemical reaction.

15. The coefficients of the balanced equations are:
a. 1, 1, 1, 2 **b.** 1, 4, 1, 2, 1 **c.** 2, 9, 6, 6 **d.** 2, 2, 1
e. 3, 2, 1, 6 **f.** 3, 1, 2, 3 **g.** 1, 3, 1, 1 **h.** 1, 1, 1, 1
i. 1, 1, 1, 2 **j.** 1, 1, 4, 1

16. A single product.

17. a. $Ca + Br_2 \rightarrow CaBr_2$ **b.** $3Mg + N_2 \rightarrow Mg_3N_2$
c. $SO_2 + H_2O \rightarrow H_2SO_3$ **d.** $2Be + O_2 \rightarrow 2BeO$

18. A single reactant.

19. a. $2H_2O_2 \xrightarrow{Mn} 2H_2O + O_2$
b. $Mg(ClO_3)_2 \rightarrow MgCl_2 + 3O_2$ **c.** $2HI \rightarrow H_2 + I_2$
d. $2NaNO_3 \rightarrow 2NaNO_2 + O_2$

20. Metal A will displace the ion of metal B from a compound if metal A is above metal B on the activity series of metals.

21. a. $2Al + 3CuSO_4 \rightarrow Al_2(SO_4)_3 + 3Cu$
b. $Ca + 2H_2O \rightarrow Ca(OH)_2 + H_2$
c. $Zn + Pb(NO_3)_2 \rightarrow Zn(NO_3)_2 + Pb$ **d.** no reaction
e. $F_2 + 2KCl \rightarrow 2KF + Cl_2$

22. Formation of a gas, precipitate, and molecular compound.

23. a. $CdCl_2 + H_2S \rightarrow CdS + 2HCl$
b. $NH_4C_2H_3O_2 + AgNO_3 \rightarrow AgC_2H_3O_2 + NH_4NO_3$
c. $H_2C_2O_4 + 2NaOH \rightarrow Na_2C_2O_4 + 2H_2O$
d. $Fe(NO_3)_3 + 3LiOH \rightarrow Fe(OH)_3 + 3LiNO_3$
e. $3BaCl_2 + 2H_3PO_4 \rightarrow Ba_3(PO_4)_2 + 6HCl$

24. In complete combustion all of the carbon is oxidized to carbon dioxide. In incomplete combustion carbon monoxide and/or elemental carbon are also produced.

25. a. $HC_2H_3O_2 + 2O_2 \rightarrow 2CO_2 + 2H_2O$
b. $2C_{10}H_{22} + 31O_2 \rightarrow 20CO_2 + 22H_2O$
c. $2C_3H_8O_3 + 7O_2 \rightarrow 6CO_2 + 8H_2O$
d. $C_{12}H_{22}O_{11} + 12O_2 \rightarrow 12CO_2 + 11H_2O$

26. a. 6, 1, 2, 3; double-replacement **b.** 4, 1, 2; combination **c.** 1, 1, 1; decomposition **d.** 3, 1, 1, 3; double-replacement **e.** 1, 4, 3, 4; single-replacement **f.** 1, 7, 6, 3; combustion **g.** 1, 1, 2; decomposition **h.** 2, 1, 1, 2; double-replacement **i.** 1, 2, 2, 1; single-replacement **j.** 1, 3, 1, 3; double-replacement

Mastery Questions and Problems

27. a. $Mg + H_2SO_4 \rightarrow MgSO_4 + H_2$
b. $H_2 + Cl_2 \rightarrow 2HCl$ **c.** $2NH_3 \rightarrow N_2 + 3H_2$
d. $Cl_2 + 2NaI \rightarrow 2NaCl + I_2$ **e.** $4Na + O_2 \rightarrow 2Na_2O$
f. $MgCl_2 + Ca(OH)_2 \rightarrow CaCl_2 + Mg(OH)_2$

28. a. $2Fe(s) + 6HCl(aq) \rightarrow 2FeCl_3(aq) + 3H_2(g)$
b. $4HgS(s) + 4CaO(s) \xrightarrow{\Delta} 4Hg(l) + 3CaS(s) + CaSO_4(s)$ **c.** $2Ag_2O(s) \rightarrow 4Ag(s) + O_2(g)$
d. $P_4O_{10}(s) + 6H_2O(l) \rightarrow 4H_3PO_4(aq)$
e. $Cl_2(g) + 2KI(aq) \rightarrow I_2(s) + 2KCl(aq)$
f. $I_2(s) + 3Cl_2(g) \rightarrow 2ICl_3(s)$

29. a. $NaOH + HNO_3 \rightarrow NaNO_3 + H_2O$
b. $2KF + Ca(NO_3)_2 \rightarrow 2KNO_3 + CaF_2$
c. $ZnS + H_2SO_4 \rightarrow ZnSO_4 + H_2S$
d. $CaI_2 + Hg(NO_3)_2 \rightarrow HgI_2 + Ca(NO_3)_2$

30. a. $Cl_2O_7 + H_2O \rightarrow 2HClO_4$ **b.** $H_2 + Br_2 \rightarrow 2HBr$
c. $Na_2O + H_2O \rightarrow 2NaOH$ **d.** $2Al + 3Cl_2 \rightarrow 2AlCl_3$

31. a. no reaction **b.** $Br_2 + BaI_2 \rightarrow BaBr_2 + I_2$
c. $Fe + H_2SO_4 \rightarrow FeSO_4 + H_2$ **d.** no reaction

32. a. $C_3H_8O_3 + 2O_2 \rightarrow 3CO + 4H_2O$
b. $HC_2H_3O_2 + O_2 \rightarrow 2CO + 2H_2O$
c. $C_6H_{12}O_6 + 3O_2 \rightarrow 6CO + 6H_2O$
d. $2C_2H_2 + 3O_2 \rightarrow 4CO + 2H_2O$

33. a. $MgCl_2(l) \xrightarrow{electricity} Mg + Cl_2$
b. $Ag_2CO_3 \xrightarrow{\Delta} Ag_2O + CO_2$
c. $Sn(OH)_4 \xrightarrow{\Delta} SnO_2 + 2H_2O$
d. $2Al_2O_3 \xrightarrow{energy} 4Al + 3O_2$

Review Questions and Problems

34. 35.4 g Ca

35. a. 0.467 mol NaOCl **b.** 3.32×10^{-3} mol CO
c. 3.48 mol NO_2 **d.** 3.53×10^{-2} mol Mg^{2+}

36. 425 g Au

37. $C_8H_{10}O_2N_4$

38. a. strontium nitrate **b.** cadmium sulfide **b.** sodium hydrogen carbonate **d.** hydrogen fluoride or hydrofluoric acid **e.** potassium cyanide **f.** tin(IV) bromide or stannic bromide **g.** diboron trioxide **h.** aluminum hydroxide **i.** iron(III) sulfate or ferric sulfate **j.** lithium chlorate

Challenging Questions and Problems

39. a. $2Al + 3H_2SO_4 \rightarrow 3H_2 + Al_2(SO_4)_3$; single-replacement **b.** $2H_2SO_4 \xrightarrow{\Delta} 2H_2O + O_2 + 2SO_2$; decomposition **c.** $C_5H_{12} + 8O_2 \xrightarrow{\Delta} 5CO_2 + 6H_2O$; combustion **d.** $3NaI + H_3PO_4 \rightarrow 3HI + Na_3PO_4$; double-replacement **e.** $K_2O + H_2O \rightarrow 2KOH$; combination

40. 1.01 g/mol protons, 5.48×10^{-4} g/mol electrons, 1.83×10^3 electrons/protons

41. a. $2Bi(NO_3)_3 + 3H_2S \rightarrow Bi_2S_3 + 6HNO_3$
b. $Br_2 + 2NaI \rightarrow 2NaBr + I_2$ **c.** $2Al + 3Cl_2 \rightarrow 2AlCl_3$
d. $2H_2O_2 \rightarrow 2H_2O + O_2$
e. $Ba(OH)_2 + 2HNO_3 \rightarrow Ba(NO_3)_2 + 2H_2O$
f. $2K + 2H_2O \rightarrow 2KOH + H_2$
g. $C_2H_5OH + 3O_2 \rightarrow 2CO_2 + 3H_2O$

7 Chemical Reactions

Chapter Preview

In Chapter 5 you learned the vocabulary of chemistry by learning how to write chemical formulas and name chemical compounds. We will now use this vocabulary to write chemical sentences called chemical equations. Chemical equations describe chemical reactions. To conform to the law of conservation of mass, equations must be balanced. While practicing your skills in balancing equations you will learn about five general types of reactions. Knowing these reaction types will allow you to predict what will happen when substances undergo a chemical change.

7·1 Writing Chemical Equations

Chemical reactions are continually taking place in us and around us. When our bodies digest food, a whole series of complex chemical reactions occur. A useful chemical reaction also takes place in a car battery to produce energy to start the car. At the same time, an unwanted chemical reaction may be taking place between the iron in the car fender and the oxygen in the air. Rust is being produced. All chemical reactions, whether simple or complex, involve changes in substances. One or more starting substances, the reactants, are changed into one or more new substances, the products.

$$\text{Reactants} \longrightarrow \text{products}$$

Figure 7·1
Copper reacts with nitric acid to produce nitric oxide (a colorless gas) and copper(II) nitrate (in solution). The nitric acid reacts with the oxygen in air to produce nitrogen dioxide, the brown gas shown here.

Figure 7·2
The ingredients for baking are reactants. They undergo physical and chemical changes and combine to form the product, in this case, blueberry muffins.

In a chemical reaction the ways in which atoms are joined together are changed. Bonds are broken and new bonds are formed as reactants are converted into products. The atoms are not created or destroyed. They are just rearranged.

Chemical reactions can be described in different ways. For the example of rusting we could say: "Iron reacts with oxygen to produce iron(III) oxide (rust)." Alternatively, we could identify the reactants and product in this reaction by writing a word equation.

$$\text{Iron} + \text{oxygen} \longrightarrow \text{iron(III) oxide}$$

In a word equation, the reactants are written on the left, and the products are written on the right. They are connected by an arrow ($\rightarrow$) that is read as "yields" or "reacts to produce." Other forms of the yields sign and their uses are shown in Table 7·1.

Table 7·1	Symbols Used in Equations
Symbol	Explanation
$+$	Used to separate two reactants or two products
$\longrightarrow$	"Yields," separates reactants from products
$=$	An alternative to $\longrightarrow$
$\rightleftharpoons$	Used in place of a $\longrightarrow$ for reversible reactions (Chapter 17)
(s)	Designates a reactant or product in the solid state; placed after the formula
$\downarrow$	Alternative to (s); used only for a solid product (precipitate)
(l)	Designates a reactant or product in the liquid state; placed after the formula
(aq)	Designates an aqueous solution; the substance is dissolved in water
(g)	Designates a reactant or product in the gaseous state; placed after the formula
$\uparrow$	Alternative to (g); used only for a gaseous product
$\xrightarrow{\Delta} \xrightarrow{\text{heat}}$	Indicates that heat is supplied to the reaction
$\xrightarrow{\text{Pt}}$	A formula written above or below the yield sign indicates its use as a catalyst (in this example, platinum)

A chemical equation is a concise representation of a chemical reaction.

Word equations are cumbersome. To communicate more effectively, chemists use chemical formulas for writing equations. *In a* **chemical equation,** *the formulas of the reactants (on the left) are connected by an arrow with the formulas of the products (on the right).* For instance, the chemical equation for rusting is shown here.

$$Fe + O_2 \longrightarrow Fe_2O_3$$

Such equations, which show just the formulas of the reactants and products, are skeleton equations. *A* **skeleton equation** *is a chemical equation that does not indicate the relative amounts of the reactants and products.*

Chemists generally do not use equations in skeleton form. Writing a skeleton equation is only the first step in obtaining a correctly balanced chemical equation.

The physical state of a substance in a reaction can be indicated in the equation. Symbols are used after each formula: (s) for a solid, (l) for a liquid, (g) for a gas, and (aq) for a solution in water.

$$Fe(s) + O_2(g) \longrightarrow Fe_2O_3(s)$$

In many chemical reactions, a catalyst is employed. *A* **catalyst** *is a substance that speeds up a reaction without being used up.* Because a catalyst is neither a reactant nor a product, it is written above the arrow in a chemical equation. For example, manganese dioxide (MnO_2) catalyzes the decomposition of an aqueous solution of hydrogen peroxide (H_2O_2).

$$H_2O_2(aq) \xrightarrow{MnO_2} H_2O(l) + O_2(g)$$

A chemical equation shows the rearrangement of atoms that takes place as a result of chemical change.

To write a skeleton equation, you must write the correct formulas of the reactants and products. Put the reactants to the left of the yield sign and the products to the right. Many of the symbols that are commonly used in writing chemical equations are listed in Table 7·1.

a

b

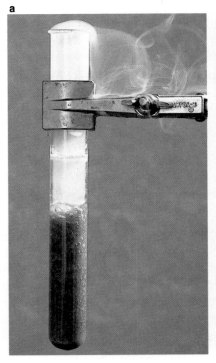
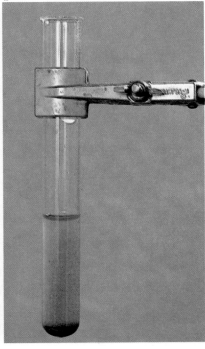

Figure 7·3
Hydrogen peroxide slowly decomposes to form water and oxygen.
a Manganese dioxide (MnO_2), a black powder, speeds up this reaction, causing bubbles to form. **b** Since it is not used up in the reaction, MnO_2 is a catalyst.

Example 1

Write a skeleton equation for this chemical reaction: When calcium carbonate is heated, calcium oxide and carbon dioxide are produced.

Solution

$$CaCO_3(s) \xrightarrow{\Delta} CaO(s) + CO_2 \uparrow$$

Problem

1. **a.** $Al(s) + O_2(g) \longrightarrow$
$Al_2O_3(s)$

b. $HgS(s) + O_2(g) \longrightarrow$
$Hg(l) + SO_2(g)$

c. $KClO_3(s) \xrightarrow{MnO_2}$
$KCl(s) + O_2(g)$

1. Write a skeleton equation for each of these chemical reactions.
   a. Aluminum metal reacts with oxygen in the air to form aluminum oxide.
   b. When solid mercury(II) sulfide is heated with oxygen, liquid mercury metal and gaseous sulfur dioxide are produced.
   c. Oxygen gas can be made by heating potassium chlorate in the presence of the catalyst manganese dioxide. Potassium chloride is a solid residue.

Example 2

Write a sentence that completely describes the chemical reaction shown in this skeleton equation.

$$NaHCO_3(s) + HCl(aq) \longrightarrow NaCl(aq) + H_2O(l) + CO_2 \uparrow$$

Solution

Solid sodium bicarbonate reacts with hydrochloric acid to produce aqueous sodium chloride, water, and carbon dioxide gas.

Problem

2. **a.** Aqueous solutions of barium chloride and sulfuric acid when mixed produce a precipitate of barium sulfate and aqueous hydrochloric acid.
   b. Gaseous ammonia and oxygen react in the presence of platinum to produce mononitrogen monoxide gas and water vapor.
   c. The gas dinitrogen trioxide reacts with water to produce an aqueous solution of nitrous acid.

2. Write sentences that completely describe each of the chemical reactions shown in these skeleton equations.
   a. $BaCl_2(aq) + H_2SO_4(aq) \longrightarrow BaSO_4 \downarrow + HCl(aq)$
   b. $NH_3(g) + O_2(g) \xrightarrow{Pt} NO \uparrow + H_2O(g)$
   c. $N_2O_3(g) + H_2O(l) \longrightarrow HNO_2(aq)$

7·2 Balancing Chemical Equations

All the equations we have written thus far have been correct in a qualitative sense. They have shown what has happened in terms of reactants changing to products. They have not been correct in a quantitative sense, however. This is because the equations have not shown the amounts of reactants and products. To represent chemical reactions correctly, equations must be balanced so that they are quantitatively correct. *In every*

balanced equation, *each side of the equation has the same number of atoms of each element*. This is necessary to be consistant with the law of conservation of mass. Remember, in a chemical reaction, atoms are not created or destroyed; they are simply rearranged.

Sometimes when we write the formulas for the reactants and products in an equation, the equation is already balanced. This is true of the equation for the burning of carbon in the presence of oxygen to produce carbon dioxide.

$$C(s) + O_2(g) \longrightarrow CO_2(g)$$

The equation is balanced. One carbon atom is on each side of the equation, and two oxygen atoms are on each side. Carbon can also react with oxygen to produce carbon monoxide.

$$C(s) + O_2(g) \longrightarrow CO(g)$$

This is a correct skeleton equation but it is not balanced. It does not obey the law of conservation of mass.

Another equation we have seen is the reaction of hydrogen with oxygen to produce water.

$$H_2(g) + O_2(g) \xrightarrow{\text{Pt}} H_2O(l)$$

This equation is not balanced even though the formulas for all the reactants and products are correct (Figure 7·4). There are two oxygen atoms on the reactant (left) side of the equation and only one oxygen atom on the product (right) side. The equation does not obey the law of conservation of mass. What can we do? Many chemical equations can be balanced by trial and error. A few guidelines, however, will speed the process. Let's look at these rules and then use them to balance the equation for the formation of water.

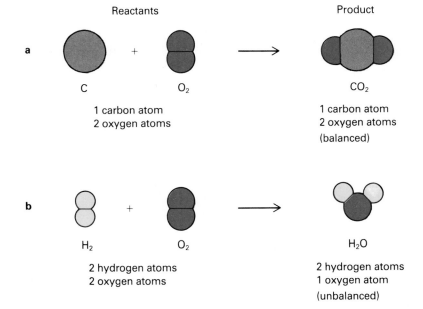

Reactants   Product

a

C O_2 CO_2

1 carbon atom   1 carbon atom
2 oxygen atoms   2 oxygen atoms
                       (balanced)

b

H_2 O_2 H_2O

2 hydrogen atoms   2 hydrogen atoms
2 oxygen atoms   1 oxygen atom
                       (unbalanced)

Figure 7·4
a A balanced chemical equation has the same number and type of atoms on each side. **b** An unbalanced equation does not have the same number and type of atoms on each side. Which kind of atom is not balanced in **b**?
Oxygen.

Rules for Balancing Equations

1. Determine the correct formulas for all the reactants and products in the reaction.

2. Write the formulas for the reactants on the left and the formulas for the products on the right with an arrow in between. If two or more reactants or products are involved, separate their formulas with plus signs.

3. Count the number of atoms of each element in the reactants and products. A polyatomic ion appearing unchanged on both sides of the equation is counted as a single unit.

4. Balance the elements one at a time by using coefficients. *A* **coefficient** *is a small whole number that appears in front of a formula in an equation.* When no coefficient is written, it is assumed to be 1. It is best to begin with an element other than hydrogen or oxygen. These two elements often occur more than twice in an equation. *You must not attempt to balance an equation by changing the subscripts in the chemical formula of a substance.*

5. Check each atom or polyatomic ion to be sure that the equation is balanced.

6. Finally, make sure that all the coefficients are in the lowest possible ratio.

Now let's use these rules to balance the equation for the formation of water from hydrogen and oxygen.

Example 3

When hydrogen and oxygen react, the product is water. Write a balanced equation for this reaction.

Solution

Since the chemical formulas of the reactants and products are known, we can write a skeleton equation.

$$H_2(g) + O_2(g) \longrightarrow H_2O(l)$$

Hydrogen is balanced but oxygen is not. If we put a coefficient of 2 in front of H_2O, the oxygen becomes balanced.

$$H_2(g) + O_2(g) \longrightarrow 2H_2O(l)$$

Now there are twice as many hydrogen atoms in the product as there are in the reactants. To correct this, put a coefficient of 2 in front of H_2. The equation is now balanced.

$$2H_2(g) + O_2(g) \longrightarrow 2H_2O(l)$$

Check the coefficients. They must be in their lowest possible ratio: $2(H_2)$, $1(O_2)$, and $2(H_2O)$. Figure 7·5 illustrates this balanced chemical equation.

Beginning students are tempted to balance this equation by placing a 2 after the O in H_2O. It should be emphasized that even a slight change in a subscript changes a substance dramatically. H_2O has very different properties than H_2O_2.

Coefficients in a balanced chemical equation that are 1's are usually not written.

Figure 7·5
A balanced chemical equation obeys the law of conservation of mass. The same number of each kind of atom is on each side of the equation.

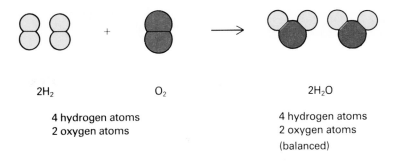

$2H_2$ O_2 $2H_2O$

4 hydrogen atoms   4 hydrogen atoms
2 oxygen atoms   2 oxygen atoms
                          (balanced)

When the same polyatomic ion is present as a reactant and a product, it is easier to balance the polyatomic ion than the individual atoms.

Figure 7·6
Copper reacts with silver nitrate to form copper nitrate and silver. Notice the silver plating on the copper strip and the characteristic blue-green color of the copper(II) ion in solution.

Never change the formula of a substance when balancing an equation.

Example 4

Balance the following equation.

$$AgNO_3(aq) + Cu(s) \longrightarrow Cu(NO_3)_2(aq) + Ag(s)$$

Solution

Since this reaction involves the polyatomic nitrate ion, we can save time if we consider the nitrate ion as a unit. Put a coefficient of 2 in front of $AgNO_3$ to balance the nitrate ion.

$$2AgNO_3(aq) + Cu(s) \longrightarrow Cu(NO_3)_2(aq) + Ag(s)$$

By inspection we see that the silver is not balanced. Put a coefficient of 2 in front of Ag.

$$2AgNO_3(aq) + Cu(s) \longrightarrow Cu(NO_3)_2(aq) + 2Ag(s)$$

Example 5

Balance the following equation.

$$Al(s) + O_2(g) \longrightarrow Al_2O_3(s)$$

Solution

First balance the aluminum by adding a coefficient of 2 in front of Al.

$$2Al(s) + O_2(g) \longrightarrow Al_2O_3(s)$$

We now have a situation that occurs quite frequently in balancing equations. We might term it the even-odd problem. Any whole-number coefficient placed in front of the O_2 will give an even number of oxygen atoms on the left. This is because we are always multiplying the coefficient by the subscript 2. The problem is that the odd number of oxygen atoms on the right has to be made even to be able to balance. The simplest way to do this is to multiply the formula with the odd number of oxygen atoms by 2.

$$2Al(s) + O_2(g) \longrightarrow 2Al_2O_3(s)$$

Now there are six oxygens on the right. Balance the oxygens on the left with a 3 and rebalance the aluminum on the left with a 4.

$$4Al(s) + 3O_2(g) \longrightarrow 2Al_2O_3(s)$$

Suppose we had written the equation for the formation of aluminum oxide as follows.

$$8Al(s) + 6O_2(g) \longrightarrow 4Al_2O_3(s)$$

This equation is balanced but incorrect because the coefficients are not in their lowest possible ratio. Each of them can be divided by 2.

Problems

3. Balance the following equations.
   a. $Al + N_2 \longrightarrow AlN$
   b. $NaCl + H_2SO_4 \longrightarrow Na_2SO_4 + HCl$
   c. $Al + CuSO_4 \longrightarrow Al_2(SO_4)_3 + Cu$
   d. $P + O_2 \longrightarrow P_2O_5$
   e. $Fe(OH)_3 \longrightarrow Fe_2O_3 + H_2O$

4. Rewrite these word equations as balanced chemical equations.
   a. sodium + water $\longrightarrow$ sodium hydroxide + hydrogen
   b. hydrogen + sulfur $\longrightarrow$ hydrogen sulfide
   c. iron(III) chloride + calcium hydroxide $\longrightarrow$ iron(III) hydroxide + calcium chloride
   d. carbon + oxygen $\longrightarrow$ carbon monoxide
   e. potassium nitrate $\longrightarrow$ potassium nitrite + oxygen

---

3. a. $2Al + N_2 \longrightarrow 2AlN$
   b. $2NaCl + H_2SO_4 \longrightarrow Na_2SO_4 + 2HCl$
   c. $2Al + 3CuSO_4 \longrightarrow Al_2(SO_4)_3 + 3Cu$
   d. $4P + 5O_2 \longrightarrow 2P_2O_5$
   e. $2Fe(OH)_3 \longrightarrow Fe_2O_3 + 3H_2O$

Be sure to count atoms correctly. $3Fe_2(SO_4)_3$ indicates 6 Fe atoms, 9 S atoms, and 36 O atoms.

4. a. $2Na + 2H_2O \longrightarrow 2NaOH + H_2$
   b. $H_2 + S \longrightarrow H_2S$
   c. $2FeCl_3 + 3Ca(OH)_2 \longrightarrow 2Fe(OH)_3 + 3CaCl_2$
   d. $2C + O_2 \longrightarrow 2CO$
   e. $2KNO_3 \longrightarrow 2KNO_2 + O_2$

Figure 7·7
St. Elmo Brady's research centered on the chemistry of plants and their products.

7·A   Passing the Torch for Chemistry: St. Elmo Brady

In 1916 St. Elmo Brady became the first black man to be awarded a doctorate in chemistry. In that year he left the University of Illinois to begin a career dedicated to inspiring young people in the study of science. Dr. Brady studied plant chemistry under Dr. George Washington Carver at Tuskegee Institute. This remained one of his research interests, along with other branches of organic chemistry. In the course of his career, he developed departments of chemistry at Tuskegee Institute, Howard University, and Fisk University. After his retirement from Fisk in 1952, he went to Tougaloo College in Mississippi to start yet another department of chemistry. Dr. Brady was known for his dedication to research and his love of teaching.

Much of the research in chemistry is done by university professors, assisted by their students. Many brilliant men and women combine scholarship in chemistry with dedication to teaching. University teachers do laboratory research, write scholarly papers, teach several courses, and advise undergraduate and graduate students. They may also have administrative duties. University teaching generally requires a doctorate in chemistry.

7·3 Combination Reactions

We can only know with certainty what the products of a chemical reaction are by carrying out that reaction in the laboratory. The reactants must be allowed to react and the products of this chemical reaction must be identified. Carrying out each reaction in the laboratory is the ideal, but it is both time consuming and costly. It is possible, however, to predict the products of some chemical reactions. To achieve this, you must be able to recognize various types of reactions. Five general types of reactions are: combination, decomposition, single-replacement, double-replacement, and combustion.

As the name implies, *in a* **combination reaction** *two or more substances react to form a single substance* (Figure 7·8). The reactants of most common combination reactions are either two elements or two compounds. One of the reactants is often water. The product of a combination (or synthesis) reaction must be a compound. Two nonmetals can often combine in more than one way. Thus for combination reactions involving nonmetals you will usually need to be told what the product is. Combination reactions usually liberate energy as they take place.

▮ The reaction of two or more substances to form a single product is a combination reaction.

Combination reactions usually liberate energy as they take place.

S (atom)   + O_2 (molecule)   ⟶ SO_2 (molecule)

Combination reaction

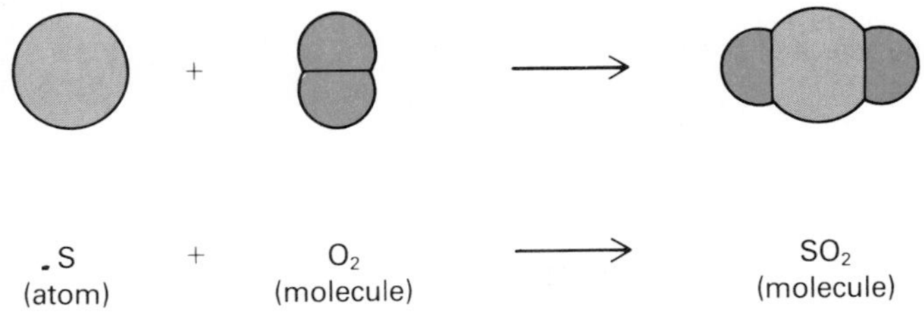

Figure 7·8
The elements sulfur and oxygen *combine* to form the compound sulfur dioxide, SO_2.

Figure 7·9
When it is ignited, sulfur will combine with oxygen to form sulfur dioxide gas.

A general equation for a combination reaction is:

$$R + S \longrightarrow RS$$

Example 6

Complete the following combination reactions.

a. $Al(s) + O_2(g) \longrightarrow$
b. $S(s) + O_2(g) \longrightarrow$
c. $Cu(s) + S(s) \longrightarrow$
d. $SO_3(g) + H_2O(l) \longrightarrow$
e. $CaO(s) + H_2O(l) \longrightarrow$

Solution

a. Write the correct formula for the compound aluminum oxide by using ionic charges. Then balance the equation.

$$Al(s) + O_2(g) \longrightarrow Al_2O_3(s) \text{ (unbalanced)}$$

$$4Al(s) + 3O_2(g) \longrightarrow 2Al_2O_3(s)$$

b. One reaction between sulfur and oxygen gives SO_2.

$$S(s) + O_2(g) \longrightarrow SO_2(g) \text{ (balanced)}$$

Another possible reaction is the formation of SO_3.

$$S(s) + O_2(g) \longrightarrow SO_3(g) \text{ (unbalanced)}$$

$$2S(s) + 3O_2(g) \longrightarrow 2SO_3(g)$$

This reaction takes place in the atmosphere and is one of the causes of acid rain. Burning sulfur-containing fuels is one source of sulfur trioxide.

c. Two reactions are possible because copper has more than one common ionic charge (Section 5·6).

$$Cu(s) + S(s) \longrightarrow CuS(s) \text{ [copper(II)]}$$

$$2Cu(s) + S(s) \longrightarrow Cu_2S(s) \text{ [copper(I)]}$$

d. Reactions between water and nonmetal oxides usually give an oxyacid. Often we can get the formula of the acid by "adding" the two molecules together.

$$SO_3(g) + H_2O(l) \longrightarrow H_2SO_4(aq)$$

e. A metal oxide reacts with water to give a metal hydroxide called a base. Use ionic charges to write the formula of the compound.

$$CaO(s) + H_2O(l) \longrightarrow Ca(OH)_2(aq)$$

Problem

5. Write balanced chemical equations for the following combination reactions. Refer to the solutions in Example 6 to help you determine the products.

a. $Ca + S \longrightarrow$
b. $Fe + O_2 \longrightarrow$ iron(II) oxide
c. $P + O_2 \longrightarrow$ diphosphorus pentoxide
d. $N_2O_5 + H_2O \longrightarrow$
e. $Na_2O + H_2O \longrightarrow$
f. $Mg + O_2 \longrightarrow$

5. a. $Ca + S \longrightarrow CaS$
   b. $2Fe + O_2 \longrightarrow 2FeO$
   c. $4P + 5O_2 \longrightarrow 2P_2O_5$
   d. $N_2O_5 + H_2O \longrightarrow 2HNO_3$
   e. $Na_2O + H_2O \longrightarrow 2NaOH$
   f. $2Mg + O_2 \longrightarrow 2MgO$

7·4 Decomposition Reactions

■ A single substance is broken down into two or more simpler substances in a decomposition reaction.

In a **decomposition reaction** *a single compound is broken down into two or more simpler products* (Figure 7·10). These products can be any combination of elements and compounds. It is usually very difficult to predict the products of decomposition reactions. When a simple binary compound breaks down, however, you know the products will be the constituent elements. Most decomposition reactions require energy in the form of heat, light, or electricity.

Decomposition reactions often absorb energy when they take place.

Figure 7·10
The compound calcium carbonate, $CaCO_3$, *decomposes* into simpler compounds: calcium oxide, CaO, and carbon dioxide, CO_2. This reaction is used to make lime (calcium oxide) from limestone (primarily calcium carbonate).

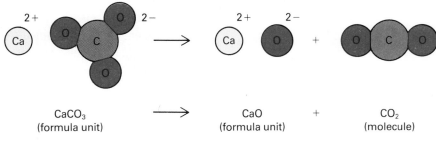

$$CaCO_3 \longrightarrow CaO + CO_2$$
(formula unit)   (formula unit)   (molecule)

Decomposition reaction

A general equation for a decomposition reaction is:

$$RS \longrightarrow R + S$$

Example 7

Write balanced equations for each of these decomposition reactions.

a. $H_2O(l) \xrightarrow{\text{electricity}}$

b. mercury(II) oxide $\xrightarrow{\Delta}$

Solution

a. Water, a binary compound, breaks down into its elements. Reminder: hydrogen and oxygen are both diatomic.

$$H_2O(l) \xrightarrow{\text{electricity}} H_2(g) + O_2(g) \quad \text{(unbalanced)}$$

$$2H_2O(l) \xrightarrow{\text{electricity}} 2H_2(g) + O_2(g)$$

b. $HgO(s) \xrightarrow{\Delta} Hg(l) + O_2(g) \quad \text{(unbalanced)}$

$$2HgO(s) \xrightarrow{\Delta} 2Hg(l) + O_2(g)$$

Problem

6. Write balanced chemical equations for each of these decomposition reactions.

a. nickel(II) carbonate $\xrightarrow{\Delta}$ nickel(II) oxide + _____

b. $AgO \xrightarrow{\Delta}$

c. ammonium nitrate $\xrightarrow{\Delta}$ dinitrogen monoxide + water

6. a. $NiCO_3 \xrightarrow{\Delta} NiO + CO_2$
 b. $2AgO \xrightarrow{\Delta} 2AgO$
 c. $NH_4NO_3 \xrightarrow{\Delta} N_2O + H_2O$

7·5   Single-Replacement Reactions

■ One element displaces another element from a compound in a single-replacement reaction.

In a **single-replacement reaction** *atoms of an element replace the atoms of a second element in a compound* (Figure 7·11). These reactions are also called displacement reactions. Whether one metal will replace another metal from a compound can be determined by the relative reactivities of the two metals. *The* **activity series of metals** (Table 7·2) *lists metals in order of decreasing reactivity.* A reactive metal will replace any metal found below it in the activity series. Thus sodium would replace zinc or silver from a compound. By contrast, sodium would not replace lithium or calcium.

A nonmetal can also replace another nonmetal from a compound. This replacement is usually limited to the halogens (F_2, Cl_2, Br_2, and I_2). The activity of the halogens decreases as you go down Group 7A on the periodic table.

$$
\begin{array}{c|c}
\text{Decreasing} & F_2 \\
\text{activity} & Cl_2 \\
& Br_2 \\
\downarrow & I_2
\end{array}
$$

General equations for single-replacement reactions are:

$$T + RS \longrightarrow TS + R$$

or

$$U + RS \longrightarrow RU + S$$

Example 8

Write balanced chemical equations for each of these single-replacement reactions.

a. $Zn(s) + H_2SO_4(aq) \longrightarrow$
b. $K(s) + H_2O(l) \longrightarrow$
c. $Sn(s) + NaNO_3(aq) \longrightarrow$
d. $Cl_2(g) + NaBr(aq) \longrightarrow$

Solution

a. According to the activity series of metals, zinc will displace hydrogen from an acid and take its place. Hydrogen as an element is diatomic.

$$Zn(s) + H_2SO_4(aq) \longrightarrow ZnSO_4(aq) + H_2 \uparrow$$

Figure 7·11
Iron is above copper in the activity series. The iron *replaces* the copper ions, forming a new compound, iron(II) sulfate, plus copper metal.

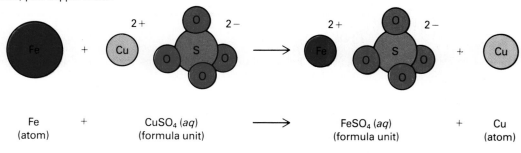

| Fe (atom) | + | CuSO$_4$ (aq) (formula unit) | $\longrightarrow$ | FeSO$_4$ (aq) (formula unit) | + | Cu (atom) |

Single-replacement reaction

Figure 7·12
The alkali metals such as potassium (shown here) displace hydrogen from water in a *single-replacement* reaction. Because these metals react so violently with water, they must be stored in mineral oil or kerosene.

Table 7·2   Activity Series of Metals

	Name	Symbol
	Lithium	Li
	Potassium	K
	Barium	Ba
	Calcium	Ca
	Sodium	Na
	Magnesium	Mg
	Aluminum	Al
	Zinc	Zn
	Iron	Fe
	Nickel	Ni
	Tin	Sn
	Lead	Pb
	(Hydrogen)	(H)*
	Copper	Cu
	Mercury	Hg
	Silver	Ag
	Gold	Au

Decreasing activity ↓

*Metals from Li to Na will replace H from acids and water; from Mg to Pb they will replace H from acids only.

b. Potassium will displace hydrogen from water. It is helpful to write water as HOH and visualize it as being made of H^+ and OH^-.

$$K(s) + H^+OH^-(l) \longrightarrow KOH(aq) + H_2 \uparrow \qquad \text{(unbalanced)}$$

$$2K(s) + 2HOH(l) \longrightarrow 2KOH(aq) + H_2 \uparrow$$

c. No reaction occurs because tin is less reactive than sodium.
d. Chlorine is more reactive than bromine and will displace bromine from a compound. Bromine is diatomic and a liquid.

$$Cl_2(g) + NaBr(aq) \longrightarrow NaCl(aq) + Br_2(l) \qquad \text{(unbalanced)}$$

$$Cl_2(g) + 2NaBr(aq) \longrightarrow 2NaCl(aq) + Br_2(l)$$

Problem

7. Use the activity series of metals to write balanced chemical equations for each of these single-replacement reactions.
 a. $Al + H_2SO_4 \longrightarrow$
 b. $Cl_2 + KI \longrightarrow$
 c. $Cu + FeSO_4 \longrightarrow$
 d. $Li + H_2O \longrightarrow$

7. a. $2Al + 3H_2SO_4 \longrightarrow$
  $Al_2(SO_4)_3 + 3H_2$
 b. $Cl_2 + 2KI \longrightarrow 2KCl + I_2$
 c. No reaction
 d. $2Li + 2H_2O \longrightarrow$
  $2LiOH + H_2$

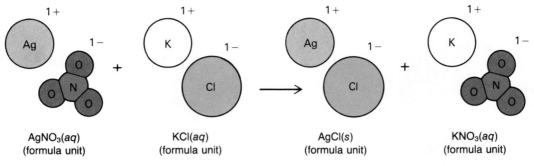

AgNO$_3$(*aq*)
(formula unit)

KCl(*aq*)
(formula unit)

AgCl(*s*)
(formula unit)

KNO$_3$(*aq*)
(formula unit)

Double-replacement reaction

Figure 7·13
The silver and potassium ions exchange places in this *double-replacement* reaction. Two new compounds are formed: silver chloride and potassium nitrate. The reaction occurs because silver chloride forms a precipitate.

■ Two ionic compounds exchange cations (or anions) in a double-replacement reaction.

A general equation for a double-replacement reaction is:

RS + TU ⟶ RU + TS

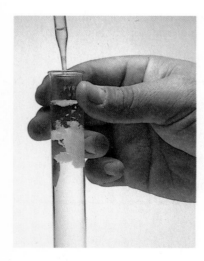

Figure 7·14
Solutions of barium chloride and potassium carbonate react in a double-replacement reaction to form barium carbonate, the white precipitate. Potassium chloride, the other product of the reaction, remains in solution.

7·6 Double-Replacement Reactions

Double-replacement reactions *involve an exchange of positive ions between two compounds* (Figure 7·13). These reactions generally take place between two ionic compounds in aqueous solution. For a double-replacement reaction to occur, one of the following statements is usually true concerning at least one of the products of the reaction. (a) It is only slightly soluble and precipitates from solution. (b) It is a gas that bubbles out of the mixture. (c) It is a molecular compound such as water.

Example 9

Write balanced chemical equations for each of these double-replacement reactions.
a. NaOH(*aq*) + H$_2$SO$_4$(*aq*) ⟶
b. BaCl$_2$(*aq*) + K$_2$CO$_3$(*aq*) ⟶
c. FeS(*s*) + HCl(*aq*) ⟶

Solution

a. This reaction takes place because of the formation of water as one of the products.

$$NaOH(aq) + H_2SO_4(aq) \longrightarrow Na_2SO_4(aq) + H_2O(l)$$

(unbalanced)

$$2NaOH(aq) + H_2SO_4(aq) \longrightarrow Na_2SO_4(aq) + 2H_2O(l)$$

b. The driving force behind the reaction is the formation of a precipitate.

$$BaCl_2(aq) + K_2CO_3(aq) \longrightarrow BaCO_3 \downarrow + KCl(aq)$$

(unbalanced)

$$BaCl_2(aq) + K_2CO_3(aq) \longrightarrow BaCO_3 \downarrow + 2KCl(aq)$$

c. A gas is formed in this double-replacement reaction.

$$FeS(s) + HCl(aq) \longrightarrow H_2S \uparrow + FeCl_2(aq) \text{ (unbalanced)}$$

$$FeS(s) + 2HCl(aq) \longrightarrow H_2S \uparrow + FeCl_2(aq)$$

8. a. $3H_2SO_4 + 2Al(OH)_3 \longrightarrow$
$Al_2(SO_4)_3 + 6H_2O$
b. $3KOH + H_3PO_4 \longrightarrow$
$K_3PO_4 + 3H_2O$
c. $SrBr_2 + (NH_4)_2CO_3 \longrightarrow$
$SrCO_3 + 2NH_4Br$

Figure 7·15
This balance is used for microanalysis because it has a precision of .001 mg or 10^{-6} g.

Problem

8. Write a balanced equation for each of these reactions.
  a. $H_2SO_4 + Al(OH)_3 \longrightarrow$
  b. $KOH + H_3PO_4 \longrightarrow$
  c. $SrBr_2 + (NH_4)_2CO_3 \longrightarrow$

7·B Qualitative and Quantitative Analysis

Finding out what is in a chemical sample is the job of the analytical chemist. The analysis may determine what elements are in a particular compound, or what compounds are in a mixture. Perhaps only a particular grouping of atoms within a large molecule is of interest. If the results must show the exact amount of each substance present, the process is called *quantitative analysis*. If the results show only what those substances are, the process is called *qualitative analysis*.

Most high school chemistry courses include a qualitative analysis experiment. Generally, this involves identifying a compound, or part of a compound, by doing simple chemical tests. These usually include single-replacement and double-replacement reactions. The tests are called "wet chemical methods" because they involve mixing chemicals in ordinary glassware and drawing conclusions from the visible reactions. Wet chemical methods used in *quantitative* analysis require very accurate mass and volume measurements. After a substance has been isolated by a chemical reaction, it must be collected very carefully and measured exactly. Professional chemists use some wet chemical methods, but most analytical work today is done with instruments.

The analytical chemist must often work with an extremely small sample. If the mass of the sample is greater than 0.1 gram, the work is called macroanalysis. If the sample mass is between 0.01 and 0.1 gram, it is called semimicroanalysis. There are also categories of micro- and submicroanalysis. The last category deals with samples that weigh less than 1×10^{-6} gram! A balance used for submicro-analysis can detect 2×10^{-8} grams.

Many instrumental methods work by detecting the type of light or other radiant energy given off or absorbed by atoms or molecules. These patterns of energy, called spectra, identify a chemical as fingerprints identify a person. (See Chapter 11 for more information on spectra.) The mass spectrometer is used to identify fragments of molecules by their mass. This is often helpful in analyzing large organic molecules such as drugs. (See Section 4·D for a description of the mass spectrometer.) Many other techniques detect characteristic behavior that occurs when molecules or atoms are subjected to

various conditions. Some of these techniques are described in later chapters (see Sections 11·B and 16·A).

Crime laboratories, medical centers, academic and government research facilities, and chemical industries of all types employ analytical chemists. A forensic chemist is asked to analyze a paint chip to determine its lead content. A surgeon requests constant monitoring of the oxygen and carbon dioxide in a patient's blood. A professor wants to determine the products of a newly devised chemical reaction. A government water-quality chemist analyzes lake water for mercury. A pharmaceutical chemist must determine the exact molecular structure of a new drug. All these situations require the skills of an analytical chemist. Analytical chemists may also specialize in designing new instruments and methods of analysis.

A person can prepare for a career in analytical chemistry by obtaining a college degree in chemistry with emphasis on analytical methods and instrumentation. A knowledge of computers is also essential because they are used to operate many instruments and to process the results.

7·7   Combustion Reactions

■ A substance burning in oxygen is a combustion reaction.

In a **combustion reaction** *oxygen reacts with another substance, often producing energy in the form of heat and light.* Combustion reactions commonly involve hydrocarbons which are compounds of hydrogen and carbon. The complete combustion of a hydrocarbon produces the compounds carbon dioxide and water. Figure 7·16 shows the combustion of methane, the major component of natural gas. If sufficient oxygen is not available during the course of a reaction, combustion will be incomplete. Elemental carbon and poisonous carbon monoxide may be additional products. A combustion reaction might be viewed as a variation of a combination reaction. The oxygen combines with both the carbon and the hydrogen. The complete combustion of a hydrocarbon produces a large amount of energy (Section 8·7). For this reason, hydrocarbons such as methane(CH_4), propane (C_3H_8), butane (C_4H_{10}), and octane(C_4H_{10}) are important fuels.

Breathing carbon monoxide is dangerous to humans because it interferes with the oxygen transport by red blood cells.

Figure 7·16
Carbon dioxide and water are the common products of the *combustion* of methane and other compounds containing carbon and hydrogen.

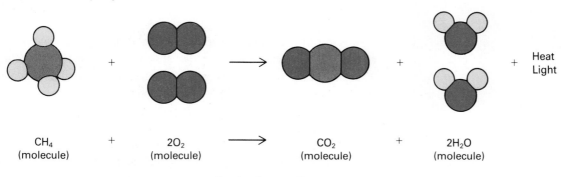

| CH_4 (molecule) | + | $2O_2$ (molecule) | ⟶ | CO_2 (molecule) | + | $2H_2O$ (molecule) |

Combustion reaction

The general equation for combustion of a hydrocarbon is:

$$C_xH_y + O_2 \longrightarrow CO_2 + H_2O$$

Safety

Combustion reactions can be very rapid, even explosive. In pure oxygen, combustion takes place much faster than in air. Use extreme care when working around a source of oxygen.

9. **a.** $C_6H_{12}O_6 + 6O_2 \longrightarrow$
$$6CO_2 + 6H_2O$$
b. $2C_8H_{18} + 25O_2 \longrightarrow$
$$16CO_2 + 18H_2O$$

Example 10

Write a balanced equation for the complete combustion of these fuels.
a. benzene, $C_6H_6(l)$ **b.** methyl alcohol, $CH_3OH(l)$

Solution

a. Oxygen is the other reactant in a combustion reaction. The products are CO_2 and H_2O.

$$C_6H_6(l) + O_2(g) \longrightarrow CO_2(g) + H_2O(g) \text{ (unbalanced)}$$

$$2C_6H_6(l) + 15O_2(g) \longrightarrow 12CO_2(g) + 6H_2O(g)$$

b. $2CH_3OH(l) + 3O_2(g) \longrightarrow 2CO_2(g) + 4H_2O(g)$

Problem

9. Write a balanced equation for the complete combustion of these compounds.   **a.** glucose, $C_6H_{12}O_6$ **b.** octane, C_8H_{18}

Figure 7·17
The different colors of a candle flame represent different stages in the combustion process.

Labels on figure:
- Dark outer cone of cooled carbon particles (soot)
- Hottest part of the flame with ample supply of oxygen and vaporized wax
- Glowing outer cone of unburned carbon particles
- Dark, oxygen-deficient inner cone
- Burning wick
- Dark, vaporized wax-deficient inner cone
- Melted wax
- Solid wax

Safety

When working with flames, be sure that there is no possibility of loose clothing or hair falling into the flame. Do not reach across a flame.

7·C   What's in a Flame?

A flame is a reaction front, an area in a gas where combustion is taking place. Vaporized fuel goes into the flame, and products come out of it. The reactants and products are usually gases, but may also include fine liquid or solid particles. Wax and methane are examples of fuels that contain compounds of hydrogen and carbon. If they are mixed with all the oxygen they need to burn completely, the products are carbon dioxide and water. The reaction also gives off energy in the form of heat and light.

A candle flame is called a diffusion flame. The air needed for combustion simply diffuses into it. When a match is held near the wick of an unlit candle, the wax melts and vaporizes. The heat of the match starts the combustion reaction of candle wax and oxygen in the air. This reaction gives off heat, which keeps the reaction going even after the match has been taken away. The air supply is drawn upward into the flame from below the burning wick. Thus the upper region of the flame has less oxygen than the area near the wick. This means that some of the vaporized wax cannot be completely burned in the upper part of the flame. Instead it remains as tiny carbon particles, which glow in the heat of the flame. The glowing carbon particles give the flame a bright yellow color. By contrast, the darker area of the flame is hotter. There is more oxygen in this region and the combustion takes place more completely.

If the air vents of a Bunsen burner are completely shut, air can only mix with the gaseous fuel by diffusing into the flame. Under these conditions the flame is like that of a candle and has the same

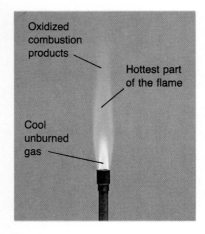

Figure 7·18
A bunsen burner flame has three distinct regions: a cool dark inner area of unburned gas, a hot middle cone where combustion takes place, and a cooler outer cone where the combustion products form carbon dioxide and water.

Recognizing reactions by type can be helpful in the prediction of the products of a chemical reaction.

bright yellow color. If the air vents are open, however, air is drawn in at the bottom of the burner tube. It mixes with the gas in the tube, and the mixture that comes out at the top of the burner has almost all the oxygen it needs to burn completely. This is called a premixed flame.

The innermost dark cone of this flame is cold unburned gas. A match suspended in this area of the flame will not light, even though it is surrounded by the flame. The bright blue inner region is actually a hollow cone. In this region the premixed fuel and air are burning, and this is the hottest part of the flame. Even here there is not enough oxygen for all of the methane to be converted to carbon dioxide and water. Some of the fuel becomes carbon monoxide and hydrogen gas. These gases leave the inner cone and enter the outermost area of the flame. There they combine with air that is diffusing into the flame and are burned to give carbon dioxide and water. Because it is a diffusion flame, this outer region is not as hot as the inner premixed region of the flame.

7·8   Summary of the Types of Reactions

Many chemical reactions can be classified as one of five general types. To classify a reaction as to type, you must look at what happens as reactants are converted into products. In a *combination reaction,* two or more elements or compounds combine chemically to form a new compound. By contrast, a single reactant is the identifying characteristic of a *decomposition reaction.* In a typical decomposition reaction, a compound is decomposed into two or more elements and/or compounds.

When oxygen reacts with a compound composed of the elements carbon and hydrogen (and perhaps, oxygen), a *combustion reaction* takes place. If all the carbon in the product is present as carbon dioxide, the reaction is complete combustion. If carbon monoxide is formed, however, the reaction is incomplete combustion. Whether a combustion reaction is complete or incomplete depends upon the amount of oxygen present. It also depends on reaction conditions, such as temperature.

Single- and double-replacement reactions are the final two general types of reactions. In a *single-replacement reaction* an element replaces another element from a compound. A new compound and a new element are formed. The activity series of metals is used to determine whether a single-replacement reaction will occur. In a *double-replacement reaction* two ionic compounds react by exchanging cations to form two different compounds. A double-replacement reaction usually takes place in aqueous solution.

Keys to identifying chemical reactions by type and the means of predicting products of a reaction are shown in Table 7·3. Nevertheless, some reactions do not fall into any of these five general types. The only way to determine the products of any reaction with certainty is to carry out the reaction in the laboratory.

Table 7·3	Keys to Identifying Types of Chemical Reactions			
General equation	Reactants	Probable reaction type	Probable products	
$R + S \rightarrow RS$	Two elements	Combination	A single compound	
	Two compounds, at least one a molecular compound	Combination	A single compound	
$RS \rightarrow R + S$	A single binary compound	Decomposition	Two elements	
	A single ternary compound	Decomposition	Two or more elements and/or compounds	
$T + RS \rightarrow TS + R$	An element and a compound	Single-replacement	A different element and a new compound	
$R^+S^- + T^+U^- \rightarrow R^+U^- + T^+S^-$	Two ionic compounds	Double-replacement	Two new compounds	
$C_xH_y + O_2 \rightarrow xCO_2 + \frac{y}{2}H_2O$	Oxygen and a compound of C, H, (O)	Combustion	CO_2 and H_2O (with incomplete combustion, C and/or CO may be additional products)	

Problem

10. After balancing each of these equations, identify them as to type.
   a. $Mg + H_2SO_4 \longrightarrow MgSO_4 + H_2$
   b. $Fe + O_2 \longrightarrow Fe_3O_4$
   c. $Pb(NO_3)_2 \longrightarrow PbO + NO_2 + O_2$
   d. $C_2H_6 + O_2 \longrightarrow CO_2 + H_2O$
   e. $Pb(NO_3)_2 + NaI \longrightarrow PbI_2 + NaNO_3$
   f. $(NH_4)_2SO_4 + NaOH \longrightarrow NH_3 + H_2O + Na_2SO_4$
   (Hint: There are two stepwise reactions in this equation.)

10. a. $Mg + H_2SO_4 \longrightarrow MgSO_4 + H_2$
single replacement
   b. $3Fe + 2O_2 \longrightarrow Fe_3O_4$
combination
   c. $2Pb(NO_3)_2 \longrightarrow 2PbO + 4NO_2 + O_2$
decomposition
   d. $2C_2H_6 + 7O_2 \longrightarrow 4CO_2 + 6H_2O$ combustion
   e. $Pb(NO_3)_2 + 2NaI \longrightarrow PbI_2 + 2NaNO_3$
double replacement
   f. $(NH_4)_2SO_4 + 2NaOH \longrightarrow 2NH_3 + 2H_2O + Na_2SO_4$
double replacement, then decomposition

7·D   The Chemistry of Firefighting

In North America more than 20,000 people are killed by fire each year. Every year over 200,000 people are injured, and millions of dollars in property damage are done by fires. Controlling fires is an important application of chemistry.

Figure 7·19
Although controlled combustions can be useful, uncontrolled combustions can be destructive and dangerous.

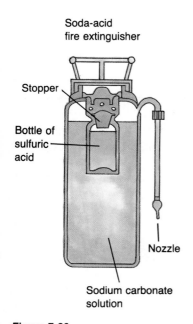

Soda-acid
fire extinguisher

Stopper

Bottle of
sulfuric
acid

Nozzle

Sodium carbonate
solution

Figure 7·20
When this fire extinguisher is inverted, the stopper falls out of the bottle containing sulfuric acid. The sulfuric acid reacts with the sodium carbonate solution to produce carbon dioxide. The carbon dioxide and water put out the fire by cutting off the oxygen supply.

Fire, or combustion, is the rapid reaction of a fuel with oxygen. The fuel is heated initially with a match, an electric current, a bolt of lightning, or intense light. Once heated, the fuel is converted into very reactive molecules, called combustion intermediates. These, in turn, can react with oxygen. Heat is liberated in the reaction, and this heat keeps the reaction going. *A fire can be put out by cooling the fuel or by cutting off the supply of oxygen.* It will also be extinguished if the combustion intermediates are tied up so that they cannot react with oxygen. All these methods are commonly used in firefighting.

Water works in two ways to put out a fire. First, it can cool the fuel below its ignition point. Second, the heat of the fire changes the water to steam. This dilutes the oxygen in the air around the fire, thus reducing the oxygen supply. Water is even more effective as a fine spray or fog. It can be made to "stick" to the burning fuel better by adding a chemical that will make it foam.

The water in pressurized fire extinguishers usually has calcium chloride or some other salt dissolved in it to prevent it from freezing at cold temperatures. The pressure is created by carbon dioxide. Some fire extinguishers have to be inverted to work. These often contain a bottle of sulfuric acid with a loose stopper and a water solution of sodium carbonate. When the extinguisher is inverted, the stopper falls out of the bottle and the acid mixes with the sodium carbonate solution. Carbon dioxide is generated by the reaction.

$$Na_2CO_3(aq) + H_2SO_4(aq) \longrightarrow Na_2SO_4(aq) + H_2O(l) + CO_2(g)$$

The carbon dioxide serves to pressurize the container and also helps to put out the fire.

A carbon dioxide fire extinguisher should not be used on a person. The gas becomes extremely cold when it is released. It could also asphyxiate the person.

Water is not always a good choice for extinguishing a fire. If the burning material is a liquid or gas (a Class B fire), a stream of water can sometimes spread the fire. For this reason, water is generally used only on Class A fires—fires that have solid fuel. Because the water in fire extinguishers usually has a salt dissolved in it, it will conduct electricity. Thus water extinguishers are not used in a Class C fire, a fire that involves an energized electrical circuit. Water can actually be a source of oxygen for burning metals (Class D fires).

Carbon dioxide extinguishes fires by cutting off the oxygen supply. Because carbon dioxide is more dense than air, it will tend to settle around the burning fire, as long as there is not much wind in the area. Pressurized carbon dioxide extinguishers contain liquid carbon dioxide at a pressure of 50 to 60 atmospheres. They must be used with care because a person entering an area full of carbon dioxide could lose consciousness from lack of oxygen. Carbon dioxide extinguishers can be used in all types of fires except Class D, where carbon dioxide may react with the hot metal.

Dry chemical fire extinguishers contain one of several types of powdered chemicals, pressurized by carbon dioxide. Some work by generating carbon dioxide, shutting off the oxygen supply to the fire. An example of this is common baking soda, sodium bicarbonate.

$$2NaHCO_3 + heat \longrightarrow Na_2CO_3 + H_2O + CO_2(g)$$

Other dry powders work by combining with the combustion intermediates, thus preventing them from reacting with oxygen. This type of extinguisher is effective against all types of fires and is most commonly used in automobiles and homes.

Figure 7·21
Airplanes can be used to dump fire retardant chemicals on brush and forest fires. The powder also contains a nutrient to help vegetation grow in the burned area.

A professional firefighter must understand the chemistry of fires and fire extinguishing methods. A firefighter must also know how to use and maintain a variety of tools and equipment. Knowledge of hydraulics, first aid, and building construction is also required. A college degree is not necessary for a job as a firefighter, but the competition for jobs is keen. Most firefighting jobs are civil service positions requiring a competitive examination. Education gives an advantage in taking the examinations and in obtaining promotions. Many community colleges offer two-year fire science programs.

Firefighters must be in top physical condition. They must be able to respond quickly in emergency situations and work well in a team. Special branches of firefighting require special training. Harbor fire protection includes the operation of fireboats. Airport fire protection requires knowledge of the design and construction of aircraft. Arson investigators collect evidence and interrogate witnesses and suspects. Fire prevention specialists educate the public and advise industries on the processing and storing of materials. Fire prevention engineers may design and install fire extinguishing systems or evaluate blueprints for fire safety. Members of the rescue and ambulance service may be trained paramedics. People may move from the position of firefighter to any of these specialized jobs, or they may train directly for them. The key to success and promotion in all these positions is the willingness to continue to learn.

7 Chemical Equations
Chapter Review

Key Terms

activity series of metals	7·5
balanced equation	7·2
catalyst	7·1
chemical equation	7·1
coefficient	7·2
combination reaction	7·3
combustion reaction	7·7
decomposition reaction	7·4
double-replacement reaction	7·6
single-replacement reaction	7·5
skeleton equation	7·1

Chapter Summary

A chemical reaction can be concisely represented by a chemical equation. The substances that undergo a chemical change are the reactants. The new substances formed are the products. In accordance with the law of conservation of matter, a chemical equation must be balanced. In balancing an equation, coefficients are placed in front of the reactants and products so that the same number of atoms of each element are on each side of the equation.

Special symbols are written after formulas in equations to show a substance's state. The designations for a solid, liquid, or gas are (s), (l), and (g)

respectively. A substance dissolved in water is designated (aq). If a catalyst is used to increase the speed of a chemical reaction, its formula is written above the arrow.

Many chemical equations can be classified as to type. In a combination reaction there is always a single product. The reactancts are two or more elements and/or compounds. In a decomposition reaction, a single compound is broken down into two or more simpler substances.

In a single-replacement reaction, the reactants and products are an element and a compound. The activity series of metals can be used to predict whether most single-replacement reactions will take place. A double-replacement reaction involves the exchange of cations (or anions) between two compounds. This reaction generally takes place between two ionic compounds in aqueous solution. One of the reactants in a combustion reaction is oxygen. The products of the complete combustion of a hydrocarbon are carbon dioxide and water.

Practice Questions and Problems

11. Write formulas and other symbols for these substances. *7·1*
   a. metallic potassium
   b. sodium chloride dissolved in water
   c. heat supplied to a chemical reaction
   d. liquid mercury
   e. zinc chloride as a catalyst
   f. carbon dioxide gas

12. What is the purpose of a catalyst? *7·1*

13. Write a sentence that describes each chemical reaction. *7·1*
   a. $2K(s) + 2H_2O(l) \longrightarrow 2KOH(aq) + H_2(g)$
   b. $NaOH(aq) + HNO_3(aq) \longrightarrow$
      $H_2O(l) + NaNO_3(aq)$
   c. $FeO(s) + C(s) \xrightarrow{\Delta} Fe(s) + CO(g)$

14. How is the law of conservation of matter related to the balancing of a chemical equation? *7·2*

15. Balance the following equations. *7·2*
   a. $Pb(NO_3)_2 + K_2CrO_4 \longrightarrow PbCrO_4 + KNO_3$
   b. $MnO_2 + HCl \longrightarrow MnCl_2 + H_2O + Cl_2$
   c. $C_3H_6 + O_2 \longrightarrow CO_2 + H_2O$
   d. $BaO_2 \longrightarrow BaO + O_2$
   e. $Zn(OH)_2 + H_3PO_4 \longrightarrow Zn_3(PO_4)_2 + H_2O$
   f. $CO + Fe_2O_3 \longrightarrow Fe + CO_2$

g. $CS_2 + Cl_2 \longrightarrow CCl_4 + S_2Cl_2$
h. $CH_4 + Br_2 \longrightarrow CH_3Br + HBr$
i. $Ba(CN)_2 + H_2SO_4 \longrightarrow BaSO_4 + HCN$
j. $(NH_4)_2Cr_2O_7 \longrightarrow Cr_2O_3 + H_2O + N_2$

16. What is a characteristic of every combination reaction? *7·3*

17. Complete and balance each of these combination reactions. *7·3*
   a. $Ca + Br_2 \longrightarrow$ **c.** $SO_2 + H_2O \longrightarrow$
   b. $Mg + N_2 \longrightarrow$ **d.** $Be + O_2 \longrightarrow$

18. What is a distinguishing feature of every decomposition reaction? *7·4*

19. Complete and balance these decomposition reactions. In some cases one of the decomposition products is given. *7·4*
   a. $H_2O_2 \xrightarrow{MnO_2} H_2O +$
   b. $Mg(ClO_3)_2 \longrightarrow MgCl_2 +$
   c. $HI \longrightarrow$
   d. $NaNO_3 \longrightarrow NaNO_2 +$

20. How can you tell if a metal can displace a metal ion from an ionic compound in an aqueous solution? *7·5*

21. Complete the equations for these single-replacement reactions that take place in water solution. Balance each equation. If a reaction does not occur (use the activity series), write "No reaction."
   a. $Al + CuSO_4 \longrightarrow$ *7·5*
   b. $Ca + H_2O \longrightarrow$
   c. $Zn + Pb(NO_3)_2 \longrightarrow$
   d. $Fe + H_2O \longrightarrow$
   e. $F_2 + KCl \longrightarrow$

22. What are the three "driving forces" for double-replacement reactions? *7·6*

23. Write the products for these double-replacement reactions. Then balance each equation. Assume that each reaction will occur. *7·6*
   a. $CdCl_2 + H_2S \longrightarrow$
   b. $NH_4C_2H_3O_2 + AgNO_3 \longrightarrow$
   c. $H_2C_2O_4 + NaOH \longrightarrow$
   d. $Fe(NO_3)_3 + LiOH \longrightarrow$
   e. $BaCl_2 + H_3PO_4 \longrightarrow$

24. Distinguish between complete and incomplete combustion. *7·7*

25. Write a balanced equation for the complete combustion of each of these compounds. *7·7*
   a. acetic acid, $HC_2H_3O_2$ **c.** glycerol, $C_3H_8O_3$
   b. decane, $C_{10}H_{22}$ **d.** sucrose, $C_{12}H_{22}O_{11}$

26. Balance each of these equations. Identify each as to type. 7·8

a. $HCl + Fe_2O_3 \longrightarrow FeCl_3 + H_2O$
b. $Li + O_2 \longrightarrow Li_2O$
c. $MgCO_3 \longrightarrow MgO + CO_2$
d. $HC_2H_3O_2 + Al(OH)_3 \longrightarrow$
$$Al(C_2H_3O_2)_3 + H_2O$$
e. $Fe_3O_4 + H_2 \longrightarrow Fe + H_2O$
f. $C_6H_5OH + O_2 \longrightarrow CO_2 + H_2O$
g. $KClO_4 \longrightarrow KCl + O_2$
h. $AgNO_3 + H_2S \longrightarrow Ag_2S + HNO_3$
i. $Cl_2 + KI \longrightarrow KCl + I_2$
j. $FeCl_3 + NaOH \longrightarrow Fe(OH)_3 + NaCl$

Mastery Questions and Problems

27. Each of these equations is "balanced" but incorrect. Find the errors and correctly balance each equation. 7·2

a. $2Mg + H_2SO_4 \longrightarrow Mg_2SO_4 + H_2$
b. $H_2 + Cl_2 \longrightarrow H_2Cl_2$
c. $NH_3 \longrightarrow N + H_3$
d. $Cl_2 + NaI \longrightarrow NaCl_2 + I$
e. $Na + O_2 \longrightarrow NaO_2$
f. $MgCl + CaOH \longrightarrow MgOH + CaCl$

28. Write a balanced chemical equation for each of these reactions. Use the necessary symbols from Table 7·1 to completely describe the reaction. 7·2

a. Bubbles of hydrogen gas and aqueous iron(III) chloride are produced when metallic iron is dropped into hydrochloric acid.
b. Mercury metal is produced by heating a mixture of mercury(II) sulfide and calcium oxide. Additional products are calcium sulfide and calcium sulfate.
c. Solid silver oxide can be heated to give silver and oxygen gas.
d. Solid tetraphosphorus decoxide reacts with water to produce phosphoric acid.
e. Bubbling chlorine gas through a solution of potassium iodide gives elemental iodine and a solution of potassium chloride.
f. Iodine crystals react with chlorine gas to form solid iodine trichloride.

29. Write balanced chemical equations for these double-replacement reactions that occur in aqueous solution. 7·6

a. Sodium hydroxide reacts with nitric acid.

b. Solutions of potassium fluoride and calcium nitrate are mixed.
c. Zinc sulfide is added to sulfuric acid.
d. A solution of calcium iodide is poured into a solution of mercury(II) nitrate.

30. Write balanced chemical equations for each of these combination reactions. 7·3

a. dichlorine heptoxide + water $\longrightarrow$
b. hydrogen + bromine $\longrightarrow$
c. sodium oxide + water $\longrightarrow$
d. aluminum + chlorine $\longrightarrow$

31. Write balanced chemical equations for each of these single-replacement reactions that take place in water solution. Then balance each equation. Write "No reaction" if they do not occur. 7·5

a. A piece of silver jewelry is dropped in hydrochloric acid.
b. Bromine reacts with aqueous barium iodide.
c. A piece of steel wool (iron) is placed in sulfuric acid.
d. Mercury is poured into an aqueous solution of zinc nitrate.

32. Write balanced equations for the incomplete combustion of each compound. Assume that the products are carbon monoxide and water. 7·7

a. glycerol, $C_3H_8O_3$
b. acetic acid, $HC_2H_3O_2$
c. glucose, $C_6H_{12}O_6$
d. acetylene, C_2H_2

33. Write balanced chemical equations for these decomposition reactions. 7·4

a. Passing an electric current through melted crystals of magnesium chloride decomposes it into its elements.
b. Silver carbonate decomposes into silver oxide and carbon dioxide when it is heated.
c. Heating tin(IV) hydroxide gives tin(IV) oxide and water.
d. Aluminum can be obtained from aluminum oxide with the addition of a large amount of electrical energy.

Review Questions and Problems

34. The white solid calcium chloride, $CaCl_2$, is used as a drying agent. How many grams of calcium are needed to make 98.0 g of $CaCl_2$?

35. Calculate the number of moles in each of the following substances.
  a. 34.8 g sodium hypochlorite
  b. 2.00×10^{21} molecules carbon monoxide
  c. 78.0 L nitrogen dioxide (at STP)
  d. 0.859 g magnesium ions

36. What mass of gold (density = 19.3 g/mL) occupies the same volume as 2.20 mol of aluminum (density = 2.70 g/mL)?

37. Coffees and colas are identified as to whether they contain the stimulant caffeine. The percent composition of caffeine is 49.5% C, 5.20% H, 16.5% O, and 28.9% N. What is the molecular formula of caffeine if its molar mass is 194.1 g/mol?

38. Name these compounds.
  a. $Sr(NO_3)_2$
  b. CdS
  c. $NaHCO_3$
  d. HF
  e. KCN
  f. $SnBr_4$
  g. B_2O_3
  h. $Al(OH)_3$
  i. $Fe_2(SO_4)_3$
  j. $LiClO_3$

Challenging Questions and Problems

39. Write balanced chemical equations for each of these reactions. Classify each as to type.
  a. Aluminum reacts with sulfuric acid to produce hydrogen and aluminum sulfate.
  b. Heating sulfuric acid produces water, oxygen, and sulfur dioxide.
  c. Pentane, C_5H_{12}, reacts with oxygen.
  d. Sodium iodide reacts with phosphoric acid to form hydrogen iodide and sodium phosphate.
  e. Potassium oxide reacts with water to form potassium hydroxide.

40. The mass of a proton and an electron are 1.67×10^{-24} g and 9.11×10^{-28} g respectively. What is the mass of a mole of protons and a mole of electrons? How many electrons are equal in mass to one proton?

41. Complete and balance these equations.
  a. $Bi(NO_3)_3 + H_2S \longrightarrow$
  b. $Br_2 + NaI \longrightarrow$
  c. $Al + Cl_2 \longrightarrow$
  d. $H_2O_2 \longrightarrow$
  e. $Ba(OH)_2 + HNO_3 \longrightarrow$
  f. $K + H_2O \longrightarrow$
  g. $C_2H_5OH + O_2 \longrightarrow$

Research Projects

1. Identify one or more everyday examples of each type of chemical equation.

2. Using your knowledge of chemical reactions, report on the burning of the Apollo I spacecraft in 1967.

3. What chemical reactions are commonly used in cooking?

4. What are plastic explosives? When and how are they used?

5. How does a miner's safety lamp work? Why was this an important invention?

6. Investigate single-replacement reactions in a gel such as agar.

7. How do matches work? What led to their invention and how did they change people's lives?

8. How are large buildings designed to control fires?

9. What are the chemical clues that tell an arson investigator that a fire was deliberately set?

Readings and References

Beller, Joel. *So You Want to Do a Science Project!* New York: Arco, 1982.

Coulson, E. H., A. E. J. Trinder, and Aaron E. Klein. *Test Tubes and Beakers: Chemistry for Young Experimenters.* New York: Doubleday, 1971.

Henahan, John F. "FIRE." *Science 80* (January/February 1980), pp. 28–39.

McMurry, Linda O. *George Washington Carver: Scientist and Symbol.* New York: Oxford U Pr., 1981.

Moorman, Thomas. *How to Make Your Science Project Scientific.* New York: Atheneum, 1974.

Smith, Norman F. *How Fast Do Your Oysters Grow? Investigate and Discover through Science Projects.* New York: Messner, 1982.

8 Stoichiometry

Chapter Planning Guide

Section		Demonstrations and Experiments	Resource Materials
8·1 Interpreting Chemical Equations	C*		Objectives Worksheet 8, SPB Skillsheet 8, SPB Beyond the Text: What Does Philosophy Have to Do With Chemistry?
8·2 Mole–Mole Calculations	C		Teaching Diagram 10
8·3 Mass–Mass Calculations	C	Exp 13 Quantitative Analysis, LM	Prelab 13, SPB Teaching Diagram 11
8·4 Other Stoichiometric Calculations	C		Quiz 8·1
8·A Chemical Sleuthing	E		
8·5 Limiting Reagent	O	Dem 8·1 Limiting Quantity	
8·6 Percent Yield	O	Exp 14 Balanced Chemical Equations, LM	Prelab 14, SPB Quiz 8·2
8·7 Energy Changes in Chemical Reactions	C	Dem 8·2 Endothermic Reactions Dem 8·3 Exothermic Reactions Dem 8·4 Photocell Dem 21·6 Electrolysis of Water	Teaching Diagram 12 Beyond the Text: Quality Control for Manufacturing Reclaiming Solid Wastes, ICT 8
8·B Calorimetry	E		
8·8 The Heat of Reaction	H	Exp 15 Heat of Reaction, LM Dem 8·5 Heat of Reaction Dem 8·6 Gas Adsorption by a Metal	Prelab 15, SPB Quiz 8·3 Reviewsheet 8, SPB Chapter 8 Test
*C = Core, O = Optional E = Enrichment, H = Honors		LM = Laboratory Manual	SPB = Skills Practice Book ICT = Issues in Chem. Tech.

Chapter Objectives

Having studied this chapter and done the problems, the student should be able to:

1. Interpret a balanced chemical equation in terms of interacting moles, representative particles, masses, and volumes of gases (at STP). *8·1*

2. Construct mole ratios from balanced chemical equations for use as conversion factors in stoichiometric problems. *8·2*

3. Perform stoichiometric calculations with balanced equations using moles, mass, representative particles, and volumes of gases (at STP). *8·3, 8·4*

4. Identify the limiting reagent in a reaction. *8·5*

5. Knowing the limiting reagent in a reaction, calculate the maximum amount of product(s) produced and the amount of any unreacted excess reagent. *8·5*

6. Given information from which any two of the following may be determined, calculate the third: theoretical yield, actual yield, and percentage yield. *8·6*

7. Classify reactions as exothermic or endothermic. *8·7*

8. Define the enthalpy of a substance. *8·8*

9. Relate a change in enthalpy to the heat of reaction or heat of combustion of a reaction. *8·8*

10. Use standard heats of formation to calculate the enthalpy change of a reaction. *8·8*

Teaching Suggestions

8·1 Interpreting Chemical Equations

This section reinforces the concept that a chemical equation is more than just a statement of mathematical equality.

Be sure the students understand that the numbers in the equation state the *relationships* between the substances involved in the reaction, not the actual quantities. Thus, an equation can be read several different ways, with each way giving a different kind of information. We can interpret an equation in terms of individual atoms, molecules, or formula units. We can interpret it in terms of moles, and from the numbers of moles, we can interpret it in terms of mass. If the substances involved are gases, then we can interpret in terms of volume as well.

The next sections rely on the ability of the student to use the mole interpretation of equations, so some time should be spent in going over this type of interpretation. If you find that they start getting confused with moles, advise them that they might try reasoning with a more familiar unit, the dozen, and then repeating the same reasoning with the mole.

8·2 Mole–Mole Calculations

It is crucial that the students be able to set up the mole ratios properly if they are to succeed with stoichiometry. Give this section plenty of emphasis. Work through representative examples with the students and have them do practice problems until they feel reasonably competent.

8·3 Mass–Mass Calculations

8·4 Other Stoichiometric Calculations

Be sure that the students understand the importance of converting measured quantities, such as mass and volume, to moles so that the reacting relationships in equations can be used.

You may wish to point out that whether they are doing mass–mass, mass–volume, volume–volume, or particle–mass calculations, they are still following the same basic pattern. These calculations always involve:

1. Changing the measured quantity to moles.

2. Using the moles of the given substance to find the moles of another substance.

3. Changing the moles of the other substance to a measured quantity.

The arrangement of conversion factors and mole ratios as shown in these two sections is done to accomplish the above three steps.

Some will have more trouble mastering stoichiometric calculations than any other topic in this course. It is

extremely important to go through these sections slowly, with plenty of time spent on doing sample problems for them, giving them plenty of practice, and giving them rapid feedback on the mistakes they are making. Do not expect all of the students to catch on right away. Stoichiometry takes time and a lot of effort.

Experiment 13 *Quantitative Analysis* is appropriate for these sections. It provides students with experience in determining the coefficients of a chemical equation. It can be done before the sections are discussed to serve as an introduction. It could also be done after the sections are covered, as reinforcement.

8·5 Limiting Reagent

Demonstration 8·1 *Limiting Quantity* shows this concept. Once a few examples are done for them, most students have little trouble with the idea that a reaction cannot continue after one of the reactants is no longer available for reacting. Discuss some possible causes why a reaction might not proceed to completion even though the equation indicates that it should.

Emphasize that the way in which we decide which is the limiting reagent is to compare the *mole* ratios of the given materials to the required mole ratio as shown in the equation.

8·6 Percent Yield

Experiment 14 *Balanced Chemical Equations and Stoichiometry* could be done after these sections have been covered. It provides good reinforcement of the concepts of limiting reagents and percent yield. If you wish to save time, try dividing the class into thirds. Have one-third do part A, one-third do part B, and one-third do part C. At the end they can then compare their results.

8·7 Energy Changes in Chemical Reactions

Until this point we have been ignoring the fact that energy is always involved when chemical reactions take place. Sometimes the amount of energy given off or taken in in a chemical reaction is too small to be of concern. But often the energy of a reaction is very important. For instance, it might be important if we are using the reaction as a source of energy for heating effects or the production of electrical energy. It could also be important if we are trying to get a reaction to occur and there is a required input of energy.

Be sure the students understand that the energy of a given chemical reaction is predictable and is just as much a part of the reaction as the atoms and molecules are a part of it. The energy term *belongs* in the equation along with the symbols and formulas. Just as the equation is not complete if a reactant or product is left out, it is also not complete if the energy term is left out.

When introducing the concept of endothermic and exothermic reactions, demonstrate some of the reactions listed in **Demonstration 8·2** *Endothermic Reactions* or **8·3** *Exothermic Reactions*. **Demonstration 21·6** *Electrolysis of Water* is an endothermic reaction requiring electrical energy. **Demonstration 8·4** *Photocell* shows a heatless exothermic reaction. Emphasize that the energy which goes into or out of a chemical reaction can be in many different forms, depending on the reaction. An exothermic reaction might give off heat, sound, light, or electrical energy, or do work (as in an explosion). An endothermic reaction might require heat energy, light energy, or electrical energy to take place.

8·8 The Heat of Reaction

Many students confuse the concepts of enthalpy and heat. To them, heat is something related to temperature. (A "hot" substance contains a large amount of heat.) Have them realize that the enthalpy refers to the amount of heat (or other forms of energy) *stored* in a substance, while the question of whether a substance is hot or cold has to do with the average kinetic energy of its molecules. As an example, you might point out that a stick of dynamite which has just been removed from a freezer has a very high heat content (enthalpy), yet is very cold!

While we cannot easily measure enthalpy, changes in enthalpy are relatively simple to monitor. The concept that changes in enthalpy are always described in terms of the stored energy of the system, and not in terms of its temperature, seems simple enough. Yet students are confused by this. For instance, when sodium hydroxide pellets are added to water in a test tube, the water gets noticeably hotter. Students will argue that since heat was produced, there must have been a gain of energy. Point out that whenever an energy change takes place, there is always something which gains energy and something which loses it. In the above case, while the water gained *kinetic* energy, the sodium hydroxide pellets lost *stored* energy (enthalpy). Thus, heat energy is a product of this reaction and so the energy term is written on the right-hand side of the equation. Since heats of reaction are always expressed in terms of changes in stored energy, the enthalpy change is given a negative sign.

When ammonium chloride is dissolved in water, the solution becomes quite cold. The water must have lost heat energy. Therefore, the ammonium chloride must have gained it. Energy is absorbed in this reaction, so we write the energy term on the left-hand side of the equation. The change in enthalpy is given a positive sign.

Experiment 15 *Heat of Reaction* gives the students excellent experience in calorimetry and calculating reaction heats. **Demonstration 8·5** *Heat of Reaction* could be used instead. **Demonstration 8·6** *Gas Adsorption by a Metal* shows an exothermic reaction.

Demonstrations

8·1 Limiting Quantity

Concept: The reactant which is consumed first in a chemical reaction determines the amount of product.

Materials: same as in **Demonstration 7·1,** balance.

Procedure: 1. Do the combination reaction of **Demonstration 7·1**. Write its chemical equation on the board. 2. Note the masses and the mole ratio of the reactants. 3. Calculate the amount of product expected based on the moles of each reactant. 4. Recover the product of the reaction and weigh it. 5. Note which of the reactants is the limiting quantity. 6. Discuss why it is the limiting quantity, noting the different mole ratios in the equation and the actual experiment.

8·2 Endothermic Reactions

Concept: Some chemical reactions absorb energy, while a decrease in temperature is observed.

Materials: cold packs (ammonium nitrate (NH_4NO_3) and water), water, 10 g of ammonium chloride (NH_4Cl) or ammonium nitrate, large test tube, stirring rod.

Procedure: 1. Break the pouch of a cold pack and pass it around so students can feel its coldness. 2. Half-fill a large test tube with water. 3. Add 1/4 test tube of either ammonium chloride or ammonium nitrate to the water and mix. The solution gets quite cold as the salts dissolve. Pass the tube around the class.

8·3 Exothermic Reactions

Concept: Many chemical reactions give off energy in the form of heat.

Materials: 5 mL of anhydrous copper(II) sulfate ($CuSO_4$), 5 mL of water, test tube, test tube rack, light sticks (emergency lights), safety goggles.

Procedure: 1. Dissolve the anhydrous copper(II) sulfate in an equal volume of water. The solution gets very hot. 2. Activate a light stick, which produces light without any noticeable heat. 3. Point out that in addition to heat, other forms of energy may be produced as well in an exothermic reaction. **Caution:** *Copper sulfate is an irritant.*

8·4 Photocell

Concept: Photocells absorb light to produce electrical energy.

Materials: photocell, 2 connecting wires with clips on the ends, bell or lamp of low voltage, flashlight or other light.

Procedure: 1. Attach the wires to the photocell leads and the lamp or bell. 2. Shine the light on the photocell. 3. Activate the lamp or bell by placing the photocell near it and facing it. 4. Note the electrical energy released.

8·5 Heat of Reaction

Concept: Chemical reactions give off or absorb heat.

Materials: thin aluminum frying pan or pie tin, 200 g dry calcium oxide (CaO), tray, water, egg, safety goggles.

Procedure: 1. Place the calcium oxide in a tray. 2. Place the pan inside the tray so that its bottom is in complete contact with the calcium oxide. 3. Fill the tray with water just to the surface of the calcium oxide. 4. Display the egg, then break it into the pan. 5. The egg cooks since the hydration of calcium oxide liberates 161 000 calories per mole. Note that this is an exothermic reaction with a very large heat of reaction, even though it is not a combustion. **Caution:** *Calcium oxide is corrosive.*

8·6 Gas Adsorption by a Metal

Concept: Gas adsorption by a metal is an exothermic reaction.

Materials: thin platinum wire, gas burner, forceps.

Procedure: 1. Using forceps, hold the wire over the unlit burner, with the gas on. 2. The adsorption of gas produces enough heat to light the burner.

Audiovisual Resources

Calculations Involving Equations (FS) Prentice-Hall Media, 1979. (Use with Sections 8·1, 8·3, and 8·4.) Explains how stoichiometric information can be obtained from a balanced equation and describes methods for solving mass–mass, mass–volume, and volume–volume problems.

Chemistry: The Ins and Outs of Energy (8 FS) Charles Clark, 1979, 12–21 min. each. (Use with Sections 8·7 and 8·8.) Discusses the potential and kinetic energy of chemical systems, enthalpy change, and reaction heats and their calculation.

Energy and Enthalpy in Chemical Change (FS) Prentice-Hall Media, 1973. (Use with Sections 8·7 and 8·8.) Discusses energy and enthalpy changes for endothermic and exothermic reactions and shows enthalpy calculations for important classes of reactants.

Energy and Rockets: Exothermic Reaction (F, V) Media Guild, 1981, 24 min. (Use with Section 8·7.) Illustrates the relationship between chemical bonding energies and rocket propulsion. Also covers topics in Chapter 17.

Beyond the Text

What Does Philosophy Have to Do With Chemistry?

The man who developed stoichiometry was as inspired by philosophy as by science. In the late eighteenth century, Jeremiah Richter was studying mathematics, science, and philosophy at the University of Konigsberg in his native Germany. At that time the famous philosopher Immanuel Kant was lecturing at the university. Richter probably attended lectures in which Kant discussed the nature of science. Kant proposed that all true science is essentially mathematics. He described the laws of chemistry as based on experimental observation, not on mathematical derivations. He concluded, therefore, that chemistry is not a pure science but a "systematic art."

Richter agreed with Kant that all science is mathematical in nature. He did not agree, however, that chemistry does not meet this definition. In his view, chemistry was concerned with amounts of matter and thus was certainly based on mathematics. In fact, he felt that if chemists would pay more attention to the mathematics of reactions, more progress would be made in chemistry!

Richter worked to establish mathematical relationships in double-displacement reactions. He found that the masses of the elements in the reactants and products were definitely related to each other. He then accumulated a wealth of data on the mass relationships of reacting substances. Other chemists saw the value of these data, perhaps more clearly than Richter did. After others had used his work to construct tables of combining masses of acids and bases, Richter also made such tables. He made a serious error, however, that kept him from getting credit for his work. He was convinced that the combining masses would form mathematical series. When the numbers did not conform to such a series, he sometimes changed his experimental numbers. Other chemists praised Richter's experiments but not his theories. When he died in 1807, the value of his work was only beginning to be understood.

Quality Control for Manufacturing

The quality of a manufactured product is the combination of characteristics that make it useful to people. Every company knows that its customers expect a product of consistently high quality. The job of the quality control staff is to maximize the usefulness of the product to those who want it. This can be relatively simple, as in the case of inspecting a sampling of finished packages of ice cream to

be sure each has the desired texture and taste. The job can be very complex, as in making sure that a medical device like an artificial heart will perform reliably.

Quality control chemists work in a wide variety of industries. These include companies that process or manufacture food, pharmaceuticals, cosmetics, agricultural chemicals, and plastics. Quality control chemists must have a thorough knowledge of how to make and interpret measurements. Experience in analytical chemistry and the ability to develop new analytical methods are particularly important. A quality control chemist must also be a specialist in the use of statistics and sampling techniques. He or she must keep up to date on regulations affecting the manufacture and marketing of the company's products. This person may also be responsible for seeing that the plant does not violate antipollution laws. The quality control chemist must be able to communicate effectively both orally and in writing.

Quality control engineers and scientists are involved in every aspect of a project. They contribute to the original research and development of a product. They help refine the manufacturing process. Then they develop methods to test the product or to determine why a particular product has failed to perform for the consumer.

Answers to End of Chapter Questions and Problems

Practice Questions and Problems

14. a. Two atoms Zn combine with 1 molecule oxygen to produce 2 formula units ZnO. **b.** Two formula units $KClO_3$ decompose to form 2 formula units KCl and 3 molecules O_2. **c.** Four molecules NH_3 react with 6 molecules NO to form 5 molecules N_2 and 6 molecules H_2O.

15. a. 2 mol Zn combine with 1 mol O_2 to form 2 mol ZnO. **b.** 2 mol $KClO_2$ decompose into 2 mol KCl and 3 mol O_2. **c.** 4 mol NH_3 react with 6 mol NO, producing 5 mol N_2 and 6 mol H_2O.

16. a. 162.8 g = 162.8 g **b.** 245.2 g = 245.2 g **c.** 248.0 g = 248.0 g

17. a. 1.26 mol CS_2 **b.** 18.1 mol C **c.** 3.05 mol CO **d.** 364 mol SO_2

18. a. 4.70 mol Sb_2S_3 **b.** 14.1 mol Fe **c.** 0.0813 mol Sb

19. a. 18.8 mol CO, 37.5 mol H_2 **b.** 280 g CO, 40 g H_2 **c.** 23 g H_2

20. a. 15.6 g Na_2O_2 **b.** 16.0 g NaOH **c.** 0.098 g O_2

21. a. 2.36 g H_3PO_4 **b.** 1.16 g CO_2 **c.** 1.28 L CO_2

22. a. 154 g H_2O **b.** 1.71×10^{24} molecules NH_3 **c.** 69.7 g Li_3N

23. The limiting reagent determines the amount of product that can be formed in a reaction. It is completely used up in the reaction.

24. a. O_2 **b.** O_2 **c.** Cl_2 **d.** P_2O_5

25. a. 4.6 mol H_2O **b.** 3.2 mol P_2O_5 **c.** 5.3 mol $AlCl_3$ **d.** .74 mol H_3PO_4

26. a. 0.4 mol H_2 **b.** 0.6 mol P **c.** 0.1 mol Al **d.** 1.4 mol H_2O

27. 86.4 g H_2O

28. The "efficiency" of a reaction; the actual yield/theoretical yield expressed as a percent.

29. 97.5%

30. 96.4%

31. Heat is the product of an exothermic reaction. Heat is a reactant in an endothermic reaction.

32. a. 96 kJ **b.** positive

33. a. 17.3 kcal **b.** 72.3 kJ

34. The amount of heat released or absorbed depends in part on the physical states of the substances involved.

35. Heat released or absorbed in a chemical change.

36. ΔH for the formation of a mole of a substance from its elements.

37. a. positive **b.** negative **c.** negative **d.** negative

38. a. 62.4 kJ **b.** −26.9 kJ **c.** 113.0 kJ

Mastery Questions and Problems

39. a. 701 L N_2 **b.** no reagent in excess

40. a. 10.7 g NO, 12.8 g H_2O, 17.1 g S **b.** 32.7 mg H_2O

41. 2.78×10^3 g NO

42. a. 2.28×10^{22} atoms Zn **b.** 285 g Zn

43. 10.7 kg $CaSO_4$

44. 92.8 kJ

45. a. 44.7 L **b.** 16.1 g H_2O

Review Questions and Problems

46. 12.8 g Be

47. a. $2Al + 3FeO \rightarrow 3Fe + Al_2O_3$
b. $NaHCO_3 + HC_2H_3O_2 \rightarrow NaC_2H_3O_2 + H_2O + CO_2$
c. $2C_3H_7OH + 9O_2 \rightarrow 6CO_2 + 8H_2O$
d. $2Pb(NO_3)_2 \rightarrow 2PbO + 4NO_2 + O_2$

48. 1.30×10^{-22} g C_6H_6

49. a. 12, 12, 14 **b.** 22, 22, 25 **c.** 8, 8, 10
d. 50, 50, 70

50. $C_2H_2O_4$

51. a. $MnCrO_4$ **b.** HBr **c.** $Al_2(CO_3)_3$ **d.** SiO_2 **e.** K_2S

Challenging Questions and Problems

52. 1.1×10^6 L air

53. 13 days

54. 0.809 g/L

55. 67.6 g $C_7H_6O_4$, 62.5 g $C_4H_6O_3$

56. 6.51 g SO_3

57. 87.3% $CaCO_3$

8 Stoichiometry

Chapter Preview

Section 8·8 is appropriate for honors students.

Chemicals are used in the manufacture of almost everything we buy, for example, soaps, foods, drugs, and paints. The processes used to manufacture these items must be carried out efficiently. Any waste will cost money. This is where balanced chemical equations come in. Equations are the recipes that tell chemists what amounts of reactants to mix and what amounts of products to expect.

Balanced equations allow us to calculate the quantities of reactants and products in a reaction. When you know the quantity of one substance, you can calculate the quantity of any other substance. By quantity, we usually mean the amount of a substance expressed in grams or moles. It could just as well be a quantity in liters, tons, or molecules. Calculations using balanced equations are called *stoichiometric* calculations. **Stoichiometry** *is the calculation of quantities in chemical equations*. For chemists it is a form of bookkeeping.

Greek: *stoikheion* = element; *metron* = to measure.

8·1   Interpreting Chemical Equations

Ammonia is widely used as a fertilizer. It is produced industrially by the reaction of hydrogen with nitrogen.

$$N_2(g) + 3H_2(g) \longrightarrow 2NH_3(g)$$

What kinds of information can be derived from this equation?

1. Particles. We might look at interacting particles. One molecule of nitrogen reacts with three molecules of hydrogen to produce two molecules of ammonia. Nitrogen and hydrogen will always react together to form ammonia in this $1:3:2$ ratio of molecules. If we could make 10

Figure 8·1
Without balance, a gymnast would fall. In a similar way, balanced chemical equations are essential for chemical calculations.

Figure 8·2
The balanced chemical equation for the formation of ammonia can be interpreted in several ways.

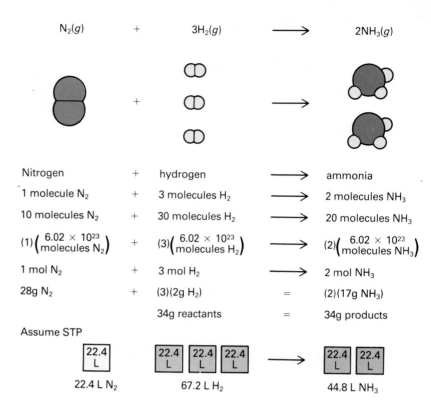

$$N_2(g) \quad + \quad 3H_2(g) \quad \longrightarrow \quad 2NH_3(g)$$

Nitrogen	+	hydrogen	$\longrightarrow$	ammonia
1 molecule N_2	+	3 molecules H_2	$\longrightarrow$	2 molecules NH_3
10 molecules N_2	+	30 molecules H_2	$\longrightarrow$	20 molecules NH_3
(1)$\left(\begin{array}{c}6.02 \times 10^{23} \\ \text{molecules } N_2\end{array}\right)$	+	(3)$\left(\begin{array}{c}6.02 \times 10^{23} \\ \text{molecules } H_2\end{array}\right)$	$\longrightarrow$	(2)$\left(\begin{array}{c}6.02 \times 10^{23} \\ \text{molecules } NH_3\end{array}\right)$
1 mol N_2	+	3 mol H_2	$\longrightarrow$	2 mol NH_3
28g N_2	+	(3)(2g H_2)	=	(2)(17g NH_3)
		34g reactants	=	34g products

Assume STP

22.4 L N_2 67.2 L H_2 $\longrightarrow$ 44.8 L NH_3

molecules of nitrogen react with 30 molecules of hydrogen, we would expect to get 20 molecules of ammonia (Figure 8·2). Of course, we cannot count out small numbers of molecules and allow them to react. We could, however, take Avogadro's number of nitrogen molecules and react them with three times Avogadro's number of hydrogen molecules. This would be the same 1 : 3 ratio of molecules of the reactants. This reaction would form two times Avogadro's number of ammonia molecules.

2. Moles. You know that Avogadro's number of representative particles is 1 mol of a substance. On the basis of the particle interpretation just given, this equation tells us the number of moles of reactants and products. One mole of nitrogen molecules reacts with three moles of hydrogen molecules. These reactants form two moles of ammonia molecules. This is the most important information that a chemical equation provides. *The coefficients of a balanced chemical equation tell us the relative number of moles of reactants and products in a chemical reaction.* From this the amounts of reactants and products can be calculated.

3. Mass. A balanced chemical equation must obey the law of conservation of mass. The mole interpretation supports this. The mass of 1 mol of nitrogen (28.0 g) plus the mass of 3 mol of hydrogen (6.0 g) does equal the mass of 2 mol of ammonia (34.0 g).

4. Volume. If we assume standard temperature and pressure, this equation also tells us about the volumes of gases. Recall that 1 mol of any gas at STP occupies a volume of 22.4 L. It follows that 22.4 L of nitrogen reacts with 67.2 L (3 × 22.4) of hydrogen to form 44.8 L (2 × 22.4) of

The coefficients in a balanced chemical equation indicate the relative number of moles of reactants and products that react in a chemical reaction.

This interpretation reflects the law of definite proportions (Section 5·3).

ammonia. Section 8·4 will show that at *any* constant temperature and pressure, nitrogen and hydrogen will react together in a 1 : 3 ratio of volume. Two volumes of ammonia will be formed.

Notice in Figure 8·2 that mass and the number of atoms are conserved in this chemical reaction. Mass and atoms will be conserved in every chemical reaction. The mass of the reactants equals the mass of the products. Representative particles, moles, and volumes of gases will not generally be conserved, although they may. Take, for example, the formation of hydrogen iodide.

$$H_2(g) + I_2(g) \longrightarrow 2HI(g)$$

In this reaction, moles, molecules, and volume all happen to be conserved. In the majority of reactions, however, they are not. In the formation of ammonia (Figure 8·2), moles, molecules, and volume of gas are not conserved. *Only mass and atoms are conserved in every chemical reaction.*

Example 1

Interpret this balanced chemical equation in terms of the interaction of relative quantities in the following four ways.
a. number of representative particles
b. number of moles
c. masses of reactants and products
d. volumes of gases at STP

$$2H_2S(g) + 3O_2(g) \longrightarrow 2SO_2(g) + 2H_2O(g)$$

Solution

a. Two molecules of H_2S react with three molecules of O_2 to form two molecules of SO_2 and two molecules of H_2O.
b. Two moles of H_2S react with 3 mol of O_2 to produce 2 mol of SO_2 and 2 mol of H_2O.
c. Apply the mole interpretation and use the gram molecular mass of the reactants and products.

$$2 \text{ mol } H_2S + 3 \text{ mol } O_2 \longrightarrow 2 \text{ mol } SO_2 + 2 \text{ mol } H_2O$$

$$(2 \text{ mol} \times 34.1 \text{ g/mol}) + (3 \text{ mol} \times 32.0 \text{ g/mol}) \longrightarrow$$

$$(2 \text{ mol} \times 64.1 \text{ g/mol}) + (2 \text{ mol} \times 18.0 \text{ g/mol})$$

$$68.2 \text{ g} + 96.0 \text{ g} \longrightarrow 128.2 \text{ g} + 36.0 \text{ g}$$

$$164.2 \text{ g} = 164.2 \text{ g}$$

d. $(2 \text{ mol } H_2S \times 22.4 \text{ L/mol}) +$

$(3 \text{ mol } O_2 \times 22.4 \text{ L/mol}) \longrightarrow (2 \text{ mol } SO_2 \times 22.4 \text{ L/mol}) +$

$(2 \text{ mol } H_2O \times 22.4 \text{ L/mol})$

Therefore, 44.8 L of H_2S reacts with 67.2 L of O_2 to form 44.8 L of SO_2 and 44.8 L of $H_2O(g)$.

Figure 8·3
Hydrogen sulfide, H_2S, smells like rotten eggs. It escapes from the ground through fumaroles in volcanic areas.

1. a. 2 mol CO + 1 mol O_2 →
                            2 mol CO_2
   88 g reactants → 88 g products
   44.8 L CO + 22.4 L O_2 →
                          44.8 L CO_2
b. 2 mol Na + 2 mol H_2O →
                     2 mol NaOH + 1 mol H_2
   82 g reactants → 82 g products
c. 2 mol C_2H_2 + 5 mol O_2 →
                     4 mol CO_2 + 2 mol H_2O
   212 g reactants →
                        212 g products
   44.8 L + 112 L →
                     89.6 L + 44.8 L

▮ Mole ratios derived from a balanced equation show the quantitative relationships between substances consumed and/or produced in a chemical reaction.

A mole ratio from an equation can be used as a conversion factor.

Safety

Ammonia solution is a common household cleaning agent. It forms toxic fumes when mixed with hypochlorite ions, found in common bleaches. Never mix chemicals, even those commonly found in the household, unless you are directed to do so by your teacher.

Problem

1. After balancing each of these equations, interpret them in terms of relative quantities in four ways. (1) number of representative particles (2) number of moles (3) masses of reactants and products (4) volumes of gases at STP (where appropriate)
a. $CO(g) + O_2(g) \longrightarrow CO_2(g)$
b. $Na(s) + H_2O(l) \longrightarrow NaOH(aq) + H_2(g)$
c. $C_2H_2(g) + O_2(g) \longrightarrow CO_2(g) + H_2O(g)$

8·2   Mole–Mole Calculations

Return now to the balanced equation for the production of ammonia.

$$N_2(g) + 3H_2(g) \longrightarrow 2NH_3(g)$$

The most important interpretation of this equation is that 1 mol of nitrogen reacts with 3 mol of hydrogen to form 2 mol of ammonia. With this interpretation we can relate moles of reactants to moles of products. The coefficients from the balanced equation can be used to write conversion factors. Then the number of moles of a product can be calculated from a given number of moles of reactant. Using other mole-quantity relationships, we can introduce mass, volume, and particles into our calculations.

Example 2

How many moles of ammonia are produced when 0.60 mol of nitrogen reacts with hydrogen?

Solution

We will work from a known number of moles of N_2 to the unknown number of moles of NH_3: mol $N_2 \longrightarrow$ mol NH_3. From the balanced equation just given, we see that 1 mol of N_2 produces 2 mol of NH_3. This relationship can be written and used as a conversion factor relating N_2 and NH_3. The conversion factor is called a *mole ratio*.

$$\frac{1 \text{ mol } N_2}{2 \text{ mol } NH_3} \quad or \quad \frac{2 \text{ mol } NH_3}{1 \text{ mol } N_2}$$

To solve the problem, we start with our given quantity, 0.60 mol of N_2. Then we multiply it by the form of the mole ratio that allows the given unit to cancel.

$$0.60 \text{ mol } N_2 \times \frac{2 \text{ mol } NH_3}{1 \text{ mol } N_2} = 1.2 \text{ mol } NH_3$$

Note that mole ratios from balanced equations are considered to be exact. They do not enter into the determination of significant figures in the answer.

Example 3

Calculate the number of moles of reactants required to make 7.24 mol of ammonia.   **a.** nitrogen **b.** hydrogen

$$N_2(g) + 3H_2(g) \longrightarrow 2NH_3(g)$$

Solution

The conversions are similar: **a.** mol $NH_3 \longrightarrow$ mol N_2;
b. mol $NH_3 \longrightarrow$ mol H_2. From the balanced equation we can get mole ratios relating each of the reactants to the product.

$$\frac{1 \text{ mol } N_2}{2 \text{ mol } NH_3} \quad or \quad \frac{2 \text{ mol } NH_3}{1 \text{ mol } N_2} \quad and \quad \frac{3 \text{ mol } H_2}{2 \text{ mol } NH_3} \quad or \quad \frac{2 \text{ mol } NH_3}{3 \text{ mol } H_2}$$

In each case, start with the given amount of product. Multiply by the appropriate mole ratio so that the given unit cancels.

a. $7.24 \text{ mol } NH_3 \times \dfrac{1 \text{ mol } N_2}{2 \text{ mol } NH_3} = 3.62 \text{ mol } N_2$

b. $7.24 \text{ mol } NH_3 \times \dfrac{3 \text{ mol } H_2}{2 \text{ mol } NH_3} = 10.86 = 10.9 \text{ mol } H_2$

Each solution in these two examples follows the same pattern. The moles of the given quantity, (G), whether reactant or product, are multiplied by a mole ratio with the given in the denominator.

$$\frac{b \text{ moles of } W}{a \text{ moles of } G}$$

In this mole ratio, W is the "wanted" quantity. The values of a and b are the coefficients from the balanced equation. A general solution for a mole–mole problem ($aG \rightarrow bW$) is given by the following equation.

$$\underset{\text{Given}}{\frac{x \text{ mol } G}{1}} \times \underset{\text{Mole ratio}}{\frac{b \text{ mol } W}{a \text{ mol } G}} = \underset{\text{Calculated}}{\frac{xb}{a} \times \text{ mol } W}$$

Problem

2. The formation of aluminum oxide from its constituent elements is represented by this equation.

$$4Al + 3O_2 \longrightarrow 2Al_2O_3$$

a. Write the six ratios of moles that can be derived from this equation.

b. How many moles of aluminum are needed to form 2.3 mol of Al_2O_3?

c. How many moles of oxygen are required to react completely with 0.84 mol of Al?

d. Calculate the number of moles of Al_2O_3 formed when 17.2 mol of O_2 reacts with aluminum.

---

2. a. $\dfrac{4 \text{ mol Al}}{3 \text{ mol O}_2}$ $\dfrac{3 \text{ mol O}_2}{4 \text{ mol Al}}$

$\dfrac{4 \text{ mol Al}}{2 \text{ mol Al}_2\text{O}_3}$ $\dfrac{2 \text{ mol Al}_2\text{O}_3}{4 \text{ mol Al}}$

$\dfrac{3 \text{ mol O}_2}{2 \text{ mol Al}_2\text{O}_3}$ $\dfrac{2 \text{ mol Al}_2\text{O}_3}{3 \text{ mol O}_2}$

b. 4.6 mol
c. 0.63 mol
d. 11.5 mol

Chemists must deal with measured quantities such as mass and volume in the laboratory. However, mass and volume have no bearing on the combining ratios of atoms and molecules. Therefore, when dealing with stoichiometric calculations we must continually translate from the language of the laboratory (mass and volume) to the language of the equation (moles) and back again.

■ Stoichiometric calculations in which quantities are measured in grams still use the mole ratio from the balanced chemical equation.

8·3 Mass–Mass Calculations

No laboratory balance can measure substances directly in moles. Instead the amount of a substance is determined by measuring its mass in grams. Thus, we must also be able to calculate the mass of a reactant or product from a chemical equation. The mole interpretation of a balanced equation still holds. If the given quantity is measured in grams, the gram formula mass is used to convert the mass to moles. Then the mole ratio from the balanced equation is used to calculate the unknown. Similarly, if we need to know the mass of the unknown, we first find the number of moles of unknown. The gram formula mass is then used to calculate the mass. As in mole–mole calculations, the unknown can be either a reactant or a product.

Example 4

Calculate the number of grams of NH_3 produced by the reaction of 5.40 g of hydrogen with nitrogen. The balanced equation is given.

$$N_2(g) + 3H_2(g) \longrightarrow 2NH_3(g)$$

Solution

We are given the mass, in grams, of hydrogen and asked to find the mass, in grams, of ammonia: g $H_2 \longrightarrow$ g NH_3. The coefficients in the equation tell us that 3 mol of H_2 can react with 1 mol of N_2 to produce 2 mol of NH_3. Thus we need two more steps to do the calculation: g $H_2 \longrightarrow$ mol $H_2 \longrightarrow$ mol $NH_3 \longrightarrow$ g NH_3.

First, change the given, 5.40 g of H_2, to moles by using the gram formula mass of hydrogen: g $H_2 \longrightarrow$ mol H_2.

The gram formula mass of a substance is used to convert moles to grams and grams to moles.

$$5.40 \text{ g H}_2 \times \frac{1 \text{ mol H}_2}{2.0 \text{ g H}_2} = 2.70 \text{ mol H}_2$$

Now use the mol ratio from the equation to calculate the number of moles of NH_3: mol $H_2 \longrightarrow$ mol NH_3.

$$2.70 \ \cancel{mol \ H_2} \times \frac{2 \ mol \ NH_3}{3 \ \cancel{mol \ H_2}} = 1.80 \ mol \ NH_3$$

Finally, convert 1.80 mol of NH_3 to grams: mol $NH_3 \longrightarrow$ g NH_3. The gram molecular mass of NH_3 is 17.0 g/mol.

$$1.80 \ \cancel{mol \ NH_3} \times \frac{17.0 \ g \ NH_3}{1 \ \cancel{mol \ NH_3}} = 30.6 \ g \ NH_3$$

The three steps just described can be combined into one "solution": g $H_2 \longrightarrow$ mol $H_2 \longrightarrow$ mol $NH_3 \longrightarrow$ g NH_3.

$$\underset{\substack{\text{Given} \\ \text{quantity}}}{5.40 \ \cancel{g \ H_2}} \times \underset{\substack{\text{Change given} \\ \text{unit to moles}}}{\frac{1 \ mol \ H_2}{2.0 \ \cancel{g \ H_2}}} \times \underset{\substack{\text{Mole ratio} \\ \text{from} \\ \text{balanced} \\ \text{equation}}}{\frac{2 \ \cancel{mol \ NH_3}}{3 \ mol \ H_2}} \times \underset{\substack{\text{Change moles of} \\ \text{"wanted" to} \\ \text{grams}}}{\frac{17.0 \ g \ NH_3}{1 \ \cancel{mol \ NH_3}}} = 30.6 \ g \ NH_3$$

In view of the law of conservation of matter, is it possible to make 30.6 g of NH_3 from only 5.40 g of H_2? Check the equation for the reaction. From it you will see that another reactant, nitrogen, is also involved.

Figure 8·5
Clouds of condensed ammonia hide the surface of Saturn.

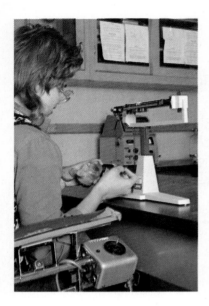

Figure 8·6
To determine the number of moles in a sample of a compound, first measure the mass of the sample. Then, use the gram formula mass to calculate the number of moles in that mass.

Example 5

How many grams of nitrogen are needed to produce the 30.6 g of NH_3 in the previous example? The equation is the same.

$$N_2(g) + 3H_2(g) \longrightarrow 2NH_3(g)$$

Solution

The balanced equation tells us that 1 mol of N_2 is needed to make 2 mol of NH_3. To use this fact, change the 30.6 g of NH_3 to moles. Then use the mole ratio to find moles of N_2. Finally, change moles of N_2 to grams of N_2. The process is: g $NH_3 \longrightarrow$ mol $NH_3 \longrightarrow$ mol $N_2 \longrightarrow$ g N_2.

$$30.6 \text{ g } NH_3 \times \frac{1 \text{ mol } NH_3}{17.0 \text{ g } NH_3} \times \frac{1 \text{ mol } N_2}{2 \text{ mol } NH_3} \times \frac{28.0 \text{ g } N_2}{1 \text{ mol } N_2} = 25.2 \text{ g } N_2$$

| Given quantity | Change given unit to moles | Mole ratio from balanced equation | Change moles of "wanted" to grams |

Our answer can be checked by using the law of conservation of matter and the answers from the last two examples.

Mass of reactants = mass of products

Mass of N_2 + mass of H_2 = mass of NH_3

25.2 g N_2 + 5.40 g H_2 = 30.6 g NH_3

30.6 g = 30.6 g

Mass–mass stoichiometric problems can be solved in basically the same way as mole–mole problems. Figure 8·7 illustrates the steps.

1. The mass of the given quantity must be changed to moles by using the ratio, 1 mol G/gfm G: mass $G \longrightarrow$ mol G.

2. The moles of G are changed to moles of W (wanted unit) by using the mole ratio from the balanced equation: mol $G \longrightarrow$ mol W.

3. The moles of W are changed to grams of W by using the ratio, gfm W/1 mol W: mol $W \longrightarrow$ mass W.

Figure 8·7
This general solution to a mass–mass problem shows how the gram formula mass is used to convert mass to moles and moles to mass. Conversion factors are shown in blue. The given substance (G) and the wanted substance (W) can be either reactants or products.

From Figure 8·7 you can also see the steps for doing mole–mass and mass–mole stoichiometric calculations. For a mole–mass problem, the first conversion (from mass to moles) is skipped. For a mass–mole problem, the last conversion (from moles to mass) is not done.

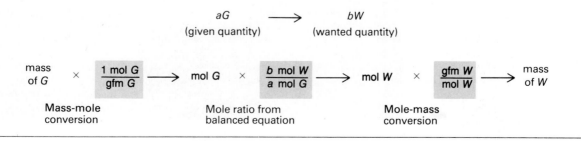

Problems

3. a. 40.0 g O_2
   b. 44.0 g CO_2, 9.0 g H_2O
   c. 53.0 g = 53.0 g
4. a. 2.03 g C_2H_2
   b. 2.72 mol CaC_2
   c. 396 g $Ca(OH)_2$

3. The combustion of acetylene gas is represented by this equation.

$$2C_2H_2(g) + 5O_2(g) \longrightarrow 4CO_2(g) + 2H_2O(g)$$

   a. How many grams of oxygen are required to "burn" 13.0 g of C_2H_2?
   b. How many grams of CO_2 and grams of H_2O are produced when 13.0 g of C_2H_2 reacts with the oxygen required to burn 13.0 g of C_2H_2?
   c. Use the answers from **a** and **b** to show that this equation obeys the law of conservation of matter.

4. Acetylene gas, C_2H_2, is produced by adding water to calcium carbide, CaC_2.

$$CaC_2(s) + 2H_2O(l) \longrightarrow C_2H_2 \uparrow + Ca(OH)_2(aq)$$

   a. How many grams of acetylene are produced by adding water to 5.00 g of CaC_2?
   b. How many moles of CaC_2 are needed to react completely with 98.0 g of H_2O?
   c. How many grams of $Ca(OH)_2$ are produced when 5.34 mol of C_2H_2 is produced?

8·4 Other Stoichiometric Calculations

Any measurement of matter related to the mole can be worked into stoichiometric calculations.

A balanced chemical equation shows us the relative number of moles of reactants and products. From this foundation, stoichiometric calculations can be expanded to include any unit of measurement that is related to the mole. The problems can include *mass–volume, volume–volume,* and *particle–mass* calculations. The given quantity can be expressed in numbers of representative particles, units of mass, or volumes of gases at STP. The given quantity is first converted to moles. Then the mole ratio from the balanced equation can be used to calculate the number of moles of the wanted substance. Once this unit has been determined, the moles can be converted to any other unit of measurement. These relationships are shown in Figure 8·8 and illustrated in the next two examples.

Figure 8·8
This diagram can help you solve various stoichiometry problems. Possible given quantities (G) are shown in green. Conversion factors are used to calculate the wanted quantities (W) shown in yellow.

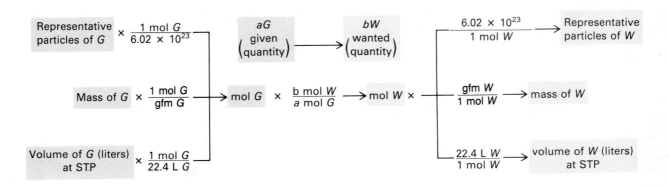

Example 6

How many molecules of oxygen are produced when 29.2 g of water is decomposed according to this balanced equation?

$$2H_2O(l) \xrightarrow{\text{electricity}} 2H_2(g) + O_2(g)$$

Solution

Figure 8·8 shows us the steps to follow.

Mass $H_2O \longrightarrow$ moles $H_2O \longrightarrow$ moles $O_2 \longrightarrow$ molecules O_2

$$29.2 \ \underbrace{\text{g } H_2O}_{\substack{\text{Given} \\ \text{quantity}}} \times \underbrace{\frac{1 \ \text{mol } H_2O}{18.0 \ \text{g } H_2O}}_{\text{Change to moles}} \times \underbrace{\frac{1 \ \text{mol } O_2}{2 \ \text{mol } H_2O}}_{\text{Mole ratio}} \times \underbrace{\frac{6.02 \times 10^{23} \ \text{molecules } O_2}{1 \ \text{mol } O_2}}_{\text{Change to molecules}}$$

$$= 4.88 \times 10^{23} \ \text{molecules } O_2$$

A mole of any substance contains 6.02×10^{23} representative particles.

Example 7

Assuming STP, how many liters of oxygen are needed to produce 19.8 L of SO_3 according to this balanced equation?

$$2SO_2(g) + O_2(g) \longrightarrow 2SO_3(g)$$

Solution

Again using Figure 8·8 as a guide, we find the steps to follow.

Liters $SO_3 \longrightarrow$ moles $SO_3 \longrightarrow$ moles $O_2 \longrightarrow$ liters O_2

$$19.8 \ \underbrace{\text{L } SO_3}_{\text{Given quantity}} \times \underbrace{\frac{1 \ \text{mol } SO_3}{22.4 \ \text{L } SO_3}}_{\text{Change to moles}} \times \underbrace{\frac{1 \ \text{mol } O_2}{2 \ \text{mol } SO_3}}_{\text{Mole ratio}} \times \underbrace{\frac{22.4 \ \text{L } O_2}{1 \ \text{mol } O_2}}_{\text{Change to liters}} = 9.9 \ \text{L } O_2$$

A mole of any gas at STP occupies a volume of 22.4 L.

Figure 8·9
In Example 8 two moles of nitrogen dioxide, a brown gas, form when 2 mol of nitrogen monoxide reacts with 1 mol of oxygen. Since the reactants and product are gases, we know that 2 L of nitrogen monoxide reacts with 1 L of oxygen to form 2 L of nitrogen dioxide.

In the previous example, did you notice that the 22.4 L/mol factors canceled out? This will always be true in a volume–volume problem. *The coefficients in a balanced chemical equation tell you the relative number of moles. The coefficients also tell the relative volumes of interacting gases.* The volume can be expressed in any unit: cubic decimeters, milliliters, liters, and so on.

Example 8

How many milliliters of nitrogen dioxide are produced when 3.4 mL of oxygen reacts with an excess of nitrogen monoxide? Assume conditions of STP.

$$2NO(g) + O_2(g) \longrightarrow 2NO_2(g)$$

Solution

The coefficients indicate the relative number of reacting milliliters of gases. The problem is solved in one step: mL $O_2 \longrightarrow$ mL NO_2.

$$3.4 \text{ mL } O_2 \times \frac{2 \text{ mL } NO_2}{1 \text{ mL } O_2} = 6.8 \text{ mL } NO_2$$

Given
quantity

Volume ratio

Problems

5. a. See the answers in Appendix C.

6. a. 966 g SnF_2
   b. 4.42 L H_2
   c. 28.4 L HF
   d. 1.08×10^{24} molecules H_2

5. Using Figure 8·8 as a guide, outline the steps necessary to convert these quantities. (G = given; W = wanted)
   a. volume of gas G (at STP) to mass of W
   b. representative particles of G to moles of W
   c. mass of G to representative particles of W

6. Tin(II) fluoride, formerly found in many toothpastes, is formed in this reaction.

$$Sn(s) + 2HF(g) \longrightarrow SnF_2(s) + H_2(g)$$

   a. How many grams of SnF_2 can be made by reacting 7.42×10^{24} molecules of HF with tin?
   b. How many liters of hydrogen gas (at STP) are produced by reacting 23.4 g of Sn with HF?
   c. How many liters of HF are needed to produce 14.2 L of H_2? (Assume STP.)
   d. How many molecules of H_2 are produced by the reaction of tin with 80.0 L of HF (at STP)?

Figure 8·10
Evidence from a crime must be carefully collected, analyzed, and preserved.

8·A   Chemical Sleuthing

Does the blood on a murder victim's hand belong to the victim or to the murderer? Does the charred material from a warehouse fire show any signs that a chemical was used to spread the fire? Is the ink on a document really 20 years old, or was it forged last week? Answering questions like these is the job of the forensic chemist.

Forensic chemistry is involved with the collection and representation of evidence that may be used in a court of law. Most forensic laboratories handle evidence involved in criminal cases. Several hundred such "crime labs" exist in the United States and Canada. Other laboratories prepare evidence in cases concerning violations of federal or state regulations. These may involve the chemical compositions of pollutants, imported materials, or products sold to the public. In both types of laboratories, standard methods are used for the analysis and comparison of materials. Because the materials may

Figure 8·11
Forensic chemists must have strong problem-solving skills, and a broad background in analytical chemistry.

be used in a court case, however, they must be collected, preserved, and analyzed according to very strict and well-documented methods.

In a crime laboratory body fluids and internal organs are commonly analyzed for poison, drugs, and alcohol. Similarly, analyses of pills, liquor, fibers, paint, glass, plastics, metals, and inks are performed. Blood, saliva, and hair can be typed. Charred documents can be restored, and fire debris can be analyzed. Many tests must be run on very tiny samples. Sometimes the tests must measure the exact amount of some substance in a sample, as in the analysis of pills for drugs. This requires the techniques of quantitative analysis. Often the tests only compare a material to some other sample, as in matching the paint on a crowbar to the paint on a door. These tests employ the methods of qualitative analysis. A forensic chemist must be an expert in both fields.

A career in forensic chemistry requires a degree in analytical chemistry and several years of on-the-job training. Skill in the use of all modern analytical instruments is very important. Specialized criminalistics courses include crime scene and firearms investigation, the identification of documents and fingerprints, and the collection and storage of evidence. Presenting evidence in court is an important part of the forensic chemist's job. Thus courses in public speaking and constitutional law are recommended. The chemist must also be able to explain complex procedures and results in simple language to the judge and jury. Lastly, a forensic chemist must have the personal strength to stand up to the threats of a criminal or the hostile cross-examination of a defense attorney.

8·5 Limiting Reagent

Most cooks follow a recipe when making a new dish. Before the actual mixing begins, sufficient quantities of all the ingredients must be available. For example it is impossible to make two loaves of bread with only one metric cup of flour. Similarly it is impossible for a chemist to make a certain amount of compound if there is an insufficient quantity of any of the reactants.

We have likened a balanced chemical equation to a chemist's recipe. This recipe can be interpreted on a microscopic scale (interacting particles) or on a macroscopic scale (interacting moles). For example, let us return to the now familiar equation for the preparation of ammonia.

$$3H_2(g) + N_2(g) \longrightarrow 2NH_3(g)$$

Two molecules (moles) of NH_3 will be produced when three molecules (moles) of H_2 are reacted with one molecule (mole) of N_2. What would happen, however, if three molecules (moles) of H_2 were reacted with two molecules (moles) of N_2? Would more than two molecules (moles) of NH_3 be formed? Figure 8·12 shows both the particle and the mole interpretations of this problem.

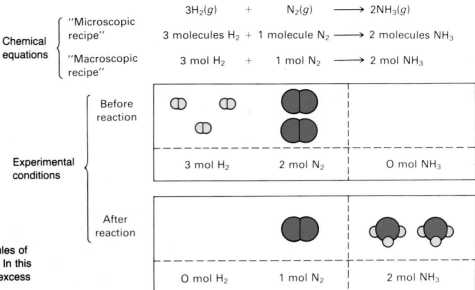

Chemical equations	"Microscopic recipe"	$3H_2(g)$	+	$N_2(g)$	$\longrightarrow$	$2NH_3(g)$
		3 molecules H_2	+	1 molecule N_2	$\longrightarrow$	2 molecules NH_3
	"Macroscopic recipe"	3 mol H_2	+	1 mol N_2	$\longrightarrow$	2 mol NH_3

Experimental conditions

Before reaction

3 mol H_2 2 mol N_2 0 mol NH_3

After reaction

0 mol H_2 1 mol N_2 2 mol NH_3

Figure 8·12
The "recipe" calls for 3 molecules of H_2 for every 1 molecule of N_2. In this particular experiment N_2 is in excess and H_2 is the limiting reagent.

■ Whenever quantities of two or more reactants in a chemical reaction are given, you must identify the limiting reagent.

Before the reaction takes place, hydrogen and nitrogen are present in a 3:2 molecule (mole) ratio. The reaction takes place according to the balanced equation. Three molecules (moles) of H_2 react with one molecule (mole) of N_2 to produce two molecules (moles) of NH_3. At this point all the hydrogen has been used up, and the reaction stops. In the reaction container one molecule (mole) of unreacted nitrogen is left in addition to the two molecules (moles) of NH_3.

In this reaction, only the hydrogen is completely used up. It is called the limiting reagent. As the name implies, *the* **limiting reagent** *limits or determines the amount of product that can be formed in a reaction.* The reaction occurs only until the limiting reagent is used up. By contrast, *the quantity of an* **excess reagent** *is more than enough to react with a limiting reagent.* In the present example, nitrogen is the excess reagent.

Figure 8·13
The amount of product is determined by the quantity of the limiting reagent. In this example, bread is the limiting reagent. No matter how much peanut butter and jelly you have, with eight slices of bread, you can make only four sandwiches.

Example 9

Sodium chloride is prepared by the reaction of sodium metal with chlorine gas.

$$2Na(s) + Cl_2(g) \longrightarrow 2NaCl(s)$$

What will occur when 6.70 mol of Na reacts with 3.20 mol of Cl_2?
a. What is the limiting reagent?
b. How many moles of NaCl are produced?
c. How much of the excess reagent remains unreacted?

Solution

a. Start with the known amount of one of the reactants. Use the mole ratio from the balanced equation to calculate the required amount of the other reactant. Sodium is chosen arbitrarily here: mol Na $\longrightarrow$ mol Cl_2.

$$6.70 \; \text{mol Na} \times \frac{1 \; \text{mol } Cl_2}{2 \; \text{mol Na}} = 3.35 \; \text{mol } Cl_2$$

Given amount   Mole ratio   Required amount
of sodium   of chlorine

This calculation shows that 3.35 mol of Cl_2 is needed to react with 6.70 mol of Na. Because only 3.20 mol of Cl_2 is available, chlorine is the limiting reagent. The sodium, then, must be in excess.

b. The given amount of limiting reagent, 3.20 mol of Cl_2, is used to calculate the maximum amount of product that can be formed: mol Cl_2 $\longrightarrow$ mol NaCl.

$$3.20 \; \text{mol } Cl_2 \times \frac{2 \; \text{mol NaCl}}{1 \; \text{mol } Cl_2} = 6.40 \; \text{mol NaCl}$$

c. The amount of the excess reagent remaining is the difference between the given amount (6.70 mol of Na) and the amount of sodium needed to react with the limiting reagent. We need to calculate the sodium that is needed: mol Cl_2 $\longrightarrow$ mol Na.

$$3.20 \; \text{mol } Cl_2 \times \frac{2 \; \text{mol Na}}{1 \; \text{mol } Cl_2} = 6.40 \; \text{mol Na}$$

Limiting   Mole ratio   Amount of excess
reagent   reagent used up

The amount of remaining sodium can now be calculated.

$$6.70 \; \text{mol} - 6.40 \; \text{mol} = 0.30 \; \text{mol Na in excess}$$

Problem

7. Two equations for the combustion of ethene, C_2H_4, are possible.

$$C_2H_4(g) + 3O_2(g) \longrightarrow 2CO_2(g) + 2H_2O(g)$$

and   (complete combustion)

$$C_2H_4(g) + 2O_2(g) \longrightarrow 2CO(g) + 2H_2O(g)$$

(incomplete combustion)

7. (1) Complete combustion
    a. 8.10 mol O_2 required, O_2
      is limiting
    b. 4.20 mol H_2O
    c. 0.60 mol C_2H_4
  (2) Incomplete combustion C_2H_4
    a. 5.40 mol O_2 required,
      C_2H_4 is limiting
    b. 5.40 mol H_2O
    c. 0.90 mol O_2

What will occur for each reaction if 2.70 mol of C_2H_4 is reacted with 6.30 mol of O_2?
a. Identify the limiting reagent.
b. Calculate the moles of water produced.
c. Calculate the moles of excess reagent remaining.

The given quantities of reactants may be expressed in units other than moles. In that case, the first step in the solution of the problem is to convert each reactant to moles. The limiting reagent is then identified as in the previous example. The amount of product is determined from the given amount of limiting reagent.

Example 10

Copper reacts with sulfur to form copper(I) sulfide.

$$2Cu(s) + S(s) \longrightarrow Cu_2S(s)$$

What is the maximum number of grams of Cu_2S that can be formed when 80.0 g of Cu reacts with 25.0 g of S?

Solution

First, find the number of moles of each reactant: g Cu $\longrightarrow$ mol Cu, and g S $\longrightarrow$ mol S.

$$80.0 \text{ g Cu} \times \frac{1 \text{ mol Cu}}{63.5 \text{ g Cu}} = 1.26 \text{ mol Cu}$$

$$25.0 \text{ g S} \times \frac{1 \text{ mol S}}{32.1 \text{ g S}} = 0.779 \text{ mol S}$$

Next, use the balanced equation to calculate the number of moles of one reactant needed to react with the given amount of the other reactant: mol Cu $\longrightarrow$ mol S.

$$1.26 \text{ mol Cu} \times \frac{1 \text{ mol S}}{2 \text{ mol Cu}} = 0.630 \text{ mol S}$$

Given   Mole   "Needed"
quantity   ratio   amount

Compare the amount of sulfur needed, 0.630 mol of S, with the given amount, 0.779 mol of S. The sulfur is in excess. Therefore, in this problem, copper is the limiting reagent.

Finally, use the limiting reagent to calculate the maximum amount of Cu_2S formed: mol Cu $\longrightarrow$ mol Cu_2S $\longrightarrow$ g Cu_2S.

$$1.26 \text{ mol Cu} \times \frac{1 \text{ mol Cu}_2\text{S}}{2 \text{ mol Cu}} \times \frac{159.1 \text{ g Cu}_2\text{S}}{1 \text{ mol Cu}_2\text{S}} = 1 \times 10^2 \text{ g Cu}_2\text{S}$$

We could have begun this last step with the given quantity of copper, 80.0 g. In that case the first step in the solution of the problem would be to change to moles of copper, which we had previously done.

Figure 8·14
Black crystalline copper(II) sulfide is formed from copper and sulfur. The reaction will take place if a mixture of the reactants is heated.

Figure 8·15
The productivity of a farm is measured in yield. Because growing conditions may vary from year to year, the actual yield often differs from the theoretical yield.

The theoretical yield is always a calculated number.

■ The percent yield is a measure of the efficiency of a reaction in changing reactants to products.

A reaction may not go 100% to completion simply because the reactants and products may reach a state of chemical equilibrium. This will be covered in Chapter 17.

Problem   **8. a.** 0.110 g H_2 **b.** 1.23 L H_2

8. Hydrogen gas can be produced in the laboratory by the reaction of magnesium metal with hydrochloric acid.

$$Mg(s) + 2HCl(aq) \longrightarrow MgCl_2(aq) + H_2(g)$$

a. How many grams of hydrogen can be produced when 4.00 g of HCl is added to 3.00 g of Mg?
b. Assuming STP, what is the volume of this hydrogen?

8·6 Percent Yield

In theory, when a teacher gives an exam to the class, everyone should get a grade of 100%. For a variety of reasons (not all of which are the teacher's fault!) this is usually not the case. Instead, the performance of the class is usually spread over a range of grades.

In doing stoichiometric problems, we have assumed that things do not "go wrong" in chemical reactions. This assumption is as faulty as assuming that all students will score 100% on an exam. *When an equation is used to calculate the amount of product that will form during a reaction, then a value for the* **theoretical yield** *is obtained.* This is the maximum amount of product that could be formed from a given amount of reactant. By contrast, *the amount of product that forms when the reaction is carried out in the laboratory is called the* **actual yield.** It is often less than the theoretical yield. *The* **percent yield** *is the ratio of the actual yield to the theoretical yield.* It measures the efficiency of the reaction.

$$Percent\ yield = \frac{actual\ yield}{theoretical\ yield} \times 100\%$$

A percent yield should not normally be larger than 100%. Many factors cause percent yields to be less than 100%. Reactions do not always go to completion. Impure reactants and competing side reactions may cause other products to be formed. Usually some of the product is lost during purification. An actual yield is an experimental value. If you are asked to calculate a percent yield, the value of an actual yield must be given. For reactions in which percent yields have been determined, an "actual" yield can be calculated if the reaction conditions remain the same.

Example 11

Calcium carbonate can be decomposed by heating.

$$CaCO_3(s) \longrightarrow CaO(s) + CO_2(g)$$

What is the percent yield of this reaction if 24.8 g of $CaCO_3$ is heated to give 13.1 g of CaO?

Figure 8·16
The masses of reactants and products must be carefully measured when the percent yield of a reaction is determined. Here the mass of sodium bicarbonate, the reactant, is measured before it is heated. The mass of the product, sodium carbonate, is measured after the reaction is completed.

Solution

The actual yield is 13.1 g of CaO. The theoretical yield can be calculated: g $CaCO_2 \longrightarrow$ mol $CaCO_3 \longrightarrow$ mol CaO $\longrightarrow$ g CaO.

$$24.8 \; \cancel{g \; CaCO_3} \times \frac{1 \text{ mol } CaCO_3}{100.1 \; \cancel{g \; CaCO_3}} \times \frac{1 \; \cancel{\text{mol } CaO}}{1 \; \cancel{\text{mol } CaCO_3}} \times \frac{56.1 \text{ g CaO}}{1 \; \cancel{\text{mol } CaO}}$$

$$= 13.9 \text{ g CaO}$$

The percent yield is the ratio of the actual yield over the theoretical yield expressed as a percent.

$$\text{Percent yield} = \frac{\text{actual yield}}{\text{theoretical yield}} \times 100\%$$

$$= \frac{13.1 \; \cancel{\text{g CaO}}}{13.9 \; \cancel{\text{g CaO}}} \times 100\% = 94.2\%$$

Problem

9. 56.7%

9. What is the percent yield if 3.74 g of copper is produced when 1.87 g of aluminum is reacted with an excess of copper(II) sulfate?

$$2Al(s) + 3CuSO_4(aq) \longrightarrow Al_2(SO_4)_3(aq) + 3Cu(s)$$

8·7 Energy Changes in Chemical Reactions

■ Energy, most often in the form of heat, is either released or absorbed in a chemical reaction.

Greek: *exo* = out of;
thermos = heat.

Energy changes occur whenever a chemical reaction takes place. Some of these energy changes involve heat. **Exothermic reactions** *release energy in the form of heat*. The combustion of coal is an exothermic reaction. Heat is one of the products.

$$C(s) + O_2(g) \longrightarrow CO_2(g) + 393.5 \text{ kJ}$$

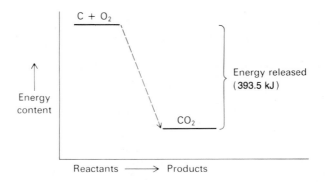

Figure 8·17
This energy diagram is typical for exothermic reactions. The energy content of C and O_2 is higher than the energy content of CO_2. Therefore, energy is released when C burns to CO_2.

Safety

Many common reactions are highly exothermic. Even dissolving chemicals in water can generate large amounts of heat. Never use glassware that is cracked because the heat of dissolving or reacting chemicals may cause it to break.

Greek: *endo* = within;
 thermos = heat.

The energy released in the combustion of carbon must have a source. This is because the law of conservation of energy states that energy is neither created nor destroyed in ordinary chemical processes. The energy source is the chemical bonds that hold the oxygen molecules together and the atoms of carbon together. The energy stored in the carbon-oxygen bonds of carbon dioxide is less than the sum of the energy stored in the oxygen-oxygen bonds of oxygen and the carbon-carbon bonds of carbon. When carbon is burned, some of the energy stored in the bonds of the reactants is released as heat. The rest of the energy in the bonds of the reactants goes into the bonds of the products (Figure 8·17).

Not all reactions are exothermic. *In an* **endothermic reaction,** *energy is absorbed*. The production of calcium oxide (lime) from calcium carbonate (limestone) is an example of an endothermic process.

$$CaCO_3(s) + 176 \text{ kJ} \xrightarrow{850°} CaO(s) + CO_2(g)$$

For each mole of calcium carbonate decomposed, 176 kJ of heat is absorbed. In this and other endothermic processes, the energy content of the products is higher than the energy content of the reactants (Figure 8·18). (The reason such reactions occur will be explained in Chapter 17.)

An equation that includes the amount of heat produced or absorbed by a reaction is a **thermochemical equation.** Standard conditions for a thermochemical equation are 25°C and 1 atm pressure. The heat term in a thermochemical equation can be treated like any other reactant or product as shown in the following example.

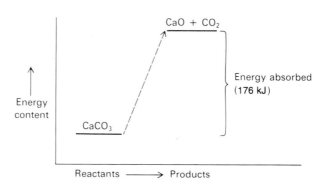

Figure 8·18
This energy diagram is typical for endothermic reactions. The energy content of $CaCO_3$ is lower than that of Ca and CO_2. Energy is absorbed when $CaCO_3$ is decomposed to Ca and CO_2.

Figure 8·19
Limestone is heated to produce lime, which is used in mortar.

10. a. 924 kJ
    b. 221 kcal
11. 6.09 × 10²³ molecules CO₂

Example 12

Using the equation just given, calculate the energy required to decompose 5.20 mol of $CaCO_3(s)$. **a.** kilojoules **b.** kilocalories

Solution

a. The equation indicates that 176 kJ are needed to decompose 1 mol of $CaCO_3$. This can be used to write a conversion factor.

$$5.20 \text{ mol } CaCO_3 \times \frac{176 \text{ kJ}}{1 \text{ mol } CaCO_3} = 915 \text{ kJ}$$

b. The number of joules can be converted to calories given that 1.00 kcal = 4.18 kJ.

$$915 \text{ kJ} \times \frac{1.00 \text{ kcal}}{4.18 \text{ kJ}} = 219 \text{ kcal}$$

Problems

10. The air pollutant sulfur trioxide reacts with water in the atmosphere to produce sulfuric acid and heat.

$$SO_3(g) + H_2O(l) \longrightarrow H_2SO_4(aq) + 129.6 \text{ kJ}$$

How much heat is released when 583 g of $SO_3(g)$ reacts with water?
a. kilojoules **b.** kilocalories

11. Carbon dioxide can be decomposed into carbon monoxide and oxygen by the absorption of heat.

$$2CO_2(g) + 43.9 \text{ kJ} \longrightarrow 2CO(g) + O_2(g)$$

How many molecules of $CO_2(g)$ can be decomposed by the addition of 22.2 kJ of heat energy?

Figure 8·20
A foam cup calorimeter can be used to measure the heat given off by a reaction.

8·B Calorimetry

Many chemists have been curious about the heat effects that accompany chemical reactions. In the early 1780s the French chemist Lavoisier (see Section 2·A) measured the heat given off by a guinea pig. He kept the animal in an enclosed container so that its body heat would melt ice. From the amount of ice melted, he calculated the heat produced by the animal.

The apparatus used to contain the guinea pig and measure its body heat was an ice calorimeter. It was a forerunner of a family of devices used to measure heat in chemical reactions. In all calorimeters a reaction is allowed to take place inside an insulated container. The heat given off by the reaction is transferred (with as little loss as possible) to some other material. The heat can then be calculated from the change in temperature.

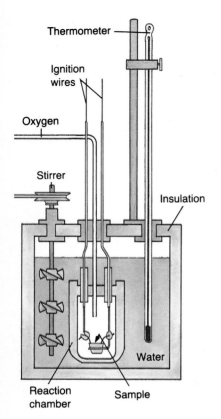

Figure 8·21
To start the combustion in a bomb calorimeter, oxygen is pumped into the reaction chamber containing the sample, and an electric charge is sent through the ignition wire. A thermometer measures the change in temperature of the water in the insulated water bath. This temperature is related to the heat given off by the reaction.

Thermometer

Ignition wires

Oxygen

Stirrer

Insulation

Water

Reaction chamber

Sample

High school chemistry courses often include an experiment using a disposable foam cup as a calorimeter. A reaction involving aqueous solutions of chemicals is done in the cup. The initial temperature of the solutions and the final temperature of the mixture are measured. Using the change in temperature, the specific heat capacity of water, and the total volume of water involved in the reaction, the heat given off can be calculated (see Sections 2·12 and 2·13). There are some obvious sources of error in this type of experiment. Heat from the reaction will also go into heating the cup. Some will be lost to the environment because the cup is not closed. If reactants are not completely mixed, the temperature measurements will not be accurate. The mixture in the cup is not water but an aqueous solution. Its heat capacity will be different from that of pure water.

More sophisticated calorimeters are designed to overcome these problems. In most, the reaction takes place in a closed chamber surrounded by a material that absorbs heat. The heat of the reaction is transferred to all parts of the calorimeter, raising its temperature. The amount of heat that is given off is equal to the heat capacity of the calorimeter times the change in temperature. The heat capacity of the calorimeter is calculated by doing a reaction for which the heat produced is known. Thereafter, the calculated heat capacity can be used to measure the heat given off by any reaction.

The material in the reservoir may be water, other liquids, or a metal. The choice depends on what the highest temperature in the calorimeter will be. The reservoir is equipped with a thermometer to measure its change in temperature. If the reservoir contains a liquid, it also has a mechanical stirrer. The reservoir is surrounded by an insulating jacket to reduce heat loss to the environment. It may be made of an insulating material, like plastic foam.

A bomb calorimeter is used to measure the heat released by the combustion of a compound. A sample of the compound with a measured mass is placed in the inner chamber of the calorimeter. This chamber is filled with oxygen at high pressure, up to 30 atmospheres. A wire leads into the sample from outside of the calorimeter. When current is passed through this wire, it glows and ignites the sample which reacts with the oxygen. The heat from this reaction passes through the walls of the chamber into the water in the reservoir, which is constantly stirred. The temperature increase of the calorimeter is measured and used to calculate the heat given off by the compound.

8·8 The Heat of Reaction

At the start of any reaction each of the reactants has a heat content. **Enthalpy** *is the amount of heat that a substance has at a given temperature and pressure.* Enthalpy is symbolized by H. Unfortunately, the enthalpy of individual substances cannot be measured directly. Nevertheless, changes in enthalpy can be measured. A change in enthalpy is

Appropriate for honors students.

An exothermic reaction has a $-\Delta H$.
An endothermic reaction has a $+\Delta H$.

Figure 8·22
The number of calories in a food sample is determined by measuring the heat of reaction of the sample in a calorimeter.

Fractional coefficients are needed here because we are dealing with the production of 1 mol of H_2O.

12. 585 cal/g

The heat of a reaction is calculated from the standard heats of formation of the reactants and products.

The (^{0}) in ΔH_f^0 indicates the use of standard conditions (25°C and 1 atm). The subscript ($_f$) indicates that the change in enthalpy is for the *formation* of the compound.

symbolized by ΔH (read "delta H"). Changes in enthalpy occur whenever heat is released or absorbed in chemical reactions. The standard conditions for measuring ΔH are 25°C and 1 atm. A reaction may be conducted at other conditions, say, at 50°C and 1 atm. In this situation, ΔH includes the heat changes involved in raising the temperature of the reactants from 25°C and lowering the temperature of the products back to that.

The heat that is released or absorbed during a chemical reaction is the **heat of reaction.** It is equivalent to ΔH, the change in enthalpy. For example, if 1 mol of carbon in its standard state is burned, 393 kJ of heat is released. The ΔH for this reaction is -393.5 kJ per mole.

$$C(s) + O_2(g) \longrightarrow CO_2(g) \qquad \Delta H = -393.5 \text{ kJ}$$

The sign of ΔH is always negative for an exothermic reaction. As Figure 8·17 shows, the products have *less* energy than the reactants. *In the special case in which one mole of a substance is completely burned, ΔH is called the* **heat of combustion.**

The sign of ΔH is always positive for an endothermic reaction. When calcium carbonate is decomposed, the products absorb 176 kJ of energy per mole of calcium carbonate decomposed. The heat content of the products is higher than that of the reactants by 176 kJ (Figure 8·18).

$$CaCO_3(s) \longrightarrow CaO(s) + CO_2(g) \qquad \Delta H = +176 \text{ kJ}$$

Note that the physical state of the reactants and products in a thermochemical reaction must be stated. (The symbols are *g* for *gas*, *l* for *liquid*, and *s* for *solid*.) Compare the following two equations.

$$H_2(g) + \tfrac{1}{2}O_2(g) \longrightarrow H_2O(g) \qquad \Delta H = -241.8 \text{ kJ}$$
$$H_2(g) + \tfrac{1}{2}O_2(g) \longrightarrow H_2O(l) \qquad \Delta H = -285.8 \text{ kJ}$$

In one case the product is a liquid. In the other case the product is a gas. The condensation of 1 mol of water vapor to 1 mol of liquid water at 25°C produces 44.0 kJ of heat.

Problem

12. If 44.0 kJ of heat is liberated when $H_2O(g) \longrightarrow H_2O(l)$, calculate the energy released in calories when 1 g of $H_2O(g)$ at 25°C is changed to 1 g of $H_2O(l)$ at the same temperature.

Enthalpy changes occur when a compound is formed from its elements. In enthalpy measurements the ΔH of a free element in its standard state is arbitrarily set to zero. For example, for the diatomic molecules—$H_2(g)$, $N_2(g)$, $O_2(g)$, $F_2(g)$, $Cl_2(g)$, $Br_2(l)$, and $I_2(s)$—the enthalpy is 0. Similarly, the enthalpy for carbon in the form of graphite, $C(s, \text{graphite})$ is also 0. *The ΔH for a reaction in which 1 mol of a compound is formed from its elements is the* **standard heat of formation,** ΔH_f^0, *of that compound.* Table 8·1 gives ΔH_f^0 for some common substances. The more negative the value of ΔH_f^0, the more stable the compounds.

Table 8·1 Standard Heats of Formation (ΔH_f^0) at 25°C and 1 atm

Substance	ΔH_f^0 (kJ/mol)
$Al_2O_3(s)$	−1676.0
$Br_2(g)$	30.91
$Br_2(l)$	0.0
$C(s, \text{diamond})$	1.9
$C(s, \text{graphite})$	0.0
$CH_4(g)$	−74.86
$CO(g)$	−110.5
$CO_2(g)$	−393.5
$CaCO_3(s)$	−1207.0
$CaO(s)$	−635.1
$Cl_2(g)$	0.0
$F_2(g)$	0.0
$Fe(s)$	0.0
$Fe_2O_3(s)$	−184.2
$H_2(g)$	0.0
$H_2O(g)$	−241.8
$H_2O(l)$	−285.8
$H_2O_2(l)$	−187.8
$HCl(g)$	−92.31
$H_2S(g)$	−20.1
$I_2(g)$	62.4
$I_2(s)$	0.0
$N_2(g)$	0.0
$NH_3(g)$	−46.19
$NO(g)$	90.37
$NO_2(g)$	33.85
$Na_2CO_3(s)$	−1131.1
$NaCl(s)$	−411.2
$O_2(g)$	0.0
$O_3(g)$	142.0
$P(s, \text{white})$	0.0
$P(s, \text{red})$	−18.4
$S(s, \text{rhombic})$	0.0
$S(s, \text{monoclinic})$	0.30
$SO_2(g)$	−296.8
$SO_3(g)$	−395.7

Standard heats of formation of compounds are useful for calculating heats of reaction under conditions of standard temperature and pressure. Because of the law of conservation of energy, the ΔH for a reaction is the difference between the standard enthalpies of formation of all reactants and all products.

$$\Delta H = \Delta H_f^0(\text{products}) - \Delta H_f^0(\text{reactants})$$

This is demonstrated in the following example.

Example 13

What is the change in enthalpy (ΔH) for the following reaction when all reactants and products are in the gaseous state?

Sulfur dioxide + oxygen ⟶ sulfur trioxide

Solution

First, write a balanced equation, including the physical states of all products and reactants.

$$2SO_2(g) + O_2(g) \longrightarrow 2SO_3(g)$$

Then, use Table 8·1 to find the standard heats of formation per mole.

$$\Delta H_f^0 \ O_2(g) = 0.0 \text{ kcal/mol (free element)}$$

$$\Delta H_f^0 \ SO_2(g) = -296.8 \text{ kJ/mol}$$

$$\Delta H_f^0 \ SO_3(g) = -395.7 \text{ kJ/mol}$$

Sum the ΔH_f^0 of the reactants while taking into account the number of moles of each.

$$2 \text{ mol } SO_2 \times \frac{-296.8 \text{ kJ}}{1 \text{ mol } SO_2} + 1 \text{ mol } O_2 \times \frac{0.0 \text{ kJ}}{1 \text{ mol } O_2} = -593.6 \text{ kJ}$$

Sum the ΔH_f^0 of the products in a similar way.

$$2 \text{ mol } SO_3 \times \frac{-395.7 \text{ kJ}}{1 \text{ mol } SO_3} = -791.4 \text{ kJ}$$

The change in enthalpy is equal to the heats of formation of the products minus the heats of formation of the reactants.

$$\Delta H = (-791.4 \text{ kJ}) - (-593.6 \text{ kJ}) = -197.8 \text{ kJ}$$

The reaction of oxygen and sulfur dioxide to give sulfur trioxide is exothermic.

Problem

13. a. −890.2 kJ   b. −566 kJ

13. Calculate the change in enthalpy for these reactions.
   a. $CH_4(g) + 2O_2(g) \longrightarrow CO_2(g) + 2H_2O(l)$
   b. $2CO(g) + O_2(g) \longrightarrow 2CO_2(g)$

Key Terms

actual yield	8·6	limiting reagent	8·5
endothermic		percent yield	8·6
reaction	8·7	standard heat of	
enthalpy (H)	8·8	formation (ΔH_f^0)	8·8
excess reagent	8·5	stoichiometry	8·0
exothermic reaction	8·7	theoretical yield	8·6
heat of combustion	8·8	thermochemical	
heat of reaction	8·8	equation	8·7

Chapter Summary

A balanced chemical equation may be interpreted in several different ways. For example, the coefficients tell us the relative number of moles of reactants and products. Chemists use moles to do chemical arithmetic, or stoichiometry. All stoichiometric calculations involving chemical reactions begin with a balanced equation. Balanced equations are necessary because mass is conserved in every chemical reaction. The number and kinds of atoms in the reactants equal the number and kinds of atoms in the products.

Stoichiometric problems are solved using conversion factors derived from a balanced chemical equation. The conversion factor relates the moles of a given substance to the moles of the desired substance. Units such as mass, volume of gases (at STP), and particles are converted to moles when working stoichiometry problems.

Whenever quantities of two or more reactants are given in a stoichiometry problem, we must identify the limiting reagent. A limiting reagent is completely used up in a chemical reaction. The amount of limiting reagent determines the amount of product that is formed in a chemical reaction. If there is a single limiting reagent in a reaction, all the other reactants are in excess.

A theoretical yield is the maximum amount of product that can be obtained from a given amount of reactants in a chemical reaction. An actual yield is the amount of product obtained when the reaction is carried out in the laboratory. A ratio of the actual yield to the theoretical yield, expressed as a percent, is the percent yield of a reaction.

Energy changes are always associated with chemical reactions. The enthalpy change (ΔH) is a measure of the heat absorbed or released during a chemical reaction. A reaction in which heat is released (negative ΔH) is termed exothermic. In an endothermic reaction heat is absorbed, and ΔH is positive. The heat absorbed or evolved when one mole of a compound is formed from its elements is the standard heat of formation.

Practice Questions and Problems

14. Interpret each of these chemical equations in terms of interacting particles. *8·1*
  a. $2Zn(s) + O_2(g) \longrightarrow 2ZnO(s)$
  b. $2KClO_3(s) \longrightarrow 2KCl(s) + 3O_2(g)$
  c. $4NH_3(g) + 6NO(g) \longrightarrow 5N_2(g) + 6H_2O(g)$

15. Interpret each of the equations in Problem 14 in terms of interacting numbers of moles of reactants and products. *8·1*

16. Calculate and compare the mass of the reactants with the mass of the products for each of the equations in Problem 14. Show that each balanced equation obeys the law of conservation of mass. *8·1*

17. Carbon disulfide is an important industrial solvent. It is prepared by the reaction of coke with sulfur dioxide. *8·2*

$$5C + 2SO_2 \longrightarrow CS_2 + 4CO$$

  a. How many moles of CS_2 form when 6.30 mol of C reacts?

b. How many moles of carbon are needed to react with 7.24 mol of SO_2?

c. How many moles of carbon monoxide form at the same time that 0.762 mol of CS_2 forms?

d. How many moles of SO_2 are required to make 182 mol of CS_2?

18. Heating an ore of antimony, Sb_2S_3, in the presence of iron gives the element antimony and iron(II) sulfide.   *8·2*

$$Sb_2S_3(s) + 3Fe(s) \longrightarrow 2Sb(s) + 3FeS(s)$$

a. How many moles of Sb_2S_3 are needed to react with an excess amount of iron to produce 9.40 mol of antimony?

b. How many moles of Fe are needed to produce 9.40 mol of antimony?

c. Calculate the number of moles of Sb produced when 0.122 mol of FeS is produced.

19. Methanol, CH_3OH, is used in the production of many chemicals. Methanol is made by reacting carbon monoxide and hydrogen at high temperature and pressure.   *8·3*

$$CO(g) + 2H_2(g) \longrightarrow CH_3OH(g)$$

a. How many moles of each reactant are needed to form 6.00×10^2 g of CH_3OH?

b. Calculate the number of grams of each reactant needed to produce 10.0 mol of CH_3OH.

c. How many grams of hydrogen are necessary to react with 5.74 mol of CO?

20. Oxygen is produced by the reaction of sodium peroxide and water.   *8·3*

$$2Na_2O_2(s) + 2H_2O(l) \longrightarrow O_2(g) + 4NaOH(aq)$$

a. Calculate the mass of Na_2O_2 in grams needed to form 3.20 g of oxygen.

b. How many grams of NaOH are produced when 3.20 g of O_2 is formed?

c. When 0.48 g of Na_2O_2 is dropped in water, how many grams of O_2 are formed?

21. Calcium carbonate reacts with phosphoric acid to produce calcium phosphate, carbon dioxide, and water.   *8·4*

$$3CaCO_3(s) + 2H_3PO_4(aq) \longrightarrow$$
$$Ca_3(PO_4)_2(aq) + 3CO_2(g) + 3H_2O(l)$$

a. How many grams of phosphoric acid, H_3PO_4, react with excess calcium carbonate, $CaCO_3$, to produce 3.74 g of $Ca_3(PO_4)_2$?

b. Calculate the number of grams of CO_2 formed when 0.473 g of H_2O is produced.

c. Assuming STP, how many liters of carbon dioxide are produced when 5.74 g of $CaCO_3$ reacts with an excess of H_3PO_4.

22. Lithium nitride reacts with water to form ammonia and aqueous lithium hydroxide.   *8·4*

$$Li_3N(s) + 3H_2O(l) \longrightarrow NH_3(g) + 3LiOH(aq)$$

a. What mass of water is needed to react with 98.7 g of Li_3N?

b. When the above reaction takes place, how many molecules of NH_3 are produced?

c. Calculate the number of grams of Li_3N that must be added to an excess of water to produce 45.0 L of NH_3 (at STP).

23. How would you identify a limiting reagent in a chemical reaction?   *8·5*

24. For each of these balanced equations, identify the limiting reagent for the given combination of reactants.   *8·5*

a. $2H_2\ +\ \ O_2\ \ \longrightarrow\ 2H_2O$
     5.0 mol 2.3 mol

b. $4P\ +\ \ 5O_2\ \ \longrightarrow\ 2P_2O_5$
     7.0 mol 8.0 mol

c. $2Al\ +\ \ 3Cl_2\ \ \longrightarrow\ 2AlCl_3$
     5.4 mol 8.0 mol

d. $2P_2O_5\ +\ 6H_2O\ \longrightarrow\ 4H_3PO_4$
    0.37 mol 2.50 mol

25. For each reaction in Problem 24, calculate the number of moles of product formed.   *8·5*

26. For each reaction in Problem 24, calculate the number of moles of excess reagent remaining after the reaction.   *8·5*

27. Acetylene, C_2H_2, will burn in the presence of oxygen.   *8·6*

$$2C_2H_2(g) + 5O_2(g) \longrightarrow 4CO_2(g) + 2H_2O(g)$$

How many grams of water can be produced by the reaction of 4.80 mol of C_2H_2 with 14.8 mol of O_2?

28. What is a percent yield of a chemical reaction a measure of?   *8·6*

29. When 84.8 g of iron(III) oxide reacts with an excess of carbon monoxide, then 57.8 g of iron is produced.

$$Fe_2O_3(s) + 3CO(g) \longrightarrow 2Fe(s) + 3CO_2(g)$$

What is the percent yield of this reaction?   *8·6*

30. When 50.0 g of silicon dioxide is heated with an excess of carbon, 32.2 g of silicon carbide is produced.

$$SiO_2(s) + 3C(s) \longrightarrow SiC(s) + 2CO(g)$$

What is the percent yield of this reaction?

31. Distinguish between an exothermic reaction and an endothermic reaction. *8·7*

32. The reaction of iron with carbon dioxide to form iron(III) oxide and carbon monoxide is an endothermic reaction. *8·7*

$$2Fe(s) + 3CO_2(g) + 26.3 \text{ kJ} \longrightarrow Fe_2O_3(s) + 3CO(g)$$

a. How many kilojoules of energy are needed for 7.3 mol of Fe to react with an excess of CO_2?
b. Is this a positive or negative enthalpy change?

33. The burning of magnesium in oxygen is a very exothermic reaction. *8·7*

$$2Mg(s) + O_2(g) \longrightarrow 2MgO(s) + 288 \text{ kcal}$$

a. How much heat, in kilocalories, is given off when 0.12 mol of Mg reacts with an excess of oxygen?
b. Express the answer in kilojoules of energy.

34. Why must the physical state of a substance be given in a thermochemical reaction? *8·7*

35. What is the enthalpy change (or heat of reaction) of a chemical reaction? *8·8*

36. What is the standard heat of formation of a compound? *8·8*

37. Which of these compounds has a negative standard heat of formation? *8·8*
a. $NO_2(g)$ **b.** $SO_2(g)$ **c.** $CaO(s)$, **d.** $H_2O_2(l)$

38. Calculate the change in enthalpy (ΔH) for these reactions. *8·8*
a. $I_2(s) \longrightarrow I_2(g)$
b. $3CO(g) + 2Fe_2O_3(s) \longrightarrow Fe(s) + 3CO_2(g)$
c. $2NO_2(g) \longrightarrow 2NO(g) + O_2(g)$

Mastery Questions and Problems

39. Hydrazine, N_2H_4, is used as a rocket fuel. It reacts with oxygen to form nitrogen and water. *8·5*

$$N_2H_4(l) + O_2(g) \longrightarrow N_2(g) + 2H_2O(g)$$

a. How many liters of N_2 (at STP) form when 1.0 kg of N_2H_4 reacts with 1.0 kg O_2?
b. How many grams of the excess reagent remain after the reaction?

40. Elemental sulfur is one of the products of the gas-phase reaction of nitric acid and hydrogen sulfide. The other products are nitrogen monoxide and water. *8·3*

$$3H_2S(g) + 2HNO_3(g) \longrightarrow 2NO(g) + 4H_2O(g) + 3S(s)$$

a. How many grams of each product are formed when 18.2 g of H_2S reacts with an excess of HNO_3?
b. How many milligrams of water are produced when 43.7 mg of sulfur is formed?

41. The formation of nitrogen monoxide from its elements is an endothermic process.

$$N_2(g) + O_2(g) + 43.2 \text{ kcal} \longrightarrow 2NO(g)$$

Given an unlimited amount of nitrogen and oxygen, how many grams of NO can be formed using 2.0×10^3 kcal of heat energy? *8·7*

42. Zinc reacts with nitric acid to form zinc nitrate, ammonium nitrate, and water. *8·4*

$$4Zn(s) + 10HNO_3(aq) \longrightarrow 4Zn(NO_3)_2(aq) + NH_4NO_3(aq) + 3H_2O(l)$$

a. How many atoms of zinc react with 5.96 g of HNO_3?
b. Calculate the number of grams of zinc that must react with an excess of HNO_3 to form 87.3 g of NH_4NO_3.

43. The pollutant sulfur dioxide can be removed from the emissions of an industrial plant by reaction with calcium carbonate and oxygen.

$$2CaCO_3(s) + 2SO_2(g) + O_2(g) \longrightarrow 2CaSO_4(s) + 2CO_2(g)$$

If this reaction proceeds with a 96.8% yield, how many kilograms of $CaSO_4$ are formed when 5.24 kg of SO_2 reacts with an excess of $CaCO_3$ and O_2? *8·6*

44. The combustion of ethene, C_2H_4, liberates 1.39×10^3 kJ/mol.

$$C_2H_4(g) + 3O_2(g) \longrightarrow 2CO_2(g) + 2H_2O(l) + 1.39 \times 10^3 \text{ kJ}$$

Calculate the amount of heat liberated when 1.87 g of C_2H_4 reacts with excess oxygen. *8·7*

45. Ammonium nitrate will decompose explosively at high temperatures to form nitrogen, oxygen, and water vapor. *8·4*

$$2NH_4NO_3(s) \longrightarrow 2N_2(g) + 4H_2O(g) + O_2(g)$$

a. What is the total number of liters of gas formed when 45.6 g of NH_4NO_3 is decomposed? (Assume STP.)
b. Calculate the number of grams of water formed when 10.0 L of N_2 is produced in this reaction. (Assume STP.)

Review Questions and Problems

46. How many grams of beryllium are in 255 g of the mineral beryl, $Be_3Al_2Si_6O_{18}$?

47. Write a balanced chemical equation for each of these reactions.
a. When a mixture of aluminum and iron(II) oxide is heated metallic iron and aluminum oxide are produced.
b. Sodium bicarbonate reacts with acetic acid to produce sodium acetate, water, and carbon dioxide.
c. The complete combustion of isopropyl alcohol, C_3H_7OH, produces carbon dioxide and water vapor.
d. Lead(II) nitrate when heated decomposes to form lead(II) oxide, nitrogen dioxide, and molecular oxygen.

48. What is the mass, in grams, of a molecule of benzene, C_6H_6?

49. How many electrons, protons, and neutrons are in an atom of each isotope?
a. magnesium-26   c. oxygen-18
b. titanium-47   d. tin-120

50. What is the molecular formula of oxalic acid, a compound found in rhubarb leaves? The gram molecular mass of oxalic acid is 90 g/mol. Its percent composition is 71.1% O, 26.7% C, and 2.2% H.

51. Write these formulas.
a. manganese(II) chromate
b. hydrobromic acid
c. aluminum carbonate
d. silicon dioxide
e. potassium sulfide

Challenging Questions and Problems

52. A car gets 9.2 kilometers to a liter of gasoline. Assuming that gasoline is 100% octane, C_8H_{18} (which has a specific gravity of 0.69), how many liters of air (21% oxygen by volume at STP) will be required to burn the gasoline for a 1250-km trip? Assume complete combustion.

53. Ethyl alcohol, C_2H_5OH, can be produced by the fermentation of glucose, $C_6H_{12}O_6$. If it takes 5.0 hr to produce 8.0 kg of alcohol, how many days will it take to consume 1.0×10^3 kg of glucose? An enzyme (biological catalyst) is used to increase the rate of this reaction.

$$C_6H_{12}O_6 \xrightarrow{\text{enzyme}} C_2H_5OH + CO_2$$

54. A 435.0-g sample of $CaCO_3$ that is 95.0% pure gives 225 L of CO_2 when reacted with an excess of hydrochloric acid.

$$CaCO_3 + HCl \longrightarrow CaCl_2 + CO_2 + H_2O$$

What is the density (in grams/liter) of the CO_2?

55. Aspirin, $C_9H_8O_4$, is made by the reaction of salicylic acid, $C_7H_6O_3$, and acetic anhydride, $C_4H_6O_3$.

$$C_7H_6O_3 + C_4H_6O_3 \longrightarrow C_9H_8O_4 + HC_2H_3O_2$$

A student is told that if a 25.0% excess of the acetic anhydride is used, she can expect to get an 85.0% yield. How many grams of each reactant should the student use to produce 75.0 g of aspirin?

56. SO_3 can be produced in this two-step process.

$$FeS_2 + O_2 \longrightarrow Fe_2O_3 + SO_2$$
$$SO_2 + O_2 \longrightarrow SO_3$$

Assuming that all the FeS_2 reacts, how many grams of SO_3 are produced when 20.0 g of FeS_2 reacts with 16.0 g of O_2?

57. Limestone contains a large percentage of calcium carbonate, $CaCO_3$. A sample of limestone weighing 84.4 g reacts with an excess of hydrochloric acid to form calcium chloride.

$$CaCO_3 + 2HCl \longrightarrow CaCl_2 + H_2O + CO_2$$

The mass of calcium chloride formed is 81.8 g. What is the percent of calcium carbonate in the limestone?

Research Projects

1. Some reactions such as those between copper and sulfur are nonstoichiometric (or seemingly so). Study the conditions that influence the combinations of copper and sulfur that can be obtained.

2. Investigate the factors that affect the percent yield of a reaction.

3. What chemistry is used in the detection of fingerprints?

4. Find out more about the methods used by forensic chemists. Write a short story that includes a mystery which is solved by a forensic chemist.

5. Why was the development of Portland cement important? How is cement used to make concrete? What are the principal types of concrete and how are they used?

6. Compare the chemical composition of earth, the moon, and asteroids. How do scientists identify the source of meteorites?

7. Compile a list of common everyday chemical reactions that are exothermic and a list of reactions that are endothermic.

8. How are waste products turned into energy sources?

9. Discuss some exothermic reactions in which the heat given off is useful, and some in which it is not useful. Do the same for endothermic reactions and the heat absorbed.

Readings and References

Blassingame, Wyatt. *Science Catches the Criminal.* New York: Dodd, 1975.

Gerber, Samuel M., ed. *Chemistry and Crime: From Sherlock Holmes to Today's Courtroom.* Washington, DC: American Chemical Society, 1983.

O'Connor, Rod, and Charles Mickey. *Solving Problems in Chemistry: With Emphasis on Stoichiometry and Equilibrium.* New York: Harper & Row, 1974.

Smyth, Frank. *Cause of Death: The Study of Forensic Science.* New York: Van Nostrand Reinhold, 1980.

9 The States of Matter

Chapter Planning Guide

Section			Demonstrations and Experiments	Resource Materials
9·1	Kinetic Theory and the Nature of Gases	C*	Dem 9·1 Molecular Motion Dem 9·2 Molecular Motion Tube Dem 9·3 Brownian Motion Dem 9·4 Brownian Motion Cell	Objectives Worksheet 9, SPB Skillsheet 9, SPB Beyond the Text: Balloon Ascensions

9·2	Kinetic Energy and Temperature	C	Dem 9·5 Determination of Absolute Zero	Beyond the Text:
				   Cryogenics: The Science of the
				   Very Cold

9·3	Pressure	C	Dem 9·6 Atmospheric Pressure
			Dem 9·7 Atmospheric Pressure vs
			   Volume
				Beyond the Text:
				   Other Ways of Measuring
				   Pressure

9·A	Measuring Pressure	E		
9·4	Avogadro's Hypothesis	C		Quiz 9·1
9·5	The Nature of Liquids	C		
9·6	Vaporization	C	Dem 9·8 Vapor Pressure	Teaching Diagram 13
9·7	The Boiling Point of a Liquid	C	Dem 9·9 Boiling Cold Water Dem 9·10 Boiling Water with Cold Water Dem 9·11 Boiling a Liquid with Hand Heat	
9·B	Liquid Crystals	E		Cigarettes and Passive Smoking, ICT 9
9·8	The Nature of Solids	C	Dem 9·12 Unit Cells Dem 9·13 Tempering	Quiz 9·2
9·9	Phase Changes	C	Exp 16 Changes of Physical State, LM	Prelab 16, SPB Teaching Diagram 14
9·10	Energy and Phase Changes	H	Exp 17 Heat of Fusion of Ice, LM Dem 9·14 Heat of Evaporation	Prelab 17, SPB Quiz 9·3 Reviewsheet 9, SPB Chapter 9 Test
9·C	Plasma: The Fourth State of Matter	E		

*C = Core, O = Optional E = Enrichment, H = Honors	LM = Laboratory Manual	SPB = Skills Practice Book ICT = Issues in Chem. Tech.

Chapter Objectives

Having studied this chapter and done the problems, the student should be able to:

1. Describe the motion of particles of a gas according to the kinetic theory. *9·1*

2. Distinguish between contained gases and uncontained gases. *9·1*

3. Relate temperature to the average kinetic energy of the particles in a substance. *9·2*

4. Explain the significance of absolute zero, giving its value in degrees Celsius and Kelvin. *9·2*

5. Use the kinetic theory to explain gas pressure. *9·3*

6. Convert between the units of pressure of Pa, atm, and mm Hg. *9·3*

7. State the values of standard temperature and pressure (STP). *9·3*

8. State and explain the significance of Avogadro's hypothesis. *9·4*

9. Describe the nature of a liquid in terms of the attractive forces between its particles. *9·5*

10. Explain why a liquid has a vapor pressure, and why a change in temperature causes a change in vapor pressure. *9·6*

11. Describe what happens on a particle level at the melting point and the boiling point of a substance. *9·7*

12. Explain the significance of the unit cell to the shape of the crystal. *9·8*

13. Name six possible phase changes that matter can undergo. *9·9*

14. Determine the following from a heating curve of a substance: specific heat, heat of fusion, heat of solidification, melting point, heat of vaporization, heat of condensation, and boiling point. *9·10*

Teaching Suggestions

9·1 Kinetic Theory and the Nature of Gases

Although they may be able to state the basic assumptions of the kinetic theory from memory, many students do not have an intuitive grasp of their significance. To say that a gas has empty space between the molecules is to understate the case. How much empty space is there? You might raise this question and then point out the amount of expansion which takes place when a liquid changes to a gas. If you made the models for **Demonstration 6·2** *Molar Volumes,* show them the small volume a mole of liquid nitrogen occupies (34.6 cm³) and the large volume a mole of gaseous nitrogen occupies (22 400 cm³).

The amount of empty space in the gas can be roughly estimated by subtracting the volume of the liquid phase from the volume of the gaseous phase. This gives a value of about 22 365 cm³ for the empty space in a mole of gaseous nitrogen. In other words, the gas is only 0.15% nitrogen molecules and 99.85% space! In reality the actual difference is even greater since the calculation assumes no empty space between the molecules in the liquid phase.

You may need to spend some time helping the students understand the concept of elastic collisions. They have had no direct experience with this type of collision, since all the collisions they have ever observed are inelastic. Have them imagine a ball which collides with surfaces in a perfectly elastic manner. When dropped from a given height the ball will return to that same height bounce after bounce after colliding with a flat surface below it. In other words, the ball never loses energy when it collides with the surface. Point out that, in a similar fashion, molecules never "run down" or lose energy when they collide. It is important for them to realize that an individual molecule may transfer its energy to another molecule and thus slow down, but the *total* energy of the molecules remains constant.

How do we know that the molecules of a gas collide elastically and never slow down? The proof is simple. If gas molecules slowed down over a period of time, the gas would lose pressure and collapse. This has never been observed to occur.

To help the students visualize the motion of gas molecules you could set up **Demonstration 9·1** *Molecular Motion* or **9·2** *Molecular Motion Tube.* **Demonstration 9·3** *Brownian Motion* or **Demonstration 9·4** *Brownian Motion Cell* would also help. **Demonstration 10·6** *Diffusion of Gases* helps get across the idea that gas molecules are indeed in motion and that their speeds depend upon their masses.

9·2 Kinetic Energy and Temperature

It is important that the students realize that in any given sample of gas the molecules are not moving identically. They may wonder how this could be when the molecules could be identical and at the same temperature. To help them with this concept, have them visualize the "life" of one molecule in a gas. It is hit from one side, travels a short distance, collides with another molecule, is hit again, and so forth. Each of these collisions can give it a different speed. A collision from behind could make it go faster. A

head-on collision could make it move in the opposite direction. If it were hit from the rear and the front at the same time, it could even come to an absolute halt. Thus, the speed of an individual molecule must be continually changing. To define temperature we can use only the *average* energy of all of the molecules.

Students will need some help, too, in understanding that molecules of different masses can have the same average amounts of kinetic energy. Kinetic energy depends upon two factors, mass and velocity. In order for a molecule with a low mass to have the same amount of kinetic energy as a more massive molecule, it must be moving more rapidly than the more massive molecule. In fact, the ratio of their speeds must be proportional to the square root of the inverse ratio of their masses:

$$v_1/v_2 = \sqrt{m_2}/\sqrt{m_1}$$

The concept of an absolute zero is easy for students to grasp. They can understand that as temperature drops, molecules slow down. So eventually a point is reached where no motion is present. There are always some students who will question whether it is possible to obtain temperatures below absolute zero. Try to get them to answer this question themselves, using the concept that temperature is a measure of the average kinetic energy of molecules. (Molecules cannot possibly have less than zero kinetic energy.)

The value of absolute zero was known long before the science of cryogenics was established. **Demonstration 9·5** *Determination of Absolute Zero* shows one method of predicting absolute zero and illustrates the necessity of the Kelvin scale.

9·3 Pressure

Most students are unaware of the tremendous amount of force being exerted by the earth's atmosphere. Try to relate this to the pressure people feel when they dive into very deep water. The weight of the water above them exerts considerable pressure. In a similar fashion we can think of ourselves as being at the bottom of a very deep "ocean" of air. The weight of all of the air above us is also exerting considerable pressure.

You can do **Demonstration 9·6** *Atmospheric Pressure* to illustrate how atmospheric pressure is powerful enough to crush a metal can. You could also demonstrate the effect of the removal of atmospheric pressure by doing **Demonstration 9·7** *Atmospheric Pressure vs Volume*. This demonstration could also be referred to when the inverse relationship between pressure and volume (Boyle's law) is discussed in Chapter 10.

9·4 Avogadro's Hypothesis

Emphasize that Avogadro's hypothesis works *only* for gases. Similar statements do not apply to solids and liquids. The factor which makes gases so different from solids and liquids is the very large proportion of volume

which is empty space. The volumes of the individual molecules are absolutely negligible compared to the space that is between them. Therefore, the volume of a gas depends upon the *number* of gas particles present, not their size. Equal volumes of gases should then contain the same number of particles.

9·5 The Nature of Liquids

This section makes the transition from the study of gases to the study of liquids. In a later section solids will also be discussed.

At this point you might wish to give the students an analogy to help them visualize the three states of matter. Have them imagine themselves as being molecules of solids, then liquids, and then gases with the school environment as their container. In the "solid" state, the students in your classroom would be confined to their seats. They could still move (wiggle, turn around, talk to each other, etc.), but they would be unable to leave their fixed positions. (At absolute zero they could not talk or move.) In the "liquid" state, they would all leave their seats and walk randomly about the room, often colliding and changing direction. The volume of the class would not have increased significantly, however. In the "gaseous" state they would have burst from the room and be running wildly about the entire campus! Their volume would have increased tremendously, with a large amount of empty space between them.

9·6 Vaporization

Any liquid when placed in a sealed container evaporates and produces a vapor pressure. Vapor pressure is an important concept, since we will use it to explain boiling. **Demonstration 9·8** *Vapor Pressure*, which illustrates the effect of temperature on vapor pressure, will assist the students in understanding this concept and pave the way for Section 9·7.

9·7 The Boiling Point of a Liquid

Boiling is a process which is different from evaporation. Evaporation is entirely a surface effect. It can occur at nearly any temperature. Boiling, on the other hand, is a phenomenon in which bubbles form anywhere in the liquid and then rise to the surface. Boiling takes place at a specific temperature.

Boiling cannot occur unless bubbles are able to form and last within the liquid. Whether or not a bubble can exist is decided by the relative strengths of the liquid's vapor pressure and atmospheric pressure.

The reason a bubble forms in the first place has to do with vapor pressure. If a tiny space appears momentarily in the liquid, vapor fills it and exerts a pressure on the outer edges of the space. If this pressure is sufficient, the bubble

grows and fills with even more vapor. Being less dense than its surroundings, the bubble rises to the surface. Boiling occurs.

The force which is opposing this process is atmospheric pressure. Atmospheric pressure is pushing down on the container of liquid with such force that most bubbles are crushed before they can even form. It is only when the internal pressure of a bubble (vapor pressure) is equal to or greater than atmospheric pressure that a bubble can exist and boiling can occur.

The traditional way in which we make water boil is, of course, to heat it. This works because the vapor pressure of any liquid increases as temperature increases. If water is heated enough, its vapor pressure equals atmospheric pressure, and boiling occurs. You might ask your students how we could get water to boil at a higher temperature. They should be able to come up with the idea that an increase in atmospheric pressure would be needed. This leads to the idea of using pressure cookers.

It may not be as obvious to the students that the boiling point of water may be lowered as well. To do this we need to drop the atmospheric pressure. This occurs naturally at high altitudes. Food takes much longer to cook at 10,000 feet than at sea level because the boiling point of water is lower and so the food cannot get as hot. Boiling point lowering can also be accomplished by placing the liquid to be boiled in an artificial "atmosphere" with pressure lowered by a vacuum pump.

Demonstration 9·9 *Boiling Cold Water* and **9·10** *Boiling Water with Cold Water* illustrate two methods by which you can show your students that water can boil at temperatures far below 100°C. **Demonstration 9·11** *Boiling a Liquid with Hand Heat* could also be used.

9·8 The Nature of Solids

Emphasize that the particles in solids are in their most orderly state, and are restricted to fixed positions. *Yet they are still in motion.* Instead of moving from place to place, they vibrate back and forth. Particles in solids have kinetic energy, and this kinetic energy varies directly with temperature changes just as in liquids and gases. **Demonstration 9·12** *Unit Cells* shows the structure of crystals. **Demonstration 9·13** *Tempering* shows the effect of heating and cooling a metal.

9·9 Phase Changes

Demonstration 23·9 *Sublimation of Iodine* shows a solid to vapor phase change.

9·10 Energy and Phase Changes

Energy is a required part of any phase change. Most students readily see that energy is needed to produce a phase change from solid to liquid or liquid to gas. This energy does not change the temperature of the substance, but is absorbed in accomplishing the phase change itself. In this kind of phase change work is being done to separate the particles from each other. More difficult for them to grasp is the fact the reverse phase changes (gas to liquid and liquid to solid) *must* give off energy as the change occurs. The energy absorbed in pulling the particles away from each other during a liquid–gas phase change is given back to the environment as the particles come back together in a gas–liquid phase change. **Experiment 17** *Heat of Fusion of Ice* shows the energy change in a phase change, as does **Demonstration 9·14** *Heat of Evaporation*.

When graphs are made of temperature–time measurements for the heating or cooling of substances, flat spots (plateaus) are seen. These plateaus are regions where the energy flowing into or out of the system is being used in changing the phase, rather than in changing the temperature. The temperature at which this plateau occurs is the melting/freezing or boiling/condensation temperature of the substance.

Have the students do **Experiment 16** *Changes in Physical State* to get experience with heating and cooling curves. In addition to the steps required in the experiment you might have them interpret their graphs. For example, you could have them state the phase or phases present in each part of the graph.

Not all students are aware that phase changes occur at the same temperature, regardless of from which direction they are approached. As an example, point out that liquid water always freezes at 0°C and solid water (ice) always melts at 0°C. Liquid water boils at 100°C (at 1 atm), while steam condenses to liquid water at 100°C.

Demonstrations

9·1 Molecular Motion

Concept: Molecules are in continuous motion.

Materials: overhead projector, screen, apparatus from a scientific supply company or glass beads in a square wooden frame covered with a clear plastic sheet.

Procedure: 1. Place the frame on the overhead projector. 2. Place glass beads in the frame and agitate it. (The commercial version uses a motor to vibrate the frame). 3. The beads' movements simulate those of molecules, colliding with each other and the walls of the frame. 4. Put in an opaque or colored bead and follow its motion to emphasize its random path. 5. Use different sized beads to show the differences in speed which result from differences in mass.

9·2 Molecular Motion Tube

Concept: Molecules are in continuous motion.

Materials: molecular vibration tubes (from a supplier), gas burner, clamp, clamp holder, stand, matches, safety goggles.

Procedure: 1. The demonstration tubes give direct evidence of molecular motion. These clear glass tubes contain colored pieces of glass and mercury. 2. When the mercury is brought to a boil by heating the tube evenly with the burner, bombardment by the invisible mercury vapor results in violent random motion of the glass particles. 3. Mercury condenses in the cooler end of the tube. 4. The tube is reusable. **Caution:** *Use a mercury sponge to clean up spills.*

9·3 Brownian Motion

Concept: Molecular motion causes random motion of larger particles.

Materials: 1 mL of india ink, water, microscope, slides, cover slips.

Procedure: 1. Dilute 1 mL of india ink with 10 mL water. 2. Put a drop of the mixture on a slide and put on a cover slip. 3. Use 100× to view the carbon particles in this ink mixture. 4. The carbon particles of the ink are seen vibrating rapidly and moving randomly. This motion is the result of the bombardment of the carbon particles by the invisible water molecules.

9·4 Brownian Motion Cell

Concept: Molecular motion causes random motion of larger particles.

Materials: Brownian motion cell, microscope, matches.

Procedure: 1. View the cell at 50×. 2. Light and extinguish a match. 3. Draw the smoke into the chamber of the cell. 4. Focus the microscope. 5. Change to 100× to see the particles (as spots of light) in random motion.

9·5 Determination of Absolute Zero

Concept: A pressure–temperature graph can be used to extrapolate the value of absolute zero on the Celsius scale.

Materials: absolute zero demonstrator apparatus (a sealed air-filled metal bulb connected to a large-size pressure gauge), water, ring stand, gas burner, matches, ring, gauze, wide range thermometer, ice, salt, dry ice, acetone, graph paper, safety goggles.

Procedure: 1. The bulb is placed in liquids of various temperatures, and pressure readings are taken. The liquids are: boiling water, water at room temperature, and a salt–ice mixture. With proper mixing a salt–ice mixture can easily produce a temperature of −10°C or lower. A mixture of dry ice and acetone produces even lower temperatures (−78°C). 2. After the readings are made, have the students prepare a graph with pressure on the vertical axis and degrees Celsius on the horizontal axis. 3. The plot produces a straight line. 4. At absolute zero, all molecular motion has theoretically stopped. Have the students extrapolate their graphs to the point of zero pressure. The temperature at that point is absolute zero. The value obtained should be fairly close to −273°C. 5. As an additional exercise, students can search for a numerical relationship between the pressure and temperature readings. Suggest that they add, multiply or divide their two numbers. They will find no relationship. 6. Repeat this using temperature readings expressed in degrees Kelvin. Dividing pressure by temperature will now give a constant value. 7. Point out that there is a constant relationship between gas pressure and temperature which holds *only if the temperature is expressed in degrees Kelvin.* The pressure–temperature relationship will be explored further in the next chapter. **Caution:** *Acetone is extremely flammable. Keep it away from all sources of heat, and store in a cool place. Dry ice can cause frostbite if it comes into contact with skin. Use tongs in handling.*

9·6 Atmospheric Pressure

Concept: The atmosphere exerts a strong pressure.

Materials: empty duplicating fluid can with lid, ring stand, water, gas burner, matches, vacuum pump (optional), one-hole stopper, safety goggles.

Procedure: 1. Mount the can on the stand. 2. Ask if the can is empty. (No, it is *full* of air.) 3. Ask if there is any pressure inside the can. (Yes, there is the pressure exerted by the air molecules, about 1 atm.) 4. Point out that there is also pressure exerted on the outside of the can by air molecules. The pressure on the inside and outside of the can are equal. 5. Pour water into the can to a depth of 1/2 cm. 6. With the lid off, boil the water with a gas burner. 7. Let the water boil vigorously for a few minutes. 8. While this is taking place, point out that the water is changing to steam and is expanding. The steam is replacing the air in the can and is pushing it out. 9. Remove the heat source and replace the cap to seal it tightly. 10. Hissing, popping, and thumping noises can be heard as the can cools. 11. The can is crushed by the atmospheric pressure until the sides collapse inward. 12. Explain that it is not suction *pulling* the sides in, but atmospheric pressure *pushing* them in. When the can cools, the steam condenses back to water. The part of the can above the water is left essentially empty. With no gas to exert pressure on the inner walls of the can, there is no resistance to the external pressure and the can collapses. 13. This demonstration can also be done by connecting a vacuum pump directly to the

can through an oversized one-hole stopper inserted into the opening of the can.

9·7 Atmospheric Pressure vs Volume

Concept: The volume of a sample of a gas varies as the pressure of its surroundings changes.

Materials: vacuum pump, large bell jar, pump plate, small party balloon, safety goggles.

Procedure: 1. Inflate the balloon to about 1/3 maximum. 2. Seal it and place it inside the bell jar. 3. Mention that you are going to pump some of the air out of the jar. Ask the students to predict what will happen to the balloon. 4. Pump out the air and observe that the balloon expands. 5. Before it pops, turn off the vacuum pump. 6. Ask why the balloon has expanded. They may respond that because the pressure on the outside is less, the balloon expanded. 7. Ask about the pressure inside the balloon: is it the same, greater, or lower than before the vacuum was applied? (The volume of the gas has increased, so its pressure has *decreased*.) 8. Continue pumping out the air until the balloon explodes. The students will be surprised at how quietly it breaks. Only the sound of the rubber fragments hitting the sides of the bell jar is heard. Sound cannot travel through a vacuum.

9·8 Vapor Pressure

Concept: A liquid exerts a vapor pressure that increases with temperature.

Materials: manometer*, meter stick, thick rubber hose, 1-L flask, two-hole rubber stopper for flask, separatory funnel inserted into one of the holes of the stopper, stopper for funnel, glass tubing with 90° bend inserted into the other hole, 50 mL of acetone (C_3H_6O), ice, hot plate, beaker, water, safety goggles. (*A manometer can be constructed by bending a 100-cm length of small bore glass tubing into a narrow "U" shape. Mount the tube to a meterstick with open ends upwards. Pour the mercury into the tube until a 30 cm column stands on either side.)

Procedure: 1. Insert the rubber stopper into the mouth of the flask. Anchor the stopper to the flask with a piece of wire. 2. Pour the acetone into the funnel and stopper it. 3. Connect the bent piece of glass tubing to one end of the manometer with the hose. Be sure the hose fits both connections tightly. 4. Measure the pressure by finding the difference between the heights of the mercury columns on either side of the "U." 5. Mention that you are going to introduce a few mL of acetone into the flask and ask them to predict the effect this will have on the pressure. 6. Point out that adding a few mL of liquid to a gas which has a volume of nearly 1-L should not increase the pressure by much since the change in volume is small. 7. Add the acetone to the flask. The pressure rises immediately as the

acetone evaporates. It slowly climbs to a maximum. This maximum is the vapor pressure of the acetone at room temperature. 8. Emphasize that the evaporation of the liquid has produced a pressure above the liquid. This pressure is *in addition* to the air pressure. The vapor pressure increases until an equilibrium is established between the liquid and gas. 9. Place the bottom of the flask in warm (50°C) water. The pressure climbs dramatically. 10. Place the flask in ice-water. The pressure drops. This behavior illustrates the dependence of vapor pressure on temperature, a concept which is crucial for the understanding of boiling. 11. To repeat this demonstration, you *must* start with a clean, dry flask. **Caution:** *Acetone is extremely flammable. Keep it away from all sources of heat. Use a mercury sponge to clean up mercury spills.*

9·9 Boiling Cold Water

Concept: Water can be boiled at low temperatures.

Materials: bell jar, pump plate, piston-type vacuum pump, 500-mL beaker, thermometer, water, drying tube filled with calcium chloride ($CaCl_2$), safety goggles.

Procedure: 1. Place a beaker of room temperature water inside a bell jar connected to a vacuum pump. 2. Place a thermometer in the water so that it can be read from the outside. 3. Check for air-tight connections between the bell jar and the vacuum pump. 4. To protect the pump from moisture damage, place a drying tube filled with calcium chloride in series with the hose that connects the pump plate to the pump. 5. Have a student read the temperature of the water before you turn on the pump. 6. Evacuate the bell jar. The water may take some time to boil, since the pressure must drop from 760 mm Hg to 20 mm Hg. 7. If your system is leak free, bubbles of dissolved gas form as the water nears its boiling point. 8. Eventually the water reaches a full boil and steam condenses on the walls of the bell jar. 9. Have the student read the thermometer both when the water starts to boil and then after it has boiled awhile. The class will be surprised to learn that the water is not only boiling at room temperature but is also getting *colder!* 10. Reinforce the point that the liquid–gas phase change is energy absorbing. The heat of vaporization is taken from the liquid as the phase change takes place. 11. Mention that if the vacuum system were good enough, the water could be cooled by the boiling process until it reached 0°C and froze!

9·10 Boiling Water With Cold Water

Concept: Cold water can induce boiling of water in a flask at low pressure.

Materials: 500-mL round bottom Pyrex flask, ring, wire gauze, ring stand, gas burner, water, one-hole stopper with a glass tube and rubber hose with clamp, cold water, matches, safety goggles.

Procedure: 1. Fill the flask 1/4 full with water. 2. Boil the water for a few minutes. The steam drives the air out of the flask. 3. Remove the source of heat and, when boiling has subsided, tightly stopper the flask. 4. Pour cold water on the part of the flask containing steam. This will renew the boiling. This can be repeated several times. 5. A lively class discussion can ensue as the students try to explain the demonstration. (Pouring the cold water on the flask causes the steam to condense to water. When the steam condenses, the pressure in the flask drops to the point where the vapor pressure of the water inside the flask is equal to the pressure in the flask.) 6. After the demonstration, the stopper may seem stuck. To release it, simply release the hose clamp so that air can enter the flask.

9·11 Boiling a Liquid with Hand Heat

Concept: Lowering pressure lowers the boiling point.

Materials: vacuum flask with side arm, vacuum hose, vacuum pump or aspirator, water, safety goggles.

Procedure: 1. Fill the flask 1/4 full of water. 2. Connect the flask to the vacuum pump with the hose. 3. Seal the flask by placing a hand on top of it. 4. Turn on the pump or aspirator. 5. Invert the flask after a few minutes. 6. A slow, rolling boil occurs if the hand is warm. 7. State that lowering pressure lowers the boiling point. Raising the pressure raises the boiling point. (Pressure cookers use this idea. Water boils at a higher temperature when the pressure is increased; as a result, food cooks faster.)

9·12 Unit Cells

Concept: Crystalline solids are made of unit cells.

Materials: large watch glass, 10 mL of water, 10 drops of liquid detergent, straw, overhead projector.

Procedure: 1. Place the water in the watch glass and add the detergent. 2. Use the straw to blow bubbles into the solution. 3. The bubbles simulate the unit cells; they organize themselves into a regular, repeating pattern. 4. Place the watch glass on the overhead projector.

9·13 Tempering

Concept: Heating and cooling a metal changes its physical properties.

Materials: three metal hair pins, forceps, gas burner, matches, small beaker of water, glass plate, safety goggles.

Procedure: 1. Using the forceps, heat one hair pin to red-hot and place it on the glass plate to cool. 2. Heat another pin to red-hot and drop it in the water. 3. Show the flexibility of the three pins. 4. The flexibility is greatest for the water-cooled one. It has the greatest degree of hexagonal close-packing of molecules.

9·14 Heat of Evaporation

Concept: The loss of thermal energy when a liquid evaporates will lower the temperature of the liquid.

Materials: acetone or Freon, thermometer in units of 1°C, safety goggles.

Procedure: 1. Read the thermometer *exactly*. 2. Dip its bulb in the acetone and let it evaporate. Repeat five times. 3. Read the thermometer again. 4. Note that the temperature of the bulb is lowered as its thermal energy is used to evaporate the liquid. **Caution:** *Acetone is extremely flammable. Keep it away from all sources of heat. Store in a cool place.*

Audiovisual Resources

Brownian Motion and Random Walk (F) Kalmia, 1974, 3 min. (Use with Section 9·1.) Demonstrates the concept of molecular motion and random walk using computer-generated diagrams that show gas molecule collisions.

Chemistry: Matter and Energy Changes (5 FS) Charles Clark, 12–18 min. each. (Use with Sections 9·1, 9·2, 9·5, 9·8, or 9·10.) Compares properties of solids, liquids, and gases, explains the Celsius and Kelvin temperature scales, and discusses changes of temperature and phase.

Chemistry: The Forces in Solids, Liquids, and Gases (5 FS) Charles Clark, 1978, 14–15 min. each. (Use with Sections 9·1, 9·5, or 9·8.) Introduces attractive forces in solids, liquids, and gases. Also covers topics in Chapters 13 and 14.

Crystallization (F) Churchill Films, 1975, 11 min. (Use with Section 9·8.) Shows crystal growth and melting through a polarizing microscope; only a small amount of initial commentary.

Crystals and Their Structures (F, V) Chem Study, 1963, 22 min. (Use with Section 9·8.) Demonstrates how crystal structures are determined and describes their properties.

Gases and How They Combine (F, V) Chem Study, 1962, 22 min. (Use with Sections 9·1 or 9·4.) Shows properties of gases and demonstrates Avogadro's hypothesis.

High Temperature Research (F, V) Chem Study, 1963, 19 min. (Use with Section 9·6.) Presents a study of the bond strength of gaseous titanium monosulfide at about 2000 K.

Molecular Motions (F, V) Chem Study, 1963, 13 min. (Use with Sections 9·1, 9·5, 9·6, 9·8, and 9·9.) Describes properties of matter in terms of molecular motion.

The Behavior of Matter (F, V) Encyclopaedia Brittanica, 1982, 15 min. (Use with Sections 9·1. 9·5, 9·6, 9·7, 9·8, and 9·9.) Discusses the three states of matter and physical and chemical change using animated models.

The Molecular Theory of Matter (F) Encyclopaedia Brittanica, 1965, 11 min. (Use with Sections 9·1 or 9·9.) Demonstrates kinetic theory by showing gaseous diffusion and phase changes.

Beyond The Text

Cryogenics: The Science of the Very Cold

Cryogenics is the science of producing very low temperatures and studying the behavior of matter at such temperatures. Scientists were interested in this subject as early as the eighteenth century. Progress was slow, however, because of the difficulty in liquefying gases. After this problem was solved, cryogenics developed very rapidly. Since World War II it has become an important field of scientific research.

Much of the work of cryogenics involves liquefied gases. The gases are used in a wide variety of manufacturing and research applications. A common use is to cool or freeze other materials. Because of the very low temperature of liquid nitrogen, about 77 K, materials immersed in it freeze very quickly. This prevents the water loss that occurs during slow freezing. Thus the sample is damaged less. The food industry uses liquid nitrogen to freeze food and to keep it frozen during transportation. At very low temperatures, biological reactions will slow down or stop. Biologists can use this effect to study reactions more easily. In medicine some body tissues can be preserved by freezing without losing their ability to be used in the body when thawed later. Blood, sperm, and cartilage are a few such materials. Doctors also perform cryosurgery by freezing tissue instead of cutting it. There is little or no bleeding in the operation, and the wound heals rapidly with little scarring.

By far the most exciting application of cryogenics is the use of liquid helium to cool metals to very low temperatures where they become superconductive. Any metal conducts electricity, and when it is cooled it becomes an even better conductor. At a very low temperature, called the transition temperature of the metal, the electrical resistance of certain metals and alloys suddenly becomes zero. If a current is passed through a loop of such a metal at this temperature, it will continue to circulate in the loop indefinitely. This property is called superconductivity. The current will not diminish even if the metal loop is disconnected from the source of electricity!

Mercury was the first metal found to be superconductive. Its transition temperature is 4 K. Helium boils at 4 K and can be cooled to very near absolute zero. By cooling mercury with liquid helium, its superconductive properties can be observed. Zinc becomes superconductive at less than 1 K, tin at 3.7 K, and lead at 7.3 K. Other metals and alloys have been found to become superconductive at temperatures as high as 18 K–20 K. Even some organic compounds can be superconductive.

Many applications of superconductivity involve the use of superconducting magnets. In comparison to an ordinary electromagnet, a superconducting magnet can produce a much larger magnetic field using a much smaller amount of electrical energy.

Superconducting circuits are also used in very large computers where ordinary circuits would generate too much heat. Superconductors can be substituted for conventional conductors in electric generators and motors, increasing efficiency and reducing size. These lighter machines would be especially useful in aircraft. These are only a few of the many possibilities being explored in the field of cryogenics.

Other Ways of Measuring Pressure

Whereas barometers measure atmospheric pressure, manometers measure the pressure of a gas sample. Manometers are U-shaped tubes half-filled with mercury or water. The tubes have a sample flask attached at one end and may be open or closed on the other end. In either case, the pressure of the gas sample is related to the difference in the heights of liquid in the two arms of the tube. In a closed-arm manometer, the gas-sample pressure is being measured against the pressure of the vacuum in the closed arm of the tube. In this case, the difference in the levels of liquid is the gas-sample pressure.

In an open-arm manometer, the liquid in the open end of the tube is subject to atmospheric pressure. If the two levels are equal, then the gas-sample pressure equals atmospheric pressure. If the level in the sample arm is higher than the level in the open arm, then the gas-sample pressure is lower than atmospheric pressure. The difference in levels is subtracted from atmospheric pressure to obtain the gas-sample pressure. If the level in the open arm is higher than the level in the sample arm, then the gas-sample pressure is higher than atmospheric pressure. The difference in levels is added to atmospheric pressure to obtain the gas-sample pressure.

Micromanometers use water instead of mercury to detect very small gas pressures. Water is used instead of mercury because the density of water is 1/13 that of mercury. Therefore smaller changes in pressure can be detected. In a micromanometer the location of a piece of metal floating in one of the arms is detected electrically to

give the sample-gas pressure. Pressures as low as 1×10^{-6} atmospheres can be measured.

Some substances have different electrical resistance at different pressures. Others, like quartz, form piezoelectric crystals that produce a small electric current when subjected to pressure. Both kinds of substances can be used to make pressure transducers. These devices will respond to pressure by giving an electrical signal. Transducers can be very small, and they can be connected by wires to a meter at a distant point. One common and very important use of these devices is in monitoring the pressure of body fluids during surgery.

Balloon Ascensions

French adventures and inventors were trying to make use of the thermal expansion of gases even before Charles had formulated his law. The sight of smoke rising above a flame inspired Joseph and Jacques Montgolfier to float a large paper bag by filling it with hot air in 1782. By 1783 the first people to fly had done so in the Montgolfier brothers' hot air balloons.

In the same year, the French physicist Jacques Charles invented the hydrogen-filled balloon. Because hydrogen is much lighter than hot air, Charles' balloon was much smaller than the Montgolfiers', yet it had equal lifting power. Charles equipped his balloon with scientific instruments: a thermometer and barometer. He rode to an altitude of 6300 feet.

Balloons were widely used for sport and entertainment. The use of hydrogen, a highly flammable gas, to fill the balloons led to a number of spectacular and tragic accidents. One famous accident involved a well-known French woman entertainer and balloonist, Madame Blanchard. She made the mistake of going aloft in her hydrogen balloon to set off fireworks!

The use of balloons for scientific research also grew. The first balloon flight purely for science was in 1803. German scientists reached an altitude of 23,500 feet from where they studied the earth's magnetism. In 1804 Joseph Gay-Lussac and a colleague floated up to 23,000 feet with a collection of scientific instruments and caged animals. They studied the behavior of insects, birds, and frogs at the high altitude. They observed, among other things, that a bee flew happily away when released, but a bird refused to leave the balloon. They also studied the earth's magnetic effects and the composition of air at high altitudes. Gay-Lussac collected air samples in flasks that had been evacuated in the laboratory. Back on land, he discovered that the atmospheric pressure at 23,000 feet was about one-half that at sea level. The percentage composition of air, however, remained the same: about 20% oxygen to 80% nitrogen.

Balloons are used today for a variety of scientific work. Generally, modern balloons are filled with helium to eliminate the possibility of explosions. Sealed weather balloons can circle the globe at 40,000 feet for almost a year, sending back meteorlogical information. Spacecraft, such as the Mars Viking lander, are hauled up to great heights by balloons and dropped. This is to test their reaction to impact on landing. Balloons are also used for aerial photography, television relay stations, communication platforms, and military surveillance.

Answers to End of Chapter Questions and Problems

Practice Questions and Problems

11. An elastic collision transfers energy from one particle to another. There is no change in the total kinetic energy.

12. $460 \dfrac{m}{s}$

13. Heat the water.

14. Average kinetic energy is zero.

15. One-half.

16. The random collisons of gas molecules on the surface of an object; pascals (Pa), millimeters of mercury (mm Hg), standard atmospheres (atm).

17. One atmosphere is equal to 760 mm Hg.

18. 0.50 atm

19. 2.4×10^3 mm Hg

20. 53 kPa

21. *S*tandard *T*emperature and *P*ressure, 0°C and 1 atm.

22. 273 K; 760 mm Hg

23. 0.10 mol

24. a. The particles of a liquid are held together by attractive forces. They are therefore denser than gases. Gas molecules have negligible forces between them. They remain far apart. **b.** The molecules of liquids are in contact and cannot be squeezed together because of repulsive electrostatic forces. The molecules of gases are far apart and can be compressed closer.

25. When the molecules leave, the average kinetic energy is lowered and the temperature decreases.

26. A larger percentage of molecules have enough energy to escape attractions within the liquid.

27. No. Vapor continuously leaves the surface of the liquid, preventing dynamic equilibrium.

28. Increases the kinetic energy which increases the vapor pressure.

29. The boiling point is the temperature at which the vapor pressure of the liquid equals the external pressure. The normal boiling point is the boiling point when the external pressure is 1 atm.

30. If the external pressure is lowered, less kinetic energy is required to separate the liquid molecules. They therefore separate at a lower temperature. At higher external pressure, separation is harder and a higher temperature is needed, because more kinetic energy is required.

31. ~82°C

32. a. ~76°C **b.** ~50°C **c.** ~62°C

33. ~250 mm Hg

34. Molecules escaping the liquid have energy higher than the average kinetic energy. This lowers the average kinetic energy.

35. The molecules of a solid at its melting point have sufficient kinetic energy to overcome the attractive forces holding them in place.

36. The forces between the molecules are weaker.

37. The regular, repeating, three-dimensional pattern of the atoms, ions, or molecules in a crystal.

38. Added heat is removed by the molecules escaping the liquid. The average kinetic energy remains the same.

39. Sublimation is the change of state from solid to vapor without passing through the liquid state. Substances can be dried without heating or boiling.

40. a. The heat needed to melt one gram of a solid at its melting point. **b.** The heat needed to boil off one gram of liquid at its boiling point.

Mastery Questions and Problems

41. 1275 cal

42. The average kinetic energy increases.

43. Vaporization is the conversion of a liquid to a gas or vapor when the liquid is below its boiling point. The vapor pressure is the force per unit area exerted by the vaporized particles on the walls of a sealed container. The boiling point is the temperature at which the vapor pressure of the liquid becomes equal to the external pressure.

44. A substance has sufficient average kinetic energy to disrupt the forces holding the solid crystal together.

45. The mass of the air pressing on molecules below it causes it. The mass of air above the mountain is less than the mass above sea level.

46. 2.44×10^4 cal; 1.02×10^5 J

47. 6.72 L

48. A dynamic equilibrium involves a continual exchange of particles even though net amounts stay constant.

49. 819 K

50. 2.85×10^3 cal; 1.19×10^4 J

51. ~77°C

52. 40.0 g water; 960 g ice

Review Questions and Problems

53. a. $V_2O_5 + 2H_2 \rightarrow V_2O_3 + 2H_2O$
  b. $(NH_4)_2Cr_2O_7 \rightarrow Cr_2O_3 + N_2 + 4H_2O$
  c. $4NH_3 + 5O_2 \rightarrow 4NO + 6H_2O$
  d. $2C_6H_{14} + 13O_2 \rightarrow 12CO + 14H_2O$

54. a. 51.2 g Cl_2O_7 **b.** 30.6 mL H_2O

55. $0.00374 \, \dfrac{g}{cm^3}$ Kr

56. a. $MoCl_4$ **b.** CH_3Cl **c.** Ag_2Te

57. a. 13.9 mol SO_2 **b.** 0.0472 mol NH_3
  c. 0.021 mol CO_2

58. a. exothermic **b.** 303 kJ **c.** C_2H_4

Challenging Questions and Problems

59. a. 4.74×10^4 cal **b.** 4.74×10^1 kcal
  c. 1.98×10^5 J

60. A unit cell is the smallest group of atoms, ions, or molecules that retains the geometric shape of the crystal. A crystal lattice is the regular, repeating, three-dimensional pattern of atoms, ions, or molecules in a crystal.

61. The vapor pressure above a liquid depends only on the kinetic energy of the escaping molecules and, therefore, the temperature.

62. Na^+ Cl^- Na^+
  Cl^- Na^+ Cl^-
  Na^+ Cl^- Na^+

63. a. 3200 cal, 3.20 kcal, 1.34×10^4 J **b.** 128 g H_2O

9 The States of Matter

Chapter Preview

Section 9·10 is appropriate for honors students.

We know that matter exists as solids, liquids, and gases. Liquids solidify, and gases liquefy when cooled. Why do changes in the state of matter occur with changes in temperature? We will find out in this chapter with the help of a model called the kinetic theory.

9·1 Kinetic Theory and the Nature of Gases

If you open a bottle of perfume, the aroma soon reaches the nose of anyone nearby. Obviously, the molecules of the fragrance have diffused from the bottle. This diffusion is simple evidence that molecules move.

Greek: *kinetos* = to move.

■ The kinetic theory describes the motion of particles.

The word *kinetic* means motion. *The **kinetic theory** says that the tiny particles in all forms of matter are in constant motion*. These particles may be atoms, ions, or molecules of gases, liquids, or solids. For the present let us concentrate on the kinetic theory as it applies to gases. We know that a gas is easily compressed and fills whatever container it is in. This behavior and many other properties of gases can be explained by the kinetic theory.

Here are the basic assumptions of the kinetic theory of gases.

1. *A gas is composed of particles, usually molecules or atoms*. These particles are considered to be small hard spheres with negligible volume and far from one another. Between the particles is empty space, absolute nothingness. No attractive or repulsive forces exist between the particles.

Figure 9·1
Life on planet Earth is dependent on water in all three states: as a solid, liquid and gas. Water vapor (a gas) is invisible, but it is an important component of air.

Figure 9·2
a Gas particles have random and chaotic movements. They are constantly colliding with one another and with the walls of the container.
b As a single gas particle moves through space it frequently changes direction due to collisions with other particles.

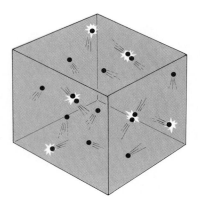
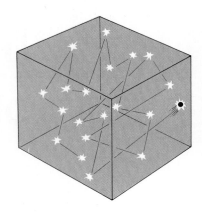

The assumptions of the kinetic theory are valid only when a gas has an extremely low density. If a gas is compressed or cooled sufficiently, the intermolecular attractions and the relative size of the particles become significant.

Temperature and pressure affect the volume of a gas.

2. *The particles in a gas move rapidly in constant random motion.* They travel in straight lines and move independently of each other. The particles change direction when they rebound from collisions with one another or with other objects (Figure 9·2).

3. *All collisions are perfectly elastic.* Perfectly elastic means that energy is transferred from one particle to another during collisions, but the total kinetic energy remains constant.

Measurements indicate that the average speed of oxygen molecules in air at 20°C is about 1656 km/hr. We say "average speed" because some particles are moving faster and some slower. At such high speeds the molecules in a bottle of perfume opened in Washington, D.C. should reach Vancouver, B.C. in about three hours. They never get there, however, because their path of unimpeded travel is very short. The perfume molecules are constantly striking air molecules and rebounding in other directions. The aimless path they take is called a *random walk* (Figure 9·2).

The physical behavior of a gas depends on its volume, temperature, and pressure. Gases in sealed containers are *contained gases*. The volume of a contained gas is the volume of the container, because gases expand to completely fill their containers. Gases that are not in sealed containers are *uncontained gases*. Air is usually an *uncontained gas*, although it may be contained by sealing it in a closed vessel. *Temperature* and *pressure* are terms we often use rather loosely, but what do they really mean? We will find out in the next two sections.

9·2 Kinetic Energy and Temperature

Motion suggests energy. *The energy an object has because of its motion is kinetic energy.* Because gas particles are in motion, they have kinetic energy. When a gas is heated, the particles in the gas absorb thermal energy. Some of it goes into increasing the energy within the particles. The rest goes into increasing the motion of particles, that is, increasing their kinetic energy.

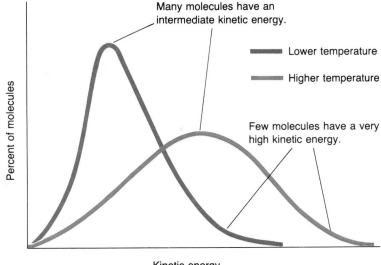

Many molecules have an intermediate kinetic energy.

▬▬ Lower temperature

▬▬ Higher temperature

Few molecules have a very high kinetic energy.

Percent of molecules

Kinetic energy

$KE = \frac{1}{2}mv^2$

■ Temperature measures the average kinetic energy of particles in a
substance.

Molecules of different masses at
the same temperature have the
same average kinetic energy. The
molecules with the lower masses
move more rapidly and the molecules with greater mass move
more slowly $\left(v = \sqrt{\dfrac{2\,KE}{m}} \right)$.

1. It is not affected.
2. It is the same.
3. It increases.

In a collection of molecules there will be a wide range of kinetic energies from very low to very high. Most molecules will have speeds in
between (Figure 9·3). As the temperature rises so does the kinetic energy. When discussing the kinetic energy of a substance, scientists use
the average kinetic energy of the particles. *The average kinetic energy of
the particles of a substance is proportional to the temperature of the substance.* We can measure how much the average kinetic energy has been
increased by measuring the temperature increase. Temperature is a measure of the average kinetic energy of the particles in a substance. Note
that it is not the total thermal energy the substance has absorbed.

Particles of all substances at the same temperature have the same average kinetic energy. An increase in the temperature of a substance
signifies an increase in the average kinetic energy of the particles of the
substance. A decrease in temperature signifies a decrease in the average
kinetic energy. Figure 9·3 shows the distribution of kinetic energies at
two different temperatures. Notice that at the higher temperature, there is
a wider range of energies.

Problems

1. How is the average kinetic energy of water molecules affected when
   hot water is poured from a kettle into cups at the same temperature
   as the water?

2. Is the average kinetic energy of the particles in a block of ice at 0°C
   the same as or different from the average kinetic energy of the particles in a gas-filled dirigible at 0°C?

3. Does the average kinetic energy of the gas particles in an inflated life
   raft increase or decrease if the sun heats the life raft from 25°C to
   37°C?

Figure 9·4
Many substances have no electrical resistance at temperatures close to absolute zero. This property is known as superconductivity. Superconducting circuits are used in large computers where ordinary circuits would generate too much heat.

The motions of the atoms themselves cease at 0 K. The motion of the subatomic particles within the atoms continues.

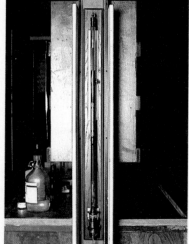

Figure 9·5
Barometers measure atmospheric pressure. This type of barometer is commonly used in laboratories. The average atmospheric pressure at sea level is 1 atm, or 760 mm Hg.

The temperature to which a substance can be raised has no theoretical upper limit. By contrast, however, there is a lower limit. At some low temperature, the particles of all substances should stop moving. The particles would have no kinetic energy at this temperature because they would have no motion. *The temperature at which the motion of particles ceases is known as absolute zero.* It falls at about −273°C. Taking a substance to a temperature *below* this lower limit is impossible. The Kelvin temperature scale is based on the idea of an absolute zero (Section 2·11). Zero degrees Kelvin (0 K) is −273° on the Celsius scale. There are no minus numbers on the Kelvin scale because they are not needed. The Kelvin scale is extremely useful because it is a direct measure of the average kinetic energy of the particles of a substance. For example, the particles in a substance at 200 K have twice the average kinetic energy of the particles in a substance at 100 K.

Problem 4. The average kinetic energy triples.

4. By what factor does the average kinetic energy of the molecules of a gas in an aerosol container increase when the temperature is raised from 300 K (27°C) to 900 K (627°C)?

9·3 Pressure

Moving bodies exert forces when they collide with other bodies. Although a gas particle is a moving body, the force exerted by a single gas particle would not make a gnat hair twitch. It is not hard to imagine, however, that many simultaneous collisions would produce a measurable force on an object. **Gas pressure** *is the result of simultaneous collisions of billions upon billions of gas particles on an object.*

Air exerts pressure because gravity holds air molecules in the earth's atmosphere. **Atmospheric pressure** *results from the collisions of air molecules with objects.* It decreases with an increase in elevation. This is because the air layer around the earth thins out at high elevations.

Collisions of gas particles with objects in their paths generate gas pressure.

1 atm = 760 mm Hg = 101.3 kPa.

Another unit of pressure, the *torr*, is named after Evangelista Torricelli (1608–1647), who invented the barometer. 1 torr = 1 mm Hg.

Barometers *are commonly used to measure atmospheric pressure.* This pressure varies slightly, depending on the weather. *The SI unit of pressure is the* **pascal** (Pa). Atmospheric pressure at sea level is about 101.3 kilopascal (kPa). Two older units of pressure are millimeters of mercury and the atmosphere. **One millimeter of mercury** (1 mm Hg) *is the pressure needed to support a column of mercury 1 mm high.* This unit developed from the early use of mercury barometers. **One standard atmosphere** (1 atm) *is the pressure required to support 760 mm of mercury* (760 mm Hg) *in a mercury barometer at 25°C.* This is the average atmospheric pressure at sea level. Thus 1 atm equals 760 mm Hg. We will use atmospheres and mm Hg as the units of pressure. *Standard conditions when working with gases are a temperature of 0°C and a pressure of 1 atm.* This is standard temperature and pressure (STP).

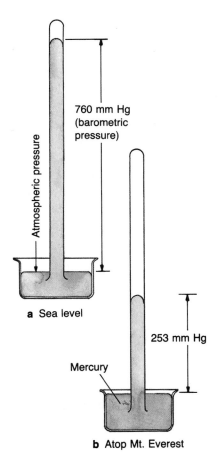

760 mm Hg (barometric pressure)

Atmospheric pressure

a Sea level

253 mm Hg

Mercury

b Atop Mt. Everest

Figure 9·6
Normal atmospheric pressure pushing on a simple mercury barometer supports a column of mercury about 760 mm high. On top of Mt. Everest (at 9000-m altitude) the air exerts enough push to support a column of mercury only 253 mm high.

Example 1

How many millimeters of mercury does a gas exert at 1.50 atm of pressure?

Solution

$$1.50 \text{ atm} \times \frac{760 \text{ mm Hg}}{1 \text{ atm}} = 1140 \text{ mm Hg} = 1.14 \times 10^3 \text{ mm Hg}$$

Problems

5. 0.25 atm
6. 253 mm is greater than 0.25 atm

5. Convert 190 mm Hg to atmospheres of pressure.

6. The pressure at the top of Mount Everest is 253 mm Hg. Is this greater or less than 0.25 atm?

9·A Measuring Pressure

The first barometers were straight glass tubes closed at one end. Each tube was filled with mercury and inverted so that the open end was below the surface of a dish of mercury. The level of mercury in the tube depended on the number of collisions of air molecules with the pool of mercury in the dish. At sea level these collisions are sufficient to support a 760 mm column of mercury in the tube. This pressure, 760 mm Hg, is called one standard atmosphere (1 atm).

Today many barometers do not contain mercury. They are called aneroid barometers. In these devices atmospheric pressure is related to the number of collisions of air molecules with a sensitive metal diaphragm. The diaphragm controls the movement of a pointer, which gives the pressure reading.

9·4 Avogadro's Hypothesis

The particles that make up different gases must have different sizes. For example, chlorine molecules have large numbers of electrons, protons, and neutrons. They must be bigger and occupy more volume than hydrogen molecules, which have only two protons and two electrons. Early scientists recognized this. Thus many reacted in disbelief in 1811 when they heard of **Avogadro's hypothesis:** *Equal volumes of gases at the same temperature and pressure contain equal numbers of particles.* It was as if Amedeo Avogadro were suggesting that two rooms of the same size could be filled by the same number of objects, no matter whether the objects were marbles or oranges.

What Avogadro had in mind is not so mysterious. It makes sense if the particles in a gas are very far apart with nothing but space in between (Figure 9·7). You can suspend ten marbles or ten oranges in a ballroom without decreasing the volume of the room very much. If we put the marbles or oranges into motion, they would occasionally collide with one another or with the walls of the room. On the average there would be large expanses of space between them. The same concept can be applied to gases. This was Avogadro's great insight, and it is easily demonstrated by experiment. At STP, 1 mol (6.02×10^{23} particles) of any gas, regardless of the size of the particles, occupies 22.4 L.

We can also understand Avogadro's hypothesis by thinking of the modern explanation for gas pressure. The same number of particles in a given volume at the same temperature should exert the same pressure. This is because the particles have the same average kinetic energy and are contained within an equal amount of space. *Whenever we have equal volumes of gases at the same temperature and pressure, the volumes must contain equal numbers of particles.*

■ A gas is mostly empty space.

Avogadro's hypothesis: At the same conditions of temperature and pressure, equal volumes of gases contain the same number of particles.

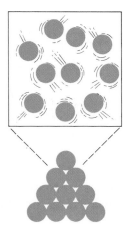 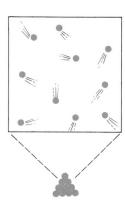

Figure 9·7
The volume of a container easily accommodates an equal number of rapidly moving large or small particles as long as the particles are not tightly packed. When the particles are tightly packed, large particles take up more space than small particles.

Example 2

Determine the volume, in liters, occupied by 0.030 mol of a gas at STP.

Solution

We know that 1 mol of a gas has a volume of 22.4 L.

$$0.030 \; \cancel{mol} \times \frac{22.4 \; L}{1 \; \cancel{mol}} = 0.67 \; L$$

1 mol of any gas at STP is 6.02×10^{23} particles and occupies 22.4 L.

Example 3

How many oxygen molecules are in 3.36 L of oxygen gas at STP?

Solution

At STP, 22.4 L of oxygen contains 1 mol. One mole of oxygen contains 6.02×10^{23} oxygen molecules.

$$3.36 \; \cancel{L \; O_2} \times \frac{1 \; \cancel{mol \; O_2}}{22.4 \; \cancel{L \; O_2}} \times \frac{6.02 \times 10^{23} \; molecules \; O_2}{1 \; \cancel{mol \; O_2}}$$
$$= 9.03 \times 10^{22} \; molecules \; O_2$$

Problems

7. 0.500 mol,
   3.01×10^{23} particles
8. 5.6 L
9. 11.2 L O_2

7. How many moles is 11.2 L of hydrogen gas at STP? How many particles (hydrogen molecules) does it contain?

8. What is the volume occupied by 0.25 mol of a gas at STP?

9. Hydrogen reacts with oxygen to give water according to this familiar combustion reaction.

$$2H_2 + O_2 \longrightarrow 2H_2O$$

What volume of oxygen (liters) at STP is required to combine with 1 mol of hydrogen?

Example 4

Determine the volume in liters occupied by 14.0 g of nitrogen gas at STP.

Solution

Nitrogen is a diatomic molecule (N_2). One mole of nitrogen gas has a mass of 28.0 g and occupies a volume of 22.4 L at STP.

$$14.0 \; \cancel{g \; N_2} \times \frac{1 \; \cancel{mol \; N_2}}{28.0 \; \cancel{g \; N_2}} \times \frac{22.4 \; L \; N_2}{1 \; \cancel{mol \; N_2}} = 11.2 \; L \; N_2$$

Problem

10. What is the volume of a container if it holds 8.8 g of carbon dioxide at STP?

9·5 The Nature of Liquids

Attractive forces tend to balance disruptive forces in liquids.

We have been able to explain many properties of gases by assuming that gas particles have motion and that there is no attraction between them. The particles that constitute liquids are also in motion. They are free to slide past one another. Hence both liquids and gases flow (Figure 9·9). Unlike gas particles, the particles of a liquid are held together by weak attractive forces. Most particles of a liquid do not have enough kinetic energy to overcome the attractive forces and escape. The forces also reduce the amount of space between the particles of the liquid (Figure 9·8). Thus liquids are much denser than gases. Increasing the pressure on a liquid has hardly any effect on its volume. For this reason, liquids and solids are known as the *condensed states of matter*. Many physical properties of liquids are determined by the interplay between the disruptive motions of particles and the attractive forces between them. Several of these properties are the vapor pressure, the heat of vaporization, and the boiling point of a liquid.

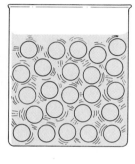

Figure 9·8
The particles in a liquid change places because of their motions. Most of the particles do not escape the liquid because of weak attractive forces between them.

Figure 9·9
Both liquids and gases flow. If a gas is denser than air, then it can be poured from one container to another.

9·6 Vaporization

Vaporization is the escape of molecules from the surface of a liquid.

The scientific term for the conversion of a liquid to a gas or vapor below its boiling point is **vaporization.** We all know that water in an open vessel goes into the air upon standing (Figure 9·10). *When vaporization of an uncontained liquid occurs, we commonly call it* **evaporation.**

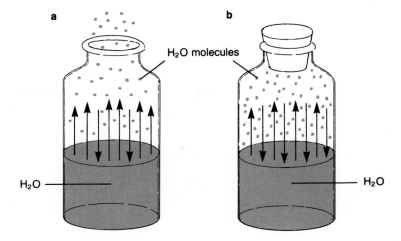

Figure 9·10

a In an open container, water molecules evaporate from the liquid and escape from the container. Equilibrium cannot be established in this system.

b In a closed container, water molecules do not escape but collect as a vapor above the liquid. A dynamic equilibrium between the vapor and the liquid is established.

a

b

H₂O molecules

H₂O

H₂O

Figure 9·11
This terrarium is at equilibrium. The rate of evaporation equals the rate of condensation. Notice the condensation on the inner surface of the glass.

Molecules at the surface of the liquid break away and go into the gas phase. Only those liquid molecules that possess a certain minimum kinetic energy can leave the surface. Some escaping particles collide with air molecules and return to the liquid, but others escape completely.

A liquid evaporates faster when heated because the kinetic energy of its particles increases. This enables more particles to overcome the attractive forces keeping them in the liquid. Although it requires heat, evaporation itself is a cooling process. This is because the particles with the highest kinetic energy (highest temperature) escape first. The particles left in the liquid have a lower average temperature than the particles that have escaped. When water molecules in perspiration evaporate from the skin's surface, the remaining perspiration is cooler. Therefore the remaining perspiration cools us by absorbing more body heat.

The vaporization of a liquid in a closed container is somewhat different from evaporation. This is because no particles can escape into the atmosphere (Figure 9·10). When a partially filled container of liquid is sealed, some of the particles in the liquid vaporize. *As vaporized particles collide with the walls of a sealed container, they produce a* **vapor pressure** *above the liquid.* As the container stands, the number of particles entering the vapor increases. Eventually some of the particles will condense and return to the liquid state.

$$\text{Liquid} \underset{\text{condensation}}{\overset{\text{evaporation}}{\rightleftharpoons}} \text{vapor (gas)}$$

After a time, the number of liquid particles vaporizing equals the number of particles condensing. The container is now saturated with vapor. A *dynamic equilibrium* exists between the gas and the liquid.

Rate of evaporation = rate of condensation

At equilibrium, the particles in the system are still vaporizing and condensing. At this point, there is no net change in either number of particles. One sign that equilibrium is established is that the inner walls of the container "sweat." The liquid that once vaporized is now condensing.

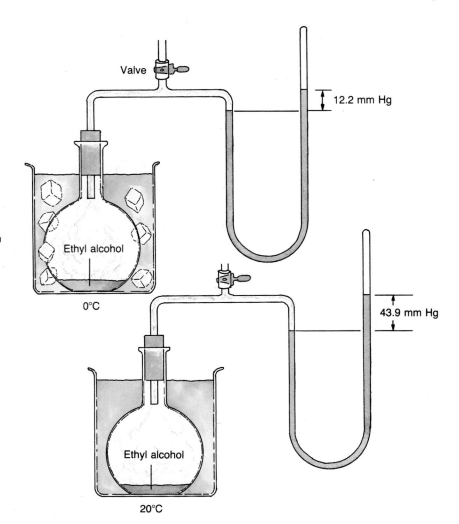

Figure 9·12

A manometer is similar to a barometer and is used to measure the pressure of a gas sample. This illustration shows how the vapor pressure of a liquid can be measured at two different temperatures. The height difference in the U-tube equals the vapor pressure at that temperature.

Valve

12.2 mm Hg

Ethyl alcohol

0°C

43.9 mm Hg

Ethyl alcohol

20°C

An increase in the temperature of a contained liquid increases the vapor pressure. This is because the particles in the warmed liquid have an increased kinetic energy. As a result, more of them will have the minimum kinetic energy necessary to escape the surface of the liquid. The particles escape the liquid and collide with the walls of the container. The vapor pressures of some common liquids at various temperatures are given in Table 9·1. Figure 9·12 illustrates one way of determining the vapor pressure of a liquid.

Table 9·1	Vapor Pressures (mm Hg) of Several Substances at Various Temperatures					
	0°C	20°C	40°C	60°C	80°C	100°C
Water	4.6	17.5	55.3	149.4	355.1	760.0
Ethyl alcohol	12.2	43.9	135.3	352.7	812.6	1693.3
Diethyl ether	185.3	442.2	921.1	1730.0	2993.6	4859.4

9·7 The Boiling Point of a Liquid

The rate of evaporation of a liquid in an open container increases with the addition of heat. This allows even larger numbers of particles at the liquid's surface to break the attractive forces keeping them in the liquid. The remaining particles in the liquid grow more and more agitated as they absorb thermal energy. Hence their average kinetic energy increases. When the liquid is finally heated to its boiling point, many of the particles in the liquid (not just those at its surface) have enough kinetic energy to vaporize. *The* **boiling point** (bp) *is the temperature at which the vapor pressure of the liquid is just equal to the external pressure.* Bubbles of vapor form throughout the liquid. The vapor pressure in these bubbles is equal to the atmospheric pressure. Vapor escapes to the atmosphere (Figure 9·13). This stage marks the onset of boiling.

The boiling point of a liquid at a pressure of 1 atm is the **normal boiling point** (Table 9·2). The boiling point of a liquid changes as the pressure changes. At lower external pressures, the boiling point decreases. This is because particles in the liquid need less kinetic energy to escape. The normal boiling point of water is 100°C. In Denver, however, water boils at 95°C. At 1600 m above sea level, Denver has an average

Evaporation is a process that occurs only at the surface of a liquid. Boiling occurs throughout a liquid.

At the normal boiling point, the vapor pressure of a liquid is 1 atm.

Figure 9·13
A liquid boils when the vapor pressure of particles in the bulk of the liquid equals the atmospheric pressure. **a** At 70°C and 760 mm Hg the atmospheric pressure at the surface of the liquid is greater than the vapor pressure of the liquid. Bubbles of vapor cannot form in the liquid. **b** At the boiling point the vapor pressure is equal to atmospheric pressure. Bubbles of vapor form inside the liquid, and the liquid boils. **c** At higher altitudes the atmospheric pressure is lower than at sea level. Thus the liquid boils at a lower temperature.

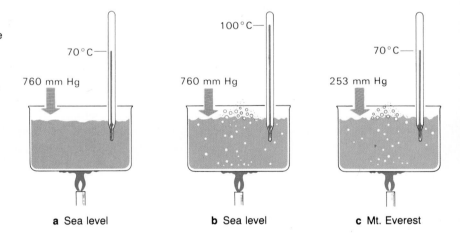

a Sea level   **b** Sea level   **c** Mt. Everest

Table 9·2	The Normal Boiling Points of Several Common Substances	
Name and formula		Boiling point (°C)
Carbon disulfide (CS_2)		46.0
Chloroform ($CHCl_3$)		61.7
Ethanol (C_2H_6O)		78.5
Octane (C_8H_{18})		126.0
Water (H_2O)		100.0

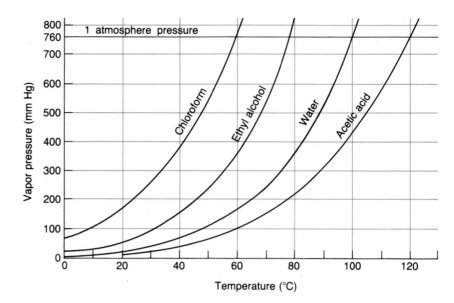

atmospheric pressure of only 640 mm Hg. Similarly, at higher external pressures, a liquid's boiling point increases. This is because the particles in a liquid need more kinetic energy to escape. Pressure cookers reduce cooking time because at high pressure water boils at well above 100°C.

Odd as it may seem, boiling is a cooling process like evaporation. As in evaporation, the particles with the highest kinetic energy escape first when the liquid is at the boiling point. If no more heat is supplied, the temperature of the liquid will drop below its boiling point. If more heat is supplied, however, more particles acquire enough kinetic energy to escape. The result is a continual cooling effect on the remaining liquid. *Therefore the temperature of a boiling liquid never rises above its boiling point.* No matter how much heat is supplied, the liquid only boils faster. Eventually all the liquid boils away.

Any liquid remains at a constant temperature while it is boiling.

9·B Liquid Crystals

Not all substances change sharply from orderly solids to disorganized nized liquids when they melt. Some substances flow like liquids even though their molecules are still orderly. These materials are called liquid crystals.

The molecules in liquid crystals are shaped like rods. The three types of liquid crystals differ in the way the rodlike molecules are organized. In *nematic* substances, the rods remain parallel to each other as they move back and forth in the liquid. In *smectic* liquid crystals, the rods are not only parallel but also are arranged in layers. The layers can move, but individual molecules remain fixed within a layer. The molecules in one layer are parallel to those in another layer. In a *cholesteric* liquid crystal, the molecules are also in layers. Within a layer, the molecules are free to move back and forth, remaining parallel to each other, as they do in nematic crystals. In contrast to the smectic crystal, the molecules in one layer of a cholesteric crystal are not parallel to those in another layer.

When light strikes a smectic or cholesteric liquid crystal, it is reflected by the layers of molecules within the crystal. The color of light that is reflected depends on the distance between layers. The distance between layers changes as the temperature changes. Thus a temperature change in the crystal will show up as a color change. Liquid crystal thermometers can be placed on the skin to take body temperature or to locate a "hot spot," like an artery or a vein.

In a digital wristwatch or calculator, a nematic liquid crystal is contained between two layers of glass. The surface of the top layer of glass can be electrically charged in segments that can be grouped to create numbers. Under the influence of these charged segments, the molecules of the liquid crystal orient themselves in a way that prevents light from passing through. The numbers therefore appear black.

Liquid crystals flow like liquids but at certain temperatures may possess crystal-like ordered structures.

Figure 9·16
The molecules in liquid crystals are usually rod-like. **a** In nematic crystals the molecules are all parallel. **b** In smectic crystals the molecules are in layers as well as being parallel. **c** In cholesteric crystals the molecules are parallel within a layer but the layers are aligned as in a spiral.

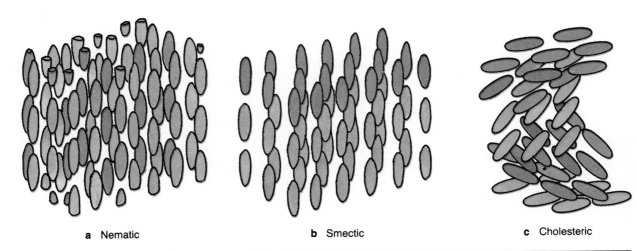

a Nematic   b Smectic   c Cholesteric

Figure 9·17
The regular shape of this sodium chloride crystal (**a**) can be explained by the arrangement of sodium ions and chloride ions (**b**) within the crystal.

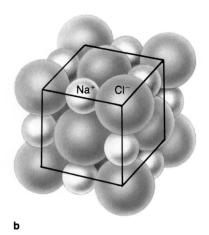

a   b

9·8   The Nature of Solids

■ The particles in a solid vibrate about fixed points.

The motions in liquids are chaotic. In most solids, however, the particles are packed against one another in a highly organized fashion. Rather than sliding from place to place, they vibrate and rotate about fixed points (Figure 9·18). Solids are dense and incompressible. Because of the fixed position of their particles, solids do not flow to fit their containers.

When a solid is heated, its particles vibrate more rapidly. The kinetic energy of the particles increases. *The **melting point** (mp) is the temperature at which the solid turns into a liquid.* At this temperature, the disruptive vibrations of some of the particles are strong enough to overcome the interactions that hold them in fixed positions. The solid begins to melt. The melting and freezing points of a substance are the same. It is the temperature at which liquid and solid exist in equilibrium.

$$\text{Solid} \quad \underset{\text{freezing}}{\overset{\text{melting}}{\rightleftarrows}} \quad \text{liquid}$$

In general, ionic solids have high melting points because they are held together by relatively strong forces. Sodium chloride, an ionic compound, has a melting point of 801°C. By contrast, molecular solids have relatively low melting points. For example, hydrogen chloride, a molecular compound, melts at −112°C. Not all solids melt. Wood, for example, decomposes when heated.

Most solid substances are crystalline in nature. *In a **crystal** the atoms, ions, or molecules are arranged in an orderly, repeating, three-dimensional pattern.* This array is called the crystal lattice. All crystals have a regular shape. The shape reflects the arrangement of the particles within the solid. The angles at which the faces of a crystal intersect are always the same for a given substance and are characteristic of that substance. Crystals are classified into seven crystal systems. They have characteristic shapes as shown in Figure 9·19. The seven crystal systems differ according to the angles between the faces and by how many of the edges of the faces are equal.

Figure 9·18
The particles in a solid do not change places but vibrate about fixed points. A solid melts when its temperature is raised to a point at which the vibrations of the particles become so intense that they disrupt the ordered structure.

Figure 9·19
Crystals occur in a multitude of shapes. They are classified into the seven crystal systems shown here according to the lengths of the sides and the angles between the sides.

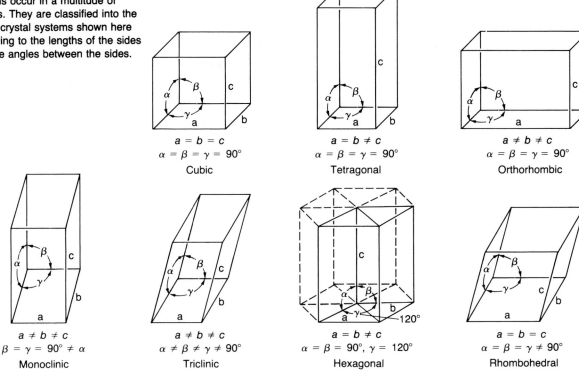

$a = b = c$
$\alpha = \beta = \gamma = 90°$
Cubic

$a = b \neq c$
$\alpha = \beta = \gamma = 90°$
Tetragonal

$a \neq b \neq c$
$\alpha = \beta = \gamma = 90°$
Orthorhombic

$a \neq b \neq c$
$\beta = \gamma = 90° \neq \alpha$
Monoclinic

$a \neq b \neq c$
$\alpha \neq \beta \neq \gamma \neq 90°$
Triclinic

$a = b \neq c$
$\alpha = \beta = 90°, \gamma = 120°$
Hexagonal

$a = b = c$
$\alpha = \beta = \gamma \neq 90°$
Rhombohedral

Figure 9·20
Three unit cells are part of the cubic crystal system. **a** In the simple cubic unit cell the atoms or ions are at the corners of an imaginary cube. **b** In a face-centered cubic unit cell the atoms or ions are also in the center of each face of the imaginary cube. **c** In a body-centered cubic unit cell the atoms or ions are at the corners and in the center of an imaginary cube.

The shape of a crystal depends on the arrangement of the particles within it. *The smallest group of particles within a crystal that retains the geometric shape of the crystal is known as a* **unit cell.** A crystal lattice is a repeating array of any one of the fourteen known unit cells. The three unit cells that are part of the cubic crystal system are shown in Figure 9·20. Each crystal system has from one to four types of unit cells that are associated with that crystal system. The melting points of crystals are determined by how the atoms are bonded.

Some substances can exist in more than one type of solid state. A good example is the element carbon. Diamond is one crystalline form of carbon (Figure 9·21). It forms when carbon crystallizes under tremendous pressure (thousands of atmospheres). The other crystalline form of carbon is graphite. The "lead" in a pencil is actually graphite. In graphite

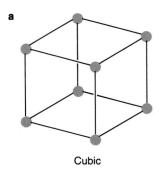

Cubic

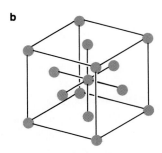

Face-centered cubic

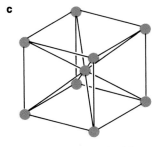

Body-centered cubic

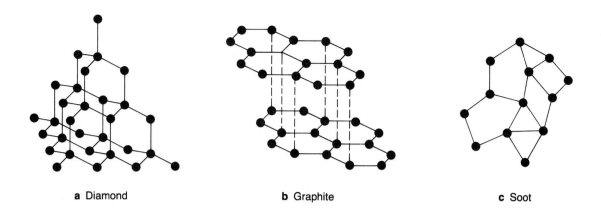

a Diamond   **b** Graphite   **c** Soot

Figure 9·21
The arrangement of carbon atoms affects the properties of the three forms of carbon. **a** In diamonds, atoms are packed in a compact symmetrical array. Each atom is bonded to four others. **b** In graphite the atoms are bonded together in sheets. Weak bonds between these sheets allow them to slide over each other. **c** In soot, the atoms are randomly bonded to one another.

the carbon atoms are packed more loosely than in diamond. The physical properties of diamond and graphite are quite different. Diamond has a high density and is very hard; graphite has a low density and is soft.

Not all solids are crystalline in form; some solids are amorphous. **Amorphous** *solids lack an ordered internal structure.* Rubber, plastic, and asphalt are amorphous solids. Soot, a third form of solid carbon is also amorphous. Its atoms are in a random arrangement (Figure 9·21).

Glasses are amorphous solids which are sometimes called **supercooled liquids.** They are transparent fusion products of inorganic substances that have cooled to a rigid state without crystallizing. The irregular internal structures of glasses are intermediate between those of a crystalline solid and a free-flowing liquid. Glasses do not melt at a definite temperature but gradually soften when heated.

When a crystalline solid is shattered, the fragments have the same surface angles as the original solid. By contrast, when an amorphous solid such as glass is shattered, the fragments have irregular angles and jagged edges.

Safety

Glass retains heat well, and hot glass looks just like cool glass. To avoid burns, be careful when bending or fire-polishing glass in the laboratory.

Figure 9·22
Glass does not have a definite melting point because it is an amorphous solid.

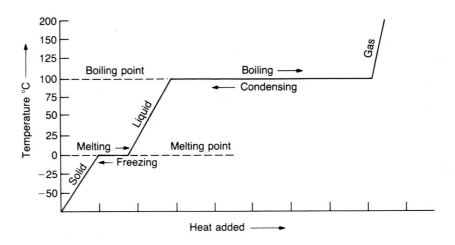

The temperature of a substance does not change while a phase change is taking place.

Figure 9·24
When solid iodine is heated, the crystals sublime, going directly from the solid to a gas. When the gas cools, solid crystals form without passing through the liquid state.

9·9   Phase Changes

A **phase change** *occurs whenever the physical state of a substance changes.* Melting, freezing, evaporation, and condensation involve phase changes. Imagine slowly warming a piece of ice, originally at −50°C and normal atmospheric pressure (Figure 9·23). As heat energy is added, the temperature of the ice increases, but the ice does not change its physical appearance. At 0°C, however, if we continue to supply heat, the ice begins to melt and liquid water appears. The ice continues to melt, but the temperature stays at a constant 0°C until all the ice is gone. During this and other phase changes, adding or removing heat does not raise or lower the temperature of the system. It just changes the physical state of the substance. In the case of melting ice, the heat energy disrupts the forces that hold the ice crystal together.

If heating is continued after all the ice has melted, the temperature of the water rises steadily until it reaches 100°C. Then the water reaches its boiling point. Another phase change occurs as liquid water turns to vapor or steam. While vaporization (boiling) is taking place, the temperature again remains constant. The heat energy added at the boiling point does not change the temperature of the liquid, but it does cause the liquid to change to vapor. As long as liquid water is present, the temperature is at 100°C. Once all the water is vaporized (turned to steam), the addition of heat raises the temperature of the steam.

Many substances undergo the physical change from solid to liquid and from liquid to gas as the temperature is raised. One exception is iodine. This violet-black solid ordinarily changes into a purple vapor without passing through a liquid state (Figure 9·24). *The change of a substance from a solid to a gas or vapor without passing through the liquid state is called* **sublimation.** A violet-black solid unchanged in appearance and composition from the original solid is obtained when iodine vapor is cooled. If wet laundry is hung on a clothes line to dry on a very cold day, the water in the clothes quickly freezes to ice. After several hours, however, the clothes are dry although the ice never thaws. The ice goes to water vapor without passing through the liquid state.

9·10 Energy and Phase Changes

Substances vary in the way in which they absorb heat. The specific heat of a substance (Section 2·13) is one measure of this property. The specific heat of liquid water is 1 cal/g°C. This means that 1 cal of heat raises the temperature of 1 g of water 1°C. Therefore, 100 cal of heat is needed to raise the temperature of 1 g of water from 0°C to 100°C. By contrast, ice has a specific heat of 0.5 cal/g°C. Half a calorie of heat will raise the temperature of 1 g of ice 1°C. Thus the temperature of ice changes twice as much as the temperature of water for every calorie of heat absorbed. The specific heat of steam is 0.4 cal/g°C. The specific heat is indicated by the slope of the line on a heating curve (Figure 9·25).

When a phase change occurs, the temperature of the substance remains constant. As heat is absorbed, the energy causes a change of state instead of a change of temperature. The heat of fusion describes the energy changes as a substance melts. *The heat required to melt one gram of a solid at its melting point is its* **heat of fusion.** For example, 80 cal of energy is needed to change 1 g of ice to 1 g of water at 0°C. Thus the heat of fusion for ice is 80 cal/g. The reverse of this process is solidification. *The* **heat of solidification** *is the amount of heat given up as one gram of liquid changes to a solid at the melting point.* Because melting and freezing are reverse processes, the magnitudes of the heat of fusion and heat of solidification are identical.

Similar energy changes take place when a liquid changes to a gas. *The number of calories required to change 1 g of a liquid to gas at the boiling point at atmospheric pressure is the liquid's* **heat of vaporization.** When a vapor condenses to a liquid, the opposite transfer of heat occurs. The heat of vaporization is passed to anything on which the vapor condenses. The temperature of the condensed liquid does not decrease until the heat of vaporization is lost. *The heat released when 1 g of a gas condenses to a liquid at the boiling point is the* **heat of condensation.**

▪ The state of a substance determines the effect of heat on changing the temperature of that substance.

The heat of fusion and heat of solidification quantify the energy changes that take place when melting and freezing occur. The heat of vaporization and heat of condensation quantify the energy changes that take place when varporization and condensation occur.

Safety

Steam is invisible, but it can cause severe burns. Do not reach across a container of boiling water.

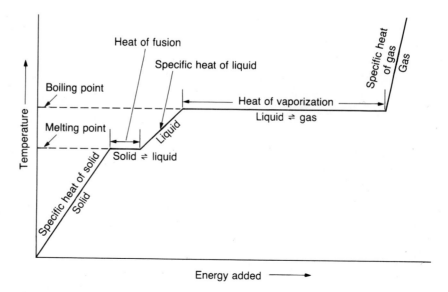

Figure 9·25
A phase diagram contains a wealth of information. Notice that the slope of the heating curve indicates the specific heat of the substance for a given state.

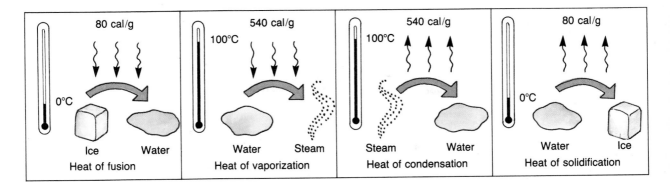

80 cal/g	540 cal/g	540 cal/g	80 cal/g
0°C	100°C	100°C	0°C
Ice → Water	Water → Steam	Steam → Water	Water → Ice
Heat of fusion	Heat of vaporization	Heat of condensation	Heat of solidification

Figure 9·26
The heat of fusion equals the heat of solidification. The heat of vaporization equals the heat of condensation.

Since vaporization and condensation are reverse processes, the heat of vaporization of a substance must be equal in magnitude to its heat of condensation. As you might expect, various liquids have different heats of vaporization and boiling points. This is because their intermolecular attractive forces vary.

Figure 9·27
The aurora borealis is caused by the presence of low density plasma in the upper atmosphere.

The fusion process and the problems faced in producing and containing hot plasma are described in Section 24·7.

9·C Plasma: The Fourth State of Matter

What happens if you heat a gas to a very high temperature? First the kinetic energy of the molecules becomes great enough to separate molecules into atoms. Then at even higher temperatures, electrons are stripped off the gaseous atoms. The substance now consists of a mixture of electrons and positive ions. This new substance behaves like ordinary gases in some ways. It also has some very peculiar properties. It is really a fourth state of matter, called *plasma*.

A gas can be ionized at low temperatures by common events. Partial plasmas are created in fluorescent lights, neon signs, lightning bolts, and even in flames. In all of these examples, only a few of the atoms present are ionized at any moment. Even these will not remain ionized. A free electron will lose energy when it collides with anything, including other particles or the walls of its container. When it has lost enough energy, it can be recaptured by a gas ion. Because of this, plasmas in the atmosphere or those created in lights and flames are only weakly ionized.

A tremendous amount of energy is required to create highly ionized plasmas. Some materials can be mostly converted into plasmas at temperatures of 50 000 K–100 000 K. These are called "cold plasmas." In contrast, some plasmas require temperatures of 10 000 000 K–100 000 000 K and more. These "hot plasmas" are the material of the stars. Scientists are trying to create hot plasmas to produce energy by nuclear fusion, the same process that produces energy in our sun. No material can contain matter at these temperatures. In the sun the hot plasmas are held together by gravity due to the huge mass of the sun. In the laboratory, of course, the mass of plasma is much too small to be held together by gravity.

Even weakly ionized plasmas have unique properties that make them useful. The free electrons and ions in a plasma make it very corrosive. Metal surfaces can be made more receptive to certain kinds of coatings by etching them with a plasma. Many other applications make use of the electrical properties of plasmas. Because plasmas consist of charged particles, they conduct electricity. Because the charged particles are moving, plasmas generate a magnetic field. Like any conducting material, a plasma generates an electric current when it moves through an external magnetic field. Scientists hope to make use of these properties to develop plasma motors and electric generators.

Low-density plasma technology is the basis of a promising alternative source of electric power, called magnetohydrodynamic power generation, or MHD. The heat from burning a fossil fuel (coal, oil, or natural gas) is used to partially ionize a gas. This low-density plasma is passed through a strong magnetic field. An electric current is generated in the plasma. This is more efficient than the conventional way of producing electricity from burning coal. MHD research is only one of the challenging problems in the rapidly expanding field of plasma physics.

9 The States of Matter

Chapter Review

Key Terms

Chapter Summary

The kinetic theory describes the motion of particles (atoms, ions, or molecules) in matter and the forces of attraction between them. The theory assumes that the volume occupied by a gas is mostly empty space and that the particles of a gas are far apart, move rapidly, and have chaotic motion. Avogadro knew that a gas is mostly empty space. He stated that equal volumes of gases, at the same temperature and pressure, contain equal numbers of particles. The pressure of a gas results from the countless collisions of the gas particles with an object. Barometers are used to measure atmospheric pressure.

Standard conditions when working with gases are a temperature of 0°C and a pressure of 1 atm. The temperature of a gas is directly proportional to the average kinetic energy of the particles. When the temperature of a gas is lowered, the particles slow down, and the gas condenses to a liquid. As

the temperature is lowered further, the liquid solidifies. Solids are rigid and have fixed volumes. In a solid the movement of particles is restricted to vibrations about fixed points. Liquids have a fixed volume and characteristic vapor pressure. A liquid boils when its vapor pressure equals the external pressure. The normal boiling point of a liquid is the temperature at which the vapor pressure is equal to 1 atm.

Most substances change their physical state and melt or vaporize as the temperature is raised. They freeze or condense as the temperature is lowered. When the physical state of a substance changes, a phase change occurs. During a phase change the temperature of the system remains constant.

The particles in a solid vibrate more rapidly when heated. Solids melt when the vibrations are greater than the forces holding the particles together. Most solids are crystalline. The particles are arranged in a repeating three-dimensional pattern known as a crystal lattice. The smallest subunit of a crystal lattice is the unit cell. Each crystal belongs to one of seven crystal systems depending upon the shape of its unit cell. Some solids have a disordered array of particles and are amorphous.

Practice Questions and Problems

11. What is meant by the term "elastic collision"? *9·1*

12. Change 1656 km/hr to m/s. *9·1*

13. How can you raise the average kinetic energy of the water molecules in a glass of water? *9·2*

14. What is significant about the temperature absolute zero? *9·2*

15. A cylinder of oxygen gas is cooled from 300 K (27°C) to 150 K (−123°C). By what factor does the average kinetic energy of the oxygen molecules in the cylinder decrease? *9·2*

16. What is gas pressure and in what units is it measured? *9·3*

17. How are the units *mm Hg* and *atm* related? *9·3*

18. What pressure in atmospheres does a gas exert at 380 mm Hg? *9·3*

19. How many millimeters of mercury pressure does a gas exert at 3.1 atm? *9·3*

20. Express 400 mm Hg in kilopascals. *9·3*

21. What does the abbreviation *STP* represent? *9·4*

22. Express standard temperature in Kelvin and standard pressure in millimeters of mercury. *9·4*

23. A gas has a volume of 2.24 L at STP. How many moles of gas is this? *9·4*

24. Explain why liquids and gases differ. *9·5*
  a. in physical state
  b. in compressibility

25. Why does evaporation lower the temperature of a liquid? *9·6*

26. Explain why increasing the temperature of a liquid increases its rate of evaporation. *9·6*

27. Would you expect an equilibrium vapor pressure to be reached above a liquid in an open container? Why? *9·6*

28. Describe the effect that increasing temperature has on the vapor pressure of a liquid. *9·6*

29. Describe the terms *boiling point* and *normal boiling point*. *9·7*

30. Explain why the boiling point of a liquid varies with atmospheric pressure. *9·7*

31. Use Figure 9·14 to determine the temperature at which water will boil in an open vessel when the atmospheric pressure is 400 mm Hg. *9·7*

32. Use Figure 9·14 to determine the boiling point of each of these liquids. *9·7*
  a. acetic acid at 200 mm Hg
  b. chloroform at 600 mm Hg
  c. ethyl alcohol at 400 mm Hg

33. At the top of Mt. Everest, water boils at only 69°C. Use Figure 9·14 to estimate the atmospheric pressure at the top of this mountain. *9·7*

34. Explain how boiling is a cooling process. *9·7*

35. Describe what happens when a solid is at its melting point. *9·8*

36. In general, molecular solids have lower melting points than ionic solids. Why? *9·8*

37. Explain the term *crystal lattice*. *9·8*

38. Any liquid stays at a constant temperature while it is boiling. Why? *9·9*

39. Describe the process of sublimation. What practical use can be made of this process? *9·9*

40. Define the terms. *9·10*
a. heat of fusion
b. heat of vaporization

Mastery Questions and Problems

41. Calculate the energy in calories that is required to change 15.0 g of ice at $-10°C$ to 15.0 g of water at $0°C$. *9·10*

42. What happens to the average kinetic energy of all the water molecules in your body when you get a fever? *9·2*

43. Describe vaporization, vapor pressure, and boiling point. *9·7*

44. Explain what happens at the melting point of a substance. *9·9*

45. What causes atmospheric pressure, and why is it much lower on the top of a mountain than at sea level? *9·3*

46. Calculate the energy in calories when 45.2 g of steam at $100°C$ condenses to water at the same temperature. What is this energy in joules? *9·10*

47. What is the volume occupied by 0.30 mol of a gas at STP? *9·4*

48. Why do we call the equilibrium that exists between a liquid and its vapor in a closed container a *dynamic equilibrium*? *9·6*

49. The temperature of the gas in an aerosol container is $0°C$ (273 K). To what new temperature must the gas be raised to increase the average kinetic energy of the gas molecules by a factor of three? *9·2*

50. How much energy in calories is required to change 35.6 g of ice at $0°C$ to water at the same temperature? What is this energy in joules? *9·10*

51. Mt. McKinley (6194 m) in Alaska is the tallest peak in North America. The normal atmospheric pressure at the summit is 330 mm Hg. Use Figure 9·14 to estimate the temperature (in degrees Celsius) at which water would boil there. *9·7*

52. If 3.20 kcal of energy is added to 1.00 kg of ice at $0°C$, how much water, at $0°C$, is produced? How much ice is left? *9·10*

Review Questions and Problems

53. Balance these equations.
a. $V_2O_5 + H_2 \longrightarrow V_2O_3 + H_2O$
b. $(NH_4)_2Cr_2O_7 \longrightarrow Cr_2O_3 + N_2 + H_2O$
c. $NH_3 + O_2 \longrightarrow NO + H_2O$
d. $C_6H_{14} + O_2 \longrightarrow CO + H_2O$

54. Perchloric acid is formed by the reaction of water with dichlorine heptoxide.

$$Cl_2O_7 + H_2O \longrightarrow HClO_4$$

a. How many grams of Cl_2O_7 must be reacted with an excess of H_2O to form 56.2 g of $HClO_4$?
b. How many mL of water are needed to form 3.40 mol of $HClO_4$?

55. What is the density of krypton gas at STP?

56. What is the empirical formula of each of these compounds?
a. The compound is 40.2% Mo and 59.8% Cl.
b. The compound has three times as many hydrogen atoms as carbon or chlorine atoms.
c. A sample of the compound contains 21.0 g of silver and 12.4 g of tellurium.

57. How many moles is each substance?
a. 888 g of sulfur dioxide
b. 2.84×10^{22} molecules of ammonia
c. 0.47 L of carbon dioxide (at STP)

58. Hydrogen reacts with ethene (C_2H_4) to form ethane (C_2H_6).

$$C_2H_4 + H_2 \longrightarrow C_2H_6 + 137.2 \text{ kJ}$$

a. Is this an exothermic or endothermic reaction?
b. How many kJ of energy are produced when 66.2 g of C_2H_6 are made?
c. What is the limiting reagent when 40.0 g C_2H_4 reacts with 3.0 g H_2?

Challenging Questions and Problems

59. Calculate the energy required to change 42.6 g of ice at $-27.6°C$ to steam at $856°C$.
a. in calories b. in kilocalories c. in joules

60. What is a unit cell? What is a crystal lattice? Describe the relationship between them.

61. If the volume of the container in which there is a liquid–vapor equilibrium is changed, the vapor pressure is not affected. Why?

62. The ions in sodium chloride are arranged in a face-centered cubic pattern. Sketch a layer of the ions in a crystal of sodium chloride.

63. An ice cube with a mass of 40.0 g melts in water that was originally at 25.0°C.
  a. How much heat does the ice cube absorb from the water when it melts? Report your answers in calories, kilocalories, and joules.
  b. Calculate the number of grams of water that can be cooled to 0°C by the melting ice cube.

Research Projects

1. Report on what was learned about carbon dioxide as a gas, as a liquid, and as a solid starting with the work of Joseph Black.

2. Measure the vapor pressure of several liquids.

3. How do scientists use cryogenics to study rates of reactions?

4. How are liquid crystals manufactured?

5. How can crystal formation be used to determine the structure of an unknown substance? How did Eilhardt Mitscherlich invent this technique?

6. Can you influence the crystalline form of ice by varying the conditions under which ice forms?

7. Compare the crystalline and amorphous structures of rocks and minerals using a hand lens or a low power microscope. How do the structures contribute to the properties of these substances?

8. How is glass made, and how do various glasses differ?

9. What are ceramics? In what ways have they traditionally been used? Describe some new applications that have been or are being developed.

10. How is X-ray crystallography used to study the structures of large molecules? What discoveries has this technique made possible?

11. How are plasmas currently used in industry? In what ways are they important in microelectronic research?

Readings and References

Haines, Gail Kay. *Supercold/Superhot; Cryogenics and Controlled Thermonuclear Fusion.* New York: Watts, 1976.

Holden, Alan, and Phylis Morrison. *Crystals and Crystal Growing.* Cambridge, MA: MIT Press, 1982.

Morgan, Ralph A. *Collisions, Coalescence and Crystals: The States of Matter and Their Models.* New York: Methuen Educational (dist. by Harper & Row), 1973.

Scientists from Westinghouse Research Laboratories. *Science by Degrees.* New York: Walker, 1965.

Trefil, James S. "A Magic Trick Moves Out of the Lab and Into Our Everyday Lives." *Smithsonian.* (July 1984), pp. 78–89.

Wilson, David. *The Colder the Better.* New York: Atheneum, 1980.

10 The Behavior of Gases

Chapter Planning Guide

Section	Demonstrations and Experiments	Resource Materials
10·1 The Effect of Adding or Removing Gas C*		Objectives Worksheet 10, SPB Skillsheet 10, SPB
10·2 The Effect of Changing the Size of the Container C	Dem 10·1 The Cartesian Diver Dem 9·6 Atmospheric Pressure Dem 9·7 Atmospheric Pressure vs Volume Dem 10·2 Barometer	Beyond the Text: Bottled Gases
10·3 The Effect of Heating or Cooling a Gas C	Dem 9·8 Vapor Pressure	
10·4 Real vs Ideal Gases C		Quiz 10·1
10·A The Liquefaction of Gases E		
10·5 Dalton's Law of Partial Pressures C	Dem 10·3 Dalton's Law	
10·6 Boyle's Law for Pressure–Volume Changes C	Dem 10·4 The Relationship of Pressure and Volume Exp 18 Boyle's Law, LM	Teaching Diagram 15 Prelab 18, SPB
10·B Scuba Science E		
10·7 Charles' Law for Temperature–Volume Changes C	Exp 19 Charles' Law, LM	Prelab 19, SPB
10·8 Gay-Lussac's Law for Temperature–Pressure Changes C		Quiz 10·2
10·9 The Combined Gas Law C		
10·10 The Ideal Gas Law C		The Bhopal Disaster, ICT 10
10·C Explosives and the Establishment of Nobel Prizes E		
10·11 Departures from the Gas Laws H		Quiz 10·3
10·12 Diffusion and Graham's Law H	Exp 20 Graham's Law, LM Dem 10·5 Diffusion of Gases Dem 10·6 Graham's Law Dem 10·7 Talking with Helium	Prelab 20, SPB Quiz 10·4 Reviewsheet 10, SPB Chapter 10 Test

*C = Core, O = Optional
E = Enrichment, H = Honors

LM = Laboratory Manual

SPB = Skills Practice Book
ICT = Issues in Chem. Tech.

Chapter Objectives

Having studied this chapter and done the problems, the student should be able to:

1. Describe the effect on the pressure of a gas by a change in the **a.** amount of gas, **b.** volume, and **c.** temperature. *10·1-10·3*

2. Describe how the temperature of a gas changes with a change in volume. *10·3*

3. Distinguish between real and ideal gases. *10·4*

4. State and use Dalton's law of partial pressures. *10·5*

5. Use Boyle's law to account for pressure–volume changes in a gas. *10·6*

6. Use Charles' law to account for temperature–volume changes in a gas. *10·7*

7. Use Gay-Lussac's law to account for temperature–pressure changes in a gas. *10·8*

8. Do calculations using the combined gas law. *10·9*

9. State and use the ideal gas law. *10·10*

10. Explain why real gases deviate from the gas laws. *10·11*

11. State and use Graham's law of diffusion. *10·12*

Teaching Suggestions

10·1 The Effect of Adding or Removing Gas

10·2 The Effect of Changing the Size of the Container

10·3 The Effect of Heating or Cooling a Gas

There are only three factors which influence the pressure exerted by a gas: the number of particles, the volume of the gas, and the kinetic energy (temperature) of the gas. These factors are discussed in these three sections. They can be presented at one time as part of a class discussion. The logic is so straightforward that if you ask leading questions the students will easily come up with the relationships themselves. Use questions like "Here is a sample of gas. How could its pressure be raised? Why does that raise it?"

To help the students visualize these relationships, do some qualitative demonstrations. **Demonstration 10·1** *The Cartesian Diver* is an attention-getting application of

the pressure–volume relationship. If you have not already done them, do **Demonstration 9·6** *Atmospheric Pressure* or **Demonstration 9·7** *Atmospheric Pressure vs Volume* as an illustration of the effect of pressure on volume, and **Demonstration 9·8** *Vapor Pressure* as an illustration of the effect of temperature on pressure. **Demonstration 10·2** *Barometer* measures atmospheric pressure.

10·4 Real vs Ideal Gases

In an ideal gas there are no intermolecular attractions and the gas particles have no volume. This cannot be true of any gas that exists. However, if the volume of the gas is large, and its pressure is low, the behavior of the gas is very close to that of an ideal gas. Point out that the deviations from ideal gas behavior are not measurable in the gases they will encounter in this course.

10·5 Dalton's Law of Partial Pressures

The key point in this section is that the particles of each kind of gas in a mixture exert their pressure as if they were by themselves. The presence of one gas does not affect the partial pressure of another gas. Remind the students that the pressure of a gas is due to the *number* of particles hitting the walls of the container. **Demonstration 10·3** *Dalton's Law* illustrates this concept.

10·6 Boyle's Law for Pressure–Volume Changes

The presentation and application of Boyle's law is straightforward and should offer the students little difficulty.

Caution them to be sure to use consistent units when using the equation $P_1 \times V_1 = P_2 \times V_2$. They should not, for example, use mm Hg on one side of the equation and atmospheres (atm) on the other.

To demonstrate Boyle's law, you could do **Demonstration 10·4** *The Relationship of Pressure and Volume* and take quantitative data. **Experiment 18** *Boyle's Law* is a challenging experiment which gives the students practical experience in dealing with gas volume measurements and in confirming Boyle's law.

10·7 Charles' Law for Temperature–Volume Changes

Most students have an intuitive understanding of the fact that a gas sample expands when heated and contracts when cooled. They should have little trouble with Charles' law. Remind them that the quantitative relationship between temperature and pressure only holds true when temperature is expressed on the Kelvin scale. (Doubling the temperature from 100°C to 200°C does not double the volume

of a gas. Doubling the temperature from 100 K to 200 K does double the volume.)

Demonstration 9·5 *Determination of Absolute Zero* could be done during this section if it was not done in Chapter 9. **Experiment 19** *Charles' Law* can be done before this section is introduced as a "discovery" exercise. It can also be done after the section as a reinforcement.

10·8 Gay-Lussac's Law for Temperature–Pressure Changes

Most students have had enough personal experience that they will readily grasp the relationship between temperature and gas pressure. The same caution applies here as in the previous section. Temperature *must* be stated on the Kelvin scale if the quantitative relationship is to hold.

10·9 The Combined Gas Law

It is important that the three relationships, between *P* and *T*, *P* and *V*, and *T* and *V*, be covered one at a time. Once the three laws have been mastered, the combined law can be introduced. Show how each of the three laws can be obtained from the combined law. Caution the students again about using consistent units in the equation and the Kelvin temperature.

10·10 The Ideal Gas Law

The ideal gas law is even more useful than the combined gas law. It not only states a relationship between pressure, volume, and temperature, as does the combined gas law, but also relates these to the number of gas particles present. *R* is indeed a constant, but the same value does not apply to all systems. Depending upon what units are chosen for pressure and volume, *R* can have a range of values and a variety of units.

One advantage of being able to use the ideal gas equation is that it enables us to find the number of moles of a gaseous sample just by measuring the temperature, pressure, and volume of the sample. If we can measure the mass of the sample as well, then we can determine the molar mass of the gas.

10·11 Departures from the Gas Laws

Do not let the students fall into the trap of thinking that since real gases deviate from the ideal gas law, the law is not useful; for gases with large volumes and low pressure it works quite well. For other cases the *relationship* still holds if we apply the appropriate corrections to the pressure and volume terms (van der Waals equation of state for a real gas). The value of *R* simply shifts slightly.

10·12 Diffusion and Graham's Law

The terms diffusion and effusion are both used in this section. Students may have trouble distinguishing them. Help them see that diffusion is a general term which applies to molecules moving away from a region of high concentration. Effusion is a specific example of diffusion in which gas molecules move *through an opening* as they go away from a region of high concentration.

Make sure the students see the connection between the effusion rates of gases and the velocities of their molecules. This is not always apparent to them at first.

Demonstration 10·5 *Diffusion of Gases* and **Demonstration 10·6** *Graham's Law* illustrate Graham's law and could be done with quantitative measurements to calculate the relative masses. Alternatively, students could do **Experiment 20** *Graham's Law*. For fun, do **Demonstration 10·7** *Talking with Helium*.

Demonstrations

10·1 The Cartesian Diver

Concept: Boyle's law is demonstrated.

Materials: a "diver" consisting of an inverted glass vial (open on bottom and closed on top) or a medicine dropper, tall glass cylinder, plastic bottle, water, rubber sheet, rubber bands or tape.

Procedure: 1. Place the diver in a nearly full cylinder of water. Adjust the water level inside the diver until it just barely floats. Leave an air gap at the top. 2. Cover the mouth of the cylinder with a rubber diaphragm to tightly seal the top. 3. If the buoyancy of the diver has been adjusted properly, the application of pressure to the diaphragm will cause the diver to sink. This occurs because the applied pressure compresses the air in the diver. More water enters the diver as the air volume is reduced. The diver loses buoyancy and sinks. 4. As soon as the external pressure is released, the air in the diver expands. Buoyancy is regained, and the diver rises. Since the reason for the sinking and floating of the diver is not usually apparent at first, this demonstration can generate a lively discussion.

10·2 Barometer

Concept: A constructed barometer measures atmospheric pressure in units of mm Hg.

Materials: 80 cm of 6-mm diameter glass tubing, evaporating dish, hypodermic syringe (without needle), ring stand with 2 clamps, 200 mL of mercury (Hg), meter stick, rubber or plastic gloves, large plastic tray, safety goggles.

Procedure: **Caution:** *Mercury (liquid and vapor) is extremely toxic. Wear gloves and remove any gold jewelry that may come in contact with it. Keep the large tray under the apparatus at all times. In the event of a mercury spill, use a mercury clean-up sponge.* 1. Seal one end of the glass tubing in a gas burner. 2. With the syringe, fill the tube with mercury from the evaporating dish. 3. Place the evaporating dish, containing mercury to a depth of 2 cm, on the table next to the ring stand. 4. Firmly place a finger over the open end of the tube. 5. Invert the tube and place the open end (with your finger still holding it closed) into the mercury of the evaporating dish. Remove your finger from the end of the tube. 6. Clamp the tube at two points with the two clamps. 7. Tilt the tube and stand slightly to show that the height of the mercury is constant. 8. Measure the height of the mercury column. 9. The mass of the atmosphere causes a pressure on the mercury pool. The height of the mercury is about 760 mm Hg, but varies with the altitude and weather.

10·3 Dalton's Law

Concept: The total pressure is the sum of the partial pressures.

Materials: 1-L container, blackboard, chalk.

Procedure: 1. State that the container is 1 L and contains 1 L of air. 2. Write on the board the percent composition of air by volume: 21% oxygen, 78% nitrogen, 1% argon. 3. Ask the class to determine the volume of each of the gases in the container. 4. According to their calculations, there is 210 mL oxygen, 780 mL nitrogen, and 10 mL argon. 5. Point out that since each gas fills the whole container it has a volume of 1 L. 6. The pressure of each gas is different; the volumes of the gases, however, are the same. 7. The partial pressure of oxygen is 160 torr, of nitrogen 593 torr, and of argon 8 torr. The sum of the pressures equals the total pressure (approximately 760 torr).

10·4 The Relationship of Pressure and Volume

Concept: The volume of a gas affects the pressure.

Materials: manometer (as in **Demonstration 9·8**) or pressure gauge, a large clear glass bottle with strong walls (the 2.5-L bottles in which acids are shipped work well) marked in 50 mL increments, a stopper assembly with two right angle pieces of glass tubing inserted into a two-hole rubber stopper (one of the glass tubes should extend to the bottom of the bottle and the other should barely enter the bottle), water, thick rubber tubing, faucet, aspirator on faucet, safety goggles.

Procedure: 1. Pour water into the bottle until it is half-full. 2. Insert the stopper assembly. 3. With rubber tubing, connect a source of water pressure (faucet) or vacuum (aspirator) to the glass tube which extends to the bottom of the bottle. 4. Connect the manometer or pressure gauge to the other glass tube. 5. The volume of the gas in the bottle can be varied by adding or removing water. The corresponding pressures can be noted on the manometer or pressure gauge. **Caution:** *Wear safety goggles. Small volume changes are preferable. Do not reduce the air volume to less than half of its original value, as the system might not be able to withstand the pressure.*

10·5 Diffusion of Gases

Concept: Gases spread by diffusion to areas of lower concentration.

Materials: glass tube 40 cm long and 1 cm in diameter, ring stand, clamp, clamp holder, cotton balls, 5 drops of concentrated hydrochloric acid (HCl), 5 drops of concentrated ammonia solution (NH_3), forceps, 2 dropper pipets, 2 rubber stoppers, safety goggles.

Procedure: 1. Clamp the glass tube horizontally on the ring stand. 2. Use forceps to place a cotton ball in each end of the tube. 3. Add 5 drops of concentrated HCl to one cotton ball and 5 drops of concentrated NH_3 to the other cotton ball. 4. Stopper the ends of the glass tube. 5. The gases diffuse toward each other and form a white cloud of ammonium chloride where they meet. 6. This meeting point is not in the center of the tube but is nearer the hydrochloric acid end. 7. Discuss the significance of this, relating it to the molecular masses of the two gases. **Caution:** *Hydrochloric acid is corrosive. Ammonia is an irritant.*

10·6 Graham's Law

Concept: Gases diffuse through a porous cup at rates inversely proportional to the square roots of the molecular masses.

Materials: 75 mm high × 38 mm diameter porous cup (available from scientific supply house), 60 cm of 6-mm diameter glass tubing, 38 mm diameter one-hole rubber stopper for the porous cup, 100 mL of food coloring solution, two 250-mL beakers, ring stand with 2 clamps, helium tank, carbon dioxide or Freon tank, safety goggles.

Procedure: 1. Place the food coloring solution in a beaker. 2. Insert the tubing in the stopper and stopper the porous cup. 3. Mount the tubing on the ring stand with two clamps so that the open end of the tube is in the beaker. 4. Place an inverted beaker over the cup. 5. Fill the inverted beaker with helium, the less dense of the two gases.

6. Bubbles come out the open tube because helium, which is lighter than air, diffuses into the cup faster than air can diffuse out. This raises the pressure. 7. Remove the beaker from the cup. 8. Liquid is pulled up the tube as the gas diffuses out faster than air goes in. 9. Repeat the procedure using the heavier-than-air gas (carbon dioxide or Freon). 10. The process is now reversed, since carbon dioxide and Freon diffuse more slowly than air.

10·7 Talking with Helium

Concept: Vocal cords vibrate faster when gases that are lighter-than-air pass through them.

Materials: helium tank, reading material.

Procedure: 1. Regulate the flow of helium from the tank so that it can be inhaled comfortably. Place the reading material in front of a student. 2. Instruct the student to exhale completely and then inhale the helium. One inhalation is sufficient. 3. Have the student start reading immediately. **Caution:** *Do not use hydrogen gas or any other gas as a substitute for helium!*

Audiovisual Resources

Chemistry: Gaseous Volume and the Mole (3 FS) Charles Clark, 1978, 18–21 min. each. (Use with Section 10·8.) Explains Gay-Lussac's law.

Chemistry: Properties of Gases (6 FS) Charles Clark, 1978, 15–22 min. each. (Use with Sections 10·6, 10·8, 10·9, and 10·10.) Demonstrates Boyle's law, Gay-Lussac's law, and the ideal gas law and shows gas law calculations.

Chemistry: Vapor Pressure and Partial Pressure (3 FS) Charles Clark, 1978, 20–21 min. each. (Use with Section 10·5.) Explains vapor pressure and partial pressure and shows partial pressure calculations.

Gas Pressure and Molecular Collisions (F, V) Chem Study, 1962, 21 min. (Use with Sections 10·1, 10·3, 10·8, or 10·12.) Shows the effect of varying temperature and molecular concentration on pressure and demonstrates the relative rates of effusion for several gases.

Laws of Science (10 FS) Eyegate, 1971, 15–25 min. each. (Use with Sections 10·6 and 10·7.) Develops Boyle's and Charles' laws through laboratory demonstrations.

Pressure, Volume, and Boyle's Law (F) Kalmia, 1974, 4 min. (Use with Sections 10·2 or 10·6.) Demonstrates Boyle's law using a computer-generated gas particle display.

Beyond the Text

Bottled Gases

Cylinders of gas, such as those used to inflate helium balloons, contain a gas under high pressure, around 130 atmospheres. The "bottle," or cylinder, is heavy because it must be strong enough to withstand the high pressure needed to contain a large amount of gas in a small space. A standard oxygen cylinder when full weighs 73 kilograms of which 9 kilograms is the mass of the oxygen.

Pressurized cylinders of gas have many advantages. They can be stored at room temperature indefinitely. A large amount of gas can be transported in a relatively small volume. Bottled gases such as nitrous oxide and oxygen are used in the health industry by dental offices, hospitals, and nursing homes. Restaurants use bottled carbon dioxide to make soft drinks. Welders and science laboratories use bottled acetylene, oxygen, and other gases.

Mention to your students that with a modest chemistry background, there are job opportunities in the gas industry. The gas industry employs chemists, chemical engineers, and chemical technicians. Salespeople who work at businesses that distribute gases must know enough chemistry to understand the needs of scientific and industrial customers. Drivers need only a basic knowledge of chemical symbols and safety procedures required in handling high pressure materials.

Answers to End of Chapter Questions and Problems

Practice Questions and Problems

14. Doubles.

15. Quadruples.

16. One-third of what it was.

17. The increased kinetic energy causes collisions to occur with more force.

18. 1 atm

19. Its particles have no volume, no forces between them, and elastic collisions. It follows the gas laws at all temperatures and pressures.

20. The total pressure is the sum of the partial pressures at constant volume and temperature. $P_{total} = P_1 + P_2 + \cdots + P_n$ for n gases in a mixture.

21. 25 mm Hg

22. The volume of a gas varies inversely with the pressure for a given mass and temperature of the gas. $P_1 \times V_1 = P_2 \times V_2$

23. 18 L

24. 4.5 atm

25. 24 L

26. The volume of a gas is directly proportional to its Kelvin temperature if the mass and pressure of the gas are constant. $\dfrac{V_1}{T_1} = \dfrac{V_2}{T_2}$

27. 8 L

28. The pressure of a gas is directly proportional to the Kelvin temperature if the mass and volume are kept constant. $\dfrac{P_1}{T_1} = \dfrac{P_2}{T_2}$

29. 330 K

30. $\dfrac{P_1 \times V_1}{T_1} = \dfrac{P_2 \times V_2}{T_2}$

31. 956 mm Hg

32. **a.** 56 L N_2 **b.** 6.72 L H_2 **c.** 30.2 L O_2 and He

33. 17.6 L O_2

34. 16.9 atm

35. 16.8 L

36. Real gases have attractions between molecules, and their molecules have volume. At low temperatures the attractions between molecules pull them together and reduce the volume. At high pressures the volume occupied by the molecules is a significant part of the total volume since the molecules are close together.

37. Diffusion is the movement of molecules or ions from regions of higher concentration to regions of lower concentration. Effusion is the escape of gas through an opening in a container of gas.

38. The rate of effusion of a gas is inversely proportional to the square root of its formula mass.

$$\frac{\text{rate}_A}{\text{rate}_B} = \frac{\sqrt{\text{formula mass}_B}}{\sqrt{\text{formula mass}_A}}$$

39. Oxygen.

40. 2.25

Mastery Questions and Problems

41. 3.56 atm

42. 846 K

43. At low pressures and high temperatures the attractions between molecules and the relative volume of the molecules are negligible.

44. 11 atm

45. 0.979 atm

46. 2 amu

47. 1800 mL

48. 165°C

49. $P_{\text{total}} = 6$ atm; $P_{\text{partial}} = 2$ atm

50. 200 amu

Review Questions and Problems

51. **a.** 158.1 g **b.** 98.0 g **c.** 342.0 g **d.** 331.2 g

52. **a.** tin(II) bromide **b.** barium sulfate **c.** magnesium hydroxide **d.** iodine pentafluoride

53. **a.** 206 amu **b.** 82 protons, 82 electrons, 124 neutrons

54. 2.96×10^4 cal

55. **a.** $Ca + 2H_2O \rightarrow Ca(OH)_2 + H_2$
b. $P_4O_{10} + 6H_2O \rightarrow 4H_3PO_4$ **c.** $2HgO \rightarrow 2Hg + O_2$
d. $Al_2S_3 + 6H_2O \rightarrow 2Al(OH)_3 + 3H_2S$

56. **a.** single-replacement **b.** combination **c.** decomposition **d.** double-replacement

57. **a.** $C_4H_8O_2$ **b.** C_8H_8 **c.** $C_3H_6O_3$

58. $10.6 \dfrac{\text{g}}{\text{cm}^3}$

59. **a.** $4Al + 3O_2 \rightarrow 2Al_2O_3$ **b.** 309 g Al, 275 g O_2

60. 60.0% C, 13.3% H, 26.7% O

Challenging Questions and Problems

61. **a.** 2.77 L O_2 **b.** 3220 mL

62. 745 atm

63. **a.** 1.61 atm **b.** 4.44 atm

64. **a.** $2.0 \times 10^{-3}\%$ **b.** 2.0%

65. $P_{PCl_3} = 0.445$ atm; $P_{Cl_2} = 0.445$ atm; $P_{PCl_5} = 0.108$ atm

66. 46% CH_4

The Behavior
of Gases

Chapter Preview

Sections 10·11 and 10·12 are appropriate for honors students.

The atmosphere is too vast for us to have any control over atmospheric pressure. Contained gases are a different matter. We can add gas or remove it, shrink or expand the container, or heat or cool the gas. In this chapter we will examine the work of such eminent scientists as Robert Boyle, Jacques Charles, and Joseph Gay-Lussac. These scientists studied the effects of changes in the pressure, volume, and temperature of contained gases. From their results they proposed a set of relationships that together are known as the gas laws. Using the kinetic theory, however, we can often explain how gases will respond to a change of conditions without resorting to formal mathematical expressions. We will therefore begin this chapter with some examples of how simple kinetic theory is used to explain gas behavior. Our emphasis will be on gas pressure.

10·1   The Effect of Adding or Removing Gas

When we pump up a tire, the pressure inside it increases. The pressure exerted by an enclosed gas is caused by collisions of gas particles with the walls of the container. By adding gas we increase the number of gas particles. This increases the number of collisions and therefore the gas

Figure 10·1
Hot air balloonists take advantage of the behavior of gases as they take to the air.

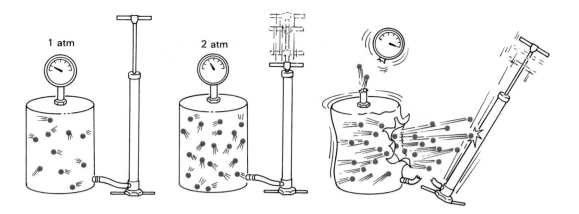

Figure 10·2
When gas is pumped into a closed rigid container, the pressure increases in proportion to the number of gas particles added. If the number of particles doubles, the pressure doubles. If the pressure exceeds the strength of the container, the container explodes.

pressure. Doubling the number of gas particles doubles the pressure if the temperature of the gas does not change (Figure 10·2). Tripling the number of gas particles triples the pressure and so forth. With a powerful pump and a strong container we can generate very high gas pressures. Once the pressure exceeds the strength of the container, however, the container will rupture. Overinflated balloons burst for this reason.

Problem

1. The volume must be doubled.

1. The manufacturer of an aerosol deodorant, wishes to produce a family-size package that will hold twice as much gas as the 150-mL regular size. The pressure in both containers must be kept the same. What will the volume of the larger package have to be?

The pressure exerted by a gas depends on the number of particles per unit volume.

Letting the air out of a tire or the gas out of a storage cylinder decreases the pressure in the container. Fewer particles are left. As you have probably already guessed, halving the number of particles in a given volume of gas decreases the pressure by one-half (Figure 10·3). When a sealed container of gas under pressure is opened, the gas always moves from the region of higher pressure to the region of lower pressure. This is

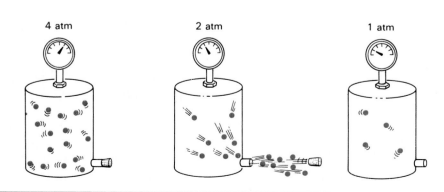

Figure 10·3
A gas under pressure in a sealed rigid container rushes into the atmosphere if the container is opened. The pressure in the container decreases in proportion to the number of gas particles released. If the number of particles decreases by one-half, the pressure also decreases by one-half.

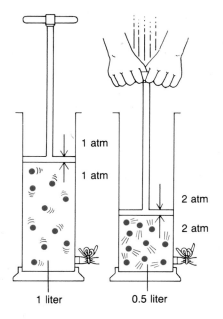

Figure 10·4
Doubling the force on a gas reduces the volume of the gas by one-half and doubles the pressure it exerts.

Gases cool when they expand and heat when they are compressed.

because there is more empty space for the gas particles to occupy. Gas particles increase their randomness by moving into this empty space, which is always a favorable process. Expansion continues until the gas pressures inside and outside the container are equal. Once the pressures are equal, the mixing of the gases in the container with gases in the surrounding atmosphere is only by diffusion.

10·2   The Effect of Changing the Size of the Container

We increase the pressure exerted by a contained gas when we reduce the size of the container. The more a gas is compressed, the greater the pressure it exerts on its container. Reducing the volume of the container by one-half has the same effect on pressure as doubling the quantity of gas while keeping the volume constant (Figure 10·4). Increasing the volume of the container has just the opposite effect. By doubling the volume we halve the gas pressure. There are now one-half as many gas particles in a given volume.

Gases cool when they expand and heat when they are compressed. When the gas is rapidly released from an aerosol can, the can becomes cooler. This is because the expanding gas absorbs some thermal energy from the container and its contents as it escapes. Compressing a gas always increases its temperature.

10·3   The Effect of Heating or Cooling a Gas

Raising the temperature of an enclosed gas increases the gas pressure. The kinetic energy of gas particles increases as they absorb thermal energy. Naturally, fast-moving particles bombard the walls of their container harder than slow-moving particles. The average kinetic energy of gas particles doubles with a doubling of the Kelvin temperature. Hence doubling the Kelvin temperature of an enclosed gas doubles the gas pressure (Figure 10·5).

Figure 10·5
When a gas in a container is heated from 300 K (27°C) to 600 K (327°C), the kinetic energy of the gas particles doubles. The particles strike the sides of the container with twice the force at 600 K as they do at 300 K. The pressure exerted by the gas therefore doubles. The pressure buildup at high temperatures may cause the container to explode.

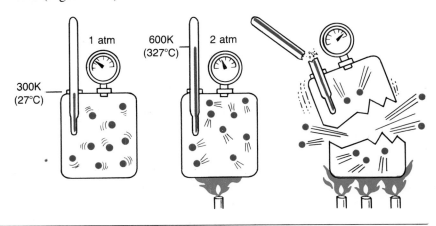

The pressure exerted by a gas depends on the average kinetic energy of the particles.

A heated gas sealed in a container generates enormous pressure. An aerosol can carelessly thrown on a fire is an explosion hazard. By contrast, as the temperature of an enclosed gas decreases, the particles move more slowly and strike the container walls with less force. By halving the Kelvin temperature of a gas in a rigid container, we decrease the gas pressure by one-half.

2. The volume decreases. The molecules with less kinetic energy cause less pressure on the inside of the balloon.

Problem

2. What happens to the volume of a balloon when it is taken outside on a cold winter day? Why?

10·4 Real vs Ideal Gases

An ideal gas follows the gas laws at all conditions of temperature and pressure.

In the discussions of the gas laws to follow, we will assume that we are dealing with ideal gases. An ideal gas is one that follows the gas laws at all conditions of pressure and temperature. An ideal gas is a substance that does not really exist. Kinetic theory assumes that the particles of an ideal gas have no volume and that the particles are not attracted to each other. There is no gas for which this is true. Nevertheless, under many conditions the behavior of a real gas is similar to that of an ideal gas.

Real gases can be liquefied and sometimes solidified by cooling them and applying pressure. Ideal gases cannot. For example when water vapor is cooled to less than 100°C, it condenses to liquid at atmospheric pressure. The behavior of other real gases is similar although lower temperatures and greater pressure may be required. Carbon dioxide goes from a gas to a solid without passing through the liquid state. The product is solid carbon dioxide, or "dry ice." Conversely, upon warming, solid carbon dioxide passes from the solid state to the gaseous state without passing through the liquid state. This is an example of sublimation.

Safety

Dry ice looks very much like ice, but it is much colder and can cause frostbite. Handle it only with tools and thick gloves.

10·5 Dalton's Law of Partial Pressures

Many gases, including air, are mixtures (Table 10·1). The particles in a gas at the same temperature have the same average kinetic energy. Gas pressure depends only on the number of gas particles in a given volume and their average kinetic energy. The kind of particle is unimportant. If we know the pressure exerted by each gas in a mixture, we can add the individual pressures and get the total gas pressure. The contribution each gas in a mixture makes to the total pressure is the partial pressure exerted by that gas. In a mixture of gases the total pressure is the sum of the partial pressures of the gases (Figure 10·6).

$$P_{total} = P_1 + P_2 + P_3$$

This equation is one mathematical form of **Dalton's law of partial pressures:** *At constant volume and temperature, the total pressure exerted by a mixture of gases is equal to the sum of the partial pressures.*

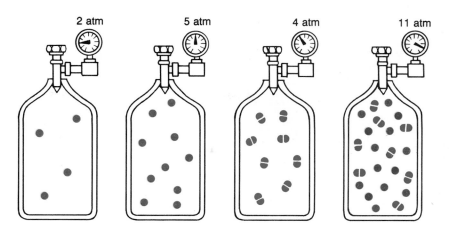

2 atm   5 atm   4 atm   11 atm

Figure 10·6
The sum of the pressures exerted by the gas in each container is the same as the total pressure exerted by a mixture of the gases in the same volume as long as the temperature stays the same. Dalton's law of partial pressures holds because each gas exerts its own pressure independent of the pressure exerted by other gases.

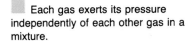

Each gas exerts its pressure independently of each other gas in a mixture.

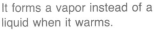

It forms a vapor instead of a liquid when it warms.

Figure 10·7
Solid carbon dioxide is known as dry ice. It can injure the skin because it is much colder ($-78.5°C$) than frozen water. Why is dry ice not as messy to use as regular ice?

Example 1

Air contains oxygen, nitrogen, carbon dioxide, and trace amounts of other gases. What is the partial pressure of oxygen (P_{O_2}) at 1 atm of pressure if $P_{N_2} = 593.4$ mm Hg, $P_{CO_2} = 0.3$ mm Hg, and $P_{others} = 7.1$ mm Hg?

Solution

We know that 1 atm = 760 mm Hg = P_{total}.

$$P_{total} = P_{O_2} + P_{N_2} + P_{CO_2} + P_{others}$$

$$P_{O_2} = P_{total} - (P_{N_2} + P_{CO_2} + P_{others})$$

$$= 760 \text{ mm Hg} - (593.4 \text{ mm Hg} + 0.3 \text{ mm Hg} + 7.1 \text{ mm Hg})$$

$$= 159.2 \text{ mm Hg}$$

Problem   3. 700 mm Hg; 0.92 atm

3. Determine the total pressure of a gas mixture that contains oxygen, nitrogen, and helium if the partial pressures of the gases are $P_{O_2} = 150$ mm Hg, $P_{N_2} = 350$ mm Hg, and $P_{He} = 200$ mm Hg. Give your answer in millimeters of mercury and in atmospheres.

Table 10·1	Composition of Dry Air		
Component	Volume (%)	Partial pressure (mm Hg)	(atm)
Nitrogen	78.08	593.4	0.781
Oxygen	20.95	159.2	0.209
Carbon dioxide	0.04	0.3	0.001
Argon	0.93	7.1	0.009
	100.00	760.0	1.000

Figure 10·8
Why must high altitude pilots have a separate oxygen supply available? At high elevations the partial pressure of O_2 is insufficient for normal breathing.

For a given mass of gas at constant temperature, the volume varies inversely with pressure.

The proportionate pressure exerted by each gas in a mixture does not change as the temperature, pressure, or volume changes. This fact has important implications for aviators and mountain climbers. When the total atmospheric pressure is reduced to 253 mm Hg (1/3 atm), as it is atop Mount Everest, the partial pressure of oxygen is reduced to 53 mm Hg. This is one-third the partial pressure of oxygen at 1 atm. This oxygen pressure is insufficient for respiration. Breathing air with a P_{O_2} of about 80 mm Hg supplies the minimum amount of oxygen. Airplanes and mountaineering expeditions must carry a supply of oxygen.

10·6 Boyle's Law for Pressure–Volume Changes

Consider the effect of pressure on the volume of a contained gas while the temperature is held constant. When the pressure goes up, the volume goes down. Similarly, when the pressure goes down, the volume goes up. In 1662 the British chemist Robert Boyle (1627–1691) proposed a law to describe this behavior of gases. **Boyle's law** *states that for a given mass of gas at constant temperature, the volume of the gas varies inversely with pressure.* In an inverse relationship, the product of the two quantities that change is always constant. This is shown in Figure 10·9.

In the figure, a volume of 1 L (V_1) is at a pressure of 1 atm (P_1). When the volume is increased to 2 L (V_2), the pressure decreases to 0.5 atm (P_2). Observe that the product $P_1 \times V_1$ (1 atm × 1 L = 1 L-atm) is the same as the product of $P_2 \times V_2$ (0.5 atm × 2 L = 1 L-atm). When the volume is decreased to 0.5 L, the gas pressure increases to 2 atm. Once again, the product of pressure times volume equals 1.0 L-atm. When an inverse relationship is graphed, the result is a curved line, as shown in Figure 10·10. The product of pressure and volume at any two sets of conditions is always constant at a given temperature. We can write Boyle's law as follows.

$$P_1 \times V_1 = P_2 \times V_2$$

Figure 10·9
Boyle's law and pressure–volume relationships are studied by using a cylindrical container fitted with a frictionless, weightless piston. When the pressure of a gas at constant temperature decreases (P_2), the volume increases (V_2). When the pressure increases (P_3), the volume decreases (V_3).

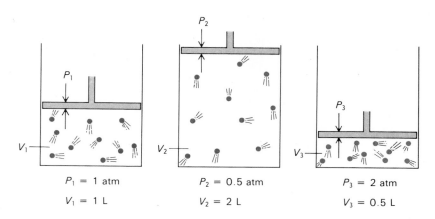

$P_1 = 1$ atm
$V_1 = 1$ L

$P_2 = 0.5$ atm
$V_2 = 2$ L

$P_3 = 2$ atm
$V_3 = 0.5$ L

$P_1 \times V_1 = P_2 \times V_2 = P_3 \times V_3 = 1$ L-atm

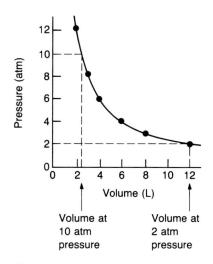

Pressure (atm)

Volume (L)

Volume at 10 atm pressure

Volume at 2 atm pressure

Figure 10·10
This graph illustrates Boyle's law. When the pressure of a gas decreases at constant temperature, the volume increases. At any point on this curve the product of pressure (P) times volume (V) is a constant: in this case, $P \times V = 24$ L-atm.

4. 6.25 L

Example 2

A balloon is filled with 30 L of helium gas at 1 atm. What is the volume when the balloon rises to an altitude where the pressure is only 0.25 atm? (Assume that the temperature remains constant.)

Solution

We know that $P_1 = 1$ atm, $V_1 = 30$ L, and $P_2 = 0.25$ atm. We need to solve for V_2. Rearrange the expression for Boyle's law to obtain V_2.

$$P_1 \times V_1 = P_2 \times V_2 \qquad \text{Therefore:} \qquad V_2 = V_1 \times \frac{P_1}{P_2}$$

Substitute values for P_1, V_1, and P_2.

$$V_2 = 30 \text{ L} \times \frac{1 \text{ atm}}{0.25 \text{ atm}} = 120 \text{ L}$$

The balloon will expand to a volume of 120 L at 0.25 atm. This agrees with what kinetic theory predicts. At a constant temperature a decrease in pressure must correspond to an increase in volume.

4. The pressure on 2.50 L of anesthetic gas is changed from 760 mm Hg to 304 mm Hg. What will be the new volume if the temperature remains constant?

10·A   Scuba Science

In 1943 Jacques-Ives Cousteau and Emile Gagnan invented scuba: a Self-Contained Underwater Breathing Apparatus. No longer did divers need to be tethered to the surface by air hoses. The increased maneuverability and convenience gave rise to the sport of scuba diving. It also greatly increased the use of diving for scientific research. All divers must have a good understanding of the science involved in diving in order to dive safely.

At the water's surface, the pressure on your body due to the mass of air around you is 1 atmosphere. Under water, the pressure increases due to the added mass of the water. Every 10 meters of depth adds 1 atmosphere pressure. Thus the total pressure on your body at a depth of 10 m will be 2 atm, at 20 m 3 atm, and so on. At around 40 m the pressure on your chest would make it impossible for you to inflate your lungs to breathe. If the pressure in your lungs had also increased as you went down, however, you would be able to breathe normally. Scuba equipment provides air to the lungs at a pressure to match that of the underwater environment. This enables the diver to breathe comfortably.

A diver at 20 meters is under a pressure of 3 atmospheres. The scuba equipment is maintaining the same pressure in his or her lungs. The average lung capacity of a human being is 6–7 liters. According to Boyle's law, this amount of air will expand to three times its volume if the pressure is reduced to 1 atmosphere. If a diver ascends to the surface without exhaling steadily along the way, the air held in the lungs will expand as the pressure drops. The increase in volume can rupture the lungs.

An understanding of partial pressure is also important in scuba diving. When the pressure on a mixture of gases increases, the partial pressure of each of the gases increases proportionately. This means that in the compressed air that a diver breathes, every ingredient is at higher pressure. At depths of 30 meters the partial pressure of carbon dioxide in air is sufficient to poison a diver. Even oxygen can be toxic if the total gas pressure is 2 atmospheres. At depths over 10 meters the length of the dive becomes very important in preventing such toxic effects.

Decompression sickness, or "the bends," is explained by another important gas law. The solubility of a gas in a liquid is proportional to the pressure of the gas above the liquid. A diver is breathing air at higher than atmospheric pressure. Thus the nitrogen in the air will be more soluble in his or her blood. When the pressure drops as the diver ascends, the nitrogen again becomes less soluble. If the drop in pressure occurs too rapidly, the nitrogen will come out of the blood in the form of tiny bubbles. This effect is just like the bubbles that form in a carbonated drink when you open the cap and relieve the pressure in the bottle. If nitrogen bubbles form in the joints or muscles, they cause a great deal of pain. If they form in the spinal cord, brain, or lungs they can cause paralysis or death. Decompression sickness can be prevented by ascending from a dive slowly. If that is not possible, the diver can be brought to the surface rapidly and put in a recompression chamber. Here he or she is recompressed to a pressure of 6 atmospheres. Then the pressure is gradually reduced so that the nitrogen can be eliminated through the lungs.

Figure 10·11
Scuba divers must be careful not to stay down too long or to ascend too rapidly. The high partial pressures of carbon dioxide, nitrogen, and oxygen can become dangerous over time. Nitrogen bubbles can form in the blood if divers come up too quickly.

 The volume of a fixed mass of gas varies directly with the Kelvin temperature.

10·7 Charles' Law for Temperature–Volume Changes

In 1787 a French physicist, Jacques Charles (1746–1823), investigated the effect of temperature on the volume of a gas at constant pressure. In every experiment, he observed an increase in the volume of gas with an increase in temperature. Charles summarized his observations in a law. **Charles' law** *states that the volume of a fixed mass of gas is directly proportional to its Kelvin temperature if the pressure is kept constant.*

In a direct relationship the ratio of the two quantities that change is a constant. In Figure 10·12, for example, a 1-L sample of gas (V_1) is at a

Figure 10·12
This apparatus illustrates Charles' law. When a gas at constant pressure is heated, the volume increases. When a gas at constant pressure is cooled, the volume decreases.

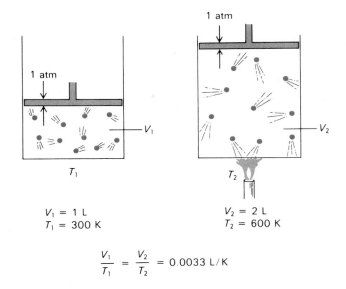

$$V_1 = 1 \text{ L}$$
$$T_1 = 300 \text{ K}$$

$$V_2 = 2 \text{ L}$$
$$T_2 = 600 \text{ K}$$

$$\frac{V_1}{T_1} = \frac{V_2}{T_2} = 0.0033 \text{ L/K}$$

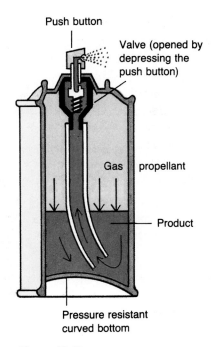

Figure 10·13
The propellant in an aerosol container is a pressurized gas. When product is released, the propellant expands, cooling the container and the product.

temperature of 300 K (T_1). (*Temperature in gas law problems is always in Kelvin.*) When the temperature is increased to 600 K (T_2), the volume increases to 2 L (V_2). Observe that the ratio $V_1 \div T_1$ (1 L $\div$ 300 K = 0.0033 L/K) is equal to the ratio $V_2 \div T_2$ (2 L $\div$ 600 K = 0.0033 L/K). Moreover, the ratio of volume to Kelvin temperature at any two sets of conditions is constant. Thus we can write Charles' law as

$$\frac{V_1}{T_1} = \frac{V_2}{T_2}$$

as long as the pressure is held constant. The graph of a relationship that is a direct proportion is a straight line, as shown in Figure 10·14. This line intersects the temperature axis at −273°C. That is, starting at 0°C the volume of a gas decreases by 1/273 for every decrease of 1°C. William Thompson (Lord Kelvin) realized that −273°C is the temperature at which the average kinetic energy of gas particles would theoretically be zero. This is the basis of the Kelvin, or absolute temperature, scale in which 0 K corresponds to −273.14°C. Absolute zero has never been reached, but temperatures within one degree of 0 K have been produced.

Figure 10·14
This graph illustrates Charles' law. When the temperature of a gas increases, the volume increases if the pressure is held constant. At any point on this curve the ratio of volume (V) to temperature (T) is a constant: in this case, $V/T = 0.0033$ L/K.

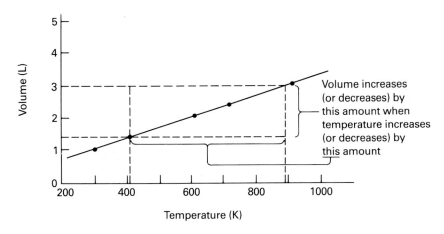

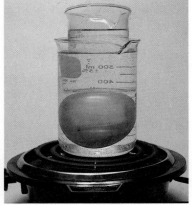

Figure 10·15
The size of a balloon is less in a beaker of ice than if the same balloon is in a beaker of boiling water. Why does this happen?
The volume of air in the balloon increases with an increase in temperature.

The pressure of a fixed mass of gas varies directly with the Kelvin temperature.

Example 3

A balloon, inflated in an air-conditioned room at 27°C, has a volume of 4.0 L. It is heated to a temperature of 57°C. What is the new volume of the balloon if the pressure remains constant?

Solution

Temperature in all gas problems is expressed as degrees Kelvin. Therefore we must convert degrees Celsius to degrees Kelvin.

$$T_1 = 27°C + 273 = 300 \text{ K}$$

$$T_2 = 57°C + 273 = 330 \text{ K}$$

We know that $V_1 = 4.0$ L, $T_1 = 300$ K, and $T_2 = 330$ K. Therefore we use Charles' law to solve for V_2. First we rearrange the expression for Charles' law to obtain V_2.

$$\frac{V_1}{T_1} = \frac{V_2}{T_2} \qquad \text{Therefore: } V_2 = V_1 \times \frac{T_2}{T_1}$$

Then the values for T_1, V_1, and T_2 are substituted.

$$V_2 = \frac{4.0 \text{ L} \times 330\,\cancel{K}}{300\,\cancel{K}} = 4.4 \text{ L}$$

The balloon will expand from a volume of 4.0 L at 27°C to a volume of 4.4 L at 57°C. Using the kinetic theory, we would predict that the volume would increase with an increase in temperature (at constant pressure).

Problem   5. 3.4 L

5. If a sample of gas occupies 6.8 L at 327°C, what will be its volume at 27°C if the pressure does not change?

10·8   Gay-Lussac's Law for Temperature–Pressure Changes

On a hot summer day a rigid car tire builds up a very high pressure. This illustrates a relation discovered in 1802 by Joseph Gay-Lussac (1778–1850), a French chemist. **Gay-Lussac's law** *states that the pressure of a gas is directly proportional to the Kelvin temperature if the volume is kept constant.* If the Kelvin temperature is doubled, for example, the gas pressure is doubled (Figure 10·16). Because Gay-Lussac's law involves direct proportions, the ratios $P_1 \div T_1$ and $P_2 \div T_2$ should be constant at constant volume. (Work out these ratios for the quantities shown in Figure 10·16 to assure yourself this is true.) Therefore, assuming the volume is held constant, we can write Gay-Lussac's law as follows.

$$\frac{P_1}{T_1} = \frac{P_2}{T_2}$$

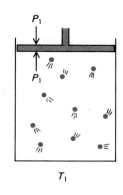 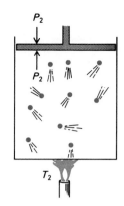

$$P_1 = 1 \text{ atm}$$
$$T_1 = 300 \text{ K}$$

$$P_2 = 2 \text{ atm}$$
$$T_2 = 600 \text{ K}$$

$$\frac{P_1}{T_1} = \frac{P_2}{T_2}$$

Safety

Never heat a closed container.

Example 4

The gas left in a used aerosol can is at a pressure of 1 atm at 27°C (room temperature). If this can is thrown onto a fire, what is the internal pressure of the gas when its temperature reaches 927°C?

Solution

First convert degrees Celsius to degrees Kelvin.

$$T_1 = 27°C + 273 = 300 \text{ K}$$

$$T_2 = 927°C + 273 = 1200 \text{ K}$$

We know that $P_1 = 1$ atm, $T_1 = 300$ K, and $T_2 = 1200$ K. Therefore we can solve Gay-Lussac's equation for P_2. We rearrange the expression to obtain P_2.

$$\frac{P_1}{T_1} = \frac{P_2}{T_2} \qquad \text{Therefore:} \qquad P_2 = \frac{P_1 \times T_2}{T_1}$$

Then we insert values for P_1, T_2, and T_1 into the equation.

$$P_2 = \frac{1 \text{ atm} \times 1200\,K}{300\,K} = 4 \text{ atm}$$

This is the pressure buildup in a can containing 1 atm of gas when it is heated from 27°C to 927°C. Once again, from the kinetic theory we would expect the increase in temperature of a gas at constant volume to give an increase in pressure.

Problem

6. 18.5 mm Hg

6. A gas has a pressure of 50.0 mm Hg at 540 K. What will be the pressure at 200 K if the volume does not change?

10·B The Liquefaction of Gases

Early chemists and physicists knew that solids turned to liquids and then to gases if enough heat was added. In the late eighteenth century, the great French chemist Lavoisier speculated that the reverse could also happen. If the earth's atmosphere could be made cold enough, he thought, it would turn to a liquid and then to a solid. Because he had no way of creating very low temperatures, Lavoisier had no way of testing this idea.

In the 1800s scientists were trying to liquefy gases by applying very high pressure. This work caused a good many spectacular explosions. In 1877 a French mining engineer, Louis Cailletet, was trying to liquefy acetylene gas. Unfortunately, his apparatus burst from the high pressure. Just as the accident took place, Cailletet saw a drop of liquid form. At the same time, the temperature of the acetylene gas dropped suddenly. Cailletet had witnessed adiabatic expansion, the cooling of a gas when it rapidly expands. He went on to use this phenomenon to bring gases to lower and lower temperatures. Eventually he was able to liquefy oxygen and nitrogen.

Today liquid oxygen, nitrogen, and argon are produced from liquid air. Hydrogen is produced as a gas by the electrolysis of water and then liquefied. Helium is liquefied after being separated from natural gas.

A gas can be liquefied in several ways. All of them depend on cooling the gas below its critical temperature. Above this temperature, no matter how much pressure is applied, the gas will not liquefy. The critical temperature of oxygen is 155 K, of nitrogen 126 K, of hydrogen 33 K, and of helium 5 K. Gases can be cooled to these low temperatures by first compressing them and then allowing them to expand rapidly. When a gas is compressed, it becomes warmer. If the heat is removed as the gas is compressed, however, it can be maintained at a constant temperature. Then if the gas is

Figure 10·17
Air is liquefied by compressing and cooling it. In the liquefaction chamber the highly compressed air is allowed to expand so that it cools sufficiently to become a liquid.

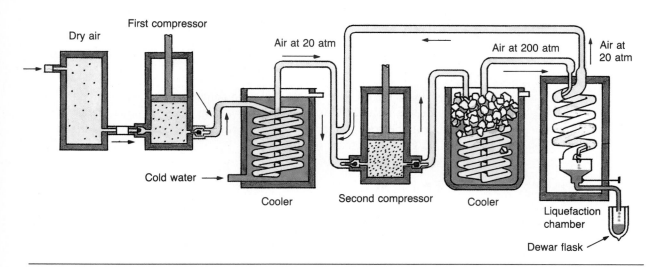

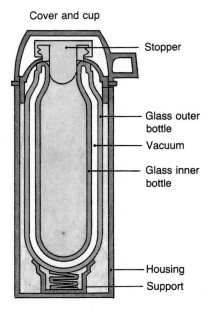

Cover and cup

Stopper

Glass outer bottle

Vacuum

Glass inner bottle

Housing

Support

Figure 10·18
A thermos bottle has basically the same construction as a Dewar flask. A vacuum is the best way to insulate against the transfer of heat.

allowed to expand rapidly, it will cool. This is the phenomenon that Cailletet observed. The gas can be repeatedly compressed and expanded until its temperature is below the critical temperature. It can then be liquefied by applying pressure.

A gas can also be cooled by surrounding it with a cold material. For example, helium can be cooled by putting it in a bath of liquid nitrogen. Liquid nitrogen boils at 77 K at room pressure. It can be made to boil at a lower temperature, however, by reducing the pressure in its container. A series of such baths can be used one after the other to cool another gas. When the temperature is low enough, the gas can be compressed to liquefy it.

The containers in which liquefied gases are stored and transported are called cryostats. They are designed to prevent heat from being transferred from the environment to the cold liquid. The most widely used cryostats are called Dewars after Sir James Dewar, who invented them in 1892. They are double-walled vessels with a vacuum between the walls, like the familiar thermos bottle used to carry hot or cold drinks. Cryostats are very light in comparison to pressure cylinders. A substance has a much smaller volume as a liquid than as a gas, even if the gas is under pressure. For these reasons, large amounts of gas can be stored and transported much more easily as a liquid than as a gas.

10·9 The Combined Gas Law

The pressure-volume and temperature-volume laws are joined in the *combined gas law*.

The three gas laws we have just discussed can be combined into a single expression called the **combined gas law.**

$$\frac{P_1 \times V_1}{T_1} = \frac{P_2 \times V_2}{T_2}$$

If you have been wondering how to remember the expressions for the other gas laws, it turns out that there is really no need. The other laws can be obtained from the combined gas law by holding one quantity (pressure, volume, or temperature) constant.

To illustrate, suppose we hold *temperature* constant ($T_1 = T_2$).

$$\frac{P_1 \times V_1}{T_1} = \frac{P_2 \times V_2}{T_2} \qquad \text{Therefore:} \qquad P_1 \times V_1 = \frac{P_2 \times V_2 \times \cancel{T_1}}{\cancel{T_2}}$$

We see that T_1 and T_2 cancel, and $P_1 V_1 = P_2 V_2$ (Boyle's law).

7. $\dfrac{P_1 \times V_1}{T_1} = \dfrac{P_2 \times V_2}{T_2}$

$\dfrac{V_1}{T_1} = \dfrac{V_2 \times P_2}{T_2 \times P_1}$

8. $\dfrac{P_1}{T_1} = \dfrac{P_2 \times V_2}{T_2 \times V_1}$

Problems

7. Show how Charles' law can be derived from the combined gas law.

8. Show how Gay-Lussac's law can be derived from the combined gas law.

Figure 10·19
When the temperature, pressure, and volume of a gas is measured, the ideal gas law allows the number of moles of the gas to be calculated. If the percent composition is known, the number of moles allows the molecular formula to be calculated.

Example 5

A cylinder of compressed oxygen gas has a volume of 30 L and 100 atm pressure at 27°C. The cylinder is cooled until the pressure is 5.0 atm. What is the new temperature of the gas in the cylinder?

Solution

First we convert degrees Celsius to Kelvin: 27°C + 273 = 300 K.

We know that T_1 = 300 K, P_1 = 100 atm, and P_2 = 5.0 atm; V_1 and V_2 are both equal to 30 L. We can now rearrange the combined gas law to obtain T_2.

$$\frac{P_1 \times V_1}{T_1} = \frac{P_2 \times V_2}{T_2} \qquad \text{Therefore:} \qquad T_2 = \frac{P_2 \times V_2 \times T_1}{P_1 \times V_1}$$

Now we can substitute the known quantities into the expression for the combined gas law.

$$T_2 = \frac{5.0 \text{ atm} \times 300 \text{ K}}{100 \text{ atm}} = 15 \text{ K}$$

We then convert 15 K back to degrees Celsius.

$$\text{K} = °\text{C} + 273 \qquad \text{Therefore:} \qquad °\text{C} = \text{K} - 273$$
$$= 15 - 273$$
$$= -258°\text{C}$$

Problem   9. 0.31 L

9. A container with an initial volume of 1.0 L is occupied by a gas at a pressure of 1.5 atm at 25°C. By changing the volume, the pressure of the gas increases to 6.0 atm as the temperature is raised to 100°C. What is the new volume?

10·10   The Ideal Gas Law

Sometimes we wish to calculate the number of moles of a gas in a fixed volume at a known temperature and pressure. Such a calculation is possible if the combined gas law is modified. The modification may be understood by recognizing that the volume occupied by a gas at a specified temperature and pressure is directly proportional to the number of particles in the gas. The number of moles, n, of gas is also directly proportional to the number of particles. Hence moles must be directly proportional to volume as well. Therefore moles may be introduced into the combined gas law by placing n in the denominator on each side of the equation.

$$\frac{P_1 \times V_1}{T_1 \times n_1} = \frac{P_2 \times V_2}{T_2 \times n_2}$$

This equation says that $(P \times V)/(T \times n)$ is a constant for any ideal gas.

Table 10·2   Units and Numerical Values for the Gas Constant

Units of R	Numerical value	Units of P	Units of V
$(L \times atm)/(K \times mol)$	0.0821	atm	L
$(L \times mm\ Hg)/(K \times mol)$	62.4	mm Hg	L
$(L \times Pa)/(K \times mol)$	8.31×10^3	Pa	L

If we were able to evaluate the constant $(P \times V)/(T \times n)$, we could then calculate the number of moles of gas at any specified conditions of P, V, and T.

We have sufficient information to evaluate the constant because we know that 1 mol of every ideal gas occupies 22.4 L at STP. Inserting the values of P, V, T, and n into the right side of the equation, we obtain a constant.

$$\frac{P_1 \times V_1}{T_1 \times n_1} = \frac{1\ atm \times 22.4\ L}{273\ K \times 1\ mol} = 0.0821 \frac{L \times atm}{K \times mol}$$

The **ideal gas constant** *(R) is 0.0821 (L $\times$ atm)(K $\times$ mol).* As shown in Table 10·2, the numerical value of R depends on the units used. For example, R is 62.4 (L $\times$ mm Hg)/(K $\times$ mol), if 760 mm Hg is used for standard pressure. Rearranging the equation for R and dropping the subscript we obtain the usual form of the **ideal gas law.**

$$\frac{P_1 \times V_1}{T_1 \times n_1} = R \quad or \quad P \times V = n \times R \times T$$

An obvious advantage of the ideal gas law over the combined gas law is that it permits us to solve for the number of moles of a contained gas when P, V, and T are known.

The value of R, the ideal gas constant, depends on the units used.

The ideal gas law describes the pressure, volume, temperature, or number of particles of a gas when any three of these four conditions are given.

Safety

Gas cylinders should always be securely strapped to the wall or to the cart on which they are transported. Each cylinder is very heavy. A cylinder could injure a person if it fell.

Example 6

A rigid steel cylinder with a volume of 20.0 L is filled with nitrogen gas to a final pressure of 200 atm at 27°C. How many moles of N_2 gas does the cylinder contain?

Solution

First we convert degrees Celsius to degrees Kelvin.

$$27°C + 273 = 300\ K$$

The conditions are $P = 200$ atm, $V = 20.0$ L, and $T = 300$ K. Because we want to find the number of moles of N_2 gas, we may rearrange the ideal gas law to obtain n.

$$n = \frac{P \times V}{R \times T}$$

Now we can substitute the known quantities into the equation.

$$n = \frac{200 \text{ atm} \times 20.0 \text{ L}}{0.0821 \dfrac{\text{L} \times \text{atm}}{\text{K} \times \text{mol}} \times 300 \text{ K}} = 162 \text{ mol}$$

Problem

10. 2.5×10^2 mol

10. When a rigid hollow sphere containing 680 L of helium gas is heated from 300 K to 600 K, the pressure of the gas increases to 18 atm. How many moles of helium does the sphere contain?

Example 7

A deep underground cavern contains 2.24×10^6 L of methane gas at a pressure of 15.0 atm and a temperature of 42°C. How many grams of methane does this natural gas deposit contain?

Solution

The problem calls for an answer in grams, but the ideal gas law permits us to obtain the solution only in moles. We must first find the number of moles, then convert to grams.

We know that $P = 15.0$ atm, $V = 2.24 \times 10^6$ L, and $T = 315$ K (42°C + 273). As in the previous example, we substitute the known quantities into the equation.

$$n = \frac{P \times V}{R \times T} \qquad n = \frac{15.0 \text{ atm} \times (2.24 \times 10^6 \text{ L})}{0.0821 \dfrac{\text{L} \times \text{atm}}{\text{K} \times \text{mol}} \times 315 \text{ K}}$$

The cavern contains 1.30×10^6 mol of methane.

One mole of methane has a mass of 16.0 g (C = 12 amu; 4 H = 4 amu). The number of grams of methane can be calculated using a mole $\longrightarrow$ mass conversion.

$$1.30 \times 10^6 \text{ mol CH}_4 \times \frac{16.0 \text{ g CH}_4}{1 \text{ mol CH}_4} = 20.8 \times 10^6$$

$$= 2.08 \times 10^7 \text{ g CH}_4$$

The cavern contains nearly 21 million grams of methane gas.

Figure 10·20
Geologists use explosions to help map underground features. Explosives are also used in both the mining and road construction industries.

Problem

11. 2.5 g air

11. A child has a lung capacity of 2.2 L. How many grams of air do her lungs hold at a pressure of 1 atm and a normal body temperature of 37°C? Air is a mixture, but you may assume a "formula mass" of 29 g/mol for air because air is about 20% oxygen (gram formula mass of $O_2 = 32$) and 80% nitrogen (gram formula mass of $N_2 = 28$). Thus 0.20 × 32 g/mol + 0.80 × 28 g/mol = 29 g/mol.

10·C Explosives and the Establishment of Nobel Prizes

An explosion is an extremely rapid combustion or decomposition reaction that produces gaseous products and heat. The most forceful explosions occur when liquid or solid reactants are instantaneously converted to gases. The volume of the gases will be much larger than that of the reactants. If the gases are confined, the resultant pressure will be great. Furthermore, the heat given off will increase this pressure. If the reaction is fast enough, however, the pressure will build up even if the gases are not confined. When the gas expands, the resulting release of pressure causes a shock wave. The kinetic energy of this "wave," the wind that follows it, and the heat from the reaction are the destructive force of the explosion.

An explosion reaction involves a fuel and an oxidizer. If the oxidizer is separate from the fuel, the reaction is called combustion. An example is the combustion of methane.

$$CH_4(g) + 2O_2(g) \longrightarrow CO_2(g) + 2H_2O(g) + \text{heat}$$

Such an explosion could occur if natural gas leaked into a building and was subsequently ignited by a spark or flame. If the fuel is its own oxidizer, a decomposition reaction takes place. An example of this type of explosive is nitroglycerine, $C_3H_5O_9N_3$. This compound is a thick, pale, oily liquid. It decomposes to give a variable mixture of products such as CO, CO_2, H_2O, and nitrogen oxides.

Some high explosives that are fuel and oxidizer in one, like nitroglycerine, are unstable. Even jarring them may be enough to cause detonation. Alfred Nobel (1833–1896) was very aware of this fact when his family started manufacturing nitroglycerine for use in the mining industry. In spite of their care, however, the Nobel family's factory exploded killing Alfred's brother.

At this point Nobel set to finding a way to make nitroglycerine less hazardous. He experimented on a barge in the middle of a lake to minimize the danger to others. At one point he found a cask of nitroglycerine that had leaked. Fortunately, the diatomaceous earth in which the cask was packed had absorbed the liquid. Nobel experimented with the mixture of nitroglycerine and diatomaceous earth. He found that it could be set off only by using a blasting cap. Moreover, it was equally explosive as the pure liquid. Nobel named his invention dynamite. It was soon one of the most widely used explosives because it could be handled relatively safely.

When Nobel died, he left his entire estate to establish a fund to provide annual prizes in five fields. He chose the fields of chemistry, physics, physiology and medicine, literature, and peace. Nobel Prizes are considered the highest honor a person can receive for achievements in these fields.

Safety

If you notice a strong odor of gas at home or in the laboratory, air out the room before lighting any flame or using any electrical switch. (Methane is odorless, but contains compounds that do have odors so that it can be detected.)

Figure 10·21
Nobel Prize winners receive this medal and an award of over $100,000. The prestige of receiving the award is even greater than its monetary value.

Appropriate for honors students.

No gas behaves as an ideal gas at all temperatures and pressures.

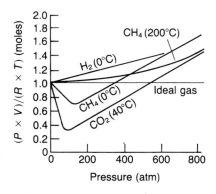

Figure 10·22
For an ideal gas, $(P \times V)/(R \times T)$ always equals 1 mol. By contrast, real gases deviate from ideality. What is the value of $(P \times V)/(R \times T)$ for CO_2 at 40°C and 100 atm?
0.3 mol

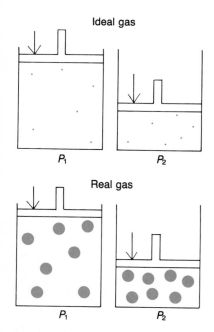

Figure 10·23
As pressure increases, the volume occupied by gas molecules is no longer negligible.

10·11 Departures from the Gas Laws

A gas that adheres to the gas laws at some conditions of temperature and pressure is said to exhibit ideal behavior. No gas behaves ideally, however, at all temperatures and pressures.

At any pressure the ideal gas law gives this ratio for an ideal gas: $(P \times V)/(R \times T) = 1$ mol. Figure 10·22 shows that this constant ratio plotted against pressure gives a horizontal line. The figure also shows that for several real gases at high pressures, $(P \times V)/(R \times T)$ departs rather widely from the ideal. The ratio may be greater or less than 1 mol. The explanation for these departures from ideality is that two different factors are operating. These factors are attractions between molecules and the volume of gas molecules.

Simple kinetic theory assumes that gas particles are not attracted to each other and that the particles occupy a negligible volume. These assumptions are not strictly true. Gases and vapors could not be liquefied if there were no attractions between molecules. Of course, real gas particles must also occupy space. Furthermore, intermolecular forces tend to hold the particles in a gas together. This effectively reduces the distance between particles. The gas therefore occupies less volume than is assumed by the kinetic theory, and $(P \times V)/(R \times T)$ tends to be less than one. At the same time, the molecules themselves occupy some volume and $(P \times V)/(R \times T)$ tends to become greater than one. One or the other of these effects will usually dominate. In portions of the curves below the line, the intermolecular attractions dominate. In portions of the curves above the line, the volume of the molecules dominates. Which of these two effects dominates is determined by the temperature.

Compare the curves for CH_4 at 0°C and 200°C. At 0°C the methane molecules are moving relatively slowly. The attractions between the molecules are strong enough that part of the curve, at the lower pressures, is below the $(P \times V)/(R \times T) = 1$ mol line. At higher pressures, the space between the molecules is reduced. The actual volume of the methane molecules becomes important, and the curve is above the $(P \times V)/(R \times T) = 1$ mol line. Raising the temperature to 200°C increases the average kinetic energy of the methane molecules sufficiently to overcome weak attractive effects when the molecules collide. Thus $(P \times V)/(R \times T)$ is near one mol at lower pressures. The ratio increases to greater than one as the volume of the gas particles becomes important.

Problem   12. See the answer in the appendix.

12. Small gas molecules such as N_2 and O_2 give the expected molar volumes of 22.41 L at STP. The nonideal behavior of gases is not limited, however, to extreme pressures and temperatures. The molar volumes of CH_4, CO_2, and NH_3 are respectively 22.37 L, 22.26 L and 22.06 L at the same conditions. Explain the reasons for these departures from ideality.

10·12 Diffusion and Graham's Law

Diffusion *is the tendency of molecules and ions to move toward areas of lower concentration until the concentration is uniform throughout the system.* For example, when a perfume bottle is opened, perfume molecules diffuse throughout a room.

Much of the early work on diffusion was done in the 1840s by the Scottish chemist Thomas Graham (1805–1869). Graham actually measured the rates of **effusion,** *which occurs as a gas escapes through a tiny hole in a container of gas.* Graham noticed that lighter gases effuse faster than heavier gases. From his observations, he proposed **Graham's law of effusion:** *The rate of effusion of a gas is inversely proportional to the square root of its formula mass.* Subsequently this relationship has also been shown to be true for the diffusion of gases. *The rate of diffusion of a gas is inversely proportional to the square root of its formula mass.*

Graham's law may be understood by an examination of the relationship of the mass and speed of a moving body to the force the body exerts when it strikes a stationary object. The mathematical expression that relates the mass (m) and the speed or velocity (v) of an object to its kinetic energy (KE) is $KE = \frac{1}{2}mv^2$. The kinetic energy is the force the body is capable of exerting. Suppose a ball bearing with a mass of 2 g traveling at 5 m/s has just enough kinetic energy to shatter a pane of glass. A ball bearing with a mass of 1 g would need to travel at slightly more than 7 m/s to have the same kinetic energy. The lighter ball bearing would therefore have to move faster to shatter the same pane of glass.

There is an important principle here. *When two bodies of different mass have the same kinetic energy, the lighter body moves faster.* The particles in two gases at the same temperature have the same average kinetic energy. Thus a gas of low-formula mass should diffuse faster than a gas of high-formula mass at the same temperatures. It is easy to show this is true by comparing two balloons, one filled with helium and the other filled with air. Balloons filled with air stay inflated longer. This is because the main components of air, oxygen molecules and nitrogen molecules, move more slowly and therefore diffuse more slowly than helium atoms. Fast-moving helium atoms, with atomic masses of only 4 amu, rapidly diffuse through small pores in the balloon. The pores are large enough for both helium atoms and air molecules to pass through freely. Thus the rate of diffusion is related only to the particle's speed.

Figure 10·24
The diffusion of one substance through another is a relatively slow process. Here bromine is diffusing through air. The process is complete in the cylinder on the left.

Occasionally students will try to refer to the sizes of gas particles in comparing their speeds. This is not quite correct, since the speeds are related only to the masses of the particles through the kinetic energy relationship.

Molecules with small mass diffuse more rapidly than molecules of large mass.

HCl was introduced at the left end, closest to the white band. Ammonia, which diffuses faster, was at the right.

Figure 10·25
When ammonia (NH_3) and hydrochloric acid (HCl) are placed at either end of a tube, a white band of ammonium chloride (the reaction product) appears in the tube. At which end was the ammonia introduced, and at which end was hydrochloric acid introduced? *Hint:* Which molecule will diffuse faster?

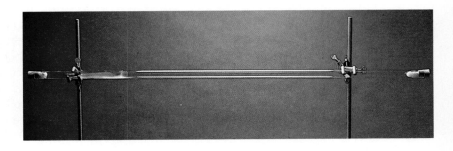

In a mathematical form Graham's law can be written as follows.

$$\frac{\text{Rate}_A}{\text{Rate}_B} = \frac{\sqrt{\text{formula mass}_B}}{\sqrt{\text{formula mass}_A}}$$

That is, the rates of effusion of two gases are inversely proportional to the square roots of their formula masses. Now let us compare the rates of effusion of nitrogen (formula mass, 28 amu) and helium (formula mass, 4 amu).

$$\frac{\text{Rate}_{He}}{\text{Rate}_{N_2}} = \frac{\sqrt{28}}{\sqrt{4}} = \frac{5.3}{2} = 2.7$$

We see that helium effuses nearly three times faster than nitrogen at the same temperature.

13. At any temperature hydrogen gas diffuses faster than chlorine gas by a factor of six.

Problem

13. Which gas effuses faster: hydrogen or chlorine? How much faster?

10 The Behavior of Gases

Chapter Review

Key Terms

Boyle's law	*10·6*	Gay-Lussac's law	*10·8*
Charles' law	*10·7*	Graham's law of effusion	*10·12*
combined gas law	*10·9*	ideal gas constant (*R*)	*10·10*
Dalton's law of partial pressures	*10·5*	ideal gas law	*10·10*
diffusion	*10·12*	partial pressure	*10·5*
effusion	*10·12*		

Chapter Summary

Gases expand to fill any volume available to them, and they diffuse from a region of high gas concentration to one of lower concentration. The smaller the formula mass of a gas, the greater its rate of diffusion (Graham's law). The collision of the particles in a gas with the walls of the container is gas pressure. Gas pressure is measured in atmospheres or millimeters of mercury; 1 atm of pressure, at sea level, is 760 mm Hg. At a pressure of 1 atm and a temperature of 273 K (STP), the volume of 1 mol of any gas is 22.4 L. This is called the molar volume. Air is a mixture of gases, approximately 20% oxygen and 80% nitrogen. The total pressure in a mixture of gases is equal to the sum of the partial pressures of each gas present (Dalton's law).

The pressure and volume of a fixed mass of gas are inversely related. If one decreases, the other increases. This relationship is Boyle's law. The *pressure* of a fixed volume of gas is directly related to its Kelvin temperature (Gay-Lussac's law); the *volume* of a gas at constant pressure is directly related to its Kelvin temperature (Charles' law). These three separate gas laws can be written as a single expression called the combined gas law. Another expression is the ideal gas law, $PV = nRT$, that relates the moles of a gas to its pressure, temperature, and volume. The letter R is called the ideal gas constant. Its value depends on the units used.

Practice Questions and Problems

14. A metal cylinder contains 1 mol of nitrogen gas at STP. What will happen to the pressure if another mole of gas is added to the cylinder but the temperature and volume do not change?   *10·1*

15. If a gas is compressed from 4 L to 1 L and the temperature remains constant, what happens to the pressure?   *10·2*

16. A gas with a volume of 4 L is allowed to expand to a volume of 12 L. What happens to the pressure in the container if the temperature remains constant?   *10·2*

17. Heating a contained gas at constant volume makes its pressure higher. Why?   *10·3*

18. The gas in a container has a pressure of 3 atm at 27°C (300 K). What will the pressure be if the temperature is lowered to −173°C (100 K)?   *10·3*

19. Describe an *ideal gas*.   *10·4*

20 State the law of partial pressures (Dalton's law) and express it in the form of an equation.   *10·5*

21. A gas mixture containing oxygen, nitrogen, and carbon dioxide has a pressure of 250 mm Hg. If $P_{O_2} = 50$ mg Hg and $P_{N_2} = 175$ mm Hg, what is P_{CO_2}?   *10·5*

22. State the pressure–volume law (Boyle's law) and express it in the form of an equation.   *10·6*

23. A gas with a volume of 4.0 L at a pressure of 0.90 atm is allowed to expand until the pressure drops to 0.20 atm. What is the new volume?   *10·6*

24. A gas is compressed at constant temperature from 27 L to 3.0 L. If the initial pressure of the gas is 0.50 atm, what is the final pressure?   *10·6*

25. A given mass of air has a volume of 6.0 L at 1 atm. What volume will it occupy at 190 mm Hg if the temperature does not change?   *10·6*

26. State the temperature–volume law (Charles' law) and express it in the form of an equation. *10·7*

27. Five liters of air at −50°C are warmed to 100°C. What is the new volume if the pressure remains constant?   *10·7*

28. State the temperature–pressure law (Gay-Lussac's law) and express it in the form of an equation.   *10·8*

29. The pressure in an automobile tire is 2.0 atm at 27°C. At the end of a journey on a hot sunny day the pressure has risen to 2.2 atm. What is the temperature of the air in the tire? (Assume that the volume has not changed.)   *10·8*

30. State the combined gas law in the form of an equation.   *10·9*

31. A 5.0-L air sample at a temperature of −50°C has a pressure of 800 mm Hg. What will be the new pressure if the temperature is raised to 100°C and the volume expands to 7.0 L?   *10·9*

32. Calculate the number of liters occupied, at STP.
  a. 2.5 mol N_2
  b. 0.600 g H_2
  c. 0.350 mol O_2 *10·10*

33. What volume will 12.0 g of oxygen gas (O_2) occupy at 25°C and a pressure of 0.520 atm? *10·10*

34. What pressure will be exerted by 0.450 mol of a gas at 25°C if it is contained in a vessel whose volume is 650 cm^3?   *10·10*

35. Determine the volume occupied by 0.582 mol of a gas at 15°C if the pressure is 622 mm Hg.   *10·11*

36. No gas exhibits ideal behavior at all temperatures and pressures. Explain the meaning of this statement.   *10·11*

37. Distinguish between the terms *diffusion* and *effusion*.   *10·12*

38. State Graham's law of effusion and express it in the form of an equation.   *10·12*

39. Which gas effuses faster at the same temperature: molecular oxygen or atomic argon?   *10·12*

40. Calculate the ratio of the velocity of helium atoms to neon atoms at the same temperature. *10·12*

Mastery Questions and Problems

41. If 4.50 g of methane gas (CH_4) is introduced into an evacuated 2.00-L container at 35°C, what is the pressure in the container, in atmospheres? *10·10*

42. A gas with a volume of 300 mL at 150°C is heated until its volume is 600 mL. What is the new temperature of the gas if the pressure is unaltered?   *10·7*

43. At what conditions do real gases behave like ideal gases? Why? *10·11*

44. A gas cylinder contains nitrogen gas at 10 atm pressure and a temperature of 20°C. The cylinder is left in the sun, and the temperature of the gas increases to 50°C. What is the pressure in the cylinder? *10·8*

45. A 5.00-L flask, at 25°C, contains 0.200 mol of Cl_2. What is the pressure in the flask? *10·10*

46. A certain gas effuses four times as fast as oxygen, O_2. What is its molecular mass? *10·12*

47. Calculate the volume of a gas in liters at 1 atm if its volume at 900 mm Hg is 1500 mL. *10·6*

48. A 3.50-L gas sample at 20°C and a pressure of 650 mm Hg is allowed to expand to a volume of 8.00 L. What is the final temperature in degrees Celsius if the final pressure of the gas is 425 mm Hg? *10·9*

49. Two liters each of nitrogen, argon, and oxygen, all at 1 atm pressure, are forced into a single container with a volume of 1 L. Assume that the temperature does not change. What will be the new total pressure and the partial pressure of each component gas? *10·5*

50. During an effusion experiment, it took 75 seconds for a certain number of moles of an unknown gas to pass through a tiny hole. Under the same conditions, the same number of moles of oxygen gas passed through the hole in 30 seconds. What is the molecular mass of the unknown gas? *10·12*

Review Questions and Problems

51. Calculate the gram formula mass of each of these substances.
a. $Ca(C_2H_3O_2)_2$ c. $C_{12}H_{22}O_{11}$
b. H_3PO_4 d. $Pb(NO_3)_2$

52. Name these compounds.
a. $SnBr_2$ c. $Mg(OH)_2$
b. $BaSO_4$ d. IF_5

53. An atom of lead-206 weighs 17.16 times as much as an atom of carbon-12.
a. What is the atomic mass of this isotope of lead?
b. How many protons, electrons, and neutrons are in this atom of lead?

54. How many kcal of heat are required to raise 40.0 g of water from −12°C to 130°C?

55. Write balanced equations for each of these chemical reactions.
a. Calcium reacts with water to form calcium hydroxide and hydrogen gas.
b. Tetraphosphorus decoxide reacts with water to form phosphoric acid.
c. Mercury and oxygen are prepared by heating mercury(II) oxide.
d. Aluminum hydroxide and hydrogen sulfide form when aluminum sulfide reacts with water.

56. Classify each of the reactions in problem 55 as to type.

57. Calculate the molecular formula of each of these compounds.
a. The empirical formula is C_2H_4O and the gmm = 88 g/mol.
b. The empirical formula is CH and the gmm = 104 g/mol.
c. The gmm = 90 g/mol. The percent composition is 26.7% C, 71.1% O and 2.2% H.

58. A piece of metal has a mass of 9.92 g and it measures 4.5 cm × 1.3 cm × 1.6 mm. What is the density of the metal?

59. Aluminum oxide is formed from its elements.

$$Al + O_2 \longrightarrow Al_2O_3$$

a. Balance the equation.
b. How many grams of each reactant is needed to form 583 g of Al_2O_3?

60. Calculate the percent composition of isopropyl alcohol, C_3H_7OH.

Challenging Questions and Problems

61. Oxygen is produced in the laboratory by heating potassium nitrate.

$$2KNO_3 \longrightarrow 2KNO_2 + O_2$$

a. At STP, how many liters of O_2 could be produced from 25.0 g KNO_3?
b. If the oxygen collected was at 750 mm Hg and 40°C, what would its volume in mL be?

62. Nitroglycerine has a density of 1.59 g/mL. It explodes to form several gases.

$$4C_3H_5O_9N_3 \longrightarrow 12CO_2 + O_2 + 6N_2 + 10H_2O$$

A sealed container filled with nitroglycerine is detonated. Assuming standard temperature and assuming that the container would not break upon detonation, what is the pressure inside the container in atmospheres?

63. The following reaction takes place in a sealed 40.0-L container at a temperature of 120°C.

$$4NH_3(g) + 5O_2(g) \longrightarrow 4NO(g) + 6H_2O(g)$$

a. When 34.0 g NH_3 reacts with 96.0 g O_2, what is the partial pressure (in atm) of NO in the container?

b. What is the total pressure (in atmospheres) in the container?

64. A 0.100-L container holds 3.0×10^{20} molecules of H_2 at 1.00 atm and 0°C.

a. If the volume of a hydrogen molecule is 6.7×10^{-24} mL, what percent of the volume of the gas is occupied by the molecules of the gas?

b. If the pressure is increased to 1000 atm, the volume of the gas is 1×10^{-4} L. What fraction of the total volume do the hydrogen molecules now occupy?

65. A sample of PCl_5 weighing 0.538 g was placed in a 0.200-L flask and completely vaporized at 250°C. The pressure in the flask was 1.00 atm. Some of the PCl_5 decomposed according to this equation.

$$PCl_5(g) \longrightarrow PCl_3(g) + Cl_2(g)$$

What are the partial pressures of PCl_3, Cl_2, and PCl_5 in the flask?

66. A mixture of acetylene, C_2H_2, and methane CH_4, occupied a certain volume at a total pressure of 126 torr. Upon burning the sample to form CO_2 and H_2O, the CO_2 was collected and its pressure found to be 192 torr in the same volume and at the same temperature as the original mixture. What percent of the original mixture was methane?

Research Projects

1. How did early hot air balloonists such as the Montgolfier brothers influence the work of Charles and Gay-Lussac?

2. How were the first hot air balloons used for scientific research? How are they used today?

3. Report on the uses of bottled gases.

4. How are liquefied gases used in scientific experiments?

5. Write a short biography of Robert Boyle. How did he influence the use of experiments to describe nature?

6. How are modern submarines equipped to withstand high pressures underwater and to provide sufficient oxygen for the crew members?

7. What are plastic explosives? When and how are they used?

8. Report on the research of one of the Nobel laureates in chemistry.

9. Trace the development of diving equipment.

10. Who invented the first "gas mask"? Report on the development of this type of equipment.

Readings and References

Marcante, Duilio. *This is Diving*. Boston: Sail Books, 1976.

Morgan, Ralph A. *Collisions, Coalescence and Crystals: The States of Matter and Their Models.* New York: Methuen Educational (dist. by Harper & Row), 1973.

Nobel, Iris. *Contemporary Women Scientists of America*. New York: Messner, 1979.

Pierce, Conway, and R. Nelson Smith. *General Chemistry Workbook: How to Solve Chemistry Problems*, 5th ed. San Francisco: Freeman, 1975.

Walker, Mort. *Sport Diving, the Instructional Guide to Skin and Scuba*. Chicago: Regnery, 1977.

Electrons in Atoms

Chapter Planning Guide

Section		Demonstrations and Experiments	Resource Materials
11·1 The Development of Atomic Models	C*	Dem 11·1 Energy Levels	Objectives Worksheet 11, SPB Skillsheet 11, SPB
11·2 The Quantum Mechanical Model of the Atom	C		
11·3 Atomic Orbitals	C	Dem 11·2 Electron Repulsion in Orbitals	Beyond the Text: Other Types of Lighting
11·A The Chemistry of Lighting	E		
11·4 Electron Configurations	C		Teaching Diagram 16
11·5 Exceptional Electron Configurations	O		Quiz 11·1
11·B Flame Tests	E		
11·6 Light and Atomic Spectra	O	Dem 11·3 Continuous Spectra Dem 11·4 Emission Spectra Dem 11·5 Borax Bead Tests Exp 21 Identification of Metals: Flame Tests, LM Exp 22 Introduction to the Spectrometer Dem 11·6 Absorption Spectra	Prelab 21, SPB Prelab 22, SPB
11·C Spectroscopy: Identifying Atoms and Molecules	E		
11·7 The Quantum Concept	H		Beyond the Text: Lasers
11·8 Light as Particles: The Photoelectric Effect	H		
11·9 An Explanation of Atomic Spectra	H	Exp 23 Energies of Electrons, LM	Prelab 23, SPB
11·10 The Wave Motion of Matter and Quantum Mechanics	H		Quiz 11·2 Reviewsheet 11, SPB Chapter 11 Test
11·D Technical Illustration: Drawing the Unseen	E		X-rays and the Effects of Low Level Radiation, ICT 11
*C = Core, O = Optional E = Enrichment, H = Honors		LM = Laboratory Manual	SPB = Skills Practice Book ICT = Issues in Chem. Tech.

Chapter Objectives

Having studied this chapter and done the problems, the student should be able to:

1. Describe the contributions that Thomson and Rutherford made to the development of atomic theory. *11·1*

2. Explain how Bohr's model of the atom differed from its predecessors. *11·1*

3. Explain the significance of quantized energies of electrons. *11·1*

4. Compare the quantum mechanical model of the atom with previous models. *11·2*

5. Distinguish among principal energy level, energy sublevel, and atomic orbital. *11·3*

6. Describe the general shape of *s, p,* and *d* orbitals. *11·3*

7. Use the Aufbau principle, the Pauli exclusion principle, and Hund's rule to write the electron configurations of the elements. *11·4*

8. Explain why the electron configuration for chromium and copper differ from those assigned using the Aufbau diagram. *11·5*

9. Given the wavelength of light, calculate the frequency and vice versa. *11·6*

10. Calculate the energy of a photon associated with a given wavelength or frequency of light. *11·7*

11. Use quantum theory to explain the photoelectric effect. *11·8*

12. Explain the origin of the atomic emission spectrum of an element. *11·9*

13. Explain the wave–particle duality of matter. *11·10*

Teaching Suggestions

11·1 The Development of Atomic Models

The history of the development of the modern model of the atom has already been discussed in Chapter 4. Do not spend too much time explaining the Bohr model. The concept of electrons moving in fixed orbits is erroneous and misleading. The important outcome of the Bohr model is the concept of electron energy levels and the quantization of energy. **Demonstration 11·1** *Energy Levels* will help explain this idea.

11·2 The Quantum Mechanical Model of The Atom

The quantum mechanical model of the atom is abstract and complex. In the quantum mechanical model the behavior of the electron is described in terms of *wave* behavior. This description is far too removed from the range of experience of most beginning chemistry students. Do not concern yourself with getting the students to "understand" the quantum mechanical model. Be content with having them accept it as the modern theory which works so well to describe, explain, and predict the behavior of the electrons of the atom, and having them learn and apply some of the fundamental postulates of the theory.

It may be helpful to use an analogy to help the students understand how the quantum mechanical model describes the location of the electron in terms of probability. One which works well is the locating of bees around their hive.

Imagine that there is a beehive in the middle of a large, flower-filled field. Imagine also that we could take photographs every few minutes to locate the bees in the field. Using these photographs we could then mark the bees' positions on a map.

From our photographs we would get a great deal of information about the instantaneous locations of the bees. However, we would not gain information about how they moved from location to location.

The density of marks on our plot would show where we would be most likely to find the bees should we want to observe them further. The density is greatest where the probability of finding them would be the greatest. Only a few bees would be at a great distances from the hive. The density of the plot would be very low there. Most bees would be found in a region near or at the hive. The density of the plot would be very high there. If enough photographs are taken, we can obtain a good visualization of the movements of the bees in the field. However, we could *never* predict the exact location of any bee at any given instant.

Like any analogy, this one is not perfect. For example, bees *can* enter the hive, but electrons *cannot* enter the nucleus. Nevertheless, the analogy can help emphasize that the quantum mechanical model does not pretend to predict the exact location of an electron or to explain how it gets from place to place. Instead, it describes electron location in terms of the probability of finding one in a given region.

11·3 Atomic Orbitals

Do not try to explain the shapes of the various kinds of orbitals. Once we get beyond the *s* shaped orbital, there is no way of understanding the shapes of the *p, d,* and *f* orbitals. Simply present them as an outgrowth of the quantum mechanical model. This is the way the quantum

mechanical model predicts them to be and this is the way experiments show them to be. There is no easily-grasped "reason" they have to be that way.

It helps to show the students models and diagrams of the *s, p, d,* and *f* orbitals. Caution them that whatever representation we use, an orbital is only a region of probability. It does not have sharp boundaries as models and diagrams would have us believe. **Demonstration 11·2** *Electron Repulsion in Orbitals* may help.

Beginning students often erroneously picture the *p* orbital as containing two electrons, one in each lobe. Point out that a *p* orbital could also contain only one or even zero electrons. That electron spends its time equally in each lobe. It could also contain two electrons, each spending half of its time in each lobe.

If students have trouble remembering how many orbitals there are at each level, point out to them that there are always n^2 orbitals per energy level (where n = principal quantum number). The number of orbitals increases with distance from the nucleus because new shapes are added. Thus we progress from 1*s* orbital to 3*p* orbitals, 5*d* orbitals, and 7*f* orbitals. We do not need to concern ourselves with orbitals beyond the *f* shaped orbital since the electrons of all known elements are accommodated by these.

11·4 Electron Configurations

This is an important section. We will use configurations to explain and predict a great deal of chemical behavior. Work through several examples of applications of the three rules for obtaining correct electron configurations.

They may ask why an orbital never contains more than two electrons. Since electrons are negatively charged, the repulsion of like charges should make it difficult for them to be found simultaneously in the same region. The answer lies in the spins of the electrons. Each electron can be thought of as spinning on an axis. This spin makes the electron act as a tiny magnet, with a north pole at one end and a south pole at the other. (As a matter of fact, the magnetism of a steel magnet is the result of an alignment of the spins of many electrons in the atoms within.) If two electrons with opposite spins are placed in one orbital (one is "upside down" in relation to the other), then their magnetic poles can attract, and counteract some of the electrical repulsive force.

If a third electron tries to enter a region already occupied by two electrons, its spin will always be the same as one of them. It will therefore be repelled from the region.

11·5 Exceptional Electron Configurations

As with many rules, the rules for the filling of orbitals have some exceptions. This section points out how the configurations for Cr and Cu deviate slightly from what we would predict from the rules in Section 11·4. Other exceptions occur with Nb, Mo, Tc, Ru, Rh, Pd, Ag, La, Ir, Pt, Au, and Ac. The fact that there are exceptions does not invalidate the rules. Just be sure the students are aware that there are a few elements which must be treated differently.

11·6 Light and Atomic Spectra

The study of light and atomic spectra gave the first indication of the fact that the electrons in atoms are restricted to energy levels. The light that is being emitted or absorbed in a spectrum is being produced or absorbed by the transition of electrons between energy levels in an atom.

Point out that the term *light* refers only to that part of the electromagnetic spectrum which we can perceive with the human eye. The electromagnetic spectrum also includes radio waves, microwaves, visible light, ultraviolet and infrared light, X-rays, and gamma rays. Atoms can emit and absorb radiation in many parts of the electromagnetic spectrum.

After covering the nature of light do **Demonstration 11·3** *Continuous Spectra,* **11·4** *Emission Spectra* (and/or **11·5** *Borax Bead Tests*), or **11·6** *Absorption Spectra,* to give students direct experience with viewing spectra. **Experiment 21** *Identification of Metals: Flame Tests* may also be done at this time.

11·7 The Quantum Concept

It is important that the students see the importance of the fact that each element emits a line spectrum rather than a continuous spectrum. Each spectral line corresponds to an exact frequency of light. Each frequency of light corresponds to an exact amount of energy being given off. Thus we see that the electrons which are making transitions to produce light are restricted to giving off only certain fixed amounts of energy. In other words, they are restricted to movements between fixed energy levels.

11·8 Light as Particles: The Photoelectric Effect

The most reasonable explanation of the photoelectric effect is that light is delivering its energy in fixed amounts, which we call quanta or photons. If this light was produced by electrons making energy level transitions, then the energy of these transitions must have been quantized as well. For this to happen, the electrons must be moving between levels which have fixed amounts of energy. Thus, the photoelectric effect gives direct evidence for the quantization of light energy, and supports the existence of energy levels and the quantum mechanical model of the atom.

The photoelectric effect also demonstrates the fact that light (which is a form of energy) has a dual nature.

Sometimes light behaves as if it is composed strictly of waves. At other times it behaves as if it is composed of a flow of very tiny particles.

11·9   An Explanation of Atomic Spectra

This section ties together the production of spectral lines and the quantum mechanical model of the atom.

Be sure that the students understand that an energy level corresponds to a distance from the nucleus, and that an electron is allowed to position itself only at certain permitted distances from the nucleus. It is never allowed to be at any intermediate position. The ladder analogy works well to get this point across, but be sure that the students realize that unlike the ladder, the spacing between the energy levels is not equal. The spacing gets smaller and smaller as higher energy levels are approached.

Emphasize that an energy level corresponds also to an amount of energy. Energy is needed to pull an electron away from the attractive force of the nucleus, and so an electron gains potential energy if it is moved to a greater distance from the nucleus. Thus there is a correspondence between distance from the nucleus and the amount of energy the electron possesses. A lower energy level is closer to the nucleus. A higher energy level is farther away from the nucleus.

An electron at any given distance from the nucleus possesses a fixed amount of potential energy. To change its potential energy, the electron must change its distance from the nucleus. This also involves a fixed amount of energy. An electron cannot possess, give off, or absorb random amounts of energy, only fixed amounts. These fixed amounts of energy with which the electron is involved are called quanta.

Be sure the students realize that an electron *must absorb* a quantum of energy to move away from the nucleus. If the electron drops back to its original level, it *must release* this same quantum of energy. The energy released is always in the form of electromagnetic radiation.

You may find it helpful to construct the simple model described in **Demonstration 11·1** *Energy Levels* to get across the energy–distance relationship.

Experiment 21 is appropriate here if it has not already been done. It provides experience with viewing spectra, as does **Experiment 22** *Introduction to the Spectrometer*. **Experiment 23** *Energies of Electrons* reinforces the concepts of this section.

11·10   The Wave Motion of Matter and Quantum Mechanics

We have already seen that light has both a wave and particle nature. In this section we see evidence that matter also has a dual nature. It can behave as particles (a behavior with which we all have had experience) and as waves (a behavior which none of us has directly witnessed). If we can understand that such pieces of matter as electrons and other subatomic particles behave as waves when they are within the atom, then perhaps it is not as difficult to accept the quantum mechanical model and its description of atomic orbitals.

Demonstrations

11·1   Energy Levels

Concepts: Electrons emit or absorb energy as they change energy level.

Materials: a 1 kg mass, 2″ styrofoam ball, 15″ rubber band or a chain of small rubber bands, strong wire.

Procedure: 1. A simple model of the hydrogen atom will help your students visualize the energy relationships in electron transitions. 2. Use a one kilogram mass to represent the nucleus. 3. Attach a rubber band to it. 4. Use the ball to represent the electron. 5. Push a strong piece of wire through the ball. Bend both ends of the wire into "U" shapes so that one end catches the ball and the other forms a hook. 6. The electrical force between the nucleus and electron is represented by the rubber band. 7. Connect the "nucleus" to the "electron" with the rubber band. 8. Hold the electron at such a distance that it tightens the rubber band without stretching it. Inform the students that this corresponds to the distance from the nucleus for the electron in the ground state. 9. Holding one hand at the ground state level, move the electron away from the nucleus. Point out that you had to invest energy to do so. The energy is stored in the rubber band. 10. Release the electron. It snaps back to your hand. Emphasize that energy has now been released. In an atom this energy is *always* released in the form of electromagnetic waves. 11. You can use this model to discuss permitted distances from the nucleus (energy levels), the spacing of these levels, and how different transitions can produce different amounts of energy (and therefore different colors of light).

11·2   Electron Repulsion in Orbitals

Concept: Electrons in orbitals repel each other.

Materials: oval balloons, thread, wool cloth.

Procedure: 1. Tie four balloons together. 2. Rub each with a wool cloth. 3. They repel each other and form a tetrahedral shape. 4. Point out that electron orbital shapes are affected by electron repulsion, as the negative charges maintain maximum separation. 5. The model can also help explain that an electron's position cannot be precisely determined. The orbital (balloon) is the region in space where there is a high probability of finding the electron.

11·3 Continuous Spectra

Concept: Incandescent and fluorescent lamps show continuous spectra.

Materials: spectroscopes*, clear incandescent bulb with vertical filament, fluorescent bulb.
(* There are many kinds of spectroscopes available from scientific supply houses. They range from sophisticated prism spectrometers to low cost diffraction grating spectroscopes. You can also construct your own. A diffraction grating can be taped across a small hole at one end of a long, narrow box, such as a shoe box. At the other end of the box, cut a 2 mm wide vertical slit. Be sure that the lid of the box fits tightly so that stray light cannot enter.)

Procedure: 1. Have students view the two bulbs with spectroscopes. 2. To use a spectroscope, the observer holds the slit end of the tube toward the light source and the grating end to one eye. Two spectra will appear, one on each side of the slit. 3. If the room is darkened, all students can view the same light source simultaneously. If you prefer, various light sources could be placed at viewing stations in different parts of the room. 4. Students should see a difference in the red/blue balances of the incandescent and fluorescent bulbs. With either source, students will see a continuous spectrum.

11·4 Emission Spectra

Concept: Emission spectra show lines of monochromatic light.

Materials: spectroscopes, gas burner, matches, high voltage DC power supply, platinum or nichrome wire, spectrum tubes: mercury (Hg), blue; neon (Ne), red; helium (He), red; argon (Ar), red; hydrogen (H_2), blue; and oxygen (O_2), red; and the following compounds: copper(II) chloride ($CuCl_2$), blue-green; sodium chloride (NaCl), yellow; barium chloride ($BaCl_2$), green-yellow; potassium chloride (KCl), purple; lithium chloride (LiCl), red; calcium chloride ($CaCl_2$), orange; strontium chloride ($SrCl_2$), red, safety goggles.

Procedure: 1. Observe the range of colors of emitted light from different spectrum tubes connected to the power supply. 2. Observe the color of the chlorides heated on a platinum wire in a burner. 3. Note that different elements have different lines of emission. 4. Observe the spectral lines of the chlorides with the spectroscopes.

11·5 Borax Bead Tests

Concept: Different elements emit different colored spectra.

Materials: 10 g of borax ($Na_2B_4O_7$), gas burner, matches, platinum or nichrome wire, 1 g of cobalt chloride ($CoCl_2$), 1 g of iron(II) nitrate ($Fe(NO_3)_2$), 1 g of nickel chloride ($NiCl_2$), 1 g of manganese dioxide (MnO_2), safety goggles.

Procedure: 1. Form a loop in the wire and hook a borax crystal into the loop. 2. Heat the borax in the burner flame to make a glassy bead. 3. Press the bead into one of the three minerals and reheat. 4. Repeat steps *1*, *2*, and *3* for the other minerals. The bead turns blue for cobalt, gray to green for nickel, green or brown for iron, and pink for manganese. 5. Point out that atoms of different elements emit characteristic spectra.

11·6 Absorption Spectra

Concept: Absorption spectra remove lines from spectra.

Materials: spectroscopes, lamps, solutions of blue and red food coloring, beakers, 100 mL of $0.1M$ solutions of the following: copper(II) chloride ($CuCl_2$), nickel chloride ($NiCl_2$), potassium permanganate ($KMnO_4$), and potassium chromate ($KCrO_4$), safety goggles.

Procedure: 1. Place the lamp behind the beakers of the different solutions. 2. With the spectroscopes, observe the absorption lines. Each colored solution has absorbed a certain range of wavelengths. **Caution:** *Potassium chromate is corrosive. Potassium permanganate and copper(II) chloride are irritants.*

Audiovisual Resources

Chemistry: Dissecting the Atom (7 FS) Charles Clark, 1975, 11–20 min. each. (Use with Sections 11·3, 11·4, or 11·6.) Discusses light as a form of energy, energy levels, and orbitals.

Models of the Atom (5 FS) AudioVisual Narrative Arts, 1980, 12–17 min. each. (Use with Sections 11·1 and 11·2.) Presents a history of the development of atomic concepts from the 19th century to the late 1920s.

Models of the Atom (5 FS) Charles Clark, 1981, 15–22 min. each. (Use with Sections 11·1 and 11·2.) Describes the development of atomic physics from about 1900 to the present.

Quantum Numbers (V) EME, 1982, 20 min. (Use with Section 11·3.) Illustrates the four quantum numbers with graphic techniques and shows how they describe an element's electron orbitals.

The Hydrogen Atom—As Viewed by Quantum Mechanics (standard version) (F, V) Chem Study, 1963, 13 min. (Use with Sections 11·2 and 11·3.) Explains the energy levels and line spectrum of the hydrogen atom in terms of quantum mechanics and discusses the meaning of a 1s orbital.

The Hydrogen Atom—As Viewed by Quantum Mechanics (advanced version) (F, V) Chem Study, 1963, 20 min. (Use with sections 11·2 and 11·3.) Contrasts electron distributions of *1s*, *2s*, and *2p* orbitals and introduces the principal quantum number, *n,* in addition to material presented in the standard version.

Beyond the Text

Other Types of Lighting

A new type of incandescent lamp, the halogen lamp, contains some iodine in addition to the argon or nitrogen. When the tungsten atoms vaporize, they react with the iodine to form tungsten iodide. This material remains a gas until it drifts near the hot filament. There the much higher temperature is enough to decompose it, giving tungsten metal and iodine once again. The life of the bulb is doubled because tungsten is constantly redeposited on the filament. This lamp produces a very bright light because it operates at high temperatures. In addition, the light produced is not decreased by a deposit of tungsten "ash" on the bulb surface. The bulb is small, about 1 centimeter in diameter, to maintain the 250°C temperature needed for the tungsten-iodine reaction. For all these reasons, halogen lamps are becoming popular wherever bright light in a small package is needed.

If the street lights in your community cast a golden glow, they are probably high-pressure sodium vapor lamps. Electric current produces heat that vaporizes sodium in the lamp. The atoms of sodium absorb energy and reradiate it as light. Sodium vapor at low pressure gives off a very bright yellow light. At high pressures, though, the light is more like white light with a yellow tint. High-pressure lamps containing mercury vapor instead of sodium will give bluish-white light. High-pressure vapor lamps are efficient, long-lasting, and give a bright, but not truly white, light. They are popular for lighting streets and parking lots. In these places good illumination, low maintenance, and high efficiency are more important than a faithful rendition of colors.

Lasers

When atoms in the ground state are struck by radiation, their electrons can absorb energy and move to a higher energy level. Sometime later the electrons will spontaneously give off their extra energy. At that point they return to the ground state directly or in steps. This is called *spontaneous emission.* The energy that the electrons give off represents many different energy level transitions. Thus the energy has many different wavelengths. In addition, it is given off in all directions and at different times because each electron operates independently.

In 1917 Albert Einstein (1879–1955) correctly predicted a different result from atoms that are already excited and then are exposed to high energy. Rather than absorbing this extra energy, the excited atoms are stimulated to emit the excess energy that they already have. This is called *stimulated emission.* The word *laser* is an acronym: Light Amplification by Stimulated Emission of Radiation.

In a laser the excited atoms may be a mixture of gases in a tube or a tubular crystal of ruby or other material. The stimulating energy may be a very bright flash of light (for the ruby) or a high electrical current (for the gas). A laser is designed so that this energy travels parallel to the tube or crystal. The energy given off by the atoms travels in the same direction. Mirrors are located at each end of the tube or crystal. The radiation that is emitted by the atoms reflects back and forth between the two mirrors as long as it is parallel to the axis of the tube. Any radiation traveling in other directions leaves the laser. The intensity of the radiation continues to build if the distance between the mirrors accommodates an exact number of wavelengths. All other wavelengths eventually die out. In practice, one of the mirrors reflects only enough of the emitted radiation to keep building the intensity of the light. The rest leaves the tube or crystal and is put to work.

Thus the light that was initially put into the tube is amplified. The beam of radiation emerges from the device as a thin pencil of light of sharply defined wavelength. This light is coherent; that is, all the waves are traveling in the same direction with their peaks and troughs lined up. This means that the laser beam remains tightly focused even after it has traveled a great distance. Because it does not spread out as ordinary light would, it is very intense.

The focused beam and sharply defined wavelength of laser light and the impressive power output of some lasers have led to many applications. Scanners in supermarkets and libraries use lasers. Lasers are used in weaponry and welding, surveying and spectroscopy, stereo sets and computer printers. They are also used extensively in the field of photochemistry, the study of chemical reactions involving light. Laser light can create catalysts, get rid of impurities, produce a desired product, or separate isotopes. Lasers are used to perform delicate surgery on the eye or skin. Because a laser cauterizes as it cuts, it is useful in any surgery where bleeding could be heavy, as in the liver or tonsils.

Answers to End of Chapter Questions and Problems

Practice Questions and Problems

10. In Rutherford's model, negatively charged electrons surround a dense, positively charged nucleus. In Bohr's model, the electrons are assigned to concentric circular orbits of fixed energy.

11. The electrons have a fixed energy level. They jump to other energy levels only by emitting or absorbing a quantum of energy.

12. In an atom, the electrons can only exist in certain fixed energy levels. To move from one energy level to another requires the emission or absorption of an exact amount of energy, or quantum.

13. The quantum mechanical model of the atom states that electrons have fixed energy levels. Electrons are in orbitals that may be visualized as clouds of various shapes, at different distances from the nucleus.

14. The $1s$ orbital is spherical. The $2s$ orbital is spherical with a diameter larger than that of the $1s$ orbital. The $2p$ orbital is dumbbell shaped.

15. The Aufbau principle states that electrons occupy the lowest possible energy levels. The Pauli exclusion principle states that an atomic orbital can hold at most two electrons. Hund's rule states that one electron occupies each of a set of orbitals with equal energies before any pairing of electrons occurs.

16. a. $1s^2\,2s^2\,2p^6\,3s^2\,3p^3$ **b.** $1s^2\,2s^2\,2p^6\,3s^2$
c. $1s^2\,2s^2\,2p^5$ **d.** $1s^2\,2s^2\,2p^6\,3s^2\,3p^6$

17. a. 10 **b.** 2 **c.** 6 **d.** 14

18. The p orbitals in the third quantum level have three electrons.

19. a. $1s^2\,2s^2\,2p^2$ **b.** $1s^2\,2s^2\,2p^6\,3s^2\,3p^6$
c. $1s^2\,2s^2\,2p^5$ **d.** $1s^2\,2s^2\,2p^6\,3s^2\,3p^6\,4s^2\,3d^{10}\,4p^6\,5s^1$

20. a. correct **b.** incorrect **c.** incorrect **d.** correct

21. a. 8 **b.** 8 **c.** 8

22. a. 2 **b.** 6 **c.** 2 **d.** 10 **e.** 6 **f.** 2 **g.** 14 **h.** 6

23. Lithium has three electrons. According to the exclusion principle, the $1s$ orbital can hold only 2 electrons.

24. a. $1s^2\,2s^2\,2p^6\,3s^2\,3p^6\,4s^2\,3d^{10}\,4p^4$
b. $1s^2\,2s^2\,2p^6\,3s^2\,3p^6\,4s^2\,3d^3$
c. $1s^2\,2s^2\,2p^6\,3s^2\,3p^6 4s^2\,3d^8$
d. $1s^2\,2s^2\,2p^6\,3s^2\,3p^6\,4s^2$

25. a. incorrect **b.** incorrect **c.** incorrect **d.** correct

26. The $4s$ orbital is lower in energy than the $3d$ orbital.

27. Violet, indigo, blue, green, yellow, orange, red.

28. d, a, e, b, c.

29. a. the distance from crest to crest of a wave **b.** the height of a wave **c.** the distance from two consecutive origins of a wave

30. The number of cycles per unit of time; Hertz, Hz; inversely proportional.

31. 2.00×10^{-3} cm, longer wavelength than red light

32. 2.61×10^4 cm

33. Planck showed that radiation is emitted and absorbed in quanta, dependent on the frequency of the radiation.

34. Light shining on a metal causes electrons to leave the surface. Classical physics assumed any wavelength of light could cause the photoelectric effect. Actually, however, only light with some minimum frequency and threshold energy can cause it.

35. a. Electrons are emitted with a low velocity.
b. More electrons are emitted; velocity stays low.
c. Electrons emitted have higher velocity.

36. A photon is a quantum of light energy. A quantum is a discrete amount of energy.

37. The outermost electron of sodium absorbs photons of wavelength 589 nm as it jumps to a higher orbital.

38. 1.3×10^{-38} m

Mastery Questions and Problems

39. a. Ar **b.** Ru **c.** Gd

40. $1s^2\,2s^2\,2p^6\,3s^2\,3p^6\,3d^{10}\,4s^2\,4p^6\,4d^{10}\,4f^{14}\,5s^2\,5p^6$ $5d^{10}\,5f^3\,6s^2\,6p^6\,6d^1\,7s^2$ 2, 8, 18, 32, 21, 9, 2; levels 5, 6, and 7 are not full.

41. a. 2 **b.** 4 **c.** 10 **d.** 6

42. a. 4.36×10^{-5} cm **b.** visible **c.** 6.88×10^{14} s^{-1}

43. $1s^2\,2s^2\,2p^3$, nitrogen; 3 unpaired electrons.

44. 7.64×10^{-19} J

45. 3.84×10^{-19} J

46. 3.08×10^{-19} J; higher energy.

47. a. Na, sodium **b.** N, nitrogen **c.** Si, silicon
d. O, oxygen **e.** K, potassium **f.** Ti, titanium

Review Questions and Problems

48. 4.06×10^{-10} m, 4.06×10^{-4} μm

49. a. 46.8% Si, 53.2% O **b.** 34.4% Fe, 65.6% Cl
c. 11.1% H, 88.9% O **d.** 2.1% H, 32.7% S, 65.2% O

50. a. $2KNO_3 + H_2SO_4 \rightarrow K_2SO_4 + 2HNO_3$
b. $Cu_2O + H_2 \rightarrow 2Cu + H_2O$
c. $2NO + Br_2 \rightarrow 2NOBr$
d. $SnO_2 + 2CO \rightarrow Sn + 2CO_2$

51. 12.5 L

52. a. Fe^{3+} **b.** Hg^{2+} **c.** N^{3-} **d.** HCO_3^- **e.** O^{2-} **f.** MnO_4^-

53. 6.2×10^7 mg

54. 154 g, 0.154 kg

55. a. 55 protons, 78 neutrons, 55 electrons **b.** 47 protons, 61 neutrons, 46 electrons **c.** 48 protons, 64 neutrons, 46 electrons **d.** 34 protons, 45 neutrons, 36 electrons

56. 1.46 atm

Challenging Questions and Problems

57. 6.93×10^2 s

58. Outermost electrons are ejected first. Then electrons at lower energy levels, requiring greater escape energy, are ejected.

59. For H: $\dfrac{1312 \text{ kJ}}{\text{mol}}$ $(n = 1)$, $\dfrac{328 \text{ kJ}}{\text{mol}}$ $(n = 2)$

For Li^{2+}: $\dfrac{11\,800 \text{ kJ}}{\text{mol}}$ $(n = 1)$

11

Electrons in Atoms

Chapter Preview

Sections 11·7 through 11·10 are appropriate for honors students.

Near the end of the nineteenth century, science was in turmoil. At that time, physicists began to probe the submicroscopic world of atoms. They found that ideas about matter and energy that had been relied on for over a century were inadequate. Chemists were confused about the reasons for the similarity in the chemistry of certain elements. When the fog lifted nearly 25 years later, the quantum mechanical model of the atom had emerged. The new model integrated the experimental discoveries and the theories of both chemists and physicists.

11·1   The Development of Atomic Models

For about 50 years past the time of John Dalton (1766–1844), the atom was considered to be a solid indestructible mass. Dalton's atomic theory was a great advance in explaining the nature of chemical reactions. It included, however, the idea of indivisible atoms. The discovery of subatomic particles shattered every theory people had about indivisible atoms.

The nineteenth-century discoverer of the electron, Joseph Thomson (1856–1940), realized that the accepted model of an indivisible atom did not take electrons and protons into account. Thomson therefore proposed

Figure 11·1
In this chapter you will learn how the brilliant colors of neon lights are due to the movements of electrons in atoms.

Figure 11·2
While he was still a student, Niels Bohr used his knowledge of light to develop a new atomic model.

a revised model that was referred to as the "plum pudding atom" (Figure 11·3). It had negatively charged electrons (raisins) stuck into a lump of positively charged protons (the dough). Thomson's model did not include neutrons because they had not yet been discovered. The plum pudding model explained some electrical properties of atoms. It said nothing, however, about the number of protons, their arrangement in the atom, or the ease with which atoms are stripped of electrons to form ions.

Based on his discovery of the nucleus, Ernest Rutherford proposed the nuclear atom in which electrons surround a dense nucleus. He thought of the rest of the atom as empty space. Later experiments showed that the nuclei of atoms are composed of protons and neutrons.

Oppositely charged particles attract each other. Thus one could argue that the negative electrons should be drawn into a positive nucleus. This would cause the atom to collapse. If the Rutherford model is correct, what prevents the electrons from falling into the nucleus?

In 1913 Niels Bohr (1885–1962), a young Danish physicist and a student of Rutherford's, came up with a new model. He proposed that electrons are arranged in concentric circular paths, or orbits, around the nucleus. This model was patterned after the motions of the planets around the sun and is often referred to as the planetary model. Bohr answered in a novel way the question of what prevents electrons from falling into the nucleus. He proposed that the electrons in a particular

■ Our understanding of the atom has been refined by successive atomic theories.

Figure 11·3
These drawings show how the model of the atom has changed as physicists have learned more about its structure. **a** In the nineteenth century, Thompson described the atom as a ball of electricity containing a number of electrons. **b** In the early twentieth century, Rutherford showed that most of an atom's weight is concentrated in a small positively charged area called the nucleus. **c** Later, Bohr proposed that electrons travel around the nucleus in definite orbits. **d** Modern physicists maintain that the atom has no defined shape and that electrons do not have precise orbits.

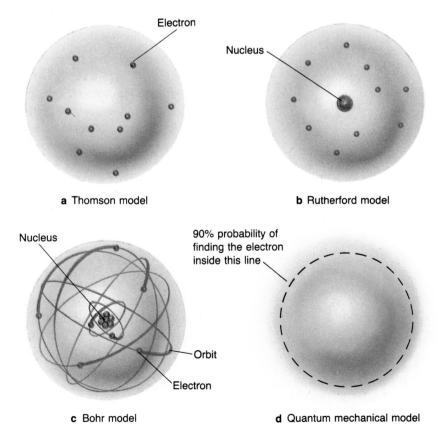

a Thomson model

b Rutherford model

c Bohr model

d Quantum mechanical model

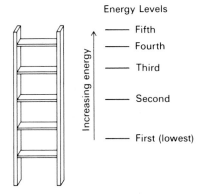

Energy Levels

Increasing energy →

—— Fifth

—— Fourth

—— Third

—— Second

—— First (lowest)

Figure 11·4
The rungs of a ladder are analogous to the energy levels in an atom. The higher the energy level occupied by the electron, the more energetic it is and the further it usually is from the nucleus.

■ The quantum mechanical model of the atom describes the probability of finding an electron in a region of space around the nucleus.

This is analogous to locating the position of a rapidly rotating fan blade. At any instant it may be in any one of a number of possible positions. Over a period of time these positions all blend to form a round blur. We know with high probability that the fan blade is somewhere within this blur. Similarly, the electron cloud gives us a time-averaged view of the electron.

path have a fixed energy. Thus they do not lose energy and fall into the nucleus. *The **energy level** of an electron is the region around the nucleus where it is likely to be moving.* The rungs of a ladder are analogous to the fixed energy levels of electrons. The lowest rung of the ladder corresponds to the lowest energy level (Figure 11·4). A person can climb up or down a ladder by going from rung to rung. Similarly, an electron can jump from one energy level to another. A person on a ladder cannot stand between the rungs. Similarly, the electrons in an atom cannot stop between energy levels. To move from one energy level to another, an electron must gain or lose just the right amount of energy.

The amount of energy gained or lost by every electron is not always the same. Unlike the rungs of a ladder, the energy levels in an atom are *not* equally spaced. *A **quantum** of energy is the amount of energy required to move an electron from its present energy level to the next higher one.* Thus the energies of electrons are said to be *quantized*. The term *quantum leap,* used to describe an abrupt change, comes from this concept. In general, the higher an electron is placed on the energy ladder, the larger is the diameter of the circular path or orbit of that electron.

11·2 The Quantum Mechanical Model of the Atom

In 1926 the Austrian physicist Erwin Schrödinger (1887–1961) took atomic models one step further. He used the new quantum theory to write and solve a mathematical equation describing the location and energy of an electron in a hydrogen atom. *The modern description of the electrons in atoms,* **the quantum mechanical model,** *derives from the mathematical solution to the Schrödinger equation.* Previous models were essentially physical models based on the extension of our knowledge of the motion of large objects. In contrast, the quantum mechanical model is primarily mathematical. It has few, if any, analogies in the visible world.

Like the Bohr model, the quantum mechanical model of the atom leads to quantized energy levels for an electron. Unlike the Bohr model, however, the quantum mechanical model does not define the exact path an electron takes around the nucleus. It is concerned with the likelihood of finding an electron in a certain position. This probability can be portrayed as a blurry cloud of negative charge. The cloud is most dense where the probability of finding the electron is large. It is less dense where the probability of finding the electron is small. Hence it is difficult to say where an electron cloud ends. There is at least a slight chance of finding the electron a considerable distance from the nucleus. A model is needed, however, to show where the electron probably is. By convention, a surface is drawn around the model of an electron cloud so that the electron is inside the surface 90% of the time. The surface is shaped so that the probability for finding the electron inside is the same for all points on the surface. The shape of the surface can now give us a useful picture of the shape of the cloud. Figure 11·3 illustrates this idea.

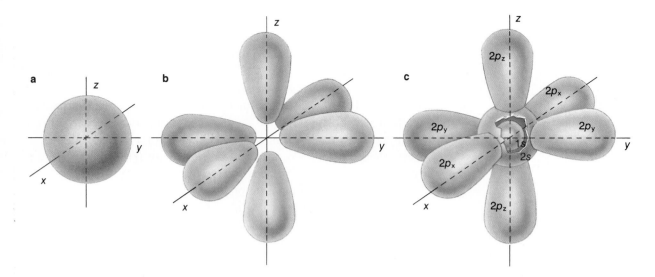

Figure 11·5
a All *s* orbitals are spherical. **b** All *p* orbitals are dumbbell shaped.
c A composite of one 1*s*, one 2*s*, and three 2*p* orbitals is shown.

Do not confuse orbitals of the quantum mechanical model with orbits of the Bohr model.

■ An atomic orbital is identified by a principal quantum number and an energy sublevel. Together these identify the shape and location of the atomic orbital.

The designations *s*, *p*, *d*, and *f* are derived from the names of spectral lines studied by early spectroscopists. They have no significance as far as the actual shapes of the orbitals.

s = spherical orbital
p = dumbbell-shaped orbital

11·3 Atomic Orbitals

In the quantum mechanical model of the atom, the energy levels of electrons are designated by *principal quantum numbers* (*n*). These are assigned certain values: $n = 1, 2, 3, 4, 5, 6$, and so forth. Within each *principal energy level*, the complex mathematics of quantum mechanics gives us *several* electron cloud shapes. This occurs because the quantum mechanical model divides the energy levels into *energy sublevels*. Each sublevel corresponds to a different cloud shape. Each cloud shape can be calculated from a mathematical expression called an *atomic orbital*. (These are different from the orbits of the Bohr model.) *We may think of an* **atomic orbital** *as a region in space where there is a high probability of finding an electron.* Different atomic orbitals are denoted by letters. The *s orbitals* give spherical clouds, and *p orbitals* give dumbbell-shaped clouds. The shapes of *d orbitals* and *f orbitals* are far more complex.

The lowest principal energy level ($n = 1$) has only one sublevel, called 1*s*. This orbital is spherical. The second principal energy level ($n = 2$) has two sublevels. The 2*s* orbital is spherical, and the 2*p* orbitals are dumbbell-shaped. The 2*p* sublevel is of higher energy than the 2*s*. The 2*p* sublevel consists of three *p* orbitals of equal energy. The long axis of each dumbbell-shaped *p* orbital is perpendicular to the other two. It is convenient to label the axes $2p_x$, $2p_y$, and $2p_z$. Thus the second principal energy level has four orbitals: 2*s*, $2p_x$, $2p_y$, and $2p_z$.

The third principal energy level ($n = 3$) has three sublevels, called 3*s*, 3*p*, and 3*d*. The 3*d* sublevel consists of five *d* orbitals of equal energy. Thus the third principal energy level has nine orbitals (one 3*s*, three 3*p*, and five 3*d* orbitals). The fourth principal energy level ($n = 4$) has four sublevels, called 4*s*, 4*p*, 4*d*, and 4*f*. The 4*f* sublevel consists of seven *f* orbitals of equal energy. The fourth principal energy level, then, has 16 orbitals (one 4*s*, three 4*p*, five 4*d*, and seven 4*f* orbitals). The shapes of the *f* orbitals are not shown. The sublevels and orbitals for each principal energy level are summarized in Table 11·1.

Figure 11·6
Four of the five *d* orbitals have the
same shape but different orientations
in space.

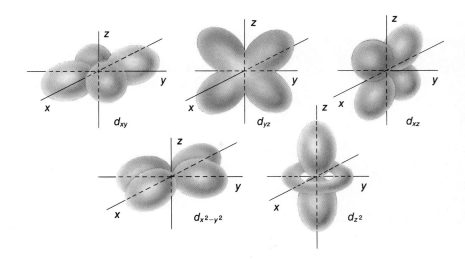

The principal quantum number always equals the number of sublevels within that principal energy level. Furthermore, the maximum number of electrons that can occupy a given energy level is given by the formula, $2n^2$. Here *n* is the principal quantum number. The number of electrons allowed in each of the first four energy levels is as follows.

Increasing energy
(increasing distance from nucleus)

Energy level *n*	1	2	3	4
Maximum number of electrons allowed	2	8	18	32

Problem

1. How many orbitals are in the following sublevels?
  a. 3*p* sublevel   **d.** 4*p* sublevel
  b. 2*s* sublevel   **e.** 3*d* sublevel
  c. 4*f* sublevel   **f.** third principal energy level

1. a. 3   **d.** 3
    b. 1   **e.** 5
    c. 7   **f.** 9

Table 11·1	Summary of Principal Energy Levels, Sublevels, and Orbitals	
Principal energy level	Number of sublevels	Type of sublevel
n = 1	1	1*s* (1 orbital)
n = 2	2	2*s* (1 orbital), 2*p* (3 orbitals)
n = 3	3	3*s* (1 orbital), 3*p* (3 orbitals) 3*d* (5 orbitals)
n = 4	4	4*s* (1 orbital, 4*p* (3 orbitals), 4*d* (5 orbitals,), 4*f* (7 orbitals)

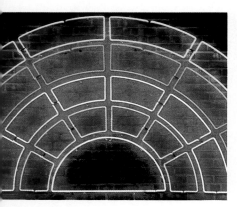

Figure 11·7
When the noble gases are energized they give off light of characteristic colors. Helium produces a yellowish light, and argon produces lavender. Krypton gives a whitish light, xenon gives blue, and neon shines orange-red.

Figure 11·8
Sodium vapor lamps produce a bright yellowish light. An electric current produces heat that vaporizes the sodium in the lamp. Atoms of sodium absorb energy and reradiate it as light. Sodium vapor lamps are used where energy efficiency and low maintenance are more important than realistic color.

11·A The Chemistry of Lighting

The famous, flashing neon lights of Times Square and Las Vegas shine because of electron orbitals. These lights contain neon gas or other gases at low pressure. When electric current passes through the gas, the atoms absorb some of the electrical energy by some of their electrons moving to higher orbitals. In dropping back to lower orbitals, the electrons give off the energy in the form of light. The color of the light is characteristic of the gas in the tube. Neon gives a bright orange light. By combining neon with other gases, other colors can be obtained. Sodium and mercury vapor lamps work in a similar way except that these metals must first be vaporized.

The light bulbs used in most homes are incandescent lamps. Their light is produced by a tungsten wire heated to white heat by an electric current. At such high temperatures the tungsten atoms give off white light much like sunlight. White light is really a combination of all the colors. This type of light is given off by hot solids and liquids and even by dense gases. Colors seen in incandescent light appear much as they do in natural light. The tungsten filament would rapidly burn up in the presence of oxygen. To prevent this an incandescent bulb is filled with argon or nitrogen. At such high temperatures the tungsten slowly vaporizes. Eventually the filament will break. Then we say the bulb is burned out. Even before the filament breaks, the vaporizing tungsten will condense on the inner surface of the bulb. This darkens the bulb and reduces the light given off.

Incandescent lighting is very inefficient at producing light from electricity. The heat that you feel when you hold your hand near a tungsten-filament bulb is energy that is lost rather than being converted to light. In fact, tungsten-filament lamps can be designed to radiate even more of their energy as heat. Fast-food restaurants keep food warm in the red glow of such infrared heat lamps.

Fluorescent lighting is much more efficient than incandescent lighting because no hot filament is involved. The long glass tube of a typical fluorescent bulb contains small amounts of mercury vapor and argon gas. The inside of the bulb is coated with a powder called a phosphor. When current passes through the bulb, electrons in the mercury atoms are excited to higher energy levels. In dropping back to the ground state, they emit ultraviolet (UV) light which is not visible. The UV light is absorbed by the electrons in the molecules of the phosphor coating of the tube. When the phosphor electrons return to their ground state, they emit visible white light that has more blue and less red than sunlight. Colors seen under this light seem "cold" in comparison to the same colors seen in natural light. A 40-watt fluorescent bulb produces as much light as a 150-watt incandescent bulb. It is no wonder that more than 75% of the lighting used in North America is fluorescent.

Figure 11·9
The energy levels of the various atomic orbitals are shown on this Aufbau diagram. Orbitals of greater energy are shown higher on the page.

■ The electron configurations of most elements can be written using three rules.

11·4 Electron Configurations

It is the nature of things to seek the lowest possible energy. High-energy systems are unstable. Unstable systems lose energy to become more stable. In the world of the atom, electrons and the nucleus interact to make the most stable arrangement possible. *The ways in which electrons are arranged around the nuclei of atoms are called* **electron configurations.**

Three rules govern the filling of atomic orbitals by electrons within the principal energy levels. These rules are the Aufbau principle, the Pauli exclusion principle, and Hund's rule. It is important to realize that these rules provide a way to obtain correct electron configurations for atoms. It is *not* the way that atoms are formed.

1. **The Aufbau principle:** *Electrons enter orbitals of lowest energy first.* The various orbitals within a sublevel of a principal energy level are always of equal energy. Further, within a principal energy level the *s* sublevel is always the lowest energy sublevel. Yet the range of energy levels within a principal energy level can overlap the energy levels of an adjacent principal energy level. This is shown on the Aufbau diagram

(Figure 11·9). A box (☐) is used to represent an atomic orbital. Electrons enter the orbitals of lowest energy first. As a result, the filling of atomic orbitals does not follow a simple pattern beyond the second energy level. For example, the 4s orbital is lower in energy than the 3d. The 4f orbital is also lower in energy than the 5d.

2. **The Pauli exclusion principle:** *An atomic orbital may describe at most two electrons.* To occupy the same orbital, two electrons must have opposite spins; that is, the electron spins must be paired. Spin is a quantum property of electrons and may be clockwise or counterclockwise. A vertical arrow (↑) is used to indicate an electron and its direction of spin (↑ or ↓). An orbital containing paired electrons is written as ↑↓.

3. **Hund's rule:** *When electrons occupy orbitals of equal energy, one electron enters each orbital until all the orbitals contain one electron with spins parallel* (↑ ↑ ↑). Second electrons then add to each orbital so that their spins are paired with the first electrons in the orbital.

Consider the electron configurations of atoms of the nine elements in Table 11·2. An oxygen atom, for example, contains eight electrons. The orbital of lowest energy, 1s, gets one electron, then a second of opposite spin. The next orbital to fill is 2s. Three electrons then go, one each, into the three 2p orbitals, which have equal energy. The remaining electron now pairs with an electron occupying one of the 2p orbitals. The other two 2p orbitals remain only half filled.

Problem

2. 3d, 4s, 3p, 3s, 2p

2. Arrange the following sublevels in order of decreasing energy: 2p, 4s, 3s, 3d, and 3p.

Table 11·2	Electron Configurations for Some Selected Elements						
	Orbital filling						Electron configuration
Element	$1s$	$2s$	$2p_x$	$2p_y$	$2p_z$	$3s$	
H	↑	☐	☐	☐	☐	☐	$1s^1$
He	↑↓	☐	☐	☐	☐	☐	$1s^2$
Li	↑↓	↑	☐	☐	☐	☐	$1s^2\,2s^1$
C	↑↓	↑↓	↑	↑	☐	☐	$1s^2\,2s^2\,2p^2$
N	↑↓	↑↓	↑	↑	↑	☐	$1s^2\,2s^2\,2p^3$
O	↑↓	↑↓	↑↓	↑	↑	☐	$1s^2\,2s^2\,2p^4$
F	↑↓	↑↓	↑↓	↑↓	↑	☐	$1s^2\,2s^2\,2p^5$
Ne	↑↓	↑↓	↑↓	↑↓	↑↓	☐	$1s^2\,2s^2\,2p^6$
Na	↑↓	↑↓	↑↓	↑↓	↑↓	↑	$1s^2\,2s^2\,2p^6\,3s^1$

A convenient shorthand method for showing the electron configuration of an atom can be used. This involves writing the energy level and the symbol for every sublevel occupied by an electron. A superscript indicates the number of electrons occupying that sublevel. For hydrogen, with one electron in a $1s$ orbital, the electron configuration is written $1s^1$. For helium, with two electrons in a $1s$ orbital, it is $1s^2$. For oxygen, with two electrons in a $1s$ orbital, two electrons in a $2s$ orbital, and four electrons in $2p$ orbitals, it is $1s^2\,2s^2\,2p^4$. Note that the sum of the superscripts equals the number of electrons in the configuration.

Example 1

Use Figure 11·9 to write the electron configuration of these atoms.
a. phosphorus **b.** nickel.

Solution

Phosphorus has 15 electrons; nickel has 28 electrons. Using Figure 11·9, start placing electrons in the orbitals with the lowest energy ($1s$). Remember that there is a maximum of 2 electrons in each orbital. Electrons do not pair up in orbitals of equal energy until necessary.

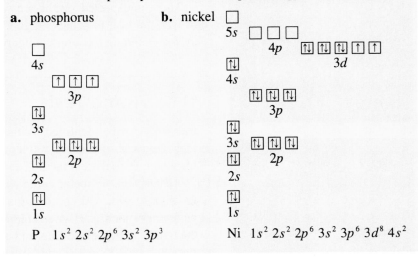

P $1s^2\,2s^2\,2p^6\,3s^2\,3p^3$

Ni $1s^2\,2s^2\,2p^6\,3s^2\,3p^6\,3d^8\,4s^2$

When the configurations are written, the sublevels within the same principal energy level are written together. This is not always the same order as given on the Aufbau diagram.

Problems

3. Write electron configurations for atoms of the following elements. How many unpaired electrons do these atoms have?
a. boron   **b.** fluorine

4. How many electrons are in the highest occupied energy level of these atoms?   **a.** barium   **b.** sodium   **c.** aluminum   **d.** oxygen

Figure 11·10
Erwin Schrödinger developed and solved an equation which is the basis of the quantum mechanical model of the atom.

3. a. $1s^2\,2s^2\,2p^1$;
   one unpaired electron
b. $1s^2\,2s^2\,2p^5$;
   one unpaired electron
4. a. 2   **c.** 3
b. 1   **d.** 6

11·5 Exceptional Electron Configurations

We obtain correct electron configurations for the elements up to vanadium (atomic number 23) if we follow the Aufbau diagram for orbital filling. If we were to continue, we would assign chromium (atomic number 24) and copper (atomic number 29) the following configurations.

$$\text{Cr } 1s^2\ 2s^2\ 2p^6\ 3s^2\ 3p^6\ 3d^4\ 4s^2$$

$$\text{Cu } 1s^2\ 2s^2\ 2p^6\ 3s^2\ 3p^6\ 3d^9\ 4s^2$$

The correct electron configurations, confirmed experimentally, are shown below.

$$\text{Cr } 1s^2\ 2s^2\ 2p^6\ 3s^2\ 3p^6\ 3d^5\ 4s^1$$

$$\text{Cu } 1s^2\ 2s^2\ 2p^6\ 3s^2\ 3p^6\ 3d^{10}\ 4s^1$$

These arrangements give chromium a half-filled d sublevel and copper a filled d sublevel. Scientists have determined that filled energy sublevels are more stable than partially filled sublevels. Half-filled levels are not as stable as filled levels. Nevertheless, they are more stable than other configurations. With only one electron in the $4s$ sublevel, chromium atoms and copper atoms are more stable.

These unexpected results are worth knowing. It is more important, however, for you to achieve a good understanding of the general procedure for obtaining electron configurations.

a

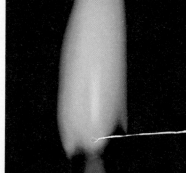

b

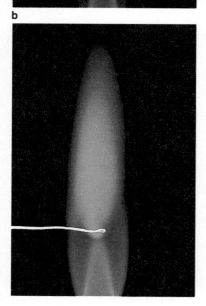

Figure 11·11
These two flame tests show the characteristic colors of barium (a) and strontium (b).

11·B Flame Tests

Elements can be identified by the color of light they give off when their atoms absorb energy. Recognition of these colors is the basis for a simple analytical method called a flame test.

The metal or metal compound to be tested is dissolved in hydrochloric acid. This produces a solution of the metal chloride. A platinum or nichrome wire is dipped in the solution. It is then held in the hot, blue flame of a Bunsen burner. The metal ions absorb energy from the heat of the flame. When they return to the ground state, they give off light of a characteristic color. Chemists learn to recognize the colors: pale green for barium, yellow for sodium, crimson for lithium, and so on. This simple test works for metals that form volatile chlorides.

The flame test was perfected by Robert Bunsen (1811–1899), a great German chemist of the nineteenth century. Bunsen was a university teacher and research chemist all his working life. He was famous for his emphasis on experimentation. Early in his career he lost an eye in a laboratory explosion. He also survived extensive work with arsenic compounds by developing an antidote for arsenic poisoning. He often invented or perfected the equipment that he needed, including batteries, calorimeters, and, of course, the Bunsen burner.

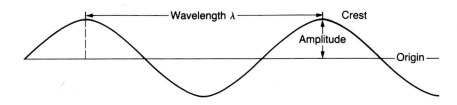

Figure 11·12
The amplitude of a wave is the height of the wave from the origin to the crest. The wavelength is the distance between crests.

11·6 Light and Atomic Spectra

The work that led to the development of the quantum mechanical model of the atom grew out of the study of light. Isaac Newton (1642–1727) had thought of light as consisting of particles. By the year 1900, however, the idea that light was a wave phenomenon was firmly ingrained among scientists.

The visible region is only a small portion of the electromagnetic spectrum.

In the wave model, light is considered to consist of electromagnetic waves that travel in a vacuum at a speed of 3.0×10^{10} cm/s. **Electromagnetic radiation** *includes radio waves, microwaves, visible light, infrared and ultraviolet light, X-rays, and gamma rays.* The parts of a wave at an instant of time are shown in Figure 11·12. Each wave cycle begins at the origin, then returns to the origin. *The **amplitude** of a wave is the height of the wave from the origin to the crest. The **wavelength** (λ, the Greek letter lambda) is the distance between the crests.* This can vary. In a traveling wave (Figure 11·13) **frequency** (ν, the Greek letter nu) *is the number of wave cycles to pass a given point per unit of time.* The frequency and wavelength of light are inversely related.

Light and other electromagnetic radiation consist of waves of many lengths and frequencies.

$$\nu = \frac{c}{\lambda}$$

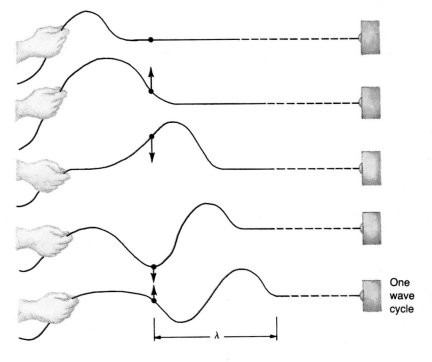

Figure 11·13
The frequency of a wave is the number of wave cycles to pass a given point per unit time. This diagram shows the generation of one wave cycle.

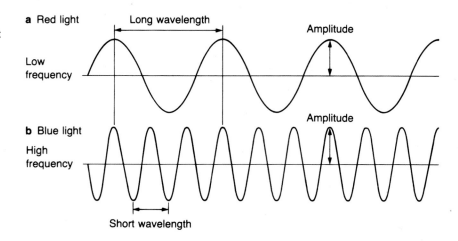

Figure 11·14
The frequency and wavelength of light waves are inversely related. As the wavelength increases, the frequency decreases. The wavelength and frequency do not affect the amplitude.

Long wavelength means low frequency. Short wavelength means high frequency.

As the wavelength of light increases, the frequency decreases (Figure 11·14). Hence the product of frequency and wavelength always equals a constant, c, the speed of light. The units of frequency are usually cycles per second. *In the SI, units of cycles per second are called* **hertz,** Hz. Frequency is expressed as reciprocal seconds (s^{-1}) because the term "cycles" is assumed as being understood.

Sunlight consists of light with a continuous range of wavelengths and frequencies. The wavelength and frequency of yellow light is different from that of red. *When sunlight is passed through a prism the light is separated into a* **spectrum** *of colors.* Each color blends into the next in order: red, orange, yellow, green, blue, indigo, and violet. In the visible spectrum, red light has the longest wavelength and the shortest frequency. Violet light has the shortest wavelength and highest frequency.

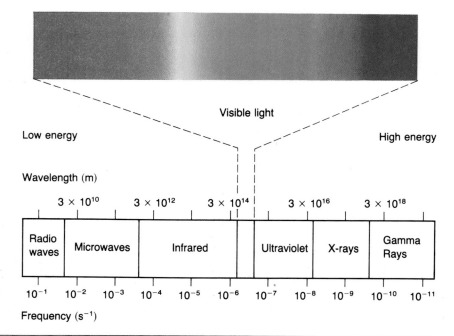

Figure 11·15
The electromagnetic spectrum consists of radiation over a broad band of wavelengths. The visible light portion is very small. It is in the 10^{-7} m wavelength range and 10^{15} Hertz (s^{-1}) frequency range. What types of nonvisible radiation have wavelengths close to those of red light? To those of blue light?

Infrared is close to red. Ultraviolet is close to blue.

Example 2

Calculate the wavelength of the yellow light emitted by a sodium lamp if the frequency of the radiation is 5.10×10^{14} s^{-1}.

Solution

First rearrange the equation $\nu = c/\lambda$ to give $\lambda = c/\nu$. Substitute values for c and ν.

$$\lambda = \frac{3.00 \times 10^{10} \text{ cm/s}}{5.10 \times 10^{14} \text{ s}^{-1}}$$

$$= \frac{3.00 \times 10^{10} \text{ cm s}^{-1}}{5.10 \times 10^{14} \text{ s}^{-1}}$$

$$= 5.88 \times 10^{-5} \text{ cm}$$

Remember that s^{-1} equals 1/s.

Problem

5. 6.00 $\times 10^{15}$ s^{-1}; ultraviolet

5. What frequency is radiation whose wavelength is 5.00×10^{-6} cm? In what region of the electromagnetic spectrum is this radiation?

Every element emits light if it is heated by passing an electric discharge through its gas or vapor. The atoms absorb energy, then lose the energy and emit it as light. *Passing the light emitted by an element through a prism gives the* **atomic emission spectrum** *of the element.* The emission spectra of elements are quite different from the spectrum of white light. White light gives a continuous spectrum. By contrast the atomic emission spectra consist of relatively few lines of colored light. Thus atomic emission spectra are line spectra or discontinuous spectra. Each line in an emission spectrum corresponds to one exact frequency of light being given off by the atom. Therefore each line corresponds to one exact amount of energy being given off. Figure 11·16 shows part of the emission spectrum of hydrogen.

The emission spectrum of each element is unique to that element. This makes these spectra extremely useful for the identification of unknown and sometimes otherwise inaccessible substances. Much of our knowledge of the composition of the universe, for example, comes from the atomic spectra of the stars, which are hot glowing bodies of gases.

Figure 11·16
The emission spectrum of an element consists of a series of bands which are characteristic for the element. **a** The emission spectrum of atomic hydrogen consists of a few widely spaced bands. **b** Molecular hydrogen gives off light at more frequencies and thus has more bands in its spectrum.

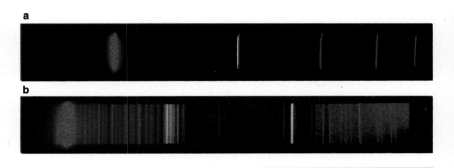

Problem

6. A hydrogen lamp emits several lines in the visible region of the spectrum. One of these lines has a wavelength of 6.56×10^{-5} cm. What is the color and frequency of this radiation?

11·C Spectroscopy: Identifying Atoms and Molecules

Spectroscopy is the process of producing and analyzing spectra. Robert Bunsen and Gustav Kirchhoff built the first spectroscope from two telescope eyepieces, a prism, and a Bunsen burner. With this apparatus they discovered a number of new elements including cesium and rubidium. They named these elements for the color of the spectra.

Spectroscopy is the chemist's most important means of identifying substances. Spectra can give both qualitative and quantitative information. The wavelengths detected tell the spectroscopist what is in the sample. The relative intensity of each wavelength tells how much of the substance is present.

A spectrum that is created by exciting atoms and then observing the light that they emit as they return to lower energy states is called an *emission spectrum*. In flame spectrophotometry, elements are excited by being burned in a flame. The ultraviolet or visible light emitted is then dispersed into its various wavelengths and detected.

A spectrum may also be created by determining the energy absorbed by an atom or molecule. Light or other energy is directed at a sample. The sample absorbs the quanta that it can. The remainder of the light passes through unchanged. The beam that comes out of the sample is compared to the beam that goes in, to determine which wavelengths have been absorbed. This is called an *absorption spectrum*. Atomic absorption spectroscopy is similar to flame spectrophotometry. The difference is that the light absorbed by the atoms is measured rather than the light emitted.

Spectral lines may be due to the emission or absorption of light. White light passed through the vapor of an element gives dark spectral lines because some of the wavelengths of light are absorbed by atoms of the element.

Figure 11·17
The emission spectra of the elements show different patterns. These spectra are for sodium (**a**), calcium (**b**), strontium (**c**), and barium (**d**).

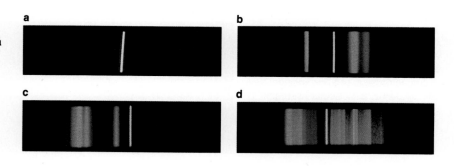

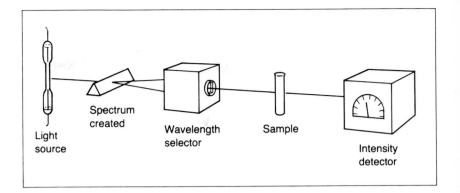

Like atoms, molecules also have quantized electron energy levels. In addition, they have energy levels due to their vibrations. In a molecule of water, for example, the hydrogen–oxygen bonds vibrate at particular frequencies. If the molecule absorbs energy, it can begin to vibrate at a different frequency, corresponding to a different energy. These vibrational energies are quantized, just like electron energies. Jumps from one vibrational level to another correspond to wavelengths in the infrared region. These wavelengths are very characteristic of the element. They depend on the atoms in the molecule, the forces in the molecular bonds, and the geometry of the molecule. These three characteristics uniquely define a particular molecule. Thus the vibrational spectrum also uniquely identifies that molecule. It is often called the "molecular fingerprint." The infrared spectra of thousands of compounds have been cataloged. Infrared absorption spectroscopy is the most common method of analysis used for covalently bonded molecules.

Many other types of spectroscopy have been developed. The source of the incident energy may be a lamp, an electric arc or spark, a flame, a laser, an X-ray tube, or a radioactive substance. The energy may change the energy level of electrons, bond vibrations or rotations, or even a nucleus. The resulting spectrum may be in any region of the electromagnetic spectrum. All these techniques are used to identify substances and to study chemical reactions.

Figure 11·19
Chemists use infrared spectroscopy to identify organic molecules. The tracing is characteristic for each compound. Each valley in this infrared spectrum of ethene (C_2H_4) indicates bond stretching or bending in the molecule when it is subjected to infrared radiation.

Appropriate for **honors** students.

The laws of classical physics are inadequate to explain atomic spectra.

11·7   The Quantum Concept

The laws of classical physics hold that there is no limit to how small the energy gained or lost by an object may be. According to these laws, when a gaseous element or the vapor of an element is heated to glowing, the spectrum of the emitted light should be continuous. Thus classical physics is no help in explaining the emission spectra of atoms, which consist of lines. The seed of an idea that explained atomic spectra came in 1900 from the German physicist Max Planck (1858–1947).

Planck was trying to quantitatively describe why a body like a chunk of iron appears to change color as it is heated. First it appears black, then red, yellow, white, and blue as its temperature increases. Planck found he could explain this if he assumed that the energy of a body changes only in small discrete units. By analogy, a brickwall can be increased or decreased in size only by units of one or more bricks.

Problem

7. Classical physics views energy changes as continuous. In the quantum concept energy changes occur in tiny discrete units called quanta.

7. Explain the difference between the laws of classical physics and the quantum concept, for example, when describing the energy lost or gained by an object.

Since period and frequency are reciprocals, 6.6262×10^{-34} J s can also be expressed as 6.6262×10^{-34} J/Hz. Thus the energy of a photon can be calculated directly without having to change frequency into s^{-1} first.

Planck showed mathematically that the amount of radiant energy, E, absorbed or emitted by a body is proportional to the frequency of the radiation.

$$E \propto \nu \quad \text{or} \quad E = h \times \nu$$

Here h is a constant now called **Planck's constant,** *which has a value of* 6.6262×10^{-34} J s (J is the joule, the SI unit of energy). The energy of a quantum equals $h \times \nu$. Any attempt to increase or decrease the energy of a system by a fraction of $h \times \nu$ must fail. The size of an emitted or absorbed quantum depends on the size of the energy change. A small energy change involves the emission or absorption of low-frequency radiation. A large energy change involves the emission or absorption of high-frequency radiation.

 Planck showed that the emission spectra of atoms are best explained by assuming that electromagnetic radiation is quantized.

Planck's proposal of absorption or emission of quanta of energy was revolutionary. Everyday experience had led chemists to believe that there was no limitation to the smallness of permissible energy changes in a system. It appears, for example, that thermal energy may be continuously supplied to heat liquid water to any temperature between 0°C and 100°C. Actually, the water temperature increases by infinitesimally small steps. This occurs as individual molecules absorb quanta of energy. We are unable, however, to detect such small changes in temperature. Thus our everyday experience gives us no clue to the fact that energy is quantized.

Appropriate for honors students.

11·8 Light as Particles: The Photoelectric Effect

In 1905 Albert Einstein, then a patent examiner in Zurich, Switzerland, returned to Newton's idea of particles of light. Einstein proposed that light could be described as quanta of energy that behave as particles. *Light quanta are called* **photons.** The energy of photons is quantized according to the familiar equation $E = h \times \nu$.

Example 3

Calculate the energy, in joules, of a quantum of radiant energy (the energy of a photon) whose frequency is 5.00×10^{15} s^{-1}.

Solution

Use the equation $E = h \times \nu$. Substitute values for h and ν to give E.

$$E = 6.62 \times 10^{-34} \text{ J s} \times 5.00 \times 10^{15} \text{ s}^{-1}$$
$$= 3.31 \times 10^{-18} \text{ J}$$

Problem   **8.** 2.12×10^{-22} J

8. What is the energy of a photon of microwave radiation whose frequency is 3.20×10^{11} s^{-1}?

Figure 11·21
Albert Einstein is considered one of the greatest scientists of the twentieth century. His mathematical derivations helped usher in the atomic age. His work on the photoelectric effect resulted in the invention of the photoelectric cell, a device that made possible sound motion pictures, television, and other inventions.

The photoelectric effect occurs when Group 1A metals give off electrons when subjected to light of a given energy.

The dual wave-particle behavior of light was difficult for scientists trained in classical physics to accept. It was even more difficult to dispute because it provided an explanation for the previously mysterious photoelectric effect.

In the **photoelectric effect,** *electrons called photoelectrons are ejected by metals when light shines on them.* The alkali metals (Li, Na, K, Cs, and Rb) are particularly subject to the effect. Not just any light will do. Red light ($\nu = 4.3$–4.6×10^{14} s^{-1}) will not cause the ejection of photoelectrons from potassium no matter how intense the light. Yet even a very weak yellow light ($\nu = 5.1$–5.2×10^{14} s^{-1}) shining on potassium begins the effect.

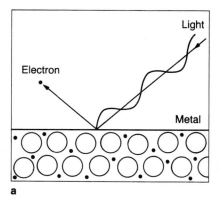
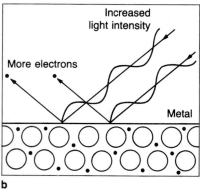
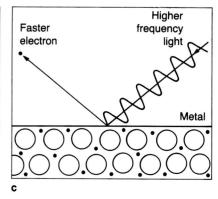

a   b   c

Figure 11·22
a When light strikes a metal surface, electrons are ejected. **b** If the threshold frequency has been reached, increasing the intensity only increases the number of electrons ejected. **c** If the frequency is increased, the ejected electrons will travel faster.

Figure 11·23
Photoelectric cells convert light energy into electrical energy. They are not used to generate electricity on a large scale because the cells are relatively expensive.

Appropriate for honors students.

The photoelectric effect could not be explained by classical physics, which had no quantum concept. Classical physics correctly viewed light as a form of energy. It assumed, however, that under weak light of any wavelength, an electron in a metal should eventually collect enough energy to be ejected. Obviously, the photoelectric effect presented a serious problem for the classical wave theory of light.

Einstein used his particle theory of light to explain the photoelectric effect. He recognized that there is a threshold value of energy below which the photoelectric effect does not occur. Because $E = h \times \nu$, all the photons in a beam of light of only one frequency (monochromatic light) have the same energy. If the frequency and therefore the energy of the light is too low, then no photoelectron will be ejected. It does not matter whether a single photon or a steady stream of low-energy photons strike an electron in the metal. Only if the frequency of light is above the threshold frequency will the photoelectric effect occur.

An analogous situation occurs with table tennis balls that strike a billiard ball. The table tennis balls are not energetic enough to budge the stationary billiard ball, no matter how many balls collide with it. By contrast, one golf ball moving at the same speed as the table tennis balls sets the target ball in motion. The golf ball is above the energy threshold. With the photoelectric effect, any excess energy of a photon beyond that needed to eject a photoelectron causes the ejected electron to travel faster. Increasing the intensity of light, however, only increases the number of photons striking the metal. Above the threshold frequency, increasing the intensity increases the number of electrons ejected. It does not, however, make them travel faster (Figure 11·22).

11·9   An Explanation of Atomic Spectra

Bohr's application of quantum theory to the energy levels of the electrons in atoms resulted in an explanation of the hydrogen spectrum. The lines observed in the spectrum are consistent with the idea that quantization limits the possible energies that an electron in a hydrogen atom can attain. Consider the lone electron of the hydrogen atom in *the lowest energy level, or* **ground state.** This energy level is designated by a quantum number, *n*. For the ground state, *n* = 1. Excitation of the electron

raises it to an excited state so that $n = 2, 3, 4, 5,$ or 6, and so forth. If the energy levels are quantized, it takes a quantum of energy, $h \times \nu$, to raise the electron from the ground state to an excited state. The same amount of energy is emitted as a photon when the electron drops from the excited state to the ground state. Only electrons in transition from higher to lower energy levels lose energy and emit light.

Figure 11·24 shows the explanation for the three groups of lines observed in the emission spectrum of hydrogen atoms. The positions of lines at the infrared end of the hydrogen spectrum are the Paschen series. These match expected values for the emission due to transitions from higher energy levels to $n = 1$. The lines in the visible spectrum are the Balmer series. They are the result of transitions from higher energy levels to $n = 2$. Those in the ultraviolet spectrum are the Lyman series. They correspond to transitions from higher energy levels to $n = 3$. Lines for the transitions from higher energy levels to $n = 4$ and $n = 5$ also exist but are not shown in the figure. Note that the spectral lines in each group become more closely spaced at increased values of n. This means that the energy differences between higher energy levels are smaller than those between lower levels. There is an upper limit to the frequency of emitted light for each set of lines. This is because a very excited electron completely escapes the atom.

Bohr's theory of the atom was only partially satisfactory. It only explained the emission spectra of atoms and ions containing one electron. Moreover, it was of no help in understanding how atoms bond to form molecules. Eventually the Bohr model of the atom was displaced by a new and better model. The latter is based on the description of the motion of material objects as waves.

Bohr explained the spectrum of the hydrogen atom using the quantum concept.

The lines in the emission spectrum of hydrogen result from the transitions of electrons from higher to lower energy levels.

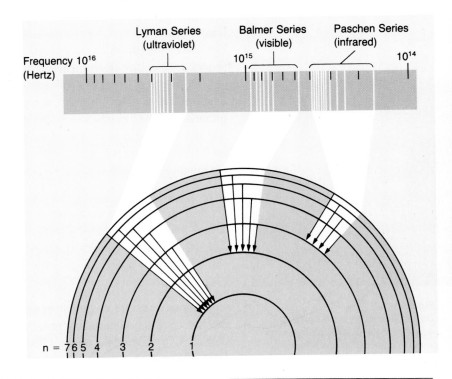

Figure 11·24
The three groups of lines in the hydrogen spectrum correspond to transitions from higher to lower energy levels. The Paschen series lines correspond to the transition to the $n = 1$ energy level. The Balmer series lines correspond to the transition to the $n = 2$ energy level. The Lyman series lines correspond to the transition to the $n = 3$ energy level.

9. The electron of the hydrogen atom is raised (excited) to the next highest energy level.

Appropriate for honors students.

It can be shown that all the units except meters cancel in the de Broglie equation if you substitute in for joules (1J = Nm) and then for newtons (1N = kg m s⁻²).

In using this equation express the mass in kg and the velocity in m/s.

■ De Broglie's claim that all moving bodies have wavelike properties stimulated the development of quantum mechanics.

Problem

9. What happens when a hydrogen atom absorbs a quantum of energy?

11·10 The Wave Motion of Matter and Quantum Mechanics

Such strange goings on! Energy absorbed or emitted in packages. Light behaving as waves *and* particles. Stranger things were yet to come. In 1924 Louis de Broglie, a French graduate student, asked an important question. Since light behaves as waves and particles, can particles of matter behave as waves? De Broglie derived an equation that described the wavelength, λ, of a moving particle.

$$\lambda = \frac{h}{mv}$$

Here h is Planck's constant, m is the mass of the particle, and v is the velocity of the particle. From this equation it is easy to calculate the wavelength of a moving electron. With a mass of 9.11×10^{-28} g and moving at the speed of light, an electron has a wavelength of about 2×10^{-8} cm. This is about the diameter of an atom.

Indeed, **de Broglie's equation** *predicts that all matter exhibits wavelike motions*. Why then are we unaware of this wave motion? As with quanta, the answer is concerned with the size of the object in motion. Wavelengths of objects that are visible to the naked eye are too small to measure. A 200-g baseball moving at 30 m/s has a wavelength of approximately 10^{-32} cm. This is too small to detect by any experiment that we can perform. By contrast, an electron moving at the same speed has a wavelength of about 2×10^{-3} cm. This is easily measured by appropriate scientific instruments.

De Broglie's proposal of matter waves set the stage for an entirely new method of describing the motions of subatomic particles, atoms, and molecules. Since mechanics is the study of the motion of bodies, the new method is called quantum mechanics. Let us summarize the most important differences between classical mechanics and quantum mechanics that we have previously seen.

1. Classical mechanics adequately describes the motions of bodies much larger than the atoms of which they are composed. It appears that such a body gains or loses energy in any amount.

2. Quantum mechanics describes the motions of subatomic particles and atoms as waves. These particles gain or lose energy in packages called quanta.

Another feature of quantum mechanics that is not found in classical mechanics is the uncertainty principle. This was derived by the German physicist Werner Heisenberg (1901–1976) in 1927. One form of the **Heisenberg uncertainty principle** *states that it is impossible to know*

Figure 11·25
DeBroglie said all matter exhibits wavelike motions. This phenomenon is more apparent in some forms of matter than in others.

Figure 11·26
a The location of an electron can be determined only if it is struck by another particle such as a photon.
b After the impact, the electron velocity changes. Thus, it is impossible to know both the position and velocity of the electron at the same time.

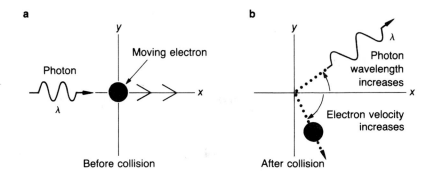

a

Photon

Moving electron

Before collision

b

Photon wavelength increases

Electron velocity increases

After collision

both the velocity and the position of a particle at the same time. As the measurement of velocity is made more accurately, the measurement of the position must become less accurate. Conversely, if the position of a moving particle is known accurately, the velocity is less well known.

The uncertainty principle is much more obvious with small bodies like electrons than with large objects like baseballs. The uncertainty in the position of a baseball traveling at 30 m/s is only about 10^{-21} cm, which is not measurable. The uncertainty in the position of an electron with a mass of 9.11×10^{-28} g moving at the same speed is nearly a billion centimeters! The quantum mechanical description by Schrödinger of the electrons in atoms shaped the concept of electron orbitals and configurations. It incorporates both the wave properties of the motions of bodies and the uncertainty principle.

Figure 11·27
Technical illustrators work with scientists and engineers to help make their material clearer and more interesting.

11·D Technical Illustration: Drawing the Unseen

If you glance through this textbook, you will see many illustrations that attempt to explain technical concepts. Often the objects pictured are things that have never been seen, like electron orbitals or the nucleus of an atom. Producing such pictures and diagrams is the job of the technical illustrator.

A technical illustrator must have artistic ability, a good background in drawing and design, and experience with various art media. General knowledge of the subject matter of the drawings also helps. Knowledge of chemistry, for example, is very helpful in illustrating a chemistry textbook. Most important is the ability to communicate with scientists, engineers, and technical writers to establish what is to be shown in the art.

Technical illustrators work on textbooks, scientific papers, operating manuals, product brochures, and many other types of publications. They may be employed by private industry, government agencies, or publishing concerns. They may also work on a free-lance basis. Technical illustration is an excellent field for a person who is interested in both art and science.

Key Terms

amplitude	*11·6*	hertz (Hz)	*11·6*
atomic emission		Hund's rule	*11·4*
spectrum	*11·6*	Pauli exclusion	
atomic orbital	*11·3*	principle	*11·4*
Aufbau principle	*11·4*	photoelectric effect	*11·8*
de Broglie's		photon	*11·8*
equation	*11·10*	Planck's constant	
electromagnetic		(*h*)	*11·7*
radiation	*11·6*	quantum	*11·1*
electron		quantum mechanical	
configuration	*11·4*	model	*11·2*
energy level	*11·1*	spectrum	*11·6*
frequency (*ν*)	*11·6*	wavelength (λ)	*11·6*
ground state	*11·9*		
Heisenberg uncertainty			
principle	*11·10*		

ple, the Pauli exclusion principle, and Hund's rule. The Aufbau principle tells us the sequence in which the orbitals are filled. The Pauli exclusion principle states that a maximum of only two electrons can occupy each orbital. Hund's rule states that the electrons pair up only after each orbital in a sublevel is occupied by a single electron.

The concept of quantized electron energy levels in atoms grew out of the study of the interaction of light and matter. The line emission spectra of atoms are best explained if energy levels are quantized. The quantum concept developed in part from Planck's studies of light radiation from heated objects and Einstein's explanation of the photoelectric effect. De Broglie's proposal that all matter in motion has wavelike properties further stimulated the development of a new mathematical description of electron configuration. Ernest Schrödinger devised the most successful of these early quantum mechanical models. It also incorporates the Heisenberg uncertainty principle.

Chapter Summary

Rutherford pictured the atom as a dense nucleus surrounded by electrons. Rutherford's model was refined by Niels Bohr. In the Bohr model of the atom, the electrons move in fixed circular paths around a dense, positively charged nucleus.

The energies of electrons in an atom are quantized. The quantum mechanical model is the modern description of the electrons in atoms. This model does not define the exact path of an electron. It does show the probability of finding an electron as a cloud of negative charge. Each cloud shape can be calculated from a mathematical expression called an atomic orbital.

The ways in which electrons are arranged around the nuclei of atoms are called electron configurations. Correct electron configurations for atoms may be written by using the Aufbau princi-

Practice Questions and Problems

10. Describe Rutherford's model of the atom and compare it with the model proposed by his student Niels Bohr. *11·1*

11. How did Bohr answer the objection that an electron traveling in a circular orbit would radiate energy and fall into the nucleus? *11·1*

12. The energies of electrons are said to be *quantized*. Explain. *11·1*

13. In general terms, explain how the quantum mechanical model of the atom describes the electron structure of an atom. *11·2*

14. Sketch 1*s*, 2*s*, and 2*p* orbitals using the same scale for each. *11·3*

15. What are the three rules that govern the filling of atomic orbitals by electrons? *11·4*

16. Write electron configurations for the elements that are identified only by these atomic numbers.   **a.** 15   **b.** 12   **c.** 9   **d.** 18   *11·4*

17. What is the maximum number of electrons allowed in each of the following sublevels?   *11·4*
a. *d*   **b.** *s*   **c.** *p*   **d.** *f*

18. What is meant by $3p^3$?   *11·4*

19. Write complete electron configurations for each of the following kinds of atoms.
  a. carbon   **c.** fluorine
  b. argon   **d.** rubidium   *11·4*

20. Indicate which of these orbital designations is incorrect.   **a.** *4s*   **b.** *3f*   **c.** *2d*   **d.** *3d*   *11·4*

21. How many electrons are in the second energy level of an atom of these elements?   **a.** chlorine   **b.** phosphorus   **c.** potassium   *11·4*

22. What is the maximum number of electrons that can go into each of the following sublevels?   *11·4*
  a. *2s*   **c.** *4s*   **e.** *4p*   **g.** *4f*
  b. *3p*   **d.** *3d*   **f.** *5s*   **h.** *5p*

23. Explain why one of the electrons in a lithium atom goes into the second energy level.   *11·4*

24. Write electron configurations for atoms of these elements.   *11·4*
  a. selenium   **c.** nickel
  b. vanadium   **d.** calcium

25. Which of the following is a correct electron configuration of an atom?   *11·4*
  a. $1s^2\ 2s^2\ 2p^5\ 3s^2\ 3p^3$
  b. $1s^2\ 2s^2\ 2p^6\ 3s^2\ 3p^6\ 3d^2$
  c. $1s^2\ 2s^2\ 2p^8$
  d. $1s^2\ 2s^2\ 2p^6\ 3s^2\ 3p^4$

26. Why does one electron in a potassium atom go into the fourth energy level instead of squeezing into the third energy level along with the eight already there?   *11·5*

27. List the colors of the visible spectrum in order of increasing wavelength.   *11·6*

28. Arrange the following electromagnetic radiations in order of decreasing wavelength.   *11·6*
  a. infrared radiation from a heat lamp
  b. ultraviolet light from the sun
  c. dental X-rays
  d. the signal from a short-wave radio station
  e. green light

29. Use a diagram to illustrate the following terms.
  a. wavelength   **b.** amplitude   **c.** wave cycle   *11·6*

30. What is meant by the term *frequency* of a wave? What are the units of frequency? Describe the relationship between frequency and wavelength.   *11·6*

31. What is the wavelength of radiation whose frequency is $1.50 \times 10^{13}\ s^{-1}$? Does this radiation have a longer or shorter wavelength than red light?   *11·6*

32. Suppose that your favorite AM radio station broadcasts at a frequency of 1150 kHz. What is the wavelength in centimeters of the radiation from the station?   *11·6*

33. How did Planck influence the development of modern atomic theory?   *11·7*

34. Briefly describe the photoelectric effect and explain why it could not be explained by classical physics.   *11·8*

35. What will happen if the following occur?   *11·8*
  a. Monochromatic light shining on the alkali metal cesium is just above the threshold frequency?
  b. The intensity of light increases, but the frequency remains the same?
  c. Monochromatic light of a shorter wavelength is used?

36. Explain the difference between a photon and a quantum.   *11·8*

37. When white light is viewed through sodium vapor in a spectroscope, the spectrum is continuous except for a dark line at 589 nm. How can you explain this observation?   *11·9*

38. What is the wavelength of a 2500-kg truck traveling at a rate of 75 km/hr?   *11·10*

Mastery Questions and Problems

39. Give the symbol for the atom whose electron configuration corresponds to each of the following electron configurations.   *11·5*
  a. $1s^2\ 2s^2\ 2p^6\ 3s^2\ 3p^6$
  b. $1s^2\ 2s^2\ 2p^6\ 3s^2\ 3p^6\ 3d^{10}\ 4s^2\ 4p^6\ 4d^7\ 5s^1$
  c. $1s^2\ 2s^2\ 2p^6\ 3s^2\ 3p^6\ 3d^{10}\ 4s^2\ 4p^6\ 4d^{10}\ 4f^7\ 5s^2$
  $5p^6\ 5d^1\ 6s^2$

40. Write the electron configuration for a uranium atom. Calculate the total number of electrons in each level and state which levels are not full. *11·5*

41. How many paired electrons are there in an atom of each of these elements? *11·4*
  a. helium   **c.** sodium
  b. boron   **d.** oxygen

42. A mercury lamp emits radiation with a wavelength of 4.36×10^{-7} m. *11·6*
  a. What is this wavelength in centimeters?
  b. In what region of the electromagnetic spectrum is this radiation?
  c. Calculate the frequency of this radiation.

43. An atom of an element has two electrons in the first energy level and five electrons in the second energy level. Write the electron configuration and name the element. How many unpaired electrons does an atom of this element have? *11·4*

44. The threshold photoelectric effect in tungsten is produced by light of wavelength 260 nm. Give the energy of a photon of this light in joules. *11·7*

45. What is the energy of a photon of green light whose frequency is 5.80×10^{14} s^{-1}? *11·7*

46. Calculate the energy of a photon of red light whose wavelength is 6.45×10^{-5} cm. Compare your answer to that of the previous question and say whether red light is of higher or lower energy than green light. *11·7*

47. Give the symbol and name of the elements whose atoms have these configurations. *11·4*
  a. $1s^2\, 2s^2\, 2p^6\, 3s^1$
  b. $1s^2\, 2s^2\, 2p^3$
  c. $1s^2\, 2s^2\, 2p^6\, 3s^2\, 3p^2$
  d. $1s^2\, 2s^2\, 2p^4$
  e. $1s^2\, 2s^2\, 2p^6\, 3s^2\, 3p^6\, 4s^1$
  f. $1s^2\, 2s^2\, 2p^6\, 3s^2\, 3p^6\, 3d^2\, 4s^2$

Review Questions and Problems

48. A potassium atom has a diameter of about 0.406 nm. Express this in meters and micrometers.

49. Calculate the percent composition of each of these compounds.
  a. SiO_2 **c.** H_2O
  b. $FeCl_3$ **d.** H_2SO_4

50. Balance the following chemical equations.
  a. $KNO_3 + H_2SO_4 \longrightarrow K_2SO_4 + HNO_3$
  b. $Cu_2O + H_2 \longrightarrow Cu + H_2O$
  c. $NO + Br_2 \longrightarrow NOBr$
  d. $SnO_2 + CO \longrightarrow Sn + CO_2$

51. Calculate the volume of O_2 at STP required for the complete combustion of 5.00 L of acetylene (C_2H_2) at STP.

$$2C_2H_2(g) + 5O_2 \longrightarrow 4O_2 + 2H_2O(l)$$

52. Write symbols for the following ions.
  a. iron(III)   **d.** bicarbonate
  b. mercury(II)   **e.** oxide
  c. nitride   **f.** permanganate

53. A person has a mass of 62 kg. What is the mass in milligrams?

54. The density of gold is 19.3 g/cm^3. What is the mass in grams of a cube of gold 2.00 cm on each edge? In kilograms?

55. Give the number of protons, neutrons, and electrons in each of the following.
  a. Cs   **b.** Ag$^+$ **c.** Cd^{2+} **d.** Se^{2-}

56. The temperature of a gas at STP is changed to 125°C at constant volume. Calculate the final pressure of the gas in atmospheres.

Challenging Questions and Problems

57. The average distance between Earth and Mars is about 2.08×10^8 km. How long does it take to transmit television pictures from the *Mariner* spacecraft to Earth from Mars?

58. In a photoelectric experiment a pair of students shine light of greater than the threshold frequency upon the surface of a metal. They observe that after a long time the maximum energy of the ejected electrons begins to decrease. Can you explain why?

59. Bohr's atomic theory can be used to calculate the energy required to remove an electron from an orbit of a hydrogen atom or an ion containing only one electron. This is the *ionization energy* for that atom or ion. The formula for determining the ionization energy E is

$$E = \frac{Z^2 \times k}{n^2}$$

where Z is the atomic number, k is 1312 kJ per mole, and n is the energy level. What is the energy required to eject an electron from a hydrogen atom when the electron is in the ground state ($n = 1$)? In the second energy level? How much energy is required to eject a ground state electron from the species Li^{2+}?

Research Projects

1. Make a timeline that traces the development of different atomic models starting with Democritus and ending with the modern atomic model.

2. Compare different sources of light such as fire, sun, and incandescent bulbs. How is the light generated and how is it used?

3. What materials were used in the early development of light bulbs?

4. What types of incandescent light bulbs are available? How is their usefulness dependent on the materials from which they are constructed?

5. What are the chemical causes and effects of lightning?

6. Describe Robert Hare's invention of the blow torch and how it led to the development of theater lights called "limelights."

7. How do microwaves compare to visual light waves? Describe some common applications of microwaves and the concerns about their use.

8. Construct a simple spectroscope. Use it to identify unknowns.

9. Compare absorption and emission spectroscopy. How is each of these techniques used in the laboratory?

10. How is spectroscopy used in astronomy?

11. How did Einstein's work on the photoelectric effect lead to the invention of sound motion pictures and television?

12. How do solar cells work? How are they being used? What are their limitations?

13. How is the laser used as a tool in chemistry? As a tool in medicine?

Readings and References

Born, Max. *My Life: Recollections of a Nobel Laureate*. New York: Scribner, 1978.

Pagels, Heinz R. *The Cosmic Code: Quantum Physics as the Language of Nature*. New York: Simon and Schuster, 1982.

Soloman, Burt. "Will Solar Sell?" *Science 84* (April 1982), pp. 70–76.

Trefil, James S. *From Atoms to Quarks: An Introduction to the Strange World of Particle Physics*. New York: Scribner, 1980.

Townes, Charles H. "Harnessing Light." *Science 84* (November 1984), pp. 153–155.

Wolf, Fred Alan. "Taking the Quantum Leap." *Discover* (December 1981), pp. 88–92.

12 Chemical Periodicity

Chapter Planning Guide

Section	Demonstrations and Experiments	Resource Materials
12·1 The Development of the Periodic Table C*		Objectives Worksheet 12, SPB Skillsheet 12, SPB
12·A Mendeleev and Moseley: Building on the Work of Others E		
12·2 The Modern Periodic Table C		Beyond the Text: A Periodic Table of the Future Teaching Diagram 17
12·3 Electron Configurations and Periodicity C		Quiz 12·1 Teaching Diagram 18
12·4 Periodic Trends in Atomic Size C		
12·5 Periodic Trends in Ionization Energy C		
12·6 Periodic Trends in Electron Affinity O		
12·7 Periodic Trends in Ionic Size C		
12·8 Periodic Trends in Electronegativity C	Exp 24 The Periodic Law, LM	Prelab 24, SPB Quiz 12·2
12·B Technical Writing: Communicating Clearly E		
12·9 The Noble Gases C	Dem 12·1 Properties of the Elements Dem 11·4 Emission Spectra	
12·10 The Alkali Metals and the Alkaline Earth Metals C	Dem 5·1 Ionization of Sodium Metal Dem 5·2 Formation of Sodium Chloride Dem 12·2 The Alkaline Earth Metals	
12·11 The Aluminum Group C		
12·12 The Carbon Group C		Quiz 12·3 Beyond the Text: Tetraethyl Lead: The Poison of Cities
12·13 The Nitrogen Group C		Asbestos: A Hazard in the Workplace, ICT 12
12·14 The Oxygen Group C	Dem 7·9 Combustion Reactions	
12·15 The Halogens and Hydrogen C		
12·16 The Transition Metals and Inner Transition Metals C	Dem 1·18 Copper in Acid Dem 5·3 Multiple Proportions Dem 7·1 Combination of Sulfur and Zinc	Quiz 12·4 Reviewsheet 12, SPB Chapter 12 Test
12·C Before the Elements: The Big Bang E		

*C = Core, O = Optional
E = Enrichment, H = Honors

LM = Laboratory Manual

SPB = Skills Practice Book
ICT = Issues in Chem. Tech.

Chapter Objectives

Having studied this chapter and done the problems, the student should be able to:

1. Explain the origin of the periodic table. *12·1*

2. Distinguish between a period and a group in the periodic table. *12·2*

3. State the periodic law. *12·2*

4. Classify the elements into four categories according to the configuration of their outermost electrons. *12·3*

5. Recognize the demarcation of the periodic table into an *s* block, *p* block, *d* block, and *f* block. *12·3*

6. Write the electron configuration of elements using the periodic table as a guide. *12·3*

7. Describe how the atomic radii vary within a group and within a period of the periodic table. *12·4*

8. Tell how the ionization energies vary within a group and within a period of the periodic table. *12·5*

9. Explain how the electron affinities change within a group and within a period of the periodic table. *12·6*

10. Describe how the ionic size changes within a group and within a period of the periodic table. *12·7*

11. Tell how electronegativities change within a group and within a period of the periodic table. *12·8*

12. Explain how the shielding effect influences periodic trends. *12·4*

13. Classify an element as a representative element, noble gas, transition metal or inner transition metal. *12·3*

14. Point out the similarities and differences in the physical and chemical properties of the elements in any group of representative elements. *12·9–12·15*

15. Identify an element as an alkali metal, alkaline earth metal, halogen, or noble gas. *12·9, 12·10, 12·15*

16. Name the two series of inner transition metals. *12·16*

Teaching Suggestions

12·1 The Development of the Periodic Table

Point out that it would be extremely difficult to keep track of the properties of the elements if it were not for our ability to organize them. Have the students compare Mendeleev's table (Figure 12·2) to the modern table (Figure 12·4) to discover similarities and differences.

12·2 The Modern Periodic Table

The students can readily see that the periodic table is organized in order of increasing atomic number. They will very likely make the assumption that as atomic number increases, so does atomic mass. Ask them to examine the chart to find any exceptions to this generalization. They should be able to notice that argon and potassium, cobalt and nickel, and tellurium and iodine are reversed from their expected atomic mass.

Emphasize that although there are some general trends which can be stated, the chemical and physical properties of the elements differ considerably from group to group.

Emphasize as well that the chemical and physical properties of the representative elements in some of the vertical columns are similar, but they are not *identical*. For instance, the halogens do not all have the same physical state at room temperature. Fluorine and chlorine are gases, bromine is a liquid, and iodine is a solid.

12·3 Electron Configurations and Periodicity

The organization of the periodic table is really a reflection of the fact that elements within a group have identical electron configurations in their outermost energy level.

One graphic way to get this idea across is to have the students write configurations for all of the representative elements and noble gases, and examples of the transition elements, the lanthanide series, and the actinide series. Of course, this is too much work for one student. The class can be divided into groups of two or three students. Each group can then work out the configurations for a part of the periodic table. If you have enough blackboard space, have them write the configurations for the rest of the class to see. As an alternative, you can give each group a transparency to write on for use on an overhead projector. When all of these configurations are placed in front of them, the students will have no trouble in seeing the similarities within a family.

12·4 Periodic Trends in Atomic Size

Try to get the students to understand the reasons behind the trends in atomic size rather then just memorizing them.

In explaining the decrease of atomic size within a period be sure that the students realize that as atomic number increases, the number of positive charges in the nucleus increases. Since the added electrons are put in at essentially the same distance, the increased attraction pulls all of the electrons closer to the nucleus. To get this point across you might wish to "build" an atom diagrammatically on the board. Start with the third element, lithium. Sketch its nucleus and its 1*s* and 2*s* orbitals. Then one at a time, add a proton and an electron to the diagram,

adding orbitals as necessary. Keep adding protons and electrons until the end of the period (neon with 10 electrons and protons) is reached. By this time the students should be able to visualize the effect of the steadily increasing nuclear charge.

If you add one more proton and electron to your diagram of Ne, you have the eleventh element, sodium. This electron must be placed in the next energy level, which is at a greater distance from the nucleus. The students should have no trouble seeing that the atom is now larger than any of the previous ones.

12·5 Periodic Trends in Ionization Energy

Ionization energy is a measure of the difficulty in removing an electron from the outermost energy level of an atom. Emphasize that there are two factors which affect ionization energy, nuclear charge and distance from the nucleus. Point out that within a period, nuclear charge increases from left to right and so does the difficulty in removing an electron. Thus ionization energy increases with increasing atomic number within a period.

Stress that increasing atomic number within a group produces larger atoms. An electron is easier to remove from a larger atom since it is more distant from the nucleus. Thus, ionization energy decreases with increasing atomic number within a group.

12·6 Periodic Trends in Electron Affinity

With electron affinity we are dealing with the idea of the attraction of an atom for electrons. The factors of nuclear charge and distance from the nucleus are again important. Emphasize that the trends for electron affinities are essentially the same as for ionization energies. Affinities generally increase with increasing atomic number within a period and generally decrease with increasing atomic number within a group. Note that the noble gases do not attract any extra electrons.

12·7 Periodic Trends in Ionic Size

To help the students understand why such drastic changes in size take place when ions are formed you might wish to sketch diagrams like the ones suggested in Section 12·4 above. Once you have shown the arrangement of electrons in a neutral atom, remove or add electrons to change these atoms to the appropriate ions. Show that positive ions are formed by the removal of electrons and that means, in the case of the representative elements, the outermost occupied energy level is emptied. Show also that the formation of negative ions usually fills the last energy level. The repulsive effect of the added electron(s) tends to make all of the electrons move outward and produces a larger ion.

12·8 Periodic Trends in Electronegativity

Ionization energy has to do with the tendency of an atom to lose an electron. Electron affinity has to do with the tendency of an atom to gain an electron. Electronegativity is a numerical scale which combines both ionization energy and electron affinity. Stress that electronegativity allows us to predict whether atoms gain or lose electrons when chemically bonded to other atoms. This will be extremely important in later chapters.

At the conclusion of your development of Sections 12·1 through 12·8, have the students do **Experiment 24** *The Periodic Law* to reinforce the concept of periodicity.

12·9 The Noble Gases

12·10 The Alkali Metals and the Alkaline Earth Metals

12·11 The Aluminum Group

12·12 The Carbon Group

12·13 The Nitrogen Group

12·14 The Oxygen Group

12·15 The Halogens and Hydrogen

12·16 The Transition Metals and Inner Transition Metals

These sections each offer brief descriptions of the chemical and physical properties of the major chemical groups. Try to get the students to focus on those characteristics which all of the group members share in common.

There is a great deal of information in these sections which needs to be assimilated, so you may wish to do more than just lecture about them. Consider the following a possible ways to help the students to master the material:

1. Break the class into teams of 3–4 students. Have each team do library research on the behavior and properties of one of the chemical groups and then make a short oral presentation to the class. The class could be required to take notes from the presentation. Each team could submit test questions to you which could be incorporated into the chapter test.

2. Develop worksheets which focus on the details found in the reading of these sections.

3. Prepare a display of as many elements from each group as possible. Show also typical compounds of these elements. Have the students view the display and list the obvious properties of these substances.

4. Do a series of demonstrations in which you show the properties of a few selected elements. See **Demonstration 12·1** *The Properties of the Elements*. The chemical behavior of the alkali metals can be demonstrated by **Demonstration 5·1** *Ionization of Sodium Metal* or **5·2** *Formation of Sodium Chloride*. **Demonstration 12·2** *The*

Alkaline Earth Metals shows a reaction of those metals. **Demonstrations 1·18, 5·3, 7·1,** and **7·9** show the reactions of elements. The spectra of the elements can be shown by spectrum tubes, as in **Demonstration 11·4.**

Demonstrations

12·1 The Properties of the Elements

Concept: Elements of different groups and periods have different properties.

Materials: samples of various elements. (Spectrum tubes can be used as examples of gases.)

Procedure: 1. Show samples of the elements. 2. Make lists of their properties. Look for similarities in elements of the same group, and for any periodic trends that can be observed.

12·2 The Alkaline Earth Metals

Concept: The chemical reactivity of two alkaline earth metals is compared.

Materials: 40 mL of $6M$ hydrochloric acid (HCl), two 50-mL glass beakers, overhead projector, forceps, 20 cm of magnesium (Mg) ribbon, 1 g of calcium (Ca).

Procedure: 1. Pour 20 mL of hydrochloric acid into each of the two beakers. 2. Place the beakers on the overhead projector. 3. Coil the magnesium ribbon and drop it into one beaker and the calcium into the other. 4. Compare the rate of dissolving and hydrogen production in the two beakers. Point out the relationship between calcium and magnesium on the periodic table. Both are alkaline earth metals, one period apart.

Audiovisual Resources

Carbon and Its Compounds (F) Coronet, 1971, 16 min. (Use with Section 12·12.) Shows the various forms of carbon and discusses bonding, carbon compounds, and radiocarbon dating.

Chemical Families (F, V) Chem Study, 1962, 22 min. (Use with Section 12·1.) Demonstrates how chemical similarities among elements led to their classification into chemical families.

Chemistry: The Periodic Table and Periodicity (F, V) Coronet, 1983, 23 min. (Use with Sections 12·3, 12·4, 12·5, 12·6, 12·7, and 12·8.) Presents a comprehensive review of the principles of periodicity.

Dust of Life (F, V) Films Inc., 1976, 30 min. (Use with Section 12·12.) Describes carbon in its elemental and combined forms.

Ionization Energy (F, V) Chem Study, 1962, 22 min. (Use with Section 12·5.) Demonstrates photoionization and electron bombardment methods of measuring ionization energy and explains the relationship of ionization energy to chemical reactivity.

Metals and Nonmetals (F) Coronet, 1964, 13 min. (Use with Section 12·8.) Describes the relationship between the properties of metals and nonmetals and their tendency to lose or gain electrons.

The Periodic Table (F, V) Media Guild, 1981, 24 min. (Use with Sections 12·1, 12·2, and 12·3.) Presents the history, terminology, and structure of the periodic table and explains the relationship between electron configurations and periodicity.

Vanadium—A Transition Element (F, V) Chem Study, 1962, 22 min. (Use with Section 12·16.) Illustrates the different oxidation states of vanadium, provides correlation with electronic structure, and shows complex ion formation.

Beyond the Text

A Periodic Table of the Future

Mendeleev's periodic table has stood the test of time. The new elements that have been discovered since he first designed the table fit into the chemical families that he outlined. What might the periodic table look like in the future?

First, there will be more elements. All the elements after uranium are synthetic. New elements are created in linear accelerators by bombarding other nuclei with high-energy particles. Scientists expect to continue to create more elements. They also expect that these elements will fit into the families in the periodic table. The element with atomic number 118, for example, will be a noble gas. Elements 122–153 would be a separate group, as the rare earth metals are separate. It is not likely that all these heavy elements will be made because they are extremely unstable. Some of the elements between numbers 108 and 118, however, are expected to be stable enough to study in the laboratory.

Second, the names and symbols of the new elements may have a new form. The naming of the synthetic elements has caused considerable controversy. It is difficult to establish who really discovered a new element because scientists throughout the world are doing similar accelerator experiments. For example, both American and Russian scientists have claimed element 104. The Americans call it rutherfordium, the Russians kurchatovium.

The International Union of Pure and Applied Chemistry (IUPAC) is the ultimate authority regarding naming of chemical elements and compounds. They have established a system of naming new elements that avoids such disputes. This system is based on the numerical roots shown in Table 12·1. The element is named by combining the three roots that "spell out" its atomic number and then ending the name with "-ium". For example, element 104 is un-nil-quad-ium; element 106 is un-nil-hex-ium, and so on. The symbol for an element named in this way has three letters, the first letter of each of the roots in its name. The symbol for unnilquadium is Unq; unnilhexium is Unh. Some chemists have even suggested using this system to rename all the elements.

Third, the Arabic numbers and Roman letters that label groups and subgroups in the periodic table will probably change. If you look at several periodic tables printed at different times in different places, you may see that A and B are used differently. A number of suggestions have been made to clear up this confusion. The American Chemical Society recommends elminating A and B. Instead, the subgroups would be marked in a way that reflects electron configurations. Their suggested format is shown in Figure 12·5.

Tetraethyl Lead: The Poison of Cities

The last member of the carbon family of elements is lead. Lead is one of the heavy metals having a density at least eleven times that of water. Most heavy metals are toxic to humans although small amounts of them may be necessary for life. Lead has not been shown to be essential to life, but it is certainly toxic. It affects the central nervous system causing headaches, dizziness, and insomnia. In higher doses it can cause hallucinations and death. In children lead poisoning can cause mental retardation. Birth defects may also result from exposure to lead. Lead poisoning can occur when a source of lead is inhaled or swallowed.

The major use of lead is in automobile batteries (see Chapter 21). It is also used to make tetraethyl lead. This very poisonous compound is added to gasoline to improve its burning qualities. Gasoline consists of a mixture of hydrocarbons. Some hydrocarbons, like iso-öctane, burn smoothly in a car engine. Others burn explosively causing "engine knock." The octane rating of gasoline is a measure of how well a particular mixture will burn in an engine. Adding a few milliliters of tetraethyl lead to a gallon of gasoline will increase its octane rating considerably. This change also makes the engine more efficient so that it uses less gasoline.

The lead in tetraethyl lead will foul the engine unless it is removed. Chemicals are added to the gasoline to ensure that the lead leaves the engine in the exhaust. Because of this, the combustion of leaded gasoline by cars, trucks, and buses accounts for 98% of the lead emitted to the atmosphere. The lead concentration in the air of large

citiies is 20 times that of rural areas and 2000 times that of the mid-Pacific Ocean area.

Because of concern about lead pollution, unleaded gasoline was developed in the mid-1970s. Over a four-year period, the amount of lead used in gasoline in the United States decreased from 212 000 tons per year to 96 000 tons. At the same time, the amount of lead detected in blood tests of people dropped 37%. This drop was attributed to the decreased use of leaded gasoline.

Unfortunately, car engines do not operate as efficiently using unleaded gasoline. This means that oil supplies will be consumed more quickly if all vehicles use unleaded gasoline. In addition, if more gasoline is burned, larger volumes of other pollutants will enter the atmosphere. Finally, unleaded gas is more expensive to produce. More efficient engines, catalytic exhaust systems to reduce emissions, and other antiknock agents are being developed to help solve the problem of lead pollution.

Answers to End of Chapter Questions and Problems

Practice Questions and Problems

7. Mendeleev arranged his periodic table by columns of elements with similar properties listed in order of increasing atomic weight. The modern periodic table has horizontal rows in order of increasing atomic number, and columns of elements with similar properties.

8. A periodic repetition of the physical and chemical properties of the elements.

9. A period is a horizontal row. A group is a vertical column.

10. Representative elements: Groups 1A–7A, Group 0. Transition elements: Groups 1B–8B. Inner transition elements: a separate section between Groups 3B and 4B.

11. Na, Mg, Cl

12. An element's outer electron configuration places it in a particular column of the periodic table.

13. s block: Groups 1A and 2A. p block: Groups 3A through 7A and 0. d block: transition metals. f block: inner transition metals.

14. a. $1s^2 2s^2 2p^5$ **b.** $1s^2 2s^2 2p^6 3s^2 3p^6 3d^{10} 4s^2$ **c.** $1s^2 2s^2 2p^6 3s^2 3p^1$ **d.** $1s^2 2s^2 2p^6 3s^2 3p^6 3d^{10} 4s^2 4p^6 4d^{10} 5s^2 5p^2$

15. a. H, Li, Na, K, Rb, Cs, Fr **b.** O, S, Se, Te, Po **c.** Zn, Cd, Hg

16. Sodium, aluminum, sulfur, chlorine; periodic trend.

17. a. sodium **b.** strontium **c.** germanium **d.** selenium

18. The energy needed to remove an electron from a gaseous atom.

19. Nonmetals. Nuclear charge is increasing and the shielding effect is the same, creating a greater electron attraction.

20. a. boron **b.** magnesium **c.** aluminum

21. a. Sr, Mg, Be **b.** Cs, Ba, Bi **c.** Na, Al, S

22. No. It already has full outermost orbitals.

23. a. fluorine **b.** nitrogen **c.** magnesium **d.** arsenic

24. Helium: balloons. Helium and neon: deep-sea diving. Neon, argon, krypton, and xenon: flashbulbs and aluminum welding.

25. To prevent contact with oxygen in the air; to prevent contact with water.

26. It reacts with oxygen in the air to form a thin protective coating of aluminum oxide that resists further oxidation.

27. Diamond and graphite.

28. Nitrogen fixation carried out in the roots of legumes.

29. White and red forms; white form is more reactive.

30. Oxygen: steel production, welding. Sulfur: sulfuric acid, vulcanization. Selenium: photoelectric cells, photographic exposure meters.

31. Chlorine: yellow-green gas. Bromine: dark red liquid. Iodine: purple-black crystalline solid.

32. $2H_2 + O_2 \rightarrow 2H_2O + heat$

33. Copper, silver, and gold are the best electrical conductors. Copper is the cheapest.

Mastery Questions and Problems

34. The radii decrease and the ionization energies increase. The increase in the number of protons creates a stronger electrostatic force.

35. Mg^{2+} has more protons in its nucleus. The electron attraction is therefore greater.

36. Zinc has more protons than calcium, attracting the $4s$ electrons more.

37. a. potassium, K **b.** aluminum, Al **c.** sulfur, S **d.** barium, Ba

38. a. Li, Na, K, Rb, Cs, Fr
b. Be, Mg, Ca, Sr, Ba, Ra
c. F, Cl, Br, I, At

39. Scandium, Sc, $(Ar) 3d^1 4s^2$. Titanium, Ti, $(Ar) 3d^2 4s^2$. Vanadium, V, $(Ar) 3d^3 4s^2$. Chromium, Cr, $(Ar) 3d^5 4s^1$. Manganese, Mn, $(Ar) 3d^5 4s^2$. Iron, Fe, $(Ar) 3d^6 4s^2$. Cobalt, Co, $(Ar) 3d^7 4s^2$. Nickel, Ni, $(Ar) 3d^8 4s^2$. Copper, Cu $(Ar) 3d^{10} 4s^1$. Zinc, Zn, $(Ar) 3d^{10} 4s^2$.

40. Representative elements, 43%; transition metals, 30%; inner transition metals, 27%.

41. $4s$ electrons; $1s$ electrons.

Review Questions and Problems

42. $P_{CO_2} = 1.23$ atm; $P_{N_2} = 0.880$ atm

43. a. $2Ag + S \rightarrow Ag_2S$
b. $Na_2SO_4 + Ba(OH)_2 \rightarrow BaSO_4 + 2NaOH$
c. $Zn + 2HNO_3 \rightarrow Zn(NO_3)_2 + H_2$
d. $2H_2O + 2SO_2 + O_2 \rightarrow 2H_2SO_4$

44. 69.9 g Fe

45. a. Li_2SO_4 **b.** $Zn_3(PO_4)_2$ **c.** $KMnO_4$ **d.** $SrCO_3$

46. 7.60 L

Challenging Questions and Problems

47. The radius of the ions decreases from S^{2-}, Cl^-, Ar, K^+, Ca^{2+}, to Sc^{3+} as the number of protons increases. The radius decreases from O^{2-}, F^-, Ne, Na^+, Mg^{2+}, to Al^{3+} for the same reason.

48. Ar to K, Co to Ni, Th to Pa, U to Np, Pu to Am, possibly from Cm to Bk, and Md to No. The proton to neutron ratio required for the stability of the atom varies for different elements. It depends on the proton–neutron organization of that atom.

49. The table shows gradually increasing atomic masses and decreasing ionization potentials for these elements. All need two atoms of chlorine and one atom of oxygen for compounds.

12 Chemical Periodicity

Chapter Preview

During the nineteenth century, chemists began to categorize the elements according to similarities in their physical and chemical properties. The end result of these studies was the modern periodic table. In this chapter you will learn how the periodic table is organized and its relationship to the atomic structure and properties of the elements.

12·1   The Development of the Periodic Table

Figure 12·1
These elements exhibit widely different chemical and physical properties. Keeping track of these properties would be quite difficult without the periodic table. It is our tool for understanding the periodicity of the elements.

About 70 elements had been described by the mid-1800s, but no common feature that would relate them had been found. Dmitri Mendeleev (1834–1907), a Russian chemist, had more success than most. Mendeleev listed the elements in several vertical columns in order of increasing atomic mass. He noticed a regular (periodic) recurrence of their physical and chemical properties. This led him to arrange the columns so that elements with the most similar properties were side by side. Mendeleev

Figure 12·2
Mendeleev designed his periodic table by grouping elements with similar properties in rows, and by ordering the rows according to the atomic masses.

			Ti=50	Zr=90	?=180.
			V=51	Nb=94	Ta=182.
			Cr=52	Mo=96	W=186.
			Mn=55	Rh=104,4	Pt=197,4
			Fe=56	Ru=104,4	Ir=198.
			Ni=Co=59	Pl=106,6,	Os=199.
H=1			Cu=63,4	Ag=108	Hg=200.
	Be=9,4	Mg=24	Zn=65,2	Cd=112	
	B=11	Al=27,4	?=68	Ur=116	Au=197?
	C=12	Si=28	?=70	Sn=118	
	N=14	P=31	As=75	Sb=122	Bi=210
	O=16	S=32	Se=79,4	Te=128?	
	F=19	Cl=35,5	Br=80	I=127	
Li=7	Na=23	K=39	Rb=85,4	Cs=133	Tl=204
		Ca=40	Sr=87,6	Ba=137	Pb=207.
		?=45	Ce=92		
		?Er=56	La=94		
		?Yt=60	Di=95		
		?In=75,6	Th=118?		

The periodic table organizes the chemical elements according to their properties.

thus constructed the first periodic table. This is an arrangement of the elements according to similarities in their properties. Numerous blank spaces had to be left in the table because there were no known elements with the appropriate properties (Figure 12·2).

Mendeleev noted the properties of the elements adjacent to the blank spaces. Then he and others were able to predict the physical and chemical properties of the missing elements. Eventually these missing elements were discovered and found to have properties similar to those predicted.

In 1913 Henry Moseley (1887–1915), a young British physicist, determined the nuclear charge, also called the atomic number, of the atoms of the elements. Moseley arranged the elements in a table by order of atomic number. This is the way that periodic tables are arranged today.

12·A Mendeleev and Moseley: Building on Other's Work

Dmitri Mendeleev's periodic table was the triumph of an outstanding career in chemistry. As a professor at the University of St. Petersburg, Mendeleev found no textbook that met the needs of his class. He decided to write a book that emphasized the similarities in the chemical properties of elements. Investigating the elements, Mendeleev wrote their names and characteristics on cards. Then he more or less played solitaire, arranging the elements into groups. Years of work led to his periodic law: Elements arranged according to their atomic masses present a clear periodicity of properties.

Figure 12·3
Mendeleev consolidated and interpreted the findings of many other chemists. He then used his periodic theory to predict the existence and properties of elements which had not yet been discovered.

Mendeleev's work was made possible by the Karlsruhe Conference held in Germany in 1860. This scientific meeting was held to standardize the atomic and molecular masses that were being used by chemists throughout the world. Once all masses were calculated by a common standard, Mendeleev was able to see the relationship among the elements. Using the experimental results of many chemists, Mendeleev formulated the periodic law.

This process of predicting a general theory from known details is called inductive reasoning. The opposite, predicting details from a known general theory, is called deductive reasoning. If general laws are known, the results can be reliably predicted. Inductive reasoning has more risk of error. It also has greater potential, however, for leading to a significant breakthrough. Mendeleev used inductive reasoning to build the periodic table. Then he used deductive reasoning to predict the properties of elements still unknown. When gallium was discovered in 1875, Mendeleev insisted that its discoverer recalculate its density. The experimental value did not agree with Mendeleev's prediction. To the astonishment of the scientific world, the recalculation proved that Mendeleev was right!

One scientist who built on Mendeleev's theory was Henry Moseley. If you look closely at the periodic table, you will find several places where the elements are not in order according to atomic mass. Moseley's work proved that the elements should be arranged by atomic number instead. Like Mendeleev, he predicted several missing elements which were later found. Unfortunately for science, Moseley was killed in World War I when he was only 28 years old. As a result of Moseley's death, the British government no longer assigns scientists to combat duty in time of war.

12·2 The Modern Periodic Table

The most commonly used form of the modern periodic table, sometimes called the long form, is shown in Figure 12·4 on the next page. In this table the elements are arranged in seven horizontal rows in order of increasing atomic number. Each element is identified by its symbol placed in a block. The atomic number of the element is shown above the symbol. The atomic mass and the name of the element are shown below the symbol. The colored dot in the upper right corner indicates the physical state of the element at 25°C.

The horizontal rows of the periodic table are called **periods.** There are seven periods. The vertical columns are called groups, or families. Each group is identified by a numeral and the letter A or B. Groups 1A through 7A and Group 0 make up the *representative elements*. They exhibit a wide variety of both physical and chemical properties. The elements in any group of the periodic table have similar physical and chemical properties. The properties of the elements in the periods change from group to group. The sequence of change is the same, however, in

Horizontal rows = periods.
Vertical columns = groups or families.

Elements within a group have similar properties.

Figure 12·4 **Periodic Table of the Elements**

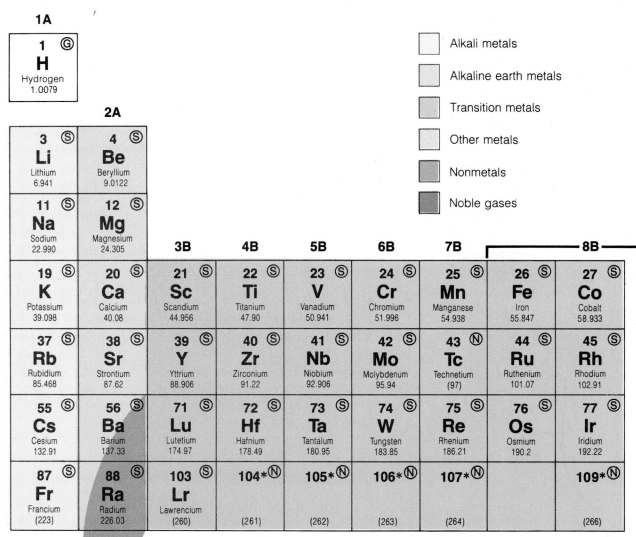

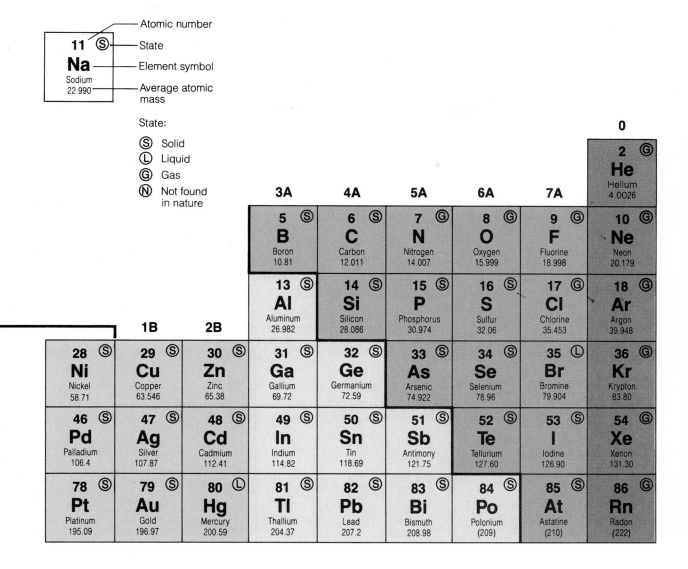

State:
ⓈSolid
ⓁLiquid
ⓖGas
ⓃNot found in nature

all the periods. Because of this situation, we have the **periodic law:** *When the elements are arranged in order of increasing atomic number, there is a periodic pattern in their physical and chemical properties.* Without the periodic table, learning and remembering the chemical and physical properties of over 100 individual elements would be a formidable task. Instead, you need only learn the general behavior and trends within the major groups to have a useful working knowledge of most of the elements.

12·3 Electron Configurations and Periodicity

Of the three subatomic particles, the electron plays the greatest part in determining the physical and chemical properties of an element. The arrangement of elements in the table depends on these properties. Thus there should be some relationship between the electron configuration of elements and their arrangement in the table. Elements can be classified into four different categories according to their electron configuration.

The properties of an element are related to the element's electron configuration.

1. The noble gases *are elements in which the outermost s and p sublevels are filled.* The noble gases belong to Group 0. The elements in this group are sometimes called the *inert gases* because they do not participate in many chemical reactions. The electron configurations for the first four noble gas elements are shown below. These elements have filled outermost *s* and *p* sublevels.

Helium	$1s^2$
Neon	$1s^2\, 2s^2\, 2p^6$
Argon	$1s^2\, 2s^2\, 2p^6\, 3s^2\, 3p^6$
Krypton	$1s^2\, 2s^2\, 2p^6\, 3s^2\, 3p^6\, 3d^{10}\, 4s^2\, 4p^6$

2. The representative elements *are elements whose outermost s or p sublevels are only partially filled.* The representative elements are usually called the Group A elements. They may also include the noble gases. For any representative element the group number is equal to the number of electrons in the outermost occupied energy level. For example, the elements in Group 1A (lithium, sodium, potassium, rubidium, and cesium) have one electron in the outermost energy level.

Lithium	$1s^2\, 2s^1$
Sodium	$1s^2\, 2s^2\, 2p^6\, 3s^1$
Potassium	$1s^2\, 2s^2\, 2p^6\, 3s^2\, 3p^6\, 4s^1$

Carbon, silicon, and germanium, in Group 4A, have four electrons in the outermost energy level.

Carbon	$1s^2\, 2s^2\, 2p^2$
Silicon	$1s^2\, 2s^2\, 2p^6\, 3s^2\, 3p^2$
Germanium	$1s^2\, 2s^2\, 2p^6\, 3s^2\, 3p^6\, 3d^{10}\, 4s^2\, 4p^2$

The groups of the periodic table are groups of elements which have similar electron configurations.

3. The transition metals *are elements whose outermost s sublevel and the nearby d sublevel contain electrons.* The transition elements are called the Group B elements. They are characterized by having electrons added to the *d* orbitals.

4. The inner transition metals *are elements whose outermost s sublevel and the nearby f sublevel generally contain electrons.* The inner transition metals are characterized by the filling of *f* orbitals.

If we consider both the electron configurations and the positions of elements in the periodic table, another pattern emerges. The periodic table may be divided into sections, or blocks, that correspond to the sublevels that are filled with electrons (Figure 12·5).

The *s* block is the part of the periodic table that contains the elements with s^1 and s^2 electron configurations. It is composed of the elements in Groups 1A and 2A and the noble gas helium.

The *p* block is composed of elements in Groups 3A, 4A, 5A, 6A, 7A, and 0 with the exception of helium.

The transition metals belong to the *d* block, and the inner transition metals belong to the *f* block.

The electron configurations of elements can be determined by using the periodic table in Figure 12·5. Simply read the periodic table like a book from left to right and top to bottom until the element of interest is

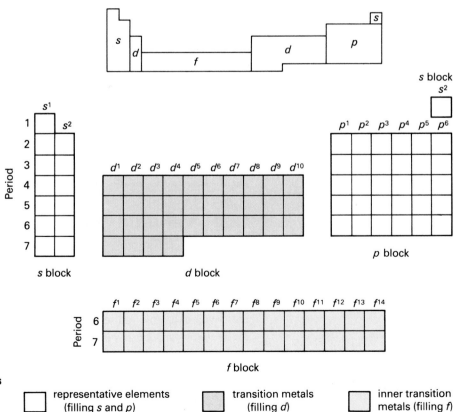

Figure 12·5
This block diagram identifies groups of elements according to the sublevels that are filled with electrons.

representative elements (filling *s* and *p*)

transition metals (filling *d*)

inner transition metals (filling *f*)

reached. Each period number on the periodic table corresponds to the principal energy level. The number of electrons in a partially filled sublevel is determined by counting over to the element, starting at the left side of the sublevel. For the transition elements, electrons are added to a *d* sublevel with a principal energy level that is one less than the period number. For the inner transition metals, the principal energy level is two less than the period number.

Example 1

Use the periodic table in Figure 12·5 to write the electron configuration of these elements.   **a.** nitrogen   **b.** nickel   **c.** iodine

Solution

a. Nitrogen has seven electrons. From the periodic table in Figure 12·5 the first period is $1s^2$, and the second period is $2s^2 2p^3$. There are three electrons in the $2p$ sublevel because nitrogen is the third element in the $2p$ block.

b. Nickel has 28 electrons. From Figure 12·5 the first three periods are $1s^2 2s^2 2p^6 3s^2 3p^6$. Next is $4s^2$ and finally $3d^8$. Remember that the principal energy level number for the d block is always one less than the period number. The complete configuration is $1s^2 2s^2 2p^6 3s^2 3p^6 4s^2 3d^8$.

c. Iodine has 53 electrons. Using Figure 12·5 we find the electron configuration to be $1s^2 2s^2 2p^6 3s^2 3p^6 3d^{10} 4s^2 4p^6 4d^{10} 5s^2 5p^5$.

Problems

1. Use Figure 12·5 to write the electron configuration for these elements.   **a.** boron   **b.** magnesium   **c.** vanadium   **d.** strontium

2. Write the electron configuration of these elements.   **a.** the inert gas in period 3   **b.** the element in Group 4A, period 4   **c.** the element in Group 2A, period 6

1. a. $1s^2 2s^2 2p^1$
  b. $1s^2 2s^2 2p^6 3s^2$
  c. $1s^2 2s^2 2p^6 3s^2 3p^6 3d^3$
   $4s^2$
  d. $1s^2 2s^2 2p^6 3s^2 3p^6 3d^{10}$
   $4s^2 4p^6 5s^2$
2. a. Ar: $1s^2 2s^2 2p^6 3s^2 3p^6$
  b. Ge: $1s^2 2s^2 2p^6 3s^2 3p^6$
   $3d^{10} 4s^2 4p^2$
  c. Ba: $1s^2 2s^2 2p^6 3s^2 3p^6$
   $3d^{10} 4s^2 4p^6 4d^{10} 5s^2 5p^6$
   $6s^2$

12·4   Periodic Trends in Atomic Size

We know from the quantum mechanical model that an atom does not have a sharply defined boundary to set the limit of its size. Therefore the radius of an atom cannot be measured directly. There are, however, several ways to estimate the relative sizes of atoms. The one we will use is the covalent atomic radius. *The **covalent atomic radius** is half of the distance between the nuclei of two atoms in a homonuclear diatomic molecule.* For example, the separation between the nuclei in the bromine molecule (Br_2) is 22.8 nm. Thus a value of 11.4 nm (22.8 ÷ 2) is assigned as the radius of the bromine atom. Figure 12·6 shows atomic radii for most of the representative elements.

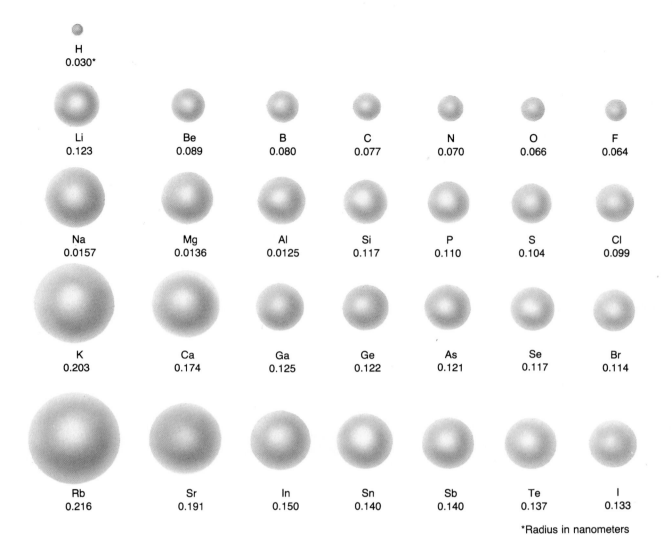

H 0.030*						
Li 0.123	Be 0.089	B 0.080	C 0.077	N 0.070	O 0.066	F 0.064
Na 0.0157	Mg 0.0136	Al 0.0125	Si 0.117	P 0.110	S 0.104	Cl 0.099
K 0.203	Ca 0.174	Ga 0.125	Ge 0.122	As 0.121	Se 0.117	Br 0.114
Rb 0.216	Sr 0.191	In 0.150	Sn 0.140	Sb 0.140	Te 0.137	I 0.133

*Radius in nanometers

Figure 12·6
The atomic radii of the representative elements are given here in nanometers. Note that the radii decrease as you read across, but they increase as you read down.

Atomic size decreases from left to right in a period and increases down a group.

Group trends. Atomic size generally increases as we move down a group of the periodic table. As we descend, electrons are added to successively higher principal energy levels, and the nuclear charge increases. The outermost orbital is larger as we move downward. The shielding also increases with the additional number of occupied orbitals between the outermost orbital and the nucleus. These two effects decrease the pull of the nucleus on the outermost electrons. The vertical columns in Figure 12·6 show how atomic size increases as we go down a group.

Periodic trends. Atomic size generally decreases as we move from left to right across a period. As we go across a period we remain in the same principal energy level. Each element has one proton and one electron more than the preceding element. The electrons are being added to the same principal energy level. The effect of the increasing nuclear charge on the outermost electrons is to pull them closer to the nucleus. Atomic size therefore decreases. If a plot is made of atomic radii versus

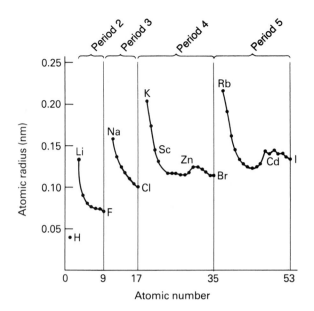

Figure 12·7
This plot of atomic radii versus atomic number shows a periodic variation.

atomic numbers, a periodic trend becomes obvious (Figure 12·7). The trend is less pronounced in periods where there are more electrons in the occupied principal energy levels between the nucleus and the outermost electrons. This is because these inner electrons help shield the outermost electrons and the nucleus from each other. In any period the number of electrons between the nucleus and the outermost electrons is the same for all the elements. Consequently, the *shielding effect* of these electrons on the nucleus is constant within a period.

3. F has a smaller atomic radius than O because F has one more nuclear charge. F has a smaller radius than Cl because F has eight fewer electrons.

Problem

3. Explain why fluorine has a smaller atomic radius than both oxygen and chlorine.

12·5 Periodic Trends in Ionization Energy

When an atom gains or loses an electron it forms an ion. *The energy to remove an electron from a gaseous atom is the* **ionization energy.** Removing one electron results in the formation of a positive ion with a 1+ charge.

$$Na(g) \longrightarrow Na^+(g) + e^-$$

The ionization energy is a measure of the ease with which an electron can be removed from a gaseous atom or ion.

The energy required to remove this first outermost electron is called the first ionization energy. To remove the outermost electron from the gaseous 1+ ion requires an amount of energy called the second ionization energy, and so forth. Table 12·1 gives the first three ionization energies of the first 20 elements.

The ionization energy is the energy required to remove a *single* electron from an atom. The amount of energy to do this is very small. A more realistic quantity is the amount of energy required to ionize a mole of atoms simultaneously. Therefore the unit used is kilojoules per mole.

A useful generalization is that the noble gas structure is particularly stable and therefore difficult to "break". As electrons are removed from an atom one by one there is a steady rise in ionization energy until the structure of a noble gas is reached. Then there is a dramatic rise in ionization energy.

Table 12·1	Ionization Energies of the First 20 Elements (in kilojoules per mole)		
Symbol of element	Ionization Energy (kJ/mol)		
	First	Second	Third
H	1 312		
He (noble gas)	2 371	5 247	
Li	520	7 297	11 810
Be	900	1 757	14 840
B	800	2 430	3 659
C	1 086	2 352	4 619
N	1 402	2 857	4 577
O	1 314	3 391	5 301
F	1 681	3 375	6 045
Ne (noble gas)	2 080	3 963	6 276
Na	495.8	4 565	6 912
Mg	737.6	1 450	7 732
Al	577.4	1 816	2 744
Si	786.2	1 577	3 229
P	1 012	1 896	2 910
S	999.6	2 260	3 380
Cl	1 255	2 297	3 850
Ar (noble gas)	1 520	2 665	3 947
K	418.8	3 069	4 600
Ca	589.5	1 146	4 941

We can use the concept of ionization energy to explain how we were able to predict some of the ionic charges in Chapter 5. Look at the three Group 1A metals in Table 12·1. You will see a large increase in energy between the first and second ionization energies. It is relatively easy to remove one electron from a Group 1A metal to form an ion with a 1+ charge. It is very difficult, however, to remove an additional electron. For the three Group 2A metals, the large increase in ionization energy occurs between the second and third ionization energies. It is fairly easy to remove two electrons from a Group 2A metal (resulting in a 2+ ionic charge), but it is difficult to remove a third electron. We know that aluminum, in Group 3A, forms a 3+ ion. The large increase in ionization energy for aluminum occurs after the third electron is removed.

Groups trends. The data in Table 12·1 show that, in general, the first ionization energy decreases as we move down a group of the periodic table. The size of the atoms is increasing as we descend. Thus the outermost electron is farther from the nucleus. It should be more easily removed and therefore have a lower ionization energy.

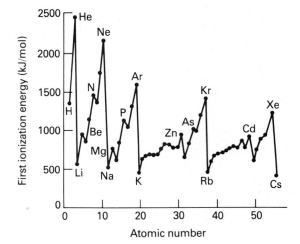

Figure 12·8
Here the first ionization energy is graphed versus the atomic number. Notice the ease with which Group 1A elements are ionized and the difficulty of ionizing noble gases.

The ionization energy increases with atomic number within a period and decreases with atomic number within a group.

Periodic trends. For the representative elements the first ionization energy generally increases as we move from left to right across a period. The nuclear charge is increasing, and the shielding effect is constant as we move across. A greater attraction of the nucleus for the electron therefore leads to the increase in ionization energy. The periodic trends of first ionization energies are shown in Figure 12·8.

12·6 Periodic Trends in Electron Affinity

The energy change that accompanies the addition of an electron to a gaseous atom is the **electron affinity** (EA). For example, energy is released when a fluorine atom gains an electron to become a negative ion.

$$F(g) + e^- \longrightarrow F^-(g)$$

The gain of an electron is the reverse of ionization. Because taking away an electron requires energy, gaining an electron releases energy. Electron affinities (Table 12·2) give an indication of the relative ease by which atoms gain an electron. The halogens as a group have the highest electron affinities. The accepted convention is to assign a negative sign to an electron affinity when energy is released upon gain of an electron. A positive sign is assigned when energy is absorbed.

A negative electron affinity means the gain of an electron is favorable because energy is released. Positive electron affinities are unfavorable.

$$F(g) + e^- \longrightarrow F^-(g) + 328 \text{ kJ} \qquad EA = -328 \text{ kJ/mol}$$

$$Be(g) + e^- + 240 \text{ kJ} \longrightarrow Be^-(g) \qquad EA = +240 \text{ kJ/mol}$$

It is experimentally very difficult to get reliable electron affinity values. In contrast to ionization energies, the trends in electron affinity values are less clear. Referring to Table 12·2, we see that electron affinity generally increases as we move from left to right across a period. This is because atoms become smaller and the nuclear charge increases. As we move down a group, electron affinities generally decrease with increasing atomic size.

Table 12·2	Electron Affinities for the Representative Elements (in kilojoules per mole)*						
1A	2A	3A	4A	5A	6A	7A
H −73						
Li −60	Be (+240)†	B −27	C −122	N +9	O −141	F −328
Na −53	Mg (+230)	Al −44	Si −134	P −72	S −200	Cl −348
K −48	Ca (+156)	Ga (−30)	Ge −120	As −77	Se −195	Br −325
Rb −47	Sr (+170)	In −30	Sn −121	Sb −101	Te −190	I −295
Cs −45	Ba (+52)	Tl −30	Pb −110	Bi −110	Po (−183)	At (−270)

*Negative values mean that the process $M + e^- \rightarrow M^-$ is exothermic, where M stands for any element.
†The values in parentheses are estimated.

4. They have large negative electron affinities because by gaining electrons they acquire noble gas configurations.

Problem

4. In general, would you expect nonmetals to have larger electron affinities than metals? Why or why not?

12·7   Periodic Trends in Ionic Size

The atoms of metallic elements have low ionization energies. They form positive ions easily. By contrast, the atoms of nonmetallic elements readily form negative ions. How does the gain or the loss of electrons affect the size of the ion produced? Positive ions (cations) are always *smaller* than the neutral atoms from which they are formed. This is because the loss of outer shell electrons results in increased attraction by the nucleus for the fewer remaining electrons. The radius of the Na^+ ion, 0.095 nm, is only about one-half that of the Na atom, 0.186 nm. In contrast, negative ions (anions) are always *larger* than the neutral atoms from which they are formed. This is because the effective nuclear attraction is less for an increased number of electrons. The additional electron also increases the repulsive forces between the electrons. The radius of the Cl^- ion, 0.181 nm, is about twice that of the Cl atom, 0.099 nm.

Cations are smaller and anions are larger than the atoms from which they are produced.

A periodic relationship among ionic radii of the elements is seen when the ions are arranged in the periodic table (Figure 12·9). Going from left to right, across a row, there is a gradual decrease in the size of positive ions. Then, beginning with Group 5, the negative ions (which are much larger in size) gradually decrease in size as you continue to move right. The atomic radius increases with both anions and cations as you go down each group.

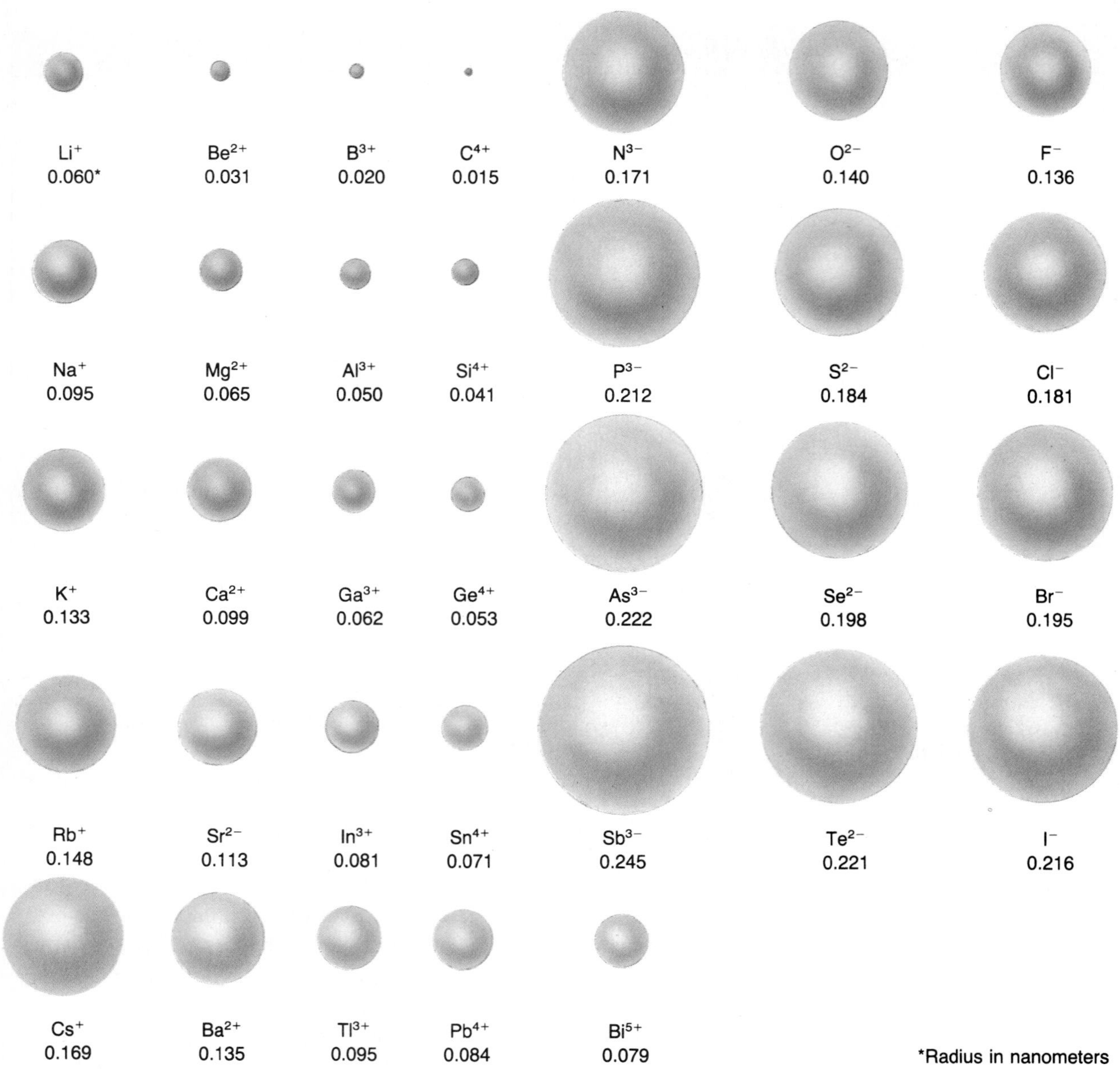
Li^{+} 0.060*
Be^{2+} 0.031
B^{3+} 0.020
C^{4+} 0.015
N^{3-} 0.171
O^{2-} 0.140
F^{-} 0.136
Na^{+} 0.095
Mg^{2+} 0.065
Al^{3+} 0.050
Si^{4+} 0.041
P^{3-} 0.212
S^{2-} 0.184
Cl^{-} 0.181
K^{+} 0.133
Ca^{2+} 0.099
Ga^{3+} 0.062
Ge^{4+} 0.053
As^{3-} 0.222
Se^{2-} 0.198
Br^{-} 0.195
Rb^{+} 0.148
Sr^{2-} 0.113
In^{3+} 0.081
Sn^{4+} 0.071
Sb^{3-} 0.245
Te^{2-} 0.221
I^{-} 0.216
Cs^{+} 0.169
Ba^{2+} 0.135
Tl^{3+} 0.095
Pb^{4+} 0.084
Bi^{5+} 0.079
*Radius in nanometers

Figure 12·9
The ionic radii shown here demonstrate a periodic variation in size. Why are ionic radii different from atomic radii (Figure 12·6)?
Ions have either more or fewer electrons than the atoms from which they form. An increased number of electrons are held more loosely forming a larger ion. A decreased number of electrons are held more tightly forming a smaller ion.

12·8 Periodic Trends in Electronegativity

The **electronegativity** *of an element is the tendency for an atom to attract electrons to itself when it is chemically combined with another element.* Electronegativities have been calculated for the elements. They are expressed in arbitrary units on the *Pauling electronegativity scale*. This scale is based on a number of factors including the electron affinity and ionization potential of the atoms.

The electronegativities, arranged in the form of the periodic table, are presented in Table 12·3. Note that the noble gases are omitted because they do not form many compounds. Otherwise, each element is assigned an electronegativity number. Cesium, the least electronegative

Table 12·3	Electronegativity Values for Atoms of Selected Elements					
H 2.1						
Li 1.0	Be 1.5	B 2.0	C 2.5	N 3.0	O 3.5	F 4.0
Na 0.9	Mg 1.2	Al 1.5	Si 1.8	P 2.1	S 2.5	Cl 3.0
K 0.8	Ca 1.0	Ga 1.6	Ge 1.8	As 2.0	Se 2.4	Br 2.8

element is 0.7 and fluorine, the most electronegative element is 4.0. When fluorine is chemically bonded to any other element, it attracts the shared electrons, or it tends to form a negative ion. In contrast, cesium with the lowest electronegativity has the least tendency to attract electrons. It loses the electron tug-of-war and forms a positive ion.

As we go across a period from left to right, the electronegativity of the representative elements *increases*. The metallic elements at the far left of the periodic table have low electronegativities. By contrast, the nonmetallic elements at the far right (excluding the noble gases) have high electronegativities. Ordinarily, electronegativity decreases as we move down a given group. The trends in electronegativities among the transition metals are not so regular. As you will see in Chapters 13 and 14, electronegativity values help us to predict the type of bonding that can exist between atoms in compounds.

Electronegativity increases with atomic number within a period and decreases with atomic number within a group.

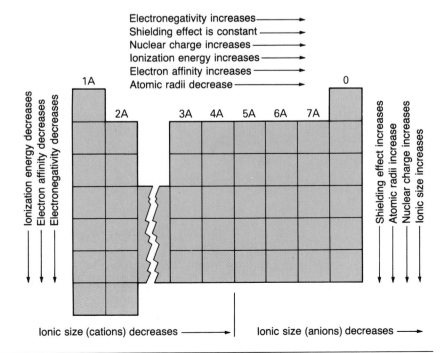

Figure 12·10
Periodic properties are those that vary as you move across and down the periodic table. These properties include the atomic radius, electron affinity, ionization energy, nuclear charge, shielding effect, and electronegativity of the elements.

We have explained five periodic trends by looking at variations in atomic structure. Figure 12·10 on the previous page summarizes the trends in atomic radii, ionization energy, electron affinity, ionic size, and electronegativity.

Problem

5. Which of these elements has a larger ionization energy?
   a. sodium or potassium   **b.** magnesium or phosphorus

12·B Technical Writing: Communicating Clearly

The job of a technical writer is to communicate complex ideas clearly. Most technical writing explains something. The explanation must be clear and brief without sacrificing detail or accuracy.

Technical writers may write instruction manuals or contracts that involve scientific or technical issues. They may also write magazine features on science and technology, press releases, sales presentations, or articles for professional journals or books. Almost every company employs writers to help its scientists and engineers communicate their work. This may be for the public or for others in their profession. Large companies often have publication divisions that employ many technical writers, editors, and illustrators. The semiconductor and aerospace industries and the government are major employers in this field.

Some companies try to hire writers who have degrees in the area about which they will be writing. Other companies prefer to have writers with English or journalism degrees. Many colleges are now offering courses in technical writing in response to the high demand for able writers. A person looking for a job as a technical writer should have a college degree in one of these fields. Like other writers, a technical writer must have good writing skills, an extensive vocabulary, and a strong knowledge of grammar and spelling. An interest in science and the ability to communicate with scientists and engineers are very important.

Figure 12·11
Technical writers should have a broad science background and strong English skills. Reference books are important tools for their work.

Noble gas is the preferred term, because inert implies *no* chemcial reactivity, and some of these gases do form compounds.

The noble gases rarely form compounds.

12·9 The Noble Gases

Helium, neon, argon, krypton, xenon, and radon are all Group 0 elements. The name, *rare gases,* was originally used to describe these elements because they occur in the atmosphere in very small amounts. Early chemists also called these elements *inert gases* because they rarely combine with other elements. In 1962, however, a Canadian chemist named

Figure 12·12

Underwater living quarters, such as the one shown, commonly have an artificial atmosphere consisting primarily of oxygen and a noble gas.

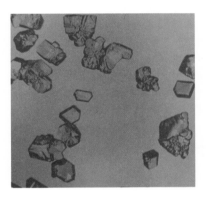

Figure 12·13

Xenon tetrafluoride is one of the few compounds that can be formed from a noble gas.

The alkali metals in Group 1A and the alkaline earth metals in Group 2A react with water to produce alkaline solutions.

Arabic: *al aqali* = the ashes.

Neil Bartlett prepared xenon tetrafluoride (XeF_4), a compound of xenon. Since that time, compounds of krypton and radon have also been prepared. Nevertheless, compared with all other elements, Group 0 elements are extremely unreactive. For this reason these elements are now called *noble gases*. This name emphasizes the tendency of these elements to exist as separate atoms rather than in combination with other atoms.

Despite their unreactivity, the noble gases have many uses. Helium is used to fill weather balloons. Although it is more dense than hydrogen, it is not explosive. Both helium and neon are used in artificial atmospheres such as those required in deep-sea diving. In a neon atmosphere, speech is less distorted than it is in a helium atmosphere. This is because the speed of sound is slower in neon than in helium. Neon, argon, krypton, and xenon are used to produce the inert atmospheres needed for photographic flashbulbs and aluminum welding.

12·10 The Alkali Metals and the Alkaline Earth Metals

The elements in Group 1A are the **alkali metals.** They have low densities, low melting points, and good electrical conductivity. They are soft enough to be cut with a knife. The freshly cut surface is shiny, but it quickly dulls on exposure to air. This is due to a rapid reaction with oxygen and moisture. These elements are not found in nature in the uncombined state. Many compounds of sodium and potassium were isolated from wood ash by early chemists. Each of the alkali metals reacts violently with cold water, producing hydrogen gas and a solution of the metal hydroxide (an alkali). The alkali metals react vigorously with water. Thus they should not be allowed to come into contact with your skin. In the stockroom they are usually stored under oil or kerosene to protect the metal from oxygen and moisture in the air.

a

b

Figure 12·14
a Freshly cut sodium is shiny, but it quickly reacts with oxygen in the air to become dull.
b Magnesium is present in asbestos, which is a fibrous form of the mineral serpentine. Asbestos was used as an insulation material until it was discovered that inhalation of its fibers causes lung cancer.

The elements in Group 2A are called **alkaline earth metals.** In their reaction with water they also produce alkaline solutions. They are extracted from the mineral ores that since early times have been called "earths." The alkaline earth metals are not found uncombined in nature, but they are less chemically reactive then the Group 1A metals. They need not be stored under oil. The alkaline earth metals are harder than the alkali metals. They have a gray-white luster but tarnish quickly in air with a thin oxide coating. The coating protects the metal, particularly beryllium and magnesium, from further oxidation. This allows alloys of these metals to be used as low-density structural materials.

12·11 The Aluminum Group

The elements in Group 3A include both metals and nonmetals. The nonmetallic solid boron at the top of the group is followed by four metallic elements: aluminum, gallium, indium, and thallium.

Aluminum is a mechanically strong metal of low density that is especially corrosion-resistant. Like magnesium in Group 2A, it reacts

Aluminum is the most common Group 3A element.

Figure 12·15
Aluminum is particularly useful in the construction of aircraft because it is lightweight and very strong. It also forms a protective coating that will not react with water.

Figure 12·16
Rubies are aluminum oxide in which a few of the aluminum ions are replaced by chromium ions.

rapidly with the oxygen in air. This reaction forms a thin, tough, protective coating of aluminum oxide. Aluminum, or its alloy with magnesium, is used widely as a lightweight structural material in aircraft production and in the manufacture of cookware. Because of its protective coating, aluminum does not react with water. Nevertheless, it will react rapidly with acids or bases, which dissolve the coat, liberating hydrogen.

Aluminum does not exist in the uncombined state in nature but is a major component of many rocks and minerals. Aluminum is commonly found as corundum (impure aluminum oxide). This very hard material is used as the abrasive in emery powder and grinding wheels. Gallium, indium, and thallium are quite rare and have few practical uses. One interesting use of gallium is in thermometers because of its extraordinarily wide liquid range. It has a melting point of 30°C and a boiling point of 1980°C.

12·12   The Carbon Group

■ Group 4A, the carbon group, contains important nonmetals, metalloids, and metals.

The elements in Group 4A continue the trend we saw in Group 3A. Carbon, at the top of the group, is a nonmetal. Silicon and germanium are metalloids with metallic and nonmetallic properties. Tin and lead are both metals.

Diamond and graphite are two forms of carbon. Diamond behaves like a typical nonmetal and is a nonconductor of electricity. Graphite has some of the properties of a metal and is a good conductor of electricity. Coke is a fairly pure form of carbon. Carbon-containing compounds, of which there are about 4 million, are called organic compounds. Organic compounds constitute the bulk of all living things.

Silicon, the second most abundant element of earth, occurs in nature in the combined state as sand and in rocks, soils, and clays. Silicon and germanium are semiconductors. Both substances are insulators at low temperatues. At high temperatures, however, they conduct electricity. These two elements when highly purified form the foundation of transistor technology. They are also used in photocells for solar power units.

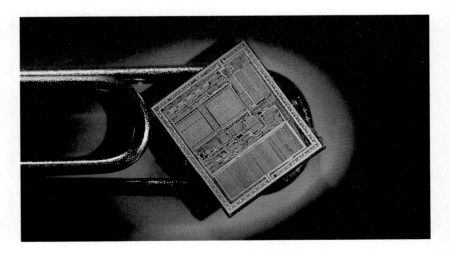

Figure 12·17
Semiconductors made of silicon are used in calculators and computers. Each chip may contain over a million transistors.

Many toxic substances can be absorbed through the skin. Avoid skin contact with chemicals whenever possible. Wash your hands thoroughly after handling chemicals, and never eat or drink in the laboratory.

Nitrogen is the most common Group 5A element.

Tin and lead are both typical metals. Tin is important in the manufacture of tinplate in which a thin coating of tin is applied to an iron can to prevent it from rusting. Plumber's solder is an alloy of tin and lead. Tetraethyl lead, an organic lead-containing compound, is the familiar antiknock additive in gasoline. It is highly toxic to humans. For this reason its use has been greatly decreased in recent years.

12·13 The Nitrogen Group

Another periodic trend, a change in physical state, is introduced with Group 5A. The first element, nitrogen, is a gas at room temperature. In descending order the next elements are phosphorus (a solid nonmetal) and arsenic and antimony, which are metalloids. The last element, bismuth, is a metal.

Nitrogen is essential to living organisms. Pairs of nitrogen-containing compounds called bases are the steps on the spiral staircase of double-stranded DNA (deoxyribonucleic acid). Proteins and enzymes are long chainlike molecules with carbon–nitrogen backbones. Although 80% of the air we breathe is nitrogen, we cannot use it to make these essential substances. Fortunately, bacteria that live in the root nodules of peas, beans, and other legumes can "fix" atmospheric nitrogen. Plants can use ammonia to synthesize proteins and other biologically important nitrogen-containing compounds.

Phosphorus is also essential to living organisms. It is present in the double strands of DNA, bones, and teeth. It is also part of ATP (adenosine triphosphate), which is the principal energy-storage molecule in living systems. Phosphorus occurs mainly in the form of phosphate rock. Pure phosphorus is prepared in a white form and a red form. The white form is very reactive. It is usually stored under water to prevent a reaction with oxygen from the air. Red phosphorus is a less active form used in the manufacture of matches.

Figure 12·18
The seeds of legumes are an excellent source of protein. Legumes are the only plants which do not depend on nitrogen in the soil.

Safety

Even the friction of cutting can ignite white phosphorus. Make a point of remembering which chemicals are toxic or flammable. Handle all chemicals with care.

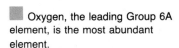 Oxygen, the leading Group 6A element, is the most abundant element.

Figure 12·20
Oxygen is present in combined form in silicate rocks and minerals. Those shown here (clockwise from the top) are feldspar ($KAlSi_3O_8$), talc ($Mg_3Si_4O_{10}(OH)_2$), biotite mica ($K_3AlSi_3O_{10}(OH)_2$), and jasper (primarily SiO_2).

Arsenic, antimony, and bismuth occur in nature in the form of sulfide ores. They are not essential to living organisms. Alloys containing antimony and bismuth are used in making metal type because they expand as they solidify.

12·14 The Oxygen Group

The Group 6A elements are oxygen, sulfur, selenium, tellurium, and polonium. Oxygen is a gas and thereby continues the periodic trend started by nitrogen in the previous group. Sulfur is a nonmetal that occurs free in nature as a brittle yellow solid. Selenium and tellurium are both solids. They are borderline between metals and nonmetals. Polonium, the last element in the group, is a radioactive metal that occurs only in trace quantities in radium-containing ores.

Oxygen is the most abundant element. It accounts for 20% by volume of the air we breathe, 60% by mass of the human body, and 50% by mass of the earth's crust. Most oxygen is combined in the silicate rocks of the earth's crust. It is produced by plants in photosynthesis. Oxygen gas is used in medicine, in the manufacture of steel (to remove impurities), and along with acetylene in oxyacetylene welding.

Sulfur occurs in the elemental state in large underground deposits. It is also a minor component of coal and petroleum. Sulfur is essential to living organisms where it is found mainly in disulfide bridges. These are the crosslinks that hold protein chains together. The major uses of sulfur are in the manufacture of sulfuric acid and in the vulcanization of rubber. Sulfuric acid is the most widely used industrial chemical.

Selenium is a semiconductor. It is a poor conductor of electricity in the dark, but its conductivity increases greatly in the light. Because of this property, selenium is used in photoelectric cells, in exposure meters for cameras, and in light-sensitive switches. The xerographic process of photocopying also depends on the photoconductivity of selenium.

Tellurium is one of the rarest elements. Its compounds are toxic, and the element itself plays no known role in living organisms.

12·15   The Halogens and Hydrogen

The **halogens** *are fluorine, chlorine, bromine, iodine, and astatine.* The halogens form a homogeneous family of nonmetals. The first two elements, fluorine and chlorine, are yellowish-green gases at room temperature and atmospheric pressure. They continue the periodic trend shown by nitrogen and oxygen. Bromine is a dark red liquid. Iodine is a purple-black crystalline solid with a metallic sheen. Tincture of iodine, a 3% solution of iodine in alcohol, was formerly widely used as an antiseptic. The last element, astatine, is an exceedingly rare radioactive solid that has not been well investigated.

The halogens do not exist in nature in the uncombined state, but their compounds are fairly abundant. These elements are named halogens because they are usually found as salts of the Group 1A or 2A metals. For example, the salts sodium chloride, sodium bromide, and sodium iodide are found in seawater and salt beds. Calcium fluoride is the mineral fluorspar. The free halogens are very reactive and must be handled with extreme caution. Nevertheless, compounds of fluorine, chlorine, and iodine are essential to our well-being and must be included in our diet. Fluorine, as fluoride ion, is beneficial in the formation and maintenance of healthy teeth. Chlorine, as chloride ion, is a major component of the blood and other body fluids. Iodine, as the iodide ion, is necessary to prevent goiter, an enlargement of the thyroid gland.

The halogens have many other uses in the home and in industry. A dilute solution of chlorine is used as a bleaching and disinfecting agent. Silver chloride and silver bromide are light-sensitive and are used to make photographic film. Fluorine is used in the manufacture of nonstick Teflon coatings that are applied to frying pans and other cookware.

Hydrogen is a group by itself. It is a reactive gas in that it forms an explosive mixture with oxygen. It also reacts violently with many other elements. Hydrogen is usually put at the top of Group 1A in the periodic table. It is not a metal, nor is it a good conductor of heat or electricity like the alkali metals. Like the alkali metals, however, hydrogen does react with the halogens. In some periodic tables hydrogen also appears at the top of Group 7A. This position has some validity because, like the halogens, hydrogen has one electron less than helium, the noble gas it precedes. Like the halogens, it reacts with the alkali metals. Thus hydrogen is unique.

12·16   The Transition Metals and Inner Transition Metals

The remainder of the elements are the transition metals and inner transition metals. Like the representative elements, most transition metals possess similar physical and chemical properties. They are therefore divided into groups. Starting with Group 3B on the left, they continue through 7B on the right. Group 7B is followed by three groups that together make up Group 8B. The last two groups are Groups 1B and 2B.

■ The halogens in Group 7A include two gases, a liquid, and two solids.

Greek: *halos* = salt; *gen* = born.

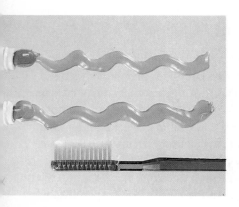

Figure 12·21
The fluoride ion is widely used in toothpastes to promote dental health.

Figure 12·22
Because of its high luster, metallic silver is used to plate mirrors.

The transition metals are the Group B elements, and the inner transition metals are the lanthanides and actinides.

Similarly, there are 14 inner transition metals in the sixth period of the periodic table. These elements, from cerium through lutetium, are called the *lanthanides*. The pattern repeats in the seventh-period elements. The elements thorium through lawrencium are also inner transition metals and are called the *actinides*.

The transition and inner transition elements are typical metals. They have a metallic luster and are very good conductors of electricity and heat. Tungsten, a hard brittle solid with a melting point of 3400°C, is used in light-bulb filaments. At the other end of the scale is mercury, with a melting point of −38°C; it is used in making thermometers. The excellent reflective qualities of silver (the high luster) make it the ideal coating for mirrors. The production of copper wire in enormous quantities attests to the high electrical conductivity of copper. Steels with widely different characteristics are made by adding small amounts of cobalt, copper, chromium, nickel, or vanadium to iron. Our bodies also need transition metals to function normally. Iron is required in the production of hemoglobin. Cobalt is part of vitamin B_{12} molecules. Both zinc and copper are necessary components of many enzymes.

The transition and inner transition metals vary greatly in their chemical reactivity. The elements scandium, yttrium, and lanthanum are similar to the Group 1A and 2A metals. They are easily oxidized on exposure to air and react with water to liberate hydrogen. In contrast, platinum and

Figure 12·23
Chemistry is an important tool for the study of nutrition. It is used to determine the presence and availability of various nutrients. Some important transition element nutrients for humans are iron, zinc, copper, manganese, cobalt, chromium, selenium, iodine, and molybdenum.

gold are extremely unreactive and resist oxidation. Most compounds of the transition and inner transition metals are colored and show multiple-formula combinations with other elements.

Problem

6. a. Ge, Germanium
b. Mg, Magnesium
c. Nb, Niobium
d. P, Phosphorus
e. Ti, Titanium
f. F, Fluorine

6. Give the symbol and name for the element that occupies each of the designated positions in the periodic table.
a. period 4, Group 4A
b. period 3, Group 2A
c. period 5, Group 5B
d. period 3, Group 5A
e. period 4, Group 4B
f. period 2, Group 7A

Figure 12·24
Scientists speculate that the universe began with a big bang. Galaxies and stars are matter that has gathered because of gravitational attraction.

12·C   Before the Elements: The Big Bang

The orderly structure of the elements, each with its unique number of protons and electrons, leads us to wonder how they were formed. We know that in our sun, hydrogen nuclei are fused together to give helium nuclei. Physicists create new heavier elements by smashing small particles into heavy nuclei in accelerators. It is reasonable to think that all nuclei are built-up of lighter nuclei in this way. But what was in the universe even before hydrogen nuclei?

Physicists theorize that the universe began with an explosion of undescribable power, the Big Bang. At the moment of this explosion the temperature was many billions of degrees. All matter was in the form of quarks (see Section 4·C).

Within 10^{-43} second, strange new particles formed that could change quarks into leptons. At 10^{-4} s after the Big Bang, quarks formed neutrons, protons, and hundreds of other types of particles. By 10^{-2}s after the Big Bang, the temperature had cooled to 10^{11} K.

The lightest nuclei began to form just three minutes after the Big Bang. The temperature then was still at least 70 times the temperature of our sun. Matter was in the form of a plasma, a sea of positive nuclei and negative electrons. It probably took 500 000 years for electrons and nuclei to cool enough to combine to form atoms!

The data that lead to these theories come largely from experiments done with particle accelerators. When very high-energy collisions take place in an accelerator, energy is transformed into strange new particles. It is reasonable to think that such particles must have existed after the tremendous energy release of the Big Bang.

Scientists cannot test these ideas by creating another Big Bang. Furthermore, the strange particles and events that are predicted by the Big Bang theory would be extraordinarily rare under normal conditions. Statistically, however, they should occur sometime. Experiments are under way to try to detect free quarks, the decay of protons, or other occurrences that would support this theory.

Key Terms

alkali metal	*12·10*	electronegativity	*12·8*
alkaline earth		halogen	*12·15*
metal	*12·10*	ionization energy	*12·5*
covalent atomic		noble gas	*12·3*
radius	*12·4*	period	*12·2*
electron affinity	*12·6*	periodic law	*12·2*

Chapter Summary

The periodic table organizes the elements into groups (vertical columns) and periods (horizontal rows) in order of increasing atomic number. Most of the elements in the periodic table are metals. The nonmetals are confined to a triangular area on the upper right-hand side of the table and are separated from the metals by a diagonal zigzag line. The table is constructed so that elements that have similar chemical properties are in the same group. The properties of any element are generally intermediate between those of its neighbors on either side in the same period and similar to those elements above and below it in the same group. The elements in Groups 1A through 7A are called the representative elements. They exhibit a wide range of both physical and chemical properties. The noble gases make up Group 0. They may be considered part of the representative elements. The elements in Groups 2A and 3A are interrupted in periods 4 and 5 by the transition metals and in periods 6 and 7 by the inner transition metals.

Elements that have similar properties also have similar electron configurations and are members of the same group. The atoms of the noble gas elements have their outermost *s* and *p* sublevels filled. The outermost *s* and *p* sublevels of the representative elements are only partially filled. The outermost *s* and nearby *d* sublevels of transition metals contain electrons. The outermost *s* and nearby *f* sublevels of inner transition metals contain electrons.

The regular changes in the electron configuration of the elements cause gradual changes in both the physical and the chemical properties of the elements within a group and within a period. Atomic radii generally decrease as we move from left to right in a given period of the periodic table because there is an increase in the nuclear charge while the number of inner electrons, and hence the shielding effect, remains constant. Atomic size generally increases within a given group because there are more occupied energy levels and an increased shielding effect as well as an increase in nuclear charge. The ionization energy, the energy required to remove an electron from an atom, generally increases as we move from left to right across a period. It decreases as we move down a group. Electron affinity is the ease with which an atom gains an electron. It increases as we move from left to right across a period and decreases as we move down a group. Electronegativity is the ability of a bonded atom to attract electrons to itself. It generally increases as we move from left to right across a period.

Practice Questions and Problems

7. What criterion did Mendeleev use in arranging his periodic table? What criterion was used in constructing the modern periodic table? *12·1*

8. What is the periodic law? *12·2*

9. How do the terms *group* and *period* relate to the periodic table? *12·2*

10. What are the representative elements, the transition elements, and the inner transition elements? *12·2*

11. Which of the following are representative elements: Na, Mg, Fe, Ni, Cl? *12·2*

12. How is an element's outer electron configuration related to its position in the periodic table? *12·3*

13. Which sections of the periodic table correspond to the various energy sublevels? *12·3*

14. Use Figure 12·5 to write the electron configuration of these atoms. *12·3*
  a. fluorine **b.** zinc **c.** aluminum **d.** tin

15. What are the symbols for all the elements that have the following outer configurations? *12·3*
  a. s^1 **b.** s^2p^4 **c.** s^2d^{10}

16. Arrange these elements in order of decreasing atomic size: sulfur, chlorine, aluminum, and sodium. Does your arrangement demonstrate a periodic or a group trend? *12·4*

17. Indicate which element in each of the following pairs has the greatest atomic radius. *12·4*
  a. sodium, lithium   **c.** carbon, germanium
  b. strontium, magnesium **d.** selenium, oxygen

18. What does the term *ionization energy* mean? *12·5*

19. In general, would you expect metals or nonmetals to have higher ionization energies? Why? *12·5*

20. Indicate which element in each of the following pairs has the greatest ionization energy. *12·5*
  a. lithium, boron   **c.** cesium, aluminum
  b. magnesium, strontium

21. Arrange the following elements in order of increasing ionization energy. *12·5*
  a. Be, Mg, Sr **b.** Bi, Cs, Ba **c.** Na, Al, S

22. Would you expect the noble gas neon to have a negative electron affinity? Explain your answer. *12·6*

23. In each of the following pairs, which element is the most electronegative? *12·8*
  a. chlorine, fluorine   **c.** magnesium, neon
  b. carbon, nitrogen   **d.** arsenic, calcium

24. Name three practical uses of various noble gas elements. *12·8*

25. Why are alkali metals stored under kerosene or mineral oil? Why must they be kept dry? *12·10*

26. Why is aluminum so corrosion resistant? *12·11*

27. Name two forms of pure carbon. *12·12*

28. What is the process by which plants convert atmospheric nitrogen gas into nitrogen-containing compounds? *12·13*

29. What are two forms of elemental phosphorus? How do they differ in reactivity with oxygen? *12·13*

30. Name at least one industrial use of oxygen, sulfur, and selenium. *12·14*

31. Give colors and physical states at STP of chlorine, bromine, and iodine. *12·15*

32. Write a balanced equation for the explosive reaction of hydrogen with oxygen. *12·15*

33. Suggest reasons why copper, silver, and gold are valued for the manufacture of electronic devices. Why is copper preferred to silver and gold for home wiring? *12·6*

Mastery Questions and Problems

34. How is the change in the radii of the atoms in the period from potassium through krypton related to the change in ionization energies in the same period? What causes this trend? *12·5*

35. The Mg^{2+} and Na^+ ions each have ten electrons surrounding the nucleus. Which ion would you expect to have the smaller radius? Why? *12·7*

36. Explain why it takes more energy to remove a $4s$ electron from zinc than calcium. *12·5*

37. Give the name and symbol for the element found at each of the following locations in the periodic table. *12·3*
  a. Group 1A, period 4   **c.** Group 6A, period 3
  b. Group 3A, period 3   **d.** Group 2A, period 6

38. Give the symbols for the elements in these groups. *12·15*
  a. alkali metals
  b. alkaline earth metals
  c. halogens

39. Give the names, symbols, and electron configurations for the ten first-row transition metals. *12·2*

40. Name the three major categories into which the elements are divided. What is the approximate percentage of elements in each category? *12·2*

41. For the element calcium, atomic number 20, which electrons experience the smallest effective nuclear charge? Which electrons experience the largest nuclear charge? *12·4*

Review Questions and Problems

42. A 2.00-L flask at 27°C contains 4.40 g of carbon dioxide and 2.00 g of nitrogen gas. What is the pressure, in atmospheres, of each of the two components?

43. Balance the following chemical equations.
  a. $Ag + S \longrightarrow Ag_2S$
  b. $Na_2SO_4 + Ba(OH)_2 \longrightarrow BaSO_4 + NaOH$
  c. $Zn + HNO_3 \longrightarrow Zn(NO_3) + H_2$
  d. $H_2O + SO_2 + O_2 \longrightarrow H_2SO_4$

44. The smelting of iron ore consists of heating the ore with carbon.

$$2Fe_2O_3 + 3C \longrightarrow 4Fe + 3CO_2$$

What mass of iron can be obtained from 100 g of the ore?

45. Write chemical formulas for the following compounds.
  a. lithium sulfate
  b. zinc phosphate
  c. potassium permanganate
  d. strontium carbonate

46. If a gas sample at 25°C occupies a volume of 2.93 L, what will be the volume at 500°C if the pressure is unchanged?

Challenging Questions and Problems

47. The ions S^{2-}, Cl^-, K^+, Ca^{2+}, Sc^{3+} have the same *total* number of electrons as the noble gas argon. How would you expect the radii of these ions to vary? Would you expect to see the same variation in the series O^{2-}, F^-, Na^+, Mg^{2+}, and Al^{3+}, in which each ion has the same total number of electrons as the noble gas neon? Why or why not?

48. The elements are arranged in the periodic table in order of increasing atomic number. We might logically expect that they would also be arranged in order of increasing atomic mass. For the most part this is true, but there are a number of exceptions. Can you find them? Can you explain them? To confirm your answer, see the article by F. H. Firsching in the June 1981 issue of the *Journal of Chemical Education*.

49. Using a handbook of chemistry, make a table for the Group 2A elements. Include densities, atomic masses, formulas of the chlorides and oxides, and first ionization potentials. Can you justify placing these elements in one group on the basis of these data?

Research Projects

1. How did the work of Jöns Berzelius lay the foundation for a periodic table of the elements? What other scientists were influenced by his work?

2. Design a three-dimensional periodic table.

3. Report on the discoveries of elements by Smithson Tennant and William Wollaston. How did they discover the composition of diamond?

4. What contributions did Glenn Seaborg make to the discovery of the actinide rare earth elements?

5. What are the current allowable levels of lead in gasoline? How has this changed in the last 20 years?

6. Report on selenium pollution and the use of selenium as a dietary supplement.

7. Design a method for detecting a toxic metal such as lead or selenium in the environment.

8. Read a research article in a technical journal. Make a diagram of how the contents are arranged and write a short summary of the article.

9. What other theories besides the Big Bang have been proposed to explain the origin of the universe?

Readings and References

Asimov, Isaac. *Building Blocks of the Universe.* New York: Abelard-Schuman, 1974.

Sandage, Allan. "Inventing the Beginning." *Science 84* (November 1984), pp. 111–113.

Tate, Cassandra. "American Dilemma of Jobs, Health in an Idaho Town." *Smithsonian* (September 1981), pp. 74–83.

Trefil, James S. "Closing in on Creation." *Smithsonian* (May 1983), pp. 32–42.

Waldrop, M. Mitchell. "Before the Beginning." *Science 84* (November 1984), pp. 44–51.

13 Ionic Bonds

Chapter Planning Guide

Section		Demonstrations and Experiments	Resource Materials
13·1 Valence Electrons	C*		Objectives Worksheet 13, SPB Skillsheet 13, SPB Teaching Diagram 19
13·2 Stable Electron Configurations for Cations	C		
13·3 Stable Electron Configurations for Anions	C		Quiz 13·1
13·4 Ionic Compounds	C	Dem 13·1 Ionic Reactions Dem 13·2 Formation of Cubic Crystals	
13·A The Mixed Blessing of Curing Salts	E		Food Additives, ICT 13
13·5 Properties of Ionic Compounds	C	Dem 13·3 Electrical Conductivity Dem 13·4 Change in Electrical Conductivity	Beyond the Text: X-Ray Diffraction Crystallography The Foundation of Geochemistry
13·6 Metallic Bonds	C	Exp 25 Crystal Structures, LM	Prelab 25, SPB Quiz 13·2 Reviewsheet 13, SPB Chapter 13 Test
13·B Alloys	E		
*C = Core, O = Optional E = Enrichment, H = Honors		LM = Laboratory Manual	SPB = Skills Practice Book ICT = Issues in Chem. Tech.

Chapter Objectives

Having studied this chapter and done the problems, the student should be able to:

1. Use the periodic table to find the number of valence electrons in an atom. *13·1*

2. Draw electron dot formulas of the representative elements. *13·1*

3. State the octet rule. *13·2*

4. State the importance of the noble-gas electron configuration in the formation of ions. *13·2*

5. Describe the formation of a cation from an atom of a metallic element. *13·2*

6. Describe the formation of an anion from an atom of a nonmetallic element. *13·3*

7. Give the characteristics of an ionic bond. *13·4*

8. Recognize a compound as having ionic bonds. *13·4*

9. Relate the coordination number of ions to the crystal structure of the compound of which they are a part. *13·5*

10. Identify characteristics of ionic compounds. *13·5*

11. Explain the electrical conductivity of melted and of aqueous solutions of ionic compounds. *13·5*

12. Use the theory of metallic bonds to explain the physical properties of metals. *13·6*

Teaching Suggestions

13·1 Valence Electrons

When starting the study of bonding, make sure the students understand that the interaction which takes place between atoms and produces bonding occurs only with the outermost electrons of the atoms. The inner electrons are locked tightly in filled energy levels and do not participate in bonding. The outermost electrons are found in the highest occupied energy level and are called the valence electrons. For the representative elements the group number is also the number of valence electrons.

Electron dot structures are a means by which the valence electrons can be shown diagrammatically. Be sure the students understand that the electron dot structure does not show the actual arrangement of electrons in the atom.

In practice, when writing electron dot structures for the representative elements we show only the *s* and *p* electrons. Point out to the students that because of this, each electron dot diagram has no more than eight electrons represented for each atom (except for hydrogen and helium which can have no more than two).

Be sure that the students are aware that the dots representing electrons are not drawn randomly, but arranged symmetrically about the element symbol. Emphasize that each position relative to the element symbol represents an orbital, which can hold no more than two electrons.

13·2 Stable Electron Configurations for Cations

13·3 Stable Electron Configurations for Anions

The underlying concept in these sections is simple and straightforward. Possessing the noble gas electron structure imparts a special stability to an atom. The chemical reactions of a great many of the elements can be explained as atoms attempting to attain the noble gas structure by gaining or losing electrons.

You may wish to review with some of the students the process by which ions are formed. Some may have forgotten how the loss of electrons produces positive ions and the gain of electrons produces negative ions.

Show the students examples of how various atoms of the representative elements form their ions and achieve the noble gas structures. Write equations for the formation of the ions as you do this.

Use examples to illustrate that there are elements which would have to gain or lose too many electrons to achieve the noble gas structure and so cannot achieve stability in this manner. These are the transition metals and the actinides and lanthanides.

Emphasize how the stability of the noble gas structure is reflected in the chemistry of the ions by comparing their reactivity to the reactivity of the elements from which they were derived. A good example is the high reactivity of the alkali metals and the halogens as elements, and the absence of reactivity in their ions.

Some students will at first misinterpret the meaning of the term *isoelectronic*. Point out that it refers to having *identical* electronic structures, not just similar. Show how F^-, Ne, Na^+, Mg^{2+}, and Al^{3+} all have the same (noble gas) electron configuration and so are isoelectronic. Point out that, in contrast, the elements within a group have similar configurations but are not isoelectronic. For instance, the alkali metals all have only one *s* electron in their outermost energy level, but have a different total number of electrons. They cannot be isoelectronic.

13·4 Ionic Compounds

Until now we did not concern ourselves with what happens to the electrons which are given up when positive ions form, nor with the source of the electrons which cause negative ions to form. In reality, positive ions cannot form in chemical reactions unless there are other atoms present which can receive those electrons. Negative ions cannot form from neutral atoms unless there are other atoms present which can donate electrons.

Help the students to see that the formation of positive ions and negative ions are simultaneous and interdependent processes. An ionic compound is the result of the transfer of electrons from one set of atoms to another set of atoms, and consists entirely of ions.

Emphasize again that an ionic solid is a collection of independent ions. There is no joining of individual particles to form molecules. Each ion "belongs" as much to one of its nearest neighbors as it belongs to any other. The arrangement in an ionic crystal is such that each ion is surrounded by ions of opposite charge. The attraction between positive and negative charges produces a relatively strong force. The strong ionic bonds interlink the entire crystal, producing solids which tend to be high melting, hard, and brittle.

Students may have trouble with the concept of coordination number unless they can actually visualize the crystal structures. Make models of the various crystal shapes available to them so that they can get some hands-on experience with counting nearest neighbors.

Demonstrations 13·1 *Ionic Reactions* and **13·2** *Formation of Cubic Crystals* may be done in this section.

13·5 Properties of Ionic Compounds

The fact that ionic solids characteristically form conducting solutions is unique to them. It is worthwhile to bring up at this point the whole issue of conducting solutions and how they form. This can be done by having the students do

Experiment 30 *Electrolytes and Nonelectrolytes* now instead of in Chapter 15. Alternatively, you can do **Demonstration 13·3** *Electrical Conductivity*. This demonstration is similar to **Experiment 28,** but covers the topic in greater depth. **Demonstration 13·4** *Change in Electrical Conductivity* is a challenging demonstration.

13·6 Metallic Bonds

The bonding in metals involves highly mobile electrons which are shared in a very general way by all of the nuclei in a metallic solid. Be sure that the students see how the electron mobility explains the high thermal and electrical conductivities of the metals. Emphasize also how the strong but flexible bonding allows metals to possess the ductility and malleability which is unique to them.

The fact that the metals have a compact structure that allows planes of atoms to slip under stress can be demonstrated with a model. To make the model connect 2″ styrofoam spheres together with toothpicks or pieces of pipe cleaner in layers of about 20 spheres per layer. Connect the atoms within a layer but do not connect the layers. If you stack several layers together, you can then show how the layers will slip over each other in response to a horizontal force without the crystal structure shattering.

If the students are expected to remember and distinguish the body-centered cubic, face-centered cubic, and hexagonal close-packed arrangements of metallic atoms, be sure they have plenty of experience with models. These can be easily constructed from styrofoam spheres held together by toothpicks or pipe cleaners. **Experiment 25** *Crystal Structures* is appropriate at this time.

Demonstrations

13·1 Ionic Reactions

Concept: Reactions of ionic compounds are double-replacement reactions.

Materials: 100 mL of 0.2% acetic acid ($C_2H_4O_2$) in a 250-mL beaker, 10 mL of 0.1% methyl red indicator, 10 g of sodium acetate ($NaC_2H_3O_2$), safety goggles.

Procedure: 1. Add 5 drops of methyl red solution to the acetic acid solution. 2. The solution turns violet-red. 3. Add crystals of sodium acetate until the solution turns yellow. 4. Note that the acetate ion reacts with the hydrogen ions.

13·2 Formation of Cubic Crystals

Concept: Ionic bonding in sodium chloride results in a cubic crystal.

Materials: 10 each of 2 sizes of styrofoam balls, toothpicks, sodium chloride (NaCl) crystals, sand, microscope or large magnifying glass.

Procedure: 1. Use the balls and toothpicks to build a model of sodium chloride, which is a face-centered cubic crystal. 2. Examine crystals of sodium chloride and sand under the microscope or glass. 3. Indicate the cubic nature of the crystal. 4. Note that each sodium ion is surrounded by six chloride ions, and vice versa. Free ions are attracted to the ions already there, increasing the size of the crystal.

13·3 Electrical Conductivity

Concept: Electrolytes and nonelectrolytes have different conductivities in solution.

Materials: conductivity apparatus (see **Experiment 30** *Electrolytes and Nonelectrolytes*) with a neon glow lamp in a third socket (lamps wired in parallel), eight 50-mL beakers, paper towel, screwdriver, water (tap and distilled), ethanol or methanol, sodium chloride (NaCl) in three forms: dry crystals, dissolved in water, and dissolved in ethanol or methanol; sucrose in three forms: dry crystals, dissolved in water, and dissolved in ethanol or methanol, safety goggles.

Procedure: 1. With the power off, wash the electrodes with distilled water and wipe dry. **Caution:** *When using the apparatus, be sure it is disconnected except when testing. Do not touch the electrodes or test solutions when the power is on.* 2. Pour a small portion of each substance (tap water, distilled water, the three forms of NaCl, and the three forms of sucrose into eight different 50-mL beakers. 3. Immerse the electrodes to a depth of about 2 cm. 4. Turn on the power and test each substance. As each test is completed, turn off the power, remove the sample, and rinse and dry the electrodes. 5. Strong electrolytes are good electrical conductors and cause the filaments of all three bulbs to glow brightly. Weak electrolytes cause only the neon glow lamp and the smaller bulb to light. Extremely weak electrolytes only light the neon lamp. If none of the bulbs light when testing weak and very weak electrolytes, disconnect the higher watt bulbs one at a time until one of the bulbs lights. Because of self-ionization, even distilled water displays some conductivity with the neon glow lamp. 6. Have the students record observations as the substances are tested. They can write a summary explaining the observed differences in conductivity. Be sure that the students pay particular attention to the following observations:

1. Neither dry sodium chloride nor distilled water conducts electricity appreciably when separate, but form an excellent conductor when mixed.

2. Sugar is highly soluble in water, yet does not produce a conducting solution.

13·4 Change in Electrical Conductivity

Concept: Precipitation removes ions from solution and alters conductivity.

Materials: medicine dropper, 50-mL beaker, 20 mL of 0.01*M* calcium hydroxide ($Ca(OH)_2$), 20 mL of 0.01*M* sulfuric acid (H_2SO_4), conductivity apparatus (see **Experiment 30**), distilled water, wipers, safety goggles.

Procedure: 1. Place the calcium hydroxide in a beaker. 2. With the medicine dropper, slowly add the sulfuric acid a drop at a time. 3. Note the conductivity of the solution after each addition. 4. In this titration, the lamps go out one after another until the end point is reached and burn again after the end point is passed. 5. Have the students explain why the conductivity of this solution increases, then decreases to a minimum, and then increases again.

Audiovisual Resources

Atoms and Molecules: Building Blocks of Matter (6 FS) Science and Mankind, 1981, 12–18 min. each. (Use with Section 13·4.) Describes the nature of ionic bonds. Also covers topics in Chapters 14 and 26.

Chemical Bonding and Atomic Structure (F) Coronet, 1983, 15 min. (Use with Sections 13·1, 13·4, 13·5, and 13·6.) Discusses valence electrons, demonstrates ionic and metallic bonds, and explains how bonding affects properties. Also covers topics in Chapter 14.

Chemistry: Bonding of Atoms (13 FS) Charles Clark, 1977, 10–18 min. each. (Use with Sections 13·2, 13·3, 13·4, and 13·5.) Explains why and how atoms form ionic bonds and discusses the relationship between physical properties and bonding. Also covers topics in Chapter 14.

Chemistry: Chemical Bonding and Atomic Structure (F, V) Coronet, 1983, 23 min. (Use with Sections 13·2, 13·3, 13·4, 13·5, and 13·6.) Explains properties of metals and ionic compounds in terms of the nature of their bonds and describes the transfer of electrons to achieve a noble gas configuration. Also covers topics in Chapter 14.

Chemistry: The Forces in Solids, Liquids, and Gases (5 FS) Charles Clark, 1978, 14–15 min. each. (Use with Section 13·6.) Discusses bonding in metals. Also covers topics in Chapter 14.

Beyond the Text

X-Ray Diffraction Crystallography

In the early 1900s, Max Theodor Felix von Laue, a German physicist, wanted to measure the wavelength of X-rays. The most common technique for measuring wavelengths of light involved passing a beam of light of only one wavelength through a grating. When the light passed through the grating, it formed a characteristic pattern of light and shadows called a *diffraction* pattern. The pattern was developed on photographic paper. Then the distances and angles of this pattern could be related to the wavelength of light. When sunlight passes through a picket fence it forms bars of shadows on the other side of the fence. In a similar way, the diffraction pattern depended on the width of the bars in the grating and the distances between them.

Laue found that X-ray wavelengths were too short to be measured with even the finest gratings. He then experimented with a crystal of zinc sulfide which he knew was composed of rows of regularly spaced ions. He measured the distances and angles in the pattern produced when X-rays were aimed through the zinc sulfide crystal. From this he found the wavelength of the X-rays. Laue received the Nobel prize in physics in 1914 for his work.

Laue used crystals with known structures to determine the unknown dimensions of X-rays. After this discovery, scientists reasoned that unknown crystal structures could be determined by passing a beam of X-rays of a known wavelength through crystals. This is the basis of modern crystallography. An X-ray diffraction spectrometer is used to obtain X-ray diffraction patterns of crystals. In this instrument, a source of X-rays of known wavelength passes through the crystal sample. The resulting diffraction pattern is recorded on a photographic plate and is characteristic for the compound. The distances and angles in the pattern are related to the distances between atoms in the crystal lattice. From measurements of the diffraction pattern and subsequent calculations the arrangement of atoms in a crystal can be determined. X-ray crystallography was first used to study simple ionic compounds. Today, the technique is used to study more complicated macromolecules such as DNA.

The Foundation of Geochemistry

The science of geochemistry began in the eighteenth century with the work of a Scottish scientist, Sir James Hall. Geology itself was a young science at that time. The most influential geologist of the day believed that the rocks of the earth were less than 6000 years old. It was believed that all of the earth's rocks were sedimentary, laid down by a global flood. These views were challenged by James Hutton, a Scottish doctor and farmer. Through field studies, he

recognized that rocks were eroded by rain and rivers. He thought that the particles were then carried to the ocean and deposited on the sea floor. He theorized that under great pressure and high temperatures these layers of sediment were changed into new forms of rock. He also recognized that other rocks must have once been molten inside the earth. He thought that this hot liquid rock cooled to form crystalline solids as it came to the surface.

To prove that Hutton's revolutionary ideas were possible, Hall tried to reproduce geological processes in the laboratory. Other scientists had found that limestone decomposed when it was heated. They concluded that heat could not transform limestone into marble as Hutton had suggested. Hall heated the rock to 1000°C and kept it under a pressure of more than 270 atmospheres. This pressure is comparable to the pressure under 2700 meters of seawater. His experiment proved that under these conditions limestone did not decompose but instead changed its form.

In another experiment Hall demonstrated that crystalline rock could form from molten lava. Prior to Hall's work, molten rock that cooled in the laboratory had formed amorphous solids, not crystalline ones. Hall showed that if the rock was cooled very slowly, it would form a crystalline solid.

Modern geochemists study the chemical composition of rocks and the distribution of elements on the earth and in the solar system. Many geochemists work for mineral exploration companies. Others work for the government and in universities. In addition to finding and planning the development of mineral deposits, geochemists evaluate pollution in the soil, air, and water of our planet. They also study the earth's geochemical processes, like those that occur in volcanoes, hot springs, and ocean vents.

Education for a career in geochemistry begins with a strong science program in high school. This is followed by a bachelor's degree in either chemistry or geology with strong coursework in the other. Geochemistry is generally studied as a specialty in graduate school. Related subjects that are helpful are statistics, economics, and computer science. As in all fields of science, skill in oral and written communication is extremely important.

Answers to End of Chapter Questions and Problems

Practice Questions and Problems

8. Electrons in the highest occupied energy level.

9. Group 2A: Be, Mg, Ca, two valence electrons. Group 3A: B, Al, Ga, three valence electrons.

10. Fluorine F, chlorine Cl, bromine Br, iodine I; Group 7A; seven valence electrons.

11. **a.** 7, Group 5A **b.** 3, Group 1A **c.** 15, Group 5A **d.** 56, Group 2A

12. **a.** $:\!\overset{\cdot\cdot}{\underset{\cdot\cdot}{Cl}}\!\cdot$ **b.** $:\!\overset{\cdot\cdot}{S}\!\cdot$ **c.** $\cdot\overset{\cdot}{Al}\cdot$ **d.** Li·

13. **a.** ·Ca· **b.** $:\!\overset{\cdot\cdot}{Se}\!\cdot$ **c.** $\cdot\overset{\cdot}{As}\!\cdot$ **d.** ·Be·

14. They have stable electron configurations.

15. After reaction, atoms have eight electrons in their highest energy level.

16. **a.** 2 **b.** 3 **c.** 1 **d.** 1 **e.** 2 **f.** 2

17. An atom (or group of atoms) with a positive charge; formed by a loss of electrons to achieve a noble gas electron configuration.

18. **a.** Al^{3+} **b.** Li^+ **c.** Ba^{2+} **d.** K^+ **e.** Ca^{2+} **f.** Sr^{2+}

19. **a.** $1s^2\, 2s^2\, 2p^6\, 3s^2\, 3p^6$ **b.** $1s^2\, 2s^2\, 2p^6$
Each has a noble gas electron configuration.

20. It does not have a noble-gas electron configuration, but does have all occupied shells filled with electrons.

21. An atom (or group of atoms) with a negative charge; formed by a gain of electrons to achieve a noble gas electron configuration.

22. **a.** 1 **b.** 2 **c.** 3 **d.** 1 **e.** 3 **f.** 2

23. **a.** Br^- **b.** O^{2-} **c.** H^- **d.** F^- **e.** As^{3-} **f.** Se^{2-}

24. **a. b. c.** and **d.** $1s^2\, 2s^2\, 2p^6$ All have the same configuration as neon.

25. A group of ions with a net charge of zero; held together by electrostatic forces.

26. The positive charges of the cations equal the negative charges of the anions.

27. An ionic compound.

28. a, e, g.

29. a, b, d.

30. **a.** K_2S **b.** CaO **c.** Na_2SO_4 **d.** $AlPO_4$

31. **a.** K^+Cl^- **b.** $Na^+NO_3^-$ **c.** $Ba^{2+}SO_4^{2-}$ **d.** $Mg^{2+}Br^-$ **e.** K^+OH^- **f.** $Li^+CO_3^{2-}$

32. **a.** potassium bromide **b.** silver chloride **c.** calcium sulfate **d.** iron(II) oxide **e.** copper(I) chloride **f.** sodium hydrogen carbonate

33. **a.** KNO_3 **b.** Na_2CO_3 **c.** $BaCl_2$ **d.** $MgSO_4$ **e.** Li_2O **f.** $(NH_4)_2CO_3$ **g.** $Ca_3(PO_4)_2$ **h.** $Al(OH)_3$

34. It is a solid containing atoms, ions, or molecules in a regular, repeating three-dimensional pattern.

35. The charges and relative sizes of the ions.

36. Their network of electrostatic attractions and repulsions forms a rigid structure.

37. In molten $MgCl_2$ the ions are free to move toward an electrode. In crystalline $MgCl_2$ the ions cannot move and there are no free electrons.

38. Attraction between stationary positive metal ions and mobile valence electrons.

39. Ductile: can be drawn into wires; malleable: can be hammered into different shapes.

40. Under pressure, the cations in a metal slide past each other. The ions in ionic crystals are forced into each other by the rigid structure.

41. They have many free electrons. The electrons leaving the metal are replaced by electrons in the entering current.

42. Body-centered cubic: Na, K, Fe, Cr, or W. Face-centered cubic: Cu, Ag, Au, Al, or Pb. Hexagonal close-packed: Mg, Zn, or Cd.

Mastery Questions and Problems

43. a, c, e, f.

44. Group number: 1A 2A 3A 5A 6A 7A
Valence electrons lost: 1   2   3   5   6   7
Formula of ion: Na^+ Ca^{2+} Al^{3+} N^{3-} S^{2-} Br^-

45. a. $\cdot\dot{C}\cdot$ **b.** $\cdot Be\cdot$ **c.** $\cdot Mg\cdot$ **d.** $:\dot{O}:$ **e.** $He:$
f. $:\dot{F}\cdot$ **g.** $Na\cdot$ **h.** $:\dot{P}\cdot$

46. It has lost valence electrons.

47. b, d, e, f.

48. 12

49. a. $1s^2\,2s^2\,2p^6\,3s^2\,3p^6\,3d^6$
b. $1s^2\,2s^2\,2p^6\,3s^2\,3p^6\,3d^7$
c. $1s^2\,2s^2\,2p^6\,3s^2\,3p^6\,3d^8$

50. a. $:\dot{I}:$ **b.** $\cdot Sr\cdot$ **c.** $:\dot{Te}\cdot$ **d.** $Cs\cdot$ **e.** $\cdot\dot{Sb}\cdot$
f. $:\dot{Xe}:$

51. It has gained valence electrons.

52. They have unfilled outermost orbitals and are reactive. Stable ions with filled orbitals are produced.

53. For the representative elements the number of electrons in the electron dot structure is the group number.

54. a. $1s^2\,2s^2\,2p^6\,3s^2\,3p^6\,3d^3$
b. $1s^2\,2s^2\,2p^6\,3s^2\,3p^6\,3d^4$
c. $1s^2\,2s^2\,2p^6\,3s^2\,3p^6\,3d^5$

55. Hexagonal close-packed unit cells have 12 neighbors for every atom or ion but differ from the face-centered cubic cell. Face-centered cubic unit cells also have 12 neighbors for every atom or ion, with an atom or ion in the center of each face. Body-centered cubic unit cells have 8 neighbors for every atom or ion, with an atom or ion at the center of each cube.

56. a, b, c, and **d:** $1s^2\,2s^2\,2p^6\,3s^2\,3p^6$ **e.** All have the noble gas electron configuration.

Review Questions and Problems

57. 11.2 L

58. Gases and liquids assume the shape of their containers. Solids have a definite shape. Liquids and solids have a definite volume; gases do not. Gases have a low density. Liquids have an intermediate density. Solids have a high density. The molecules of a gas move freely and randomly. The molecules of a liquid flow. The molecules of a solid vibrate and rotate around a fixed position.

59. 5.6 L

60. Increases the average kinetic energy and speed of the gas molecules.

61. 11 cm³

62. a. At 40°C more water molecules have energies that allow them to overcome the intermolecular attractions than at 20°C. **b.** Steam at 100°C has more potential energy. **c.** The molecules have more kinetic energy, creating a greater vapor pressure. **d.** Diethyl ether has very weak attractions between molecules. Water is polar and has hydrogen bonding between molecules. **e.** Ice absorbs energy. The kinetic energy of the tea decreases. **f.** Heating may rupture chemical bonds within the food and change its flavor or quality.

63. a. decreases **b.** increases **c.** decrease **d.** increase **e.** decrease **f.** increase or decrease depending on the relative sizes of the changes of T and P.

64. 1020 mm Hg

65. 596 K, or 323°C

66. 1.2×10^4 cm³

Challenging Questions and Problems

67. The sodium ion and the cesium ion are greatly different in size. The sizes of the sodium ion and the chloride ion are similar to the sizes of the sulfide ion and the manganese(II) ion.

68. 0.1445 nm

13

Ionic
Bonds

Chapter Preview

In Chapters 11 and 12 you learned about the electron structure of atoms and the organization of the periodic table. This knowledge of atomic structure and periodicity will help you understand the chemical bonding that occurs between atoms. For example, the electron configurations of the sodium and chlorine atoms help explain why one atom of sodium combines with one atom of chlorine. It also explains why the formula unit for sodium chloride is NaCl and not Na_2Cl, $NaCl_2$, or Na_2Cl_2. Why does sodium chloride conduct an electric current when it is in the molten state? Why is sodium chloride a solid at room temperature with a melting point of 800°C whereas hydrogen chloride is a gas? Why do the metallic elements form positive ions whereas the nonmetallic elements form negative ions? Questions like these and many others will be answered in this chapter.

13·1 Valence Electrons

■ Valence is the capacity of an element to combine with another.

Latin: *valere* = to be strong.

Figure 13·1
Most ionic compounds are crystalline solids with high melting points. For example, calcium fluoride, the mineral fluorite, melts at 1360° C.

Knowing electron configurations is important because the number of valence electrons largely determines the chemical properties of an element. **Valence electrons** *are the electrons in the highest occupied energy level of an element's atoms*. You may recall that when Mendeleev organized his periodic table, he did so with the properties of the elements in mind. Scientists later learned that all the elements in a particular group of the periodic table have the same number of valence electrons. For example, the elements in Group 1A (hydrogen, lithium, sodium, potassium, and so forth) all have one valence electron. For the representative elements an atom's number of valence electrons can be determined by looking up the

group number of that element. Carbon and silicon, in Group 4A, have four valence electrons. Nitrogen and phosphorus, in Group 5A, have five valence electrons; and oxygen and sulfur, in Group 6A, have six. The noble gases (Group 0) are the one exception to this rule. Helium has two valence electrons, and all the others have eight.

Problem

1. a. 1   c. 2
b. 4   d. 6

1. How many valence electrons does each of the following atoms have?
   a. potassium **b.** carbon **c.** magnesium **d.** oxygen

Electron dot structures are also called *Lewis dot structures* in honor of Gilbert N. Lewis (1875–1946), an American chemist whose ideas concerning the nature of chemical bonds are very much a part of modern chemistry.

Valence electrons are usually the only electrons used in the formation of chemical bonds. Thus it is customary to show only the valence electrons in electron dot structures. **Electron dot structures** *depict valence electrons as dots. The inner electrons and the atomic nuclei are represented by the symbol for the element being considered.* Table 13·1 shows electron dot structures for atoms of some Group A elements.

Table 13·1	Electron Dot Structures of Some Group A Elements							
	Group							
Period	1A	2A	3A	4A	5A	6A	7A	0
1	H·						H·	He:
2	Li·	·Be·	·Ḃ·	·Ċ·	·N̈·	:Ö·	:F̈·	:N̈e:
3	Na·	·Mg·	·Al̇·	·Si̇·	·P̈·	:S̈·	:C̈l·	:Är:
4	K·	·Ca·	·Gȧ·	·Gė·	·Äs·	:S̈e·	:B̈r·	:K̈r:

Electron dot structures do not distinguish between *s* and *p* electrons.

13·2 Stable Electron Configurations for Cations

Why are some elements found mainly as ions? *It is because the nature of things is to adjust to achieve the lowest possible energy.* Noble gas atoms are stable. They are of low energy and low chemical reactivity because they have *stable electron configurations*. The atoms of all other elements are less stable. They are of higher energy and higher chemical reactivity because they do not have stable electron configurations. In forming compounds, atoms make adjustments to achieve the lowest possible energy.

Most stable means *lowest energy.*

In 1916 Gilbert Lewis provided an explanation for why atoms tend to form certain types of ions and molecules. He proposed the **octet rule:** *Atoms react by changing the number of their electrons so as to acquire the stable electron structure of a noble gas.* Recall that each noble gas,

Greek: *okto* = eight.

An outer structure of eight electrons is a stable configuration.

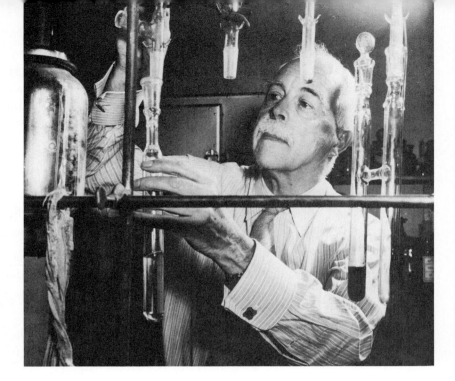

Figure 13·2
Gilbert Lewis proposed the octet rule
and the electron dot method of showing valence electrons. He was also an
important contributor to acid–base
theory and thermodynamics.

Anion, a negative ion; cation, a
positive ion.

The metallic elements tend to form
positive ions, cations.

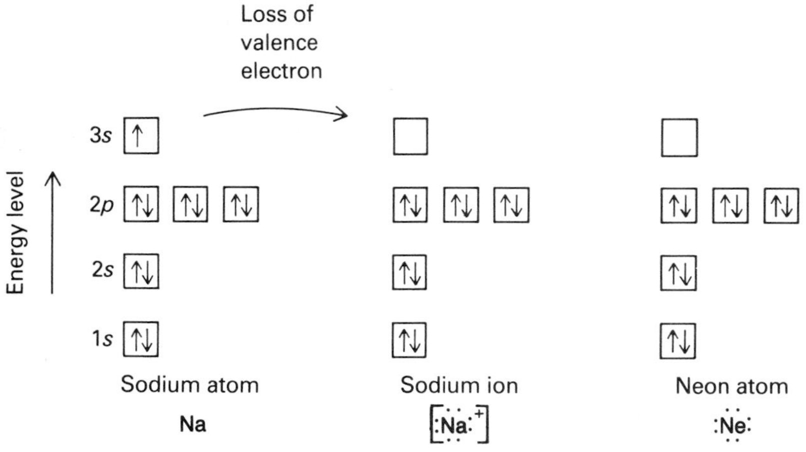

except helium, has eight electrons (ns^2 np^6) in its highest energy level.
The octet rule takes its name from this fact. Atoms of the metallic elements obey the octet rule by losing electrons. Atoms of some nonmetallic
elements obey the rule by gaining electrons. *The loss of valence electrons
from an atom produces a cation, or positively charged ion. The gain of
valence electrons produces an anion, or negatively charged ion.*

You may recall from Section 5·2 that a *cation* is any atom or group
of atoms with a positive charge. The most common cations are those produced by the loss of electrons from metal atoms. These atoms usually
have up to three valence electrons that are easily removed. Sodium, in
Group 1A of the periodic table, is typical. Sodium atoms have a total of
11 electrons, including 1 valence electron. When forming a compound, a
sodium atom loses its 1 valence electron. It then has the same electron
configuration as neon, a noble gas (Figure 13·3). The sodium *ion* has an
octet (eight electrons) in its highest energy level. Because the number of

Figure 13·3
A sodium atom loses an electron to
become a positively charged sodium
ion. The sodium ion has an electron
configuration like that of the noble gas
neon. There are eight electrons (an
octet) in the highest energy levels of
Na^+ and Ne.

Loss of
valence
electron

Energy level

	Sodium atom	Sodium ion	Neon atom
3s	↑	□	□
2p	↑↓ ↑↓ ↑↓	↑↓ ↑↓ ↑↓	↑↓ ↑↓ ↑↓
2s	↑↓	↑↓	↑↓
1s	↑↓	↑↓	↑↓

Sodium atom **Na** Sodium ion $[:Na\cdot]^+$ Neon atom :Ne:

protons in the sodium nucleus is still 11, the lack of one unit of negative charge produces a sodium ion with a charge of 1+. We can show the electron loss, or ionization, of the sodium atom by drawing the complete electron configuration of the atom and the ion formed.

$$Na \qquad 1s^2\ 2s^2\ 2p^6\ 3s^1$$

$$Na^+ \qquad 1s^2\ \underbrace{2s^2\ 2p^6}_{octet}$$

The electron configuration of the sodium ion is the same as that of the neon atom. Both have an octet of outer electrons.

$$Ne \qquad 1s^2\ \underbrace{2s^2\ 2p^6}_{octet}$$

The ionization can be shown more simply by using an electron dot structure for the atom.

$$Na\cdot \xrightarrow[\text{ionization}]{\substack{\text{loss of valence} \\ \text{electron}}} Na^+ \quad + \quad e^-$$

Sodium atom (electrically neutral, charge = 0) Sodium ion (plus sign indicates one unit of positive charge) Electron (minus sign indicates one unit of negative charge)

Magnesium (atomic number 12) belongs to Group 2A of the periodic table and therefore has two valence electrons. Magnesium atoms attain the electron configuration of neon by losing both valence electrons. The loss of the valence electrons produces a magnesium ion, a cation with twice the positive charge of a sodium ion.

$$\cdot Mg\cdot \longrightarrow Mg^{2+} + 2e^-$$

Magnesium atom   Magnesium ion

We have said that the cations of Group 1A elements always have a charge of 1+. Similarly, the cations of Group 2A elements always have a charge of 2+. We can now explain this constancy in terms of the loss of valence electrons by atoms of metals to attain the electron configuration of a noble gas. The elements in Group 2A all have two valence electrons. In losing these two electrons they form 2+ cations. The charge of transition metal cations may vary. An atom of iron loses two electrons to form the iron(II), or ferrous, ion, Fe^{2+}. It loses three electrons in forming the iron(III), or ferric, ion, Fe^{3+}.

Many ions do not have noble-gas electron configurations ($ns^2\ np^6$). These ions are exceptions to the octet rule. Let us consider silver with the electron configuration of $1s^2\ 2s^2\ 2p^6\ 3s^2\ 3p^6\ 3d^{10}\ 4s^2\ 4p^6\ 4d^{10}\ 5s^1$ as an example. To achieve the structure of the noble gas krypton, a silver atom would have to lose 11 electrons. Alternatively, it could gain 7 electrons to acquire the electron configuration of the noble gas xenon. Since ions with a charge of greater than three are uncommon, neither of these possibilities is likely.

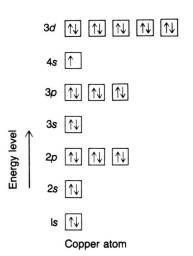

Figure 13·4
The electron configuration of a copper atom is shown. By losing the 4s electron, copper attains a pseudo noble gas electron configuration. It then becomes a copper(I) ion, Cu⁺.

2. Cu$^+$: $1s^2\,2s^2\,2p^6\,3s^2\,3p^6\,3d^{10}$
Au$^+$: $1s^2\,2s^2\,2p^6\,3s^2\,3p^6\,3d^{10}$
$4s^2\,4p^6\,4d^{10}\,4f^{14}\,5s^2\,5p^6\,5d^{10}$
Cd^{2+}: $1s^2\,2s^2\,2p^6\,3s^2\,3p^6$
$3d^{10}\,4s^2\,4p^6\,4d^{10}$
Hg^{2+}: $1s^2\,2s^2\,2p^6\,3s^2\,3p^6$
$3d^{10}\,4s^2\,4p^6\,4d^{10}\,4f^{14}\,5s^2\,5p^6$
$5d^{10}$

The nonmetallic elements tend to form negative ions with an octet of valence electrons.

Silver cannot acquire a noble-gas configuration. Yet its outer electron configuration will be $4s^2\,4p^6\,4d^{10}$ if it loses its $5s^1$ electron. This configuration, with 18 electrons in the outer energy level, is relatively stable. It is known as the *pseudo noble-gas* electron configuration. Silver forms a unipositive ion in this way. Other elements that behave similarly to silver are at the right of the transition metal series. Cu$^+$, Au$^+$, Cd^{2+}, and Hg^{2+} ions have pseudo noble-gas electron configurations.

Problem

2. Write electron configurations for the unipositive ions of copper and gold and the dipositive ions of cadmium and mercury.

13·3   Stable Electron Configurations for Anions

An anion is an atom or a grouping of atoms with a negative charge. Atoms of nonmetallic elements attain stable electron configurations more easily by gaining electrons than by losing them. For example, chlorine belongs to Group 7A, the halogen family, of the periodic table. A gain of one electron converts a chlorine atom into a chloride ion. It is an anion with a single negative charge. Chlorine atoms therefore need one more valence electron to achieve the electron configuration of the nearest noble gas, argon.

$$\text{Cl} \quad 1s^2\,2s^2\,2p^6\,3s^2\,3p^5$$
$$\text{Cl}^- \quad 1s^2\,2s^2\,2p^6\,\underbrace{3s^2\,3p^6}_{\text{octet}}$$

The chloride ion has eight electrons (an octet) in its highest energy level. It has the same electron configuration as the noble gas argon.

$$\text{Ar} \quad 1s^2\,2s^2\,2p^6\,3s^2\,3p^6$$

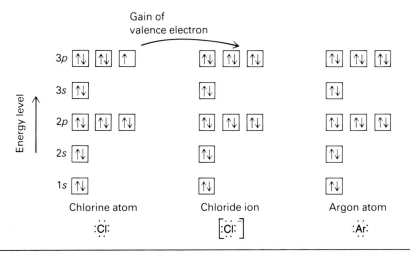

Figure 13·5
A chlorine atom gains an electron to become a negatively charged chloride ion. The chloride ion has an electron configuration like that of the noble gas argon. Each has an octet of electrons.

Electron dot structures can also be used to write the ionization of chlorine to form a chloride ion.

$$:\ddot{\underset{..}{Cl}}\cdot \;+\; e^- \xrightarrow[\text{(ionization)}]{\overset{\text{gain of one}}{\underset{\text{valence electron}}{}}} \; :\ddot{\underset{..}{Cl}}:^-$$

Chlorine atom   Chloride ion (Cl^-)

Anions of chlorine and the other halogens gain electrons to form **halide ions.** An atom of each halogen has seven valence electrons. It needs to gain one electron to achieve the electron configuration of a noble gas. Therefore, as we have seen, all halide ions have a charge of $1-$: F^-, Cl^-, Br^-, and I^-.

Oxygen atoms each have six valence electrons. They attain the electron configuration of neon by gaining two electrons. The resulting oxide ions have charges of $2-$ and are written as O^{2-}.

$$:\ddot{O}\cdot \;+\; 2e^- \longrightarrow \; :\ddot{\underset{..}{O}}:^{\,2-}$$

Oxygen atom   Oxide ion

Problems

3. a. lose 2   **c.** lose 3
    b. gain 1   **d.** gain 2
4. a. S^{2-} **c.** F^-
    b. Na^+ **d.** Ba^{2+}

3. How many electrons will the following elements gain or lose in forming an ion?
    a. calcium (Ca)   **c.** aluminum (Al)
    b. fluorine (F)   **d.** oxygen (O)

4. What will be the formula of the ion formed when the following elements gain or lose valence electrons and attain noble gas configurations?
    a. sulfur (S)   **c.** fluorine (F)
    b. sodium (Na)   **d.** barium (Ba)

13·4 Ionic Compounds

Electrically charged objects can exert forces on each other even though they are not touching. Electrostatic forces result from the interaction of positive and negative charges.

■ Ionic compounds are composed of oppositely charged ions in fixed ratios.

Metals react with nonmetals to form ionic compounds.

Anions and cations have opposite charges. They attract one another by electrostatic forces. *The forces of attraction that bind oppositely charged ions together are called* **ionic bonds.** Ionic compounds are electrically neutral groups of ions joined by electrostatic forces. They are also known as salts. In any sample of an ionic compound, the positive charges of the cations must equal the negative charges of the anions. We made use of this principle in using ionic charges to write formulas of ionic compounds in Chapter 5.

To learn about ionic bonds, consider the reaction between a sodium atom and a chlorine atom. In forming a compound, sodium has a single valence electron that it can easily lose. Chlorine has seven valence electrons and can easily gain one. When sodium and chlorine react to form a compound, they must do so in a one-to-one ratio. The sodium atom gives its one valence electron to a chlorine atom.

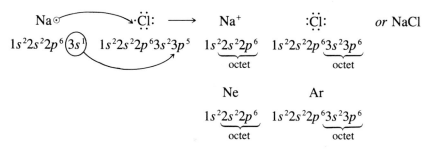

$$\text{Na} \odot \longrightarrow \overset{\cdot}{\underset{\cdot\cdot}{\text{Cl}}}\text{:} \longrightarrow \text{Na}^+ \qquad \text{:}\overset{\cdot\cdot}{\underset{\cdot\cdot}{\text{Cl}}}\text{:} \qquad \text{or NaCl}$$

$$\underbrace{1s^2 2s^2 2p^6}_{} \boxed{3s^1} \quad \underbrace{1s^2 2s^2 2p^6 3s^2 3p^5} \quad \underbrace{1s^2 2s^2 2p^6}_{\text{octet}} \quad \underbrace{1s^2 2s^2 2p^6 3s^2 3p^6}_{\text{octet}}$$

$$\text{Ne} \qquad\qquad \text{Ar}$$

$$\underbrace{1s^2 2s^2 2p^6}_{\text{octet}} \quad \underbrace{1s^2 2s^2 2p^6 3s^2 3p^6}_{\text{octet}}$$

The chemical formula, NaCl, is a *formula unit*. It represents the smallest sample of an ionic compound that has the composition of the compound. The formula NaCl shows that one formula unit of sodium chloride contains one sodium ion and one chloride ion.

Aluminum and bromine react to form an ionic compound. Each aluminum atom has three valence electrons to lose. A bromine atom has seven valence electrons. It will easily gain an additional electron. When aluminum and bromine react, three bromine atoms react with each aluminum atom.

$$\text{Al} \odot + \begin{matrix} \cdot\overset{\cdot\cdot}{\text{Br}}\text{:} \\ \cdot\overset{\cdot\cdot}{\text{Br}}\text{:} \\ \cdot\overset{\cdot\cdot}{\text{Br}}\text{:} \end{matrix} \longrightarrow \text{Al}^{3+} \begin{matrix} \text{:}\overset{\cdot\cdot}{\underset{\cdot\cdot}{\text{Br}}}\text{:}^- \\ \text{:}\overset{\cdot\cdot}{\underset{\cdot\cdot}{\text{Br}}}\text{:}^- \\ \text{:}\overset{\cdot\cdot}{\underset{\cdot\cdot}{\text{Br}}}\text{:}^- \end{matrix} \quad or \quad \text{AlBr}_3$$

The formula for aluminum bromide is therefore $AlBr_3$.

Figure 13·6
Aluminum and bromine combine to form aluminum bromide. Why do three bromine atoms combine with each aluminum atom?

Aluminum can obtain a noble gas structure if it loses three electrons. Each bromine atom needs to gain only one electron to obtain a noble gas configuration.

Example 1

Use electron dot formulas to predict the formulas of the ionic compounds formed from these elements.
a. potassium and oxygen
b. magnesium and nitrogen

Solution

Write down the correct electron dot formulas of each atom in the compound. Atoms of metals lose their valence electrons when forming an ionic compound. Atoms of nonmetals gain electrons to have an electron configuration like a noble gas (usually eight electrons). Enough atoms of each element must be used in the formula so that electrons lost equals electrons gained.

a. Start with the atoms: $K\cdot$ and $\cdot\overset{\cdot\cdot}{\underset{\cdot}{O}}\text{:}$

Oxygen needs two electrons. These electrons can come from two potassium atoms.

$$\begin{matrix} K\cdot \\ K\cdot \end{matrix} + \cdot\overset{\cdot\cdot}{\underset{\cdot}{O}}\text{:} \longrightarrow \begin{matrix} K^+ \\ K^+ \end{matrix} \text{:}\overset{\cdot\cdot}{\underset{\cdot\cdot}{O}}\text{:}^{2-}$$

Electrons *lost* now equals electrons *gained*. The formula of potassium oxide is K_2O.

b. Start with the atoms: $\dot{M}g$ and $\cdot\ddot{N}:$

Nitrogen needs three electrons, but each magnesium atom can lose only two. Thus we need three magnesium atoms for every two nitrogen atoms.

$$\begin{matrix} \dot{M}g \\ \dot{M}g \\ \dot{M}g \end{matrix} \quad + \quad \begin{matrix} \cdot\ddot{N}: \\ \\ \cdot\ddot{N}: \end{matrix} \quad \longrightarrow \quad \begin{matrix} Mg^{2+} \\ Mg^{2+} \\ Mg^{2+} \end{matrix} \quad \begin{matrix} :\ddot{N}:^{3-} \\ \\ :\ddot{N}:^{3-} \end{matrix}$$

The formula of magnesium nitride is Mg_3N_2.

Problems

5. Use electron dot formulas to determine chemical formulas of the ionic compounds formed when the following elements combine.
   a. potassium and iodine
   b. calcium and sulfur
   c. aluminum and oxygen
   d. sodium and phosphorus

6. Name the compounds formed in Problem 5.

7. Use ionic charges to write chemical formulas of the compounds named in Problem 5.

5. **a.** KI **c.** Al_2O_3
   b. CaS **d.** Na_3P
6. **a.** potassium iodide
   b. calcium sulfide
   c. aluminum oxide
   d. sodium phosphide.
7. **a.** K^+ I^-: KI
   b. Ca^{2+} S^{2-}: CaS
   c. Al^{3+} O^{2-}: Al_2O_3
   d. Na^+ P^{3-}: Na_3P

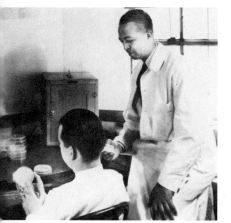

Figure 13·7
The meat-packing industry was revolutionized when Lloyd Hall and others developed new types of curing salts.

Safety

Nitrates enhance the combustion of other materials, and can cause explosions. Handle with care.

13·A   The Mixed Blessing of Curing Salts

Curing salts are ionic substances used to preserve meat. For centuries people have packed meat and fish in sodium chloride or soaked it in a salt solution to prevent bacterial growth. Many recipes for curing salts and pickling solutions used today are the work of Lloyd Hall. At one time he held more than 25 patents for food processing and packaging methods, which he developed as a research chemist.

One controversial substance used in meat processing is sodium nitrite. The nitrates and nitrites of sodium and potassium are used to help preserve ham, bacon, frankfurters, sausage, and other cured meats. These salts are used in small amounts along with sodium chloride. The nitrate ion is easily converted by enzymes or bacteria into nitrite. This ion prevents the growth of the bacteria that cause botulism, an extremely dangerous form of food poisoning. Nitrate and nitrite also enhance the flavor of meat and give it a pink color.

At high temperatures, nitrite ions react with amines, substances present in all meat. The product of this reaction is a group of chemicals called nitrosoamines. These compounds have been found to cause cancer in every species of animal in which they have been tested. In addition, in high concentrations they can cause mutations and birth defects. Nitrosoamines can form if meat containing nitrites is cooked at a high temperature, such as when bacon is fried.

Figure 13·8
Curing salts are used to prevent bacterial growth in meat.

■ An ionic compound is characterized by a high-melting point, conductivity of electricity in the molten state, existence in a crystalline form, and tendency to dissolve in water.

Figure 13·9
Cesium chloride and sodium chloride both form clear cubic crystals. Nevertheless their internal crystal structures differ. The unit cell of sodium chloride is face-centered cubic. By contrast the unit cell of cesium chloride is body-centered cubic. How many chlorine atoms surround each sodium atom? How many chlorine atoms surround each cesium atom? 6; 8

No conclusive evidence exists that nitrites themselves cause cancer. They can react with the hemoglobin in blood, however, to reduce the capacity of blood to carry oxygen. This condition is particularly serious in babies and unborn children.

Cured meats are not the only source of nitrite we encounter. Saliva contains nitrite, and nitrate that is present naturally in food and water is converted to nitrite in the intestines. Thus it is advisable to control nitrite consumption wherever possible. Some experts feel, however, that a total ban on the use of nitrites in cured meats could cause an outbreak of botulism. The amount of nitrite that can be used in foods is restricted by government regulations. Scientists are also looking for ways to inhibit the formation of nitrosoamines.

13·5 Properties of Ionic Compounds

Most ionic compounds are crystalline solids at room temperature. *The component molecules, atoms, or ions of a crystal are arranged in repeating three-dimensional patterns.* The composition of a crystal of sodium chloride is typical. In solid NaCl each sodium ion is surrounded by six chloride ions and each chloride ion is surrounded by six sodium ions. In this arrangement each ion is attracted strongly to each of its neighbors and repulsions are minimized. The large attractive forces result in a very stable structure. This is reflected in the fact that NaCl and ionic compounds in general have very high melting temperatures.

The three dimensional arrangement of ions in NaCl is shown in Figure 13·9. Because each Na^+ ion is surrounded by six Cl^- ions, it has a coordination number of 6. *The* **coordination number** *gives the number of ions of opposite charge that surround each ion in a crystal.* Each Cl^- ion is surrounded by six Na^+ ions and also has a coordination number of 6.

Cesium chloride (CsCl) has a formula unit that is similar to NaCl. Both these compounds have cubic crystals but their internal crystal structures are different. Each Cs^+ ion is surrounded by eight Cl^- ions, and each Cl^- ion is surrounded by eight Cs^+ ions. Both the anion and cation in cesium chloride have a coordination number of 8.

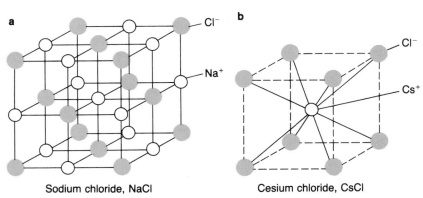

Sodium chloride, NaCl

Cesium chloride, CsCl

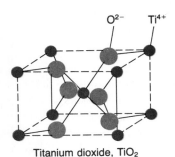

Titanium dioxide, TiO$_2$

Figure 13·10
The shape of a crystal depends on its internal structure. Crystals of the mineral rutile (titanium dioxide) are tetragonal.

Safety

Many chemicals are similar in appearance yet different in chemical and biological properties. Always label containers used even temporarily to store chemicals. Use the proper chemical formula and/or name.

Rutile is the crystalline form of titanium dioxide (TiO$_2$). In this compound the coordination number for the cation (Ti^{4+}) is 6. Each Ti^{4+} ion is surrounded by six O^{2-} ions. The coordination number of the anion (O^{2-}) is 3. Each O^{2-} ion is surrounded by three Ti^{4+} ions. The crystals are tetragonal instead of cubic (Figure 13·10). The internal structures of crystals are determined using a technique known as x-ray diffraction crystallography. Patterns are formed when x-rays pass through a crystal onto x-ray film. These patterns are used to calculate the positions of ions in the crystal (Figure 13·14).

Ionic compounds conduct an electric current when in the molten state. For example, when sodium chloride is melted (melting point 800°C) the orderly crystal structure breaks down. Each ion is then free to move throughout the molten mass. If a voltage is applied across this melt, cations will migrate to one electrode and anions will migrate to the other. This movement of ions means that there is a flow of electricity between the two electrodes. It is a characteristic property of ionic compounds that they conduct an electric current when melted. Ionic compounds also produce electrical conductivity if they can be dissolved in water. When such compounds dissolve, their ions are free to move about.

Figure 13·11
When sodium chloride melts, the sodium and chloride ions move freely through the molten salt. If a voltage is applied, the sodium ions will migrate to the negatively charged electrode (the cathode), and the chloride ions will migrate to the positively charged electrode (the anode).

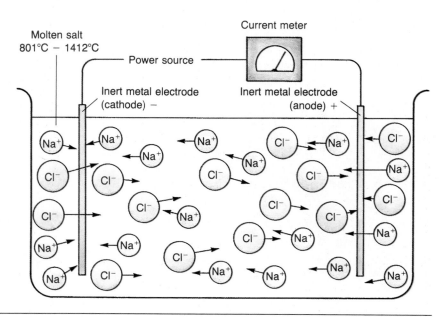

Figure 13·12
Because they are malleable, metals
can be bent and hammered into
different shapes.

Elements which display metallic
bonding must meet two requirements. They must have vacant
valence orbitals, and they must
have low ionization energies so
that loosely held electrons are
available for bonding.

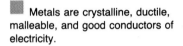 Metals are crystalline, ductile,
malleable, and good conductors of
electricity.

Safety

Metals are excellent conductors of
heat. When heating glassware, position clamps or iron rings so that they
will not be heated by the flame. Be
careful not to burn yourself when dis-
assembling the equipment.

Ions of like charge would be
pushed together and would repel
each other.

Figure 13·13
a A metal rod can be forced through a
narrow opening in a *die* to produce
wire. **b** As this occurs, the metal
changes shape but remains in one
piece. **c** If an ionic crystal were forced
through the die it would shatter. Why?

a

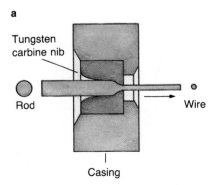

13·6 Metallic Bonds

Scientists believe that a piece of pure metal such as copper or iron consists not of metal atoms but of closely packed cations. The cations are
surrounded by mobile valence electrons that are free to drift from one
part of the metal to another. **Metallic bonds** *consist of the attraction of
the free-floating valence electrons for the positively charged metal ions.*
These are the forces of attraction that hold metals together.

Scientists have accounted for many physical properties of metals on
the basis of this picture of metallic bonding. *Metals are good conductors
of electrical current* (flow of electrons) *because as electrons enter one
end of a bar of metal, an equal number leave the other end.* Metals are
also *malleable* in that they can be hammered into different shapes (Figure
13·13). They are *ductile* in that they can be drawn into wires. The electron mobility theory says that the metal cations are insulated from one another by electrons. When a metal is subjected to pressure, the metal
cations easily slide past one another like ball bearings immersed in oil. In
contrast, if an ionic crystal is struck with a hammer, the blow tends to
push ions of like charge into contact. They repel, and the crystal shatters
(Figure 13·13).

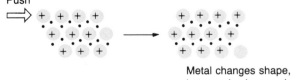

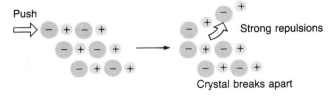

Figure 13·14

The techniques of X-ray diffraction and electron diffraction are used to determine the arrangement of atoms within a metal. This electron diffraction pattern is for stainless steel 306. Calculations based on the distances and angles within the pattern indicate that stainless steel has a body-centered cubic structure.

The atoms in metals are packed in several compact crystal forms:
1. body-centered cubic
2. face-centered cubic
3. hexagonal close-packed

Metals are among the simplest crystalline solids. Each metal contains just one kind of atom. Metal atoms are arranged in a very compact and orderly pattern, just as we might pack tennis balls in a box. Several arrangements give the closest packing possible for spheres of identical size, like metal atoms. These are body-centered cubic, face-centered cubic, and hexagonal close-packed (Figure 13·15).

In a *body-centered cubic* structure, every atom (except those on the surface) has 8 neighbors. The metallic elements sodium, potassium, iron, chromium, and tungsten crystallize in the body-centered cubic pattern.

In a *face-centered cubic* arrangement, every atom has 12 neighbors. Among the metals that form a face-centered cubic lattice are copper, silver, gold, aluminum, and lead.

In a *hexagonal close-packed* arrangement, every atom has 12 neighbors. The pattern is different, however, from the face-centered cubic. Metals that have this crystal structure include magnesium, zinc, and cadmium.

Figure 13·15

The three most common arrangements for atoms in metals are body-centered cubic (**a**) face-centered cubic (**b**) and hexagonal close-packed (**c**).

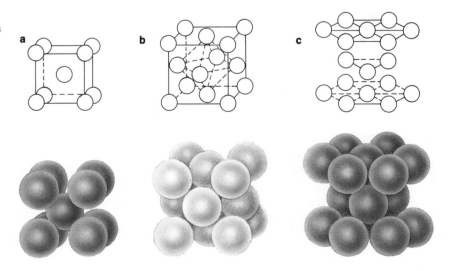

13·B Alloys

The properties of alloys are different from those of pure metals.

Solid solutions made by dissolving metals in other metals are called alloys. They are prepared by melting the metals together and cooling the mixture. If the atoms of the metals are about the same size, they can replace each other in the metal crystals. This type of mixture is called a substitutional alloy. Sterling silver, an alloy of copper and silver, is an example of a substitutional alloy.

Sometimes the atomic sizes of the metals in the alloy are quite different. Then the smaller atoms can fit into the interstices, the spaces between the larger atoms. This is called an interstitial alloy. In the various types of steel, for example, carbon atoms occupy the spaces between the iron atoms.

Alloys of mercury are called amalgams. They may be liquids or solids. Dental amalgam, used for filling cavities in teeth, is an alloy of mercury, silver, and zinc. It is a liquid when first prepared but hardens quickly.

The properties of alloys differ from those of their component metals. Sterling silver is harder than pure silver but still soft enough to be made into jewelry and tableware. Stainless steel, an alloy of iron, carbon, chromium, and nickel. This steel is stronger than iron and more resistant to corrosion. Table 13·2 gives the composition and use of some common alloys.

Figure 13·16
a The component metals of substitutional alloys have atoms of similar sizes.
b The component elements of an interstitial alloy have atoms of very different sizes.

Metal A	Metal B	Substitutional alloy
Metal A	Metal B	Interstitial alloy

Table 13·2	Composition of Some Common Alloys	
Name	Composition (by mass)	Use
Sterling silver	Ag 92.5%; Cu 7.5%	Jewelry, tableware
Coinage silver	Ag 90%; Cu 10%	Medals, coins
Plumber's solder	Pb 67%; Sn 33%	Soldering joints
Pewter	Sn 85%; Cu 7.3%; Bi 6%; Sb 1.7%	Tableware
Brass	Cu 60%; Zn 39%; Sn 1%	Gears
Steel	Fe 99%; C 1%	Structural material
Cast iron	Fe 96%; C 4%	Castings
Stainless steel	Fe 80.6%; Cr 18%; C 0.4%; Ni 1%	Cutlery
Spring steel	Fe 98.6%; Cr 1%; C 0.4%	Cutting tools, springs
Surgical steel	Fe 67%; Cr 18%; Ni 12%; Mo 3%	Skeletal implants
18-Carat gold	Au 75%; Ag/Cu 25%	Gold jewelry
Duraluminum	Al 94.5%; Cu 5%; Mg 0.5%	Aircraft parts

Ionic Bonds

Chapter Review

13

Key Terms

coordination number		ionic bond	13·4
	13·5	metallic bond	13·6
electron dot structure		octet rule	13·2
	13·1	valence electron	13·1
halide ion	13·3		

Chapter Summary

Atoms are held together in compounds by chemical bonds. Chemical bonds result from the sharing or transfer of valence electrons between pairs of atoms. Bonded atoms attain the stable electron configuration of a noble gas. The noble gases themselves exist as isolated atoms because that is their most stable condition. The transfer of one or more valence electrons between atoms produces positively and negatively charged ions: cations and anions.

The attraction between an anion and a cation is an ionic bond. A substance with ionic bonds is an ionic compound. Nearly all ionic compounds are crystalline solids at room temperature. They generally have high melting points. These solids consist of positive and negative ions packed in an orderly arrangement. The total positive charge is balanced by the total negative charge. Ionic compounds, also known as salts, are electrically neutral. Many ionic compounds contain polyatomic ions. The coordination number indicates the number of ions of opposite charge that surround each ion in a crystal.

Metals are like ionic compounds in some ways. They consist of positive metal ions packed together and surrounded by a sea of their valence electrons. This arrangement constitutes the metallic bond. The valence electrons are mobile and can travel from one end of a piece of metal to the other. This electron mobility accounts for the excellent electrical conductivity of metals and helps explain why metals are malleable and ductile. Metals are among the simplest crystalline solids. The metal atoms are commonly packed in a body-centered cubic, a face-centered cubic, or a hexagonal close-packed arrangement.

Practice Questions and Problems

8. Define the term *valence electrons*.   13·1

9. List the first three elements in Group 2A and Group 3A and determine how many valence electrons each of them has.   13·1

10. Name the first four halogens. What group are they in, and how many valence electrons does each of them have?   13·1

11. How many electrons does each of the following atoms have? What groups are they in?   13·1
  a. nitrogen   **c.** phosphorus
  b. lithium   **d.** barium

12. Write electron dot structures for each of the following elements.   13·1
  a. Cl   **c.** Al
  b. S   **d.** Li

13. Write electron dot structures for each of these elements.   13·1
  a. calcium   **c.** arsenic
  b. selenium   **d.** beryllium

14. The atoms of the noble gas elements are stable. Explain.   13·2

15. In your own words state the *octet rule*.   13·2

16. How many electrons must be lost by each of the following atoms to attain a noble gas electron configuration?   13·2
  a. Ca   **d.** Li
  b. Al   **e.** Ba
  c. Na   **f.** Mg

17. What are cations? How and why are cations produced? *13·2*

18. Write the formula for the ion you get when the following elements lose their valence electrons. *13·2*
   a. aluminum
   b. lithium
   c. barium
   d. potassium
   e. calcium
   f. strontium

19. Write complete electron configurations for the following atoms and ions. For each group, comment on the results. *13·2*
   a. Ar, K^+, Ca^{2+}
   b. Ne, Na^+, Mg^{2+}, Al^{3+}

20. What is meant by a *pseudo noble-gas* electron configuration? *13·2*

21. What are anions? How and why are anions produced? *13·3*

22. How many electrons must be gained by each of the following atoms to achieve a stable electron configuration? *13·3*
   a. I
   b. S
   c. N
   d. Cl
   e. P
   f. O

23. Write the formula for the ion you get when each of the following elements gains electrons and attains a noble gas configuration. *13·3*
   a. Br
   b. O
   c. H
   d. F
   e. As
   f. Se

24. Write electron configurations for the following and comment on the result. *13·3*
   a. N^{3-}
   b. O^{2-}
   c. F^-
   d. Ne

25. What is an ionic compound? What holds an ionic compound together? *13·4*

26. Why are ionic compounds electrically neutral? *13·4*

27. What is a *salt*? *13·4*

28. Which of the following pairs of elements are most likely to form ionic compounds? *13·4*
   a. magnesium and bromine
   b. chlorine and bromine
   c. potassium and helium
   d. nitrogen and sulfur
   e. lithium and fluorine
   f. carbon and oxygen
   g. iodine and sodium

29. Which pairs of elements will not form ionic compounds? *13·4*
   a. sulfur and oxygen
   b. sodium and calcium
   c. sodium and sulfur
   d. oxygen and chlorine
   e. barium and chlorine

30. Write the correct chemical formula, the formula unit, for the following pairs of ions. *13·4*
   a. K^+, S^{2-}
   b. Ca^{2+}, O^{2-}
   c. Na^+, SO_4^{2-}
   d. Al^{3+}, PO_4^{3-}

31. Write the formula for the ions in the following compounds. *13·4*
   a. KCl
   b. $NaNO_3$
   c. $BaSO_4$
   d. $MgBr_2$
   e. KOH
   f. Li_2CO_3

32. Name these compounds. *13·4*
   a. KBr
   b. AgCl
   c. $CaSO_4$
   d. FeO
   e. CuCl
   f. $NaHCO_3$

33. Write formulas for the following compounds. *13·4*
   a. potassium nitrate
   b. sodium carbonate
   c. barium chloride
   d. magnesium sulfate
   e. lithium oxide
   f. ammonium carbonate
   g. calcium phosphate
   h. aluminum hydroxide

34. In your own words describe a *crystal*. *13·5*

35. What determines the crystal structure of an ionic compound? *13·5*

36. Most ionic substances are brittle. Why? *13·5*

37. Why does molten $MgCl_2$ conduct an electric current although crystalline $MgCl_2$ does not? *13·5*

38. In your own words define a *metallic bond*. *13·6*

39. Describe what is meant by the terms *ductile* and *malleable*. *13·6*

40. Why is it possible to bend metals but not ionic crystals? *13·6*

41. Explain briefly why metals are good conductors of electricity. *13·6*

42. Name the three crystal arrangements that give close-packing of metal atoms. Give an example of a metal that crystallizes in each arrangement. *13·6*

Mastery Questions and Problems

43. Which of the following substances are most probably *not* ionic? *13·4*
  a. H_2O
  b. Na_2O
  c. CO_2
  d. CaS
  e. NH_3
  f. SO_2

44. Construct a table that shows the relationship among the group number, valence electrons lost, and the formula of the cation or anion produced for the following metallic and nonmetallic elements. Na, Ca, Al, N, S, Br *13·3*

45. Write electron dot formulas for the following atoms. *13·1*
  a. C
  b. Be
  c. Mg
  d. O
  e. He
  f. F
  g. Na
  h. P

46. Why does a cation have a positive charge? *13·2*

47. Which of the following species would not be present in a crystal of sodium chloride? *13·4*
  a. Na^+
  b. Cl
  c. Cl^-
  d. Na^{2+}
  e. Cl_2
  f. $NaCl_2$

48. Metallic cobalt crystallizes in a hexagonal close-packed structure. What is the coordination number of a cobalt atom? *13·6*

49. Write electron configurations for the dipositive ions of these elements. *13·2*
  a. Fe **b.** Co **c.** Ni

50. Write electron dot structures for each of the following atoms. *13·1*
  a. I
  b. Sr
  c. Te
  d. Cs
  e. Sb
  f. Xe

51. Why does an anion have a negative charge? *13·3*

52. Some elements are found in nature mainly as their ions. Why? *13·2*

53. Show the relationship between the electron dot structure of an element and the location of the element in the periodic table. *13·1*

54. Write electron configurations for the tripositive ions of these elements. *13·2*
  a. Cr **b.** Mn **c.** Fe

55. Explain how hexagonal close-packed, face-centered cubic, and body-centered cubic unit cells are different. *13·6*

56. Write electron configurations for these atoms and ions, and comment on the result. *13·3*
  a. Ar
  b. Cl^-
  c. S^{2-}
  d. P^{3-}

Review Questions and Problems

57. Hydrogen and oxygen react to give water according to this equation.

$$2H_2 + O_2 \longrightarrow 2H_2O$$

How many liters of hydrogen at STP are needed to produce 0.50 mol of water? *9·4*

58. Distinguish among gases, liquids, and solids with respect to shape, volume, relative density, and motion of particles. *9·8*

59. What is the volume in liters occupied by 8.0 g of oxygen gas at STP? *9·4*

60. If you raise the temperature of a gas, what actually happens to the gas particles? *9·2*

61. A gas occupies 750 cm³ at 27°C and 0.016 atm. Find its volume at STP.

62. Explain each of these observations on the basis of the kinetic theory and the forces of attraction that exist between the particles in matter.
  a. Water evaporates faster at 40°C than 20°C.
  b. A burn from steam at 100°C is worse than a burn from water at 100°C.
  c. A cap "pops" off a bottle of root beer that has been kept in the trunk of a car on a hot day.
  d. Diethyl ether, $C_4H_{10}O$, has a vapor pressure of 442 mm Hg at 20°C, whereas the vapor pressure of water at this temperature is only 17.5 mm Hg.
  e. A melting ice cube cools a glass of tea.
  f. Foods are dehydrated (water is removed) by using low pressures rather than high heat.

63. Use the gas laws and the kinetic theory to complete these statements. Unless otherwise stated, assume a constant amount of gas.
  a. As the volume of a gas increases at constant temperature, its pressure _____ .

b. As the temperature of a gas increases and its pressure decreases, its volume _____ .

c. At constant pressure, a decrease in the volume of a gas is caused by a/an _____ in its temperature.

d. An increase in the volume and pressure of a gas is caused by a/an _____ in its temperature.

e. At constant volume, a decrease in the temperature of a gas causes the pressure to _____ .

f. If the volume of a gas is increased while its temperature is increased, the pressure will _____ .

64. A gas mixture contains 1.50 g of O_2 and 1.50 g of N_2. If the partial pressure of O_2 is 475 mm Hg, what is the total pressure of the mixture?

65. At what temperature will the average kinetic energy of a nitrogen molecule be twice that at 25°C?

66. Calculate the volume of hydrogen in cm^3 at STP that will be produced when 35.0 g of zinc metal reacts with an excess of dilute sulfuric acid.

Challenging Questions and Problems

67. The chemically similar alkali metal chlorides NaCl and CsCl have different crystal structures whereas the chemically different NaCl and MnS have the same crystal structures. Why?

68. Silver crystallizes in a face-centered cubic unit cell. A silver atom is at the edge of each lattice point. The length of the edge of the unit cell is 0.4086 nm. What is the atomic radius of silver?

Research Projects

1. Grow samples of crystals. Test the effects of varying temperature, varying concentrations, and impurities.

2. Devise a way to compare the space occupied by an ion and by an atom of the same element.

3. What is the historical significance of salt (NaCl)?

4. Trace the history of food preservation.

5. What are some common chemical food additives? Why are some considered harmful in high concentrations?

6. Report on studies linking nitrosoamines to cancer.

7. Describe the techniques used by geochemists to analyze rock samples. How do other scientists use this information?

8. Are alloys mixtures or compounds? Devise experiments to test your answer.

9. Construct a model for each type of unit cell, and find a chemical example of each.

10. What alloys are used in structural materials? Why are they used?

Readings and References

Freydberg, Nicholas, and Willis A. Gortner. *The Food Additives Book*. New York: Bantam Books, 1982.

Hansen, James. "Metals that Remember." *Science 81* (June 1981), pp. 44–47.

Packard, Vernal S., Jr. *Processed Foods and the Consumer*. Minneapolis: University of Minnesota Press, 1976.

Sanders, Kevin. "Muscle Metal." *Discover* (October 1981), pp. 92–96.

Stine, William R. *Chemistry for the Consumer*. Boston: Allyn and Bacon, 1978.

Winter, Ruth. *A Consumer's Dictionary of Food Additives*. New York: Crown, 1978.

Section		Demonstrations and Experiments	Resource Materials
14·1 Single Covalent Bonds	C*		Objectives Worksheet 14, SPB Skillsheet 14, SPB
14·2 Double and Triple Covalent Bonds	C		
14·3 Covalent Compounds	C	Exp 26 Model Building, LM	Prelab 26, SPB
14·4 Coordinate Covalent Bonds	O		
14·5 Resonance	O		
14·6 Exceptions to the Octet Rule	H		Quiz 14·1
14·7 Molecular Orbitals	H		
14·A Molecular Models	E		
14·8 VSEPR Theory	C		Teaching Diagram 20
14·9 Hybrid Orbitals	H		Quiz 14·2
14·10 Polar Bonds	C		
14·11 Polar Molecules	C	Dem 14·1 Polar Molecules	Formaldehyde: A Hazard in the Home, ICT 14
14·12 Bond Dissociation Energies	H		
14·B Johannes van der Waals: Using the Power of Reason	E		
14·13 Intermolecular Attractions	C	Dem 14·2 Hydrogen Bonding	
14·C Bonding with Adhesives	E		
14·14 Properties of Molecular Substances	C		Quiz 14·3 Reviewsheet 14, SPB Chapter 14 Test

*C = Core, O = Optional E = Enrichment, H = Honors	LM = Laboratory Manual	SPB = Skills Practice Book ICT = Issues in Chem. Tech.

Chapter Objectives

Having studied this chapter and done the problems, the student should be able to:

1. Describe the formation of a covalent bond between two nonmetallic elements.   *14·1*

2. Describe double and triple covalent bonds.   *14·2*

3. Draw electron dot formulas for simple covalent molecules containing single, double, or triple bonds.   *14·3*

4. Explain the formation of a coordinate covalent bond.   *14·4*

5. Define resonance.   *14·5*

6. Show why some molecules which are exceptions to the octet rule may be paramagnetic.   *14·6*

7. Describe the molecular orbital theory of covalent bonding.   *14·7*

8. Distinguish between bonding and antibonding molecular orbitals.   *14·7*

9. Describe the features of sigma and pi bonds.   *14·7*

10. Use VSEPR theory to describe the shapes of simple covalently bonded molecules. *14·8*

11. Describe the shapes of simple molecules using orbital hybridization. *14·9*

12. Use electronegativity values to determine whether a bond is nonpolar covalent, polar covalent, or ionic. *14·10*

13. Show the relationship between polar covalent bonds and polar molecules. *14.11*

14. Define bond dissociation energy. *14·12*

15. Name and describe the weak attractive forces that hold molecules together. *14·13*

16. Identify the characteristics of molecular substances. *14·14*

Teaching Suggestions

14·1 Single Covalent Bonds

The stability of the noble gases is the stability of filled energy levels. Be sure your students understand that covalent bonding results from two atoms sharing electrons in an effort to fill energy levels. As electrons move back and forth between two half-filled orbitals, there are moments when both electrons will be in the same orbital. For that brief time the orbital will be filled, and the noble gas configuration achieved. As these electrons are being shared they are attracted simultaneously to both nuclei. This attraction pulls the nuclei together and forms the covalent bond.

Point out that the covalent bond can be represented in different ways, each with its own advantages. Electron dot diagrams and structural formulas can both be used to give information about the arrangement of atoms in a molecule. An electron dot formula does not give information as to the kind of bonding present since it can be used for both covalent compounds and ionic compounds. A structural formula is easier to write, and can only be used for molecules. Neither attempts to give the exact shape of the molecule.

14·2 Double and Triple Covalent Bonds

Some students may have forgotten that an orbital can contain no more than two electrons at any one time. Remind them that each half-filled orbital of an atom can only share with a single half-filled orbital of another atom. One covalent bond always consists of a pair of electrons being shared between two orbitals. Stress that a double bond between two atoms always involves two pairs of orbitals and a triple bond always involves three pairs of orbitals.

Show the students how to draw electron dot representations of multiple bonding. In multiple bonding diagrams, the bonding electrons are always rotated into the space between the element symbols. Have them note, also, that this text uses a modified electron dot representation in which the bonding electron pairs are shown as dashed lines (as in structural formulas), while the unshared pairs of electrons are shown as electron dots.

14·3 Covalent Compounds

Be sure that the students realize that atoms of Groups 2A, 3A, and 4A promote electrons to increase their bonding capacity. Spend some time showing the students examples of each group's bonding after promoting.

After the students have had experience in writing representations of bonding, have them do **Experiment 26** *Model Building*. This will reinforce the work they have just done and help them visualize molecules in later sections.

14·4 Coordinate Covalent Bonds

Coordinate covalent bonding is the exception to the rule that covalent bonding occurs between half-empty orbitals. In this case, one atom has an empty orbital and the other has a filled orbital not yet involved in a chemical bond. It is important to note that even in this case the bonding still involves only one pair of electrons and one pair of orbitals.

Stress that the negative polyatomic ions have gained their charges by the addition of one or more electrons. Show the students that these electrons are not placed randomly in the polyatomic ion structure, but go into half-filled orbitals and thus help the ion gain stability. This is illustrated well by the example of the OH^- ion. Oxygen has two half-empty orbitals. Hydrogen has one. If an O atom joins an H atom, there still is a half-empty orbital left in the oxygen atom. An electron placed in that orbital fills it, producing the stable ion.

14·5 Resonance

You might introduce this topic by having your students draw electron dot diagrams for SO_2. Emphasize that they should satisfy the bonding requirements for all three atoms in the molecule. They should end up with a structure which has one of the oxygen atoms single bonded, and the other double bonded. Then point out that experiments show that both bonds are identical. Explain that this shows that the true bonding cannot be shown with the diagrams they have just done and that the bonding in SO_2 must be some intermediate between the single and double bonds. You can then introduce the concept of resonance.

Stress that resonance can be expected whenever it is possible to write two equally valid electron dot structures.

14·6 Exceptions to the Octet Rule

The octet rule works nicely in explaining the ways in which most atoms combine. However, it does not cover all cases. This section lists some of the more important exceptions. Advise the students that this should not upset them. They should use the octet rule whenever possible and simply realize that exceptions appear now and then.

14·7 Molecular Orbitals

The explanations of bonding that we have been using have served chemistry well over the years. However, there are some phenomena (such as paramagnetism) which are not satisfactorily explained by these models. These deficiencies arise from the assumption that the electrons in a molecule occupy orbitals of the individual atoms.

The molecular orbital theory attempts to treat bonds in terms of orbitals which involve an entire molecule. It assumes that the atomic orbitals of atoms are combined to give a new set of molecular orbitals which have their own characteristics. These orbitals are arranged in order of increasing energy, and the valence electrons of the molecule distributed among the available molecular orbitals. Electrons are placed in these orbitals following the same rules as for atomic orbitals. (Two electrons per orbital, electrons in the lowest energy level, and Hund's rule.)

Emphasize that the combining of two atomic orbitals always produces two molecular orbitals. The most stable bonds occur if there are *two* electrons in the bonding orbital and *none* in the antibonding orbital. Work out the bonding diagrams of several examples, showing the formation of the sigma and pi bonds.

14·8 VSEPR Theory

This theory does not attempt to explain how bonds form, but does explain why molecules take the shapes they do. The best way to get the students to understand it is to work through examples. Take steps to help them visualize the various shapes. Refer to diagrams or drawings, or use molecular models (space filling or ball and stick) to show the various atoms and their positions.

14·9 Hybrid Orbitals

Hybridization not only explains how atoms bond, but also the shapes of the molecules they form. The key concept in hybridization is that atomic orbitals blend together to form entirely new orbitals which have new characteristics.

The most important examples of hybridization occur with the element carbon. However it can occur with any of the elements in Groups 2A, 3A, and 4A (the ones which promote electrons.) Again, use diagrams and/or models to get the idea of hybridization across.

14·10 Polar Bonds

Point out that so far we have taken a simplistic approach to bonding. We have referred to a bond as being either covalent or ionic, as if the two were mutually exclusive. The reality is, however, that most chemical bonds are neither totally covalent nor totally ionic. In these bonds the electrons are not shared equally, but displaced more toward one atom than the other. In other words, the bond is polar.

Using Tables 12·3 and 14·3, go over examples of various combinations of atoms with the students. Have them predict whether the bonding is predominately covalent or ionic and which atom(s) are positively charged and which are negatively charged.

14·11 Polar Molecules

In this section emphasize that a polar molecule must have at least one polar bond within it. However, not all molecules that have polar bonds are polar molecules. It is possible that the dipoles within the molecule are oriented in such a manner as to cancel. This is a difficult concept to get across, since the cancellation of dipoles involves visualizing the bonding geometry and the addition of vectors.

Use plenty of examples, and refer continually to diagrams and models. Avoid situations in which you are trying to find the resultant of unequal dipoles. Then as a simplification you can reasonably assume that dipoles which are equal in strength and symmetrically oriented in opposite directions cancel each other. As an illustration have the students consider what happens to a methane molecule as its hydrogen atoms are substituted one at a time by chlorine atoms. As you go through the series, CH_4, CH_3Cl, CH_2Cl_2, $CHCl_3$, CCl_4, you can show that the first and last are nonpolar and the middle three are polar.

A simple test of whether a liquid is polar or not is to pass it through an electric field and observe its behavior. If you wish to show the students the effect of an electric field on polar and nonpolar molecules, try doing **Demonstration 14·1** *Polar Molecules*.

14·12 Bond Dissociation Energies

The main point here is that the bond dissociation energy is a measure of the stability of a bond. Stress that the higher the bond dissociation energy, the greater the stability of the bond.

14·13 Intermolecular Attractions

14·14 Properties of Molecular Substances

Start off this section by emphasizing that the bonding we have considered up to now is the bonding which holds atoms together to form molecules. The sharing of electrons ties the atoms together and isolates the electrons from any

further interaction with other atoms. If there were no other forces present, then all substances made of covalently bonded molecules would be gases at any temperature. The purpose of this section is to acquaint the students with some of the forces that exist *between* covalently bonded molecules and cause them to form liquids and solids.

The weakest forces of all are the van der Waals forces. Be sure the students realize that all molecules (and atoms) have these forces between them and if no other forces are present, these are the forces which allow them to form liquids and even solids. Van der Waals forces are negligible, however, when *any* other bonding forces (such as dipole interactions or hydrogen bonding) are possible.

Be sure the students understand the nature of hydrogen bonding and its importance. It explains many of the properties of water and is very much involved in the chemistry of living systems.

Demonstration 14·2 *Hydrogen Bonding* shows these intermolecular attractions.

Demonstrations

14·1 Polar Molecules

Concept: Polar molecules show electrostatic attractions to charged materials.

Materials: fur, rubber or amber rod, vinyl strip, wool, glass rod, silk, acetate strip, cotton, water, two burets, ring stands, buret clamps, turpentine.

Procedure: 1. Fill one buret with water and the other with turpentine. 2. Rub the vinyl strip with wool and the rubber rod with fur to give them negative charges. 3. Bring the vinyl strip near the open end of the water-containing buret as you slowly let the water out. Carefully observe the behavior of the stream of water. Repeat using the rubber rod. 4. Repeat step *3* with the turpentine-containing buret. 5. Rub the acetate strip with cotton and the glass rod with silk to give them positive charges. 6. Repeat step *3* with the acetate strip and rubber rod. 7. Repeat step *3* with the turpentine-containing buret. 8. Point out that the polar water molecules are attracted to both the positively and negatively charged materials, but the nonpolar turpentine molecules are not attracted to either. 9. This demonstration may be extended to determine if various liquids are polar. **Caution:** *Turpentine is an irritant.*

14·2 Hydrogen Bonding

Concept: Hydrogen bonding increases the surface tension and viscosity of liquids.

Materials: 100 mL each of glycerin, ethylene, glycol, water, ethanol, and kerosene in 300-mL stoppered bottles, safety goggles.

Procedure: 1. Gently rotate one of the bottles so that its contents begin to swirl. 2. Note how long it takes before the swirling vortex that is formed disappears. 3. Repeat for each of the fluids. It is important that each bottle be rotated an equal amount. 4. If done carefully, the times should be in the same order in which the materials are listed above. Since hydrogen bonding increases surface tension and viscosity, liquids with a relatively high degree of hydrogen bonding will stop moving earlier. 5. Show the structural formulas of the compounds to determine the origins of the hydrogen bonding. **Caution:** *Kerosene is flammable.*

Audiovisual Resources

Chemistry: Bonding of Atoms (13 FS) Charles Clark, 1977, 10–18 min. each. (Use with Sections 14·7, 14·9, 14·11, or 14·14.) Discusses molecular orbitals and shapes, hybrid orbitals, polar and nonpolar molecules and relates physical properties and bonding.

Chemistry: Chemical Bonding and Atomic Structure (F, V) Coronet, 1983, 23 min. (Use with Sections 14·1 or 14·11.) Illustrates covalent bonding using the octet rule and introduces unequal electron sharing in polar molecules.

Quest into Matter (F, V) Films Inc., 1976, 30 min. (Use with Sections 14·8, 14·9, or 14·11.) Develops the relationship between molecular symmetry and shape and the general properties of materials.

Answers to End of Chapter Questions and Problems

Practice Questions and Problems

10. Helium already has a stable electron configuration. Hydrogen atoms achieve stability by sharing an electron with another hydrogen atom.

11. a. H:Ö:H **b.** H:Ö:Ö:H **c.** :C̈l:P̈:C̈l: **d.** H:N̈:H
                                    :C̈l: H

12. a. ionic **b.** covalent **c.** ionic **d.** covalent **e.** ionic **f.** covalent

13. a. A pair of electrons is shared between two atoms; hydrogen molecule. **b.** A pair of valence electrons belongs to one atom only; the non-bonding electrons of fluorine.

14. Chemical bonds form when atoms attain a stable electron configuration of low energy. Ionic bonds depend on electrostatic attractions between ions. Covalent bonds depend on electrostatic attractions between shared electrons and protons of the combining atoms.

15. A double covalent bond has four shared electrons; a triple covalent bond has six.

16. a. :F:F: **b.** H:Cl: **c.** H:C:::C:H **d.** H:C:::N:

17. a. :I:I: **b.** :F:O:F: **c.** H:S:H **d.** :I:N:I:
　　　　　　　　　　　　　　　　　　　　　　　:I:

18. One atom provides both bonding electrons.

19. An unshared pair of electrons is needed. There are no unshared pairs in C—H or C—C bonds.

20. [:O:N::O:]⁻ ⟷ [:O::N:O:]⁻

21. :O::S:O: ⟷ :O:S::O:

22. [:O:C:O: / :O:]²⁻ ⟷ [:O:C::O: / :O:]²⁻ ⟷ [:O:C:O: / :O:]²⁻

23. a. :F:B:F: 　　 **b.** [:O:O:]⁻
　　　:F:
　　diamagnetic　　　　paramagnetic

c. :O:N::O:　　　**d.** :F:F:
　paramagnetic　　　diamagnetic

24. :N::O: It is paramagnetic because it has an unpaired electron.

25. a. :O: :N:O: 　　 **b.** [:O:H]⁻
　　　　:O:
　　diamagnetic　　　　diamagnetic

c. H:O:O·　　　**d.** :O:S::O:
　　　　　　　　　　　　:O:
　diamagnetic　　　　diamagnetic

26. They are larger atoms than nitrogen and oxygen and have *d* orbital electrons.

27.
　　　　:F:
　:F　|　　:F:
　　　Br
　:F　　　:F:

28.
$2s^1$ —[↑] — H ⟨hexagon⟩ [↑]—$2s^1$
　　　　　H　　　　　H
　　　　　　[↑↓]
　　　　　　　H

The molecule has two electrons in a bonding molecular orbital. It theoretically should exist as a diatomic molecule. The Li_2 molecule is actually moderately stable in the gas phase.

29. a. 2 sigma, 2 pi **b.** 4 sigma **c.** 6 sigma, 2 pi **d.** 6 sigma, 2 pi

30. a. The four valence-electron pairs repel each other to the corners of a tetrahedron in which they are equidistant. The angle between bonds is 109.5°. **b.** The four valence-electron pairs repel each other but the unshared pair is closer to the nitrogen than are the bonding pairs. The unshared pair repels bonded pairs more strongly. As a result, the angle between bonds is 107°. **c.** The four valence-electron pairs repel each other but the two unshared pairs are closer to the oxygen than are the bonding pairs. The unshared pairs repel bonded pairs more strongly. Therefore, the angle between bonded pairs is 105°.

31. The four valence-electron pairs repel each other but the one shared with chlorine is closer to the chlorine. The repulsion is weaker. Consequently, the bond angles between carbon and hydrogen are slightly more than 109.5°.

32. a. linear **b.** tetrahedral **c.** triangular planar **d.** bent **e.** linear **f.** bent

33. :O::C:Cl: The shape is triangular and planar.
　　　:Cl:

34. The 2s and two 2p orbitals form three sp^2 hybrid orbitals in the carbon and two oxygens. One sp^2 hybrid orbital from each atom forms a sigma bond between each oxygen and the carbon. The pi bonds between each oxygen and the carbon are formed by the unhybridized 2p orbitals.

35. The 2s and the three 2p orbitals form four sp^3 hybrid orbitals. Three of these form sigma bonds to the hydrogens and one is the unshared pair. The shape is pyramidal.

36. a. sp **b.** sp^3 **c.** sp^2 **d.** sp

37. a. ionic **b.** polar covalent: $\overset{\delta+}{C}—\overset{\delta-}{S}$ **c.** ionic **d.** polar covalent: $\overset{\delta+}{N}—\overset{\delta-}{O}$ **e.** polar covalent: $\overset{\delta+}{H}—\overset{\delta-}{O}$ **f.** polar covalent: $\overset{\delta+}{S}—\overset{\delta-}{O}$

38. c, d, a, f, b, e.

39. b, d, e, a, c, f.

40. a. $\overset{\delta+}{H}:\overset{\delta-}{O}:\overset{\delta-}{O}:\overset{\delta+}{H}$ **b.** $:\overset{\delta+}{Br}:\overset{\delta-}{Cl}:$ **c.** $\overset{\delta+}{H}:\overset{\delta-}{Br}:$ **d.** $\overset{\delta+}{H}:\overset{\delta-}{O}:\overset{\delta+}{H}$

41. a. polar **b.** polar **c.** nonpolar **d.** nonpolar

42. The energy needed to break a single bond.

43. Nitrogen and oxygen have more protons than carbon. The electrons are held closer to each nucleus, reducing the overlap between orbitals and decreasing bond strength.

$$\text{H—C} \quad \text{C} \equiv \text{C} \quad \text{H—C}$$

44. H:C:::C:H 393 + 908 + 393 = 1694 kJ/mol

45. Dispersion forces are caused by the motion of electrons. Atoms with more electrons have larger attractions between them. Dipole interactions electrostatically attract polar molecules to each other.

46. A hydrogen atom covalently bonded to a fluorine, oxygen, or nitrogen atom is electrostatically attracted to an unshared pair of a nearby atom.

47. a. H_2O **b.** HF **c.** HCl **d.** H_2O

48. They require more energy to separate the molecules.

49. Atoms are covalently bonded to each other; diamond and silicon carbide.

Mastery Questions and Problems

50. The $3s$ and three $3p$ orbitals of P hybridize to form four sp^3 hybrid orbitals. The resulting shape is pyramidal with a bond angle of 107° between the sigma bonds.

51. :N::N::O: :N: : :N:O: It is diamagnetic and linear.

52. :Cl:S:Cl:
　　　:O:

53. a. Carbon does not have an octet. $[:C:::N:]^-$
b. A fluorine atom has 10 electrons. :F:P:F:
　　　　　　　　　　　　　　　　　　:F:
c. Carbon and oxygen do not have octets. H:C::O:
　　　　　　　　　　　　　　　　　　　　　　:Cl:
d. Boron does not follow the octet rule. (There are too many electrons.) :F:B:F:
　　　　　　　　　　　　　　　　　　　　:F:

54. a. Sigma bonds have an overlap of the orbitals between two nuclei. Pi bonds involve an overlap of unhybridized p orbitals. **b.** Polar bonds have a difference in electronegativity of the atoms in a covalent bond. Polar molecules have a dipole caused by bond polarity that is not canceled by any symmetry in the molecule. **c.** Diamagnetic molecules are weakly repelled by a magnetic field and have only paired electrons in their orbitals. Paramagnetic molecules are attracted by a magnetic field and have unpaired electrons in their orbitals. **d.** The sp^2 hybrid orbitals are formed from one s and two p orbitals, have a bond angle of 120°, and

have a triangular shape. The sp^3 hybrid orbitals are formed from one s and three p orbitals, have a bond angle of about 109°, and have a tetrahedral shape.

55. $\Delta H = -55 \dfrac{\text{kJ}}{\text{mol}}$

56. a. tetrahedral, 109.5° **b.** triangular, 120°
c. tetrahedral, 109.5° **d.** bent, 105°

57. a. 109.5° **b.** 120° **c.** 180°

58. An antibonding orbital has a higher energy because the atomic orbitals overlap on opposite sides of the nuclei, not between them.

Review Questions and Problems

59. a, b, c, d.

60. .10 mol $BaSO_4$, 23 g $BaSO_4$

61. a. $1s^2\,2s^2\,2p^6\,3s^1$ **b.** $1s^2\,2s^2\,2p^6\,3s^2\,3p^4$
c. $1s^2\,2s^2\,2p^6\,3s^2\,3p^3$ **d.** $1s^2\,2s^2\,2p^3$

62. a. $136.2\,\dfrac{\text{g}}{\text{mol}}$ **b.** $98.1\,\dfrac{\text{g}}{\text{mol}}$ **c.** $394.7\,\dfrac{\text{g}}{\text{mol}}$
d. 162.3 g/mol

63. a. 1.20×10^{22} **b.** 9.27×10^{20} **c.** 5.26×10^{15}
d. 1.81×10^{18}

64. a. manganese, Mn **b.** indium, In **c.** francium, Fr
d. polonium, Po

Challenging Questions and Problems

65.　　H
　　　H:C:H
　　　　H

The first sketch is tetrahedral. The second sketch is a tetrahedron. The bond angles in the first sketch are not all the same, with some of 90°. The bond angles in the second sketch are all 109.5°. The second sketch is correct. (Note: the wedge-shaped lines come out of the paper; the dotted lines recede into the paper.)

66.　　　:P·　　　　:S:　　　　:I:

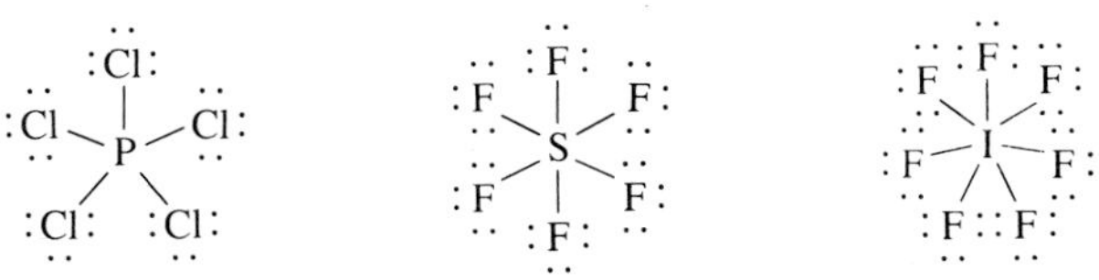

:Cl:
:Cl～P—Cl:
:Cl:　:Cl:

（:F: / :F: around S with :F: :F: :F: and :F:）

（:F: :F: :F: / :F:—I—:F: / :F::F:）

P forms 5 hybrid orbitals (dsp^3), S forms 6 hybrid orbitals (d^2sp^3), and I forms 7 hybrid orbitals from its s and p electrons.

14 Covalent Bonds

Chapter Preview

Sections 14·6, 14·7, 14·9, and 14·12 are appropriate for honors students.

The previous chapter showed how ions are formed from atoms by the gain or loss of electrons. Electrostatic attractions between ions result in ionic bonds. This chapter covers the sharing of electrons between atoms to form a different kind of bond, the covalent bond.

14·1   Single Covalent Bonds

In the previous chapter the Lewis theory of bonding was applied to the formation of cations, anions, and ionic bonds. Another part of the Lewis theory holds that some atoms share electrons to attain noble-gas electron configurations. Covalent bonds are the result of electron-sharing between atoms. Atoms of hydrogen and the nonmetallic elements in Groups 4A, 5A, 6A, and 7A of the periodic table are particularly prone to form covalent bonds. This tendency is summarized in the octet rule for covalent bonding: *The sharing of electrons occurs when the atoms involved can thus acquire particularly stable electron configurations*. Often the configurations contain eight valence electrons (an octet). The notable exception is hydrogen, which must share two electrons to acquire the stable electron configuration of helium.

Hydrogen is the simplest molecule. A hydrogen atom has a single valence electron. Pairs of hydrogen atoms share electrons to form simple

■ Atoms share electrons in covalent bonds.

Figure 14·1
Chemists use molecular models to help explain the behavior of substances. This is a ball-and-stick model of propanol (rubbing alcohol)

diatomic molecules. Each hydrogen gets the stable electron configuration of helium, which has two valence electrons. *A **single covalent bond** is formed when a pair of electrons is shared between two atoms*. The chemical formula for the hydrogen molecule is therefore H_2.

$$H\cdot \quad + \quad \cdot H \quad \longrightarrow \quad H:H \quad \text{shared pair of electrons}$$

Hydrogen atom   Hydrogen atom   Hydrogen molecule

Sometimes it is helpful to show the pair of electrons in a covalent bond as a dash, as in H—H for hydrogen. Notations of this type are structural formulas. **Structural formulas** *are chemical formulas that show the arrangement of atoms in molecules and polyatomic ions*. The dashes between the atoms in structural formulas always indicate a pair of shared electrons. The dashes are never used to show ionic bonds.

The formula of hydrogen, H_2, brings up a difference between the chemical formulas of ionic and covalent compounds. The chemical formulas of ionic compounds are correctly described only as *formula units*. The chemical formulas of covalent compounds are correctly described only as *molecular formulas*. Ionic compounds do not have molecular formulas because they do not contain molecules. The formula unit of copper(II) oxide is CuO and not Cu_2O_2 because CuO represents the smallest electrically neutral sample that is representative of the composition of

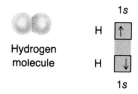

Figure 14·2
The two bonding electrons in the hydrogen molecule come from the 1s atomic orbitals of the hydrogen atoms.

The quantum mechanical model of the atom was not yet developed when Lewis developed his theory of bonding. Thus Lewis did not use electron configurations to show the electrons that are involved in bonding. The electron configurations are included here as an alternate way of showing which electrons are involved in bonds.

Figure 14·3
Sodium chloride, an ionic compound, and water, a molecular compound, are compared here. How do molecular compounds differ from ionic compounds?
Ionic compounds are made up of arrays of ions. Molecular compounds are collections of molecules.

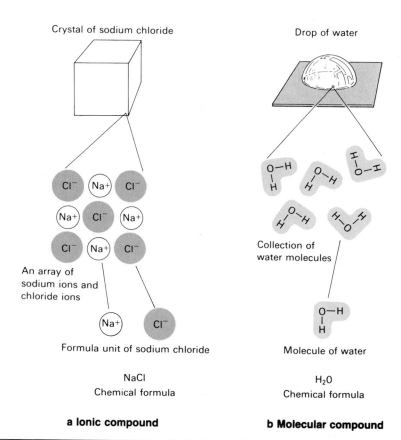

a Ionic compound

b Molecular compound

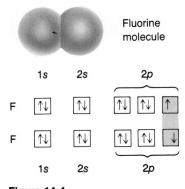

Figure 14·4
The two bonding electrons in the fluorine molecule come from the $2p$ atomic orbitals of the fluorine atoms.

1. **a.** $:\ddot{Cl}:\ddot{Cl}:$

   b. $:\ddot{Br}:\ddot{Br}:$

   c. $:\ddot{I}:\ddot{I}:$

▇ Some pairs of atoms share two or three pairs of electrons.

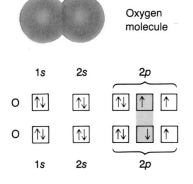

Figure 14·5
The oxygen molecule is an exception to the octet rule. It forms only a single bond, and it has two unpaired electrons.

copper(II) oxide. In a similar way, only one pair of shoes, not two, is needed to show someone what a pair of shoes is. On the other hand, a single hydrogen molecule actually contains two hydrogen atoms bonded together. Writing the molecular formula of hydrogen as H would be similar to showing one shoe to someone who asks to see a pair. Sometimes the correct formulas of molecular compounds have subscripts that are multiples of the lowest whole number ratio, as in C_3H_6 or C_4H_{10}. Those of ionic compounds seldom do. Figure 14·3 illustrates the essential difference between ionic compounds and covalent compounds.

The halogens also form single covalent bonds in their diatomic molecules. Fluorine is one example, and the other halogens are similar. Because a fluorine atom has seven valence electrons, it needs one more to attain the electron configuration of neon. By electron-sharing, two fluorine atoms gain stability. By this process they form a single covalent bond.

$$:\ddot{F}\cdot \quad + \quad \cdot\ddot{F}: \quad \longrightarrow \quad :\ddot{F}:\ddot{F}: \quad or \quad :\ddot{F}{-}\ddot{F}:$$

| Fluorine atom | Fluorine atom | Fluorine molecule |

Notice that each fluorine nucleus shares only one pair of valence electrons. *The pairs of valence electrons that are not shared between atoms are called unshared pairs of electrons, or* **unshared pairs.** They are also called *lone pairs* or *nonbonding pairs.*

Problem

1. Draw electron dot structures for these diatomic halogen molecules.
   a. chlorine **b.** bromine **c.** iodine

14·2 Double and Triple Covalent Bonds

Atoms can sometimes share more than one pair of electrons to attain stable, noble-gas electron configurations. **Double covalent bonds** *involve two shared pairs of electrons.* **Triple covalent bonds** *include three shared pairs of electrons.*

Oxygen, O_2, is an example of a molecule that should have a double covalent bond according to the octet rule. Oxygen atoms, with six valence electrons, could share two of these electrons with another oxygen molecule to form the double bond.

$$:\ddot{O}: \quad + \quad :\ddot{O}: \quad \longrightarrow \quad :\ddot{O}::\ddot{O}: \quad or \quad :\ddot{O}{=}\ddot{O}:$$

| Oxygen atom | Oxygen atom | Oxygen molecule |

Experimental evidence indicates, however, that the electrons in the oxygen molecule are not all paired (see Section 14·6). Thus oxygen represents an exception to the octet rule.

The nitrogen molecule contains a triple covalent bond. Each nitrogen atom has five valence electrons. It needs three more to attain the electron

Table 14·1	The Diatomic Elements		
Name	Chemical formula	Structure	Properties and Uses
Fluorine	F_2	:F̤—F̤:	Greenish-yellow reactive toxic gas. Compounds of fluorine, a halogen, are added to drinking water and toothpaste to promote healthy teeth.
Chlorine	Cl_2	:C̤l—C̤l:	Greenish-yellow reactive toxic gas. Chlorine is a halogen used in household bleaching agents.
Bromine	Br_2	:B̤r—B̤r:	Dense red-brown liquid with pungent odor. This Compounds of bromine are used in the preparation of photographic emulsions.
Iodine	I_2	:I̤—I̤:	Dense gray-black solid that produces purple vapors; a halogen. A solution of iodine in alcohol (tincture of iodine) is used as an antiseptic.
Hydrogen	H_2	H—H	Colorless, odorless, tasteless gas. Hydrogen is the lightest known element.
Nitrogen	N_2	:N≡N:	Colorless, odorless, tasteless gas. Air is 80% nitrogen by volume.
Oxygen	O_2	:O̤—O̤:	Colorless, odorless, tasteless gas that is vital for life. Air is 20% oxygen by volume.

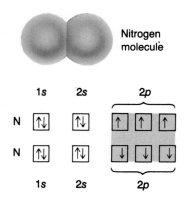

Figure 14·6
Three pairs of electrons are shared in a nitrogen molecule.

Generally as the number of multiple bonds increases, so does the chemical reactivity. Ethane, C_2H_6, is more stable than ethene, C_2H_4. Ethene is more stable than ethyne, C_2H_2.

configuration of neon. In the nitrogen molecule each nitrogen has one unshared pair of electrons.

$$:\overset{\cdot}{N}\cdot \ + \ \cdot\overset{\cdot}{N}: \ \longrightarrow \ :N::N: \quad or \quad :N≡N:$$

Nitrogen atom   Nitrogen atom   Nitrogen molecule

Up to this point, the examples of covalent bonds have all been in molecules of diatomic elements. Table 14·1 lists these elements and their properties.

14·3 Covalent Compounds

Electron dot formulas for molecules of compounds can be written in much the same way as for molecules of the diatomic elements. This will be shown with four examples: water, ammonia, methane, and carbon dioxide.

Water is a triatomic molecule. Two hydrogen atoms share electrons with one oxygen atom. The hydrogen and oxygen atoms attain stable noble-gas configurations by electron-sharing. The oxygen nucleus in water has two unshared pairs of valence electrons.

$$2H\cdot \ + \ :\overset{\cdot\cdot}{O}\cdot \ \longrightarrow \ :\overset{\cdot\cdot}{O}:H \quad or \quad :\overset{\cdot\cdot}{O}—H$$

Hydrogen atoms   Oxygen atom   Water molecule

Figure 14·7

a In the water molecule two hydrogen atoms form single covalent bonds with an oxygen atom.
b In the ammonia molecule three hydrogen atoms form single covalent bonds with a nitrogen atom.

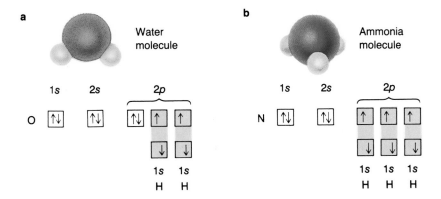

a Water molecule
b Ammonia molecule

■ Covalent molecules share electrons thus obtaining stable noble gas configurations.

Ammonia, a suffocating gas, is formed in a similar way. The ammonia molecule has one unshared pair of electrons.

$$3\text{H·} \quad + \quad \text{:}\dot{\text{N}}\text{·} \quad \longrightarrow \quad \begin{matrix} \text{H} \\ \text{:N:H} \\ \text{N} \end{matrix} \quad or \quad \begin{matrix} \text{H} \\ | \\ \text{:N—H} \\ | \\ \text{N} \end{matrix}$$

Hydrogen atoms   Nitrogen atom   Ammonia molecule

The carbon atom has four valence electrons and needs four more to attain a noble-gas configuration. The methane molecule contains four hydrogen atoms that each share one electron with carbon. In this way four identical carbon–hydrogen bonds are formed.

$$4\text{H·} \quad + \quad \text{·}\dot{\text{C}}\text{·} \quad \longrightarrow \quad \begin{matrix} \text{H} \\ \text{H:C:H} \\ \text{H} \end{matrix} \quad or \quad \begin{matrix} \text{H} \\ | \\ \text{H—C—H} \\ | \\ \text{H} \end{matrix}$$

Hydrogen atoms   Carbon atom   Methane molecule

When carbon bonds with other atoms it usually forms four bonds. You might not have predicted this from the electron configuration of atomic carbon.

$$1s^2 \quad 2s^2 \qquad 2p^2$$

Any attempt to generate covalent C—H bonds for methane by combining the two $2p$ electrons of the carbon with two $1s$ electrons of hydrogen atoms would produce a molecule with the formula CH_2. Yet carbon tends to form four bonds to other atoms. This can be explained if a small amount of energy is used to promote a $2s^2$ electron to the vacant $2p$ orbital.

$$1s^2 \qquad 2s \text{ and } 2p$$

The electron promotion provides four electrons of carbon capable of entering into covalent bonds with four hydrogen atoms (Figure 14·8).

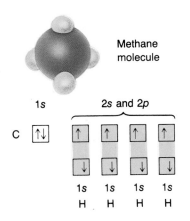

Methane molecule

1s   2s and 2p

C

1s 1s 1s 1s
H   H   H   H

Figure 14·8
The methane molecule has four carbon-hydrogen bonds. In each bond the carbon and a hydrogen share an electron from a 1s hydrogen orbital and an electron from a carbon orbital.

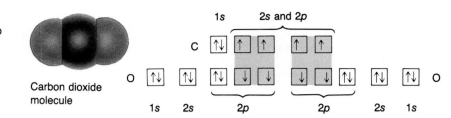

The carbon dioxide molecule contains two oxygens that each share two electrons with carbon to form two carbon–oxygen double bonds.

$$:\overset{..}{O}: \ + \ \cdot\overset{.}{\underset{.}{C}}\cdot \ + \ :\overset{..}{O}: \longrightarrow \ :\overset{..}{O}::C::\overset{..}{O}: \ or \ :\overset{..}{O}{=}C{=}\overset{..}{O}:$$

| Oxygen atom | Carbon atom | Oxygen atom | Carbon dioxide molecule |

If it did not promote an electron, the carbon atom would still have an unfilled orbital. By promoting and entering into covalent bonding it can have electrons in all of its orbitals and thus achieve stability. Atoms of groups 2A, 3A, and 4A promote when possible.

Example 1

Hydrogen chloride (HCl) is a diatomic molecule with a single covalent bond. Draw the electron dot structure for HCl.

Solution

To form a single covalent bond, hydrogen and chlorine atoms must share a pair of electrons. First write electron dot structures for the two atoms. Then show the electron-sharing.

$$H\cdot \ + \ \cdot\overset{..}{\underset{..}{C}l}: \longrightarrow \ H:\overset{..}{\underset{..}{C}l}:$$

| Hydrogen atom | Chlorine atom | Hydrogen chloride molecule |

Through electron-sharing, hydrogen and chlorine atoms attain the electron configurations of the noble gases helium and argon.

Problem

2. Draw electron dot structures for the following covalent molecules which have only single covalent bonds.
   a. H_2S **b.** PH_3 **c.** ClF

2. a. $H:\overset{..}{\underset{..}{S}}:H$

b. $H:\overset{..}{\underset{..}{P}}:H$
$\quad \quad H$

c. $:\overset{..}{\underset{..}{C}l}:\overset{..}{\underset{..}{F}}:$

In a coordinate covalent bond one atom contributes both bonding electrons.

Safety

Carbon monoxide, is a colorless, odorless, toxic gas. It may be formed when fuels burn in a limited supply of oxygen. Do not burn a fuel in an enclosed area.

14·4   Coordinate Covalent Bonds

When one atom contributes both bonding electrons in a covalent bond, a **coordinate covalent bond** *is formed.* An example is carbon monoxide. A carbon atom is four electrons short of the electron configuration of neon. An oxygen atom is two electrons short. Yet it is possible for both atoms to achieve stable electron configurations by coordinate covalent bonding. To see how, begin by making a double covalent bond between carbon and oxygen.

$$\cdot\overset{.}{\underset{.}{C}}\cdot \ + \ :\overset{..}{O}: \longrightarrow \ :C::\overset{..}{O}:$$

| Carbon atom | Oxygen atom |

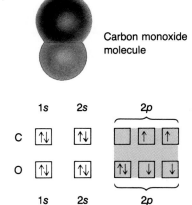

Carbon monoxide molecule

	1s	2s	2p
C	⇅	⇅	↑ ↑
O	⇅	⇅	⇅ ↓ ↓
	1s	2s	2p

Figure 14·10
In a coordinate covalent compound such as is formed by carbon monoxide, one atom contributes both electrons of a bonding pair.

With the double bond in place, the oxygen atom has a stable configuration but the carbon atom does not. The dilemma is solved if the oxygen also donates one of its unshared pairs of electrons to make a coordinate covalent bond.

$$:C::O: \longrightarrow :C::O:$$

Carbon monoxide molecule

Coordinate covalent bonds are shown in structural formulas as arrows. They point from the atom donating the pair of electrons to the atom receiving them. The structural formula of carbon monoxide, with two covalent bonds and one coordinate covalent bond, is $C \equiv O$. Coordinate covalent bonds are often shown by arrows. It is important to realize though, that once formed, a coordinate covalent bond is like any other covalent bond. The only difference is the source of the bonding electrons. The polyatomic ammonium ion (NH_4^+) has a coordinate covalent bond. It is formed when a hydrogen ion is attracted to the unshared electron pair of an ammonia molecule.

Unshared electron pair

$$H^+ + :N:H \longrightarrow \left[H:N:H \right]^+ \quad or \quad H \leftarrow N^+ - H$$

| Hydrogen ion (proton) | Ammonia molecule (NH_3) | Ammonium ion (NH_4^+) |

Most polyatomic cations and anions contain covalent and coordinate covalent bonds. Table 14·2 lists some common covalent compounds.

Example 2

The polyatomic hydronium ion (H_3O^+) contains a coordinate covalent bond. It forms when a hydrogen ion is attracted to an unshared electron pair of a water molecule. Write the electron dot structure for the hydronium ion.

Solution

$$H^+ + :O:H \longrightarrow \left[H:O:H \right]^+ \quad or \quad H \leftarrow O - H$$

| Hydrogen ion (proton) | Water molecule (H_2O) | Hydronium ion (H_3O^+) |

Many polyatomic ions have a negative charge. Because the atoms in polyatomic ions are covalently bonded, electron dot structures can be written for these ions. The negative charge of a polyatomic ion shows the number of electrons *in addition* to the valence electrons of the atoms

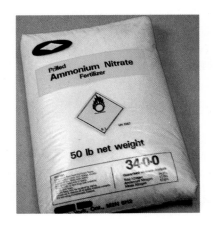

Figure 14·11
The polyatomic ammonium ion is an important component of fertilizer.

Table 14·2 Some Common Covalent Compounds

Name	Chemical formula	Structure	Properties and Uses
Carbon monoxide	CO	:C≡O:	Colorless, highly toxic gas. It is a major air pollutant present in cigarette smoke and automobile exhaust.
Carbon dioxide	CO_2	:O=C=O:	Colorless unreactive gas. This normal component of the atmosphere is exhaled in the breath of animals and is essential for plant growth.
Water	H_2O	H—O: H	Colorless, odorless, tasteless liquid with melting point of 0°C and boiling point of 100°C. The human body is approximately 60% water.
Hydrogen peroxide	H_2O_2	H :O—O: H	Colorless, unstable liquid when pure. It is used as rocket fuel. A 3% solution is used as a bleach and antiseptic.
Sulfur trioxide	SO_3	:O=S O: / :O=S O:	Oxides of sulfur are produced in combustion of petroleum products and coal. They are major air pollutants in industrial areas, where they cause smog. Oxides of sulfur can lead to respiratory problems.
Ammonia	NH_3	H—N—H H	Colorless gas with pungent odor; extremely soluble in water. Household ammonia is a solution of ammonia in water.
Nitric oxide	NO	:O=N·	Oxides of nitrogen are major air pollutants produced by the combustion of fossil fuels in automobile engines. They irritate the eyes, throat, and lungs. Nitrogen dioxide, a dark brown gas, readily converts to colorless dinitrogen tetroxide.
Nitrogen dioxide	NO_2	:O=N :O:	
Dinitrogen tetroxide	N_2O_4	:O N—N O: :O: O:	
Nitrous oxide	N_2O	:O←N≡N:	Colorless sweet-smelling gas. It is used as an anesthetic commonly called laughing gas.
Hydrogen cyanide	HCN	H—C≡N:	Colorless toxic gas with the smell of almonds.
Hydrogen fluoride	HF	H—F:	Four hydrogen halides, all extremely soluble in water. Hydrogen chloride, a colorless gas with pungent odor, readily dissolves in water to give a solution called hydrochloric acid.
Hydrogen chloride	HCl	H—Cl:	
Hydrogen bromide	HBr	H—Br:	
Hydrogen iodide	HI	H—I:	

present. Because a polyatomic ion is found as part of an ionic compound, these additional electrons are balanced by the positive charge of the cation of the compound.

The hydroxide ion is OH^-. The components of this ion are $H\cdot$, $\cdot\ddot{O}\cdot$, and an electron ($\cdot$). The additional electron is signified by the $1-$ charge. The stable electron dot formula is $[H\!:\!\ddot{O}\!:]^{1-}$.

Example 3

Draw the electron dot structure for sulfite, SO_3^{2-}, where sulfur is the central atom.

Solution

Start with the atoms and their valence electrons and the two "extra" electrons indicated by the charge.

$$:\!\ddot{O}\cdot \quad \cdot\ddot{S}\!: \quad \cdot\ddot{O}\!: \quad + \quad \cdot\cdot$$
$$\cdot\ddot{O}\!:$$

Join two of the oxygens to sulfur by single covalent bonds.

$$:\!\ddot{O}\!:\!\ddot{S}\!: \quad \cdot\ddot{O}\!:$$
$$\cdot\ddot{O}\!:$$

Join the remaining oxygen by a coordinate covalent bond, and add the "extra" two electrons.

$$:\!\ddot{O}\!:\!\ddot{S}\!:\!\ddot{O}\!: \quad + \quad \cdot\cdot \quad \left[:\!\ddot{O}\!:\!\ddot{S}\!:\!\ddot{O}\!:\right]^{2-}$$
$$\cdot\ddot{O}\!: \qquad\qquad :\!\ddot{O}\!:$$

Problem

3. Draw the electron dot structures for sulfate, SO_4^{2-}, and carbonate, CO_3^{2-}. Sulfur and carbon are the central atoms, respectively.

3.

14·5   Resonance

Consider the two electron dot structures for ozone shown below. Notice that the structure on the left can be converted to the one on the right by shifting electron pairs *without changing the positions of the oxygen atoms*.

$$:\!\ddot{O}\cdot\cdot\ddot{O}\!:\!:\!\ddot{O}\!: \quad \longleftrightarrow \quad :\!\ddot{O}\!:\!:\!\ddot{O}\cdot\cdot\ddot{O}\!:$$

The structures suggest that the bonding in ozone consists of one coordinate covalent bond and one double covalent bond. Double covalent bonds are usually shorter than single covalent bonds. Experimental measurements show, however, that the two bonds in ozone are the same length. This result can be explained if the actual bonding in the ozone molecule is the average of the two electron dot structures.

A resonance structure cannot be adequately represented by a single electron dot diagram.

Figure 14·12
Resonance is similar to the mixing of two colors. The result is intermediate between the two extremes and different from each of them.

Appropriate for honors students.

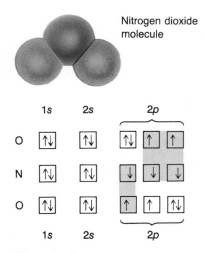

Nitrogen dioxide molecule

Figure 14·13
The nitrogen dioxide molecule is unusual in that it contains an unpaired electron.

Resonance *occurs when two or more equally valid electron dot structures can be written for a molecule*. How resonance is envisioned has changed somewhat with time. Earlier chemists imagined the electron pairs rapidly flipping back and forth, or resonating, between the various electron dot structures. Thus double-headed arrows are used to indicate that two or more structures are in resonance. A more modern interpretation is that electron pairs do not resonate. The actual resonance bonding is considered to be a hybrid, or mixture, of the extremes represented by the resonance forms. A mule is an example of a hybrid animal. The offspring of a donkey and a horse, a mule is a distinct creature with some characteristics of both parents. It is neither half-donkey nor half-horse, nor does it change continually between donkey and horse. Likewise, a resonance hybrid has some characteristics of its resonance forms, but it is a distinct species. The more resonance structures that can be drawn, the more stable is the ion or molecule.

14·6   Exceptions to the Octet Rule

Sometimes it is impossible to write electron dot structures that fulfill the octet rule. This happens whenever the total number of valence electrons in the species is an odd number. The NO_2 molecule, for example, contains a total of 17 valence electrons. Each oxygen contributes six electrons and the nitrogen contributes five. Two plausible resonance structures can be written for the NO_2 molecule.

$$\ddot{O} = \ddot{N} - \ddot{O} \cdot \quad \longleftrightarrow \quad \cdot \ddot{O} - \ddot{N} = \ddot{O}$$

An unpaired electron is present in each of these structures. No Lewis structure in which all of the atoms achieve an octet can be written.

Electrons may be considered as small, spinning, electric currents. These electric currents create magnetic fields, much as the current in an electric motor creates a magnetic field. Paired electrons can be thought of as having spins in opposite directions. The magnetic effect of paired electrons essentially cancels. Substances in which all of the electrons are paired are said to be *diamagnetic*. Diamagnetic substances are weakly repelled by an external magnetic field. In contrast, **paramagnetic** *substances show a relatively strong attraction to an external magnetic field*. These substances have molecules containing one or more unpaired electrons. Paramagnetism can be detected by measuring the mass of a substance in the absence and then in the presence of a magnetic field. The mass of the substance will appear to be greater in the magnetic field if the substance is paramagnetic (Figure 14·14).

Paramagnetism should not be confused with ferromagnetism. The latter is a much stronger attraction of iron, cobalt, and nickel for magnetic fields. The ions Fe^{2+}, Co^{2+}, and Ni^{2+} all have unpaired electrons. Large groups of ions are randomly dispersed throughout the metals. In a magnetic field these groups of ions line up in an orderly fashion with the field. This creates a strong magnetic attraction. The order remains even when the magnetic field is removed, leading to permanent magnetism.

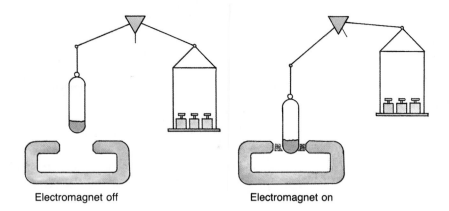

Electromagnet off   Electromagnet on

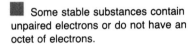
Some stable substances contain
unpaired electrons or do not have an
octet of electrons.

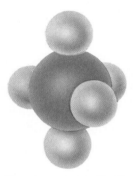

Phosphorus pentachloride

Sulfur hexafluoride

Figure 14·15
Phosphorus pentachloride and sulfur
hexafluoride are exceptions to the
octet rule.

A structure can be written for the oxygen molecule in which both
oxygen atoms are surrounded by eight electrons. In this structure all the
electrons are paired. We said in Section 14·2, however, that this structure
is incorrect. The experimental evidence for this statement is that oxygen
is paramagnetic. This property can be explained only if the oxygen
molecule contains unpaired electrons. The measured distance between
the oxygen atoms indicates that the oxygen molecule has some multiple
bond character. This information suggests that oxygen is a resonance hybrid of these structures.

$$:\ddot{O}—\ddot{O}: \quad \longleftrightarrow \quad :\ddot{O}=\ddot{O}: \quad \longleftrightarrow \quad :O\equiv\ddot{O}:$$

Several other molecules such as some compounds of boron also fail
to follow the octet rule. The boron atom of boron trifluoride (BF_3), for
example, is deficient by two electrons. Boron trifluoride readily reacts
with ammonia to make the compound $BF_3 \cdot NH_3$. By doing so, the boron
atom accepts the unshared electron pair from ammonia and completes the
octet.

A few elements, especially phosphorus and sulfur, sometimes expand the octet to include ten or twelve electrons. Phosphorus trichloride
(PCl_3) and phosphorus pentachloride (PCl_5) are stable compounds (Figure
14·15). In both compounds all of the chlorines are bonded to the phosphorus. Covalent bonding in PCl_3 follows the octet rule, because all the
atoms acquire eight electrons. An electron dot structure for PCl_5 can be
written only if phosphorus has ten valence electrons. In sulfur hexafluoride (SF_6) the sulfur atom must have twelve valence electrons.

14·7 Molecular Orbitals

■ Molecular orbital theory is the logical extension to molecules of the quantum mechanical description of the atom.

There are other models for covalent bonding besides the one we have described. Just as there is a quantum mechanical description of the atom, there is also a quantum mechanical description of bonding. As discussed in Section 11·3, the quantum mechanical model describes the electrons in atoms by means of atomic orbitals. Similarly, quantum mechanics describes the electrons in molecules by *molecular orbitals.*

When two atoms combine, their atomic orbitals overlap to produce **molecular orbitals.** The overlap of two atomic orbitals produces two molecular orbitals. One is a **bonding orbital,** *a molecular orbital whose energy is lower than that of the atomic orbitals from which it is formed.* The other is an **antibonding orbital,** *a molecular orbital whose energy is higher than that of the atomic orbitals from which it is formed.*

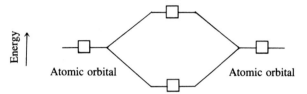

An atomic orbital belongs to a particular atom. A molecular orbital belongs to the molecule as a whole. The number of molecular orbitals is equal to the number of atomic orbitals which overlap.

Each atomic orbital describes at most two electrons. Thus an atomic orbital is half-filled if it contains one electron. It is filled if it contains two electrons. Similarly, two electrons are required to fill the energy level corresponding to a bonding or an antibonding molecular orbital.

■ Do not confuse orbitals with electrons. An orbital, a region of space, has a predictable shape and energy regardless of whether it contains electrons.

These concepts can be used to explain bonding in the hydrogen molecule, H_2. The $1s$ atomic orbitals of two hydrogen atoms overlap in the formation of a hydrogen molecule. Two electrons, one from each hydrogen atom, are available. Since electrons seek the lowest energy, they fill the bonding molecular orbital energy level.

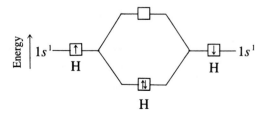

The energy of the electrons in the bonding orbital is lower than it is in separate hydrogen atoms. This makes the hydrogen molecule stable. Figure 14·16 shows the formation of the bonding and antibonding molecular orbitals in the hydrogen molecule.

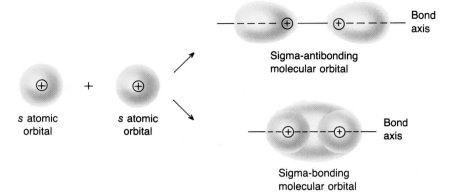

Figure 14·16

The overlap of *s* orbitals produces sigma-bonding and sigma-antibonding molecular orbitals. In a bonding molecular orbital, the electron density between the nuclei is high. In an antibonding orbital the electron density between the nuclei is extremely low. In the hydrogen molecule the two electrons occupy the bonding orbital.

In the bonding molecular orbital there is a high probability of finding the electrons between the nuclei of the combining atoms. This orbital is symmetrical along the axis between the hydrogen atoms. *A* **sigma bond** *is formed when two atomic orbitals combine to form a molecular orbital that is symmetrical along the axis connecting two atomic nuclei.* The symbol for the Greek letter sigma is σ.

Bonding results from an imbalance between attractive and repulsive forces. Because they are oppositely charged, nuclei and electrons attract each other. Because they are similarly charged, nuclei repel other nuclei and electrons repel other electrons. In the hydrogen molecule the attraction of hydrogen nuclei to electrons tips the balance in favor of the attractive forces. In higher-energy or antibonding molecular orbitals, however, the electrons are *not* between the nuclei. Thus the balance favors the repulsive forces. Repulsive forces would occur if two helium atoms were to combine into a He_2 molecule. Each atom has two $1s$ electrons. Two of these electrons can go into the bonding energy level, but the other two must go into the antibonding level.

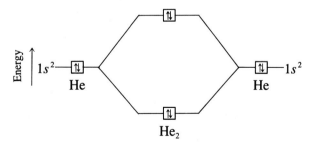

In this case the bonding forces are almost exactly offset by the antibonding forces. Hence a He_2 molecule is unstable compared with two separate helium atoms, and helium exists only as atoms.

Atomic *p* orbitals also overlap to form molecular orbitals. For example, a fluorine atom has a half-filled $2p$ orbital. When two fluorine atoms combine, these orbitals overlap to make a filled bonding molecular orbital (Figure 14·17). The bonding molecular orbital shows a high probability of finding a pair of electrons between the positively charged nuclei of the two fluorines. The fluorine nuclei are attracted to this region of

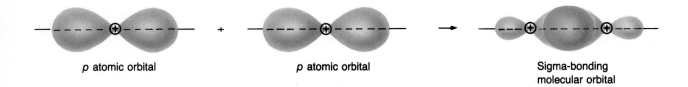

| p atomic orbital | p atomic orbital | Sigma-bonding molecular orbital |

Figure 14·17
Two p atomic orbitals can combine to form a sigma-bonding molecular orbital.

high-electron density. This attraction holds the atoms together in the fluorine molecule, F_2. The overlap of the $2p$ orbitals produces a symmetrical bonding molecular orbital when viewed along the F—F bond axis. Therefore the F—F bond is a sigma bond.

Problem

4. A sigma bond is formed by the overlap of two s orbitals, the overlap of an s with a p orbital, or end-to-end overlap of two p orbitals.

4. What is a sigma bond? Describe, with the aid of a diagram, how the overlap of two half-filled $1s$ orbitals produces a sigma bond.

In the fluorine molecule the p atomic orbitals overlap end-to-end. In some molecules these orbitals can also overlap side-by-side. The side-by-side overlap of atomic p orbitals produces pi molecular orbitals (Figure 14·18). A pi bond results when a pi molecular orbital is filled with two electrons. The symbol for the Greek letter pi is π. *In a* **pi bond,** *the bonding electrons are most likely to be found in sausage-shaped regions above and below the nuclei of the bonded atoms.* Orbital overlap in pi bonding is not as extensive as it is in sigma bonding. Therefore pi bonds tend to be weaker than sigma bonds. We will return to pi bonding when we discuss the shapes of molecules in Section 14·9.

Figure 14·18
The side-by-side overlap of two p atomic orbitals produces a pi-bonding molecular orbital. The *two* sausage-shaped regions in which a bonding electron pair is most likely to be found constitute *one* pi-bonding molecular orbital.

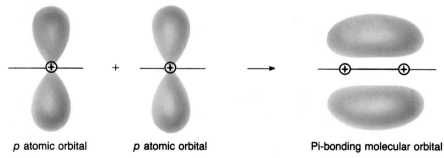

| p atomic orbital | p atomic orbital | Pi-bonding molecular orbital |

14·A Molecular Models

In the sections ahead you will see that the properties of a substance depend on the shape of its molecules. Physical models of molecules help us to visualize them and better understand their behavior.

Ball-and-stick models represent atoms by means of balls of different colors. Yellow usually represents hydrogen, black carbon, and red oxygen. Bonds are represented by wooden sticks or metal springs that fit into holes drilled into the balls at angles of 109.5°. The

Figure 14·19
The ball-and-stick and space-filling models of methane show the advantages and disadvantages of each model. **a** The bond angles for methane are most apparent from the ball-and-stick model. **b** The relative sizes of the atoms are more apparent from the space-filling models. **c** Computers can generate 3-dimensional models of large molecules.

a Ball-and-stick model

b Space filling model

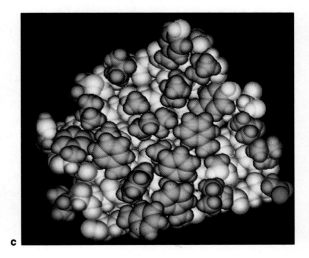

c

number of holes in each ball is the same as the number of bonds that atom makes. Hydrogen has one, oxygen two, and carbon four. Unshared pairs are not shown. Ball-and-stick models show very clearly the bond angles in a molecule. They do not, however, accurately represent the relative size of the atoms or the bond lengths.

Space-filling models are made of plastic balls. The size of each ball accurately represents the relative size of the atom. Bond lengths are also to scale. These models do not give the erroneous impression of empty space between the atoms of a molecule. They do make it more difficult, however, to see bond angles.

Organic chemists and biochemists use computers to create models of molecules composed of hundreds of atoms. Many biochemical reactions depend on a compound having the proper shape as well as the proper formula. Using a special viewing apparatus, chemists are able to see three-dimensional representations of complex molecules on the computer monitor. It is possible to turn the molecule over to see the other side, to shrink it, or to cut it in pieces on the monitor.

14·8   VSEPR Theory

A photograph or sketch may fail to do justice to a person's appearance. Similarly, electron dot structures and structural formulas fail to reflect the three-dimensional shapes of molecules. For example, the electron dot structure and structural formula of methane (CH_4) show the molecule in only two dimensions.

$$\begin{array}{c} H \\ H\!:\!\overset{\displaystyle\cdot\cdot}{\underset{\displaystyle\cdot\cdot}{C}}\!:\!H \\ H \end{array} \qquad\qquad \begin{array}{c} H \\ | \\ H\!-\!C\!-\!H \\ | \\ H \end{array}$$

Methane
(electron dot
structure)

Methane
(structural
formula)

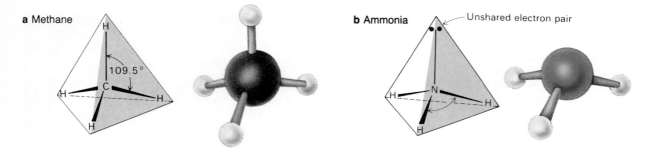

a Methane

109.5°

b Ammonia — Unshared electron pair

Figure 14·20

a Methane is a good example of a tetrahedral molecule. The hydrogens in methane are at the four corners of a regular tetrahedron.
b An ammonia molecule is pyramidal. The unshared pair of electrons repels the bonding pairs causing the bond angle to be about 107°.

■ Molecules and ions have three-dimensional shapes.

Electron pair repulsions are not always equal. The repulsions can be ranked as follows.

strongest: two unshared pairs
medium: one unshared and one shared pair
weakest: two shared pairs

In reality, methane molecules exist in three dimensions. The hydrogens in the methane molecule are at the four corners of a geometric solid, the regular tetrahedron. In this arrangement, all the H—C—H angles are *109.5°, the* **tetrahedral angle** (Figure 14·20). The *v*alence-*s*hell *e*lectron-*p*air *r*epulsion theory, or VSEPR theory, explains this shape. **VSEPR theory** *states that because electron pairs repel, molecules adjust their shapes so that the valence-electron pairs are as far apart as possible.* The methane molecule has four bonding electron pairs and no unshared pairs. The bond pairs are farthest apart when the angle between the central carbon and its attached hydrogens is 109.5°. This is the H—C—H bond angle found by experiment. Any other arrangement tends to bring two bonding pairs of electrons closer together.

Unshared pairs of electrons are important when we are trying to predict the shapes of molecules. The nitrogen in ammonia (NH_3) is surrounded by four pairs of valence electrons, but one of these is an unshared pair (Figure 14·20). No bonding atom is vying for the unshared electrons. Thus they are held closer to the nitrogen than are the bonding pairs. The unshared pair strongly repels the bonding pairs, pushing them closer together. The experimentally measured H—N—H bond angle is only 107°. The shape of the ammonia molecule is *pyramidal*.

In a water molecule, oxygen forms single covalent bonds with two hydrogen atoms. The two bonding pairs and two unshared pairs of electrons form a tetrahedral arrangement around the central oxygen (Figure 14·21). Thus the water molecule is planar (flat) but *bent*. With two unshared pairs repelling the bonding pairs, the H—O—H bond angle is compressed. The experimentally measured bond angle is about 105°.

The carbon in CO_2 has no unshared pairs. The double bonds joining the oxygens to the carbon are farthest apart when the O=C=O bond angle is 180° (Figure 14·21). Thus CO_2 is a *linear* molecule. Figure 14·22 shows some common molecular shapes.

Figure 14·21

a The water molecule is bent because the bonding electrons are repelled by the unshared pairs.
b By contrast, the carbon dioxide molecule is linear. It has no unshared pairs of electrons.

a Water

Unshared electron pairs

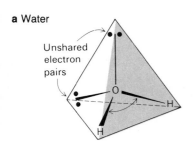

b Carbon dioxide

Figure 14·22
Some commonly found shapes
of molecules are linear triatomic,
trigonal planar, bent triatomic,
pyramidal, tetrahedral, and trigonal
bipyramidal.

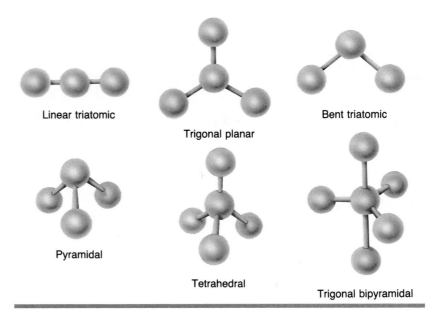

Linear triatomic

Trigonal planar

Bent triatomic

Pyramidal

Tetrahedral

Trigonal bipyramidal

Problem

5. Tetrahedral

5. The BF_3 molecule is planar. The attachment of a fluorine ion to the boron in BF_3 through a coordinate covalent bond creates the BF_4^- ion. What is the geometric shape of this ion?

Appropriate for honors students.

14·9   Hybrid Orbitals

Electron dot structures and the combination of unpaired electrons in boxes representing orbitals are two ways of describing covalent bonding. The VSEPR theory does a good job of describing molecular shapes. Another way to describe molecules that is informative of *both* bonding and shape is orbital hybridization. *With* **hybridization** *several atomic orbitals mix to form the same number of equivalent hybrid orbitals.*

The number of hybrid orbitals is always the same as the number of orbitals mixed.

Orbital hybridization can be used to describe the methane molecule. One $2s$ orbital and three $2p$ orbitals of a carbon atom mix to form four

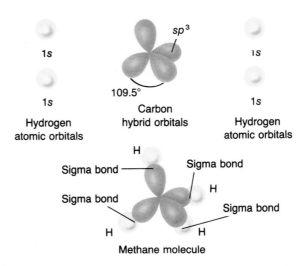

1*s*

1*s*

Hydrogen
atomic orbitals

sp^3

109.5°

Carbon
hybrid orbitals

1*s*

1*s*

Hydrogen
atomic orbitals

Sigma bond

Sigma bond

Sigma bond

Sigma bond

H

H

H

H

Methane molecule

Figure 14·23
In methane, each of the four sp^3 hybrid orbitals of carbon overlap with a 1*s* orbital of hydrogen. The result of each overlap is a sigma bond.

Figure 14·24
In ethene, two sp^2 hybrid orbitals from each carbon overlap with a $1s$ orbital of hydrogen to form a sigma bond. The other sp^2 orbitals overlap to form a carbon–carbon sigma bond. The p atomic orbitals overlap to form a pi bond which occupies regions above and below the carbons.

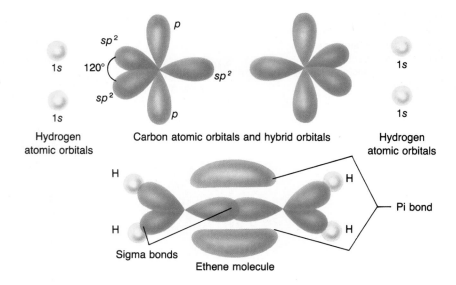

Hydrogen atomic orbitals

Carbon atomic orbitals and hybrid orbitals

Hydrogen atomic orbitals

Ethene molecule

The orbitals which combine to form the hybrid orbital lose their individual identities. The shape and orientation of the hybrid cannot be predicted from the shapes of the combining orbitals.

sp^3 hybrid orbitals. These are at the tetrahedral angle of 109.5°. The four sp^3 orbitals of carbon overlap with the $1s$ orbitals of the four hydrogen atoms (Figure 14·23). The sp^3 orbitals extend farther into space than either s or p orbitals. Thus the overlap with a hydrogen $1s$ orbital can be greater. The eight available valence electrons fill the molecules's orbitals to form four C—H sigma bonds. The greater overlap results in an unusually strong covalent bond.

Hybridization is also useful in describing double covalent bonds. Ethene is a relatively simple molecule. It has one carbon–carbon double bond and four carbon–hydrogen single bonds.

Ethene

Experimental evidence indicates that the H—C—H bond angles are 120°. In ethene, sp^2 hybrid orbitals form from the combination of one $2s$ and two $2p$ atomic orbitals of carbon (Figure 14·24). Each hybrid orbital is separated from the other two by 120°. Two sp^2 hybrid orbitals of each carbon form sigma-bonding molecular orbitals with the four available hydrogen $1s$ orbitals. The third sp^2 orbitals of the two carbons overlap to form a carbon–carbon sigma–bonding orbital. The nonhybridized $2p$ (carbon) orbitals overlap side-by-side to form a pi-bonding orbital. A total of twelve electrons fill the six bonding orbitals. (The two carbons each contribute four electrons and the four hydrogens each contribute one.) Thus the ethene molecule is held together by five sigma bonds and one pi bond.

Both sigma and pi bonds are two-electron covalent bonds. These bonds are drawn alike in structural formulas. Pi bonds are weaker than sigma bonds. In chemical reactions of carbon–carbon double bonds, the pi bond is broken in preference to the sigma bond.

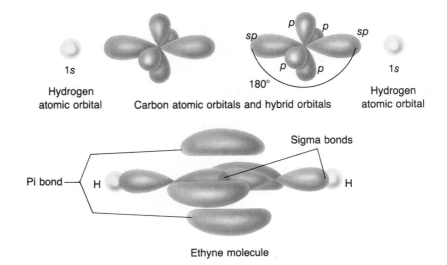

Figure 14·25
In ethyne, one *sp* hybrid orbital from each carbon overlaps with a 1*s* orbital of hydrogen to form a sigma bond. The other *sp* hybrid orbital of each carbon overlaps to form a carbon–carbon sigma bond. The two *p* atomic orbitals from each carbon overlap to form two pi bonds.

A third type of covalent bond is a triple bond such as is found in ethyne, C_2H_2. Another name for this compound is acetylene.

$$H—C\equiv C—H$$

As with other molecules, the hybrid orbital description of ethyne is guided by the properties of the molecule. Ethyne is a linear molecule. The best hybrid orbital description is obtained if a 2*s* atomic orbital of carbon mixes with only one of the three 2*p* atomic orbitals. The result is two *sp* hybrid orbitals for each carbon (Figure 14·25). A carbon–carbon sigma–bonding molecular orbital forms from the overlap of one *sp* orbital from each carbon. The other *sp* orbital of each carbon overlaps with the 1*s* orbital of each hydrogen. Sigma-bonding molecular orbitals are formed. The remaining pair of *p* atomic orbitals on each carbon overlap side-by-side. They form two pi-bonding molecular orbitals. These surround the central carbons. The ten available electrons completely fill the five bonding molecular orbitals. Thus the bonding of ethyne consists of three sigma bonds and two pi bonds.

14·10 Polar Bonds

Covalent bonds are formed by electron-sharing between atoms. Not all covalent bonds are the same. The character of these bonds in a given molecule depends on the kind and number of atoms joined together. These features in turn determine the properties of the molecules.

The bonding pairs of electrons in covalent bonds are pulled, as in a tug of war, between the nuclei of the atoms sharing the electrons. *When the atoms in a molecule are the same, the bonding electrons are shared equally, and the bond is a* **nonpolar covalent bond.** Hydrogen (H_2), oxygen (O_2), and nitrogen (N_2) have nonpolar covalent bonds. *When two different atoms are joined by a covalent bond, and the bonding electrons are shared unequally, the bond is a* **polar covalent bond,** *or simply a* **polar bond.** The atom with stronger electron attraction (the more

Figure 14·26
The nuclei of atoms pull the bonding electrons as in a tug-of-war between two children.

Figure 14·27
This electron cloud picture for hydrogen chloride shows that the chlorine atom attracts more of the electron cloud than does the hydrogen atom. Chlorine is more electronegative than hydrogen.

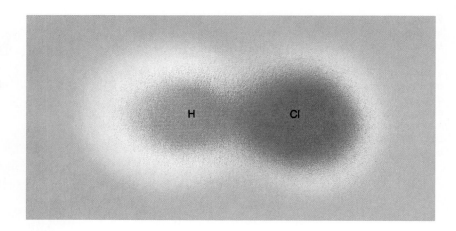

Covalent bonds joining unlike atoms are often polar.

We can interpret unequal sharing as meaning that an electron spends more time in the vicinity of one atom than the other. Thus there is a higher probability of finding it near a particular atom than there is in finding it near the other atom.

In no event is the unequal sharing so extreme that one atom entirely possesses the electron and forms an ion. Thus, the charge formed on each atom is always less than a whole positive or whole negative charge.

electronegative atom) in a polar bond acquires a slightly negative charge. The less electronegative atom acquires a slightly positive charge. Table 12·3 gives electronegativities of some common elements. The higher the electronegativity value, the greater is the ability of an atom to attract electrons to itself.

Consider the hydrogen chloride molecule (HCl). Hydrogen has an electronegativity value of 2.1, and chlorine has an electronegativity value of 3.0. The covalent bond in hydrogen chloride is polar. The chlorine atom acquires a slightly negative charge. The hydrogen atom acquires a slightly positive charge. The Greek letter delta (δ) is used to show that atoms involved in the covalent bond acquire only partial charges, much less than $1+$ or $1-$.

$$\overset{\delta^+}{H}\!-\!\overset{\delta^-}{Cl}$$

The minus sign shows that chlorine has acquired a slightly negative charge. The plus sign shows that hydrogen has acquired a slightly positive charge. The polarity of the bond may also be represented with an arrow pointing to the more electronegative atom.

$$\overset{+\longrightarrow}{H\!-\!Cl}$$

The O—H bonds in the water molecule are also polar. The very electronegative oxygen pulls the bonding electrons away from hydrogen.

A perfectly nonpolar covalent bond can only form between two atoms which have the same electronegativies. This is most likely to occur between identical atoms, as in O_2, F_2, and N_2. Most other combinations of atoms will produce bonds which will have at least a slightly polar nature.

Table 14·3	Electronegativity Differences and Bond Types	
Electronegativity difference (approx.)	Type of bond	Example
0.0–0.4	Covalent (nonpolar)	H—H (0.0)
0.4–1.0	Covalent (moderately polar)	$\overset{\delta+}{H}\!-\!\overset{\delta-}{Cl}$ (0.9)
1.0–2.0	Covalent (very polar)	$\overset{\delta+}{H}\!-\!\overset{\delta-}{F}$ (1.9)
≥2.0	Ionic	Na^+Cl^- (2.1)

The oxygen acquires a slightly negative charge. The hydrogens acquire a slightly positive charge.

$$\underset{\delta+ \ \text{H} \qquad \ \text{H} \ \delta+}{\overset{\delta-}{\text{O}}} \qquad \text{or} \qquad \underset{\text{H} \qquad \text{H}}{\overset{\text{O}}{\diagup \diagdown}}$$

Electronegativities also indicate the type of bond that two atoms will tend to form. If the electronegativity difference between two atoms is greater than 2.0, a bond is ionic. If the electronegativity difference is less than 2.0 but greater than 0.4, a bond is covalent and polar. If the difference is less than 0.4, the bond is nonpolar covalent (Table 14·3).

Example 4

What type of bond (polar covalent, nonpolar covalent, or ionic) will form between atoms of the following pairs of elements?
a. N and H   **b.** F and F   **c.** Ca and O   **d.** Al and Cl

Solution

The types of bonds formed depend on the electronegativity differences between the bonding elements. The rules are given in Table 14·3.

Elements (electronegativities)	Electronegativity difference	Type of bond
a. N (3.0), H (2.1)	0.9	Moderately polar covalent
b. F (4.0), F (4.0)	0.0	Nonpolar covalent
c. Ca (1.0), O (3.5)	2.5	Ionic
d. Al (1.5), Cl (3.0)	1.5	Very polar covalent

Problems

6. **a.** Covalent (moderately polar)
   b. Ionic
   c. Covalent (very polar)
   d. Covalent (very polar)
   e. Ionic
   f. Covalent (nonpolar)
7. In order of increasing polarity: e. c. d. b. a.

6. Identify the bonds between atoms of the following pairs of elements as ionic, nonpolar covalent, or polar covalent.
   a. H and Br   **b.** K and Cl   **c.** C and O   **d.** Cl and F
   e. Li and O   **f.** Br and Br
7. Which covalent bond is the most polar?   **a.** H—Cl   **b.** H—Br
   c. H—S   **d.** H—C   **e.** F—F

14·11   Polar Molecules

■ A polar molecule always contains polar bonds, but some molecules with polar bonds are nonpolar.

The presence of a polar bond in a molecule often makes the entire molecule polar. *In a* **polar molecule** *one end of the molecule is slightly negative, and one end is slightly positive.* For example, in the hydrogen chloride molecule the partial charges on the hydrogen and chlorine atoms are electrically charged regions, or poles. *A molecule that has two poles is called a dipolar molecule, or* **dipole.** The hydrogen chloride molecule is a dipole.

Figure 14·28
When polar molecules are placed in an electric field, the negative ends of the molecules orient toward the positively charged plate and the positive ends of the molecules orient toward the negatively charged plate. What would happen if carbon dioxide molecules were placed in this field? Why?

They would not align because they are nonpolar.

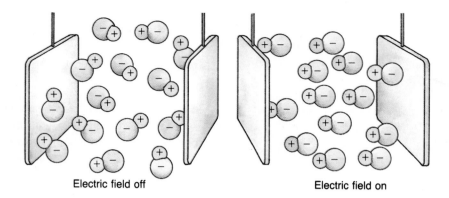

Electric field off   Electric field on

The effect of polar bonds on the polarity of an entire molecule depends on the shape of the molecule and the orientation of the polar bonds. A carbon dioxide molecule, for example, has two polar bonds and is linear.

$$O \overset{\leftharpoonup}{\equiv} C \overset{\rightharpoonup}{\equiv} O$$

The carbon and oxygens lie along the same axis. Therefore the bond polarities cancel because they are in opposite directions. Carbon dioxide is a nonpolar molecule.

The water molecule has two polar bonds, but the molecule is bent. Hence the bond polarities do not cancel, and a water molecule is polar.

14·12   Bond Dissociation Energies

A large quantity of heat is liberated when hydrogen atoms combine to form hydrogen molecules. This is evidence that the product is more stable than the reactants. Indeed, the covalent bond in the hydrogen molecule is so strong that 435 kJ of energy is required to dissociate 1 mol of hydrogen molecules to hydrogen atoms. *The energy required to break a single bond is known as the* **bond dissociation energy.** Hydrogen molecules have a bond dissociation energy of 435 kJ per mole.

■ The bond dissociation energy of a diatomic molecule is the energy required to dissociate the bond to atoms, *not* ions.

$$H-H + 435 \text{ kJ} \longrightarrow H\cdot + \cdot H$$

The carbon–carbon single covalent bond has a bond dissociation energy of about 347 kJ. The ability of carbon to form strong carbon–carbon bonds helps explain the stability of carbon compounds. Table 14·4 gives bond dissociation energies of several representative covalent bonds. Compounds with only C—C and C—H single covalent bonds are quite unreactive chemically. In part this is because of the high dissociation energies of these bonds.

Problem

8. 157 kJ

8. How many kilojoules would be required to dissociate all the C—H single bonds in 0.1 mol of methane? Assume that the bond dissociation energy is the same for each bond.

Bond lengths are usually given in picometers (pm). 1 pm = 10^{-12} m.

Table 14·4	Bond Dissociation Energies and Bond Lengths for Covalent Bonds	
Bond	Bond energy (kJ/mol)	Bond length (pm)
H—H	435	74
C—H	393	109
C—O	356	143
C=O	736	121
C≡O	1074	113
C—C	347	154
C=C	657	133
C≡C	908	121
C—N	305	147
S—S	259	208
Cl—Cl	243	199
N—N	209	140
Br—Br	192	228
I—I	151	267
O—O	142	132
O—H	464	96

Safety

Bromine is toxic and very corrosive. It has a high vapor pressure. When working with bromine solutions, avoid breathing the fumes, and keep the container tightly closed.

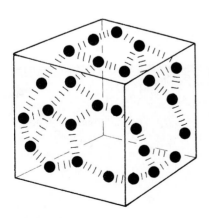

Figure 14·29
Van der Waals said that gases do not obey ideal behavior at low temperatures and high pressures because the gas molecules are weakly attracted to each other.

14·B Johannes van der Waals: Using the Power of Reason

The lifelong work of Johannes van der Waals was the study of the behavior of gases and liquids. Van der Waals observed that at higher pressures or lower temperatures gases did not really obey the ideal gas equations. He reasoned that the assumptions involved in the ideal gas laws must be incorrect.

The ideal gas laws assume that the molecules of a gas are not attracted to each other. Van der Waals noted that at low temperatures and high pressures the measured pressure is less than the calculated ideal pressure. He reasoned that under these conditions gas molecules must be weakly attracted to each other. The pressure that the molecules exert on the walls of the container is reduced because they are "held back" by the molecules around them.

By such reasoning van der Waals was able to calculate correction factors for the erroneous assumptions of the ideal gas equation. For this work he was awarded the Nobel Prize in physics in 1910. Two types of intermolecular attractions are named in his honor because his work dealt with the weak forces of attraction between molecules.

14·13 Intermolecular Attractions

Intermolecular forces determine some of the properties of substances.

Van der Waals forces are sometimes called fluctuating dipoles.

In addition to covalent bonds in molecules, there are attractions between molecules, or intermolecular attractions. These attractions are weaker than either an ionic or covalent bond. Nevertheless, do not underestimate the power of these forces. Among other things, they are responsible for whether a molecular compound is a gas, liquid, or solid.

The weakest attractions between molecules are collectively called **van der Waals forces.** They are named after the Dutch chemist Johannes van der Waals (1837–1923). Two major van der Waals forces are dispersion forces and dipole interactions.

Dispersion forces, *the weakest of all molecular interactions, are thought to be caused by the motion of electrons.* Generally speaking, the strength of dispersion forces increases as the number of electrons in a molecule increases. The halogens are an example of molecules whose major attraction for one another is caused by dispersion forces. Fluorine and chlorine, with relatively few electrons, are gases at STP. The larger number of electrons in bromine generate larger dispersion forces. Bromine molecules are therefore sufficiently attracted to each other to make bromine a liquid at STP. Iodine, with a still larger number of electrons, is a solid at STP.

Dipole interactions *occur when polar molecules are attracted to one another* (Figure 14·30). Electrostatic attractions occur between the oppositely charged regions of dipolar molecules. Dipole interactions are similar to but much weaker than ionic bonds. They are stronger than dispersion forces. Dipole interactions in water, for example, result in a weak attraction of water molecules for one another. Each O—H bond in the water molecule is highly polar. The oxygens in water acquire a slightly negative charge because of oxygen's greater electronegativity. The hydrogens in water acquire a slightly positive charge. Polar molecules attract one another. Hence the positive region of one water molecule attracts the negative region of another. This dipolar attraction is weak, however, when compared with the strength of hydrogen bonds.

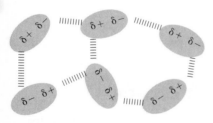

Figure 14·30
Polar molecules are attracted to one another by van der Waals forces called dipole interactions.

Figure 14·31
Liquids tend to form drops because of intermolecular attractions. Molecular substances with weak intermolecular attractions are gases at room temperature. Molecular substances with very strong intermolecular attractions are solids.

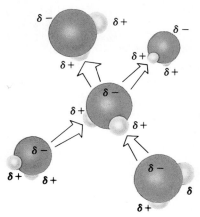

Figure 14·32
Hydrogen-bonding between water molecules accounts for many properties of water. The hydrogen bond has about 5% the strength of an average covalent bond.

9.

H   H
| |
H—N: H—N:
| |
H   H

H   H
| |
:O: ···· H—N:
| |
H   H

Hydrogen bonds *are attractive forces in which a hydrogen that is covalently bonded to a very electronegative atom is also weakly bonded to an unshared electron pair of an electronegative atom in the same molecule or in a nearby molecule.* Hydrogen-bonding always involves hydrogen. It is the only chemically reactive element whose valence electrons are not shielded from the nucleus by a layer of underlying electrons. A very polar covalent bond is formed when hydrogen bonds to an electronegative atom like oxygen, nitrogen, or fluorine. This leaves the hydrogen nucleus quite electron-deficient. The hydrogen makes up for its deficiency by sharing a nonbonding electron pair on a nearby electronegative atom. The resulting hydrogen bond has about 5% of the strength of an average covalent bond. Hydrogen bonds are the strongest of the intermolecular forces. They are extremely important in determining the properties of water and biological molecules like proteins. Figure 14·32 shows hydrogen-bonding between water molecules.

Problem

9. Depict the hydrogen-bonding between two ammonia molecules and between one ammonia molecule and one water molecule.

14·C   Bonding with Adhesives

An adhesive is a substance that can hold materials together at their surface. The earliest adhesives were natural substances like flour paste and egg white. Modern adhesives are mostly synthetic. Like their ancestors, however, they bond materials together by maximizing the intermolecular attractions.

If two perfectly smooth, clean surfaces are pressed together in a vacuum, they will stick together. If no air molecules are in the way, atoms or molecules in one surface will be attracted to those in the other surface. If the surfaces are very smooth, many atoms will be in contact. Intermolecular attractions will hold the two surfaces together.

Ordinary surfaces, however, are not smooth. They are full of microscopic ridges and valleys. The contact area between such surfaces is actually quite small, and there is little adhesion. We can make two ordinary surfaces stick together, however, by coating each surface with a liquid that can fill up all the ridges and valleys. Many atoms will be in contact. Thus the adhesion between the liquid and each of the two solid surfaces will be very strong. If the liquid itself holds together, a strong bond will form between the two surfaces. To be a good adhesive, then, a liquid must spread well, wetting all the nooks and crannies of a surface. This means that its molecules must be attracted to those in the surface to be glued. For example, it should be polar if the material to be glued is polar. It should also have strong intermolecular forces or molecular bonds.

Figure 14·33
Glue works by filling in all the nooks and crannies. It provides a large area of contact between the two surfaces.

Glues and adhesives are generally polymers. These are very long molecules that are held together by strong covalent bonds. In addition, these molecules often have branches that are polar. Intermolecular attractions between the branches bind the molecules to other similar molecules. This makes these polymers very good adhesives.

Epoxy resins are a group of very strong synthetic adhesives. An epoxy prepolymer combines chemically with a curing agent to form an interlocking polymer (Figure 14·34). The end result of this kind of chemical reaction is that the glue layer is essentially one big molecule. The polar −OH groups in the final polymer are strongly attracted to the surface to which the glue is applied. The attractions between the glue and the surface are extremely strong. So are the attractions within the glue itself. If an object glued with epoxy is subjected to stress, the object will break before the glued surface will!

Aircraft, cars, trucks, and boats are partially held together with epoxy adhesives. For example, the rear one-third of the wing surfaces of jet aircraft are glued together. The joints are strong and add little mass to the plane in comparison to welding or fastening with bolts. Approximately 500 kg of adhesive may be used in one plane.

Figure 14·34
Epoxy resins are particularly strong adhesives. An epoxy prepolymer reacts with a curing agent to form essentially one large molecule with thousands of units. In this example, a curing agent molecule links four epoxy prepolymer molecules together to form an interlocking epoxy resin polymer chain.

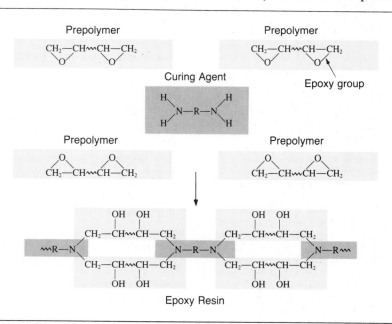

14·14 Properties of Molecular Substances

The physical properties of a compound depend on the type of bonding it displays. Some covalent compounds are gases, some are liquids, and some are solids at room temperature. We have already touched on this point by noting that most ionic compounds are crystalline solids. Table 14·5 summarizes some of the differences between ionic and molecular substances. A great variety of physical properties occurs among covalent compounds. This is in large part because of intermolecular attractions.

The melting and boiling points of most molecular compounds are low compared with those of ionic compounds. A few molecular solids resist melting, however, except in the range of 1000°C to 3000°C. Some decompose without melting at all. Most of these *very stable substances are* **network solids** (or network crystals) *in which all of the atoms are covalently bonded to each other*. Diamond is a network solid because each carbon in a diamond is covalently bonded to four other carbons. Diamond-cutting requires breaking a multitude of these bonds. Diamond does not melt, but vaporizes to a gas at 3500°C and above. Silicon carbide, with the formula unit SiC and a melting point of about 2700°C, is also a network solid. Silicon carbide is so hard that it is used in grindstones and as an abrasive. The molecular structure of silicon carbide is like diamond except that every other carbon is replaced by silicon. Samples of diamond or silicon carbide can be thought of as single molecules. The melting of silicon carbide requires that covalent bonds be broken. To melt other molecular solids we need only to break the weak attractions between molecules.

■ Properties of molecular compounds are diverse.

A network solid can be thought of as one very large covalently bonded macromolecule because all of the atoms are interconnected.

Figure 14·35
Ionic compounds have high melting points. Each ion in the crystal lattice is held firmly in place by ionic bonds. By contrast, molecular crystals generally have low melting points. Even strong intermolecular bonds are much weaker than ionic bonds.

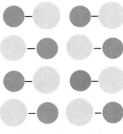

Molecular crystal

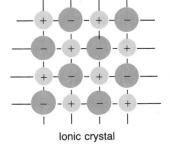

Ionic crystal

Table 14·5 Characteristics of Ionic and Covalent Compounds		
Characteristic	Ionic compound	Covalent compound
Representative unit	Formula unit	Molecule
Bond formation	Transfer of one or more electrons between atoms	Sharing of electron pairs between atoms
Type of elements	Metallic and nonmetallic	Nonmetallic
Physical state	Solid	Solid, liquid, or gas
Melting point	High (usually above 300°C)	Low (usually below 300°C)
Solubility in water	Usually high	High to low
Electrical conductivity of aqueous solution	Good conductor	Poor to nonconducting

Key Terms

antibonding orbital	14·7	pi bond (π bond)	14·7
bonding dissociation energy	14·12	polar bond	14·10
		polar covalent bond	14·10
bonding orbital	14·7		
coordinate covalent bond	14·4	polar molecule	14·11
		resonance	14·5
dipole	14·11	sigma bond (σ bond)	14·7
dipole interaction	14·13		
dispersion force	14·13	single covalent bond	14·1
double covalent bond	14·2	structural formula	14·1
		tetrahedral angle	14·8
hybridization	14·9	triple covalent bond	14·2
hydrogen bond	14·13		
molecular orbital	14·7	unshared pair	14·1
network solid	14·14	van der Waals force	14·13
nonpolar covalent bond	14·10		
paramagnetic	14·6	VSEPR theory	14·8

Chapter Summary

When atoms share electrons to gain the stable electron configuration of a noble gas, they form covalent bonds. A shared pair of valence electrons constitutes a single covalent bond. Sometimes two or three pairs of electrons may be shared to give double or triple covalent bonds. In some cases only one of the atoms in a bond provides the pair of bonding electrons; this is a coordinate covalent bond.

When like atoms are joined by a covalent bond, the bonding electrons are shared equally, and the bond is nonpolar. When the atoms in a bond are not the same, the bonding electrons are shared unequally, and the bond is polar. The degree of polarity of a bond between any two atoms is determined by consulting a table of electronegativities. Some molecules are polar because they contain polar covalent bonds. Bond dissociation energies are affected by bond polarity and the electronegativity of the joined atoms. The attractions between opposite poles of polar molecules constitute dipole interactions. The dipole interaction is one of several weak attractions between molecules. Another weak attractive force is the hydrogen bond. These weak forces determine whether a covalent compound will be a solid, liquid, or gas.

As a general rule, molecules adjust their three-dimensional shapes so that the valence-electron pairs around a central atom are as far apart as possible. This is the guiding principle in the valence-shell electron-pair repulsion, or VSEPR, theory of molecular geometries. Molecular orbital theory is a logical extension of the quantum mechanical description of the electron structure of atoms. Covalent bonding is described in terms of sigma and pi bonds. In some instances molecular geometry is adequately described by simple overlap of atomic orbitals. In others a description of molecular shape that better fits experimental results is obtained from hybridized atomic orbitals.

Practice Questions and Problems

10. Explain why helium is monatomic but hydrogen exists as diatomic molecules. *14·1*

11. The following covalent molecules have only single covalent bonds. Draw an electron dot structure for each. *14·1*
  a. H_2O **c.** PCl_3
  b. H_2O_2 **d.** NH_3

12. Classify the following compounds as ionic or covalent. *14·1*
  a. $MgCl_2$ **d.** H_2S
  b. HCl **e.** CaO
  c. Na_2S **f.** H_2O

13. Define and give an example of the following.
  a. a single covalent bond   *14·1*
  b. an unshared pair of electrons

14. Explain why atoms form chemical bonds and describe the difference between an ionic and a covalent bond. *14·1*

15. How many electrons are shared by two atoms in a double covalent bond? In a triple covalent bond? *14·2*

16. Draw the electron dot structures of these molecules. *14·3*
   a. F_2 **b.** HCl   **c.** HCCH   **d.** HCN

17. Write plausible electron dot structures for the following compounds. Each compound contains only single covalent bonds. *14·3*
   a. I_2 **b.** OF_2 **c.** H_2S **d.** NI_3

18. Define a coordinate covalent bond. *14·4*

19. Explain why compounds containing C—N and C—O single bonds can form coordinate covalent bonds with H^+ but compounds containing only C—H and C—C single bonds cannot. *14·4*

20. Using electron dot structures draw at least two resonance structures for the nitrite ion, NO_2^-. The oxygens in NO_2^- are attached to the nitrogen. *14·5*

21. Draw all resonance forms for sulfur dioxide, SO_2. The oxygens in SO_2 are attached to the sulfur. *14·5*

22. Draw resonance structures for the carbonate ion CO_3^{2-}. Each oxygen is attached to the carbon. *14·5*

23. Predict whether the following species are diamagnetic or paramagnetic. *14·6*
   a. BF_3 **b.** O_2^- **c.** NO_2 **d.** F_2

24. Do you think that the NO molecule is paramagnetic? Explain your answer. *14·6*

25. Which of the following species would you predict to be diamagnetic? Paramagnetic? *14·6*
   a. NO_3^- **b.** OH^- **c.** HO_2 **d.** SO_3

26. Can you suggest a reason why phosphorus and sulfur expand octets in many of their compounds but nitrogen and oxygen never do? *14·6*

27. Draw an electron dot structure for BrF_5. *14·6*

28. Draw molecular orbital diagrams for the possible diatomic molecule Li_2. Would you expect Li_2 to exist as a stable molecule? *14·7*

29. What is the total number of sigma bonds and pi bonds in each of the following molecules? *14·7*
   a. HCN   **b.** CH_4 **c.** H_3CNCO **d.** H_2CCCH_2

30. Explain how the VSEPR theory can be used to predict bond angles in these molecules. *14·8*
   a. methane
   b. ammonia
   c. water

31. If one of the hydrogens in methane is replaced by chlorine, explain how the shape of the molecule will change (if at all). *14·8*

32. Use VSEPR theory to predict the shapes of the following species. *14·8*
   a. CO_2 **d.** SCl_2
   b. $SiCl_4$ **e.** CO
   c. SO_3 **f.** I_3^-

33. The phosgene molecule, $COCl_2$, has the oxygen and chlorines attached directly to carbon. Write the electron dot structure and predict the shape of the phosgene molecule. *14·8*

34. The molecule CO_2 has two carbon–oxygen double bonds. Draw the bonding in the CO_2 molecule using hybridized orbitals for carbon and oxygen. *14·9*

35. Using hybridized orbitals for oxygen, describe the bonding and shape of the hydronium ion, H_3O^+. *14·9*

36. What type of hybrid orbitals are involved in bonding of each atom in the following molecules? *14·9*
   a. CO   **c.** $H_2C{=}O$
   b. H_2O **d.** $N{\equiv}C{-}C{\equiv}N$

37. Determine what type of bond (ionic, polar covalent, or nonpolar covalent) will form between atoms of the following elements and show the polarity of the bond if it is polar covalent. *14·10*
   a. Ca and Cl   **d.** N and O
   b. C and S   **e.** H and O
   c. Mg and F   **f.** S and O

38. The bonds between the following pairs of elements are covalent. Arrange them according to polarity, naming the most polar bond first. *14·10*
   a. H—Cl   **d.** H—O
   b. H—C   **e.** H—H
   c. H—F   **f.** S—Cl

39. Arrange the following bonds in order of increasing ionic character. *14·10*
   a. Cl—F   **d.** C—H
   b. N—N   **e.** S—O
   c. K—O   **f.** Li—F

40. Draw the electron dot structure for each of the following molecules. Then identify polar covalent bonds by assigning $\delta+$ and $\delta-$ to the appropriate atoms. *14·11*
 a. HOOH c. HBr
 b. BrCl d. H_2O

41. Based on the information about molecular shapes in Section 14·8, which of these molecules would you expect to be polar? *14·11*
 a. SO_2 c. CO_2
 b. H_2S d. BF_3

42. Explain what is meant by the term *bond dissociation energy*. *14·12*

43. What suggestion can you offer to account for the fact that the N—N and O—O single covalent bonds are much weaker than the C—C single bond? *14·12*

44. Assume that the total bond energy in a molecule is the sum of the individual bond energies. Calculate the total bond energy in a mole of ethyne, C_2H_2. (*Hint*: Write the electron dot structure to determine the kinds of bonds. Then refer to Table 14·4). *14·12*

45. Briefly discuss the nature and significance of van der Waals forces. *14·13*

46. What is a hydrogen bond? *14·13*

47. Which compound in each pair exhibits the stronger intermolecular hydrogen-bonding? *14·13*
 a. H_2S and H_2O c. HBr and HCl
 b. HCl and HF d. NH_3 and H_2O

48. Why do compounds with strong intermolecular attractive forces have higher boiling points than compounds with weak intermolecular attractive forces? *14·14*

49. Define and give two examples of a *network solid*. *14·14*

Mastery Questions and Problems

50. Devise a hybridization scheme and predict the shape of PCl_3 based on this scheme. *14·9*

51. Write two electron dot structures for the molecule N_2O. Predict the magnetic properties and shape of this molecule. *14·6*

52. The chlorines and oxygen in thionyl chloride, $SOCl_2$, are bonded directly to the sulfur. Write an acceptable electron dot structure for thionyl chloride. *14·3*

53. Explain why each of the following electron dot structures is incorrect. Replace each structure with one that is more acceptable. *14·6*

 a. :C::N̈: c. H:C̈::O with :Cl: above

 b. :F̈:P::F̈: with :F̈: below d. :F̈: above, :F̈:B:F̈: below

54. Describe differences between the members of each pair of terms. *14·9*
 a. sigma bonds and pi bonds
 b. polar bonds and polar molecules
 c. diamagnetic and paramagnetic molecules
 d. sp^2 and sp^3 hybrid orbitals

55. Using bond dissociation energies estimate ΔH for the following reaction. *14·12*

$$CO(g) + 2H_2(g) \longrightarrow CH_3OH(g)$$

56. Use VSEPR theory to predict the geometry of each of the following. *14·8*
 a. $SeCl_4$ c. CCl_4
 b. CO_3^{2-} d. $SnCl_2$

57. Give the angles between the orbitals of each of the following hybrids. *14·9*
 a. sp^3 hybrids
 b. sp^2 hybrids
 c. sp hybrids

58. Describe the difference between a bonding molecular orbital and an antibonding molecular orbital. How do their energies compare? *14·7*

Review Questions and Problems

59. Which of the following ions have the same number of electrons as a noble gas?
 a. Al^{3+} c. Br^-
 b. O^{2-} d. N^{3-}

60. A solution containing 0.10 mol of $BaCl_2$ is mixed with a solution containing 0.2 mol of Na_2SO_4 to give a precipitate of $BaSO_4$. What is the maximum yield in moles of $BaSO_4$? In grams?

61. Write correct electron configurations for atoms of the following elements.
  a. sodium
  b. sulfur
  c. phosphorus
  d. nitrogen

62. Calculate the gram formula mass of each of the following substances.
  a. $CaSO_4$
  b. H_2SO_4
  c. NI_3
  d. $FeCl_3$

63. Give the number of representative particles in the following molar quantities.
  a. 2.00 centimole
  b. 1.54 millimole
  c. 8.73 nanomole
  d. 3.00 micromole

64. Name and give the symbol for the element in the following position in the periodic table.
  a. Group 7B, period 4
  b. Group 3A, period 5
  c. Group 1A, period 7
  d. Group 6A, period 6

Challenging Questions and Problems

65. The electron structure and geometry of the methane molecule, CH_4, can be described by a variety of models. These include the electron dot structure, simple overlap of atomic orbitals, and orbital hybridization of carbon. Write the electron dot structure of CH_4. Sketch two molecular orbital pictures of the CH_4 molecule. For your first sketch assume that one of the paired $2s^2$ electrons of carbon has been "promoted" to the empty $2p$ orbital. Overlap each half-filled atomic orbital of carbon to a half-filled $1s$ orbital of hydrogen. What is the predicted geometry of the CH_4 molecule using this simple overlap method? In your second sketch assume hybridization of the $2s$ and $2p$ orbitals of carbon. Now what geometry would you predict for CH_4? Which picture do you think is preferable based on the facts that all H—C—H bond angles in CH_4 are 109.5° and all C—H bond distances are identical?

66. There are some compounds in which one atom has more electrons than the corresponding noble gas. Examples are PCl_5, SF_6, and IF_7. Write the electron configuration of P, S, and I, and then draw the electron dot structures for these compounds. Looking at the outer shell configuration of P, S, and I, can you develop an orbital hybridization scheme to explain the existence of these compounds?

Research Projects

1. What are the structural differences between ionic crystals and molecular crystals? Compare physical properties for an ionic compound and a molecular compound and relate the differences to their crystal structures.

2. Devise a method to measure the polarity of some covalent bonds.

3. Relate the melting points of some covalently bonded compounds to the degree of polarity of the compounds.

4. What contributions did Jacobus van't Hoff make to the understanding of the three-dimensional structures of molecules? What other property of organic molecules did his research help explain?

5. Make models of a family of compounds such as H_2O, H_2Se, and H_2Te and relate the bond angles to the predictions of VSEPR theory.

6. How did Christian Schönbein discover ozone? What role does ozone play in the atmosphere? How is it affected by fluorocarbons?

7. Trace the development of adhesives.

8. How did Linus Pauling use wave theory to describe chemical bonds?

9. Diagram a simple protein molecule. What types of bonds and attractions contribute to the structure of the molecule?

Readings and References

Drummond, A. H., *Molecules in the Service of Man*. Philadelphia: Lippincott, 1972.

Gordon, J. E. *The New Science of Strong Materials or Why You Don't Fall Through the Floor*, 2nd ed. Princeton, NJ: Princeton University Press, 1984.

Morgan, Ralph A. *Collisions, Coalescence and Crystals: The States of Matter and Their Models*. New York: Methuen Educational (dist. by Harper & Row), 1973.

Vergara, William C. *Science in Everyday Life*. New York: Harper & Row, 1980.

15 Water and Aqueous Systems

Chapter Planning Guide

Section		Demonstrations and Experiments	Resource Materials
15·1 The Water Molecule	C*		Objectives Worksheet 15, SPB Skillsheet 15, SPB
15·2 Surface Properties of Water	O	Dem 15·1 Surface Tension	Beyond the Text: Nonwettable Surfaces
15·3 The Heat Capacity of Water	O		
15·4 The Vaporization of Water	O		
15·5 Ice	O		Quiz 15·1
15·6 Aqueous Solutions	C	Exp 27 The Solvent Properties of Water, LM Exp 28 Distillation, LM Dem 15·2 Multicolored System	Prelab 27, SPB Prelab 28, SPB Teaching Diagram 21
15·7 Solvation	C	Dem 15·3 Soft Water	
15·A When the Water is Hard	E		
15·8 Water of Hydration	O	Dem 15·4 Water of Hydration Exp 29 Water of Hydration, LM	Quiz 15·2 Prelab 29, SPB
15·9 Electrolytes and Nonelectrolytes	C	Exp 30 Electrolytes and Nonelectrolytes, LM	Prelab 30, SPB
15·10 Suspensions and Colloids	O	Dem 15·5 Colloids Dem 15·6 Tyndall Effect Dem 15·7 A Slimy Substance	Quiz 15·3 Reviewsheet 15, SPB Chapter 15 Test
15·B Ellen Richards: Pioneer in Water Treatment	E		Sewage Treatment, ICT 15
*C = Core, O = Optional E = Enrichment, H = Honors		LM = Laboratory Manual	SPB = Skills Practice Book ICT = Issues in Chem. Tech.

Chapter Objectives

Having studied this chapter and done the problems, the student should be able to:

1. Describe the hydrogen-bonding that occurs in water on the basis of the structure of the polar water molecule. *15·1*

2. Use the concept of hydrogen bonding to explain the following properties of water: **a.** high surface tension **b.** low vapor pressure **c.** high specific heat **d.** high heat of vaporization and **e.** high boiling point. *15·2-15·4*

3. Explain the low density and high heat of fusion of ice. *15·5*

4. Define the terms solution, aqueous solution, solute, and solvent and give an example of each. *15·6*

5. Use the rule that "like dissolves like" to predict the solubility of one substance in another. *15·7*

6. Describe the role of solvation in the dissolving process. *15·7*

7. Define the term water of hydration. *15·8*

8. Calculate the percent of water in a given hydrate. *15·8*

9. Distinguish among strong electrolytes, weak electrolytes, and nonelectrolytes, giving examples of each. *15·9*

10. Give the characteristics of colloids and suspensions that distinguish them from solutions. *15·10*

Teaching Suggestions

15·1 The Water Molecule

The unifying theme of these sections is that water is a compound of unusual properties, and that these unusual properties are the result of hydrogen bonding.

A possible approach is to present the following sections as an illustration of this theme. Discuss each special property, give examples of the importance of that property, and then explain the property in terms of hydrogen bonding of water molecules.

15·2 Surface Properties of Water

Most students have not had much experience with surface tension effects. You can do **Demonstration 15·1** *Surface Tension* at this time to illustrate some of the interesting aspects of surface tension.

15·3 Heat Capacity of Water

15·4 The Vaporization of Water

15·5 Ice

Experiment 17 *Heat of Fusion of Ice* could be done now instead of during Chapter 9.

15·6 Aqueous Solutions

Demonstration 15·2 *Multicolored System* is appropriate at this time.

15·7 Solvation

Stress the idea that when a solid dissolves in a solvent, it breaks up into its smallest units, molecules or ions. In order for the solid to dissolve, the molecules of the solvent must be able to overcome the attractive forces that are holding the solid together. In the case of water it is the charges on the polar molecules which attract the ions in the solids. Using models, if possible, show how each ion on the surface of a solid is surrounded by molecules of water and carried away by them. Make the point that the ions do not exist as free species, but are always surrounded by water molecules. Remind the students that in a true solution the particles of solute cannot be seen even with a microscope. They cannot be filtered out of solution, and they do not settle out.

To gain further experience with solutions, have the students do **Experiment 27** *The Solvent Properties of Water* and/or **Experiment 28** *Distillation*. **Demonstration 15·3** *Soft Water* shows how water can be softened.

15·8 Water of Hydration

After dealing with the previous section the students should have no trouble with the concept of water of hydration. It is reasonable to expect that when ions precipitate out of solution, some of the solvating water molecules are carried with them into the crystal structure. Emphasize that these water molecules are no longer dissolving the ions, but are part of the crystal structure itself. Point out that the formula of a hydrated solid does not combine the formulas of the ionic solid and the water. Instead, they are written side by side with a dot between them.

The fact that the water of hydration is not tightly bound into the crystal can be illustrated by the heating of a hydrate. **Experiment 29** *Water of Hydration*, or **Demonstration 15·4** *Water of Hydration* will be helpful.

15·9 Electrolytes and Nonelectrolytes

Be sure the students see the difference in the manner in which metals conduct electricity and in which solutions and molten liquids conduct electricity.

Emphasize the role of ions in the conductivity of solutions and molten liquids. Stress that the classification of a solution as a nonelectrolyte, a strong electrolyte, or a weak electrolyte is solely determined by the relative number of ions in the solution. It is strongly recommended that you do **Demonstration 13·3** *Electrical Conductivity* at this point, if you have not already done it as part of Chapter 13. The students could also do **Experiment 30** *Electrolytes and Nonelectrolytes*.

15·10 Suspensions and Colloids

When they reach this section, students may become confused by the subtle differences between solutions, suspensions, and colloids. Explain that the main difference is in particle size. Solution particles are characteristically less than 1 nm in diameter. Colloid particles are between 1 nm and 100 nm in diameter; this includes large molecules, such as proteins. Suspension particles are typically larger than 100 nm in diameter.

Have the students compare the properties of solutions, colloids, and suspensions by carefully studying Table 15·6. They should be able to deduce that the properties of colloids are in-between the properties of solutions and suspensions.

Most students are not aware that so many common substances are colloids. To get this point across you might arrange a display of common colloids. (This would also make a good student project.) See Table 15·5 for examples, and do **Demonstration 15·5** *Colloids*.

The scattering of light by a colloid is easily demonstrated. **Demonstration 15·6** *The Tyndall Effect* shows how light is scattered by colloidal sulfur. **Demonstration 15·7** *A Slimy Substance* is for fun.

Demonstrations

15·1 Surface Tension

Concept: Water has a high surface tension due to its hydrogen bonding.

Materials: overhead projector, sewing needle, beaker, water, dropper, 3 toothpicks coated with detergent or soap, clear plastic film, 3 camphor pieces, light wooden "boat" (with pointed bow in front and a notch in the rear).

Procedure: 1. Float the needle on the surface of water in a beaker. This may take some practice; you must minimize disturbance of the water surface. Be sure that the beaker and your fingers have no trace of soap or detergent. 2. Point out that a steel needle is much denser than water and should *sink*. It *floats* because it is supported by the surface tension of the water. 3. Once the needle floats, dip the coated toothpick into the top of the liquid in the beaker. 4. The needle sinks immediately, due to the effect of the surfactant on the surface tension. 5. Place water drops on a piece of clear plastic film. 6. Observe that regardless of the size of the drop, it is always round. 7. Point out that the water surface is sharply curved at the plastic/water interface. This is best observed by looking at the drop from the side. 8. Dip the end of a coated toothpick into one of the drops. 9. The drop flattens as the surfactant breaks the surface tension. 10. Insert a piece of camphor into the notch on the wooden "boat." 11. Place the boat in water and observe its motion. 12. Explain that the outer edges of the boat are attracted to the molecules in the surface layer of the water. Without the camphor, these attractions would be equal and opposite, and would cancel. As the camphor dissolves, it breaks the surface tension behind the boat. The attractive forces at the front of the boat pull it forward.

15·2 Multicolored System

Concept: Ionization can cause color changes.

Materials: 1 g of iron(III) aluminum sulfate (FeAl(SO$_4$)$_3$), 5 mL of 1% potassium thiocyanate (KSCN), 5 mL of 1% barium chloride (BaCl$_2$), 5 mL of 1% potassium ferrocyanide (K$_3$Fe(CN)$_6$), large test tube, safety goggles.

Procedure: 1. Mix the ferric aluminum sulfate, potassium thiocyanate, barium chloride, and potassium ferrocyanide (in that order) in the test tube. 2. Red, white, and blue colors form as a result of ionizations. **Caution:** *potassium thiocyanate, potassium ferrocyanide, and barium chloride are toxic.*

15·3 Soft Water

Concept: The removal of calcium ions softens water.

Materials: two test tubes and stoppers, 100 mL distilled water, small bar of soap, beaker, 50 mL each of 0.1N: sodium sulfate (Na$_2$SO$_4$), calcium sulfate (CaSO$_4$), and sodium bicarbonate (NaHCO$_3$).

Procedure: 1. In the beaker, dissolve the soap in distilled water. 2. Half-fill one test tube with sodium sulfate, and the other with calcium sulfate. Add 1 mL of soapy water to each of the tubes. 3. Stopper each tube and shake it. The suds level is lower in the calcium sulfate tube. 4. Add sodium bicarbonate to the calcium sulfate tube to precipitate the calcium. 5. Shake the tube and observe the formation of suds. The removal of calcium has softened the water.

15·4 Water of Hydration

Concept: Water can be an integral part of a crystal.

Materials: test tube, test tube holder, glass plate, 5 g of hydrated copper(II) sulfate (CuSO$_4$·5H$_2$O), gas burner, matches, evaporating dish, ring stand, ring, clay triangle, 20 g of sodium carbonate decahydrate (Na$_2$CO$_3$·10H$_2$O), watch glass, safety goggles.

Procedure: 1. Place the hydrated copper(II) sulfate in a test tube and heat gently. 2. The blue color of the solid disappears as the water evaporates. Place a cold glass plate near the mouth of the test tube. Note the condensation of water on the plate. 3. Place the evaporating dish on the triangle in the ring stand. 4. Put the sodium carbonate in the dish and heat. 5. Observe the evaporation of water. 6. The water of hydration is trapped in the crystal lattice. As the water evaporates, the crystal structure collapses and the anhydrous salt is left. **Caution:** *Copper(II) sulfate is an irritant.*

15·5 Colloids

Concept: Colloids can form in a variety of ways.

Materials: examples of various colloidal suspensions: whipped cream (gas in liquid), marshmallow (gas in solid), milk (liquid in liquid), aerosol spray (liquid in gas), cigarette smoke (solid in gas), gelatin dessert (solid in liquid).

Procedure: 1. Show the materials and discuss their colloidal nature.

15·6 The Tyndall Effect

Concept: Colloids scatter light.

Materials: 25 g of sodium thiosulfate pentahydrate (Na$_2$S$_2$O$_3$·5H$_2$O) in 5 L of water, 25 mL of concentrated hydrochloric acid (HCl), slide projector, cardboard slide

with a small hole, aquarium or other flat-walled glass container, stirring rod, water.

Procedure: 1. Place 5 L of water in the aquarium. 2. Set up the slide projector and slide. Direct its beam through the aquarium so that it projects onto a white wall behind it. 3. Point out that water alone will not scatter light. 4. Dissolve the sodium thiosulfate in the water. 5. Add 25 mL of hydrochloric acid. 6. Stir thoroughly and wait two minutes. 7. Sulfur particles form and aggregate into colloidal-size particles. The colloid becomes cloudy and yellow from the sulfur. 8. Observe the scattering of light passing through the colloid. This effect is analogous to the scattering of light in our atmosphere. **Caution:** *Hydrochloric acid is corrosive.*

15·7 A Slimy Substance

Concept: Solids dispersed in liquids may form colloidal gels.

Materials: 600-mL beaker, two 250-mL beakers, two stirring rods, 4 g of guar gum, 3 g of borax ($Na_2B_4O_7 \cdot 10H_2O$), water, food coloring, scissors.

Procedure: 1. Add food coloring to 250 mL water in the 600-mL beaker and bring to a boil. 2. Suspend the guar gum in 80 mL of water in a 250-mL beaker. 3. Dissolve the borax in 80 mL of water in a 250-mL beaker. 4. Remove the boiling water from the heat and add the guar gum, stirring well. 5. Add the borax solution, stirring well. 6. Let cool. 7. Try to pick up the gel; it flows like a liquid. 8. Try to cut the gel with scissors. 9. Pull it slowly from the beaker. 10. Pull it again, but this time more quickly. 11. Note that it is 98% water. The guar gum consists of large molecules that become cross-linked by the borax. Hydrogen bonding of the water adds to the effect.

Audiovisual Resources

Chemistry: Looking at the Solution (5 FS) Charles Clark, 1978, 15–19 min. each. (Use with Sections 15·6, 15·7, or 15·10.) Compares solutions and suspensions and discusses the solution process. Also covers topics in Chapter 16.

Common Colloids (F, V) Sterling Educational Films, 1973, 7 min. (Use with Section 15·10.) Defines solution, mixture, and colloidal suspension and illustrates the eight possible types of colloidal suspensions in a simple way.

Groundwater (F, V) Encyclopaedia Brittanica, 1982, 18 min. (Use with Section 15·1.) Presents an overview of the role of groundwater in the environment and the need to conserve this resource.

The Quiet Crisis (F, V) Indiana University, 1980, 55 min. (Use with Section 15·6.) Examines the problems of water quality and supply.

The Water Crisis (F, V) Time-Life Video, 1981, 57 min. (Use with Sections 15·6 or 15·8.) Presents problems and politics of water shortages and pollution.

Water: A Precious Resource (F) National Geographic, 1979, 23 min. (Use with Section 15·1.) Examines the hydrologic cycle and explores ways we obtain, use, and abuse our water supply.

Beyond the Text

Nonwettable Surfaces

The feathers of ducks, the leaves of aquatic plants, and the inside of blood sampling tubes are all examples of nonwettable surfaces. Molecules that are not attracted to water are called hydrophobic. Those that are attracted to water are called hydrophilic. Surfaces coated with hydrophobic materials can be in contact with water without getting wet.

You have seen water "bead up" on a greasy surface, on a freshly waxed car, or on some plastics. The molecules in these materials are nonpolar and are not attracted to water. They are hydrophobic. A duck coats its feathers with oil from a gland near its tail. The duck can remain in water for hours without getting wet because of this hydrophobic oil coating. The leaves of many aquatic plants are coated with wax. Because of this they never get waterlogged and sink.

Blood in contact with glass, a hydrophilic surface, clots very quickly. Glass blood-sample tubes are coated on the inside with silicone, a hydrophobic polymer. Blood will not interact with the hydrophobic silicone surface of the sample tube. Silicone is also used to waterproof leather, textiles, and masonry.

Answers to End of Chapter Questions and Problems

Practice Questions and Problems

4. Oxygen is more electronegative than hydrogen. Because of the bent shape, the bond polarities do not cancel.

5. High surface tension, low vapor pressure, high specific heat, high heat of vaporization, high boiling point, high melting point.

6. A hydrogen atom covalently bonded to a highly electronegative atom is electrostatically attracted to an unshared electron pair of a nearby atom.

7. It is the inward pulling force which minimizes the surface area of a liquid. Surface molecules are attracted to the other liquid molecules on one side but not to the air. Molecules inside the liquid are attracted in all directions.

8. Drops are spherical; objects denser than water float.

9. Water molecules are hydrogen-bonded to each other, but not to air molecules. The net attraction is inward, minimizing the water surface.

10. It physically interferes with hydrogen bonding and reduces surface tension.

11. The pressure of the vapor above a liquid; hydrogen bonding prevents escape of water molecules.

12. Water, 2.0×10^4 cal; iron, 2.2×10^3 cal

13. 1.3×10^4 cal

14. Hydrogen bonds hold water molecules together, making it harder for them to escape.

15. Ice has an open, honeycomb-like structure of hydrogen bonded water molecules. Water has a less rigid structure in which water molecules are closer together. The density of ice is less than that of water because of ice's lattice structure. As a result, ice floats on water.

16. Bodies of water would freeze from the bottom up. This would kill many forms of aquatic life.

17. **a.** 15.9 kJ **b.** 3.81 kcal

18. The polar water molecules electrostatically attract and repel ions and polar covalent molecules. Polar compounds will dissolve but nonpolar compounds are unaffected because they have no charges.

19. Solutions are homogeneous mixtures in which a solute is dissolved in a solvent. Aqueous solutions have water as the solvent.

20. **a.** whipped cream or beaten egg whites **b.** alcohol in water **c.** salt or sugar in water **d.** oxygen in nitrogen in the air

21. No. The molecules are smaller than the pores of the filter.

22. Polar solvents dissolve polar compounds, and nonpolar solvents dissolve nonpolar compounds. *Like* refers to the relative polarity of the substances.

23. The positive ions are attracted by the negatively charged end of the polar water molecule; the negative

ions are attracted by the positively charged end. As the ions are pulled away from the crystal, they are surrounded by the water molecules.

24. **a.** no; nonpolar **b.** yes; ionic **c.** no; nonpolar **d.** yes; ionic **e.** yes; polar covalent **f.** no; ionic

25. Water in the crystal structure of a substance.

26. **a.** tin(IV) chloride pentahydrate **b.** iron(II) sulfate heptahydrate **c.** aluminum chloride hexahydrate **d.** barium bromide tetrahydrate **e.** iron(III) phosphate tetrahydrate

27. $CaCl_2 + 6H_2O \rightarrow CaCl_2 \cdot 6H_2O$

28. $MgSO_4 \cdot 7H_2O \xrightarrow{150°C} MgSO_4 \cdot H_2O + 6H_2O$

29. Electrolytes can conduct an electrical current in aqueous solution or in the molten state; nonelectrolytes cannot.

30. A strong electrolyte forms solutions that are mostly ions. A weak electrolyte forms solutions with few ions.

31. Its ions are free to move toward an electrode.

32. An aqueous solution of a strong electrolyte conducts electricity much better.

33. A suspension is a mixture with relatively large particles which slowly settle upon standing. A colloid is a mixture with particles of intermediate size which do not settle.

34. Particle size.

35. The particles are the *dispersed phase* in a colloidal suspension. They are in the *dispersion medium*.

36. The scattering of visible light by the particles in a colloid or suspension.

37. The molecules or ions are too small to have reflective surfaces.

38. The random motion of the dispersion medium molecules.

39. The random movement of colloidal particles.

40. Emulsions are colloidal dispersions of liquids in liquids. An emulsifying agent attracts both of the liquids and holds them in suspension.

41. Emulsion.

Mastery Questions and Problems

42. Water molecules at 4°C are tightly packed and have maximum density. Below 4°C the attractions between water molecules arrange them in a regular network. Molecules are farther apart because of water's bond

angles. As a result, ice has a lower density than water and floats.

43. Hexane, chloroform, ethanol, water.

44. a. sodium tetraborate decahydrate, 47.2% H_2O
b. sodium carbonate monohydrate, 14.5% H_2O
c. magnesium sulfate heptahydrate, 51.5% H_2O
d. calcium sulfate hemihydrate, 6.2% H_2O

45. a. 2.95×10^3 cal **b.** 2.95 kcal

46. Ions in solution are surrounded by water molecules. Negative ions are attracted to the hydrogen atoms and positive ions are attracted to the oxygen atoms.

47. 3.52×10^3 cal, 3.52 kcal, 1.47×10^3 J, 14.7 kJ; 132.0 g H_2O

48. a. no **b.** tasting, drying to examine the crystals, testing for electrical conductivity, doing a flame test

49. a. water **b.** gasoline **c.** water **d.** gasoline **e.** water **f.** neither

50. a. 1,2 **b.** 2,3 **c.** 1 **d.** 3 **e.** 2,3 **f.** 1,2 **g.** 2 **h.** 1 **i.** 2

51. a. Water expands when it turns to ice. **b.** Water is polar and wax is nonpolar, and water has a high surface tension. **c.** Sweat evaporates from skin to carry away the heat of vaporization. **d.** Freezing damages plants because water expands when frozen. Water on the surface of plants gives off the heat of fusion to the plants when it freezes. **e.** Steam carries the heat of vaporization.

52. Ethyl alcohol has a polar hydroxyl end (—OH) that dissolves in water, and a nonpolar hydrocarbon end (C_2H_5—) that dissolves in gasoline.

53. 4.5×10^7 kcal, 1.9×10^8 kJ

54. Nonpolar molecules do not dissolve in polar molecules.

55. a. $NH_4Cl \rightarrow NH_4^+ + Cl^-$
b. $Cu(NO_3)_2 \rightarrow Cu^{2+} + 2NO_3^-$ **c.** $HNO_3 \rightarrow H^+ + NO_3^-$
d. $HC_2H_3O_2 \rightarrow H^+ + C_2H_3O_2^-$
e. $Na_2SO_4 \rightarrow 2Na^+ + SO_4^{2-}$
f. $HgCl_2 \rightarrow Hg^{2+} + 2Cl^-$

Review Questions and Problems

56. a. 195 g **b.** 1.95×10^5 mg **c.** 0.195 kg

57. 1.27 atm

58. a. raises the boiling point **b.** lowers the boiling point

59. 3.60×10^{-2} g H_2O, 2.24×10^{-2} L O_2

60. 9.00 g H_2, 72.0 g O_2

61. 25.7 g H_2O

62. 636 g C_2H_4O

63. 0.300 mol O_2, 6.72 L O_2

64. a. $6CO_2 + 6H_2O \rightarrow C_6H_{12}O_6 + 6O_2$
b. $2Na + 2H_2O \rightarrow 2Na^+ + 2OH^- + H_2$
c. $2C_6H_6 + 15O_2 \rightarrow 12CO_2 + 6H_2O$
d. $2NaHCO_3 \rightarrow Na_2CO_3 + H_2O + CO_2$

65. 1.5×10^{20} molecules H_2O

66. a. H_2O, HBr, and HCl have decreasing boiling points. Even though H_2O has low molecular mass, it has hydrogen bonding. The molecular attractions in HBr and HCl are similar, but HBr has greater molecular mass and increased dispersion forces. **b.** H_2O, NH_3, and CH_4 have decreasing boiling points. The molecular masses are similar. Hydrogen bonding is greater in H_2O than in NH_3, and CH_4 has no hydrogen bonding.

67. 5.74 atm

68. a. 11.1% H, 88.9% O **b.** 5.9%H, 94.1% S **c.** 2.5% H, 97.5% Se **d.** 1.5% H, 98.5% Te

69. 4.9×10^7 mg H_2O, 49 kg H_2O

70. $1s^2\, 2s^2\, 2p^6$; neon.

71. $H^+ + \overset{..}{\underset{..}{O}}:H \rightarrow \left[H:\overset{..}{\underset{..}{O}}:H \right]^+$

Challenging Questions and Problems

72. The gfm of water is 18.0 g. The gfm of deuterium oxide is 20.0 g. Deuterium oxide boils and freezes at a higher temperature and is denser. Deuterium oxide can be used to replace hydrogen with deuterium in compounds, and as a moderator for nuclear reactors.

73. a. The volume of 1 g ice at 0°C is greater. **b.** The volume of 1 g water at 100°C is less.

74. a. hydrogen **b.** 4.9×10^{-2} g H_2O **c.** oxygen **d.** 10 cm^3 O_2

75. Volume of ice above H_2O (0°C) = 3.2×10^8 cm^3
Mass of ice above H_2O (0°C) = 2.9×10^5 kg
The answers are the same at 4°C.

76. The water molecules fit into the spaces between the ethyl alcohol molecules and the total volume is reduced. In some mixtures, electrostatic repulsions keep the different molecules further apart and increase the volume.

77. Ice freezes first at the top surface. The heavier sodium and chloride ions fall below the surface. Also, the formation of ice crystals is hindered by the ions.

Water and Aqueous Systems

Chapter Preview

Figure 15·1
The unique chemical properties of water make it well suited to be the basis of life on our planet.

Polar bonds

Molecule has net polarity

Figure 15·2
The water molecule is bent. The bond polarities are equal, but the two dipoles do not cancel each other. There is a net polarity, and the molecule as a whole is polar.

Water has a unique story because it is a unique compound. Liquid water covers about three-quarters of the surface of the earth, providing us with oceans, lakes, and rivers. Immense aquifers store water deep underground. Ice dominates the vast polar regions of the globe. It appears as icebergs in the oceans, and it whitens the temperate zones as snow in winter. Water vapor from the evaporation of surface water and from steam spouted from geysers and volcanoes is ever-present in the earth's atmosphere. Water is the foundation of everything that lives. Without it neither plant nor animal life as we know it could exist.

15·1 The Water Molecule

Water is a simple triatomic molecule. Each O—H covalent bond in the water molecule is highly polar. Because of its greater electronegativity, oxygen attracts the electron pair of the covalent O—H bond and acquires a slightly negative charge. The less electronegative hydrogens acquire a slightly positive charge. The water molecule has a H—O—H bond angle of 105°. Because of the water molecule's bent shape, the two O—H bond polarities do not cancel, and the water molecule as a whole is polar. The region around oxygen is slightly negatively charged. The region around the hydrogens is slightly positively charged.

One property of polar molecules is that they attract one another. This leads to a dipolar interaction between the positive region of one water molecule and the negative region of another. This attraction is very weak, however, when compared with the strength of intermolecular

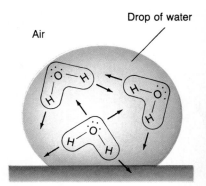

Air

Drop of water

Figure 15·3
Water molecules at the surface experience an uneven attraction. Because they cannot hydrogen-bond with air molecules, they tend to be drawn into the body of the liquid, producing surface tension.

Water molecules are polar, and they participate in hydrogen-bonding.

Water has unusual surface properties because of hydrogen-bonding.

hydrogen bonds. In water the molecules change position by sliding over one another. Because of hydrogen-bonding, however, most do not have enough kinetic energy to escape. *Hydrogen bonds* are the cause of many unique and important properties of water. They are responsible for its high surface tension, low vapor pressure, high specific heat, high heat of vaporization, and high-boiling point.

15·2   Surface Properties of Water

You have probably seen a glass so filled with water that the water surface bulges above the rim. You also may have noticed that water forms nearly spherical droplets at the end of a medicine dropper or when sprayed on a greasy surface. A needle floats if placed upon the surface of water, but it sinks immediately if it breaks through the surface. Apparently the surface of water acts like a skin. This phenomenon, called *surface tension,* is explained by the ability of water to form hydrogen bonds. The molecules within the liquid are completely surrounded by, and hydrogen-bonded to, adjacent water molecules. At the surface of the liquid, however, water molecules experience an uneven attraction. They are hydrogen-bonded on only one side. They are not attracted to the air because they cannot form hydrogen bonds with air molecules (Figure 15·3). As a result, the

Figure 15·4
Surface tension tends to hold drops of liquids in a spherical shape. At the same time the force of gravity tends to flatten the drops. The higher the surface tension, the more spherical the drop of liquid. All of the drops shown are of equal volume. From left to right they are mercury, water, and water with detergent.

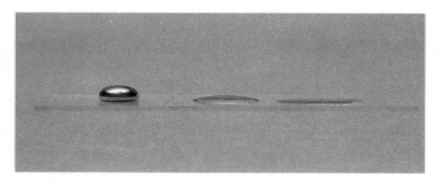

Figure 15·5
Surface tension makes it possible for some insects such as this water strider to "walk" on water. The force of gravity pulling the insect downward is less than the forces of attraction between the water molecules.

The surface tension is strong for liquids having strong intermolecular attractions.

This same effect can be observed by placing a tiny amount of detergent along the edge of a beaker which has a steel needle floating on top of the water. The instant the detergent is added, the needle will sink to the bottom.

The low vapor pressure of water is the result of strong intermolecular forces of attraction between water molecules.

surface water molecules tend to be drawn into the body of the liquid. *This inward force or pull which tends to minimize the surface area of a liquid is* **surface tension.**

A sphere has the smallest surface area for a given volume. The surface tension of a liquid tends to hold a drop of liquid in a spherical shape. A liquid that has strong intermolecular attractions has a high-surface tension. The higher the surface tension, the more nearly spherical the drop of that particular liquid (Figure 15·4).

All liquids have a surface tension, but water's surface tension is higher than most. The surface tension of water may be decreased by adding a *wetting agent* such as soap or detergent. Soaps and detergents are **surfactants** (*surf*ace *act*ive *a*gents). When a detergent is added to beads of water on a greasy surface, the detergent molecules interfere with the hydrogen-bonding between water molecules. As a result, surface tension is reduced. The beads collapse, and the water spreads out.

Hydrogen-bonding between water molecules also explains water's unusually low vapor pressure. As was covered in Section 9·6, the *vapor pressure* of a liquid is caused by the tendency of the molecules at the surface to escape. Because hydrogen bonds hold water molecules together, the tendency of these molecules to escape is low. If it were not, all the lakes and oceans, with their large surface areas, would rapidly evaporate!

15·3 The Heat Capacity of Water

You may recall from Section 2·12 that it takes 1 cal of heat energy to raise the temperature of 1 g of water 1°C. The specific heat or heat capacity of water is nearly constant at 1 cal/g°C at temperatures between 0°C and 100°C. The specific heat of water is higher than that of many other substances. Iron has a specific heat of only 0.107 cal/g°C. For the same increase in temperature, iron requires about one-tenth as much heat as does an equal mass of water. On a sunny day a puddle of water remains relatively cool. Meanwhile a nearby manhole cover gets hot enough, so it is said, to fry an egg.

Figure 15·6
People flock to the beach in hot weather because the shore is cooler than inland areas. Can you explain this phenomenon in terms of water's heat capacity?

The high heat capacity of water allows it to absorb a large amount of heat without a great increase in temperature. During the summer the air near beaches is cooled by the water.

Water has a higher specific heat than many other substances.

Water has the highest heat of vaporization of any known liquid.

Water's high heat capacity helps moderate daily air temperatures around large bodies of water. On a warm day, water absorbs heat from its warmer environment, lowering the air temperature. On a cool night the transfer of heat is from the water to its cooler environment, raising the air temperature. Thus water is a storage medium for solar energy.

15·4 The Vaporization of Water

Because of hydrogen-bonding, water absorbs a large amount of heat before it vaporizes. The heat of vaporization is the amount of energy needed to convert one gram of a substance from a liquid to a gas at the boiling point. It takes 540 cal to convert 1 g of water at 100°C to 1 g of steam at 100°C. The extensive network of hydrogen bonds holds the molecules in water tightly together. The heat of vaporization of liquid ammonia, which is less hydrogen-bonded than water, is 327 cal/g. Liquid methane, which has no hydrogen-bonding, has a heat of vaporization of only 122 cal/g.

The reverse of vaporization is condensation. When 1 g of steam at 100°C condenses to 1 g of water at 100°C, 540 cal of heat is liberated. The heat of condensation of water is therefore 540 cal/g. As expected, this heat is numerically equal to the heat of vaporization. You can get a severe burn if you allow steam to condense on your hand. Not only is the temperature of steam 100°C, but the additional heat of condensation is absorbed by your skin.

The condensation of water is also important to geographical temperatures. Temperatures in the tropics would be much higher if water did not absorb heat while evaporating from the surface of the surrounding oceans. Temperatures in the polar regions would be much colder if water vapor did not release its heat while condensing out of the air.

Compounds of low formula mass are usually gases or low-boiling liquids at normal atmospheric pressure (Table 15·1). Ammonia is a typi-

Table 15·1   Melting Points and Boiling Points of Some Substances with Low-Formula Mass

Name of substance	Formula	Formula mass (amu)	Melting point (°C)	Boiling point (°C)
Methane	CH_4	16	−183	−164
Ammonia	NH_3	17	−77.7	−33.3
Water	H_2O	18	0	100
Neon	Ne	20	−249	−246
Methanol	CH_3OH	32	−93.9	64.9
Hydrogen sulfide	H_2S	34	−85.5	−60.7

cal example. Ammonia has a formula mass of 17 amu and boils at −33°C. Yet water, with a formula mass of 18 amu, is an exception. It has a boiling point of 100°C. The reason is again hydrogen-bonding. Hydrogen-bonding is more extensive in water than in ammonia. It takes much more heat to disrupt the attractions between water molecules than between ammonia molecules. If the hydrogen-bonding in water were as weak as it is in ammonia, water would be a gas at the usual temperatures found on earth.

1. Ammonia molecules form hydrogen bonds whereas methane molecules do not. Substances whose molecules form hydrogen bonds tend to have higher boiling points.

Problem

1. Why does ammonia have a much higher boiling point (−33°C) than methane (−164°C) although their formula weights are almost the same?

15·5   Ice

Table 15·2   Density of Water and Ice

Temperature (°C)	Density (g/cm³)
100 (water)	0.9584
50	0.9881
25	0.9971
10	0.9997
4	1.0000*
0 (water)	0.9998
0 (ice)	0.9168

*Most dense.

As a typical liquid is cooled, it contracts slightly. Its density increases because its mass stays constant. (Recall that density = mass/volume.) If the cooling continues, the liquid eventually solidifies. Because the density of a typical solid is greater than that of the liquid, the solid sinks in its own liquid. (Lead shot sinks in molten lead.) As water is cooled, it first behaves like a typical liquid. Its density gradually increases until the temperature reaches 4°C. Below 4°C, the density of water starts to decrease (Table 15·2). At 0°C, ice begins to form. Ice has about 10% greater volume and therefore a lower density than water. As a result, it floats on water. This is certainly unusual behavior for a solid. Ice is one of very few solids that floats in its own liquid.

Why does ice behave so differently? The structure of ice is a very regular open framework of water molecules arranged like a honeycomb (Figure 15·7). Hydrogen-bonding holds the water molecules in place. At low temperatures they do not have sufficient kinetic energy to break out

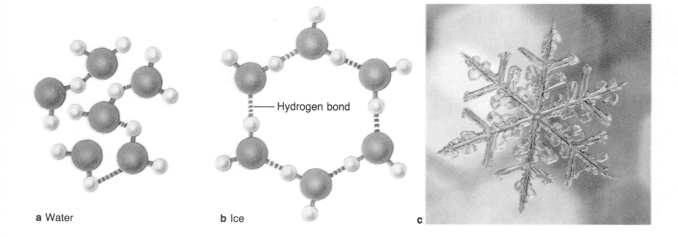

a Water **b** Ice **c**

Figure 15·7
a The molecules in liquid water are hydrogen bonded but free to move about.
b Extensive hydrogen bonding in ice causes the water molecules to be held further apart and in a more ordered arrangement than in liquid water.
c The hexagonal symmetry of snowflakes results from the hydrogen bonding of water molecules in ice.

Ice, like water, has unusual properties because of hydrogen-bonding.

of the rigid framework. When ice melts, the framework collapses. Then the water molecules pack together, and the water becomes more dense.

The fact that ice floats has important consequences for living organisms. The ice on a pond acts as an insulator for the water beneath, preventing it from freezing except under extreme conditions. Since the water at the bottom of a frozen pond is warmer than 0°C, aquatic life is able to survive. If ice were more dense than water, all bodies of water would tend to freeze solid during the winter months. Many types of aquatic life would be destroyed.

Water molecules require a considerable amount of kinetic energy to return to a liquid state from a frozen state. Ice melts at 0°C, a high temperature for such a small molecule (Table 15·1). The heat absorbed when 1 g of water changes from a solid to a liquid is 80 cal/g. This amount of energy could also raise the temperature of 1 g of water from 0°C to 80°C!

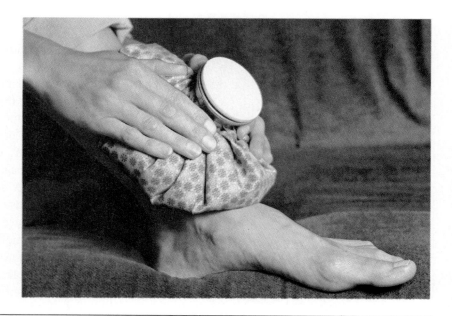

Figure 15·8
Ice packs are used to decrease swelling and pain from an injury. Water absorbs a large amount of heat as it changes from a solid to a liquid at 0°C.

15·6 Aqueous Solutions

Figure 15·9
The small size of solute particles allows them to pass through filter paper.

Safety

Many solutions look and smell just like water. Always label prepared solutions. Never taste a liquid to determine its contents.

The terms solvent and solute are arbitrary in the case of solutions formed from substances which can dissolve in all proportions. If a little water is dissolved in a large quantity of ethanol, ethanol is the solvent. On the other hand, if a small quantity of ethanol is dissolved in a large quantity of water, water is the solvent.

Figure 15·10
When an ionic solid dissolves, the ions become solvated and are surrounded by solvent molecules.

Chemically pure water never exists in nature because water dissolves so many substances. Tap water contains varying amounts of dissolved minerals and gases. *Water samples containing dissolved substances are* **aqueous solutions.** In a solution, *the dissolving medium is the* **solvent,** and *the dissolved particles are the* **solute.** If sodium chloride is dissolved in water, water is the solvent and sodium chloride is the solute.

Solutions are homogeneous and stable. For example, sodium chloride does not settle out when its solutions are allowed to stand as long as other conditions such as temperature remain constant. Solute particles can be either ionic or molecular. Their average diameters are usually less than 1.0 nm (10^{-9} m). If a solution is filtered, both the solute and the solvent pass through the filter. Solvents and solutes may be gases, liquids, or solids. Table 1·3 lists some common types of solutions.

Substances that dissolve most readily in water include ionic compounds and polar covalent molecules. Nonpolar covalent molecules like methane and like those in grease and gasoline do not dissolve in water. Nevertheless grease will dissolve in gasoline. Why the difference? To answer this question the structures of the solvent and the solute and the forces of attraction between them must be discussed.

15·7 Solvation

Water molecules are in continuous motion because of their kinetic energy. When a crystal of sodium chloride is placed in water, the water molecules collide with it. The solvent molecules (H_2O) exert attractive forces on the solute (NaCl) ions. When these forces overcome the attractive forces within the solute, the sodium chloride crystal will dissolve (Figure 15·10). **Solvation** *occurs when a solute dissolves.* The negatively and positively charged ions become solvated, that is, surrounded by solvent molecules.

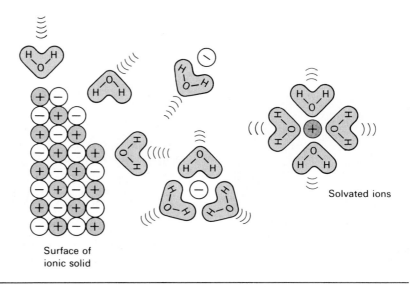

Solvated ions

Surface of
ionic solid

In some ionic compounds the attractive forces within the crystals are stronger than the attractive forces exerted by water. These compounds cannot be solvated and are therefore insoluble. Barium sulfate ($BaSO_4$) and calcium carbonate ($CaCO_3$) are examples of nearly insoluble ionic compounds.

What about dissolving grease in gasoline? Both grease and gasoline are composed of nonpolar molecules. They mix to form a solution, but not because the solute and solvent are favorably attracted. Rather, it is because there are no repulsive forces between the two. As a rule, polar solvents dissolve ionic and polar compounds. Similarly, nonpolar solvents dissolve nonpolar compounds. This relationship can be summed up in the expression "like dissolves like."

Polar solvents such as water dissolve polar compounds, whereas nonpolar solvents dissolve nonpolar compounds.

2. a. HCl (polar) will dissolve
   b. NaI (ionic) will dissolve
   c. NH_3 (polar) will dissolve
   d. $MgSO_4$ (ionic) will dissolve
   e. CH_4 (nonpolar) will not dissolve
   f. $CaCO_3$ (strong ionic forces) will not dissolve
   g. gasoline (nonpolar) will not dissolve

Problem

2. Which of the following substances dissolve in water? Give reasons for your choice.   a. HCl   b. NaI   c. NH_3 d. $MgSO_4$ e. CH_4 f. $CaCO_3$ g. gasoline

15·A   When the Water is Hard

Have you ever found it difficult to get soap to lather? If so, then you may have been trying to wash in hard water. Calcium and magnesium carbonates dissolve in water in large quantities. These compounds react with the carbon dioxide already dissolved in the water. The resulting ions stay in solution.

$$CaCO_3 + CO_2 + H_2O \longrightarrow Ca^{2+} + 2HCO_3^-$$

Similar reactions occur with magnesium carbonate, $MgCO_3$. When soap is added, however, precipitates form. Soap is composed of sodium stearate ($NaC_{18}H_{35}O_2$). Calcium and magnesium ions combine with stearate ions and form a gray scum.

$$Ca^{2+} + 2C_{18}H_{35}O_2^- \longrightarrow Ca(C_{18}H_{35}O_2)_2 \downarrow$$

When these reactions occur it is hard to get soap to lather. Hence the name "hard water."

When hard water is heated in industrial boilers, the calcium and magnesium carbonates come out of solution. They form a precipitate called "scale." This precipitate clogs boilers and pipes and can lead to overheating.

$$Ca^{2+} + 2HCO_3^- \xrightarrow{\text{heat}} CaCO_3 \downarrow + H_2O + CO_2$$

Most municipal water supplies are treated to "soften" hard water. The treatment used depends on the types of anions present in the water. Sometimes only the relatively unstable bicarbonate ion is

Figure 15·11
Industrial boiler pipes can become clogged with calcium and magnesium carbonates that form when hard water is heated.

Many methods for softening water replace Ca^{2+} and Mg^{2+} ions with Na^+ ions. People who must limit their sodium intake for medical reasons must be aware that softened water often contains elevated levels of Na^+ ions.

present. Then the water can be softened by simply boiling the water. This precipitates the calcium and magnesium carbonates and removes them from the water supply.

Often more stable anions are present in the water. Then less stable anions must be added to force the calcium and magnesium ions to precipitate. For example, sodium carbonate (Na_2CO_3) can be added. Then the calcium and magnesium ions precipitate as calcium and magnesium carbonate.

$$Ca^{2+} + Na_2CO_3 \longrightarrow CaCO_3 + 2Na^+$$

Sodium phosphate (Na_3PO_4) added to the water causes the calcium and magnesium to precipitate as phosphates. Free sodium ions do not interfere with the action of soap.

$$3Ca^{2+} + 2Na_3PO_4 \longrightarrow Ca_3(PO_4)_2 + 6Na^+$$

Sometimes ion exchange is used to soften hard water. An ion exchanger can be made from natural minerals called "zeolites." Aluminum and silicate groups form a lattice in the zeolite in which free sodium ions are distributed. When hard water is passed through a zeolite, the sodium ions dissolve in the water, and the calcium and magnesium ions are caught in the zeolite. Most household water softeners use a synthetic zeolite that reacts more rapidly than natural zeolites.

Chemists often use a cation-exchange resin to remove positively charged ions like magnesium and calcium from water. The resin contains positively charged hydronium ions (H_3O^+). Like the sodium ions in zeolite, hydronium ions change places with the calcium and magnesium ions. Water can also be passed through an anion-exchanger. In that case hydroxide (OH^-) ions are exchanged for the negatively charged ions in the water. Water that is passed through a cation-exchanger and an anion-exchanger is said to be "deionized."

Figure 15·12
Ion exchange resins are used to remove positive and negative ions from water. This is particularly important for laboratory experiments in which high concentrations of ions in the water may interfere with chemical reactions.

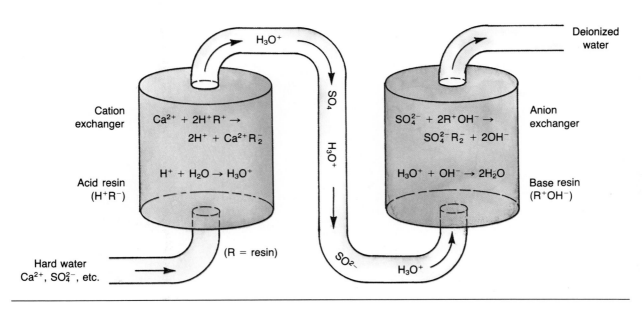

15·8　Water of Hydration

Water molecules are an integral part of the crystal structure of many substances. *The water in a crystal is called the* **water of hydration,** *or water of crystallization.* When an aqueous solution of copper(II) sulfate is allowed to evaporate, crystals of copper(II) sulfate pentahydrate are deposited. The chemical formula for this compound is $CuSO_4 \cdot 5H_2O$. A dot is used in the formula of a hydrate to connect the formula of the compound and the number of water molecules per formula unit. Crystals of copper sulfate pentahydrate always contain five molecules of water for every copper and sulfate ion pair. The deep blue crystals are dry to the touch. They are unchanged in composition or appearance in normally moist air. When heated or exposed to dry air, however, the crystals lose their water of hydration. They crumble to a white anhydrous powder whose formula is $CuSO_4$. If anhydrous copper sulfate is treated with water, the pentahydrate is regenerated.

$$CuSO_4 \cdot 5H_2O \underset{-\text{heat}}{\overset{+\text{heat}}{\rightleftharpoons}} CuSO_4 + 5H_2O$$

Table 15·3 lists some familiar hydrates. They all contain a fixed quantity of water and have a definite composition.

The forces holding the water molecules in hydrates are not very strong. This is shown by the ease with which water is lost and regained. Because the water molecules are held by weak forces, hydrates often have an appreciable vapor pressure. *If a hydrate has a vapor pressure higher than that of the water vapor in air, the hydrate will* **effloresce** *by losing the water of hydration.* For example, $CuSO_4 \cdot 5H_2O$ has a vapor

Hydrated compounds have crystals that contain specific numbers of water molecules per formula unit.

The presence of water in a hydrated crystal does not make the crystal "wet". The water molecules are chemically bonded to the ions in the crystal and so are not readily detected in the physical properties of the crystal.

Salts are not the only substances to form hydrates. Oxalic acid, an organic acid present in rhubarb leaves, forms a dihydrate $(COOH)_2 \cdot 2H_2O$. Barium hydroxide forms an octahydrate $Ba(OH)_2 \cdot 8H_2O$.

Figure 15·13
When hydrated copper sulfate **(a)** is heated, the water is driven off leaving anhydrous copper sulfate **(b)**.

a

b

Figure 15·14
Dry sodium hydroxide pellets exposed to air **(a)** will, over time, remove water from the air **(b)**.

a

b

pressure of about 7.8 mm Hg at room temperature. The average pressure of water vapor at room temperature is usually about 10 mm Hg. This hydrate is stable until the humidity decreases. When the vapor pressure drops below 7.8 mm Hg the hydrate will effloresce.

Some hydrated salts, with a low vapor pressure, remove water from moist air to form higher hydrates.

$$CaCl_2 \cdot H_2O \xrightarrow{\text{moist air}} CaCl_2 \cdot 2H_2O$$

Salts and other compounds that remove moisture from air are said to be **hygroscopic.** Calcium chloride monohydrate is hygroscopic as are phosphorus pentoxide, sodium hydroxide, and concentrated sulfuric acid. *Hygroscopic substances are used as drying agents,* or **desiccants.** Some compounds are so hygroscopic that they become wet when exposed to normally moist air. These **deliquescent** *compounds remove sufficient water from the air to completely dissolve and form solutions.* Deliquescence does not necessarily involve hydrate formation. It occurs when the solution formed has a lower vapor pressure than that of the water in the air.

To maintain an anhydrous state, hygroscopic compounds must be placed in a sealed container to keep out water vapor.

Anhydrous silica gel is quite hygroscopic. Small packets of it are often placed in containers in which valuable electronic or optical equipment is shipped for protection from moisture in the air.

Table 15·3	Some Common Hydrates	
Formula	Chemical name	Common name
$MgSO_4 \cdot 7H_2O$	Magnesium sulfate heptahydrate	Epsom salts
$Ba(OH)_2 \cdot 8H_2O$	Barium hydroxide octahydrate	
$CaCl_2 \cdot 2H_2O$	Calcium chloride dihydrate	
$CuSO_4 \cdot 5H_2O$	Copper(II) sulfate pentahydrate	Blue vitriol
$Na_2SO_4 \cdot 10H_2O$	Sodium sulfate decahydrate	Glauber's salt
$KAl(SO_4)_2 \cdot 12H_2O$	Potassium aluminum sulfate dodecahydrate	Alum
$Na_2B_4O_7 \cdot 10H_2O$	Sodium tetraborate decahydrate	Borax
$FeSO_4 \cdot 7H_2O$	Iron(II) sulfate heptahydrate	Green vitriol
$H_2SO_4 \cdot H_2O$	Sulfuric acid hydrate (m.p. 8.6°C)	

Example 1

Calculate the percent by mass of water in washing soda ($Na_2CO_3 \cdot 10H_2O$).

Solution

The gram formula mass of $Na_2CO_3 \cdot 10H_2O$ is 286 g. The mass of water per gram formula mass of $Na_2CO_3 \cdot 10H_2O$ is 10×18 g = 180 g.

$$\text{Percent } H_2O = \frac{\text{mass of water}}{\text{mass of hydrate}} \times 100\%$$

$$= \frac{180 \text{ g}}{286 \text{ g}} \times 100\% = 62.9\%$$

Problem   3. 36.1%

3. What is the percent by mass of water in $CuSO_4 \cdot 5H_2O$?

15·9   Electrolytes and Nonelectrolytes

Compounds that conduct an electric current in aqueous solution or the molten state are **electrolytes** (Figure 15·16). All ionic compounds are electrolytes. Sodium chloride, copper(II) sulfate, and sodium hydroxide are typical water-soluble electrolytes. They conduct electricity in solution and in the molten state. Barium sulfate is an example of an ionic compound that conducts electricity in the molten state but not in aqueous solution because it is insoluble.

Compounds that do not conduct an electric current in aqueous solution or the molten state are **nonelectrolytes.** Many molecular compounds are nonelectrolytes because they are nonionic. Most compounds of carbon such as cane sugar and rubbing alcohol are nonelectrolytes.

Some very polar molecular compounds are not electrolytes in the pure state, but they become electrolytes when they dissolve in water.

Safety

Even dilute aqueous solutions like tap water can conduct electricity. Do not use electrical equipment on a wet lab bench. Do not handle this equipment with wet hands or while standing on a wet floor.

All ionic compounds are electrolytes. Many water-soluble molecular compounds are nonelectrolytes.

Table 15·4 Some Examples of Strong Electrolytes, Weak Electrolytes, and Nonelectrolytes		
Strong electrolyte	Weak electrolyte	Nonelectrolyte

Acids (inorganic)
    HCl, HBr, HI, HNO_3, H_2SO_4, $HClO_4$
	Heavy metal halides
	    $HgCl_2$, $PbCl_2$
		Most organic compounds
		Sucrose (cane sugar)
		Glycerol

Bases (inorganic) NaOH, KOH	Ammonia	

Soluble salts
    KCl, $MgSO_4$, $KClO_3$, $CaCl_2$
	Organic acids and bases
	    acetic acid, aniline
	
	H_2O (very weak)	

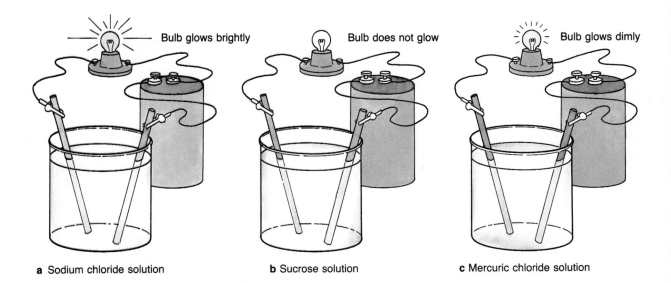

Bulb glows brightly

Bulb does not glow

Bulb glows dimly

a Sodium chloride solution

b Sucrose solution

c Mercuric chloride solution

Figure 15·15
The presence of an electrolyte in solution can be determined by a conductivity test. **a** Sodium chloride is a strong electrolyte. **b** Sucrose is a nonelectrolyte. **c** Mercuric chloride is a weak electrolyte.

Figure 15·16
In a suspension, the particles are not dissolved. Rather, they are suspended in the liquid medium. Suspended particles can be removed by filtration.

This is because they ionize in solution. For example, neither ammonia (NH_3) nor hydrogen chloride (HCl) is an electrolyte. Yet an aqueous solution of ammonia conducts electricity. This is because ammonium ions (NH_4^+) and hydroxide ions (OH^-) are formed when ammonia dissolves. Similarly, hydrogen chloride produces hydronium ions (H_3O^+) and chloride ions (Cl^-). A hydrogen chloride solution is therefore an electrolyte.

$$NH_3 + H_2O \longrightarrow NH_4^+ + OH^-$$

$$HCl + H_2O \longrightarrow H_3O^+ + Cl^-$$

Not all electrolytes conduct an electric current to the same degree (Figure 15·00). In a simple conductivity test, a bulb glows dimly with the electrodes in a mercuric chloride solution. By contrast, the bulb glows brightly for a sodium chloride solution. Mercuric chloride is a weak electrolyte. *When a **weak electrolyte** is in solution, only a fraction of the solute exists as ions.* In a solution of mercuric chloride, most of the solute exists as unionized $HgCl_2$. In contrast, *when a **strong electrolyte** is dissolved, a large portion of the solute exists as ions.* Sodium chloride is a strong electrolyte. All the dissolved sodium chloride in a solution exists as Na^+ and Cl^- ions. Table 15·4 lists some common electrolytes and nonelectrolytes.

15·10 Suspensions and Colloids

The emphasis of the chapter now shifts slightly to mixtures of water with substances that do not form true solutions. Two such mixtures are suspensions and colloids. **Suspensions** *are mixtures from which some of the particles will settle slowly upon standing.* A piece of clay shaken with water forms a suspension. The clay particles become suspended in the water, but they start to settle when shaking stops. A suspension differs from a solution because the component particles are much larger. The particles in a typical suspension have an average diameter greater than 100 nm. By contrast, in a solution the particle size is usually about 1 nm.

Table 15·5	Some Colloidal Systems		
System			
Dispersed phase	*Dispersion medium*	Type	Example
Gas	Liquid	Foam	Whipped cream
Gas	Solid	Foam	Marshmallow
Liquid	Liquid	Emulsion	Milk, mayonnaise
Liquid	Gas	Aerosol	Fog, aerosol sprays
Solid	Gas	Smoke	Dust in air
Solid	Liquid	Sols and gels	Egg white, jellies, paint, colloidal gold, blood, starch in water

Three types of liquid mixtures exist.
· Solutions are homogeneous.
· Suspensions are heterogeneous.
· Colloids are heterogeneous. The dispersion medium is one phase and the dispersed material is the other phase.

Suspensions are unstable. The particles in a suspension settle out unless it is shaken or stirred.

The word *colloid* was coined by the English scientist Thomas Graham, in 1861. Greek: *kolla* = glue.

The Tyndall effect, first reported by Michael Faraday (1791–1867) in 1857, was named for John Tyndall (1820–1893), a British physicist.

Suspensions are heterogeneous because at least two substances can be clearly identified. In our example, these were clay and water. If muddy water is filtered, the suspended clay particles are trapped by the filter and clear water passes through.

Colloids *are mixtures containing particles that are intermediate in size between those of suspensions and true solutions.* Thus the particles range in size from 1 nm to 100 nm. The particles are the *dispersed phase*. They are spread throughout the *dispersion medium*. The first colloids that were identified as such were glues. Many other materials such as blood, paint, aerosol sprays, and smoke are also colloids (Table 15·5).

The properties of colloids differ from those of solutions and suspensions. Many colloids are cloudy or milky in appearance but look clear when they are very dilute. The particles in a colloid cannot be retained by filter paper and do not settle out with time.

Colloidal particles exhibit the **Tyndall effect,** *which is the scattering of visible light in all directions.* We see a beam of light passed through a colloid just as we see a sunbeam in a dusty room. Suspensions also exhibit the Tyndall effect, but solutions never do (Figure 15·18).

Figure 15·17
Light is reflected in all directions from particles in colloids or in suspensions. This effect, called the Tyndall effect, is not observed with true solutions.

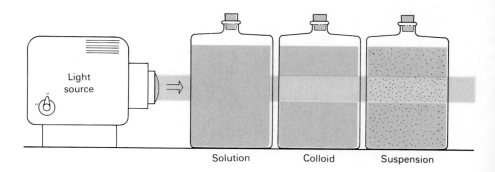

Light source   Solution   Colloid   Suspension

Table 15·6	Properties of Solutions, Colloids, and Suspensions		
	System		
Property	*Solution*	*Colloid*	*Suspension*
Particle type	Ions, atoms, small molecules	Large molecules or particles	Large particles or aggregates
Particle size (approximate)	0.1–1 nm	1–100 nm	100 nm and larger
Effect of light	No scattering	Gives Tyndall effect	Gives Tyndall effect
Effect of gravity	Stable, does not separate	Stable, does not separate	Unstable, sediment forms
Filtration	Particles not retained on filter	Particles not retained on filter	Particles retained on filter
Uniformity	Homogeneous	Borderline	Heterogeneous

Flashes of light (scintillations) are seen when colloids are studied under a microscope. Colloids scintillate because the particles reflecting and scattering the light move erratically. *The chaotic movement of colloidal particles is called* **Brownian motion.** It was first observed by the Scottish botanist Robert Brown (1773–1858). Brownian motion is caused by the water molecules of the medium colliding with the small, dispersed colloidal particles. The buffeting action exerts such a force on the particles that they cannot settle.

Colloidal particles may also absorb charged particles from the surrounding medium onto their surface. Whether or not this occurs depends on the characteristics of the particles. Some colloidal particles can absorb positively charged particles and become positively charged. Some colloidal particles can absorb negatively charged particles and become negatively charged. All the particles in a system will have the same charge. The repulsion of the like-charged particles prevents them from forming aggregates. This keeps them dispersed throughout the medium. Charged colloidal particles form aggregates and precipitate from the dispersion when ions of opposite charge are added. Table 15·6 summarizes the properties of solutions, colloids, and suspensions.

Emulsions *are colloidal dispersions of liquids in liquids.* An emulsifying agent is essential for the formation of an emulsion and for maintaining its stability. For example, oils and greases are not soluble in water. They readily form a colloidal dispersion, however, if soap or detergent is added to the water. Soap and detergents are emulsifying agents. One end of the large soap molecule is polar and is attracted to water molecules. The other end of the soap molecule is nonpolar. It is soluble in oil or grease. Soaps and other emulsifying agents thus allow the formation of tiny stable droplets of one liquid in another liquid.

Figure 15·18
Many salad dressings are liquid-in-liquid colloids or emulsions. When vinegar and oil are shaken, a temporary emulsion forms. If an emulsifying agent such as egg yolk is added, the result is mayonnaise, a permanent emulsion of vinegar and oil.

a

b

c

Figure 15·19
Three aspects of waste water treatment are shown. In a settling tank (top) suspended solids sink to the bottom and are periodically removed as sludge. Air can be added in an aeration tank (middle) to allow bacteria to break down organic materials. A trickle filter tank (bottom) also promotes the growth of bacteria.

15·B Ellen Richards: Pioneer in Water Treatment

Ellen Richards became interested in water treatment by default. For seven years she was a chemistry instructor for the "Woman's Laboratory" at the Massachusetts Institute of Technology (M.I.T.). When M.I.T. began admitting women on a regular basis in 1878, Richards was out of a job. The school offered her a position, however, as an instructor in a new sanitary chemistry department. She accepted and remained in the position until her retirement in 1911.

Richards was a strong advocate for establishing public health standards. At one point she analyzed over 40 000 state water samples for purity. Richards also initiated significant advances in water treatment and water quality. She helped develop the use of straw filters for deodorizing waste water. When water passed through the straw, bacteria present in the water would collect on the straw. These bacteria captured the nitrogen present in the water and removed the source of the odors.

Water treatment centers came into existence partly because of Richards' work. At a treatment center, water is allowed to stand from one hour to several days to allow silt, clay, and other fine particles to settle out. A light, highly absorbent material called "floc" is added to the settling pond. Colloids and bacteria become attached to the floc on the surface of the water and are removed.

Next, the water is filtered through sand, pulverized coal, or a net of fibrous material. This removes suspended solids, colloids, bacteria, and other organisms. Chlorine is added to kill any organisms not removed by filtration. The water may then be passed through an activated carbon filter or treated with ammonia to remove the taste and odor of the chlorine. If the water is "hard," it may also be treated to remove excessive amounts of calcium and magnesium ions (see Section 15·A). Finally, air may be forced through the water to remove carbon dioxide, hydrogen sulfide, and other taste-producing gases.

Sewage treatment is a related field that consists of up to three stages. In primary treatment, solids are separated from liquids and are sent to a landfill. In secondary treatment, liquid waste is treated with bacteria to remove organic substances and nitrogen. This is a step that Richards initiated. Some facilities discharge the water after secondary treatment whereas other facilities may send the water through an activated carbon filter. Finally, oxygen is added before releasing the water to a body of water.

Sanitary engineers help design and run water treatment and sewage treatment facilities. A background in chemistry allows the engineer to determine how to process the water and remove contaminants. Engineering skills are used in designing and constructing the equipment to carry out the processes.

Key Terms

aqueous solution	15·6	solute	15·6
Brownian motion	15·10	solvation	15·7
colloid	15·10	solvent	15·6
deliquescent	15·8	strong electrolyte	15·9
desiccant	15·8	surface tension	15·2
effloresce	15·8	surfactant	15·2
electrolyte	15·9	suspension	15·10
emulsion	15·10	Tyndall effect	15·10
hygroscopic	15·8	water of hydration	15·8
nonelectrolyte	15·9	weak electrolyte	15·9

Chapter Summary

Hydrogen-bonding between polar water molecules explains the high boiling point (100°C) and freezing point (0°C) of water, and it explains why ice floats. Hydrogen-bonding is also responsible for the high surface tension of water. Liquids tend to minimize their surface area and form spherical droplets because of their surface tension. Water is a polar liquid and an excellent solvent for many substances. Aqueous solutions are homogeneous mixtures of ions or molecules in water. The solubility of a solute depends on solute–solvent interactions. A good rule to remember is that "like dissolves like."

Substances that are in solution as ions are electrolytes. A solute that is completely ionized in solution is a strong electrolyte. A solute that is only partially ionized is a weak electrolyte. A solution of an electrolyte will conduct an electric current, whereas a solution of a nonelectrolyte is nonconducting.

True solutions are distinguished from colloidal dispersions and suspensions on the basis of particle size. Particles with an average diameter greater than 100 nm can be kept in suspension if the fluid (water) is kept agitated. Gravity or filtration, however, will separate the suspended particles from the liquid. The particles in a colloidal dispersion range in size from 1 nm to 100 nm. In general, they do not settle under gravity, and they pass through ordinary filter paper unchanged. Colloids are good at scattering light, as are suspensions, as evidenced by the Tyndall effect. Colloidal dispersions also exhibit Brownian motion. The particles in solutions are ions and small molecules. They cannot be trapped by filter paper, nor do they exhibit the Tyndall effect.

Many crystals are hydrates; they contain water of hydration. If water of hydration is lost from a hydrate when it is exposed to air, the process is called efflorescence. Some substances take up water from moist air and may eventually form a solution. They are deliquescent.

Practice Questions and Problems

4. Explain why water molecules are polar. *15·1*

5. Name four physical properties of water. *15·1*

6. What is meant by hydrogen-bonding? *15·1*

7. What is surface tension? Why do the particles at the surface of a liquid behave differently than those in the bulk of the liquid? *15·2*

8. Describe some observable effects that can be produced by the surface tension of a liquid. *15·2*

9. Explain how hydrogen-bonding is responsible for the high surface tension of water. *15·2*

10. What is a surfactant? Explain how it functions. *15·2*

11. Define the term *vapor pressure* and explain why the vapor pressure of water is unusually low. *15·2*

12. How many calories are required to heat 256 g of water from 20°C to 99°C? How many calories are required to heat the same mass of iron through the same range of temperature? *15·3*

13. How many calories are liberated when 24 g of steam at 100°C condenses to 24 g of water at 100°C? *15·4*

14. Explain why water has a relatively high boiling point. *15·4*

15. Distinguish between the structures of water and ice. Then explain why ice floats on water. *15·5*

16. What would be some of the consequences if ice were more dense than water? *15·5*

17. How much energy is required to change 47.6 g of ice at 0°C to 47.6 g of water at the same temperature? **a.** kilojoules **b.** kilocalories *15·5*

18. Why is water an excellent solvent for most ionic compounds and polar covalent molecules but not for nonpolar compounds? *15·6*

19. Define the terms *solution* and *aqueous solution*. *15·6*

20. Give a familiar example of solutions of each of these types. *15·6*
 a. gas in liquid **c.** solid in liquid
 b. liquid in liquid **d.** gas in gas

21. Suppose an aqueous solution contains both sugar and salt. Can you separate either of these solutes from the water by filtration? Explain. *15·6*

22. What is the significance of the statement "Like dissolves like"? What does "like" refer to? *15·6*

23. Describe how an ionic compound dissolves in water. *15·7*

24. Which of the following substances dissolve in water? Why? *15·7*
 a. CH_4 **d.** $MgSO_4$
 b. KCl **e.** cane sugar
 c. He **f.** $NaHCO_3$

25. Define water of hydration. *15·8*

26. Name each of these hydrates. *15·8*
 a. $SnCl_4 \cdot 5H_2O$ **d.** $BaBr_2 \cdot 4H_2O$
 b. $FeSO_4 \cdot 7H_2O$ **e.** $FePO_4 \cdot 4H_2O$
 c. $AlCl_3 \cdot 6H_2O$

27. Calcium chloride forms a hexahydrate. Write the equation for the formation of this hydrate from the anhydrous salt. *15·8*

28. Epsom salt ($MgSO_4 \cdot 7H_2O$) changes to the monohydrate form at 150°C. Write an equation for this change. *15·8*

29. Distinguish between an electrolyte and a nonelectrolyte. *15·9*

30. Contrast the characteristics of strong and weak electrolytes. *15·9*

31. Why does molten sodium chloride conduct electricity? *15·9*

32. What is the main distinction between an aqueous solution of a strong electrolyte and an aqueous solution of a weak electrolyte? *15·9*

33. Define the terms *suspension* and *colloid*. *15·10*

34. What is the basis for distinguishing among solutions, colloids, and suspensions? *15·10*

35. Describe the terms *dispersed phase* and *dispersion medium*. *15·10*

36. Explain the Tyndall effect. *15·10*

37. Solutions do not give the Tyndall effect. Why? *15·10*

38. What makes a colloidal dispersion stable? *15·10*

39. Define Brownian motion. *15·10*

40. Describe the term *emulsion* and tell how emulsions are stabilized. *15·10*

41. Mayonnaise is an example of what kind of colloidal dispersion? *15·10*

Mastery Questions and Problems

42. Water has its maximum density at 4°C. Explain why this is so and discuss the consequences of this fact. *15·5*

43. From your knowledge of intermolecular forces arrange these liquids in order of increasing surface tension: water, H_2O; hexane, C_6H_{14}; ethanol, C_2H_5OH; chloroform, $CHCl_3$. *15·2*

44. Name these hydrates and determine the percent by mass of water in each. *15·8*
 a. $Na_2B_4O_7 \cdot 10H_2O$ **c.** $MgSO_4 \cdot 7H_2O$
 b. $Na_2CO_3 \cdot H_2O$ **d.** $(CaSO_4)_2 \cdot H_2O$

45. If 5.0 g of steam, $H_2O(g)$, at 100°C condenses to 5.0 g of water, $H_2O(l)$, at 50°C, how much heat is liberated? **a.** calories **b.** kilocalories *15·4*

46. Explain why ions become solvated in aqueous solution. *15·7*

47. A block of ice, at 0°C, has a mass of 176.0 g. How much heat must be added to change 25% of this mass of ice to water at 0°C? (Express your answer in calories, kilocalories, joules, and kilojoules.) What is the mass of ice remaining? *15·5*

48 You are given a solution containing either sugar or salt dissolved in water.
  a. Can you tell which it is by visual inspection?
  b. Give two ways by which you could easily tell which it is. *15·9*

49. Water is a polar solvent; gasoline is a nonpolar solvent. Decide which of the following compounds are more likely to dissolve in water and which are more likely to dissolve in gasoline. *15·6*
  a. sugar ($C_{12}H_{22}O_{11}$) **d.** methane (CH_4)
  b. chloroform ($CHCl_3$) **e.** KCl
  c. Na_2SO_4 **f.** $BaSO_4$

50. Match each of the descriptions with the following terms. A description may apply to more than one term. *15·10*
  1. true solution
  2. colloidal dispersion
  3. suspension

  a. Does not settle out on standing:_____
  b. Heterogeneous mixture:_____
  c. Particle size less than 1.0 nm:_____
  d. Particles can be filtered out:_____
  e. Gives Tyndall effect:_____
  f. Particles are invisible to the naked eye:_____
  g. Milk:_____
  h. Salt water:_____
  i. Jelly:_____

51. Explain which unique properties of water are responsible for these occurrences. *15·4*
  a. Water in tiny cracks in rocks helps break up the rocks when it freezes.
  b. Water beads up on a newly waxed car.
  c. As you exercise and your body temperature increases, your body produces sweat.
  d. Grape vines are damaged at temperatures below 28°F. When severe frost is predicted, grape growers spray a mist of water on their vines.
  e. An efficient way of heating a large building is to generate steam in a boiler and circulate it through pipes to radiators throughout the entire building.

52. Explain why ethyl alcohol (C_2H_6O) will dissolve in both gasoline and water. *15·7*

53. A 25.0 m × 10.0 m swimming pool is filled with fresh water to a depth of 1.7 m. The water temperature is initially at 25°C. How much heat must be removed from the water to change it all to ice at 0°C? Express your answer in kilocalories and kilojoules. *15·5*

54. Are all liquids soluble in each other? Explain your answer. *15·6*

55. Write equations to show how these substances ionize or dissociate in water. *15·9*
  a. NH_4Cl **d.** $HC_2H_3O_2$
  b. $Cu(NO_3)_2$ **e.** Na_2SO_4
  c. HNO_3 **f.** $HgCl_2$

Review Questions and Problems

56. A cylindrical vessel, 28.0 cm in height and 3.00 cm in diameter, is filled with water at 50°C. The density of water is 0.988 g/cm^3 at this temperature. What is the mass of water in the vessel?
  a. grams   **b.** milligrams   **c.** kilograms

57. A l-L sample of steam at 100°C and l atm pressure is changed to 200°C at constant volume. Calculate the final pressure of the steam in atmospheres.

58. What effect does a change in pressure on a water surface have on the boiling point of the water?
  a. an increase   **b.** a decrease

59. The decomposition of hydrogen peroxide is given by this equation.

$$2H_2O_2(l) \longrightarrow 2H_2O(l) + O_2(g)$$

Calculate the mass of water in grams and the volume of oxygen at STP when 2.00×10^{-3} mol of hydrogen peroxide is decomposed.

60. How many grams each of hydrogen and oxygen are required to produce 4.50 mol of water?

61. Calculate the mass of water produced in the complete combustion of 8.00 L of propane (C_3H_8) at STP.

$$C_3H_8 + O_2 \longrightarrow CO_2 + H_2O$$

62. Acetaldehyde, C_2H_4O, is produced commercially by the reaction of acetylene with water.

$$C_2H_2 + H_2O \longrightarrow C_2H_4O$$

How many grams of C_2H_4O can be produced from 260 g H_2O, assuming sufficient C_2H_2 is present?

63. Hydrogen reacts with oxygen to form water.

$$2H_2 + O_2 \longrightarrow 2H_2O$$

How many moles of oxygen are required to produce 10.8 g H_2O? How many liters of oxygen is this at STP?

64. Balance these equations.
a. $CO_2 + H_2O \longrightarrow C_6H_{12}O_6 + O_2$
b. $Na + H_2O \longrightarrow Na^+ + OH^- + H_2$
c. $C_6H_6 + O_2 \longrightarrow CO_2 + H_2O$
d. $NaHCO_3 \longrightarrow Na_2CO_3 + H_2O + CO_2$

65. Give the number of molecules in 4.5×10^{-3} g of H_2O.

66. The normal boiling point of a substance depends on both the molecular mass and the intermolecular interactions. Considering these, arrange the following in order of decreasing boiling points and explain your answers.
a. HBr, HCl, H_2O
b. NH_3, H_2O, CH_4

67. If 20.0 g steam, $H_2O(g)$, occupies 6.25 L at 120°C, what is the pressure in atmospheres?

68. Calculate the percent composition.
a. H_2O
b. H_2S
c. H_2Se
d. H_2Te

69. What is the mass, in milligrams and in kilograms, of 2.7×10^3 mol H_2O?

70. Write the correct electron configuration for the oxide ion. Which noble gas has the same electron configuration?

71. When a proton is attracted to the unshared electron pair of a water molecule, the polyatomic hydronium ion (H_3O^+) is formed. Write electron dot structures to show the formation of this ion.

Challenging Questions and Problems

72. Deuterium oxide is often described as "heavy water". Why? List the differences in physical and chemical properties you would expect to exist between water and deuterium oxide. Give some uses for deuterium oxide.

73. What relationships exist between the following volumes?
a. 1 g of ice at 0°C and 1 g of water at 0°C
b. 1 g of water at 100°C and 1 g of steam at 100°C

74. A mixture of 40 cm³ of oxygen gas and 60 cm³ of hydrogen gas, at STP, is ignited. Determine the following.
a. which gas is the limiting reagent
b. the mass of water produced
c. which gas remains after reaction
d. the volume of the remaining gas

75. An iceberg with a mass of 3.50×10^6 kg is floating in fresh water at a temperature of 0°C. Calculate the mass and volume of the iceberg above the water level. How would this mass and volume change if the temperature of the water was raised to 4°C? (Use Table 15·2 and assume no melting of ice occurs.)

76. When ethyl alcohol (C_2H_6O) dissolves in water, the volume of the final solution is less than the separate volumes of the water and alcohol added together. Can you explain this result? Do you think it might be possible to mix two different liquids and get a mixture volume that is larger than the sum of the volume of the two components? Explain.

77. When an aqueous solution of sodium chloride starts to freeze, the ice that forms does not contain ions of the salt. Why?

Research Projects

1. How do water repellants work?

2. How do solutes affect the surface tension of water? Design an experiment to find the answer.

3. How does the volume of a solution compare to the volumes of the solute and the solvent? Give a few examples.

4. Compare the conductivities of solutions to various ions present.

5. What were Thomas Graham's contributions to colloid chemistry?

6. How did John Tyndall use his work on light scattering in solutions to describe why the sky is blue?

7. How does a household tap water purifier work?

8. How important is tertiary wastewater treatment? Why is it used in some areas but not in other areas?

9. How can wastewater be reused? How can sewer sludge be processed and reused?

10. What are the components of fabric softeners? How do they work?

11. What are the laws regulating water pollution in your area? What federal, state, and local agencies are responsible for enforcing the regulations?

Readings and References

Branley, Franklyn M. *Water for the World*. New York: Harper & Row, 1982.

Goldin, Augusta. *Water: Too Much, Too Little, Too Polluted?* San Diego, CA: Harcourt Brace Jovanovich, 1983.

Hansen, James. "The Delicate Architecture of Cement." *Science 82* (December 1982), pp. 48–55.

Lightman, Alan. "Snow." *Science 84* (December 1984), pp. 22–26.

Maranto, Gina. "The Creeping Poison Underground." *Discover* (March 1985), pp. 83–85.

Piasecki, Bruce. "Unfouling the Nest." *Science 83* (September 1983), pp. 76–81.

Pringle, Laurence. *Water: The Next Great Resource Battle*. New York: Macmillan, 1982.

16 Properties of Solutions

Chapter Planning Guide

Section		Demonstrations and Experiments	Resource Materials
16·1 Solution Formation	C*	Dem 16·1 Miscible and Immiscible Liquids	Objectives Worksheet 16, SPB
		Dem 16·2 Miscible and Immiscible Solutions of Varying Concentration	Skillsheet 16, SPB
		Exp 31 Factors Affecting Solution Formation, LM	Prelab 31, SPB
16·2 Solubility	C		
16·3 Factors Affecting Solubility	C	Dem 16·3 Solubility	Quiz 16·1
		Dem 16·4 Solubility and Temperature	Teaching Diagram 22
		Dem 16·5 Solubility Decrease with Increasing Temperature	
		Dem 16·6 Supersaturation	
		Exp 32 Supersaturation, LM	
		Dem 16·7 Column Chromatography	Prelab 32, SPB
		Dem 16·8 Thin Layer Chromatography	
		Dem 16·9 Adsorption on Charcoal	
16·A Chromatography	E	Exp 33 Introduction to Chromotography, LM	Prelab 33, SPB
16·4 Molarity	C	Dem 16·10 Molarity	
16·5 Making Dilutions	C		
16·B Nutrition: The Birth of a Science	E		
16·6 Percent Solutions	O		Quiz 16·2
			Beyond the Text: Environmental Testing
16·7 Colligative Properties of Solutions	C	Dem 16·11 Osmosis	Thermal Pollution, ICT 16
		Dem 16·12 Dialysis	
		Exp 34 Freezing Point Changes, LM	Prelab 34, SPB
16·8 Molality and Mole Fraction	H		
16·9 Calculating Boiling and Freezing Point Changes	H		Teaching Diagram 23
16·10 Molecular Mass Determination	H		Quiz 16·3
			Reviewsheet 16, SPB
			Chapter 16 Test

*C = Core, O = Optional
 E = Enrichment, H = Honors

LM = Laboratory Manual

SPB = Skills Practice Book
ICT = Issues in Chem. Tech.

Chapter Objectives

Having studied this chapter and done the problems, the student should be able to:

1. List three factors that determine how fast a soluble substance dissolves. *16·1*

2. Explain the difference between saturated, unsaturated, and supersaturated solutions. *16·2, 16·3*

3. Use Henry's law to solve gas solubility problems. *16·3*

4. Explain what is meant by the concentration of a solution. *16·4*

5. Define and work problems involving the molarity of a solution. *16·4*

6. Describe how to prepare dilute solutions from concentrated solutions of known molarity. *16·5*

7. Perform calculations involving percent (volume/volume) and percent (mass/volume) solutions. *16·6*

8. Describe on a particle basis why a solution has a lower vapor pressure than the pure solvent of that solution. *16·7*

9. Explain on a particle basis how the addition of a solute to a pure solvent causes an elevation of the boiling point and a depression of the freezing point of the resultant solution. *16·7*

10. Calculate the molality of a solution. *16·8*

11. Calculate the freezing point depression and the boiling point elevation of aqueous solutions. *16·9*

12. Determine the molecular mass of an unknown from experimental freezing point depression or boiling point elevation measurements. *16·10*

Teaching Suggestions

16·1 Solution Formation

The students will have little trouble in understanding the effect of agitation, temperature, and surface area on the rate of dissolving if they recall Section 15·7. Remind them that the dissolving process is one in which each particle (atom, molecule, or ion) of the solute is removed from the solid structure, one at a time, and surrounded by solvent molecules. They can then easily see why stirring the solution, raising the temperature, and increasing the surface area are so helpful in increasing the rate of solution.

In **Demonstration 16·1** *Miscible and Immiscible Liquids*, various liquids are tested for solubility in each other. **Demonstration 16·2** *Miscible and Immiscible Solutions of Varying Concentration* is also helpful.

16·2 Solubility

Be sure to emphasize that, with the exception of completely miscible liquids, the addition of solute to a solvent cannot go on indefinitely. Eventually a point is reached where no more added solute can dissolve. This is the saturation point.

Stress that the factors which affect the rate of solution determine how fast the saturation point is reached, but with the exception of temperature have no effect on the final amount of solid that dissolves.

Emphasize also that the dissolving process continues even after saturation is reached. Although there are no macroscopic changes taking place, solvent molecules are still carrying solute particles away from the solid. At the same time, particles are precipitating out of solution and returning to the solid. At saturation, the rate at which they are being carried away is equal to the rate of precipitation.

The term dynamic equilibrium refers to the fact that a balance has been reached in which macroscopic properties are no longer changing, but in which microscopic processes continue. Take time to explain this concept, since it helps pave the way for Chapter 17, in which equilibrium is covered in depth.

16·3 Factors Affecting Solubility

An examination of Table 16·2 shows that we can make the generalization that the solubility of a solid increases with temperature. Emphasize that this generalization has many exceptions. For instance, the solubility of sodium chloride barely changes over a 100°C range. The solubility of sodium sulfate *decreases* with increasing temperature, as does that of calcium acetate. **Demonstrations 16·3** *Solubility*, **16·4** *Solubility and Temperature*, and **16·5** *Solubility Decrease with Increasing Temperature* all explore these concepts. **Experiment 31** *Factors Affecting Solution Formation* is also appropriate here.

Stress that the solubility behavior of gases is *opposite* the general behavior of solids. The solubility of gases *decreases* as temperature increases. Do not bother to explain why this occurs since most students are not ready for it yet. (When a gas dissolves in a liquid, heat is evolved. Thus, the tendency toward minimum enthalpy favors the dissolving process when temperature increases. These topics are covered in Chapter 17.)

Students often show great interest in the phenomenon of supersaturation, especially the fact that crystallization can be triggered by the addition of a seed crystal. Be sure

to demonstrate this effect by doing **Demonstration 16·6** *Supersaturation.* They can also observe this effect in **Experiment 32** *Supersaturation.*

Experiment 33 *Introduction to Chromatography,* and **Demonstrations 16·7** *Column Chromatography,* **16·8** *Thin Layer Chromatography,* and **16·9** *Adsorption on Charcoal* may also be introduced here.

16·4 Molarity

There are several ways in which to express concentration. Those that involve mass and volume, such as g/mL, are the most convenient to use, since these quantities can be measured directly. Remind the students that when atoms, molecules, and ions react, the quantities involved have to do with numbers of particles, not the masses or volumes of the particles. Since so many of the reactions we study in chemistry are reactions in solutions, it is extremely important that we have a unit which allows us to count numbers of particles in these solutions. Stress that the expression of concentration in terms of molarity is the chemist's means of keeping track of the amounts of reacting quantities in solutions. It is therefore one of the most important units in this course.

To help the students grasp the concept of molarity, demonstrate the steps involved in making solutions of given molarity. **Demonstration 16·10** *Molarity* gives one possible approach.

16·5 Making Dilutions

The approach to this section is straightforward. Present the equation. Show examples of how it is used in problems. Then give the students plenty of problems that involve use of the equation.

16·6 Percent Solutions

Point out that there are advantages to using percent to express the concentrations of solutions. Percents are easy to calculate, and since they are expressed in terms of easily measured quantities, they are also convenient when making solutions. One does not have to look up any information in a reference book to decide how to make up a 20% ethanol solution, for instance.

However, the percent concentration method does not give us accurate information about the number of particles available for reaction. In fact, it may be misleading since a volume change often occurs when two liquids are mixed. For instance, if 20 mL of ethanol are mixed with 80 mL of water, the resulting volume is less than 100 mL. More water must be added to the mixture to bring its volume up to 100 mL. Thus, students should be warned to interpret 20% as meaning 20 parts of solute for every 100 parts of *final* solution.

16·7 Colligative Properties of Solutions

Emphasize that a colligative property is one which depends upon the concentration, but not the kind, of solute particles. A mole of any kind of particle has the same effect as a mole of any other kind of particle in producing colligative effects. Since a soluble ionic solid will produce two or more moles of ions for every mole of solid that dissolves, it is more effective at producing changes in colligative properties than a soluble molecular solid.

Point out that the effects of solutes on the colligative properties are definite but their magnitudes are fairly small. For a nonelectrolyte like sucrose, the boiling point elevation is only 0.51°C for 1 *m* solution. For the same solution, the freezing point is depressed 1.86°C, and the vapor pressure reduced by less than 0.4 mm Hg.

To gain experience with colligative properties, students can do **Experiment 34** *Freezing Point Changes.* Osmotic Pressure is another example of a colligative property. **Demonstration 16·11** *Osmosis* and **Demonstration 16·12** *Dialysis* would be effective here.

16·8 Molality and Mole Fraction

Molality is so similar to molarity that some students are likely to confuse these terms at first. Emphasize that 1 molar and 1 molal solutions each contain one mole of solute in a given amount of solution. The difference between the two lies in the volume of solution in which that one mole is found. Point out that in the case of molarity the amount of solvent cannot be specified, only that the final volume of the solution is to be 1 liter. In the case of molality, the final volume of the solution is not known, but the amount of solvent is specified as exactly 1000 g.

Mole fraction is another way in which concentration is shown and is often used by organic chemists. Mole fraction is a method of comparing the number of moles of solute to the number of moles of solution. As we will see in the next section, mole fractions are useful in calculations involving colligative properties.

16·9 Calculating Boiling and Freezing Point Changes

Remind the students that the elevation of boiling points and depression of freezing points are phenomena that depend upon the number of solute particles, not the kind.

The use of molality as an expression of solution concentration simplifies the calculation of boiling point and freezing point changes. The addition of a mole of particles to 1000 g of a solvent has the same effects on the boiling point and freezing points of the solvent, no matter what the solute. Therefore constants for boiling point elevation and freezing point depression can be stated for each solvent. Have the students refer to Table 16·3 and note that each solvent has its own set of constants.

Remind the students that these are colligative properties and are dependent on the number of particles. When performing calculations involving ionic solids, they must be sure to find the molality of the solution in terms of the *total* number of particles. For example, when calculating boiling point and freezing point changes, a solution that is 1 *m* in $Ca(NO_3)_2$ must be considered to be 3 *m* in solute particles.

16·10 Molecular Mass Determination

Stress that freezing point depression and boiling point elevation are of more than just academic interest. They provide the chemist with a means of finding the molar masses of substances. The principle is simple. The change in boiling point or freezing point produced by a given mass of a substance allows us to calculate the number of moles of the substance. Using the number of moles and the mass, we can calculate the molar mass.

Point out that the changes in freezing point and boiling point are relatively small. The chemist must make very precise measurements to obtain useful values for molar mass.

Demonstrations

16·1 Miscible and Immiscible Liquids

Concept: Miscible liquids dissolve in each other but immiscible liquids do not.

Materials: 20 mL each of the following liquids: water, vinegar, oil, gasoline, acetone, ethanol, methanol, 0.1*M* hydrochloric acid (HCl), 0.1*M* sodium hydroxide (NaOH), 8 small beakers, organic waste can, safety goggles.

Procedure: 1. Combine any two liquids in a small beaker. Stir to determine if they are miscible. Record which combinations are miscible and which are not. 2. Note the properties of each liquid. 3. Ask the students to try to account for these results. **Caution:** *Hydrochloric acid and sodium hydroxide are corrosive. Acetone, gasoline, ethanol, and methanol are flammable.*

16·2 Miscible and Immiscible Solutions of Varying Concentration

Concept: The concentration of a solution may vary from dilute to saturated.

Materials: 4 large test tubes and stoppers, test tube rack, water, 10 crystals of iodine (I_2), sodium chloride (NaCl) crystals (enough to 1/4 fill a test tube), and 5 mL each of the following: glacial acetic acid ($C_2H_4O_2$), ethanol, and gasoline, safety goggles.

Procedure: 1. Pour acetic acid into a test tube, noting that it is a concentrated solution. 2. Add 5 mL water to double the volume, pointing out that it is now a dilute solution. 3. Place sodium chloride crystals in another test tube. 4. Add water until the tube is 3/4 full. 5. Shake the tube, noting the undissolved crystals at the bottom of the saturated solution. 6. Place 5 iodine crystals in a test tube. 7. Add ethanol to dissolve the iodine. 8. Add water, 1 mL at a time, shaking the tube after each addition. Note that this is a miscible solution; the solute and solvent are mutually soluble in any ratio. 9. Place the remaining 5 iodine crystals in a test tube. 10. Add the gasoline. 11. Add water, 1 mL at a time, shaking after each addition. Note that they are immiscible; the liquids are mutually insoluble. 12. In each case identify the solute and solvent. Discuss the properties of each type of solution. **Caution:** *Iodine is an irritant. Gasoline and ethanol are flammable. Glacial acetic acid is corrosive.*

16·3 Solubility

Concept: Temperature affects solubility.

Materials: 30 g of sucrose (granulated sugar), test tube, water, alcohol burner, matches, test tube holder, test tube rack, stirring rod, safety goggles.

Procedure: 1. Fill a test tube with sucrose to within 3 cm of the top. 2. Add room temperature water to completely fill the tube. 3. Stir thoroughly. 4. Point out that although some sugar has dissolved, most remains in the solid state. 5. Gently heat the tube, taking care not to burn the sugar. 6. As the solution nears its boiling point, the sugar dissolves completely. 7. Discuss how solubility usually increases with increasing temperature. There are exceptions, however. (See **Demonstration 16·5** *Solubility Decrease with Increasing Temperature*.)

16·4 Solubility and Temperature

Concept: Temperature change affects solubility.

Materials: 1-L Florence flask, 2 g of lead(II) iodide (PbI_2), 800 mL water, rubber stopper for flask, hot plate or gas burner, matches, ring stand, ring, wire gauze, insulated glove, stirring rod, safety goggles.

Procedure: 1. Place the lead(II) iodide and water in a flask and stopper it. 2. Heat the flask to a boil. 3. Allow the solution to cool. Golden flakes of precipitate slowly settle out. 4. Swirl the flask to produce a beautiful shimmering effect. 5. Note that the solubility usually decreases with decreasing temperature.

16·5 Solubility Decrease with Increasing Temperature

Concept: Exceptions to the usual relation of temperature and solubility occur.

Materials: 37 g of calcium acetate, 100 mL of water, 125-mL Florence flask, hot plate or ring stand, wire gauze, ring, gas burner, matches, stirring rod, insulated glove, ice, safety goggles.

Procedure: 1. Place the calcium acetate and water in the flask. 2. Heat the calcium acetate solution. 3. It becomes cloudy as solid calcium acetate precipitates out. 4. Chill the solution with ice. The precipitate re-dissolves. 5. Calcium acetate is an exception to the usual relationship between temperature and solubility. (The solubility of calcium acetate is 37.4 g/100 mL in cold water, but decreases to 29.7 g/100 mL in hot water.)

16·6 Supersaturation

Concept: If no solid is present, solutions may have a higher solute concentration than in a saturated solution at the same temperature.

Materials: 60 g of sodium thiosulfate pentahydrate ($Na_2S_2O_3 \cdot 5\,H_2O$), 1 g of sodium chloride ($NaCl$), 3 large test tubes, 600-mL beaker, gas burner, matches, test tube holder, test tube rack, stopper, water, ice bath, safety goggles.

Procedure: 1. Fill three test tubes 2/3 full with sodium thiosulfate pentahydrate. 2. Heat until all of the sodium thiosulfate has "melted" (it actually dissolves in its own water molecules) to form a clear solution. Make sure no undissolved crystals are in the test tubes; if there are, add more water. 3. Allow to cool to room temperature in an ice bath. When cooled below 48°C, the solutions become supersaturated. 4. Show the clear solution. Drop one small crystal of sodium thiosulfate into one of the tubes to "seed" the crystal. 5. The crystal falls to the bottom, surrounded by a cluster of crystals. 6. Observe that the tube becomes very warm. The crystallization of sodium thiosulfate pentahydrate is an exothermic process. 7. Add a crystal of sodium chloride to a second tube. No crystallization occurs. 8. Stopper the tube and shake vigorously. 9. Crystallization occurs. 10. Point out that salts demonstrate varying solubilities with temperature. In this system, a salt is much less soluble at a lower temperature. Cooling the solution saturates it. No crystals appear because there is no surface on which to crystallize. The supersaturated solution is unstable. Crystals comes out of solution as soon as a crystal surface is available.

16·7 Column Chromatography

Concept: Ions can be separated by chromatography.

Materials: 200 g of aluminum oxide, 500 mL of 2.0M nitric acid (HNO_3), 10 mL of 1M potassium permanganate ($KMnO_4$), 10 mL of 1M potassium dichromate ($K_2Cr_2O_7$), 20-cm chromatography column, ring stand, two clamps, two clamp holders, two 800-mL beakers, 50-mL beaker, 5-cm tubing, hose clamp, safety goggles.

Procedure: 1. Attach the column to the stand with the clamps. Attach the tubing to the bottom of the column. Place the tubing with hose clamp attached in the beaker. 2. Soak aluminum oxide with nitric acid and fill the column with it. Take care that no air becomes trapped in the aluminum oxide slurry or in the tube. Leave 30 mL space at the top of the column. 3. Pour nitric acid solution on top of the column and allow it to run out. 4. Mix the dichromate and permanganate solutions in the small beaker and pour onto the top of the column. Let the solution into the column by loosening the hose clamp. 5. Keep the top of the column filled with nitric acid after all of the solution has entered the column. 6. As the nitric acid flows through, the yellow dichromate lags behind but the purple permanganate flows through easily. 7. Collect the permanganate in the beaker. 8. Ask how the dichromate could also be separated. **Caution:** *Nitric acid is corrosive. Potassium permanganate is an irritant and a mutagen. Potassium dichromate is toxic.*

16·8 Thin Layer Chromatography

Concept: Polar and nonpolar substances can be separated by chromatography.

Materials: thin layer chromatography kit.

Procedure: 1. Follow the instructions of the kit.

16·9 Adsorption on Charcoal

Concept: Charcoal adsorbs many substances.

Materials: activated powdered charcoal, 10 cm of 1-cm diameter glass tubing, spatula, stirring rod, 5 mL of 0.1M methylene blue solution, water, funnel with short tubing from the bottom, 400-mL beaker, ring, ring stand, 2 clamps, safety goggles.

Procedure: 1. Gently pack the charcoal into the glass tubing with spatula and stirring rod. 2. Clamp the tubing directly below the funnel and connect with the rubber tubing. 3. Place the beaker beneath the glass tubing. 4. Pour methylene blue solution into the funnel and let it run through the glass tubing. 5. Add more water to the funnel to show that only a colorless solution comes out the bottom of the tubing. The charcoal has adsorbed the methylene blue.

16·10 Molarity

Concept: Molarity is the number of moles per liter.

Materials: 3 volumetric flasks: 250-mL, 500-mL, and 1-L; water, stirring rod, 3 different-size samples of sodium chloride ($NaCl$): 58.44 g, 29.22 g, and 14.61 g.

Procedure: 1. Review the definition of *one molar*. 2. On the board, show that 1 mol sodium chloride is 58.44 g by adding atomic weights. 3. Half-fill the 1-L flask with water. 4. Add the 58.44 g sodium chloride. 5. Stir until it dissolves. 6. Fill with water to the 1 L mark, noting that there is 1 mol of solute and 1 L of solution. Emphasize that there is less than 1 L of water since sodium chloride accounts for part of the volume. 7. Ask how a 1*M* sodium chloride solution can be made in the 500-mL flask. Proceed according to their suggestions, following the steps outlined above. 8. Repeat using the 250-mL flask. 9. Repeat the demonstration using different solutes and different-size containers.

16·11 Osmosis

Concept: Osmosis is the movement of water to a region ncentration across a semipermeable membrane.

Materials: large potato, 10 mL of saturated sugar solution, drill, small one-hole stopper with 30-cm glass tubing, ring stand and clamp.

Procedure: 1. Drill a hole halfway through the potato. 2. Pour the saturated sugar solution into the hole. 3. Place the stopper with tubing attached into the hole. 4. Place the potato in a beaker and cover with water. 5. Clamp the tube to the ring stand. 6. On the following day, observe that the water has risen up the tube.

16·12 Dialysis

Concept: In dialysis, materials move across a semipermeable membrane.

Materials: 100 mL of 1*M* copper(II) sulfate (CuSO₄), 0.3 mL of 1*N* iron(III) chloride (FeCl₃), 900 mL of water, 250-mL beaker, two 600-mL beakers, wire gauze, ring, ring stand, burner, lighter, cellophane tubing, safety goggles.

Procedure: 1. Boil 100 mL water in the 250-mL beaker. 2. Add 0.3 mL iron chloride solution. A deep red ferric hydroxide colloid forms. 3. Place the colloid in a sealed cellophane tube. 4. Place the copper sulfate solution in another sealed cellophane tube. 5. Put 400 mL of water in each of the 600-mL beakers. 6. Place each of the cellophane tubes into a beaker. 7. After several days, the copper sulfate has diffused out of its tube. The ferric hydroxide, however, does not diffuse. **Caution:** *Iron(III) chloride and copper sulfate are irritants.*

Audiovisual Resources

Chemistry: Looking at the Solution (5 FS) Charles Clark, 1978, 15–19 min. each. (Use with Sections 16·1, 16·2, or 16·3.) Describes the formation of solutions, discusses their degree of saturation, and interprets solubility curves.

Chemistry: Solutions (Ionic and Molecular) (F, V) Coronet, 1983, 23 min. (Use with Sections 16·1, 16·2, or 16·7.) Discusses the nature of polar and nonpolar solutions and examines colligative properties.

Investigating Matter: Solutions (FS) Britannica, 1977, 10 min. (Use with Sections 16·1–16·3.) Discusses the properties of solutions.

Solutions (F, V) BFA Educational Films, 1969, 13 min. (Use with Sections 16·1–16·3.) Discusses how particle size affects solution formation and the scattering of light beams.

Solutions (F) Coronet, 1960, 16 min. (Use with Sections 16·1–16·3.) Demonstrates important characteristics of solutions and shows the factors that influence solubility.

Beyond the Text

Environmental Testing

For most chemical applications, the preferred unit of concentration is molarity. When very dilute solutions are being used, however, concentrations are more conveniently stated in parts per million (ppm) or parts per billion (ppb). A concentraton of 1 ppm is equivalent to one milligram of solute dissolved in 1 000 000 milligrams (1 kilogram) of solvent.

$$1 \text{ kg} \times \frac{1000 \text{ g}}{1 \text{ kg}} \times \frac{1000 \text{ mg}}{1 \text{ g}} = 1\ 000\ 000 \text{ mg}$$

Similarly, 1 ppb is equivalent to 1 microgram solute dissolved in 1 000 000 000 micrograms (or 1 kilogram) of solvent. Notice that this system of units does not require that the molecular mass of the solute be known.

These units may seem too small to be of any use, but that is far from true. The allowable concentration of toxic chemicals is measured in these units. For example, the Occupational Safety and Health Administration has set the allowable concentration of mercury in air at 0.0825 ppm, or 82 ppb. The allowable concentration of copper in drinking water is 1 ppm, that of cadmium 0.01 ppm. Iron is not toxic, but if the concentration of it in drinking water is more than 0.3 ppm the water will have a noticeable taste and color.

Chemists working in the field of environmental protection routinely measure these and much smaller concentrations of pollutants in our air and water. Their laboratories are equipped with the most sensitive analytical

instruments. Environmental chemists also develop new systems for controlling and monitoring pollution. They may search for new fuels or design new processes that generate less toxic wastes. They may work for industry, for government agencies, or for private research firms. Environmental chemistry laboratories also employ chemical technicians and chemical engineers.

Answers to End of Chapter Questions and Problems

Practice Questions and Problems

18. The *solvent* is the substance in which the *solute* is dissolved.

19. Random collisions of the solvent molecules with the solute molecules or ions provide enough force to overcome gravity.

20. Agitation, temperature, solute particle size.

21. *Solubility* is the amount of solute dissolved in a given amount of solvent to make a saturated solution at a given temperature. A *saturated* solution has the maximum amount of solute that can be dissolved in a given amount of solvent at a given temperature. An *unsaturated* solution has less dissolved solute than a saturated solution.

22. 555 g $AgNO_3$

23. The solution becomes cloudy as particles of solute crystallize.

24. *Miscible* liquids dissolve in each other, but *immiscible* liquids do not.

25. Solubility of a gas in a liquid is directly proportional to the pressure of the gas above the liquid at a given temperature.

26. Increases the solubility.

27. a. 0.016 g/L   **b.** 0.047 g/L

28. 1.0×10^{-2} atm

29. The number of moles of solute dissolved in one liter of solution.

30. a. 1.3M KCl   **b.** 0.33M $MgCl_2$ **c.** 0.050M NaCl **d.** 0.627M $CuSO_4$ **e.** 0.040M $NaHCO_3$

31. a. 0.50 mol NaCl, 29 g NaCl   **b.** 1.0 mol KNO_3, 1.0×10^2 g KNO_3 **c.** 0.025 mol $CaCl_2$, 2.8 g $CaCl_2$ **d.** 0.60 mol Na_2SO_4, 85 g Na_2SO_4

32. a. 1.3×10^2 mL   **b.** 0.80 L   **c.** 2.5 mL

33. 0.036M $Fe(NO_3)_3$

34. a. 23 g NaCl   **b.** 2.0 g $MgCl_2$ **c.** 10 g glucose **d.** 0.25 g $MgSO_4$

35. a. 3.3% KCl   **b.** 1.6% $NaNO_3$ **c.** 5.0% K_2SO_4

36. A solution with a nonvolatile solute has a lower vapor pressure than the pure solvent. The solute molecules or ions attract water molecules, making it more difficult for the water molecules to escape the solution.

37. A physical property that depends only on the number of dissolved particles; vapor pressure lowering, boiling point elevation, freezing point depression.

38. Nonvolatile solute particles attract molecules of the solvent and make it more difficult for the solvent molecules to escape from solution.

39. a. 100.26°C   **b.** 101.56°C

40. Freezing point is lowered by 5.58°C.

41. 111.2 g NaCl

42. A 1M solution has 1 mol solute dissolved in 1 L of solution. A 1 m solution has 1 mol solute dissolved in 1000 g of solvent.

43. 327 g of $Ba(NO_3)_2$ must be dissolved.

44. 0.556 m

45. 4.0 kg H_2O

46. $X_{CCl_4} = 0.437$ $X_{CHCl_3} = 0.563$

47. $X_{NaCl} = 0.101$ Mass fraction$_{NaCl} = .0259$

48. Ionic. A 1.00 molal solution lowers the freezing point 1.86°C if there is only one type of particle in solution. An ionic compound dissociates into more than one type of particle; a lower molality can give the same number of particles per 1000 g.

49. a. −0.56°C   **b.** −0.37°C   **c.** −0.74°C

50. 4.95°C

51. $169 \frac{g}{mol}$

Mastery Questions and Problems

52. Each gram of acetone requires 0.929 g of water.

53. 0.0234 L

54. If the KNO_3 solution is supersaturated, adding one crystal of KNO_3 causes crystallization. If it is saturated,

the crystal does not dissolve. If it is unsaturated, the crystal dissolves.

55. Freezing point = $-1.86°C$.
Boiling point = $100.512°C$

56. $X_{C_2H_5OH} = 0.20$ $X_{H_2O} = 0.80$

57. $-0.413°C$

58.

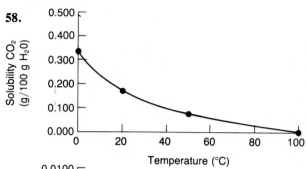

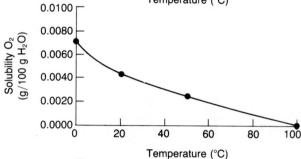

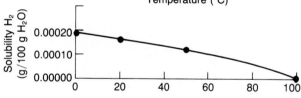

59. a. 44.2 g KCl   **b.** 5.8 g KCl

60. a. 0.30 mol   **b.** 0.40 mol   **c.** 0.50 mol
d. 0.20 mol

61.

Mass Solute	Moles Solute	Volume of Solution	Molarity
12.5 g	0.0694	219 mL	0.317
194 g	1.08	2.08 L	0.519
315 g	1.75	1.62 L	1.08

62. Unsaturated.

63. 100.680°C

64. a. 7.5 g H_2O_2 **b.** 0.88 M H_2O

65. 24 g $NaNO_3$

66. 85.5 g/mol

67. $X_{H_2O} = 0.972$ $X_{C_{12}H_{22}O_{11}} = 0.0283$

68. $\Delta T_f = -9.57°C$; $\Delta T_b = +4.73°C$

69. 1.1 m $NaHCO_3$

Review Questions and Problems

70. a. Gases are more soluble in cold water than warm water.   **b.** Vinegar is polar and oil is nonpolar.
c. Anhydrous $CaSO_4$ adsorbs water better than the surfaces of the instruments.   **d.** The greater surface area of the ground sugar increases the collisions between water and sugar molecules.   **e.** Tap water contains ions that conduct electricity.   **f.** The tea is already saturated.

71. Hydrogen chloride is polar. Water surrounds each HCl molecule, causing ionization and high solubility. Nonpolar solvents like benzene have no interaction with HCl.

72. Raises the boiling points.

73. A solution is formed. Soap molecules have a polar end that dissolves in water, a polar solvent.

74. a. the substance that is dissolved   **b.** the substance used for dissolving   **c.** No additional solute can be dissolved.   **d.** More solute can be dissolved.
e. The solution contains more solute than a saturated solution.   **f.** a solute that cannot conduct electricity
g. a solute that conducts a small amount of electricity   **h.** a solute that can conduct electricity

75. a. $NH_4Cl \longrightarrow NH_4^+ + Cl^-$
b. $Cu(NO_3)_2 \longrightarrow Cu^{2+} + 2NO_3^-$
c. $HNO_3 \longrightarrow H^+ + NO_3^-$
d. $HC_2H_3O_2 \longrightarrow H^+ + C_2H_3O_2^-$
e. $Na_2SO_4 \longrightarrow 2Na^+ + SO_4^{2-}$
f. $HgCl_2 \longrightarrow Hg^{2+} + 2Cl^-$

76. The stronger the intermolecular attractions in a liquid, the greater the surface tension.

Challenging Questions and Problems

77. a. 76°C: 15 mol/kg; 33°C; 5 mol/kg
b. 82°C   **c.** 30°C

78. 0.120M HCl

79. 20.0 mL $Cr_2(SO_4)_3$

80. 66.2 mL HNO_3

81. 0.090M Na_2SO_4

82. 99.8 g Cl^-, 54.8 g Na^+, 6.9 g Mg^{2+}, 13.3 g SO_4^{2-}, 2.2 g Ca^{2+}, 1.9 g K^+, 0.6 g HCO_3^-

Properties of Solutions

Chapter Preview

Sections 16·8, 16·9, 16·10, are appropriate for honors students.

Solutions are homogeneous mixtures that can be grouped according to their physical state. Solid, liquid, and gaseous solutions exist. Certain metal alloys are solid solutions, air is a gaseous solution, and ocean water is a liquid solution. Chemists usually work with liquid solutions. This chapter begins with discussions of solution formation and the concept of solubility. Various ways of expressing the concentrations of solutions, both qualitatively and quantitatively, will then be examined. Colligative properties of solutions are very important. They depend on the number of solute particles dissolved in a given volume of solvent. The colligative properties that will be covered are vapor pressure lowering, boiling point elevation, and freezing point depression.

16·1   Solution Formation

The rate at which a solute dissolves is influenced by agitation, temperature, and particle size.

Figure 16·1
Rock formations can be created and eroded due to the properties of solutions.

The nature of the solvent and solute affects *whether* a substance will dissolve. Several other factors determine *how fast* a soluble substance dissolves. If sodium chloride crystals are placed in a flask containing water, the crystals will eventually dissolve. If the flask and its contents are shaken, the crystals disappear more quickly than if the flask is not shaken. Agitation makes the solute dissolve more rapidly because it brings fresh solvent into contact with the solute. This is why most people stir coffee after they have added sugar. It is important to realize, however, that agitation affects only the *rate* at which a solute dissolves. It cannot influence the *amount* of solute that dissolves. An insoluble substance remains undissolved no matter how much the system is agitated.

Figure 16·2
Heat and agitation increase the rate at which a solute dissolves. Sugar dissolves faster in hot tea than it does in iced tea. Stirring also makes the sugar dissolve faster.

For most substances there is a limit to how much solute will dissolve in a given volume of solvent.

Temperature also influences the rate at which solutes dissolve. A salt crystal dissolves much more rapidly in hot water than in cold water. The kinetic energy of the water molecules is greater at the higher temperature. This leads to an increased frequency and force of the collisions of water molecules with the crystal surfaces.

A third factor that determines the rate of dissolution of a solute is its particle size. A powder dissolves more rapidly than a single crystal. This is because a greater surface area of ions is exposed to the colliding water molecules. Solvation is a surface phenomenon.

16·2 Solubility

When 36 g of sodium chloride is added to 100 g of water at 25°C, all the salt dissolves. Yet if we add one more gram of salt and stir, no matter how vigorously or how long, only 0.2 g of the last portion goes into solution. Why? After all, the kinetic theory says that water molecules are in continuous motion. They must continue to bombard the excess solid, removing and solvating the ions. Seemingly, all the sodium chloride should eventually disappear, but that does not happen. What does take place is an exchange. New particles from the solid are solvated and enter into solution. At the same time an equal number of particles come out of solution. They become desolvated and are deposited as a solid. The undissolved crystals of sodium chloride change their shape over time, but their mass remains constant.

The particles move from the solid to the solvated state and back to the solid again. Yet there is no net change in the overall system. A state of dynamic equilibrium exists between the solution and the undissolved solute, provided that the temperature remains constant (Figure 16·3). The sodium chloride solution is saturated. *A saturated solution contains the maximum amount of solute for a given amount of solvent at a constant temperature.* For example, 36.2 g of sodium chloride in 100 g of water is a saturated solution at 25°C. *The solubility of a substance is the amount of substance that dissolves in a given quantity of a solvent at a given temperature to produce a saturated solution.* Solubility is usually expressed in grams of solute per 100 g of solvent. *A solution that contains less solute than a saturated solution is unsaturated.* The solubilities of some substances are given in Table 16·1.

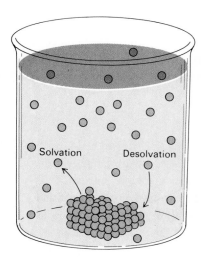

Figure 16·3
A state of dynamic equilibrium exists in a saturated solution. At these conditions the rate of solvation (dissolving) equals the rate of desolvation (crystallization).

Problem   1. 272 g NaCl

1. What weight of NaCl can be dissolved in 750 g of water at 25°C?

Two liquids are said to be **miscible** *if they dissolve in each other.* For example, water and ethanol are infinitely soluble in one another. Any amount of ethanol will dissolve in a given volume of water and *vice versa.* Such a pair of liquids is said to be completely miscible. Liquids

Figure 16·4
Which of these two beakers contains
a saturated solution?
The one on the right.

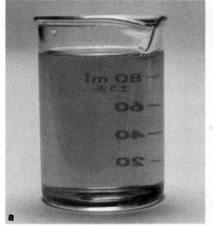

a | b

that are slightly soluble in one another, for example, water and diethyl
ether, are partially miscible. *Liquids that are insoluble in one another are*
immiscible. Gasoline is immiscible with water.

16·3   Factors Affecting Solubility

At 25°C the solubility of sodium chloride in water is 36.2 g per 100 g of
water. When the temperature is raised to 100°C, the solubility increases
to 39.2 g of NaCl per 100 g of water. As shown in Figure 16·5, the solubility of most substances increases as the temperature of the solvent is increased. For some substances, however, the reverse occurs. The solubility of sodium sulfate in water drops from 50 g per 100 g at 40°C to 41 g
per 100 g at 100°C. Table 16·1 lists the solubilities of some common
substances at various temperatures.

Remember that 100 g of H_2O =
100 mL of H_2O at 4°C. This is not
true for other liquids.

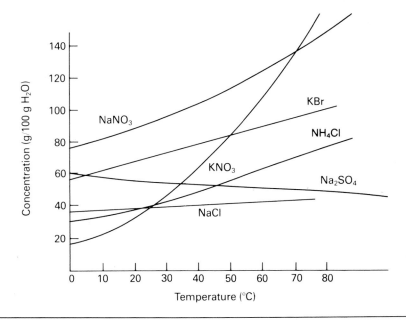

Figure 16·5
Temperature may affect the solubility
of a substance. Notice that increasing
the temperature greatly increases the
solubility of KNO_3 but decreases the
solubility of Na_2SO_4.

Table 16·1   Solubilities of Some Substances in Water at Various Temperatures

Substance	Formula	Solubility (g/100 g of H₂0)			
		0°C	20°C	50°C	100°C
Barium sulfate	$BaSO_4$	0.00019	0.00025	0.00034	—
Lead(II) chloride	$PbCl_2$	0.60	0.99	1.70	—
Lithium carbonate	Li_2CO_3	1.5	1.3	1.1	0.70
Potassium chlorate	$KClO_3$	4.0	7.4	19.3	56.0
Potassium chloride	KCl	27.6	34.0	42.6	57.6
Sodium chloride	$NaCl$	35.7	36.0	37.0	39.2
Sodium nitrate	$NaNO_3$	74	88.0	114.0	182
Sodium sulfate	Na_2SO_4	4.76	62	50.0	41.0
Silver nitrate	$AgNO_3$	122	222.0	455.0	733
Lithium bromide	$LiBr$	143.0	166	203	266.0
Cane sugar	$C_{12}H_{22}O_{11}$	179	203.9	260.4	487
Hydrogen*	H_2	0.00019	0.00016	0.00013	0.0
Oxygen*	O_2	0.0070	0.0043	0.0026	0.0
Carbon dioxide*	CO_2	0.335	0.169	0.076	0.0

*Gas at 760 mm Hg total pressure

For most substances, solubility increases as temperature increases. For gases, solubility increases as temperature decreases.

The solubilities of gases are greater in cold water than in hot water. Bubbles form in water when it is heated as the dissolved gases escape from solution. The components of air all become less soluble in water as the temperature of the solution rises (Figure 16·6). When an industrial plant takes cool water from a lake and dumps hot water back into the lake, the temperature of the lake water rises. This is known as thermal

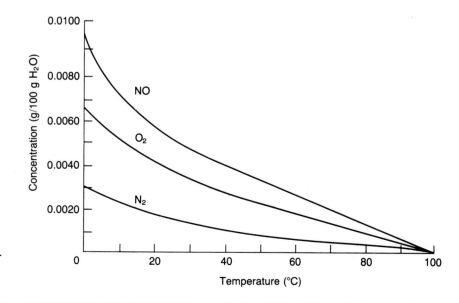

Figure 16·6
Gases have different solubilities in water at different temperatures. Generally, as the temperature increases, the solubilities of gases decrease. Notice that nitrogen, oxygen, and nitric oxide are insoluble at 100°C.

Figure 16·7
Warm but otherwise clean water can kill fish and other aquatic animals that depend on high concentrations of dissolved oxygen.

pollution. The temperature increase lowers the concentration of dissolved oxygen in the lake water. Aquatic animal life can be severely affected by the lack of oxygen.

The solubility of a gas increases as the partial pressure of the gas *above* the solution is increased. Carbonated beverages are a good example of this principle. These drinks contain large amounts of carbon dioxide (CO_2) dissolved in water. It is the dissolved CO_2 that makes your mouth tingle. The drinks are bottled under a high pressure of CO_2 gas. This forces large amounts of CO_2 into solution. When a carbonated beverage bottle is opened, the partial pressure of CO_2 above the liquid decreases, and the concentration of dissolved CO_2 decreases. Bubbles of CO_2 form in the liquid and escape from the open bottle. If the bottle is left open, the drink becomes flat as the solution loses its CO_2. **Henry's law** *states that at a given temperature the solubility of a gas in a liquid (S) is directly proportional to the pressure of the gas above the liquid (P).* In other words, as the pressure of the gas above the liquid increases, the solubility of the gas increases. Similarly, as the pressure of the gas decreases, the solubility of the gas decreases. This relationship can be written in mathematical form.

$$\frac{S_1}{P_1} = \frac{S_2}{P_2}$$

Example 1

If the solubility of a gas in water is 0.77 g/L at 3.5 atm of pressure, what is its solubility, in grams per liter at 1.0 atm of pressure? (The temperature is held constant at 25°C.)

Solution

Use the same general method that was used for solving gas law problems in Chapter 10. The knowns are: P_1 = 3.5 atm, S_1 = 0.77 g/L, and P_2 = 1.0 atm. To find S_2, begin by rearranging Henry's law to give S_2.

$$S_2 = \frac{S_1 \times P_2}{P_1}$$

Then substitute values for the other variables in the equation.

$$S_2 = \frac{0.77 \text{ g/L} \times 1.0 \text{ atm}}{3.5 \text{ atm}} = 0.22 \text{ g/L}$$

When the pressure is reduced to 1.0 atm, the solubility of the gas decreases to 0.22 g/L.

Problem

2. A gas has a solubility in water at 0°C of 3.6 g/L at a pressure of 1.0 atm. What pressure is required to produce an aqueous solution containing 9.5 g/L of the same gas at 0°C?

2. 2.6 atm

Figure 16·8
Mineral deposits form around the edges of this hot spring because the hot water is saturated with minerals. As the water cools at the surface, the minerals crystallize because they are less soluble at a lower temperature.

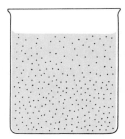

a Supersaturated solution

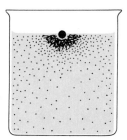

b Seed crystal added

c Excess solute crystallizes on seed

Figure 16·9
When a seed crystal **(b)** is added to a supersaturated solution **(a)**, the excess solute crystallizes **(c)**.

When the temperature of a saturated solution is raised, the excess solid will usually dissolve. If the system then cools slowly and undisturbed to its original temperature, the excess solute does not always immediately crystallize. *A solution which contains more solute than it can theoretically hold at a given temperature is a* **supersaturated solution.** In such a solution, a dynamic equilibrium cannot exist between the dissolved solute and the undissolved solid because there is no undissolved solid. Crystallization in a supersaturated solution can be initiated if a very small crystal, called a seed crystal, of the solute is added (Figure 16·9). Crystallization can also occur on a rough surface such as the inside of the container if it is scratched.

The rate at which excess solute deposits upon the surface of a seed crystal can be impressively rapid. Scientific rainmaking is done by seeding clouds, which are made of air supersaturated with water vapor. Tiny silver iodide (AgI) crystals are dusted on a cloud. Water molecules that are attracted to the ionic particles come together and form droplets that act as seeds for other water molecules. The water droplets grow and eventually fall as rain when they are large enough.

16·A Chromatography

Chemists often need to separate the components of a solution to identify them. One of the most powerful techniques available for this purpose is chromatography. It is based on the fact that different substances have different solubilities in a particular solvent.

Paper chromatography is a relatively easy procedure to perform in the laboratory. It can be used to separate a mixture of colored substances. A small drop of the sample mixture is placed near the bottom edge of a piece of filter paper and is allowed to dry. The filter paper is placed in a shallow container so that the bottom edge just touches the chosen solvent. Capillary action causes the solvent to travel up the filter paper. The substance in the sample with the great-

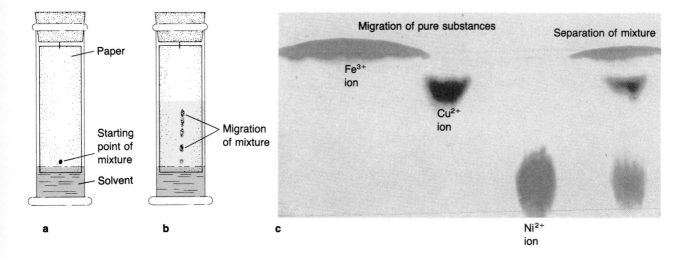

Figure 16·10
Paper chromatography can be used to detect the various ions. **a** The mixture to be identified is placed on paper which is rolled and put into a container of solvent. **b** The components of the mixture become separated as the solvent moves up the paper. **c** Three pure samples and one mixture were placed at the bottom of this chromatograph. In this case the mixture contained all three of the pure substances.

In the figure, labels read: Paper; Starting point of mixture; Solvent; Migration of mixture; Migration of pure substances; Separation of mixture; Fe^{3+} ion; Cu^{2+} ion; Ni^{2+} ion. Positions marked **a**, **b**, **c**.

est solubility in the solvent migrates up the strip almost as fast as the solvent. Components with intermediate solubilities migrate at slower rates. The further the solvent migrates, the more the component substances of the sample mixture become separated. By changing the solvent, the degree of migration and separation can be varied.

Several other types of chromatography are also available. In some of these systems the liquid solvent, also called the mobile phase, is replaced by a gas solvent. The filter paper, the stationary phase, can be substituted by a liquid, a colloid, or more appropriate type of solid. The type of chromatographic system used depends on the substances that must be separated.

Commercial laboratories and research facilities make great use of chromatography. For example, the food industry uses a gas chromatograph to isolate and identify compounds responsible for food aromas. This is a first step in the process of producing flavorings that imitate natural flavors. Chromatography is used in many areas of chemical, medical, and biological research.

16·4 Molarity

Molarity is the most important unit of concentration in chemistry.

So far this chapter has focused mainly on whether a particular substance does or does not dissolve in a particular solvent. This section focuses on ways of expressing the concentrations of solutions. *The* **concentration** *of a solution is a measure of the amount of solute that is dissolved in a given quantity of solvent.* The terms *concentrated* and *dilute* are a qualitative description of the amount of a solute in solution. *A* **dilute solution** *contains only a small amount of solute.* By contrast, *a* **concentrated solution** *contains a large amount of solute.* An aqueous solution of sodium chloride containing 1 g of NaCl per 100 g of H_2O might be described as dilute compared with another solution containing 30 g per 100 g. The first solution might be described as concentrated if it were compared with another solution containing only 1×10^{-2} g of NaCl per

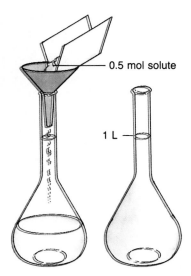

Figure 16·11
To make a 0.5 mol solution, add 0.5 mol of solute to a 1-L volumetric flask half filled with water. Swirl the flask carefully to make the solute dissolve. Then fill the flask with water exactly to the 1 L mark.

Note that molarity is per liter of *solution*, not of *solvent*.

100 g of H_2O. For this reason, describing a solution as concentrated or dilute does not really express the concentration of the solution.

Just as the most important unit of mass in chemistry is the mole, the most important unit of concentration is molarity (abbreviated *M*). **Molarity** *is the number of moles of a solute dissolved in 1 L of solution.* Note that the volume is the volume of the *total solution,* not the volume of the solvent. If 0.5 mol of a solute is dissolved in water and diluted to a volume of exactly 1 L, a 0.5 molar (0.5 mol/L) or 0.5*M* solution is created. To determine the molarity of any solution, the number of moles in 1 L of the solution can be calculated using the following equation.

$$\text{Molarity } (M) = \frac{\text{number of moles of solute}}{\text{number of liters of solution}}$$

For example, if water is added to 2 mol of glucose to give 5 L of solution, the molarity is 0.4*M*. To get this answer, divide the number of moles by the volume in liters.

$$\frac{2 \text{ mol of glucose}}{5 \text{ L of solution}} = 0.4 \text{ mol/L}$$

The solution is 0.4 molar (0.4*M*) in glucose.

Example 2

A saline solution contains 0.90 g of NaCl per 100 mL of solution. What is its molarity?

Solution

Molarity is moles per liter. The concentration must be converted from grams per 100 mL to moles per liter. To do this, start with the gram formula mass of sodium chloride.

$$\text{gfm NaCl} = 23.0 \text{ g} + 35.5 \text{ g} = 58.5 \text{ g}$$

Use a conversion factor based on the gram formula mass to calculate the moles of NaCl in 100 mL of saline.

$$\text{Moles} = 0.90 \text{ g} \times \frac{1.0 \text{ mol}}{58.5 \text{ g}} = 0.015 \text{ mol}$$

Now convert mol per 100 mL to mol per L (100 mL = 0.1 L).

$$\text{Molarity} = \frac{\text{moles}}{\text{liter}} = \frac{0.015 \text{ mol}}{0.1 \text{ L}} = 0.15M \text{ solution}$$

Problems

3. 2.8*M*
4. 0.1*M*

3. A salt solution has a volume of 250 mL and contains 0.70 mol of NaCl. What is the molarity of the solution?
4. An aqueous solution has a volume of 2.0 L and contains 36.0 g of glucose. If the gram formula mass of glucose is 180 g, what is the molarity of the solution?

Figure 16·12
A 1 molar solution contains 1 mole of solute per liter of solution. One mole of each substance is shown: 58.5 g sodium chloride, 158 g potassium permanganate, 250 g copper sulfate pentahydrate.

CuSO₄·5H₂O

KMnO₄

1 mole

1 mole

Example 3

How many moles of solute are present in 1.5 L of $0.20M$ Na_2SO_4?

Solution

Rearrange the expression for molarity to give moles of solute.

Liters of solution × molarity (M) = moles of solute

Substitute in the known information, stating the molarity in mol/L.

$$1.5 \; \cancel{L} \times \frac{0.20 \; mol}{1.0 \; \cancel{L}} = 0.30 \; mol$$

To determine the weight of solute, multiply the number of moles of Na_2SO_4 by a conversion factor based on the gram formula mass.

$$0.30 \; \cancel{mol} \times \frac{142 \; g}{1.0 \; \cancel{mol}} = 42.6 \; g = 43 \; g \; \text{(to two significant figures)}$$

Problem   5. 0.50 mol $CaCl_2$; 56 g $CaCl_2$

5. How many moles of solute are in 250 mL of $2.0M$ $CaCl_2$? How many grams of $CaCl_2$ is this?

16·5   Making Dilutions

Solutions of known molarity are usually available in the laboratory. Often other dilute solutions of known concentrations are required. A solution can be made less concentrated by diluting with solvent. *The number of moles of solute does not change when a solution is diluted.*

$$\begin{array}{c} \text{Number of moles of solute} \\ \textit{before} \text{ dilution} \end{array} = \begin{array}{c} \text{number of moles of solute} \\ \textit{after} \text{ dilution} \end{array}$$

The definition of molarity can be rearranged to show the relationship between molarity and volume.

$$\text{Molarity } (M) = \frac{\text{number of moles of solute}}{\text{number of liters of solution}}$$

Moles of solute = molarity (M) × liters of solution (V)

Changing the amount of solvent does not change the amount of solute. The total number of moles remains constant upon dilution. If a solution is diluted from V_1 to V_2, the molarity of that solution changes according to this equation.

$$M_1 \times V_1 = M_2 \times V_2$$

In this equation M_1 and V_1 are the initial solution's molarity and volume, and M_2 and V_2 are the final solution's molarity and volume. Volume was expressed in liters to get the equation, but the volumes can be in liters or milliliters as long as the same units are used for both volumes.

Diluting a solution does not change the amount of solute.

Safety

To dilute an acid, always add the acid, with stirring, to the required amount of water. Never add water to the acid. The heat generated may splash the solution out of the container.

Figure 16·13
To prepare 100 mL of 0.40*M* MgSO₄ from a stock solution of 2.0*M* MgSO₄, transfer 20 mL of the stock solution to a 100-mL volumetric flask. Carefully add water to make 100 mL of solution.

Accurate volume-measuring devices include the volumetric pipet, the buret, and the volumetric flask.

Chemists have a variety of volume-measuring devices available to them. Their choice of what to use depends on how accurate the concentration of the solution they are making must be. The following example shows how a dilute solution is prepared.

Example 4

How would you prepare 100 mL of 0.40*M* MgSO₄ from a stock solution of 2.0*M* MgSO₄?

Solution

Use the above equation to calculate the volume of 2.0*M* MgSO₄ and then describe the procedure. The knowns are: $M_1 = 2.0M$, $M_2 = 0.40M$, and $V_2 = 100$ mL. V_1 is the unknown. Rearrange the equation to give V_1.

$$M_1 \times V_1 = M_2 \times V_2 \text{ therefore } V_1 = \frac{M_2 \times V_2}{M_1}$$

Now substitute values into the equation.

$$V_1 = \frac{0.40M \times 100 \text{ mL}}{2.0M} = 20 \text{ mL}$$

Suppose the dilute solution must be very accurate. Measure 20 mL of the 2.0*M* MgSO₄ with a 20-mL volumetric pipet and transfer the solution to a 100-mL volumetric flask. (A buret can also be used to measure volumes accurately.) Next add distilled water to the flask up to the etched line. This dilutes the contents to exactly 100 mL. Then shake the flask. This produces 100 mL of 0.40*M* MgSO₄.

Safety

Never pipet a solution by mouth. Use a suction bulb.

Problem

6. Use a pipet to transfer 50 mL of the 1.0*M* solution to a 250-mL volumetric flask. Then add distilled water up to the mark.

6. You need 250 mL of 0.20*M* NaCl, but the only supply of sodium chloride you have is a solution of 1.0*M* NaCl. How do you prepare the required solution? Assume that you have the appropriate volume-measuring devices on hand.

Figure 16·14
Mary Schwartz Rose used her knowledge of chemistry to make substantial contributions to the field of nutrition.

16·B Nutrition: The Birth of a Science

When Mary Swartz Rose (1874–1941) enrolled at Columbia University in 1905, no curriculum was available in the study of nutrition. Her desire to study the chemistry of food and nutrition led her to Yale University. She obtained a Ph.D. there in physiological chemistry. She returned to Columbia and was largely responsible for establishing a Department of Nutrition.

Rose was a brilliant and talented educator. Her department became a leading university center for the study of nutrition. She taught for 31 years and published over 40 scholarly papers on such topics as energy metabolism and the nutritive value of food proteins. She served on many national and international advisory councils concerned with diet and nutrition.

Nutrition is the study of the processes by which living organisms absorb and utilize food substances. Nutrients are transferred to the cells of the body by the circulatory system. Solution chemistry is a major aspect of nutritional science because body nutrients are more easily studied in the blood than in the body cells and tissues.

The world population is increasing more rapidly than the food supply. The agricultural and nutritional sciences are vital for our future. Nutritional chemists are helping to solve food supply problems by finding which foods provide adequate amounts of nutrients.

16·6 Percent Solutions

The two common ways of representing percent concentrations are volume/volume (v/v) percent and mass/volume (m/v) percent.

If both the solute and the solvent are liquids, a convenient way to make a solution is by measuring volumes. The concentration of the solute can then be expressed as a percent of the solution by volume. Percent means "parts per hundred." If 20 mL of rubbing alcohol is diluted with water to a total volume of 100 mL, the final solution is 20% alcohol by volume. It can be written as 20 percent (volume/volume), or 20% (v/v).

The denominator in the expression is equal to the total volume of the solution.

$$\text{Percent by volume} = \frac{\text{volume of solute}}{\text{volume of solution}} \times 100\%$$

Example 5

What is the percent by volume of ethanol (ethyl alcohol, C_2H_6O) in the final solution when 75 mL of ethanol is diluted to a volume of 250 mL with water?

Solution

$$\text{Percent by volume} = \frac{75 \text{ mL}}{250 \text{ mL}} \times 100\% = 0.30 \times 100\%$$
$$= 30\% \text{ ethanol (v/v)}$$

Figure 16·15
When environmental pollution is suspected, analytical chemists are called on to measure its extent. If the levels of toxic wastes are too high in the soil or ground water, the area may be closed off.

8. 4.0 g MgSO₄
9. 3.6% CuSO₄ (m/v)

Problem   7. 5.0% (v/v)

7. If 10 mL of acetic acid (CH_3COOH) is diluted with water to a total solution volume of 200 mL, what is the percent by volume of acetic acid in the solution?

A commonly used relationship for solutions of solids dissolved in liquids is percent (mass/volume). It is usually convenient to weigh the solute in grams and to measure the volume of the resulting solution in milliliters. Percent (mass/volume) is the number of grams of solute per 100 mL of solution. A solution containing 7 g of sodium chloride in 100 mL of solution is 7 percent (mass/volume) or 7% (m/v).

$$\text{Percent (mass/volume)} = \frac{\text{mass of solute (g)}}{\text{solution volume (mL)}} \times 100\%$$

Example 6

How many grams of glucose ($C_6H_{12}O_6$) would you need to prepare 2.0 L of 2.0% glucose (m/v) solution?

Solution

A 2.0% glucose (m/v) solution means that 100 mL of the solution contains 2.0 g of glucose. Use a conversion factor to determine the number of grams per liter.

$$\frac{2.0 \text{ g}}{100 \text{ mL}} \times \frac{1000 \text{ mL}}{1.0 \text{ L}} = 20 \text{ g/L}$$

Multiply the number of grams of solute per liter by the number of liters required.

$$2.0 \text{ L} \times \frac{20 \text{ g}}{1 \text{ L}} = 40 \text{ g}$$

The required mass of glucose is 40 g.

Problems

8. How many grams of magnesium sulfate are required to make 250 mL of a 1.6% MgSO₄ (m/v) solution?

9. A solution contains 2.7 g of CuSO₄ in 75 mL of solution. What is the percent (mass/volume) of the solution?

Percent composition can often be misleading. When a label says a product contains 5% glucose, what does it mean? It is probably specifying percent (mass/volume), but we cannot be certain unless the units are given. When using percentages to express concentration, be sure to state the units.

16·7 Colligative Properties of Solutions

Colligative properties depend on the number of particles in solution. They include: vapor pressure lowering, boiling point elevation, and freezing point depression.

Electrolytes have a more pronounced effect on colligative properties than nonelectrolytes since they produce ions when they dissolve.

The physical properties of a solution are different from those of the pure solvent. Some of these differences are due to the mere presence of solute particles in the solution. **Colligative properties** *depend on the number of particles dissolved in a given mass of solvent.* They do not depend on the chemical nature of the solute or the solvent. Three important colligative properties of solutions are vapor pressure lowering, boiling point elevation, and freezing point depression.

Vapor pressure is the pressure exerted by a vapor that is in dynamic equilibrium with its liquid in a closed system. A solution that contains a nonvolatile solute always has a lower vapor pressure than the pure solvent. A nonvolatile solute is one that does not vaporize. Glucose, a molecular compound, and sodium chloride, an ionic compound, are examples of nonvolatile solutes. Both glucose and sodium chloride would lower the vapor pressure of a pure solvent. Consider an aqueous sodium chloride solution as an example. Sodium ions and chloride ions are dispersed throughout the liquid. Both within the liquid and at the surface, the ions are surrounded by shells of water of solvation. The formation of these shells occupies much of the surface water. This reduces the number of solvent molecules that have enough kinetic energy to escape as vapor (Figure 16·16). As a result, the solution has a lower vapor pressure than the pure solvent.

The decrease in the vapor pressure is proportional *to the number of particles the solute makes in solution.* A solute that dissociates into several particles, like sodium chloride, has a greater effect on the vapor pressure than the same concentration of a nondissociating solute like glucose. For example, the vapor pressure lowering caused by 0.1 mol of sodium chloride in 1000 g of water is twice the vapor pressure lowering of 0.1 mol of glucose in 1000 g of water. Each formula unit of the ionic compound sodium chloride produces two particles in solution: a sodium ion and a chloride ion. When glucose dissolves, each molecule produces only one particle, the molecule itself. Similarly, 0.1 mol of $CaCl_2$ in 1000 mL of water produces three times the vapor pressure lowering of a 0.1 mol glucose solution. Each formula unit of calcium chloride produces three particles in solution.

An ionic compound dissociates into several particles in solution; a molecular compound does not dissociate in solution.

Figure 16·16
The vapor pressure of a solution of a nonvolatile solute is lower than the vapor pressure of a pure solvent. **a** Equilibrium is established between the liquid and the vapor in the pure solvent. **b** The equilibrium is disrupted when solute is added. Solvent particles form shells around the solute particles. This reduces the number of free solvent particles able to escape the liquid.

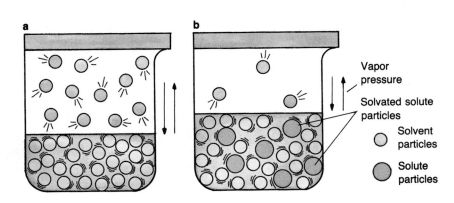

Figure 16·17
Temperatures below 0°C are needed to make ice cream. Thus rock salt is added to ice in a hand crank ice cream maker. A freezing point depression occurs and the temperature of the ice-water mixture decreases a few degrees below 0°C.

The boiling point of a solution is *higher* than the boiling point of the pure solvent.

The boiling point of a substance is the temperature at which the vapor pressure of the liquid phase equals the atmospheric pressure. Adding a nonvolatile solute to a liquid solvent decreases the vapor pressure of the solvent. Because of the decrease in vapor pressure, additional kinetic energy must be added to raise the vapor pressure of the liquid phase to atmospheric pressure. Thus the boiling point of the solution is higher than the boiling point of the pure solvent. *The* **boiling point elevation** *is the difference in temperature between the boiling points of a solution and of the pure solvent.*

Another way to think about the reason for a boiling point elevation is in terms of particles. Attractive forces exist between the solvent and solute particles. Additional kinetic energy must be added for solvent particles to overcome the attractive forces that keep them in the liquid phase. The magnitude of the boiling point elevation is proportional to the number of solute particles dissolved in the solvent. For example, the boiling point of water increases by 0.52°C for every mole of *particles* that the solute forms when dissolved in 1000 g of water. Thus boiling point elevation is a colligative property.

When a substance freezes, the particles in the solid take on an orderly pattern. The presence of a solute in water disrupts this pattern due to the shells of water of hydration. As a result, more kinetic energy must be withdrawn from a solution than from pure solvent for it to solidify. *The* **freezing point depression** *is the difference in temperature between the freezing points of a solution and of the pure solvent.* The magnitude of the freezing point depression is proportional to the number of solute particles dissolved in the solvent. Thus it is a colligative property.

The freezing point of a solution is *lower* than the freezing point of the pure solvent.

The addition of 1 mol of particles of solute to 1000 g of water lowers the freezing point by 1.86°C. When 1 mol (180 g) of glucose is added to 1000 g of water, the solution freezes at −1.86°C. If 1 mol (58.5 g) of sodium chloride is added to 1000 g of water, however, the solution freezes at −3.72°C. This is because 1 mol of NaCl produces 2 mol of particles. We take advantage of the freezing point depression of aqueous solutions to melt ice on sidewalks. Ice sprinkled with salt melts and forms a solution with a lower freezing point than that of pure water.

16·8 Molality and Mole Fraction

The colligative properties depend only on the ratio of the number of solute particles to solvent particles. Two convenient ways of expressing this ratio are in molality units and in mole fractions. **Molality** *(m)* is the number of moles of solute dissolved in 1 kilogram (1000 g) of solvent. Molality is also known as molal concentration.

$$\text{Molality} = \frac{\text{moles of solute}}{\text{kilogram of solvent}} = \frac{\text{moles of solute}}{1000 \text{ g of solvent}}$$

Note that *molality* is not the same as *molarity*. Molality refers to moles per kilogram of *solvent* rather than per liter of *solution*.

A solution that is 1.00 molal in glucose can be prepared by adding 1000 g of water to 1.00 mol (180 g) of glucose. A solution prepared by dissolving 0.500 mol (29.25 g) of sodium chloride in 1.000 kg (1000 g) of water is 0.500 molal (0.500 *m*) in NaCl.

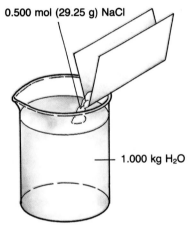

0.500 mol (29.25 g) NaCl

1.000 kg H₂O

Figure 16·18
To make a 0.500*m* solution of NaCl use a balance to measure 1.000 kg of water, and add 29.25 g of NaCl to it.

Example 7

How many grams of potassium iodide must be dissolved in 500 g of water to produce a 0.060 molal KI solution?

Solution

According to the definition of *molal*, the final solution must contain 0.060 mol KI per 1000 g H₂O. Use this as a conversion factor.

$$500 \text{ g } H_2O \times \frac{0.060 \text{ mol KI}}{1000 \text{ g } H_2O} = 0.030 \text{ mol KI}$$

Then convert 0.030 mol of KI to grams.

$$\text{gfm KI} = 39.1 + 126.9 = 166.0 \text{ g}$$

$$0.030 \text{ mol KI} \times \frac{166.0 \text{ g KI}}{1 \text{ mol KI}} = 5.0 \text{ g KI}$$

Dissolve 5.0 g KI in 500 g of H₂O to get 0.060 molal KI.

Problem

10. Calculate the molality of a solution prepared by dissolving 10.0 g of NaCl in 600 g of water.

The ratio of the moles of solute in solution to the total number of moles of both solvent and solute is the **mole fraction** *of that solute.* In a solution containing n_A moles of solute and n_B moles of solvent, the mole fraction of solute, X_A, and mole fraction of the solvent, X_B, can be expressed mathematically.

$$X_A = \frac{n_A}{n_A + n_B} \qquad\qquad X_B = \frac{n_B}{n_A + n_B}$$

Example 8

Compute the mole fraction of each component in a solution of 1.25 mol ethylene glycol (EG) and 4.00 mol water.

Solution

The mole fraction of ethylene glycol, X_{EG}, in the solution is the number of moles of ethylene glycol divided by the total number of moles in solution.

$$X_{EG} = \frac{n_{EG}}{n_{EG} + n_{H_2O}} = \frac{1.25 \text{ mol}}{1.25 \text{ mol} + 4.00 \text{ mol}} = 0.238$$

The mole fraction of water, X_{H_2O}, is the number of moles of water divided by the total number of moles in solution.

$$X_{H_2O} = \frac{n_{H_2O}}{n_{EG} + n_{H_2O}} = \frac{4.00 \text{ mol}}{1.25 \text{ mol} + 4.00 \text{ mol}} = 0.762$$

$$\text{Total} = 1.000$$

Note that mole fraction is a dimensionless quantity. *The sum of the mole fractions of all the components in a solution must equal unity.*

11. mole fraction of C_2H_5OH = 0.190
mole fraction of H_2O = 0.810

12. mole fraction of NaCl = 0.00269
mole fraction of H_2O = 0.99731

13. 0.60 mol H_2O and 0.40 mol CH_3OH
or
10.8 g H_2O and 12.8 g CH_3OH

Appropriate for honors students.

Problems

11. What is the mole fraction of each component in a solution made by mixing 300 g of ethanol (C_2H_5OH) and 500 g of water?

12. A solution is labeled 0.150 molal NaCl. What are the mole fractions of the solute and solvent in this solution?

13. Describe how you would make an aqueous solution of methanol, CH_3OH, in which the mole fraction of methanol is 0.40.

16·9 Calculating Boiling and Freezing Point Changes

Boiling and freezing point changes are proportional to the number of particles in a solution.

Elevations of boiling points and depressions of freezing points are usually quite small. They can be measured accurately only with thermometers that can measure temperature changes as small as 0.001°C.

The boiling point of a solvent is raised by the addition of a nonvolatile solute. The magnitude of the boiling point elevation is directly proportional to the molal concentration when the solute is molecular (not ionic).

$$\Delta T_b \propto m$$

The change in the boiling temperature, ΔT_b, is the elevation of the boiling point of the solvent. It is the boiling point of the solution minus the boiling point of the solvent. The term m is the molal concentration of the solution. Adding a proportionality constant makes an equality.

$$\Delta T_b = K_b \, m$$

Figure 16·19
The addition of a nonvolatile solute to water lowers its vapor pressure. This results in an increase in the normal boiling point of water and a decrease in the normal freezing point of water.

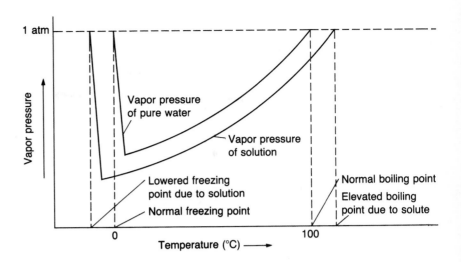

Table 16·2 K_b Values for Some Common Solvents	
Solvent	K_b (°C/m)
Water	0.512
Benzene	2.53
Acetic Acid	3.07
Nitrobenzene	5.24
Phenol	3.56

The constant, K_b, the **molal boiling point elevation constant,** *is equal to the change in boiling point for a 1 molal solution of a nonvolatile molecular solute*. The constant K_b for water and some other solvents are given in Table 16·2. The units of K_b are °C/m.

Example 9

What is the boiling point of a solution that contains 1.20 mol of sodium chloride in 800 g of water?

Solution

First determine the molality of the solution.

$$\frac{\text{mol NaCl}}{1000 \text{ g H}_2\text{O}} = \frac{1.20 \text{ mol NaCl}}{800 \text{ g}} \times \frac{1000 \text{ g}}{1 \text{ kg}} = 1.50 \text{ } m$$

Each formula unit of NaCl is ionized into two particles.

$$\text{NaCl}(s) \longrightarrow \text{Na}^+(aq) + \text{Cl}^-(aq)$$

The molality of *total* particles is $2 \times 1.50 \text{ } m = 3.00 \text{ } m$. Now determine the boiling point elevation. From Table 16·2, K_b for H_2O is 0.512°C/m.

$$\Delta T_b = K_b \times m$$
$$= 0.512°\text{C}/m \times 3.00 \text{ } m$$
$$= 1.54°\text{C}$$

The boiling point of this solution is 100°C + 1.54°C = 101.54°C.

Problem

14. 101.37°C

14. What is the boiling point of a solution that contains 1.25 mol of $CaCl_2$ in 1400 g of water?

Table 16·3 K_f Values for Some Common Solvents	
Solvent	$K_f(°C/m)$
Water	1.86
Benzene	5.12
Acetic Acid	3.90
Nitrobenzene	7.00
Phenol	7.40

15. a. −4.46°C
   b. −1.71°C
16. FeCl$_3$

Appropriate for honors students.

The molecular mass of a non-volatile solute may be determined by using the boiling point elevation or freezing point depression.

The freezing point depression of a solution can also be calculated.

$$\Delta T_f = K_f \times m$$

The change in the freezing temperature, ΔT_f, represents the freezing point depression. The molality is m. The **molal freezing point depression constant,** K_f, *is equal to the change in the freezing point for a 1 molal solution of a nonvolatile molecular solute* (Table 16·3).

Problems

15. What is the freezing point of these solutions?
   a. 1.40 mol of Na$_2$SO$_4$ in 1750 g of H$_2$O
   b. 0.60 mol of MgSO$_4$ in 1300 g of H$_2$O

16. One mole of a compound of iron and chlorine is dissolved in 1 kg of water. The boiling point of this aqueous solution is 102.05°C; the freezing point is −7.44°C. What is the formula of this compound?

16·10   Molecular Mass Determination

The changes in boiling and freezing points can be used to determine the molecular mass of a substance. A known amount of solute is added to a known amount of solvent, and the change in boiling or freezing point is measured. A solvent with a known molal freezing point depression constant (K_f) or molal boiling point elevation constant (K_b) must be used. Then the molecular mass for the solute can be calculated.

Example 10

A solution of 7.50 g of a nonvolatile compound in 22.60 g of water boils at 100.78°C at 760 mm Hg. What is the molecular mass of the solute? (Assume the solute exists as molecules and not ions.)

Solution

First use the boiling point elevation to calculate the molality of the solution. The observed boiling point elevation is: 100.78°C − 100.00°C = 0.78°C = ΔT_b.

$$\Delta T_b = K_b \times m \qquad \text{Thus} \qquad m = \frac{\Delta T_b}{K_b}$$

The K_b for water is $0.512 \dfrac{°C \times kg \text{ of water}}{mol \text{ of solute}}$

$$m = \frac{0.78°\cancel{C}}{0.512 \dfrac{\cancel{°C} \times kg \text{ of water}}{mol \text{ of solute}}}$$

$$m = 1.52 \frac{mol \text{ of solute}}{kg \text{ of water}}$$

Now calculate moles of solute in solution.

$$1.52 \frac{\text{mol of solute}}{\text{kg of water}} \times 22.6 \text{ g of water} \times \frac{1 \text{ kg}}{1000 \text{ g}} = 0.0344 \text{ mol solute}$$

Finally use the number of moles of solute and its mass to determine the molecular mass of the solute.

$$\text{Molecular mass of solute} = \frac{\text{mass of solute}}{\text{moles of solute}}$$

$$= \frac{7.50 \text{ g}}{0.0344 \text{ mol}}$$

$$= 218 \text{ g/mol}$$

Due to the difficulty of obtaining precise temperature measurements, most molecular mass determinations using boiling point elevation or freezing point depression are accurate to only two or three significant digits.

Problem

17. The freezing point for water is lowered to $-0.390°C$ when 3.90 g of a nonvolatile molecular solute is dissolved in 475 g of water. Calculate the molecular mass of the solute.

17. 39.1 g/mol

---

16 Properties of Solutions
Chapter Review

Key Terms

boiling point
  elevation   *16·7*
colligative property *16·7*
concentrated
  solution   *16·4*
concentration   *16·4*
dilute solution   *16·4*
freezing point
  depression   *16·7*
Henry's law   *16·3*
immiscible   *16·2*
miscible   *16·2*
molal boiling point
  elevation constant
  (K_b)   *16·9*

molal freezing point
  depression constant
  (K_f)   *16·9*
molality (m)   *16·8*
molarity(M)   *16·4*
mole fraction   *16·8*
saturated solution   *16·2*
solubility   *16·2*
supersaturated
  solution   *16·3*
unsaturated   *16·2*

Chapter Summary

Changes in temperature and pressure of a system affect the solubility of a solute. The extent to which a gas dissolves in a liquid is proportional to the pressure of the gas in accordance with Henry's law. The solubility of a gas decreases with increasing temperature. Polar liquids tend to be soluble (miscible) in water whereas nonpolar liquids tend to be insoluble (immiscible). Generally the solubility of a solid in water increases with increasing temperature, but there are exceptions. The rate at which a solute dissolves is influenced by a number of factors, including the temperature of the solvent and the particle size of the solute.

    The relative amounts of solute and solvent in a solution are best described by using quantitative units, including molar concentration, percent composition, molal concentration, and mole fraction.

The effects in solution of a nonvolatile solute on the properties of the solvent are called colligative properties. Colligative properties include freezing point and vapor pressure lowering and boiling point elevation. In each case, the magnitude of the effect is directly proportional to the number of solute molecules or ions present and is independent of the type of particle. Each solvent has a characteristic molal boiling point elevation constant and molal freezing point depression constant. The colligative properties are useful for demonstrating dissociation of solutes in solution and in determining molecular masses.

Practice Questions and Problems

18. Name and distinguish between the two components of a solution. *16·1*

19. Explain why the dissolved component does not settle out of a solution. *16·1*

20. Name three factors that influence the rate at which a solute dissolves in a solvent. *16·1*

21. Define the terms solubility, saturated solution, and unsaturated solution. *16·2*

22. What mass of $AgNO_3$ can be dissolved in 250 g of water at 20°C? *16·2*

23. If a clear saturated solution of sodium nitrate is cooled, what change(s) might you observe? *16·2*

24. Explain the terms *miscible* and *immiscible*. *16·2*

25. State Henry's law. *16·3*

26. What is the effect of pressure on the solubility of gases in liquids? *16·3*

27. The solubility of methane, the major component of natural gas, in water at 20°C and 1.00 atm pressure is 0.026 g/L. If the temperature remains constant, what will the solubility of this gas be at the following pressures? *16·3*
  a. 0.60 atm   **b.** 1.80 atm

28. The solubility of a gas in water at 10°C and a pressure of 1.50 atm is 4.6×10^{-4} g/L. Calculate the pressure required to produce an aqueous solution at 10°C that contains 3.2×10^{-6} g/L of the same gas. *16·3*

29. Define the term *molarity*. *16·4*

30. Calculate the molarity of each of the following solutions. *16·4*
  a. 1.0 mol of KCl in 750 mL of solution
  b. 0.50 mol of $MgCl_2$ in 1.5 L of solution
  c. 5.85 g of NaCl in 2.00 L of solution
  d. 400 g of $CuSO_4$ in 4.00 L of solution
  e. 0.060 of $NaHCO_3$ in 1500 mL of solution

31. Calculate the number of moles and the number of grams of solute in each solution. *16·4*
  a. 1.0 L of 0.50M NaCl
  b. 500 mL of 2.0M KNO_3
  c. 250 mL of 0.10M $CaCl_2$
  d. 2.0 L of 0.30M Na_2SO_4

32. You have the following stock solutions available: 2.0M NaCl, 4.0M KNO_3, and 0.50M $MgSO_4$. Calculate the volumes you must dilute to make the following solutions. *16·5*
  a. 500 mL of 0.50M NaCl
  b. 2.0 L of 0.20M $MgSO_4$
  c. 50 mL of 0.20M KNO_3

33. A solution is made by diluting 150 mL of 0.120M $Fe(NO_3)_3$ solution with water to a final volume of 0.500 L. Calculate the molarity of $Fe(NO_3)_3$ in the diluted solution. *16·5*

34. Calculate the number of grams of solute required to make the following: *16·6*
  a. 2.5 L of normal saline solution (0.90% NaCl (m/v))
  b. 50 mL of 4.0% $MgCl_2$ (m/v)
  c. 500 mL of 2.0% glucose (m/v)
  d. 250 mL of 0.10% $MgSO_4$ (m/v)

35. What is the concentration in percent (m/v) of the following solutions? *16·6*
  a. 20 g KCl in 600 mL of solution
  b. 32 g $NaNO_3$ in 2.0 L of solution
  c. 75 g K_2SO_4 in 1500 mL of solution

36. Why does salt water evaporate more slowly than fresh water at the same temperature? *16·7*

37. Define *colligative property* and name all the colligative properties of solutions studied in this chapter. *16·7*

38. A solution with a nonvolatile solute has a lower vapor pressure than the pure solvent at the same temperature. Explain why. *16·7*

39. What is the boiling point of each solution? *16·7*
  a. 0.50 mol of glucose in 1000 g of H_2O
  b. 1.50 mol of NaCl in 1000g of H_2O

40. What effect does the addition of 1.00 mol of $CaCl_2$ to 1000 g of H_2O have on the freezing point of water? *16·7*

41. How much NaCl would have to be dissolved in 1000 g of water to raise the boiling point 2.0°C? *16·7*

42. Distinguish between a lM solution and a l m solution. *16·8*

43. Describe how you would prepare an aqueous solution that is 1.25 m in $Ba(NO_3)_2$. *16·8*

44. A solution is prepared by dissolving 2.50 g of K_2CrO_4 in 23.2 g of water. Calculate the molality of K_2CrO_4. *16·8*

45. How many kilograms of water must be added to 9.0 g of oxalic acid, $H_2C_2O_4$, to prepare a 0.025 m solution? *16·8*

46. A solution contains 50.0 g of carbon tetrachloride (CCl_4) and 50.0 g of chloroform ($CHCl_3$). Calculate the mole fraction of each component in the solution. *16·8*

47. A saturated solution of NaCl at 30°C has a molality of 6.25 m. What is the mole fraction and mass fraction of NaCl in the solution? *16·8*

48. A 0.50 molal solution of an unknown compound in water freezes at $-1.86°C$. Is the compound most likely to be molecular or ionic? Why? *16·9*

49. Determine the freezing points of these 0.10 m aqueous solutions. *16·9*
 a. K_2SO_4 **b.** $CsNO_3$ **c.** $Al(NO_3)_3$

50. Estimate the freezing point of a solution of 12.0 g of carbon tetrachloride dissolved in 750 g of benzene (which has a freezing point of 5.48 °C). *16·9*

51. A solution containing 16.9 g of a nonvolatile molecular compound in 250 g of water has a freezing point of $-0.744°C$. What is the molecular mass of the substance? *16·10*

Mastery Questions and Problems

52. Describe how you would prepare an aqueous solution of acetone, CH_3COCH_3, in which the mole fraction of acetone is 0.25. *16·8*

53. You are asked to make 1.50 L of 0.250M HNO_3 by diluting concentrated 16.0M HNO_3. What volume of the concentrated acid will be required to make the dilution? *16·5*

54. You are given a clear water solution containing KNO_3. How would you determine experimentally whether the solution is unsaturated, saturated, or supersaturated? *16·3*

55. Calculate the freezing point and the boiling point of a solution that contains 15.0 g of urea, CH_4N_2O, in 250 g of water. Urea is a covalently bonded compound. *16·9*

56. Calculate the mole fractions in a solution that is made of 25.0 g of ethyl alcohol, C_2H_5OH, and 40.0 g of water. *16·8*

57. Estimate the freezing point of an aqueous solution of 20.0 g of glucose, $C_6H_{12}O_6$, dissolved in 500.0 g of water. *16·7*

58. Plot a graph of solubility versus temperature for the three gases listed in Table 16·1. *16·3*

59. The solubility of KCl in water is 34.0 g of KCl/100 g of H_2O at 20°C. A warm solution containing 50.0 g of KCl in 130 g of H_2O is cooled to 20°C. *16·2*
 a. How many grams of KCl remain dissolved?
 b. How many grams came out of solution?

60. How many moles of ions are present when 0.10 mol of the following compounds are dissolved in water? *16·7*
 a. K_2SO_4 **c.** $Al_2(SO_4)_3$
 b. $Fe(NO_3)_3$ **d.** $NiSO_4$

61. Complete the following table for aqueous solutions of glucose, $C_6H_{12}O_6$. *16·4*

Mass Solute	Moles Solute	Volume of Solution	Molarity
12.5g	—	219 mL	—
—	1.08	—	0.519
—	—	1.62 L	1.08

62. A solution contains 26.5 g of NaCl in 75.0 g of H_2O at 20°C. Determine whether the solution is unsaturated, saturated, or supersaturated. (The solubility of NaCl at 20°C is 36.0 g/100 g H_2O.) *16·2*

63. An aqueous solution freezes at $-2.47°C$. What is its boiling point? *16·9*

64. Hydrogen peroxide is often sold commercially as a 3.0% (m/v) aqueous solution. *16·6*

a. If you buy a 250-mL bottle of 3.0% (m/v) H_2O_2, how many grams of hydrogen peroxide have you purchased?

b. What is the molarity of this solution?

65. How many grams of $NaNO_3$ will precipitate if a saturated solution of $NaNO_3$ in 200 g of H_2O at 50°C is cooled to 20°C? *16·2*

66. What is the molecular mass of a nondissociating compound if 5.76 g of the compound in 750 g of benzene gives a freezing point depression of 0.460°C? *16·10*

67. The molality of an aqueous solution of sugar, $C_{12}H_{22}O_{11}$, is 1.62 *m*. Calculate the mole fractions of sugar and water. *16·8*

68. Calculate the freezing and boiling point changes for a solution containing 12.0 g of naphthalene, $C_{10}H_8$, in 50.0 g of benzene. *16·9*

69. The solubility of sodium bicarbonate, $NaHCO_3$, in water at 20°C is 9.6 g/100 g of H_2O. What is the mole fraction of $NaHCO_3$ in a saturated solution? What is the molality of the solution? *16·8*

Review Questions and Problems

70. Explain each of the following facts.

a. Fish need oxygen to survive. Goldfish in a crowded bowl have a better chance of survival in cold water than in warm water.

b. Vinegar-and-oil salad dressing separates into two layers. (Vinegar is a mixture of acetic acid ($HC_2H_3O_2$) and water.)

c. Electronic instruments that can be damaged by moisture are often packed for shipment with small packets of anhydrous $CaSO_4$.

d. Finely ground sugar dissolves more quickly in a glass of water than does a large sugar cube.

e. It is dangerous to use electric appliances around the bathtub.

f. Adding more sugar to a glass of tea that already has crystals of sugar at the bottom doesn't make the tea taste any sweeter.

71. The solubility of hydrogen chloride gas in the polar solvent water is much greater than its solubility in the nonpolar solvent benzene. Why?

72. Discuss the effect that hydrogen-bonding has upon the boiling points of compounds with low formula mass.

73. When soap is shaken with water do you get a solution, a suspension, or a colloid? Explain.

74. Explain the following terms as applied to solutions.

a. solute   e. supersaturated
b. solvent   f. nonelectrolyte
c. saturated   g. weak electrolyte
d. unsaturated   h. strong electrolyte

75. Indicate by simple equations how the following substances ionize or dissociate in water.

a. NH_4Cl d. $HC_2H_3O_2$
b. $Cu(NO_3)_2$ e. Na_2SO_4
c. HNO_3 f. $HgCl_2$

76. What relationship exists between surface tension and the intermolecular attractions in a liquid?

Challenging Questions and Problems

77. One way in which the solubility of a compound can be expressed is by moles of compound that will dissolve in 1 kg of water. Solubility depends on temperature. Plot a graph of the solubility of potassium nitrate, KNO_3, from the following data.

Temperature, °C	Solubility, mol/kg
0	1.61
20	2.80
40	5.78
60	11.20
80	16.76
100	24.50

From your graph estimate:

a. the solubility of KNO_3 at 76°C and at 33°C.

b. the temperature at which its solubility is 17.6 mol/kg water.

c. the temperature at which the solubility is 4.24 mol/kg water.

78. An excess of zinc added to 800 mL of a hydrochloric acid solution evolves 1.21 L of hydrogen

gas measured over water at 21°C and 747.5 mm Hg. What is the molarity of the acid? The vapor pressure of water at 21°C is 18.6 mm Hg.

79. How many milliliters of 0.500*M* $Cr_2(SO_4)_3$ solution are needed to react completely with 300 mL of 0.100*M* $BaCl_2$?

$$3BaCl_2 \; (aq) + Cr_2(SO_4)_3 \; (aq) \longrightarrow$$
$$2CrCl_3 \; (aq) + 3BaSO_4 \; (s)$$

80. How many milliliters of 2.50*M* HNO_3 contain enough nitric acid to dissolve an old copper penny with a mass of 3.94 g?

$$3Cu + 8HNO_3 \longrightarrow 3Cu(NO_3)_2 + 2NO + 4H_2O$$

81. A 250-mL sample of Na_2SO_4 is reacted with an excess of $BaCl_2$. If 5.28 g of $BaSO_4$ is precipitated, what is the molarity of the Na_2SO_4 solution?

82. The table below lists the most abundant ions in sea water and their molal concentrations.

Ion	Molality
Chloride	0.568
Sodium	0.482
Magnesium	0.057
Sulfate	0.028
Calcium	0.011
Potassium	0.010
Bicarbonate	0.002

Calculate the mass, in grams, of each component contained in 5.00 L of sea water. The density of sea water is 1.024 g/mL.

Research Projects

1. Describe the chemical composition of sea water. Devise a method for extracting a valuable element or compound.

2. Trace the development of chromatography starting with the work of Mikhail Tswett.

3. Compare two types of chromatography such as high-performance liquid chromatography and gas chromatography.

4. What techniques are used to measure levels of trace nutrients in foods?

5. What are the major sources of water pollution? What steps have been taken to control these sources?

6. Make a diagram of how ground water becomes contaminated. How pure is the ground water in your area? What steps have been taken to safeguard its purity?

7. What techniques are used to measure the levels of contaminants in drinking water?

8. What is the role of oxygen in water pollution, and what effects do temperature inversions have on water pollution?

9. What effects do combinations of solutes such as KCl and NaCl have on the colligative properties of solutions?

10. Compare the effect of several solutes on the vapor pressure of water.

Readings and References

Blaustein, Elliot H. *Your Environment and You: Understanding the Pollution Problems*. Dobbs Ferry, NY: Oceana, 1974.

Cagliotti, Luciano, and trans. by Mirella Giaconi. *The Two Faces of Chemistry*. Cambridge, MA: MIT Press, 1983.

Eagles, Juanita Archibald, Orrea Florence Pye, and Clara Mae Taylor. *Mary Swartz Rose, 1874–1941: Pioneer in Nutrition*. New York: Teachers College Press, 1979.

Epstein, Samuel S., Lester O. Brown, and Carl Pope. *Hazardous Waste in America*. San Francisco: Sierra Club, 1982.

Maugh, Thomas H. (II). "Laying Waste in America." *Science Year* (1984), pp. 83–97.

Stark, Norman. *The Formula Book*. New York: Avon Books, 1979.

17 Reaction Rates and Equilibrium

Chapter Planning Guide

Section			Demonstrations and Experiments	Resource Materials
17·1	Collision Theory	C*		Objectives Worksheet 17, SPB
				Skillsheet 17, SPB
				Teaching Diagram 24
17·2	Reaction Rates	C	Exp 35 Factors Affecting Chemical Reaction Rate	
			Dem 17·1 Temperature and Reaction Rate	
			Dem 17·2 Particle Size and Reaction Rate	
			Dem 17·3 Catalysis	
17·A	The Contact Process	E		
17·3	Rate Laws	H	Exp 36 The Clock Reaction, LM	Prelab 36, SPB
			Dem 17·4 Old Nassau	
17·4	Reaction Mechanisms	O		Quiz 17·1
17·5	Entropy	C		
17·6	Entropy Calculations	H		
17·7	Spontaneous Reactions	C	Dem 17·5 Spontaneous Reaction	
17·8	Free Energy	C		
17·9	Free Energy Calculations	H		
17·10	Reversible Reactions	C	Dem 17·6 Reversible Reaction	Quiz 17·2
17·B	Photochemical Smog	E		
17·11	Equilibrium Constants	C		
17·12	Le Châtelier's Principle	C	Exp 37 Disturbing Equilibrium: Le Châtelier's Principle, LM	Prelab 37, SPB
			Dem 17·7 Temperature and Le Châtelier's Principle	Quiz 17·3
			Dem 17·8 Concentration and Le Châtelier's Principle	Reviewsheet 17, SPB
				Chapter 17 Test
				Auto Exhaust and Local Air Pollution, ICT 17
17·C	Mining the Riches of the Atmosphere	E		
*C = Core, O = Optional			LM = Laboratory Manual	SPB = Skills Practice Book
E = Enrichment, H = Honors				ICT = Issues in Chem. Tech.

Chapter Objectives

Having studied this chapter and done the problems, the student should be able to:

1. Relate the ideas of activation energy and the activated complex to the rate of a reaction. *17·1*

2. Use the collision theory to explain how the rate of a chemical reaction is influenced by the temperature, concentration, particle size of reactants, and catalysts. *17·2*

3. Given the order of each reactant, write the rate law for the reaction. *17·3*

4. Given a potential energy diagram for a reaction, discuss the reaction mechanism for the reaction. *17·4*

5. Relate changes in entropy to a change of state, a change in temperature, and a change in the number of product particles compared to reactant particles. *17·5*

6. Use standard entropies to calculate the change in entropy of a reaction. *17·6*

7. Characterize spontaneous and nonspontaneous reactions. *17·7*

8. Explain how changes in energy and changes in entropy both influence the spontaneity of a reaction. *17·7*

9. Distinguish between exergonic and endergonic reactions. *17·8*

10. Determine the spontaneity of a reaction by calculating the change in free energy of the reaction. *17·9*

11. Define chemical equilibrium in terms of a reversible reaction. *17·10*

12. Write the expression for the equilibrium constant of a reaction, and calculate its value from given experimental data. *17·11*

13. Predict the equilibrium position of a reaction from a given K_{eq} value. *17·11*

14. State Le Châtelier's principle, and use it to predict the changes in the equilibrium position due to changes in concentration, temperature, and pressure. *17·12*

Teaching Suggestions

17·1 Collision Theory

17·2 Reaction Rates

Take time to explain the collision theory thoroughly. It is important for the students to understand that when one substance is mixed with another, the two substances do not react on a macroscopic basis, but react as their individual particles (atoms, molecules, or ions) come together. The factors which affect how these particles come together are the factors which influence the rate of the reaction. Collision theory explains these factors.

Use the collision theory as the unifying concept for this chapter. Rather than have the students memorize information, try to get them to understand why the various principles and relationships hold true. Most of these are easily explained in terms of the collision theory.

Emphasize the importance of relying on two-particle collisions in explaining any reaction mechanism. Random simultaneous collisions of three or more particles are so improbable as to be unimportant.

Experiment 35 *Factors Affecting the Rate of a Chemical Reaction* is designed to reinforce the concepts learned in Section 17·2. It is written in such a way that it could easily be performed as a series of demonstrations, with the students observing the results and then answering the questions. **Demonstrations 17·1** *Temperature and Reaction Rate* and **17·2** *Particle Size and Reaction Rate* are alternatives.

Another approach is to do **Experiment 36** *The Clock Reaction* to see the temperature and concentration relationship, discuss Sections 17·1 and 17·2, and then do parts B, C, and D of **Experiment 35** as demonstrations.

When discussing catalysis, be sure to do **Demonstration 17·3** *Catalysis* as a dramatic example of the effect of a catalyst on the reaction rate.

17·3 Rate Laws

In the previous sections the students learned that the concentration of each reactant has an effect on the rate of a reaction. In this section that effect is stated as a quantitative relationship. **Experiment 36** uses a discovery type approach in studying the effect of temperature and concentration on reaction rate. It is most appropriately done before starting Section 17·3. **Demonstration 17·4** *Old Nassau* is a variation of the clock reaction.

Emphasize that the order of a reaction must be determined experimentally. It cannot be easily deduced from the coefficients of the balanced equation.

The importance of the order of reactions can best be shown by looking at the effect of doubling the concentration of one reactant. With a zero order reaction the rate is independent of the concentration of the reactant. Doubling the concentration has no effect on the reaction rate. With a first order reaction, the rate is directly proportional to the concentration of the reactant. Doubling the concentration doubles the reaction rate. With a second order reaction, the rate is directly proportional to the *square* of the concentration of the reactant. Doubling the concentration increases the rate by four times (2^2).

Once the students understand how the doubling of concentration affects the rate for each order of reaction, they can analyze experimental data to decide on reaction order. They need only look at the data to see what effect doubling the concentration has had on the reaction rate.

17·4 Reaction Mechanism

The key point here is that even the most complex reactions occur as a series of simple steps. Each of these steps usually involves the collision of no more than two particles.

Try to get across the point that even "simple" reactions may have many steps in their mechanisms. Have them come up with possible hypothetical mechanisms for common "simple" reactions. This activity will help them conceptualize bond breaking and forming. You might have them progress through this series:

$$Ag^+(aq) + Cl^-(aq) \longrightarrow AgCl\ (s)$$
$$C + O_2 \longrightarrow CO_2$$
$$2H_2 + O_2 \longrightarrow 2H_2O$$
$$CH_4 + 2O_2 \longrightarrow CO_2 + 2H_2O$$

17·5   Entropy

There are two major tendencies that drive chemical reactions. The tendency toward minimum energy has already been discussed. The other driving force is the tendency toward disorder. Entropy is the term we use for the disorder of a system. The students are already aware that the things in their environment will naturally become disordered, if given enough time. They will have little trouble understanding the concept of entropy.

Using the guidelines given in this section, go over examples of common physical and chemical changes. Ask whether entropy increases or decreases in these changes.

17·6   Entropy Calculations

The students will learn how to calculate changes in entropy most easily if you do examples for them. Show where Table 17·1 is and explain how to use it.

17·7   Spontaneous Reactions

Stress that we can now explain why certain chemical reactions occur spontaneously and others do not. All spontaneous processes have only two driving forces: the tendency toward minimum energy (exothermic reactions), and the tendency toward maximum entropy. When the change from reactants to products is favored by both tendencies, the reaction is very likely to occur. When the change from reactants to products is opposed by both tendencies, the reaction is unlikely to occur.

In many cases one tendency will favor the formation of products, while the other favors the reactants staying unchanged. In this case the direction of the reaction is decided by the relative strengths of the tendencies. It is unlikely that the reaction will proceed 100% in either direction. That is, a balance is reached between the two. This explains how and why equilibrium is established in chemical reaction. Be sure to emphasize this point, since you will need to refer back to it while covering Section 17·10.

You can show an example of a spontaneous reaction by doing **Demonstration 17·5** *Spontaneous Reaction.* Stress that while most spontaneous reactions are exothermic, not all are. If the tendency of a reaction to proceed toward a state of maximum entropy is strong enough, it may overcome the opposing tendency of the reaction to proceed toward a state of minimum energy. Such is the case in the melting of ice. The process is endothermic and spontaneous. Explain that this is due to the large entropy increase in going from the solid (ice) to the liquid (water). This offsets the absorption of heat.

17·8   Free Energy

17·9   Free Energy Calculations

The concept of free energy is often confusing. Take time to go over it carefully and develop it slowly.

These sections discuss free energy in terms of work available or done. Many students may not know what is meant by work. Point out that work is what is accomplished when a force acts through a distance. For example, work is done *on* a gas if it is compressed, since a force must be applied to make it into a smaller volume. Work is done *by* a gas as it expands outward. For instance, the rapidly expanding gases in an explosion can exert very large forces on objects which happen to be in their path. Work is done in accelerating molecules from low speeds to high speeds. Thus, work is done on molecules when their temperature is raised. Work is done whenever attracting particles are moved away from each other, as when chemical bonds are broken. In all cases work involves energy. Work has the same units as energy.

Emphasize that free energy is a term that refers to more than just the enthalpy change, ΔH, that occurs in a chemical reaction. Free energy combines the energy change, ΔH, with the change in randomness that occurs in a chemical reaction. Point out that ΔH and ΔS are usually assumed to be constant with changes in temperature. Therefore, the contribution to the free energy from the $T\Delta S$ term comes mostly from the temperature itself.

Be sure the students understand the importance of G in determining whether a reaction will be spontaneous or not. Discuss why the following statements are true:

When ΔG is negative, the reaction is spontaneous.

When ΔG is positive, the reaction is nonspontaneous.

When ΔH and ΔS are both positive, the reaction is nonspontaneous at low temperatures and becomes spontaneous as the temperature is raised.

When ΔH and ΔS are both negative, the reaction is spontaneous at low temperatures and becomes nonspontaneous as the temperature is raised.

Follow up this section with **Demonstration 17·5** if it has not already been done.

17·10   Reversible Reactions

Reversible reactions occur when the reaction which favors the tendency toward minimum energy is opposed by the reaction which favors the tendency towards maximum entropy. Emphasize that when these two processes are in

opposition, they reach a balance which we call equilibrium. This state of equilibrium is dynamic. That is, these microscopic processes continue even though we see no macroscopic changes. **Demonstration 17·6** *Reversible Reaction* is appropriate here.

The point should be made that the use of = in a chemical equation can be misleading. Certainly the reactants do not equal the products, as they are different substances. This is why double arrows are often used in an equilibrium equation. At first some students will make the mistaken assumption that at equilibrium the amounts of reactants and products must be equal. Stress that the term *equilibrium* does not imply that anything in particular must be equal, except for the rates of the opposing reactions.

Make sure the students understand that when a catalyst lowers the activation energy for one reaction, it also lowers it for the opposing reaction. Thus a catalyst does not affect the equilibrium state, only how fast it is reached.

17·11 Equilibrium Constants

The main concept in this section is that whenever a chemical system reaches equilibrium, the reactants and products have a fixed numerical relationship. That relationship is stated in the equilibrium constant expression.

Even though the concentrations of the individual reactants and products may vary over a very wide range, their numerical relationship does not. Thus, K_{eq} is truly a constant. Stress that each chemical system has its own constant. Point out that the balance in equilibrium systems is very sensitive to temperature changes, however. Thus a specific value of K_{eq} is good only at a specified temperature. At any other temperature it will be different.

Point out that the only quantities which can go into the brackets, [ ], used in the equilibrium law expression are concentrations (or quantities like partial pressures which are related to concentrations). Substances for which a concentration cannot be stated or for which the concentration is unvarying are usually dropped out of the equilibrium law expression. In general, the concentrations of solids, of pure liquids, and of solvent are usually incorporated in the equilibrium constant.

The value of the equilibrium constant can be used to predict the position of equilibrium. Since the constant takes the form of products/reactants, the larger the value of K_{eq}, the more products are favored. Conversely, the smaller the value of K_{eq}, the more reactants are favored.

17·12 Le Châtelier's Principle

Introduce Le Châtelier's Principle by either **Demonstration 17·7** *Temperature and Le Châtelier's Principle,* or **Demonstration 17·8** *Concentration and Le Châtelier's Principle.* Identify the substances in the system and write the equation for the equilibrium reaction. Then change the

system to apply stress and note the response of the system. Point out that the system behaves according to Le Châtelier's principle.

Next, state Le Châtelier's principle. Give examples of stresses being applied to various systems. Emphasize that the most important changes we can impose on an equilibrium system are to add or subtract products or reactants, heat or cool the system, change the concentrations of the reactants and/or products, and raise or lower the pressure on the system. Take each change, one at a time, and predict the response of the system. As the students become more competent, have them make their own predictions.

As a follow-up, do the remainder of **Demonstrations 17·3, 17·4,** and **17·5.** Conclude with **Experiment 37** *Disturbing Equilibrium: Le Châtelier's Principle.*

Demonstrations

17·1 Temperature and Reaction Rate

Concept: Increasing temperature increases reaction rate.

Materials: 3 effervescent antacid tablets, 3 flasks, ice, hot water, safety goggles, timer with second hand.

Procedure: 1. Put ice, room temperature water, and hot water in three different flasks. 2. Add a tablet to each flask. 3. Record the time for each reaction to go to completion. Ice is the slowest and hot water the fastest.

17·2 Particle Size and Reaction Rate

Concept: Smaller particle size increases reaction rate.

Materials: corn starch, gas burner, matches, watch glass, spatula, safety goggles.

Procedure: 1. Pile the starch on a watch glass and try to light it. 2. Dust the starch into the burner flame with a spatula. 3. Note the difference in reaction: the starch dust flares up. (This is more dramatic in a darkened room.) **Caution:** *Stand back from the burner flame in step 2.*

17·3 Catalysis

Concept: Catalysts increase reaction rate.

Materials: 300 mL of 3% hydrogen peroxide (H_2O_2), 0.1 g of manganese dioxide (MnO_2), 500-mL flask, spatula, safety goggles, tray.

Procedure: 1. Write the equation for the decomposition of hydrogen peroxide: $2H_2O_2 \rightarrow 2H_2O + O_2$. 2. Point out

that this reaction occurs very slowly at room temperature. The decomposition is inevitable, but will take many months. 3. State that this reaction can be catalyzed by yeast, blood, or manganese dioxide. When catalyzed, the reaction proceeds very quickly at room temperature. 4. Pour the hydrogen peroxide into a *clean* flask and place on the tray. 5. Drop the manganese dioxide into the flask and stand back. 6. Oxygen gas is generated in the flask. 7. Show that the manganese dioxide is still present. If it were dried and weighed, we would find that none has been consumed. 8. If you plan to repeat this demonstration, use a clean flask.

17·4 Old Nassau

Concept: Increasing the concentration of a reactant increases the reaction rate.

Materials: three 100-mL graduated cylinders, three 400-mL beakers, stop watch or clock with a second hand, stirring rod, safety goggles, and the following solutions:

Solution *A*: 5 g of potassium iodate (KIO₃) dissolved in 300 mL of water.

Solution *B*: 1 g of soluble starch dissolved in 150 mL boiling water, with 5 g of sodium bisulfite (NaHSO₃) added when cool, and water added to make 300 mL.

Solution *C*: 1 g of mercury(II) chloride in 300 mL of water.

Procedure: 1. Measure 50 mL of each solution into the three graduated cylinders. 2. Instruct a student to begin timing the reaction as soon as Solution *C* is added and to stop when a black color appears. 3. Add Solution *B* to a beaker. 4. Add Solution *C*, and then *immediately* add Solution *A*. 5. Stir rapidly. The solution turns orange (mercury iodide) and then black (starch and iodine). 6. Record the time required for the color change. 7. Repeat two more times, using 40 mL and then 60 mL of Solution *C*. 8. Emphasize how increasing the concentration of reactants increases the rate of reaction. **Caution:** *Mercury(II) chloride is highly toxic.*

17·5 Spontaneous Reactions

Concept: Spontaneous reactions are exothermic and/or maximize entropy.

Materials: 3 g of potassium permanganate (KMnO₄), glass plate, 1 mL of glycerol, dropper or small beaker, safety goggles, stirring rod.

Procedure: **Caution:** *use a fume hood. Wear goggles. Potassium permanganate is an irritant. Students should stand well back.* 1. Pile the potassium permanganate on the glass plate. 2. Pour the glycerol over the crystals. 3. The reaction starts slowly at first, producing white smoke. Eventually a purple flame appears, and sparks shoot from the mixture. A dark solid remains after the reaction.

The primary reaction is:
$$14KMnO_4 + 4C_3H_5(OH)_3 \rightarrow$$
$$7K_2CO_3 + 7Mn_2O_3 + 5CO_2 + 16H_2O$$
4. Discuss the fact that a spontaneous reaction proceeds from reactants to products without an external energy source. This reaction is exothermic and has proceeded in the direction of maximum entropy: Four products have formed from two reactants.

17·6 Reversible Reaction

Concept: Some reactions are reversible.

Materials: 100 mL of 0.1*M* iron(III) chloride (FeCl₃), 100 mL of 0.1*M* ammonium thiocyanate (NH₄SCN), four 250-mL beakers, 1-L beaker, four stirring rods, safety goggles.

Procedure: 1. Mix 50 mL each of the iron chloride and ammonium thiocyanate, and stir. 2. The solution should turn orange-yellow. If it does not, add more ammonium thiocyanate. 3. Add iron chloride until the solution turns red (from the iron/thiocyanate complex, FeSCN). 4. Add ammonium thiocyanide to restore the orange-yellow color. **Caution:** *Iron(III) chloride is an irritant.*

17·7 Temperature and Le Châtelier's Principle

Concept: Increasing temperature shifts the equilibrium position of an exothermic reaction to the left.

Materials: 3 copper turnings (3 g), 10 mL of 6*M* nitric acid (HNO₃), 3 large test tubes, 2 solid stoppers, 1 one-hole stopper fitted with delivery tube and rubber hose, tongs, two 600-mL beakers, ice, water, ring stand, ring, wire gauze, gas burner, matches, dry ice/acetone slush, safety goggles.

Procedure: 1. Place the copper turnings in a test tube. 2. Add the nitric acid. 3. Insert the one-hole stopper assembly into the test tube. 4. Fill the other two test tubes with the brown gas that has formed. 5. When their brown color is the same as in the reacting test tube, stopper the two tubes. **Caution:** *Use a fume hood. Nitric acid is corrosive.* 6. Set up an ice bath and a boiling water bath in the two beakers. 7. Place one test tube in the ice bath and the other in the boiling water. 8. After a few minutes, remove the tubes and compare. The cooled tube is light brown and the heated tube is dark brown. 9. Place the tubes in the dry ice/acetone slush and observe the loss of color. 10. Move the tubes back and forth between the water baths to demonstrate that the equilibrium shifts are reversible. The reversible reaction is: $2NO_2 \rightleftharpoons N_2O_4$ + energy. Nitrogen dioxide is red-brown, while dinitrogen tetroxide is light yellow or colorless. Energy is a product of the reaction. When energy is *added* to the system, the added energy is absorbed to form more nitrogen dioxide. **Caution:** *Dry ice can cause frostbite. Use tongs! Acetone is extremely flammable. Keep away from sources of heat.*

17·8 Concentration and Le Châtelier's Principle

Concept: Concentration changes will shift the equilibrium point of a reaction.

Materials: 40 mL of $0.1M$ potassium chromate (K_2CrO_4), 40 mL of $0.1M$ potassium dichromate $(K_2Cr_2O_7)$, 100 mL of $1M$ hydrochloric acid (HCl), 100 mL of $1M$ sodium hydroxide (NaOH), 100 mL of $0.1M$ barium nitrate $(Ba(NO_3)_2)$, three 150-mL beakers, four small beakers, safety goggles.

Procedure: 1. In each of the 4 small beakers, mix 10 mL each of potassium chromate and potassium dichromate. The equilibrium equation is:
$$2H^+(aq) + 2CrO_4^{2-}(aq) \rightleftharpoons Cr_2O_7^{2-}(aq) + H_2O(l)$$
The chromate ion CrO_4^{2-} is yellow. The dichromate ion $Cr_2O_7^{2-}$ is orange. 2. Add hydrochloric acid to one of the beakers until the solution turns bright orange. (The H^+ ions shift the equilibrium to the *right*.) 3. Add sodium hydroxide to a second beaker until the solution turns yellow. (The removal of H^+ ions shifts the equilibrium to the *left*.) 4. Show that these changes are reversible by adding hydrochloric acid to the yellow solution and sodium hydroxide to the orange solution. 5. Add sodium hydroxide to a third beaker until the solution turns yellow. 6. Add a volume of barium nitrate equal to the volume of the solution in the beaker. 7. A white precipitate forms and establishes a new equilibrium:
$$BaCrO_4(s) \rightleftharpoons Ba^{2+}(aq) + CrO_4^{2-}(aq)$$
8. Add hydrochloric acid to the remaining beaker until the solution turns orange. 9. Add an equal volume of barium nitrate. No precipitate forms. 10. Slowly add hydrochloric acid to the beaker which contains the precipitate until the precipitate disappears. 11. The precipitate reappears when sodium hydroxide is added. 12. The disappearance of the precipitate is another example of Le Châtelier's principle. The addition of hydrogen ion converts the chromate ion to dichromate ion. The solid barium chromate breaks down in an attempt to replace the missing chromate ion. If enough hydrogen ion is added, the barium chromate is eventually consumed. **Caution:** *Potassium chromate is a suspected mutagen and is corrosive. Hydrochloric acid and sodium hydroxide are also corrosive. Potassium dichromate and barium nitrate are toxic.*

Audiovisual Resources

Chemistry: Reaction Rates and Equilibrium (F, V) Coronet, 1983, 23 min. (Use with Sections 17·2, 17·7, or 17·10.) Discusses the factors that affect reaction rates, introduces chemical equilibrium and explains the principles of exothermic and endothermic reactions.

Energy and Rockets: Exothermic Reaction (F, V) Media Guild, 1981, 24 min. (Use with Sections 17·7 and 17·8.) Illustrates the relationship between chemical bonding energies and rocket propulsion.

Entropy and Free Energy: Why Chemical Reactions Occur (FS) Prentice-Hall Media, 1972. (Use with Sections 17·5, 17·6, 17·7, 17·8, and 17·9.) Presents the concept of entropy, discusses the entropy contribution to free energy and shows entropy and free energy calculations.

Enzymes: Regulators of Body Chemistry (2 FS) Human Relations Media, 1982, 18–20 min. each. (Use with Section 17·2.) Explains how enzymes work, using two models of enzyme action and discusses the role of enzymes in living systems.

Mars: Chemistry Looks for Life (F, V) Chem Study, 1978, 26 min. (Use with Sections 17·1 and 17·2.) Discusses chemical reaction kinetics in the context of the Viking mission's search for life on Mars.

Reaction Rates: Molecules in Motion (9 FS) Bergwall Productions, 1980, 12–15 min. each. (Use with Section 17·2.) Illustrates different reaction rates using familiar situations.

Answers to End of Chapter Questions and Problems

Practice Questions and Problems

17. Reactions require collisions between molecules with sufficient energy to break and form bonds.

18. No. The collision must have sufficient energy to break and form bonds.

19. The number of atoms, ions, or molecules that react in a given time to form products.

20. a. usually speeds up a reaction **b.** speeds up a reaction **c.** speeds up a reaction **d.** slows down a reaction

21. A catalyst increases the rate of spontaneous reactions by providing a reaction mechanism with a lower activation energy.

22. c.

23. Gas and oxygen mix readily but do not have enough energy to react at room temperature. The flame raises the temperature and energy of collision, and the reaction rate is increased. The heat released by the reaction maintains the high temperature and the reaction continues spontaneously.

24. a. the proportionality constant relating the concentrations of the reactants to the reaction rate **b.** reaction rate proportional to the concentration of one reactant **c.** an equation relating the reaction rate to the concentrations of the reactants

25. Rate $= k$ [NO] [O$_3$]

26. 100 minutes

27. a. converts reactants to products in a single step **b.** a product of one reaction that immediately becomes a reactant in a second reaction **c.** the sequence of elementary reactions of a complex reaction

28.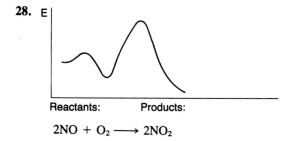

Reactants: Products:

$$2NO + O_2 \longrightarrow 2NO_2$$

29. A measure of the disorder of a system.

30. Unfavorable.

31. a. completed jigsaw puzzle **b.** 50 mL of ice **c.** sodium chloride crystals **d.** house

32. a. higher entropy **b.** lower entropy **c.** higher entropy **d.** lower entropy

33. 254.7 J/(K $\times$ mol)

34. 0.7 J/(K $\times$ mol S)

35. Spontaneous reactions yield the products under the stated conditions. The spontaneous reaction chosen might be an oxidation–reduction reaction or an acid–base reaction.

36. Change in heat content, change in entropy.

37. No. Endothermic reactions that have an increase in entropy may be spontaneous if the entropy increase is great enough.

38. No. Spontaneous chemical reactions may be slow if the activation energy is high, as in the rusting of iron or other types of corrosion.

39. The potential energy in a system that can become available to do work.

40. Endergonic: free energy is absorbed and the reaction is nonspontaneous. Exergonic: free energy is released and the reaction is spontaneous.

41. A flame or ignition wire provides sufficient energy for activation. Once started, the spontaneous reaction can proceed rapidly.

42. 130.3 kJ/mol; nonspontaneous

43. a. 98.1 kJ/mol; nonspontaneous
b. -1457.7 kJ/mol; spontaneous
c. 514.2 kJ/ mol; nonspontaneous
d. 66.04 kJ/ mol; nonspontaneous

44. Reactants are forming products and products are forming reactants at the same time.

45. The rate of formation of products from reactants and the rate of formation of reactants from products are equal.

46. The rates are equal.

47. a. $K_{eq} = \dfrac{[H_2] \times [Br_2]}{[HBr]^2}$ **b.** $K_{eq} = \dfrac{[SO_2]^2 \times [O_2]}{[SO_3]^2}$
c. $K_{eq} = \dfrac{[CO] \times [H_2O]}{[CO_2] \times [H_2]}$ **d.** $K_{eq} = \dfrac{[H_2O]^6 \times [NO]^4}{[NH_3]^4 \times [O_2]^5}$

48. a. $K_{eq} = \dfrac{[CH_4] \times [H_2S]^2}{[H_2]^4 \times [CS_2]}$ **b.** $K_{eq} = \dfrac{[PCl_3] \times [Cl_2]}{[PCl_5]}$
c. $K_{eq} = \dfrac{[NO_2]^2}{[NO]^2 \times [O_2]}$ **d.** $K_{eq} = \dfrac{[H_2] \times [CO_2]}{[CO] \times [H_2O]}$

49. 1.60×10^{-3}

50. 0.786

51. a. favorable **b.** slightly favorable **c.** highly unfavorable

52. A system in dynamic equilibrium changes to relieve the stress applied to it. Carbonated drinks in closed containers have achieved a state of dynamic equilibrium between the carbon dioxide in the liquid and in the vapor. When opened, carbon dioxide leaves the vapor. Carbon dioxide from the liquid goes into the vapor to try to re-establish equilibrium, but is lost.

53. Only in reversible reactions that involve gaseous reactants and/or products.

54. a. increase in products **b.** increase in products **c.** increase in products **d.** decrease in reactants **e.** does not affect equilibrium

55. a. increase in reactants **b.** increase in products **c.** does not affect equilibrium **d.** decrease in reactants **e.** decrease in reactants

Mastery Questions and Problems

56. c.

57. 25 kJ

58.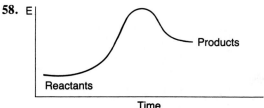

For exothermic reactions, the activation energy must be less than or equal to the total energy change.

59. a. Fanning the campfire increases the oxygen level, increasing the reaction rate. **b.** Small particles have a larger surface area. Molecular collisions and the reaction rate are increased. **c.** Powdered MnO_2 has a large surface area with properties that make it a catalyst.

60.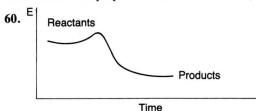

61. a. yes **b.** yes **c.** no **d.** yes

62. a. increase in products **b.** decrease in products **c.** decrease in products

63. $K_{eq} = 0.659$

64. a. $K_{eq} = \dfrac{[ICl]^2}{[I_2][Cl_2]}$ **b.** $K_{eq} = \dfrac{[NO]^2[O_2]}{[NO_2]^2}$

c. $K_{eq} = \dfrac{[SO_3]^2}{[SO_2]^2[O_2]}$ **d.** $K_{eq} = \dfrac{[PCl_5]}{[Cl_2][PCl_3]}$

65. Increasing pressure reduces volume and increases density.

66. Rate $= k[NO]^2$; Rate $= k[N_2O_2][O_2]$

67. a. $1.22 \times 10^{-4} \dfrac{mol}{L \times s}$ **b.** $1.94 \times 10^{-4} \dfrac{mol}{L \times s}$

68. a. IO^- **b.** yes **c.** two **d.** the first reaction **e.** $2H_2O_2 \rightarrow 2H_2O + O_2$

69. The reaction is never spontaneous if the entropy decreases. The reaction is endothermic because both absorb free energy.

70. The reaction is slow (activation energy is high).

71. A catalyst will help establish equilibrium more quickly, but it does not change the equilibrium position.

72. $-89.8 \dfrac{J}{K \times mol}$

73. a. increases **b.** unchanged **c.** decreases **d.** unchanged

Review Questions and Problems

74. a. fluoride ion (anion) **b.** copper(II) ion (cation) **c.** phosphide ion (anion) **d.** hydrogen ion (cation) **e.** sodium ion (cation) **f.** iodide ion (anion) **g.** oxide ion (anion) **h.** magnesium ion (cation)

75. Crystalline substances have a regular, repeating pattern of atoms, ions, or molecules in three dimensions. Amorphous substance have an irregular arrangements of molecules.

76. Solid potassium chloride is an ionic compound of K^+ and Cl^-, not of KCl molecules. Each ion is surrounded by 6 ions of opposite charge in a simple cubic unit cell crystal.

77. a. $CaCl_2$ **b.** Al_2S_3 **c.** $Mg(NO_3)_2$ **d.** $Al_2(CO_3)_3$ **e.** $Ba(OH)_2$ **f.** NH_4NO_3 **g.** K_2SO_4 **h.** $AlPO_4$

78. a. sodium perchlorate, ClO_4^- **b.** potassium permanganate, MnO_4^- **c.** calcium phosphate, PO_4^{3-} **d.** magnesium carbonate, CO_3^{2-} **e.** sodium sulfate, SO_4^{2-} **f.** potassium dichromate, $Cr_2O_7^{2-}$

79. a. $1s^2\,2s^2\,2p^6\,3s^2\,3p^6\,3d^{10}\,4s^2\,4p^2$ · Ge ·
b. $1s^2\,2s^2\,2p^6\,3s^2\,3p^6\,4s^2$ · Ca ·
c. $1s^2\,2s^2\,2p^4$:Ö:
d. $1s^2\,2s^2\,2p^6\,3s^2\,3p^6$:Är:
e. $1s^2\,2s^2\,2p^6\,3s^2\,3p^6\,3d^{10}\,4s^2\,4p^5$:Br·
f. $1s^2\,2s^2\,2p^6\,3s^2\,3p^3$:P·

80. a. Li^+ :Br:⁻ **b.** :Cl:⁻ Al^{3+} :Cl:⁻
:Cl:⁻
c. :F:⁻ Mg^{2+} :F:⁻ **d.** Na^+ :S:²⁻ Na^+

81. a. $1s^2\,2s^2\,2p^6\,3s^2\,3p^6$:Ca:²⁺
b. $1s^2$ Li:⁺
c. $1s^2\,2s^2\,2p^6\,3s^2\,3p^6\,3d^{10}\,4s^2\,4p^6$:Br:⁻
d. $1s^2\,2s^2\,2p^6\,3s^2\,3p^6$:S:²⁻

82. Positive ions: **b, e, f, g, h,** and **j.** Negative ions: **a, c, d,** and **i.**

83. Crystalline solids, high melting points, insulators when solid but conductors when molten, not malleable or ductile, soluble in water.

Challenging Questions and Problems

84. Give the person pure oxygen to breathe. Warm the oxygen. Encourage rapid deep breaths.

85. The additional H^+ reacts with the OH^-, shifting the reaction towards more products. As a result, more of the reactant, tooth enamel, is broken down.

17 Reaction Rates and Equilibrium

Chapter Preview

Sections 17·3, 17·4, 17·6, and 17·9 are appropriate for honors students.

Three questions can be asked about any single chemical reaction. Will the reaction go? How far will it go? How fast will it go? Answers to all these questions depend on the energy available in a chemical system and the energy required for a reaction to take place.

17·1 Collision Theory

How fast will a chemical reaction go? *The **reaction rate** is the number of atoms, ions, or molecules that react in a given time to form products.* Reactions proceed at different rates. The conversion of sodium metal to sodium hydroxide occurs rapidly at room temperature. The conversion of iron to iron(III) oxide (rust) occurs more slowly. Collision theory provides an explanation for why reactions proceed at different rates.

Most chemical reactions involve the transfer of atoms from one molecule to another. Thus contact between the reactants is very important. For any reaction involving two or more reactants, the reacting particles must collide. The more often the particles collide, the faster the reaction should go. Chemical reactions also involve chemical bond breaking and bond making. These processes require energy. The colliding particles must have sufficient energy for bond breaking and bond making to occur. Otherwise the particles collide without reacting. *The minimum energy colliding particles must have in order to react is the **activation energy.*** In a sense, activation energy is a barrier that the reactants must cross to be converted to products (Figure 17·2).

During a reaction, particles which are neither reactants nor products form momentarily. *An **activated complex** is the arrangement of atoms at*

■ In order to react, reactants must have sufficient energy when they collide.

Figure 17·1
Chemical reactions are the result of collisions between atoms, ions, and molecules. If a collision is not energetic enough, however, the particles will "bounce" off each other like billiard balls, without reacting.

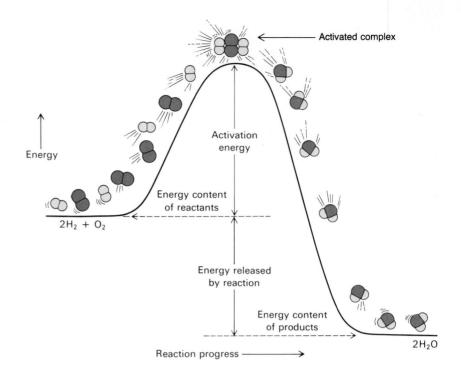

Figure 17·2
The activation energy barrier must be crossed before reactants are converted to products. The activated complex is a temporary arrangement of particles that has sufficient energy to become either reactants or products.

Energy

Activated complex

Activation energy

Energy content of reactants

$2H_2 + O_2$

Energy released by reaction

Energy content of products

$2H_2O$

Reaction progress ⟶

The activated complex is unstable. It possesses more energy than either the reactants or products.

the peak of the activation energy barrier. This group of atoms is on its way to becoming an ionic or molecular product. The lifetime of an activated complex is only about 10^{-13} seconds. The very unstable activated complex is equally likely to return to the reactants as it is to go to the products. For this reason, *the activated complex is sometimes called the* **transition state.** Studies of transition states are conducted to learn what bonds are broken and formed during a given reaction.

Collision theory explains why some exothermic reactions do not occur at room temperature. The reaction of carbon and oxygen is exothermic, but it has a high activation energy. At room temperature the collisions of oxygen and carbon molecules are not energetic enough to break O—O and C—C bonds. Virtually none of the collisions are energetic enough to surmount the activation energy barrier. Thus the reaction rate of carbon with oxygen at room temperature is essentially zero.

17·2 Reaction Rates

The rates of chemical reactions can be affected in several ways.

▪ The rate of reaction depends on the presence of catalysts and on the temperature, concentration, and particle size of the reactants.

Effect of Temperature. Usually, raising the temperature speeds up a reaction. Lowering the temperature usually slows reactions down. At higher temperatures the motions of the reactant particles are more chaotic and more energetic than at lower temperatures. The frequency of high energy collisions between reactants increases. More colliding molecules become energetic enough to slip over the activation energy barrier to become products.

Figure 17·3
A large amount of energy must be added to initiate the reaction of charcoal with oxygen even though the reaction is exothermic. Once the reaction is going it liberates enough energy to continue to drive the reactants to overcome the activation energy barrier.

As mentioned, coal coes not burn at a measurable rate at room temperature. If it is given an "energy prod" in the form of heat, however, the result is dramatic. When a flame touches coal, the reactants (carbon and oxygen) collide with greater frequency. Some of these collisions are at a high enough energy that the product (carbon dioxide) forms. The heat released by the reaction then supplies enough energy to get more carbon and oxygen over the activation energy barrier. When the flame is removed, the reaction continues. The coal burns as long as a supply of coal and oxygen is available.

Problem

1. Chemical reactions caused by bacteria occur faster at higher temperatures.

1. Refrigerated food stays fresh for long periods. The same food stored at room temperature quickly spoils. Why?

Effect of Concentration. The number of reacting particles in a given volume affects the rate at which reactions occur. Cramming more particles into a fixed volume increases the collision frequency. Therefore increasing the concentration of reactants increases the reaction rate. A lighted splint vividly illustrates the effect. A splint glows in air, which is 20% oxygen. If a glowing splint is plunged into pure oxygen, however, it immediately bursts into flame (Figure 17·4). This is why smoking is forbidden in hospital areas where oxygen is being used.

Effect of Particle Size. The total surface area of a solid or liquid reactant has an important effect on the reaction rate. The smaller the particle size, the larger the surface area for a given mass of particles. An increase in surface area increases the collision frequency, and the reaction rate. As you probably know, a bundle of kindling burns faster than a log of equal mass.

Usually the best way to increase the surface area of solid reactants is to dissolve them. This separates the particles. For example, a marble on the floor is more accessible than a marble in the middle of a box of marbles. Homogeneous mixtures of reactants usually react more rapidly than

Figure 17·4
Why will a smoldering splint burst into flame if it is placed into a bottle of pure oxygen?
The combustion reaction occurs more rapidly when the concentration of one of the reactants (oxygen) is increased.

Figure 17·5
In 1932, this explosion destroyed a Chicago grain elevator. The small size of the reactant particles (grain dust) and the mixture of the grain dust and air caused the reaction to be explosive.

Safety

Use extreme care when mixing chemicals that react rapidly. A large amount of heat may be generated in a short time.

heterogeneous mixtures. In many reactions, however, it is impossible to obtain homogeneous mixtures, or solutions, of the reactants. *Reactions carried out with heterogenous mixtures of reactants are called* **heterogeneous reactions.** When forced to conduct heterogeneous reactions, chemists often grind solids to a fine powder first. As coal miners know, coal dust suspended in the air presents an explosion hazard. By contrast, the large chunks of coal on the mine floor are no hazard at all.

Effect of Catalysts. An increase in temperature is not always the best way to increase the rate of a reaction. A catalyst, if one can be found, is often better. A catalyst is a substance that increases the rate of a reaction without being used up itself. Catalysts provide reactants with a reaction path of lower activation energy than they could normally take (Figure 17·6). Presented with this lower-energy pathway, a larger fraction of reactants at a given temperature can form products. For instance, the

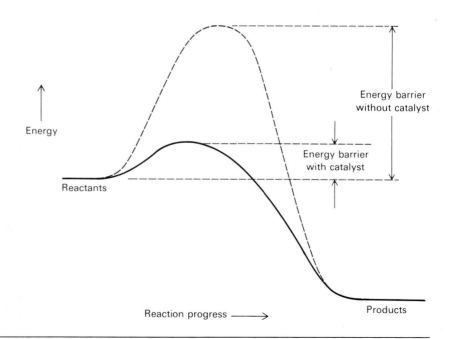

Figure 17·6
A catalyst increases the rate of a reaction by lowering the activation energy barrier.

reaction of hydrogen and oxygen at room temperature is negligible. With a trace of catalyst, however, the reaction is rapid. Finely divided platinum catalyzes this reaction.

$$2H_2(g) + O_2(g) \xrightarrow{\text{Pt}} 2H_2O(l)$$

Catalysts are not used up in a reaction. Neither do they appear as reactants or products in the equation for the reaction. Catalysts called *enzymes* increase the rates of biological reactions. Our body temperature is held at 37°C and cannot be raised or lowered significantly without imperiling our lives. Yet without catalysts, few reactions in the body would proceed fast enough at this temperature. We could not live without enzymes to catalyze these reactions.

A substance that interferes with catalysis is an **inhibitor.** Some inhibitor molecules interfere with catalysis by reacting with ("poisoning") a catalyst. This reduces the amount of catalyst available.

Safety

Finely divided metals such as zinc, aluminum, and magnesium powders are very flammable because of their large surface area. Handle with care.

Problem

2. Temperature, concentration, particle size, catalysts.

2. Name two factors that influence the rate of a chemical reaction. How are the effects of these factors explained by the collision theory?

Figure 17·7
This simplified diagram of the Contact process shows all the major steps but does not show important secondary processes such as the heating, cooling, cleaning, and purifying of the chemicals involved.

17·A The Contact Process

Sulfuric acid (H_2SO_4) was first prepared on a commerical scale in the middle of the eighteenth century. Since that time, it has become one of the most widely used compounds in the chemical industry.

The contact process is the preferred method for manufacturing sulfuric acid. Sulfur is burned in air, or iron pyrite (FeS_2) is roasted to produce sulfur dioxide (SO_2). The sulfur dioxide and oxygen are passed over a catalyst to form sulfur trioxide. The catalyst is usually

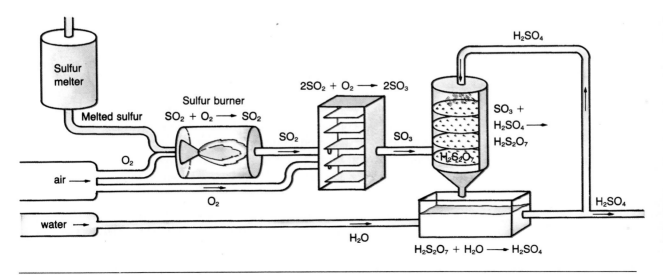

a vanadium or platinum compound. Without this catalyst the reaction would occur too slowly to be useful. The resulting sulfur trioxide is slowly mixed with water to yield sulfuric acid. Due to solubility problems, it is often preferable to mix the sulfur trioxide with concentrated sulfuric acid to form pyrosulfuric acid (H_3SO_7). This is then treated with water to produce the sulfuric acid. By carefully controlling the reaction conditions, pure H_2SO_4 can be produced.

The previous method of manufacturing sulfuric acid was called the chamber process. Under different conditions, sulfur dioxide and oxygen were allowed to react inside a lead-lined chamber. This technique could only yield concentrations of H_2SO_4 between 60% and 80%, by weight. The yield also contained many impurities. This process is considerably less expensive, however, than the contact process. It can be used when lower grade sulfuric acid is sufficient for a particular procedure.

17·3 Rate Laws

The rate of a reaction depends in part on the concentrations of the reactants. For a reaction of some reactant A going to a product B, a simple equation may be written.

$$A \longrightarrow B$$

The rate at which A is transformed to B is the change in concentration of A (ΔA) with time. Because the quantity of A is decreasing, the rate is given a minus sign.

$$\text{Rate} = -\frac{\Delta A}{\Delta t}$$

The rate of disappearance of A is proportional to its molar concentration.

$$-\frac{\Delta A}{\Delta t} \propto [A]$$

The proportionality can be expressed as a constant multiplied by $[A]$.

$$\text{Rate} = -\frac{\Delta A}{\Delta t} = k \times [A]$$

■ Rate laws are used to describe the progress of a reaction.

This equation is an example of a **rate law,** *an expression relating the rate of a reaction to the concentration of reactants. The* **specific rate constant** *for a reaction (k) is a proportionality constant relating the concentrations of reactants to the rate of the reaction.* The magnitude of the specific rate constant depends on the conditions at which the reaction is conducted. If the production of B from A is very fast, k is large. The value of k will be small for a slow reaction.

The rate of a reaction can also be followed by measuring the appearance of a product.

The order of a reaction is the power to which the concentration of a reactant must be raised to give the observed relationship between concentration and rate. *In a* **first-order reaction** *the reaction rate is proportional to the concentration of only one reactant.* The reaction is said to be first-order in A. As a first-order reaction progresses, the rate of reaction

Figure 17·8
The rate of a first-order reaction decreases in direct proportion to the concentration of one reactant. The curved line shows the decrease in concentration of reactant A with time. The short colored lines show the rate at three points in the reaction.

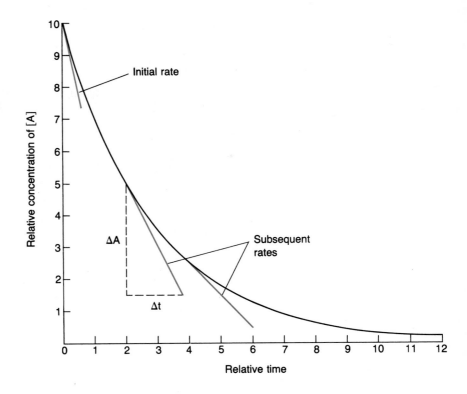

decreases (Figure 17·8). This is because the concentration of reactant decreases. On a graph, the rate at any point $(-\Delta A/t)$ equals the slope of the tangent to the curve at that point. For a first-order reaction, a halving of [A] results in a halving of the reaction rate.

Problems

3. Rate = k[A]
Rate is moles per liter per second. [A] is moles per liter.
$$k = \frac{\text{rate}}{[A]}$$
$$k = \frac{\text{(mol/liter)/s}}{\text{mol/liter}}$$
$$k = \frac{1}{s}$$

4. 0.25 mol/(L × s)
0.125 mol/(L × s)

3. Show that the unit of k for a first-order reaction is the reciprocal second (s^{-1}) or any other reciprocal unit of time.

4. A first-order reaction initially proceeds at a rate of 0.5 mol/(L × s). What will be the rate when half of the starting material remains? When one-fourth of the starting material remains?

In some kinds of reactions, such as double-replacement, two substances react to give products. The coefficients in the equation for such a reaction are represented by lower case letters.

$$a\text{A} + b\text{B} \xrightarrow{k} c\text{C} + d\text{D}$$

For a one-step reaction of A with B the rate of reaction is dependent on the concentration of both A and B.

$$\text{Rate} = k[\text{A}]^a[\text{B}]^b$$

The order of reaction in each reactant is the value of the exponent associated with that reactant. The overall order of the reaction is the sum of the exponents for each reactant.

5. For a hypothetical second-order reaction: $A + B \longrightarrow C$.

$$\text{rate} = k \times [A] \times [B]$$

$$\frac{\text{rate}}{[A] \times [B]} = k$$

$$\frac{\dfrac{\text{mol}}{L \times s}}{\dfrac{\text{mol}}{L} \times \dfrac{\text{mol}}{L}} =$$

$$\frac{L}{\text{mol} \times s} =$$

Problem

5. Show that the unit of k for a second-order reaction can be expressed in $L/(\text{mol} \times s)$. This unit is often written as L/mol-s.

Example 1

The rate law for the reaction $aA \longrightarrow B$ is of the form: Rate $= k[A]^a$. From the data in the following table, find the kinetic order of the reaction with respect to A, and the overall order of the reaction.

Initial concentration of A(mol/L)	Initial rate (mol/L-s)
0.05	3×10^{-4}
0.10	12×10^{-4}
0.20	48×10^{-4}

Solution

If a reaction is first-order in A, then $a = 1$. In that case the initial rate would be directly proportional to the initial [A]. The reaction cannot be first-order in A because a doubling of A causes the rate to increase by four times. This suggests that $a = 2$, since $2^2 = 4$. Increasing [A] by four times should therefore increase the rate sixteen-fold ($4^2 = 16$). When the initial concentration of A is increased from 0.05 mol/L to 0.20 mol/L, the initial rate increases from 3×10^{-4} mol/L-s to 48×10^{-4} mol/L-s, a sixteen fold increase. The reaction is second-order in A and second-order overall.

Problem

6. The reaction is first-order in NO_2^-, first-order in NH_4^+, and second-order overall.

6. Ammonium ions and nitrite ions react in water to form nitrogen gas.

$$NH_4^+(aq) + NO_2^-(aq) \longrightarrow N_2(g) + 2H_2O(l)$$

From the following data, decide the kinetic order of the reaction with respect to NH_4^+ and NO_2^-, and the overall order of the reaction.

Initial concentration of NO_2^- (mol/L)	Initial concentration of NH_4^+ (mol/L)	Initial rate (mol/L-s)
0.0100	0.200	5.4×10^{-7}
0.0200	0.200	10.8×10^{-7}
0.0400	0.200	21.5×10^{-7}
0.0600	0.200	32.3×10^{-7}
0.200	0.0202	10.8×10^{-7}
0.200	0.0404	21.6×10^{-7}
0.200	0.0606	32.4×10^{-7}
0.200	0.0808	43.3×10^{-7}

17·4 Reaction Mechanisms

In an **elementary reaction** *reactants are converted to products in a single step*. Such a reaction has only one intervening activated complex. Most chemical reactions consist of a number of elementary reactions. *A* **reaction mechanism** *includes all of the elementary reactions of a complex reaction*. The reaction progress curve for a complex reaction consists of a number of hills and valleys. The hills correspond to the energy levels of the activated complexes. The valleys correspond to the energy levels of the intermediate products (Figure 17·9).

An **intermediate** *is a product of a reaction that immediately becomes a reactant of another reaction*. Intermediates have a significant lifetime compared with an activated complex. They have real ionic or molecular structures and some stability. They are reactive enough, however, to react further to eventually give the final product of the reaction.

Intermediates do not appear in the chemical equation for a reaction. For example, the decomposition of nitrous oxide (N_2O) is believed to occur in two elementary steps.

$$N_2O \longrightarrow N_2 + O$$

$$N_2O + O \longrightarrow N_2 + O_2$$

$$\overline{}$$

$$2N_2O \longrightarrow 2N_2 + O_2$$

Notice that oxygen atoms are intermediates in this reaction. They disappear when the individual reactants are summed to give the final chemical equation. Thus the overall chemical equation for a complex reaction gives no information about the reaction mechanism.

▪ Most chemical reactions consist of more than one elementary step.

A complex chemical reaction occurs as a series of steps involving the collision of two particles at a time.

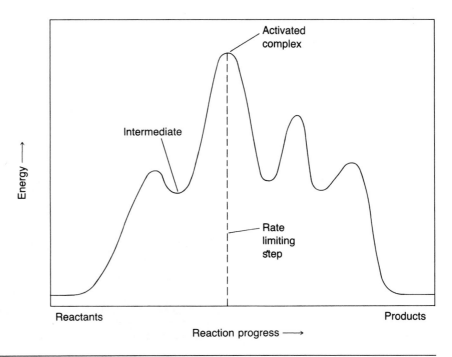

Four elementary reactions; three intermediates.

Figure 17·9
A reaction progress curve shows an activation energy peak for each elementary reaction. Valleys indicate the formation of intermediates. How many elementary reactions are part of this reaction? How many intermediates are formed?

17·5 Entropy

Energy changes accompany all chemical and physical processes. For example, the combustion of carbon is exothermic. The heat released is 393.5 kJ for each mole of carbon (graphite) burned.

$$C(s, \text{graphite}) + O_2(g) \longrightarrow CO_2(g) + 393.5 \text{ kJ/mol}$$

The heat content of the products is lower than that of the reactants in their stable states at 25°C and 1 atm.

Remember that standard conditions for thermochemical equations are 25°C and 1 atm.

Chemical systems tend to achieve the lowest possible energy. Thus we might expect that only exothermic reactions would occur. This reasonable assumption does not always work. The melting of ice, a physical process, is endothermic. One mole of ice at 25°C absorbs 6.0 kJ of heat from its surroundings as it melts from a solid to a liquid.

$$H_2O(s) + 6.0 \text{ kJ/mol} \longrightarrow H_2O(l)$$

Although the liquid is at a higher energy level than the solid, ice still melts. The change in heat content is obviously not the only factor in determining whether a reaction will proceed. Another factor, called entropy, is also involved.

The idea that physical and chemical systems attain the lowest possible energy has a corollary. *The* **law of disorder** *states that things move spontaneously in the direction of maximum chaos or disorder.* A handful of marbles is ordered in the sense that all the marbles are collected in one place. It is highly improbable that when permitted to fall, the marbles will end in the same neat arrangement. Instead, the marbles will scatter on the ground. The marbles will obey the law of disorder. *The measure of the disorder of a system is its* **entropy.** Scattered marbles have a higher entropy than gathered marbles.

Students can relate directly to this tendency. Have them consider what happens to their rooms at home as the week progresses.

Entropy can be described as the randomness of a system.

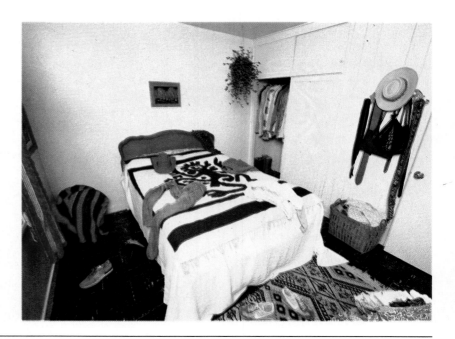

Figure 17·10
How does the entropy of your room vary over a week?

Figure 17·11
Entropy is a measure of the disorder of a system. **a** The entropy of a gas is greater than the entropy of a liquid or solid. **b** Entropy increases when a substance is divided into parts. **c** Entropy increases with an increase in temperature.

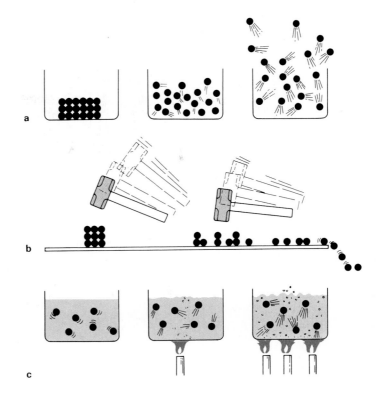

The law of disorder also operates at the level of atoms and molecules. On an atomic and molecular scale, the following concepts can be applied.

1. For a given substance, the entropy of a gas is greater than the entropy of a liquid or a solid. Similarly, the entropy of a liquid is usually greater than that of a solid. Entropy therefore increases in reactions in which solid reactants give liquid or gaseous products. It also increases when liquid reactants give gaseous products.

2. Entropy increases when a substance is divided into parts. Entropy therefore increases in chemical reactions in which the total number of product molecules is greater than the total number of reactant molecules.

3. Entropy increases with a temperature increase because the motions of molecules become more chaotic. Molecules are more disordered at high temperatures than at low temperatures. Figure 17·11 illustrates these concepts.

Problem

7. **a.** playing cards in use
   b. a dissolved sugar cube
   c. a cup of water at 50°C
   d. 1 g of powdered salt

7. Which of the following systems has the higher entropy?
   a. a new pack of playing cards or playing cards in use?
   b. a sugar cube dissolved in water or a cube of sugar?
   c. a cup of water at room temperature or a cup of water at 50°C?
   d. a 1-g salt crystal or 1 g of powdered salt?

17·6 Entropy Calculations

■ The quantity S^0 provides a way to compare entropies of different substances or different states of the same substance at a standard set of conditions.

The symbol for the entropy of a substance is S, with units of J/K. When the entropy (S) is given per mole of substance it has the unit of J/(K × mol). This unit is also written as J/K-mol. *The standard entropy of a substance in its stable state at 25°C and 1 atm is designated S^0.* Table 17·1 gives standard entropies for some common substances. The theoretical entropy of a perfect crystal at 0 K is zero. Other substances have positive entropies, even at absolute zero.

Figure 17·12
What characteristics of an explosion would lead you to believe that an increase in entropy is occurring? (Hint: see Figure 17·11).

Gases are created, and solids are broken into pieces.

Example 2

Calculate the standard entropy change, ΔS^0, that occurs when 1 mol $H_2O(g)$ at 25°C is condensed to 1 mol $H_2O(l)$ at the same temperature.

Solution

The phase change can be written as a reaction.

$$H_2O(g) \longrightarrow H_2O(l)$$

From Table 17·1 find S^0 for $H_2O(g)$ and $H_2O(l)$.

$$S^0 \text{ for } H_2O(g) = 188.7 \text{ J/K-mol}$$

$$S^0 \text{ for } H_2O(l) = 69.94 \text{ J/K-mol}$$

The change in entropy ΔS^0, can be calculated by subtraction.

$$\Delta S^0 = S^0(\text{products}) - S^0(\text{reactants})$$

Only 1 mol of each reactant and product is involved.

$$\Delta S^0 = 69.94 \text{ J/K-mol} - 188.7 \text{ J/K-mol} = -118.8 \text{ J/K-mol}$$

The condensation of 1 mol of water vapor to liquid water at 25°C results in a large decrease in entropy.

Example 3

What is the standard change in entropy for the following reaction when all reactants and products are in the specified states?

$$NO(g) + O_2(g) \longrightarrow NO_2(g)$$

Solution

First, write the balanced equation including all the physical states.

$$2NO(g) + O_2(g) \longrightarrow 2NO_2(g)$$

Then use Table 17·1 to find the standard entropies.

$$S^0 \text{ for } NO(g) = 210.6 \text{ J/K-mol}$$

$$S^0 \text{ for } O_2(g) = 205.0 \text{ J/K-mol}$$

$$S^0 \text{ for } NO_2(g) = 240.5 \text{ J/K-mol}$$

Sum the S^0 of the reactants, taking into account the number of moles.

$$S^0 \text{ for NO} = 2 \text{ mol NO} \times 210.6 \text{ J/K-mol NO} = 421.2 \text{ J/K}$$

$$S^0 \text{ for O}_2 = 1 \text{ mol O}_2 \times 205.0 \text{ J/K-mol O}_2 = 205.0 \text{ J/K}$$

$$S^0 \text{ (reactants)} = 626.2 \text{ J/K}$$

Calculate the S^0 of the products.

$$S^0 \text{ for NO}_2 = 2 \text{ mol NO}_2 \times 240.5 \text{ J/K-mol NO}_2 = 481.0 \text{ J/K} \times \text{mol}$$

Calculate the change in entropy ΔS^0 by subtraction.

$$\Delta S^0 = S^0 \text{(products)} - S^0 \text{ (reactants)}$$

$$\Delta S^0 = (481.0 \text{ J/K}) - (626.2 \text{ J/K}) = -145.2 \text{ J/K}$$

The entropy declines because a total of *three* reactant molecules are reorganized to only *two* product molecules.

Problem

8. **a.** 165 J/K
   b. −326.3 J/K
   c. 9.8 J/K

8. Calculate the change in entropy for these reactions.
   a. $CaCO_3(s) \longrightarrow CaO(s) + CO_2(g)$
   b. $2H_2(g) + O_2(g) \longrightarrow 2H_2O(l)$
   c. $H_2(g) + Cl_2(g) \longrightarrow 2HCl(g)$

Table 17·1	Standard Entropies (S^0) at 25°C and 1 atm		
Substance	S^0(J/K-mol)	Substance	S^0(J/K-mol)
$Al_2O_3(s)$	50.99	$HCl(g)$	186.7
$Br_2(g)$	245.3	$H_2S(g)$	205.6
$Br_2(l)$	152.3	$I_2(g)$	260.6
$C(s, \text{diamond})$	2.439	$I_2(s)$	117
$C(s, \text{graphite})$	5.694	$N_2(g)$	191.5
$CH_4(g)$	186.2	$NH_3(g)$	192.5
$CO(g)$	197.9	$NO(g)$	210.6
$CO_2(g)$	213.6	$NO_2(g)$	240.5
$CaCO_3(s)$	88.7	$Na_2CO_3(s)$	136
$CaO(s)$	39.75	$NaCl(s)$	72.4
$Cl_2(g)$	233.0	$O_2(g)$	205.0
$F_2(g)$	203	$O_3(g)$	238
$Fe(s)$	27.2	$P(s, \text{white})$	44.4
$Fe_2O_3(s)$	90.0	$P(s, \text{red})$	29
$H_2(g)$	130.6	$S(s, \text{rhombic})$	31.9
$H_2O(g)$	188.7	$S(s, \text{monoclinic})$	32.6
$H_2O(l)$	69.94	$SO_2(g)$	248.5
$H_2O_2(l)$	92	$SO_3(g)$	256.2

17·7 Spontaneous Reactions

A balanced equation can be written for any reaction. That does not mean, however, that the reaction will actually occur. For chemical reactions, the most important question is: Under specified conditions, will the reaction go? **Spontaneous reactions** *are reactions that are known to produce the written products*. The reaction of sodium with water to produce sodium hydroxide is a spontaneous reaction at room temperature. **Nonspontaneous reactions** *do not give products under the specified conditions*. The terms *spontaneous* and *nonspontaneous* do not refer to how fast reactants go to products. The terms refer to whether the reactants go to products at all. Some reactions that are spontaneous go so slowly that they appear to be nonspontaneous. This section presents the two factors that together determine whether a reaction is spontaneous or not. These factors are entropy and the heat released or absorbed by the reaction.

On a molecular level, a reaction tends toward spontaneity whenever the reaction is exothermic. A reaction will also tend toward spontaneity if the entropy of the products is greater than the entropy of the reactants. In a given reaction, therefore, the heat changes and the entropy changes may both act in a favorable direction. They may both act in an unfavorable direction, or they may act in opposition to each other.

The combustion of carbon has both the heat changes and entropy changes in its favor. The reaction is exothermic. The entropy also increases as *solid* carbon, is converted to *gaseous* carbon dioxide. Hence the reaction is spontaneous.

The heat changes and entropy changes work in opposition when ice melts. The process is endothermic but still spontaneous above 0°C. The absorption of heat is more than offset by a favorable entropy change. The increase in entropy is large as *solid* water (ice) goes to *liquid* water.

Another chemical reaction shows the effect of temperature on the spontaneity of a reaction. Solid calcium carbonate decomposes to give calcium oxide and carbon dioxide. In this reaction the entropy increases

Heat and entropy changes together determine whether reactants will give products.

Table 17·2 How Changes in Heat Content and Entropy Affect Reaction Spontaneity		
Heat content	Entropy	Spontaneous reaction?
Decreases (exothermic)	Increases (more disorder in products than in reactants)	Yes
Increases (endothermic)	Increases	Depends on whether unfavorable heat content change is offset by favorable entropy change
Decreases (exothermic)	Decreases (less disorder in products than in reactants)	Depends on whether unfavorable entropy change is offset by favorable heat content change
Increases (endothermic)	Decreases	No

Figure 17·13
The decomposition of calcium carbonate is an endothermic process. The reaction is not spontaneous at low temperatures because the entropy increase is not great enough to offset the heat energy absorbed.

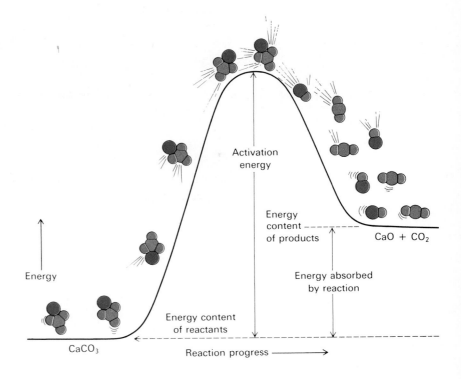

Energy

Activation energy

Energy content of products

CaO + CO_2

Energy absorbed by reaction

Energy content of reactants

$CaCO_3$

Reaction progress ⟶

because one of the products formed from the *solid* reactant is a *gas*. The entropy increase is not great enough, however, for the reaction to be spontaneous at ordinary temperatures. This is because the reaction is endothermic. The heat content of the reactants is lower than that of the products. At temperatures greater than 850°C, the entropy difference between the products and the reactants increases. The reaction is spontaneous at that temperature because the large increase in entropy offsets the heat required by the endothermic reaction.

Table 17·2 summarizes these ideas on how entropy and the heat absorbed or given off affect the spontaneity of chemical reactions.

17·8 Free Energy

Some nonspontaneous reactions can be made to be spontaneous if the conditions are changed. For instance, water does not spontaneously break down into hydrogen and oxygen. With the application of electric energy, it will decompose.

*When a reaction occurs some energy known as the **free energy** of the system becomes available to do work.* Free energy is only part of the total energy of the system. *Spontaneous reactions release free energy and are said to be **exergonic.*** As a spontaneous reaction occurs, free energy is released that can be used to cause chemical or physical changes. *Nonspontaneous reactions absorb free energy and are said to be **endergonic.***

All spontaneous reactions release free energy.

A reaction that is nonspontaneous under one set of conditions may become spontaneous under other conditions. Changing the temperature or pressure may change whether or not a reaction is spontaneous. A nonspontaneous reaction can also be linked to a spontaneous reaction. If the spontaneous reaction produces a large release of free energy, it can be used to drive the nonspontaneous reaction. The free energy transfer in coupled reactions causes many otherwise nonspontaneous reactions to occur. This occurs frequently in living systems.

Figure 17·14
The entropy of the products of photosynthesis (complex sugars such as $C_6H_{12}C_6$) is less than that of the reactants (CO_2 and H_2O). Light energy drives this process. Nonspontaneous reactions can occur when they are coupled with spontaneous reactions.

The free energy of a reaction depends on the size and direction of the heat and entropy changes. That is why these changes determine whether or not a reaction is spontaneous. If a reaction is exothermic (heat is released) and causes an increase in entropy (more disorder), then the reaction is spontaneous. A reaction will also be spontaneous if a decrease in entropy (more order) is offset by a large release of heat. Similarly, an endothermic reaction will be spontaneous if an entropy increase offsets the

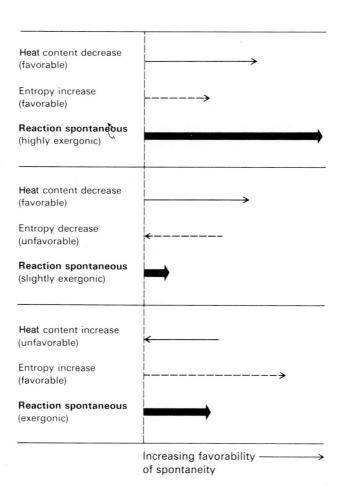

Figure 17·15
Free energy is released in spontaneous reactions. The reaction may be exothermic, the entropy of the system may increase, or both may occur.

Figure 17·16
A reaction may be nonspontaneous because the reaction is endothermic or the entropy of the system decreases, or both may occur.

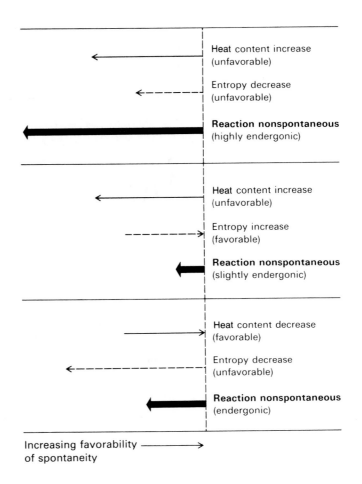

Increasing favorability ───────→
of spontaneity

heat absorbed. Figure 17·15 summarizes the relationship between heat, entropy, and free energy changes for spontaneous reactions.

In nonspontaneous reactions the free energy of the system increases. Energy must be absorbed for the reaction to occur. The reaction may involve a large decrease in entropy (increased order) and/or the reaction may be highly endothermic. In either case the other changes are not favorable enough to cause the reaction to be spontaneous. Figure 17·16 summarizes these relationships.

Appropriate for honors students.

17·9 Free Energy Calculations

In every spontaneous process, some energy becomes available to do useful work. *The* **change in Gibbs free energy,** ΔG, *is the maximum amount of energy that can be coupled to another process to do useful work*. The change in Gibbs free energy is related to the change in entropy ΔS and the change in enthalpy ΔH of the system.

$$\Delta G = \Delta H - T\Delta S$$

Temperature (T) in the equation is stated in Kelvin. All spontaneous processes release free energy; therefore, they are exergonic. The numerical

value of ΔG is negative in spontaneous processes because free energy is lost by the system. By contrast, nonspontaneous processes are endergonic. They require that work be expended to make them go at the specified conditions. The numerical value of ΔG is positive for a nonspontaneous process. In that case free energy is absorbed by the system.

The standard free energy change ΔG^0 is used to determine whether a chemical reaction is spontaneous when ΔH^0 and ΔS^0 are known.

$$\Delta G^0 = \Delta H^0 - T\Delta S^0$$

Alternatively, ΔH^0 or ΔS^0 can be determined for a reaction if the other two quantities in the equation are known. Table 17·3 gives values of ΔG^0, for some common reactions. Table 17·4 lists values of ΔG^0, the standard free energy change for the formation of substances from their elements. Note that $\Delta G_f^0 = 0$ for elemental substances. The ΔG_f^0 may be used to calculate ΔG^0 for a reaction. This is similar to the way that ΔH_f^0 is used to calculate the heats of reaction. If ΔG^0 is calculated to see whether a reaction is spontaneous, the result only applies to reactants and products in their standard states. A reaction that is nonspontaneous at one set of conditions may be spontaneous under other conditions.

■ Calculations of the standard free energy change can show whether a reaction is spontaneous or nonspontaneous at standard conditions.

Example 4

Determine whether the following reaction is spontaneous by using the ΔG_f^0 for reactants and products.

$$C(s, \text{ graphite}) + O_2(g) \longrightarrow CO_2(g)$$

Solution

Find the ΔG_f^0 of all reactants and products in Table 17·4.

$$\Delta G_f^0 \text{ for } C(s, \text{ graphite}) = 0.0 \text{ kJ/mol}$$

$$\Delta G_f^0 \text{ for } O_2(g) = 0.0 \text{ kJ/mol}$$

$$\Delta G_f^0 \text{ for } CO_2(g) = -394.4 \text{ kJ/mol}$$

Sum the G_f^0 of the reactants and sum the ΔG_f^0 of the products.

$$\Delta G_f^0 \text{ (reactants)} = 0.0 \text{ kJ/mol}$$

$$\Delta G_f^0 \text{ (products)} = -394.4 \text{ kJ/mol}$$

The ΔG^0 for the reaction is the difference between the ΔG_f^0 of the products and the ΔG_f^0 of the reactants.

$$\Delta G^0 = \Delta G_f^0 \text{ (products)} - \Delta G_f^0 \text{ (reactants)}$$

$$\Delta G^0 = -394.4 \text{ kJ/mol} - 0.0 \text{ kJ/mol}$$

$$= -394.4 \text{ kJ/mol}$$

The reaction is spontaneous. The spontaneity of the reaction can also be determined by using the changes in enthalpy and the entropies for the reactants and products, as shown in the next example.

Figure 17·17
Fireworks displays are the result of exergonic reactions. A large quantity of free energy is released.

Example 5

Using values for ΔH_f^0 and S^0, determine whether the reaction in Example 4 is spontaneous

Solution

First find the ΔH_f^0 and S^0 of all the reactants and products in Tables 8·1 and 17·1.

Substance	ΔH_f^0(kJ/mol)	S^0(kJ/(K-mol))
C(s, graphite)	0.0	5.69
$O_2(g)$	0.0	205
$CO_2(g)$	−395.5	214

The S^0 values of Table 17·1 are given in J/K-mol and must be converted to kJ/K-mol to match the units of ΔH_f^0.

$$S^0 \text{ for C}(s, \text{graphite}) = 5.7 \frac{\text{J}}{\text{K-mol}} \times \frac{1 \text{ kJ}}{1000 \text{ J}} = 0.0057 \text{ kJ/K-mol}$$

$$S^0 \text{ for } O_2(g) = 205 \frac{\text{J}}{\text{K-mol}} \times \frac{1 \text{ kJ}}{1000 \text{ J}} = 0.205 \text{ kJ/K-mol}$$

$$S^0 \text{ for } CO_2(g) = 214 \frac{\text{J}}{\text{K-mol}} \times \frac{1 \text{ kJ}}{1000 \text{ J}} = 0.214 \text{ kJ/K-mol}$$

The standard change in entropy ΔS^0 for the reaction is calculated from the standard entropies of the reactants and products.

$$\Delta S^0 = S^0(\text{products}) - S^0(\text{reactants})$$

$$\Delta S^0 = 0.214 \frac{\text{kJ}}{\text{K-mol}} - \left(0.0057 \frac{\text{kJ}}{\text{K-mol}} + 0.205 \frac{\text{kJ}}{\text{K-mol}} \right)$$

$$= 0.003 \text{ kJ/K-mol}$$

The standard enthalpy of the reaction is calculated in a similar way.

$$\Delta H^0 = \Delta H_f^0(\text{products}) - \Delta H_f^0(\text{reactants})$$

$$\Delta H^0 = -393.5 \text{ kJ/mol} - (0.0 + 0.0) = -393.5 \text{ kJ/mol}$$

The value of ΔG^0 is calculated from the changes in enthalpy and in the changes in entropy.

$$\Delta G^0 = \Delta H^0 - T\Delta S^0$$

Kelvin temperature $T = 273.15 + 25°C = 298.15$ K

$$\Delta G^0 = -393.5 \frac{\text{kJ}}{\text{mol}} - \left(298.15 \text{ K} \times 0.003 \frac{\text{kJ}}{\text{K-mol}} \right) = -394.4 \frac{\text{kJ}}{\text{mol}}$$

The reaction is spontaneous due to the large decline in ΔH^0 and due to the increase in entropy when solid graphite is converted to gaseous CO_2.

Problem

9. a. Spontaneous
   $\Delta G_f = -768.06$
   b. Spontaneous
   $\Delta G_f = -3152.8$
10. -75.2 kJ/mol

9. Determine whether the following reactions are spontaneous. Assume all substances are in their stable states at 25°C and 1 atm.
   a. $2Na(s) + Cl_2(g) \longrightarrow 2NaCl(s)$
   b. $4Al(s) + 3O_2(g) \longrightarrow 2Al_2O_3(s)$

10. When gaseous nitrogen and hydrogen are converted to gaseous ammonia, then ΔG^0 equals -16.64 kJ/mol.

$$3H_2(g) + N_2(g) \longrightarrow 2NH_3(g)$$

Using the S^0 values of Table 17·1, calculate the ΔH_f^0 for the formation of ammonia.

Table 17·3 Free Energy Values (ΔG^0) for Some Spontaneous Processes

Reaction		Free energy	
		Kilocalories/mole	Kilojoules/mole
$H_2(g) + Cl_2(g) \longrightarrow$ Hydrogen Chlorine	$2HCl(g)$ Hydrogen chloride	-45.6	-191
$S(s) + O_2(g) \longrightarrow$ Sulfur Oxygen	$SO_2(g)$ Sulfur dioxide	-71.7	-300
$2N_2O_5(s) \longrightarrow$ Dinitrogen pentoxide	$4NO_2(g) + O_2(g)$ Nitrogen Oxygen dioxide	-7.2	-30
$C_6H_{12}O_6(s) + 6O_2(g) \longrightarrow$ Glucose Oxygen	$6CO_2(g) + 6H_2O(l)$ Carbon Water dioxide	-686.0	-2868

Table 17·4 Standard Gibbs Free Energies of Formation (ΔG_f^0) at 25°C and 1 atm.

Substance	ΔG_f^0(kJ/mol)	Substance	ΔG_f^0(kJ/mol)	Substance	ΔG_f^0(kJ/mol)
$Al_2O_3(s)$	-1576.4	$Fe(s)$	0.0	$NO(g)$	86.69
$Br_2(g)$	3.14	$Fe_2O_3(s)$	-741.0	$NO_2(g)$	51.84
$Br_2(l)$	0.0	$H_2(g)$	0.0	$Na_2CO_3(s)$	-1048
$C(s, diamond)$	2.866	$H_2O(g)$	-288.6	$NaCl(s)$	-384.03
$C(s, graphite)$	0.0	$H_2O(l)$	-237.2	$O_2(g)$	0.0
$CH_4(g)$	-50.79	$H_2O_2(l)$	-114.0	$O_3(g)$	163.4
$CO(g)$	-137.3	$HCl(g)$	-95.27	$P(s, white)$	0.0
$CO_2(g)$	-394.4	$H_2S(g)$	-33.02	$P(s, red)$	-14
$CaCO_3(s)$	-1127.7	$I_2(g)$	19.4	$S(s, rhombic)$	0.0
$CaO(s)$	-604.2	$I_2(s)$	0.0	$S(s, monoclinic)$	0.096
$Cl_2(g)$	0.0	$N_2(g)$	0.0	$SO_2(g)$	-300.4
$F_2(g)$	0.0	$NH_3(g)$	-16.64	$SO_3(g)$	-370.4

17·10   Reversible Reactions

How far will a reaction go? So far we have assumed that spontaneous reactions go completely to products as written. In some reactions, however, products are favored only slightly over reactants or vice versa. Such reactions are reversible. *In* **reversible reactions** *the conversion of reactants into products and the conversion of products into reactants occur simultaneously.* The conversion of reactants to products is called the forward reaction. The conversion of products to reactants is called the reverse reaction. One example of a reversible reaction is the reaction of sulfur dioxide with oxygen to give sulfur trioxide. This is one step in the process of making sulfuric acid. The double arrows show the reaction is reversible.

$$2SO_2(g) \; + \; O_2(g) \; \Longleftrightarrow \; 2SO_3(g)$$

Sulfur   Oxygen   Sulfur
dioxide   trioxide

A spontaneous chemical reaction begins when the reactants are mixed. In a reversible reaction the rate of the reverse process is zero at first. At that point there are no products to go back to reactants. As the concentrations of products build up, however, some products revert to reactants by the reverse reaction. As the reactants are used up, their concentrations decrease. Then the forward reaction slows down. As the products build up, their concentrations increase. Then the reverse reaction speeds up. Eventually, the products are going to reactants at the same rate as reactants are going to products. *The reaction has reached* **chemical equilibrium** *when the forward and reverse reactions are taking place at the same rate.* At chemical equilibrium there is no net

■ When chemical equilibrium has been achieved, the rates of the forward and reverse reactions are the same.

Figure 17·18
A reversible reaction achieves equilibrium regardless of the direction from which it is approached. Molecules of SO_2 and O_2 react to give SO_3; molecules of SO_3 decompose to give SO_2 and O_2. At equilibrium, all three types of molecules are present in the mixture.

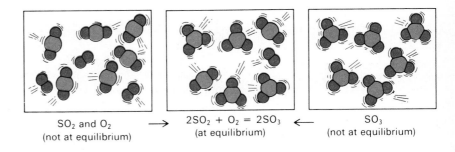

SO₂ and O₂ → 2SO₂ + O₂ = 2SO₃ ← SO₃
(not at equilibrium)   (at equilibrium)   (not at equilibrium)

Figure 17·19
These graphs show the variation with time of the concentration of O_2, SO_2, and SO_3 in two situations at 1000 K. **a** Initially twice as much SO_2 as O_2 is present. At equilibrium, a mixture of all three gases is obtained. **b** Initially only SO_3 is present. At equilibrium the amounts of O_2, SO_2, and SO_3 are the same as in **a**.

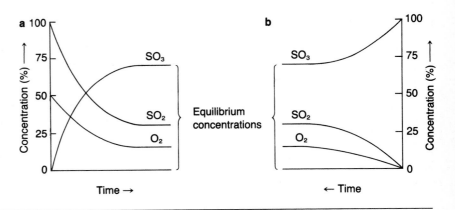

At equilibrium there are no outward signs of a chemical reaction occurring. On the molecular level, however, the forward and reverse reactions continue at equal rates.

change in the actual amounts of reactants and products in the system (Figure 17·18). Chemical equilibrium is similar to the dynamic equilibrium of a saturated solution (Section 16·2).

The equilibrium position of a reaction is given by the relative concentrations of reactants and products at equilibrium. The equilibrium position indicates whether the reactants or the products are favored in a reversible reaction. For example, if A reacts to give B and the equilibrium mixture contains 1% of A and 99% of B, then the *products* are favored.

$$A \rightleftharpoons B$$

$$1\% \qquad 99\%$$

If at equilibrium the mixture contains 99% of A and 1% of B, then the *reactants* are favored.

$$A \rightleftharpoons B$$

$$99\% \qquad 1\%$$

The longer arrow indicates the favored direction of the reaction. Reactions that are exergonic give larger amounts of products than reactants at equilibrium. Reactions that are endergonic give larger amounts of reactants than products at equilibrium.

Catalysts speed up the forward and backward reactions equally. This is because the activation energy is reduced by the same amount for both the forward and reverse directions. Therefore catalysts do not affect the amounts of reactants and products present at equilibrium. They simply decrease the time it takes for equilibrium to be established.

17·B Photochemical Smog

Environmental pollution has become a major threat to human health and general well being. Our ancestors polluted the land and water, but photochemical smog is a modern problem. The stagnant, brown air over many cities is a visible reminder of this phenomenon.

Photochemical reactions are initiated when light energy is absorbed by a light-sensitive substance. Depending on the substance, the light may be visible, infrared, or ultraviolet radiation. Some photochemical reactions are extremely beneficial. For example, photosynthesis, is a photochemical process.

Los Angeles has a severe photochemical smog problem. Hydrocarbons, ozone (O_3), and nitrogen oxides (N_xO_y) are the major compounds involved. (Several nitrogen oxides are NO, N_2O, and NO_2.) These pollutants are formed by the evaporation of industrial solvents and the combustion of fuels. The exhaust of cars and trucks contributes significantly to photochemical smog.

Ozone (O_3) damages the leaves of plants and irritates the human respiratory system. Increased concentrations of nitrogen dioxide promote the formation of ozone.

$$NO_2 + O_2 \xrightleftharpoons{\text{UV light}} NO + O + O_2 \rightleftharpoons NO + O_3$$

Note that this is a reversible reaction. In clean air ozone is usually removed from the atmosphere by the reverse reaction.

Hydrocarbons are compounds containing hydrogen and carbon. Gasoline is a mixture of volatile liquid hydrocarbons, and car exhaust contains oxidized hydrocarbons. These react with nitrogen dioxide to form PANs (peroxyl acryl nitrates), another component of smog.

$$\underset{\substack{\text{Oxidized} \\ \text{hydrocarbon}}}{C_xH_yO_3} + NO_2 \longrightarrow \underset{\text{PAN}}{C_xH_yO_3NO_2}$$

The effects of PANs are similar to those of ozone.

Two other air pollutants add to the effects of photochemical smog. Carbon monoxide (CO) is a toxic gas that results from incomplete combustion of fuels. Oxides of sulfur form acid smog. Sulfur-containing fuels form sulfur dioxide (SO_2) when they burn. Sulfuric acid is formed from sulfur dioxide in the air by these reactions.

$$SO_2 + O_2 + NO \longrightarrow SO_3 + NO_2$$

$$SO_3 + H_2O \longrightarrow H_2SO_4$$

Any efforts to control smog must take into account all the reactions involved. Catalytic systems are now being used to decrease the carbon monoxide and hydrocarbons in exhaust. Unfortunately, engines with these systems tend to emit more nitrogen oxides. Chemists are currently developing other types of catalytic systems that will reduce nitrogen oxide emissions as well.

17·11 Equilibrium Constants

The use of equilibrium constants is a concise way of stating whether reactants or products are favored in a reaction.

Chemists seldom use percentages to indicate the position of equilibrium. Rather, they use equilibrium constants. These numbers relate the amounts of reactants to products at equilibrium. Consider the hypothetical reaction in which *a* mol of reactant A and *b* mol of reactant B react to give *c* mol of product C and *d* mol of product D at equilibrium.

$$aA + bB \rightleftharpoons cC + dD$$

Because the reaction is at equilibrium, there is no *net change* in the amounts of A, B, C, or D at any given instant. *The* **equilibrium constant** K_{eq} *is the ratio of product concentrations to reactant concentrations, with each concentration raised to a power given by the number of moles of that substance in the balanced chemical equation.*

The equilibrium constant expression always takes the form of the products divided by the reactants.

$$K_{eq} = \frac{[C]^c \times [D]^d}{[A]^a \times [B]^b}$$

The brackets indicate that the amounts of substances are in moles per liter. The value of K_{eq} for a reaction depends on the temperature. If the temperature changes, the value of K_{eq} also changes.

Safety

Any reaction that generates a poisonous gas such as NO_2 should be done only under a fume hood.

Lower temperatures favor the formation of dinitrogen tetroxide.

Figure 17·21
Dinitrogen tetroxide is a colorless gas, whereas nitrogen dioxide is brown. How does temperature affect the equilibrium of a mixture of these gases?

Example 6

Dinitrogen tetroxide (N_2O_4) a colorless gas, and nitrogen dioxide (NO_2), a dark brown gas, exist in equilibrium with each other.

$$N_2O_4(g) \rightleftharpoons 2NO_2(g)$$

Write the expression for the equilibrium constant.

Solution

At equilibrium, there is no net change in the amount of N_2O_4 or NO_2 at any given instant. Nitrogen dioxide is the only product of the reaction. It has a coefficient of 2. According to the rule for writing the equilibrium constant, the concentration of nitrogen dioxide, raised to the second power, is in the numerator. The reactant is dinitrogen tetroxide. Its coefficient is 1. Thus the concentration of this substance, raised to the first power, is in the denominator.

$$K_{eq} = \frac{[NO_2]^2}{[N_2O_4]}$$

Example 7

A liter of a gas mixture at 100°C at equilibrium contains 0.0045 mol of dinitrogen tetroxide and 0.030 mol of nitrogen dioxide. Calculate the equilibrium constant, K_{eq}, for the reaction.

$$N_2O_4 \rightleftharpoons 2NO_2$$

Solution

Substitute the given data into the equilibrium constant expression of Example 6.

$$K_{eq} = \frac{[NO_2]^2}{[N_2O_4]} = \frac{(0.030 \text{ mol/L})^2}{0.0045 \text{ mol/L}} = \frac{0.030 \text{ mol/L} \times 0.030 \text{ mol/L}}{0.0045 \text{ mol/L}}$$

$$= 0.20 \text{ mol/L}$$

Example 8

One mole of hydrogen gas and 1 mol of iodine are sealed in a 1-L flask and allowed to react at 450°C. At equilibrium 1.56 mol of hydrogen iodide is present. Calculate K_{eq} for the reaction.

$$H_2(g) + I_2(g) \rightleftharpoons 2HI(g)$$

Solution

The balanced equation indicates that 1.00 mol of hydrogen and 1.00 mol of iodine form 2.00 mol of hydrogen iodide. To make 1.56 mol of hydrogen iodide therefore consumes 0.78 mol of hydrogen and 0.78 mol of iodine. First calculate how much of the H_2 and I_2 are left in the flask at equilibrium.

$$\text{mol } H_2 = \text{mol } I_2 = 1.00 \text{ mol} - 0.78 \text{ mol}$$
$$= 0.22 \text{ mol}$$

These concentrations can be substituted in the equation for K_{eq}.

$$K_{eq} = \frac{[HI]^2}{[H_2] \times [I_2]}$$

$$= \frac{(1.56 \text{ mol})^2}{0.22 \text{ mol} \times 0.22 \text{ mol}}$$

$$= \frac{1.56 \text{ mol} \times 1.56 \text{ mol}}{0.22 \text{ mol} \times 0.22 \text{ mol}}$$

$$= 50.3 = 50 \text{ (to two significant figures)}$$

Problems

11. $K_{eq} = \dfrac{[NH_3]^2}{[H_2]^3 \times [N_2]}$

12. $K_{eq} = 12$

11. Give the equilibrium-constant expression for the formation of ammonia from hydrogen and nitrogen.

$$3H_2(g) + N_2(g) \rightleftharpoons 2NH_3(g)$$

12. Analysis of an equilibrium mixture of nitrogen, hydrogen, and ammonia contained in a 1-L flask at 300°C gives the following results: hydrogen 0.15 mol; nitrogen 0.25 mol; ammonia 0.10 mol. Calculate K_{eq} for the reaction.

$$3H_2(g) + N_2(g) \rightleftharpoons 2NH_3(g)$$

Example 9

Bromine chloride, BrCl, decomposes to form chlorine and bromine.

$$2BrCl(g) \rightleftharpoons Cl_2(g) + Br_2(g)$$

At a certain temperature the equilibrium constant for the reaction is 11.1, and the equilibrium mixture contains 4.00 mol Cl_2. How many moles of Br_2 and BrCl are present in the equilibrium mixture?

Solution

$$2BrCl(g) \rightleftharpoons Cl_2(g) + Br_2(g)$$

According to the equation, when BrCl breaks down, equal moles of Cl_2 and Br_2 are formed. The measured equilibrium concentration of Cl_2 was given as 4.00 mol. Thus there must be 4.00 mol Br_2 in the equilibrium mixture. Substitute the known values in the equilibrium expression for the reaction. (K_{eq} was given as 11.1.)

$$K_{eq} = \frac{[Cl_2] \times [Br_2]}{[BrCl]^2} \qquad 11.1 = \frac{(4.00 \text{ mol}) \times (4.00 \text{ mol})}{[BrCl]^2}$$

Now solve for [BrCl].

$$[BrCl]^2 = \frac{(4.00 \text{ mol}) \times (4.00 \text{ mol})}{11.1} = \frac{16.0 \text{ mol}^2}{11.1} = 1.44 \text{ mol}^2$$

$$[BrCl] = \sqrt{1.44 \text{ mol}^2} = 1.20 \text{ mol}$$

Problems

13. $K_{eq} = \dfrac{[H_2] \times [I_2]}{[HI]^2}$

14. 3.5 mol

13. Write the equilibrium-constant expression for the decomposition of hydrogen iodide to hydrogen and iodine.

$$2HI(g) \rightleftharpoons H_2(g) + I_2(g)$$

14. The decomposition of hydrogen iodide at 450°C produces an equilibrium mixture that contains 0.50 mol of hydrogen. The equilibrium constant is 0.020 for the reaction. How many moles of iodine and hydrogen iodide are present in the equilibrium mixture?

$$2HI(g) \rightleftharpoons H_2(g) + I_2(g)$$

Equilibrium constants are valuable chemical information. Among other things, they show whether products or reactants are favored at equilibrium. An equilibrium constant is always written as a ratio of products to reactants. Thus a value of K_{eq} greater than 1 means that products are favored over reactants. Conversely, a value of K_{eq} less than 1 means that reactants are favored over products.

$$K_{eq} > 1 \qquad \text{products favored at equilibrium}$$

$$K_{eq} < 1 \qquad \text{reactants favored at equilibrium}$$

All spontaneous or exergonic reactions have $K_{eq} > 1$. All nonspontaneous or endergonic reactions have $K_{eq} < 1$.

Problem

15. A chemist has determined the equilibrium constants for several reactions. In which of these reactions are the products favored over the reactants?

a. $K_{eq} = 1 \times 10^2$ **c.** $K_{eq} = 3.5$

b. $K_{eq} = 0.003$ **d.** $K_{eq} = 6 \times 10^{-4}$

15. a. products favored
   b. reactants favored
   c. products favored
   d. reactants favored

17·12 Le Châtelier's Principle

A delicate balance exists between reactants and products in a system at equilibrium. The application of stress to the system disrupts this balance. The French chemist Henri Le Châtelier (1850–1936) studied the changes in a system that result from changed conditions. He proposed **Le Châtelier's principle:** *If a stress is applied to a system in a dynamic equilibrium, the system changes to relieve the stress.* Three types of stress are easily applied to chemical systems: changes in concentration of reactants and products, changes in temperature, and changes in pressure.

Changes in Concentration.   Changing the amount of any reactant or product in a system at equilibrium disturbs the equilibrium. The system changes to minimize the original change. When carbon dioxide dissolves in water, for example, it reacts with the water to a slight extent to form a substance known as carbonic acid. The equilibrium constant for this process is small. At equilibrium the amount of carbonic acid is only about 1%.

$$CO_2 + H_2O \rightleftharpoons H_2CO_3$$
$$99\% \qquad\qquad\qquad 1\%$$

If more carbon dioxide is added, the equilibrium will be disturbed. Suppose enough carbon dioxide is added to shift the ratio of carbonic acid to carbon dioxide (H_2CO_3/CO_2) from 1 : 99 to 0.5 : 99.5. As the carbon dioxide is added, it reacts with water to form more carbonic acid. This shifts the ratio back toward the original 1 : 99. In other words: *Adding a reactant always pushes a reversible reaction in the direction of products.* If carbon dioxide is removed, the H_2CO_3/CO_2 ratio increases to greater than 1 : 99. Then carbonic acid decomposes as the system readjusts itself toward a H_2CO_3/CO_2 ratio of 1 : 99. *Removing a reactant always pulls a reversible reaction in the direction of reactants.*

Our bodies use the removal of reactants to keep carbonic acid at low, safe levels in the blood. Blood contains dissolved carbonic acid in equilibrium with carbon dioxide and water. When we exhale carbon dioxide, the equilibrium shifts toward carbon dioxide and water. This reduces the amount of carbonic acid. The same principle applies to adding or removing products. *When a product is added to a system at equilibrium, the reaction shifts in the direction of the formation of reactants. When a product is removed a reaction shifts in the direction of formation of products.*

Removal of products is a trick often used by chemists to increase the yield of a desired product. As products are removed from a reaction mixture, the system continually changes to restore equilibrium with the products. Because the products are being removed as fast as they are formed, however, the reaction never builds up enough of them to establish an equilibrium. (If you have spent some time around henhouses, you know that a hen lays a clutch of eggs and then proceeds to hatch them. Only if you take the eggs away will she produce more eggs.) Similarly, the reactants continue to react to give products until they are completely used up.

When environmental factors such as the temperature or pressure of a system in dynamic equilibrium are changed, the position of equilibrium also changes.

Figure 17·22
The rapid exhalation of CO_2 following exercise helps reestablish the body's H_2CO_3/CO_2 equilibrium. This keeps H_2CO_3 at a low, safe level in the blood.

Changes in Temperature.
Increasing the temperature causes the equilibrium position of a reaction to shift in the direction that absorbs heat. For example, the production of SO_3 is an exothermic reaction.

$$2SO_2(g) + O_2(g) \rightleftharpoons 2SO_3(g) + \text{heat}$$

In this reaction, heat can be considered to be a product, just like SO_3. Heating the reaction mixture at equilibrium pushes the equilibrium position to the left. This favors the reactants. As a result, the product yield decreases. Cooling pulls the equilibrium to the right, and the product yield increases. Notice that the ratio of products to reactants changes with temperature. A change in temperature produces a change in K_{eq}.

Changes in Pressure.
A change in pressure will affect only an equilibrium with an unequal number of moles of *gaseous* reactants and products. For example, an equilibrium is established between ammonia gas and the gaseous elements from which it is formed.

$$3H_2(g) + N_2(g) \rightleftharpoons 2NH_3(g)$$

A pressure increase causes a stress that can be relieved by a shift in the equilibrium to the right. This is because a decrease of pressure results when 4 mol of gas reacts to form 2 mol of gas.

The equilibrium for this reaction can be made to shift to the left (favoring reactants) by decreasing the pressure. When the reaction shifts left, the pressure is increased. This is because 4 mol of gas is produced for each 2 mol of NH_3 that decomposes.

An increase of pressure on a gaseous system always favors a shift toward the side with the lowest total number of particles.

Example 10

What effect do the following changes have on the position of equilibrium for this reversible reaction?

$$PCl_5(g) + \text{heat} \rightleftharpoons PCl_3(g) + Cl_2(g)$$

a. addition of Cl_2
b. increase in pressure
c. removal of heat
d. removal of PCl_3 as it is formed.

Solution

a. The stress of adding Cl_2 is relieved if the equilibrium shifts to the left ($\longleftarrow$), forming more PCl_5.
b. There are 2 mol of gaseous products and 1 mol of gaseous reactant. The stress of an increase in pressure is relieved if the equilibrium shifts to the left ($\longleftarrow$). A decrease in the number of moles of gaseous substances gives a decrease in pressure.
c. Removal of heat causes a shift to the left ($\longleftarrow$) because the reverse reaction is heat-producing.
d. Removal of PCl_3 causes a shift to the right ($\longrightarrow$) to produce more PCl_3.

16. **a.** reactants favored
    b. reactants favored
    c. products favored

Problem

16. How is the equilibrium position of this reaction affected by the following changes?

$$C(s) + H_2O(g) + heat \rightleftharpoons CO(g) + H_2(g)$$

a. lowering the temperature
b. increasing the pressure
c. removing H_2 from the equilibrium mixture

17·C Mining the Riches of the Atmosphere

At the turn of the century, more and more land was being used as farmland in order to increase food production. Most of the best land had already been used. Much of the new cropland had marginal, nutrient-poor soil that required heavy fertilization. Fertilizers were obtained from nitrate deposits found only in scattered areas around the world. The most important element found in these fertilizers was nitrogen. It is essential for plant growth. The large demand for nitrogen-containing compounds was beginning to outstrip the supply.

The atmosphere contains huge quantities of nitrogen gas. (Air is 78% nitrogen by volume.) Unfortunately, this molecular form of nitrogen (N_2) is extremely unreactive. The German physical chemist Fritz Haber (1868–1934) was interested in the problem of synthesizing nitrogen compounds. Between 1907 and 1909, he successfully developed a laboratory procedure for making ammonia (NH_3) from nitrogen and hydrogen.

$$N_2 + 3H_2 \rightleftharpoons 2NH_3$$

The industrial production technique for this process was subsequently devised by Carl Bosch. It uses extremely high pressures and temperatures. An equally important factor, however, is an iron-containing catalyst. A basic flow diagram of the Haber–Bosch process is shown in Figure 17·23.

The Haber-Bosch process shifts the reaction equilibrium to favor the forward reaction. Since four moles of reactants form two moles of products, increased pressure favors the formation of ammonia. High temperatures and a catalyst are used to increase the rate of the reaction. Today ammonia plants use temperatures of 300°C to 600°C and pressures of 200 to 1000 atmospheres. The ammonia is separated from the reactants by dissolving it in water or by liquefaction. For their research efforts, both Haber and Bosch were independently awarded the Nobel Prize in Chemistry. Haber received the award in 1918, and Bosch in 1931.

Air.

Figure 17·23
In the Haber–Bosch process, nitrogen and hydrogen combine to form ammonia. The hydrogen is derived from the reaction of steam with methane. What is the source of the nitrogen?

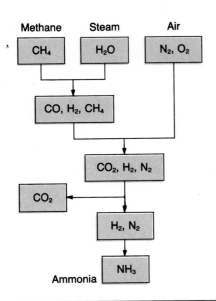

Key Terms

Chapter Summary

The speed, or rate, at which a chemical reaction goes is determined by an activation energy barrier. The activation energy is the minimum energy that reactants must have to go to products. (In the reverse direction, it is the minimum energy that products must have to go to reactants.) The higher the activation energy barrier, the slower the reaction. Chemists help reactants overcome the activation barrier in a number of ways. Their most effective method is to either increase the temperature at which the reaction is done or use a catalyst.

The natural tendency for all things to go to lower energy and greater disorder (entropy) determines whether a reaction will go. Reactions that actually occur as written are called spontaneous reactions. Equations for other reactions may be written,

but the reactions are nonspontaneous. All spontaneous reactions release energy that becomes available to do work. This energy is called free energy.

In principle all reactions are reversible. That is, reactants go to products in the forward direction and products go to reactants in the reverse direction. In practice, however, some reactions are irreversible (go completely to products). Others are reversible, and products go to reactants only to a certain extent. The point at which the rate of conversion of reactants to products and vice versa is equal is the position of equilibrium. The equilibrium constant of a reversible reaction, K_{eq}, is useful for determining the position of equilibrium. It is essentially a measure of the ratio of products to reactants at equilibrium. The direction of change in the position of equilibrium may be predicted by applying Le Châtelier's principle.

Practice Questions and Problems

17. Explain the collision theory of reactions. *17·1*

18. Does every collision between reacting particles lead to products? What other factor is involved? *17·1*

19. What is meant by the rate of reaction? *17·2*

20. How does each of the following factors affect the rate of a chemical reaction? *17·2*
a. temperature
c. particle size
b. concentration
d. inhibitor

21. How is the rate of a spontaneous reaction influenced by a catalyst? How do catalysts make this possible? *17·2*

22. Which of these statements is true? *17·2*
a. All chemical reactions can be speeded up by increasing the temperature.
b. Once a chemical reaction gets started, the colliding particles no longer have to "climb over" the activation energy barrier.
c. Enzymes are biological catalysts.

23. When the gas to a stove is turned on, the gas does not burn unless lit by a flame. Once lit, however, the gas burns until turned off. Explain these observations in terms of the effect of temperature on reaction rate. *17·2*

24. What is meant by the following terms? *17·3*
  a. specific rate constant
  b. first-order reaction
  c. rate law

25. The rate law for this reaction is first-order in NO and O_3, and second-order overall. Write the complete rate law for the reaction. *17·3*

$$NO + O_3 \longrightarrow NO_2 + O_2$$

26. The reactant in a first-order reaction has half disappeared in 50 minutes. How many minutes are required for this particular reaction to be 75% complete? *17·3*

27. Define each of the following terms as applied to chemical reactions. *17·4*
  a. elementary reaction
  b. intermediate
  c. reaction mechanism

28. Sketch a potential energy diagram for the reaction whose mechanism is shown below.

$$2NO \longrightarrow N_2O_2 \text{ (fast)}$$
$$N_2O_2 + O_2 \longrightarrow 2NO_2 \text{ (slow)}$$

Write the balanced equation for the overall reaction. *17·4*

29. What is the meaning of the term *entropy*? *17·5*

30. The products in a spontaneous process are more ordered than the reactants. Is this entropy change favorable or unfavorable? *17·5*

31. Which system has the lower entropy? *17·5*
  a. a completed jigsaw puzzle *or* the separate pieces?
  b. 50 mL of water *or* 50 mL of ice?
  c. 10 g of sodium chloride crystals *or* a solution containing 10 g sodium chloride?
  d. a house *or* a pile of bricks and lumber?

32. Predict the direction of the entropy change in each of the following reactions. *17·5*
  a. $CaCO_3(s) \longrightarrow CaO(s) + CO_2(g)$
  b. $NH_3(g) + HCl(g) \longrightarrow NH_4Cl(s)$
  c. $2NaHCO_3(s) \longrightarrow$
  $$Na_2CO_3(s) + H_2O(g) + CO_2(g)$$
  d. $CaO(s) + CO_2(g) \longrightarrow CaCO_3(s)$

33. The standard entropies are given below for some substances at 25°C. *17·6*

$$KBrO_3(s) \qquad S^0 = 149.2 \text{ J/K-mole}$$
$$KBr(s) \qquad S^0 = 96.4 \text{ J/K-mole}$$
$$O_2(g) \qquad S^0 = 205.0 \text{ J/K-mole}$$

Calculate ΔS^0 for this reaction.

$$KBrO_3(s) \longrightarrow KBr(s) + \tfrac{3}{2}O_2(g)$$

34. Based upon the data of Table 17·1, calculate ΔS^0 for conversion of the monoclinic form of sulfur to the rhombic form. *17·6*

35. What is a spontaneous reaction? Give an example (not given in the text) of a spontaneous reaction. *17·7*

36. What two factors together determine whether or not a reaction is spontaneous? *17·7*

37. Is it true that all spontaneous processes are exothermic? Explain your answer. *17·7*

38. Are spontaneous chemical reactions always fast? Why? Give examples that prove your point. *17·7*

39. What is free energy? How can knowing the free energy of a reaction help you predict whether or not the reaction will be spontaneous? *17·8*

40. What is meant by the terms *endergonic* and *exergonic*? *17·8*

41. The reaction of hydrogen and oxygen gas proceeds with a large decrease of free energy. The reaction is very slow at room temperature but occurs with explosive rapidity in the presence of a flame or ignition wire. Explain. *17·8*

42. For the decomposition of $CaCO_3(s)$ to $CaO(s)$ and $CO_2(g)$ at 298 K the ΔH^0 is 178.5 kJ/mol and the ΔS^0 is 161.6 J/K-mol. Is the reaction spontaneous or nonspontaneous at this temperature? *17·9*

43. From the data of Table 17·4, calculate the standard free energy change for each of the following reactions, and say whether the reaction is spontaneous or nonspontaneous. *17·9*
  a. $Cl_2(g) + H_2O(g) \longrightarrow 2HCl(g) + \tfrac{1}{2}O_2(g)$
  b. $4NH_3(g) + 7O_2(g) \longrightarrow 4NO_2(g) + 6H_2O(g)$
  c. $2CO_2(g) \longrightarrow 2CO(g) + O_2(g)$
  d. $2H_2S(g) \longrightarrow 2H_2(g) + 2S(s, rhombic)$

44. In your own words define a reversible reaction. *17·10*

45. A reversible reaction has reached a state of dynamic chemical equilibrium. What does this information tell you? *17·10*

46. How do the rates of the forward and reverse reactions compare at a state of dynamic chemical equilibrium? *17·10*

47. Write the expression for the equilibrium constant for each of the following. *17·11*
a. $2HBr(g) \rightleftharpoons H_2(g) + Br_2(g)$
b. $2SO_3(g) \rightleftharpoons 2SO_2(g) + O_2(g)$
c. $CO_2(g) + H_2(g) \rightleftharpoons CO(g) + H_2O(g)$
d. $4NH_3(g) + 5O_2(g) \rightleftharpoons 6H_2O(g) + 4NO(g)$

48. Write the expression for the equilibrium constant for each of the following. *17·11*
a. $4H_2(g) + CS_2(g) \rightleftharpoons CH_4(g) + 2H_2S(g)$
b. $PCl_5(g) \rightleftharpoons PCl_3(g) + Cl_2(g)$
c. $2NO(g) + O_2(g) \rightleftharpoons 2NO_2(g)$
d. $CO(g) + H_2O(g) \rightleftharpoons H_2(g) + CO_2(g)$

49. At a high temperature the following system reaches equilibrium.

$$N_2(g) + O_2(g) \rightleftharpoons 2NO(g)$$

An analysis of the equilibrium mixture in a 1-L flask gives the following results: nitrogen 0.50 mol; oxygen 0.50 mol; nitrogen monoxide 0.020 mol. Calculate K_{eq} for the reaction. *17·11*

50. At 750°C this reaction reaches an equilibrium in a 1-L container.

$$H_2(g) + CO_2(g) \longrightarrow H_2O(g) + CO(g)$$

An analysis of the equilibrium mixture gives the following results: hydrogen 0.053 mol; carbon dioxide 0.053 mol; water 0.047 mol; carbon monoxide 0.047 mol. Calculate K_{eq} for the reaction. *17·11*

51. Comment on the favorability of product formation in each of these reactions. *17·11*

a. $H_2(g) + F_2(g) \rightleftharpoons 2HF(g)$ $\quad K_{eq} = 1 \times 10^{13}$
b. $SO_2(g) + NO_2(g) \rightleftharpoons NO(g) + SO_3(g)$
$$K_{eq} = 1 \times 10^2$$
c. $2H_2O(g) \rightleftharpoons 2H_2(g) + O_2(g)$
$$K_{eq} = 6 \times 10^{-28}$$

52. What is Le Châtelier's principle? Use it to explain why carbonated drinks go flat when their containers are left open. *17·12*

53. Can a pressure change be used to shift the position of equilibrium in every reversible reaction? Explain your answer. *17·12*

54. Carbon disulfide can be made by the reaction of carbon dioxide and sulfur trioxide.

$$2SO_3(g) + CO_2(g) + heat \rightleftharpoons CS_2(g) + 4O_2(g)$$

Assuming that the reaction is at equilibrium, what effect do the following changes have on the equilibrium position? *17·12*
a. addition of CO_2
b. addition of heat
c. decrease in the pressure
d. removal of O_2
e. addition of a catalyst

55. The industrial production of ammonia is described by this reversible reaction.

$$N_2(g) + 3H_2(g) \rightleftharpoons 2NH_3(g) + 92 \text{ kJ}$$

What effect do the following changes have on the equilibrium position? *17·12*
a. addition of heat
b. increase in pressure
c. addition of catalyst
d. removal of heat
e. removal of NH_3

Mastery Questions and Problems

56. Which statement or combination of statements is sufficient to determine whether a reaction will be spontaneous or not? *17·8*
a. The reaction is exothermic.
b. Entropy is increased in the reaction.
c. Free energy is released in the reaction.

57. For the reaction: $A + B \longrightarrow C$, the activation energy of the forward reaction is 5 kJ and the total energy change is -20 kJ. What is the activation energy of the reverse reaction? *17·10*

58. By means of a sketch, show that the activation energy of an endothermic reaction must be greater than or equal to the total energy change in the reaction. Does a similar relationship exist for exothermic reactions? *17·1*

59. Explain each of the following. *17·2*
a. A campfire is "fanned" to help get it going.
b. An explosion at a grain elevator is blamed on dust.
c. A pinch of powdered manganese dioxide causes hydrogen peroxide to explode even though the manganese dioxide is not changed.

60. Sketch an energy profile curve for this gas-phase reaction.

$$F + H_2 \longrightarrow HF + H$$

The reaction has an activation energy of 22 kJ and the total energy change is -103 kJ. *17·1*

61. Would you expect the entropy to increase in each of the following reactions? *17·5*
a. $C(s) + O_2(g) \longrightarrow CO_2(g)$
b. $Al_2O_3(s) \longrightarrow 2Al(s) + \frac{3}{2}O_2(g)$
c. $2N(g) \longrightarrow N_2(g)$
d. $N_2(g) \longrightarrow 2N(g)$

62. What would be the effect on the position of equilibrium by decreasing the volume in each of the following reactions? *17·12*
a. $4HCl(g) + O_2(g) \rightleftharpoons 2Cl_2(g) + 2H_2O(g)$
b. $CO_2(s) \rightleftharpoons CO_2(g)$
c. $CaCO_3(s) \rightleftharpoons CaO(s) + CO_2(g)$

63. A mixture at equilibrium at 827°C contains 0.552 mol CO_2, 0.552 mol H_2, 0.448 mol CO, and 0.448 mol H_2O.

$$CO_2(g) + H_2(g) \rightleftharpoons CO + H_2O(g)$$

What is the value of K_{eq}? *17·11*

64. Write the equilibrium constant expression for each of the following reactions. *17·11*
a. $I_2(g) + Cl_2(g) \rightleftharpoons 2ICl(g)$
b. $2NO_2(g) \rightleftharpoons 2NO(g) + O_2(g)$
c. $2SO_2(g) + O_2(g) \rightleftharpoons 2SO_3(g)$
d. $Cl_2(g) + PCl_3(g) \rightleftharpoons PCl_5(g)$

65. The freezing of liquid water at 0°C can be written as follows.

$$H_2O(l, d = 1.00 \text{ g/cm}^3) \rightleftharpoons$$
$$H_2O(s, d = 0.92 \text{ g/cm}^3)$$

Explain why the application of pressure causes ice to melt. *17·12*

66. Write the rate law for each of the elementary rate processes of Problem 28. *17·4*

67. Consider the decomposition of N_2O_5 in carbon tetrachloride (CCl_4) at 45°C.

$$2N_2O_5 \longrightarrow 4NO_2 + O_2$$

The reaction is first order in N_2O_5, with the specific rate constant 6.08×10^{-4} per second. Calculate the reaction rate under these conditions. *17·3*
a. $[N_2O_5] = 0.200$ mole/liter
b. $[N_2O_5] = 0.319$ mole/liter

68. The decomposition of hydrogen peroxide is catalyzed by iodide ions. The mechanism is thought to be as follows. *17·4*

$$H_2O_2 + I^- \longrightarrow H_2O + IO^- \text{ (slow)}$$
$$IO^- + H_2O_2 \longrightarrow H_2O + O_2 + I^- \text{ (fast)}$$

a. What is the reactive intermediate?
b. Does I^- qualify as a catalyst?
c. What is the minimum number of activated complexes needed to describe the reaction?
d. Which of the two reactions has the smallest specific rate constant?
e. Write the balanced equation for the entire reaction.

69. The entropy decreases in an endothermic reaction. Is the reaction spontaneous? *17·7*

70. The reaction between diamond (carbon) and oxygen is spontaneous. What can you say about the speed of this reaction? *17·7*

$$C(s, \text{ diamond}) + O_2(g) \longrightarrow CO_2(g)$$

71. Predict what will happen if a catalyst is added to a slow reversible reaction. What happens to the equilibrium position? *17·10*

72. Using the standard entropy data of Table 17·1, calculate the standard entropy change ΔS^0 for this reaction. *17·6*

$$2NO(g) + 3H_2O(g) \longrightarrow 2NH_3(g) + \frac{5}{2}O_2(g)$$

73. Suppose equilibrium exists for the following reaction at 425 K.

$$Fe_3O_4(s) + 4H_2(g) \rightleftharpoons 3Fe(s) + 4H_2O(g)$$

How would the equilibrium concentration of H_2O be affected by these actions? *17·12*
a. adding more H_2 to the mixture
b. adding more Fe(s)
c. removing H_2
d. adding a catalyst

Review Questions and Problems

74. Name each of the following ions and identify it as an anion or a cation.
a. F^- **e.** Na^+
b. Cu^{2+} **f.** I^-
c. P^{3-} **g.** O^{2-}
d. H^+ **h.** Mg^{2+}

75. Explain how crystalline and amorphous substances differ.

76. What is wrong with the statement that solid potassium chloride is composed of KCl molecules?

77. Use ionic charges as a guide to write the formula for each of the following compounds.
   a. calcium chloride
   b. aluminum sulfide
   c. magnesium nitrate
   d. aluminum carbonate
   e. barium hydroxide
   f. ammonium nitrate
   g. potassium sulfate
   h. aluminum phosphate

78. Name the following compounds and give the charge on the anion for each.
   a. $NaClO_4$
   b. $KMnO_4$
   c. $Ca_3(PO_4)_2$
   d. $MgCO_3$
   e. Na_2SO_4
   f. $K_2Cr_2O_7$

79. Write electron configurations and draw electron dot structures for the following elements.
   a. Ge
   b. Ca
   c. O
   d. Ar
   e. Br
   f. P

80. Write the formulas for each of these ionic compounds using electron dot structures.
   a. LiBr
   b. $AlCl_3$
   c. MgF_2
   d. Na_2S

81. Write the electron configurations and draw electron dot structures for the following:
   a. Ca^{2+}
   b. Li^+
   c. Br^-
   d. S^{2-}

82. Which atoms from the following list would you expect to form positive ions, and which would you expect to form negative ions?
   a. Cl
   b. Ca
   c. P
   d. Se
   e. Cu
   f. Sn
   g. K
   h. Fe
   i. N
   j. Ni

83. List some properties that are typical of ionic compounds.

Challenging Questions and Problems

84. Hemoglobin is a protein molecule in the red blood cell that carries oxygen from the lungs to cells throughout the body. Carbon monoxide poisoning results from formation of a complex of carbon monoxide (CO) with the hemoglobin. This complex is 200 times stronger than the oxygen–hemoglobin complex. This makes it extremely difficult for the oxygen to compete with carbon monoxide in being carried to the cells. When too much hemoglobin is tied up by the carbon monoxide, death occurs by asphyxiation. This is the reaction.

Hemoglobin—O_2 + CO $\rightleftharpoons$

Hemoglobin—CO + O_2

What would be a logical treatment for a person suffering from carbon monoxide poisoning? Using your knowledge of the gas laws, can you suggest a way to increase the effectiveness of this treatment?

85. Is eating sugar candy really bad for your teeth? Tooth decay is the result of the dissolving of tooth enamel, $Ca_5(PO_4)_3OH$. In the mouth the following equilibrium is established.

$Ca_5(PO_4)_3OH(s) \rightleftharpoons$

$5Ca^{2+}(aq) + 3PO_4^{3-}(aq) + OH^-(aq)$

When sugar ferments on the teeth, H^+ is produced. What effect does this increased H^+ have on tooth enamel?

Research Projects

1. Investigate the effects of different catalysts on the decomposition of hydrogen peroxide.

2. Report on a catalyst used in industrial reactions. How does the catalyst operate on a molecular level?

3. What are the problems involved in the scale-up of a laboratory reaction to an industrial process?

4. What contributions did Josiah Gibbs make to chemical reaction thermodynamics? Why was his work relatively unrecognized for almost 20 years?

5. Discuss some common spontaneous reactions. What makes them spontaneous?

6. What effect do catalysts and temperature have on nonspontaneous reactions? Cite some examples.

7. What contributions did Henri Le Châtelier make to the understanding of equilibrium and reaction rates? How did his discoveries help industrial chemists?

8. What contributions did Gottlieb Kirchhoff make to industrial chemistry?

9. What chemical reactions are involved in smog formation? Compare the local, regional, and global effects of photochemical smog.

10. What are the major sources of air pollution in your community? How is it being controlled? What are the tangible and intangible costs of air pollution?

11. How does a catalytic converter reduce pollution from automobile emissions?

12. Review the effects of clean air standards since 1970.

Readings and References

Davenport, Derek A. "When Push Comes to Shove: Disturbing the Equilibrium." *Chem Matters* (American Chemical Society) (February 1985), p. 14.

Fuller, John G. *The Poison That Fell from the Sky.* New York: Random House, 1977.

Kidder, Tracy. "A Perch in the Sky." *Science 83* (March 1983), pp. 64–73.

O'Connor, Rod, and Charles Mickey. *Solving Problems in Chemistry: With Emphasis on Stoichiometry and Equilibrium.* New York: Harper & Row, 1974.

Siezen, Roland, "Pumping Oxygen." *Chem Matters* (American Chemical Society) (February 1984), pp. 6–9.

Stoker, H. Stephen, and Spencer L. Seager. *Environmental Chemistry: Air and Water Pollution,* 2nd ed. Glenview, IL: Scott, Foresman, 1976.

Verbit, Lawrence P. "Chemistry's Speedy Servants." *Science Year* (1982), pp. 194–205.

Acids and Bases

Chapter Planning Guide

Section		Demonstrations and Experiments	Resource Materials
18·1 Properties of Acids and Bases	C*	Dem 18·1 Classifying Substances as Acidic, Basic, or Neutral Dem 18·2 Etching	Objectives Worksheet 18, SPB Skillsheet 18, SPB
18·A Etching in Art and Industry	E		
18·2 Hydrogen Ions from Water	C	Dem 18·3 Cabbage Juice Indicator Dem 18·4 Universal Indicator	
18·3 The pH Concept	C	Exp 38 Acids and Bases: Determination of pH, LM Dem 18·5 pH Meter	Prelab 38, SPB Teaching Diagram 25
18·4 Calculating pH Values	H		Quiz 18·1
18·B Arrhenius Led the Way	E		
18·5 Arrhenius Acids and Bases	C		
18·6 Brønsted–Lowry Acids and Bases	C		
18·C Measuring pH	E		
18·7 Lewis Acids and Bases	H	Dem 18·6 Amphoteric Zinc Compounds	Quiz 18·2
18·8 The Strengths of Acids and Bases	C	Exp 39 Characteristic Reactions of Acids, LM Dem 18·7 Strengths of Acids and Bases	Prelab 39, SPB Beyond the Text: Acid Rain Regional Air Pollution and Acid Rain, ICT 18
18·9 Calculating Dissociation Constants	H		Quiz 18·3 Reviewsheet 18, SPB Chapter 18 Test
*C = Core, O = Optional E = Enrichment, H = Honors		LM = Laboratory Manual	SPB = Skills Practice Book ICT = Issues in Chem. Tech.

Chapter Objectives

Having studied this chapter and done the problems, the student should be able to:

1. List properties of acids and bases. *18·1*

2. Write the equation for the self-ionization of water. *18·2*

3. Given the hydrogen-ion or hydroxide-ion concentration, classify a solution as neutral, acidic, or basic. *18·2*

4. Calculate the pH of a solution given the hydrogen-ion or hydroxide-ion concentration. *18·3*

5. Calculate the hydrogen-ion or hydroxide-ion concentration given the pH of a solution. *18·4*

6. Define and give examples of Arrhenius acids and bases. *18·5*

7. Use the Brønsted–Lowry theory to classify substances as acids or bases, or as hydrogen-ion donors or hydrogen-ion acceptors. *18·6*

8. Identify conjugate acid–base pairs in acid–base reactions. *18·6*

9. Classify substances as Lewis acids or bases. *18·7*

10. Use the extent of ionization and the acid dissociation constant, K_a, to distinguish between strong and weak acids. *18·8*

11. Use the extent of ionization and the base dissociation constant, K_b, to distinguish between strong and weak bases.   *18·8*

12. Calculate an acid dissociation constant K_a, from concentration and pH measurements.   *18·9*

Teaching Suggestions

18·1 Properties of Acids and Bases

One way to introduce the topic of acids and bases is to make two lists. In one, include properties which are characteristic of acids. In the other, include properties which are characteristic of bases. Ask students to define acids and bases in terms of these properties. Such definitions are called *operational* definitions.

These definitions, of course, do not give us any clue as to *why* acids and bases have these properties. In this chapter the students will be given definitions of acids and bases which become progressively more abstract as they attempt to explain the behavior of all acids and bases. These definitions are called *conceptual* definitions.

One way to get the students started along this line of thinking is to have them observe **Demonstration 18·1** *Classifying Substances as Acidic, Basic, or Neutral*. In this demonstration, they observe the behavior of several solutions and then try to relate this behavior to their formulas. **Demonstration 18·2** *Etching* demonstrates the effect of an acid on glass.

18·2 Hydrogen Ions from Water

Because of self-ionization, all aqueous systems contain hydrogen and hydroxide ions. However small the concentration of one or the other or both may be, they are always present. Be sure the students are aware that an acid solution contains a greater concentration of hydrogen ions than hydroxide ions, while a basic solution contains a greater concentration of hydroxide ions than hydorgen ions. A neutral solution is one which contains equal concentrations of these two ions. **Demonstrations 18·3** *Cabbage Juice Indicator* and **18·4** *Universal Indicator* show how indicators are used to find the amount of hydrogen ion.

Present the self-ionization of water as an equilibrium process. Emphasize that the product of the concentrations of the hydrogen ion and the hydroxide ion is always equal to 1.0×10^{-14} at room temperature. Stress that by using this relationship, we can always find the concentration of one of the ions if given the other.

After an introduction to acids and bases the students should do **Experiment 39** *Characteristic Reactions of Acids*. In this experiment the students treat various substances with an acid and test the gas which is evolved.

18·3 The pH Concept

Introduce pH as an easy way to express hydrogen ion concentrations. Point out that it is much easier to say the pH of a solution is 3 than it is to say that the hydrogen ion concentration is equal to 1.0×10^{-3} moles per liter. For those students who have no idea of logarithms, explain that pH is found by taking the negative of the *power* of the hydrogen ion concentration and expressing it as a whole number. Explain that the positive values of pH range from 0 to 14, with the most acidic being 0, the most basic being 14, and neutral being 7. Negative values of pH are possible as well. For instance, the pH of a $10M$ HCl solution is -1.

Remind the students that if they know either the pH, hydrogen ion concentration, or hydroxide ion concentration, they can use K_w to find the other two.

Once they have mastered the concept of pH, the students should do **Experiment 38** *Acids and Bases: Determination of pH*. This is an exercise in classifying substances according to their behavior with indicators and measuring the pH. **Demonstration 18·5** *pH Meter* could also be used.

18·4 Calculating pH Values

The calculation of non-integer pH values requires a functional understanding of logarithms. This section should be omitted if the students do not have this background.

18·5 Arrhenius Acids and Bases

In Section 18·1 acids and bases were defined in terms of their properties. The Arrhenius definitions explain those properties, and so are conceptual definitions. Acids taste sour, form conducting solutions, react with hydroxide ions, and so forth, because of the hydrogen ions they release. Bases have their properties because of the hydroxide ions they release.

The Arrhenius definitions are useful since they cover nearly all common acids and bases. However the students should be warned that there are some acids and bases which do not fit these definitions. Emphasize that it is the *free* hydrogen ions and hydroxide ions which give the acid and bases their observable properties. A compound (such as CH_4 or CH_3OH) can contain hydrogen atoms or OH groups but still not be an acid or base.

18·6 Brønsted–Lowry Acids and Bases

The Brønsted–Lowry definitions of acids and bases are even more all-encompassing than the previous definitions. An acid is a substance which can produce hydrogen ions. A base is a substance which can react with hydrogen ions. Point out how these definitions not only cover those substances covered by the previous definitions, but also explain why CH_4 *is not* an acid and NH_3 *is* a base.

When discussing conjugate acids and bases be sure to stress the idea that every acid–base reaction always produces a new acid and base, called the conjugate acid and base. When hydrogen ion reacts with hydroxide ion to produce water, there is only one product instead of two. Students may think that this is an exception to the principle that an acid–base pair always produces a conjugate acid–base pair. Point out that water is amphoteric and can act in both roles. In this case, one water molecule donates a hydrogen ion, and another accepts that hydrogen ion.

18·7 Lewis Acids and Bases

The last definitions of acids and bases presented in this chapter are all-encompassing and even more abstract. The Lewis definition does not even require that a substance be able to produce hydrogen ions to be an acid, only that it be able to accept a pair of electrons. A substance need only donate a pair of electrons to be a base. Point out that these definitions do not exclude the substances we have previously identified as acids and bases. All these substances fit the Lewis definitions. In addition, the Lewis definitions include a whole class of other substances which we would not have previously considered to be acids or bases. **Demonstration 18·6** *Amphoteric Zinc Compounds* could be done to conclude this section.

18·8 The Strengths of Acids and Bases

The terms. *Strong* and *weak* as applied to acids and bases are often misconstrued as having to do with concentration. Emphasize that the dissociation of an acid or base into its ions involves the establishment of an equilibrium. Strong and weak are relative terms which refer to the position of that equilibrium. When a strong acid or base dissolves, the equilibrium favors the products (the ionic form) to a very great extent. When a weak acid or base dissolves, the equilibrium favors the reactants (the molecular form).

If students have difficulty relating strength to degree of ionization, do **Demonstration 18·7** *Strengths of Acids and Bases*. Since the dissociation of an acid or base establishes equilibrium, an equilibrium constant can be written for the reaction. The constants which are specifically for acid or base dissociation are given the special symbols K_a and K_b, respectively.

Show the students how the extent to which products or reactants are favored can be determined from the values of K_a or K_b. Show them also how to use values of K_a or K_b to compare the strengths of acids or bases.

18·9 Calculating Dissociation Constants

This section illustrates how easily the dissociation constant of an acid or base can be determined experimentally. It demonstrates that all we need know is the concentration of the solution and its pH. However, there are some limitations to the method shown. These should be discussed.

In doing the calculations it is assumed that when the acid molecule dissociates, it forms an equal number of hydrogen ions and negative ions. Thus the concentration of the negative ion is assumed to be equal to the concentration of the hydrogen ion. This is true only if there is no additional source of either hydrogen ion or the accompanying negative ion.

The calculation of K_a is also much more complicated in the case of a polyprotic substance. The complete dissociation of H_3PO_4, for instance, involves three separate ionizations, each with its own K_a. Each of the three equilibria are in competition. Thus, advise the students that in this case they could not just use a pH measurement and the solution concentration to find a K_a value.

Demonstrations

18·1 Classifying Substances as Acidic, Basic, or Neutral

Concept: Indicators show pH.

Materials: six 50-mL beakers, red and blue litmus paper, 10 mL of 0.1% bromthymol blue, dropper, 10 mL of $0.1M$ solutions of various acids (hydrochloric, nitric, sulfuric, phosphoric, acetic, or boric), bases (ammonia, sodium carbonate, or hydroxides of sodium, potassium, calcium, magnesium, or barium), and neutral substances (methanol, ethanol, sodium chloride, or water), safety goggles.

Procedure: 1. Arrange the beakers on a table or overhead projector. 2. In each beaker, place an acid, base, or neutral solution. 3. Test the solutions with litmus paper and 3 drops of bromthymol blue. Litmus turns red in an acid solution, blue in a basic solution, and a weak violet color in a neutral solution. Bromthymol blue turns yellow in an acid solution, blue in a basic solution, and green in a neutral solution. 4. Students should write the formulas of the solutions tested and classify each as an acid, base, or neutral substance. 5. Have them look for relationships between the formulas and the classification of the substance. **Caution:** *The acids and bases are corrosive.*

18·2 Etching

Concept: Acids can etch glass.

Materials: 10 g of calcium fluoride (CaF_2), 30 mL of concentrated sulfuric acid (H_2SO_4), watch glass coated with wax, lead dish to hold watch glass, file, tongs, safety goggles.

Procedure: **Caution:** *Use a fume hood. Calcium fluoride is an irritant. Sulfuric acid is corrosive. Hydrogen fluoride is toxic by inhalation, skin contact, or ingestion.*

1. Use the file to etch a design in the wax on the watch glass. 2. Add the calcium fluoride to the lead dish. 3. Pour sufficient sulfuric acid to cover the watch glass. 4. The hydrogen fluoride vapors etch the glass in about 15 minutes. 5. Take the watch glass out with tongs and rinse with hot water to remove the acid and wax. 6. The design can be seen.

18·3 Cabbage Juice Indicator

Concept: Some natural substances are weak acids.

Materials: 25 g of red cabbage, food grinder or knife, series of solutions of pH 1–13 in test tubes (made by diluting 0.1M hydrochloric acid, HCl, or 0.1M sodium hydroxide, NaOH), two test tube racks, 250-mL beaker, hot plate or ring, ring stand, gas burner, wire gauze, matches, dropper, safety goggles.

Procedure: 1. Grind or slice the cabbage and place in a beaker with 100 mL water. 2. Boil for 5 minutes. 3. Add 5 drops of cabbage juice to each test tube of acid or base. 4. Note the colors and pH of the tubes. 5. Discuss the fact that the coloring pigments of many natural materials are weak acids that change color with varying pH. These pigments are good acid–base indicators. **Caution:** *Hydrochloric acid and sodium hydroxide are corrosive.*

18·4 Universal Indicator

Concept: A universal indicator undergoes numerous color changes with varying pH.

Materials: 10 mL of 0.1% solutions of each of the following: thymol blue, methyl red, bromthymol blue, and phenolphthalein, 28 medium test tubes, 5 test tube racks, 7 large test tubes, 20 mL each of buffers at: pH 4, 5, 6, 7, 8, 9, and 10, safety goggles.

Procedure: 1. Place 7 medium test tubes in each of four racks. 2. Put 5 mL of pH 4 buffer in the first tube of each rack, 5 mL of pH 5 buffer in the second tube of each rack, etc. The seventh tube in each rack has 5 mL of pH 10 buffer. 3. Put 5 drops of one indicator in all 7 test tubes of one rack. Repeat for each indicator. 4. Note the color of each tube after each addition. 5. Place the large test tubes in a rack. 6. Pour all four of the pH 4 tubes (one from each rack) into the first large tube, all four pH 5 tubes into the second large tube, etc. All four pH 10 tubes go into the seventh large tube. 7. Note the colors of the large test tubes. 8. Ask whether it is possible for a single substance to be a universal indicator, and why different indicators change color at different pH.

18·5 pH Meter

Concept: The hydrogen ion concentration can be measured with a pH meter.

Materials: distilled water, pH meter, solutions of different pH in 50-mL beakers: fruit juice, vinegar, ammonia, detergent, soap, baking soda or powder, tomato soup, gelatin, jelly, and antacid tablets, safety goggles.

Procedure: 1. Rinse the electrodes of the meter with distilled water. 2. Test each solution, noting the pH. 3. Test the same solutions at different temperatures to show how pH varies with temperature. 4. Ask why *millivolts* appear on the meter. (pH is an electrical measurement since ions are involved.)

18·6 Amphoteric Zinc Compounds

Concept: Some substances exhibit properties of both acids and bases, depending on the reaction.

Materials: 10 mL of 0.1M zinc chloride ($ZnCl_2$), 6 mL of 1M sodium hydroxide (NaOH), 1 mL of 1M hydrochloric acid (HCl), 2 large test tubes, safety goggles.

Procedure: 1. Place half the zinc chloride in each test tube. 2. Add sodium hydroxide to each to form amphoteric zinc hydroxide, $Zn(OH)_2$, precipitate. 3. Continue adding sodium hydroxide to one tube until a soluble complex ion forms and the precipitate dissolves. The reaction is:

$$Zn(OH)_2 + 2OH^- \rightarrow Zn(OH)_4^{2-}$$

4. Add hydrochloric acid to the other tube. The precipitate dissolves as the hydroxide accepts protons. The reaction is:

$$Zn(OH)_2 + 2H^+ \rightarrow Zn^{2+} + 2H_2O$$

Caution: *Hydrochloric acid and sodium hydroxide are corrosive.*

18·7 Strengths of Acids and Bases

Concept: The strength of an acid or base depends on its ability to ionize.

Materials: 30 mL each of 1M: hydrochloric acid (HCl), acetic acid ($C_2H_4O_2$), and oxalic acid ($H_2C_2O_4$), three 50-mL beakers, electrical conductivity apparatus (from **Demonstration 13·1**), pH paper or pH meter, three 5-cm pieces of magnesium ribbon, safety goggles.

Procedure: 1. Discuss the difference between the *strength* of an acid or base and its *concentration*. 2. Use the electrical conductivity apparatus to test each of the solutions. 3. Test each solution with pH paper or a pH meter. 4. Place a magnesium ribbon in each beaker of acid. 5. Note the difference in the rates of production of hydrogen gas. (The stronger the acid, the greater the bubbling.) 6. Point out that the solutions have the same molar concentration. The difference in activity results from the difference in hydrogen ion concentration in each solution. The strongest acid, hydrochloric acid, is ionized to a greater degree and thus shows more conductivity, a lower pH, and a higher reactivity. **Caution:** *Hydrochloric acid, oxalic acid, and acetic acid are corrosive. Oxalic acid is toxic.*

Audiovisual Resources

Acid-Base Indicators (F, V) Chem Study, 1962, 19 min. (Use with Sections 18·1 or 18·6.) Explains the behavior of acid–base indicators with the Brønsted-Lowry theory and demonstrates the effects of changing acidity on indicators.

Acid Rain (2 FS) Educational Dimensions, 1982, 18 min. each. (Use with Sections 18·1 or 18·3.) Discusses the causes and effects of acid rain and examines the controversy delaying action on the issue.

Acid Rain: Requiem or Recovery (F, V) National Film Board of Canada, 1982, 27 min. (Use with Sections 18·1 or 18·3.) Shows effects of acid rain on structures, crops, forests, and lakes and stresses the need for public pressure to force action.

All About Acids and Bases (4 FS) Focus Media, 1981, 20–30 min. each. (Use with Sections 18·1 and 18·3.) Discusses properties and uses of acids and bases and explains the concept of pH. Also covers topics in Chapter 19.

Chemistry: Acids, Bases, and Salts (F) Coronet, 1983, 20 min. (Use with Sections 18·1, 18·5, 18·6, or 18·7.) Surveys the major acid–base theories, describes commercial and laboratory preparation and shows properties and uses of acids, bases, and salts.

Proton Transfer in Chemical Change (FS) Prentice-Hall Media, 1971. (Use with Sections 18·1, 18·2, 18·6, or 18·8.) Develops the Brønsted–Lowry theory to explain properties and reactions of acids and bases.

Beyond the Text

Acid Rain

What is the pH of the rain in your community? Rain tends to be mildly acidic (pH 5.6) because of the formation of carbonic acid. Since the late 1970s, however, researchers in the Great Lakes area have regularly found the rain and snow to have pHs from 5.0 to 4.0. This level of acidity is harmful to both plant and animal life. Aquatic life is the most severely affected. Many small lakes, which used to be teeming with plants and animals, are now lifeless. Forests and farm crops are affected to a lesser extent. Acid rain water leaches aluminum and other toxic metals from the soil and carries them into lakes and rivers. Acidified water also accumulates toxic lead and copper ions when it moves through household plumbing.

Air pollutants are the major cause of acid rain. Sulfur dioxide and nitrogen dioxide react with moisture in the air to form sulfuric and nitric acids. Acid rain is a problem particularly in Europe and eastern North America due to the climate and air pollutants there. Before the use of tall smokestacks most air pollutants settled out locally within a short time. Tall smokestacks solved the local pollution problem but created a global one. For example, many coal-burning utilities are located in the midwestern United States. These utilities contribute to the acid rain problems in the eastern United States and Canada.

Solving the acid rain problem will require the efforts of scientists, industries, and politicians. All of the potential solutions are costly, as is the problem itself. Lime can be added to the affected lakes, but this is only a temporary measure. The high-sulfur coal burned by utilities could be "cleaned" before it is burned. The smokestack emissions could also be reduced. Both of these solutions are very expensive.

Answers to End of Chapter Questions and Problems

Practice Questions and Problems

17. Taste sour, conduct electricity when dissolved in water, cause indicators to change color, react with metals to form hydrogen gas when dissolved in water, react with compounds containing hydroxide ions to form water and a salt.

18. Taste bitter, conduct electricity when dissolved in water, cause indicators to change color, react with acids to form water and a salt, feel slippery in aqueous solution.

19. $H_2O \rightleftharpoons H^+ + OH^-$

20. $1.0 \times 10^{-7}M$ for both H^+ and OH^- at 25°C

21. $K_w = [H^+] \times [OH^-] = 1.0 \times 10^{-14}M$ at 25°C

22. a. Hydroxide ion concentration is greater.
b. Hydrogen ion concentration is greater.
c. The concentrations are equal.

23. $1 \times 10^{-12}M$, basic

24. The negative logarithm of the hydrogen ion concentration.

25. The hydrogen ion concentration of pure water at 25°C is $1.0 \times 10^{-7}M$. The negative logarithm or pH of this concentration is 7.0.

26. a. pH = 2, acidic **b.** pH = 12, basic **c.** pH = 6, acidic **d.** pH = 6, acidic

27. a. $1.0 \times 10^{-7}M$ **b.** $1.0 \times 10^{-13}M$
c. $1.0 \times 10^{-2}M$

28. a. $1.0 \times 10^{-10}M$ **b.** $1.0 \times 10^{-6}M$
c. $1.0 \times 10^{-2}M$

29. Acids ionize to give hydrogen ions in aqueous solution. Bases ionize to give hydroxide ions in aqueous solution.

30. a. acid **b.** base **c.** acid **d.** acid **e.** base **f.** acid

31. a. monoprotic **b.** not an acid **c.** diprotic **d.** monoprotic **e.** not an acid **f.** monoprotic

32. a. $2Li + 2H_2O \rightarrow 2LiOH + H_2$
b. $Ba + 2H_2O \rightarrow Ba(OH)_2 + H_2$

33. In the Brønsted–Lowry theory, acids are hydrogen ion donors and bases are hydrogen ion acceptors. This explains why a compound without hydroxide ions behaves like a base.

34. a. HNO_3, acid; H_2O, base **b.** CH_3COOH, acid; H_2O, base **c.** H_2O, acid; NH_3, base **d.** H_2O, acid; CH_3COO^-, base

35. a. HNO_3 with NO_3^-, H_2O with H_3O^+
b. CH_3COOH with CH_3COO^-, H_2O with H_3O^+
c. H_2O with OH^-, NH_3 with NH_4^+ **d.** H_2O with OH^-, CH_3COO^- with Ch_3COOH

36. Acts as an acid or a base.

37. A Lewis acid accepts a pair of electrons to form a covalent bond. A Lewis base donates a pair of electrons to form a covalent bond. The Lewis theory explains the behavior of compounds that act like bases without accepting hydrogen ions or that act like acids without donating hydrogen ions.

38. a. $HNO_3 + H_2O \rightarrow H_3O^+ + NO_3^-$
b. $CH_3COOH + H_2O \rightleftharpoons CH_3COO^- + H_3O^+$
c. $NH_3 + H_2O \rightarrow NH_4^+ + OH^-$
d. $Mg(OH)_2 + H_2O \rightleftharpoons Mg^{2+} + 2OH^- + H_2O$

39. Strong acids and bases are completely ionized in aqueous solution. Weak acids and bases ionize only slightly in aqueous solution.

40. a. strong base **b.** strong acid **c.** strong base **d.** weak acid **e.** weak base **f.** strong acid **g.** weak acid

41. A strong acid is completely dissociated; K_a must be large.

42. $Mg(OH)_2$ and $Ca(OH)_2$ have high K_a ratios even though their concentration in saturated solution is low because of their low solubility.

43. a. $K_a = \dfrac{[H^+][I^-]}{[HI]}$ **b.** $K_a = \dfrac{[H^+][HCO_3^-]}{[H_2CO_3]}$

Mastery Questions and Problems

44. a. pH = 5.62 **b.** pH = 8.04
c. $[H^+] = 6.3 \times 10^{-14}M$ **d.** $[H^+] = 2.0 \times 10^{-7}M$

45. Yes. Acids like acetic acid dissolve well but ionize poorly.

46. a. NH_4^+ and NH_3; H_2O and H_3O^+ **b.** HCO_3^- and H_2CO_3; H_2O and OH^- **c.** CO_3^{2-} and HCO_3^-; H_2O and OH^- **d.** H_3PO_4 and $H_2PO_4^-$; H_2O and H_3O^+

47. $HPO_4^{2-} \rightarrow H^+ + PO_4^{3-}$; $HPO_4^{2-} + H^+ \rightarrow H_2PO_4^-$

48. $4.5 \times 10^{-4}M$

49. a. CO_3^{2-}, carbonate ion **b.** I^-, iodide ion **c.** NH_3, ammonia **d.** HSO_3^-, hydrogen sulfite ion

50. a. KOH is the base; HBr is the acid. **b.** HCl is the acid; H_2O is the base.

51. a. $HClO_2$, chlorous acid **b.** H_3PO_4, phosphoric acid **c.** H_3O^+, hydronium ion **d.** NH_4^+, ammonium ion

52. $1.59 \times 10^{-5}M$

53. a. $[OH^-] = 4.0 \times 10^{-10}M$ **b.** $[OH^-] = 2.0 \times 10^{-5}M$ **c.** pH = 12.25 **d.** pH = 5.86

54. $H_3PO_4 \rightleftharpoons H^+ + H_2PO_4^-$
$H_2PO_4^- \rightleftharpoons H^+ + HPO_4^{2-}$
$HPO_4^{2-} \rightleftharpoons H^+ + PO_4^{3-}$

Review Questions and Problems

55. Stirring, heating, using fine particles of solid.

56. Add 15.3 g KOH to distilled water and dissolve. Then bring the volume of the solution up to 400.0 mL.

57. a. increase **b.** increase **c.** decrease **d.** increase

58. 0.47 L

59. a. increases products **b.** no change **c.** increases products **d.** increases products **e.** increases products

60. a. $K = \dfrac{[CO]^2[O_2]}{[CO_2]^2}$ **b.** $K = \dfrac{[NH_3]^2}{[N_2][H_2]^3}$

Challenging Questions and Problems

61. $[H^+] = 6M$, $[OH^-] = 1.7 \times 10^{-15}M$, pH = −0.8

62. pH = 10.7

63. $K_w = K_a K_b = \dfrac{[H^+][A^-]}{[HA]} \times \dfrac{[HA][OH^-]}{[A^-]} = [H^+][OH^-]$

64. a. At 10°C, pH = 7.27; at 45°C, pH = 6.70.
b. At 10°C, pure water is slightly basic; at 45°C, pure water is slightly acidic.

18 Acids and Bases

Chapter Preview

Section 18·9 is appropriate for honors students.

The first section gives operational definitions of acids and bases. An operational definition defines a substance in terms of its properties.

Acids and bases are readily identified by their characteristic properties.

Acids and bases play a central role in much of the chemistry that affects our daily lives. They are widely used in manufacturing processes. They are also extremely important in the correct functioning of our bodies. This chapter covers the qualitative and quantitative aspects of these two classes of compounds. You will see how they ionize or dissociate in water. You will also see how the concept of pH is used to measure the strength of acidic and basic solutions.

18·1   Properties of Acids and Bases

Compounds that are classified as acids or bases have many distinctive properties. Acidic compounds give foods a tart or sour taste. For example, vinegar contains acetic acid. Lemons contain citric acid. Aqueous solutions of acids will conduct electricity and thus are electrolytes. Some are strong electrolytes whereas others are weak electrolytes. Acids cause certain chemical dyes, called indicators, to change color. Many metals, such as zinc and magnesium, react with aqueous solutions of acids to produce hydrogen gas. Acids react with compounds containing hydroxide ions to form water and a salt.

Bases are compounds that react with acids to form water and a salt. Milk of magnesia (magnesium hydroxide) is a base. It is used to treat the problem of excess stomach acid. Aqueous solutions of bases have a bitter taste and feel slippery. Like acids, bases are electrolytes. Like acids, bases will change the color of an acid–base indicator.

Figure 18·1
The tangy taste of a fresh orange comes from the citric acid found in all citrus fruits.

Several theories explain the observed properties of acids and bases. Before discussing these theories, we must examine water and the ways in which the hydrogen-ion concentration is measured in solutions.

Acids and bases are among the most common and industrially important chemicals.

18·A Etching in Art and Industry

For centuries printmakers have used acids to make engravings. Initially, a metal plate is coated with a thin layer of wax or other material that is acid resistant. The artist draws in the wax so that areas of the metal plate are exposed. When the drawing is complete the waxed surface is dipped in an acid. Wherever the wax was removed from the plate the exposed metal is eaten away. After an appropriate amount of time the plate is washed to stop the etching process, and the wax is removed.

To make a print the plate is inked with a roller that forces the ink into the etched areas. A piece of paper is laid on the inked surface. Pressure transfers the ink from the etched metal surface to the paper.

Printmakers commonly use copper, zinc, or iron plates and either nitric acid (HNO_3) or hydrochloric acid (HCl). The various combinations of metals and acids produce different effects. For example, nitric acid "bites" an etched line more readily on the sides than on the bottom. This makes the line wider, and the final print takes on a more diffuse appearance. Hydrochloric acid bites deeper into the metal plate. It is preferred for etching details.

Glass is etched using hydrofluoric acid (HF). The resulting frosted and transparent areas can be used to create artistic designs. The process is also used to produce the fine markings on laboratory glassware and to frost the insides of light bulbs.

Figure 18·2
Artists use acids to etch patterns in glass and metals.

Figure 18·3
All of these items contain acids or bases.

18·2 Hydrogen Ions from Water

Water molecules are highly polar. Even at room temperature they are in continuous motion. Occasionally, the collisions between water molecules are energetic enough that a hydrogen ion is transferred from one water molecule to another. *A water molecule that loses a hydrogen ion becomes a negatively charged* **hydroxide ion** (OH⁻). *A water molecule that gains a hydrogen ion becomes a positively charged* **hydronium ion** (H_3O^+).

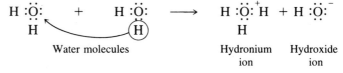

Water molecules   Hydronium   Hydroxide
                                            ion   ion

The reaction in which two water molecules react to give ions is the **self-ionization** *of water.* This reaction can be written as a simple dissociation.

$$H_2O \rightleftharpoons H^+ + OH^-$$

Hydrogen ion   Hydroxide ion

In water or aqueous solution, hydrogen ions (H^+) are always joined to water molecules as hydronium ions (H_3O^+). The hydronium ions are themselves solvated to form species such as $H_9O_4^+$. Hydrogen ions in aqueous solution have several names. Some chemists call them protons. Others prefer to call them hydrogen ions, or hydronium ions, or solvated protons. In this book we use either H^+ or H_3O^+ to represent hydrogen ions in aqueous solution.

The self-ionization of water occurs to a very small extent. In pure water at 25°C the concentration of hydrogen ions, $[H^+]$, and the concentration of hydroxide ions, $[OH^-]$, are each only 1.0×10^{-7} mol/L. Note that the concentrations of H^+ and OH^- must be equal in pure water. These ions are produced in a 1:1 ratio. Chemists describe pure water as neutral. In fact, *any aqueous solution in which the $[H^+]$ and the $[OH^-]$ are 1.0×10^{-7} mol/L is described as a* **neutral solution.**

In any aqueous solution the $[H^+]$ and the $[OH^-]$ are interdependent. If the $[H^+]$ increases then the $[OH^-]$ decreases. If the $[H^+]$ decreases then

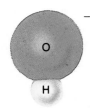

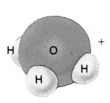

Figure 18·4
Which of these ions is a hydronium ion? Which is a hydroxide ion?
Hydroxide ion above, hydronium ion below.

Water self-ionizes.

Brackets around a chemical formula [H_2O] are used to indicate concentrations of solutions in moles per liter (molarity).

the [OH⁻] increases. Le Châtelier's principle applies here. If additional ions (either hydrogen ions or hydroxide ions) are added to the solution, the equilibrium will shift to decrease the other type of ion. More water molecules are formed in the process.

$$H^+ + OH^- \rightleftharpoons H_2O$$

For aqueous solutions the product of the hydrogen ion concentration, $[H^+]$, and the hydroxide ion concentration, $[OH^-]$, is equal to 1.0×10^{-14} (mol/L)².

$$[H^+] \times [OH^-] = 1.0 \times 10^{-14} \text{ (mol/L)}^2$$

The product of the concentrations of the hydrogen ions and hydroxide ions in water is K_w, the **ion-product constant for water.**

$$K_w = [H^+] \times [OH^-] = 1.0 \times 10^{-14} \text{ (mol/L)}^2$$

Not all solutions are neutral. When some substances dissolve in water they release hydrogen ions. For example, when hydrogen chloride dissolves in water it forms hydrochloric acid.

$$HCl(g) \xrightarrow{\text{water}} H^+(aq) + Cl^-(aq)$$

In such a solution the hydrogen ion concentration, $[H^+]$, is greater than the hydroxide ion concentration, $[OH^-]$. (The hydroxide ions are present from the self-ionization of water.) *In* **acidic solutions** *the $[H^+]$ is greater than the $[OH^-]$.* Therefore the $[H^+]$ of an acidic solution is greater than 1.0×10^{-7} mol/L.

When sodium hydroxide is dissolved in water it forms hydroxide ions.

$$NaOH(s) \xrightarrow{\text{water}} Na^+(aq) + OH^-(aq)$$

In such a solution the hydrogen ion concentration, $[H^+]$, is less than the hydroxide ion concentration, $[OH^-]$. (The hydrogen ions are present from the self-ionization of water.) *In* **basic solutions** *the $[H^+]$ is less than the $[OH^-]$.* Therefore the $[H^+]$ of a basic solution is less than 1.0×10^{-7} mol/L. *Basic solutions are also known as* **alkaline solutions.**

K_w is the equilibrium constant for aqueous systems. Its value is 1.0×10^{-14} only at 25°C. The value of K_w decreases as temperature increases.

$K_w = [H^+] \times [OH^-]$ is true for every aqueous solution regardless of the presence of any other ions.

Hydrogen and hydroxide ions will always be present in aqueous solutions, even those of acids or bases. If we know the concentration of one of the ions we can always find the concentration of the other using K_w.

HCl would increase the [H⁺]. NaOH would increase the [OH⁻].

Figure 18·5
Which of these reagents would increase the hydrogen ion concentration when added to an aqueous solution? Which would increase the hydroxide ion concentration?

Example 1

If $[H^+] = 1.0 \times 10^{-5}$ mol/L, is the solution acidic, basic, or neutral? What is the $[OH^-]$ of this solution?

Solution

The $[H^+]$ is 1.0×10^{-5} mol/L. Because this is greater than 1.0×10^{-7} mol/L, the solution is acidic. We know that $K_w = [H^+] \times [OH^-]$. Therefore the $[OH^-] = K_w/[H^+]$. Substituting the numerical values $K_w = 1.0 \times 10^{-14}$ (mol/L)² and $[H^+] = 1.0 \times 10^{-5}$ mol/L, we can compute $[OH^-]$.

$$[OH^-] = \frac{1.0 \times 10^{-14} \text{ (mol/L)}^2}{1.0 \times 10^{-5} \text{ (mol/L)}} = 1.0 \times 10^{-9} \text{ mol/L}$$

1. 1×10^{-11} mol/L; basic.

Problem

1. If the hydroxide-ion concentration of an aqueous solution is 1.0×10^{-3} mol/L, what is the $[H^+]$ in the solution? Is the solution acidic, basic, or neutral?

Before reading this section you should review logarithms by doing Section B·5 of the Math Review in Appendix B.

■ The pH scale is used to express hydrogen-ion concentrations.

18·3 The pH Concept

The expression of hydrogen-ion concentration in moles per liter is cumbersome. A more widely used system is the pH scale. It was proposed in 1909 by the Danish scientist Søren Sørensen (1868–1939). *The* **pH** *of a solution is the negative logarithm of the hydrogen-ion concentration.*

$$pH = -\log[H^+]$$

In a neutral solution the $[H^+] = 1 \times 10^{-7}$ mol/L. The pH of a neutral solution is 7.

$$\begin{aligned} pH &= -\log(1 \times 10^{-7}) \\ &= -(\log 1 + \log 10^{-7}) \\ &= -(0.0 + (-7)) \\ &= 7.0 \end{aligned}$$

To calculate pH, concentrations must be expressed in exponential form. For example, a hydrogen-ion concentration of $0.001M$ is rewritten as $1 \times 10^{-3}M$. The pH of this solution is 3.0. Neutral solutions have a pH of 7.0. A pH of 0 is strongly acidic. A pH of 14 is strongly basic.

In a similar way, the pOH of a solution equals the negative logarithm of the hydroxide ion concentration.

$$pOH = -\log[OH^-]$$

A neutral solution has a pOH of 7.0. A solution with a pOH of less than 7.0 is basic. A solution with a pOH of greater than 7.0 is acidic.

Figure 18·6
The pH scale shows the relationship between pH and the hydrogen-ion concentration. Notice that acids have lower pHs than bases.

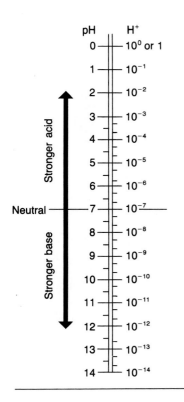

Example 2

The hydrogen-ion concentration of a solution is 1×10^{-10} mol/L. What is the pH of the solution?

Solution

We know that the $[H^+] = 1 \times 10^{-10}$ mol/L.

$$\begin{aligned} pH &= -\log[H^+] \\ &= -\log(1 \times 10^{-10}) \\ &= -(0.0 + (-10)) \\ &= 10.0 \end{aligned}$$

A solution in which the $[OH^-]$ is 1×10^{-10} mol/L has a pH of 10.0.

Problem

2. Determine the pH of the following solutions.
    a. $[H^+] = 1 \times 10^{-10}$ mol/L
    c. $[H^+] = 0.001M$
    b. $[OH^-] = 1 \times 10^{-2}$ mol/L
    d. $[OH^-] = 1 \times 10^{-11}$ mol/L

Example 3

The pH of a solution is 6.0. What is the hydrogen-ion concentration?

Solution

To do this problem we work backward.

$$pH = -\log[H^+]$$
$$6.0 = -\log[H^+]$$
$$-6.0 = \log[H^+]$$

The number whose log is -6.0 is 1×10^{-6}. Therefore the $[H^+] = 1 \times 10^{-6}$ mol/L.

Problems

3. What are the hydrogen-ion concentrations for solutions with the following pH values?   **a.** 4.0 **b.** 11.0 **c.** 8.0

4. What are the hydroxide-ion concentrations for solutions with the following pH values?   **a.** 6.0 **b.** 9.0 **c.** 12.0

3. **a.** $1 \times 10^{-4}M$
  b. $1 \times 10^{-11}M$
  c. $1 \times 10^{-8}M$
4. **a.** $1 \times 10^{-8}M$
  b. $1 \times 10^{-5}M$
  c. $1 \times 10^{-2}M$

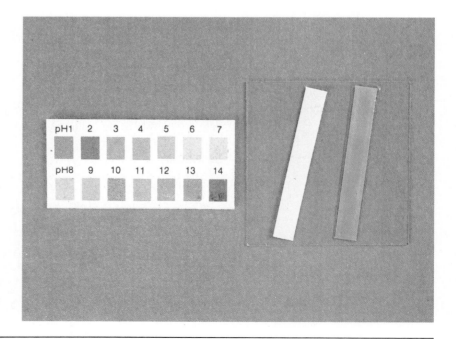

pH = 7. The sample is neutral, neither acid nor base.

Figure 18·7
You can determine the approximate pH of a substance by testing it with pH test paper and comparing the color with the standards. What is the pH of the sample tested with the pH test paper at the right? Is it an acid or base?

Table 18·1   Relationship between the [H⁺], the [OH⁻], and pH

[H⁺] (mol/L)	[OH⁻] (mol/L)	pH	Aqueous system
1×10^{0}	1×10^{-14}	0.0	$1M$ HCl (0.0)
1×10^{-1}	1×10^{-13}	1.0	$0.1M$ HCl (1.0)
1×10^{-2}	1×10^{-12}	2.0	Gastric juice (1.6–1.8)
1×10^{-3}	1×10^{-11}	3.0	Lemon juice (2.3), vinegar (2.4–3.4)
1×10^{-4}	1×10^{-10}	4.0	Soda water (3.8), tomato juice (4.2)
1×10^{-5}	1×10^{-9}	5.0	Black coffee (5.0)
1×10^{-6}	1×10^{-8}	6.0	Milk (6.3–6.6), urine (5.5–7.0)
1×10^{-7}	1×10^{-7}	7.0	Pure water (7.0), saliva (6.2–7.4)
1×10^{-8}	1×10^{-6}	8.0	Blood (7.35–7.45), bile (7.8–8.6)
1×10^{-9}	1×10^{-5}	9.0	Sodium bicarbonate (8.4), sea water (8.4)
1×10^{-10}	1×10^{-4}	10.0	Milk of magnesia (10.5)
1×10^{-11}	1×10^{-3}	11.0	Household ammonia (11.5)
1×10^{-12}	1×10^{-2}	12.0	Washing soda (12.0)
1×10^{-13}	1×10^{-1}	13.0	$0.1M$ NaOH (13.0)
1×10^{-14}	1×10^{0}	14.0	$1M$ NaOH (14.0)

Increasing acidity → *Neutral* → *Increasing basicity*

Remind the students that they are dealing with negative exponents here. 10^{-3} is a *larger* number than 10^{-6}.

Students are sometimes confused by the fact that a *lower* pH value means a *higher* degree of acidity.

In an acidic solution [H⁺] > [OH⁻]. In a basic solution [H⁺] < [OH⁻].

The pH of pure water or a neutral aqueous solution is 7.0. A solution in which the [H⁺] is greater than 1×10^{-7} mol/L has a pH less than 7.0 and is acidic. A solution that has a pH greater than 7.0 is basic and has a [H⁺] of less than 1×10^{-7} mol/L.

- *Neutral solution:* pH equals 7.0; the [H⁺] equals 1×10^{-7} mol/L.
- *Acidic solution:* pH is less than 7.0; the [H⁺] is greater than 1×10^{-7} mol/L.
- *Basic solution:* pH is greater than 7.0; the [H⁺] is less than 1×10^{-7} mol/L.

Table 18·1 gives the pH values of a number of common aqueous solutions. It also summarizes the relationships between the [H⁺], the [OH⁻], and pH. You may notice that pH can sometimes be read easily from the value of the [H⁺]. If the [H⁺] is written in standard exponential form and has a characteristic of exactly 1, the pH of the solution equals the exponent with the sign changed from minus to plus. For example, a solution with a $[H^+] = 1 \times 10^{-2}$ has a pH of 2.

Problem

5. a. 4.0   c. 9.0
   b. 3.0   d. 10.0

5. Give the pH of each of the following solutions.
   a. $[H^+] = 1 \times 10^{-4}$
   b. $[H^+] = 0.001$
   c. $[H^+] = 1 \times 10^{-9}$
   d. $[H^+] = 100 \times 10^{-12}$

18·4 Calculating pH Values

Most pH values are not whole numbers. For example, Table 18·1 shows that milk of magnesia has a pH of 10.5. Using the definition of pH, this means that the $[H^+]$ must equal $1 \times 10^{-10.5}$. Therefore the $[H^+]$ must be less than 1×10^{-10} (pH 10.0) but greater than 1×10^{-11} (pH 11.0).

When the $[H^+]$ is written in standard exponential form but its coefficient is *not* 1, then a table of common logarithms is needed to calculate pH. A four-place log table is in Appendix B·5. The following example shows how such a calculation is made.

■ The $[H^+]$ and $[OH^-]$ can be calculated from a measurement of pH.

Example 4

What is the pH of a solution if the $[OH^-] = 4.0 \times 10^{-11}$ mol/L?

Solution

To calculate pH, first calculate the $[H^+]$. Use the definition of K_w.

$$K_w = [OH^-] \times [H^+]$$

$$[H^+] = \frac{K_w}{[OH^-]} = \frac{1.0 \times 10^{-14}}{4.0 \times 10^{-11}} = 0.25 \times 10^{-3}$$

$$= 2.5 \times 10^{-4} \text{ mol/L}$$

Then solve for the pH using the definition of pH.

$$pH = -\log[H^+]$$

$$pH = -\log (2.5 \times 10^{-4})$$

$$= -(\log 2.5 + \log 10^{-4})$$

$\log (a \times b) = \log a + \log b$

Use the log table to find the value of log 2.5. By inspection, log $10^{-4} = -4$.

The log table is in Appendix B·5. Some calculators also give logs.

$$pH = -(0.40) - (-4)$$

$$= -0.40 + 4$$

$$= 3.60$$

Problem

6. a. 5.30   c. 9.30
   b. 9.08   d. 3.66

6. Calculate the pH for each solution.
   a. $[H^+] = 5.0 \times 10^{-6}$ c. $[OH^-] = 2.0 \times 10^{-5}$
   b. $[H^+] = 8.3 \times 10^{-10}$ d. $[OH^-] = 4.5 \times 10^{-11}$

The hydrogen-ion concentration of a solution can be calculated if the pH is known. If the pH of a solution is 3.0, for example, then the $[H^+] = 1 \times 10^{-3}$ mol/L. When the pH is not a whole number, log tables are needed to calculate the hydrogen-ion concentration. For example, if the pH is 3.7 the hydrogen-ion concentration must be greater than 1×10^{-4} mol/L (pH 4.0) and less than 1×10^{-3} mol/L (pH 3.0). To get an accurate value use log tables.

Example 5

What is the $[H^+]$ of a solution if the pH = 3.7?

Solution

First rearrange the equation: pH = $-\log[H^+]$.

$$\log[H^+] = -pH = -3.7$$

You cannot use a log table directly to find a number whose log is negative. To get around this problem, add and subtract the whole number that is closest to and larger than the negative log. In this case, the negative log is 3.7, and the whole number is 4.

$$\log[H^+] = (-3.7 + 4) - 4$$
$$= 0.3 - 4$$
$$[H^+] = 10^{(0.3-4)}$$
$$= 10^{0.3} \times 10^{-4}$$

From the log table, the number whose log is 0.3 is 2. Thus the antilog of 0.3 is 2. The number whose log is -4 is 10^{-4}. Therefore the $[H^+] = 2 \times 10^{-4}$ mol/L.

Problem

7. a. $1 \times 10^{-5}M$
b. $1.6 \times 10^{-6}M$
c. $6.3 \times 10^{-13}M$
d. $2.3 \times 10^{-3}M$

7. Calculate the $[H^+]$ for each solution.
 a. pH = 5.0   c. pH = 12.20
 b. pH = 5.80   d. pH = 2.64

Figure 18·8
Svante Arrhenius received a Nobel Prize for his revolutionary work in chemistry.

18·B   Arrhenius Led the Way

Svante Arrhenius (1859–1927) studied the electrical conductivity of solutions. At the time the structure of the atom was completely unknown. The nature of the particles responsible for electricity was also unknown. Certain solutions were known to be capable of conducting electricity. The solutes of those solutions were called electrolytes. Solutes that would not conduct electricity while in solution were called nonelectrolytes.

Some chemists noticed that solutes caused a depression in the freezing point of solvents (Section 16·7). It was thought that this property was related to the number of particles in the solution. The electrolyte sodium chloride (NaCl) caused twice the expected freezing point depression. Barium chloride ($BaCl_2$) produced three times the expected freezing point depression.

From these observations Arrhenius proposed that electrolytic compounds broke into particles when they dissolved. Depending upon the composition of the solute some solute particles could break

into two or more parts. This is called electrolytic dissociation. It was consistent with the idea that the freezing point depression depended on the number of particles. Arrhenius also reasoned that the constituent parts must be electrically charged. This accounted for two critical observations that had not been explained at the time. First, the elements from the compounds were not apparent in the solution. Second, the solution conducted electricity. Arrhenius later extended his concepts of electrolytic dissociation to explain certain behaviors of acids and bases.

The idea of electrically charged solute particles was not readily accepted. (This is often the case for new concepts.) Arrhenius was given the lowest possible grade for his Ph.D. defense of this theory in 1884. In the following decade, however, numerous discoveries undermined the idea that the atom was structureless. When Thomson discovered the negatively charged electron in the 1890s, Arrhenius's ideas gained acceptance. In 1903 Arrhenius's work was formally recognized when he received the Nobel Prize in Chemistry.

Arrhenius' theory is sometimes referred to as the theory of ionization.

18·5   Arrhenius Acids and Bases

In 1887 the young Swedish chemist Svante Arrhenius proposed a revolutionary way of thinking about acids and bases. He said that *acids are compounds containing hydrogen that ionize to yield hydrogen ions (H^+) in aqueous solution.* Similarly, he said that *bases are compounds that ionize to yield hydroxide ions (OH^-) in aqueous solution.*

Table 18·2 lists some important acids. Nitric acid (HNO_3) and *any acid that contains one ionizable hydrogen is called a* **monoprotic acid.** Sulfuric acid (H_2SO_4) and *any acid that contains two ionizable protons is a* **diprotic acid.** Phosphoric acid (H_3PO_4) and *any acid that contains three ionizable protons is a* **triprotic acid.** Do not assume that all compounds containing hydrogen are acids or that all the hydrogens in an acid are released as hydrogen ions. Only the hydrogens in very polar bonds are ionizable. These are bonds in which hydrogen is joined to a very electronegative element. Hydrogen ions are released when compounds

■ In aqueous solutions acids release hydrogen ions, and bases release hydroxide ions.

The acids and bases the students are most likely to encounter are Arrhenius acids and bases.

Safety

Nitric acid is very reactive and should be stored separately from other acids.

Table 18·2	Some Common Acids	
	Name	Formula
	Hydrochloric acid	HCl
	Nitric acid	HNO_3
	Sulfuric acid	H_2SO_4
	Phosphoric acid	H_3PO_4
	Acetic acid	CH_3COOH
	Carbonic acid	H_2CO_3

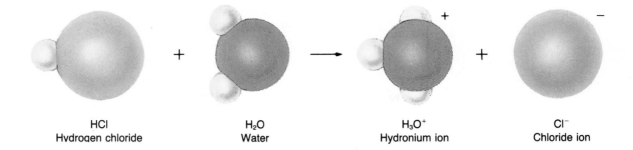

HCl	H₂O	H₃O⁺	Cl⁻
Hydrogen chloride	Water	Hydronium ion	Chloride ion

Figure 18·9
Hydrochloric acid is actually hydrogen chloride dissolved in water. The ionized hydrogen forms hydronium ions and makes this compound an acid.

that contain such bonds dissolve in water. This is because the hydrogen ions are stabilized by solvation. The hydrogen chloride molecule, for example, is a polar covalent molecule. It ionizes to form hydrochloric acid in aqueous solution.

$$\overset{\delta+ \quad \delta-}{H\text{---}Cl}(g) \xrightarrow{\text{water}} H^+(aq) + Cl^-(aq)$$

$$\underset{\text{Hydrogen chloride}}{} \qquad \underset{\substack{\text{Hydrogen} \\ \text{ion}}}{} \underset{\substack{\text{Chloride} \\ \text{ion} \\ \text{(hydrochloric acid)}}}{}$$

By contrast, the four hydrogens in methane (CH_4) are in weakly polar C—H bonds. Methane has no ionizable hydrogens and is not an acid. Acetic acid (CH_3COOH) is different. Although each molecule contains four hydrogens, acetic acid is a monoprotic acid. The structural formula shows why.

$$H\text{---}\overset{\overset{\displaystyle H}{|}}{\underset{\underset{\displaystyle H}{|}}{C}}\text{---}\overset{\overset{\displaystyle O}{\|}}{C}\text{---}O\text{---}H$$

Acetic acid
(CH_3COOH)

The three hydrogens attached to carbon are in weakly polar bonds. They do not ionize. Only the hydrogen attached to oxygen is ionizable. As you see more written formulas, you will be able to recognize ionizable hydrogens.

Problem   **8. a.** diprotic   **b.** triprotic   **c.** monoprotic

8. Identify the following acids as monoprotic, diprotic, or triprotic.
   a. H_2CO_3 **b.** H_3PO_4 **c.** HCl

Table 18·3 lists some common bases. The base with which you are perhaps most familiar is sodium hydroxide (NaOH). This is ordinary lye. Sodium metal reacts with water to form sodium hydroxide.

$$2Na + 2H_2O \longrightarrow 2NaOH + H_2$$

$$\underset{\substack{\text{Sodium} \\ \text{metal}}}{} \quad \underset{\text{Water}}{} \qquad \underset{\substack{\text{Sodium} \\ \text{hydroxide}}}{} \underset{\text{Hydrogen}}{}$$

Figure 18·10
Hydrochloric acid, commonly known as muriatic acid, is used to clean stone buildings and swimming pools.

Figure 18·11
Sodium hydroxide is used to clean clogged drains because it is very corrosive.

Table 18·3	Some Common Bases	
Name	Formula	Solubility in water
Potassium hydroxide	KOH	High
Sodium hydroxide	NaOH	High
Calcium hydroxide	$Ca(OH)_2$	Very low
Magnesium hydroxide	$Mg(OH)_2$	Very low

Potassium reacts vigorously with water to produce potassium hydroxide (KOH). Both sodium hydroxide and potassium hydroxide are ionic solids. They dissociate completely into the metal ions and hydroxide ions when dissolved in water.

$$NaOH \xrightarrow{\text{water}} Na^+(aq) + OH^-(aq)$$

Sodium
Hydroxide   Sodium   Hydroxide
                    ion   ion

Sodium and potassium are Group 1A elements. They are named the alkali metals because they react with water to produce alkaline solutions. Metal oxides also react with water to produce alkaline solutions.

Both sodium hydroxide and potassium hydroxide are very soluble in water. Concentrated solutions of these compounds are readily prepared. Such solutions would have a bitter taste and feel slippery. Note, however, that they are extremely corrosive to the skin. They can cause painful, deep, slow-healing wounds if not immediately washed off. Calcium hydroxide, $Ca(OH)_2$, and magnesium hydroxide, $Mg(OH)_2$, are both hydroxides of Group 2A metals. They are not very soluble in water. Consequently, their solutions are always very dilute, even when saturated. The concentration of hydroxide ions in such solutions is correspondingly low.

A saturated solution of calcium hydroxide contains 0.165 g of $Ca(OH)_2$ per 100 g of water. Limewater is an aqueous suspension of solid calcium hydroxide. Magnesium hydroxide is much less soluble than calcium hydroxide. A saturated solution contains only 0.0009 g of $Mg(OH)_2$ per 100 g of water. Suspensions of solid magnesium hydroxide in water contain low concentrations of hydroxide ion. They are taken internally as "milk of magnesia," an antacid or mild laxative.

Safety

Never taste bases or any other chemical in the laboratory.

Problems

9. a. $2K + 2H_2O \rightarrow 2KOH + H_2$
b. $Ca + 2H_2O \rightarrow Ca(OH)_2 + H_2$
10. a. $KOH \rightarrow K^+ + OH^-$
b. $Mg(OH)_2 \rightarrow Mg^{2+} + 2OH^-$

9. Write a balanced equation for each reaction.
   a. Potasssium metal reacts with water.
   b. Calcium metal reacts with water.

10. Write the reaction for the dissociation of each compound in water.
   a. potassium hydroxide   **b.** magnesium hydroxide

18·6 Brønsted–Lowry Acids and Bases

One problem with the Arrhenius theory is that it is not comprehensive enough. It does not explain the behavior of all compounds that behave as bases. For example, aqueous solutions of ammonia (NH_3) and sodium carbonate (Na_2CO_3) are basic. Neither of these compounds is a hydroxide. In 1923 Johannes Brønsted (Danish; 1879–1947) and Thomas Lowry (English; 1874–1936) independently proposed a new theory. *The Brønsted–Lowry theory defines an acid as a* **hydrogen-ion donor.** Similarly, a *Brønsted–Lowry base is a* **hydrogen-ion acceptor.** All the acids and bases included in the Arrhenius theory are also acids and bases according to the Brønsted–Lowry theory. Some compounds that were not included in the Arrhenius theory are classified as bases in the Brønsted–Lowry theory.

A Brønsted–Lowry acid is a hydrogen-ion donor. A Brønsted–Lowry base is a hydrogen-ion acceptor.

The behavior of ammonia as a base can be understood by the Brønsted–Lowry theory. Ammonia gas is very soluble in water. When ammonia dissolves it acts as a base because it accepts a hydrogen ion from water.

$$NH_3 \ + \ H_2O \ \rightleftharpoons \ NH_4^+ \ + \ OH^-$$

Ammonia (hydrogen-ion acceptor, Brønsted–Lowry base) Water (hydrogen-ion donor, Brønsted–Lowry acid) Ammonium ion Hydroxide ion (makes the solution basic)

In this reaction ammonia is the hydrogen-ion acceptor. Therefore it is a Brønsted–Lowry base. Water, the hydrogen-ion donor, is a Brønsted–Lowry acid. Hydrogen ions are transferred from water to ammonia. This causes the hydroxide-ion concentration to be greater than it is in pure water. As a result, solutions of ammonia are basic.

Heating an aqueous solution of ammonia drives off ammonia gas. This action causes the equilibrium in the ammonia dissolution equation to shift to the left. The ammonium ion, NH_4^+, reacts with OH^- to form NH_3 and H_2O. When the reaction goes from right to left, NH_4^+ gives up a hydrogen ion; it acts as a Brønsted–Lowry acid. The hydroxide ion accepts a H^+; it acts as a Brønsted–Lowry base. Overall then, this equilibrium has two acids and two bases.

$$NH_3 \ + \ H_2O \ \rightleftharpoons \ NH_4^+ \ + \ OH^-$$

Base Acid Conjugate acid Conjugate base

Safety

Ammonia is a very irritating gas. Use care when smelling chemicals. Wave your hand over the open container to waft the aroma to your nose.

It is not a hydroxide.
Figure 18·12
Ammonia dissolves in water to form ammonium ions and hydroxide ions. Why is ammonia not classified as an Arrhenius base?

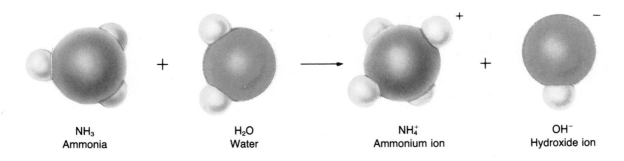

NH$_3$
Ammonia

H$_2$O
Water

NH$_4^+$
Ammonium ion

OH$^-$
Hydroxide ion

When ammonia dissolves, NH_4^+ is the conjugate acid of the base NH_3. *A* **conjugate acid** *is the particle formed when a base gains a hydrogen ion.* Similarly, OH^- is the conjugate base of the acid water. *A* **conjugate base** *is the particle that remains when an acid has donated a hydrogen ion.* Conjugate acids and bases are always paired with an acid and a base. *A* **conjugate acid-base pair** *is two substances that are related by the loss or gain of a single hydrogen ion.* The ammonia molecule and ammonium ion are a conjugate acid–base pair. The water molecule and hydroxide ion are also a conjugate acid–base pair.

The conjugate acid of a strong base is a weak acid. The conjugate base of a strong acid is a weak base.

$$\underset{\text{Base}}{NH_3} + \underset{\text{Acid}}{H_2O} \rightleftharpoons \underset{\substack{\text{Conjugate} \\ \text{acid}}}{NH_4^+} + \underset{\substack{\text{Conjugate} \\ \text{base}}}{OH^-}$$

The reaction between an acid and a base always produces a new acid and a new base.

A strong Brønsted–Lowry acid gives up its hydrogen ion easily.

The Brønsted–Lowry theory is also applicable to acids. Consider the ionization of hydrogen chloride in water.

$$\underset{\text{Acid}}{HCl} + \underset{\text{Base}}{H_2O} \rightleftharpoons \underset{\substack{\text{Conjugate} \\ \text{acid}}}{H_3O^+} + \underset{\substack{\text{Conjugate} \\ \text{base}}}{Cl^-}$$

In this reaction hydrogen chloride is the hydrogen-ion donor. It is therefore a Brønsted–Lowry acid. Water is the hydrogen-ion acceptor. It is a Brønsted–Lowry base. The chloride ion is the conjugate base of the acid HCl. The hydronium ion is the conjugate acid of the base water.

You may have noticed that water has a split personality. Sometimes water receives a hydrogen ion. At other times it donates a hydrogen ion. *A substance that can act as both an acid and a base is termed* **amphoteric.** Water is amphoteric. Brønsted–Lowry bases are substances capable of pulling a hydrogen ion from water. Brønsted–Lowry acids are substances capable of donating a hydrogen ion to water.

The hydronium ion is the conjugate acid. The hydrogen sulfate ion is the conjugate base.

Figure 18·13
When sulfuric acid dissolves in water it forms hydronium ions and hydrogen sulfate ions. Which ion is the conjugate acid and which is the conjugate base?

Problem   See the answer in Appendix C.

11. Write equations for the ionization of HNO_3 and Na_2CO_3 in water.
a. Identify the hydrogen-ion donor and hydrogen-ion acceptor in each case.   **b.** Label the conjugate acid–base pairs.

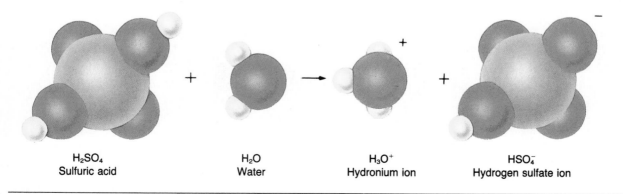

H_2SO_4
Sulfuric acid

H_2O
Water

H_3O^+
Hydronium ion

HSO_4^-
Hydrogen sulfate ion

Figure 18·14
Acid−base indicators respond to pH changes over a specific range. Methyl orange (top row) is shown at pH 2, 4, and 6 (left to right). Bromthymol blue (bottom row) is shown at pH 5, 7, and 9.

Figure 18·15
Acid rain has a pH of less than 5.6. It damages stonework, soil, and vegetation and can kill many freshwater organisms.

18·C Measuring pH

Chemists must be able to measure the pH of the solutions they use. For preliminary pH measurements and for small volume samples, indicators are often used. For precise and continuous measurements, a pH meter is preferred.

An *indicator* (In) is a weak acid or base that undergoes dissociation in a known pH range. In this range the acid (or base) is a different color from its conjugate base (or acid). The following generalized equation represents this process.

$$\underset{\text{Acid}}{\text{HIn}} \underset{\text{H}^+}{\overset{\text{OH}^-}{\rightleftharpoons}} \text{H}^+ + \underset{\substack{\text{Conjugate} \\ \text{base}}}{\text{In}^-}$$

Each indicator is only useful over a pH range of approximately two units. Many different indicators are needed to span the entire pH spectrum. Figure 18·16 shows some commonly used indicators.

Indicators are useful tools. They have certain characteristics, however, that limit their use. The listed pH values of indicators are usually given for 25°C. At other temperatures, an indicator may change color at a different pH. If the solution being tested has a color of its own, the color of the indicator may be distorted. Dissolved salts in a solution may also change the indicator's dissociation. Often, these problems can be overcome by using indicator strips. An indicator strip is a piece of paper or plastic that has an indicator bonded to it. This strip is dipped into the unknown solution and compared with a color chart. Some pH paper contains multiple indicators so that it can indicate pHs from 1 to 14.

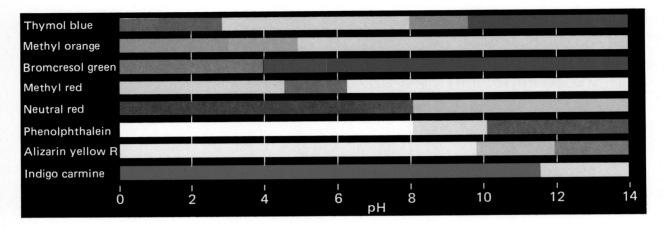

Figure 18·16
Each indicator changes color at a dif-
different pH. What indicator would
you choose to show that a reaction
solution has changed from
pH 3 to pH 6?

Bromcresol green.

Most chemistry laboratories have a pH meter. It is used to make rapid, accurate measurements of pH. If a pH meter is connected to a strip chart, it can be used to make a continuous recording of pH changes.

The structure of the pH meter is shown in Figure 18·17. It consists of two electrodes connected to a millivoltmeter. The reference electrode has a constant voltage. The voltage of the glass electrode changes with the $[H_3O^+]$ in the solution in which it is dipped. The pH meter makes an electrical measurement of pH by comparing the voltages of the two electrodes. The millivoltmeter gives a readout directly as pH.

Before a pH meter is used, it must be calibrated. The electrodes are dipped into a solution of known pH. The readout of the millivoltmeter is adjusted to that pH. The electrodes are then rinsed with distilled water and dipped into the solution of unknown pH. The electrodes may be left in the solution so that continuous readings of pH can be made.

Figure 18·17
A pH meter is used to measure
hydrogen ion concentrations. The instrument consists of two electrodes: a
glass electrode and a reference electrode. A meter measures the voltage
difference between the two electrodes
and gives a pH reading. The meter
may be connected to a strip-chart
recorder.

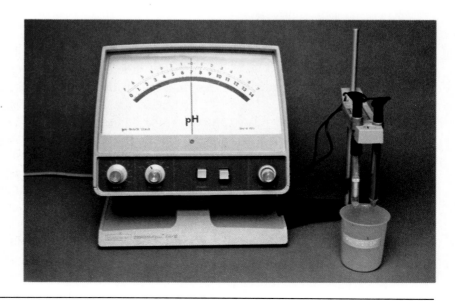

A pH meter is a valuable instrument. In many situations it is easier to use than liquid indicators or indicator strips. Values of pH obtained with a pH meter are typically accurate to within a 0.01 pH unit of the true pH. The color and cloudiness of the unknown solution do not affect the accuracy of the pH value obtained. Hospitals use pH meters to find small but meaningful changes of pH in blood and other body fluids (Figure 19·9). Sewage and industrial effluents are easily monitored with a pH meter.

18·7   Lewis Acids and Bases

A third theory of acids and bases was proposed by Gilbert Lewis (1875–1946). He focused on the donation or acceptance of a pair of electrons during a reaction. This concept is more general than either the Arrhenius theory or the Brønsted–Lowry theory. A **Lewis acid** *is a substance that can accept a pair of electrons to form a covalent bond.* A **Lewis base** *is a substance that can donate a pair of electrons to form a covalent bond.* Brønsted–Lowry acids and bases are also Lewis acids and bases. A hydrogen ion (Brønsted–Lowry acid) can accept a pair of electrons in forming a bond. A hydrogen ion, therefore, is also a Lewis acid. A substance that accepts a hydrogen ion (Brønsted–Lowry base) must have a pair of electrons available (Lewis base).

A Lewis acid is an electron-pair acceptor. A Lewis base is an electron-pair donor.

Consider the reaction of H$^+$ and OH$^-$.

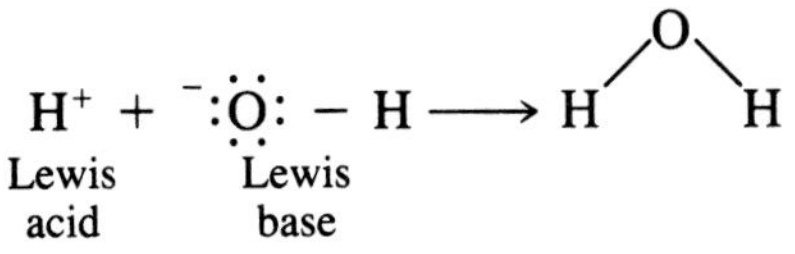

$$\text{H}^+ + \ ^-\!\!:\!\overset{..}{\underset{..}{\text{O}}}\!:\!-\text{H} \longrightarrow \text{H}\overset{\text{O}}{\diagup}\diagdown\text{H}$$

Lewis acid   Lewis base

A hydroxide ion is a Lewis base. It is also a Brønsted–Lowry base. A hydrogen ion is both a Lewis acid and a Brønsted–Lowry acid. The Lewis theory also includes some compounds that are not classified as Brønsted-Lowry acids or bases.

Example 6

Identify the Lewis acid and the Lewis base in this reaction.

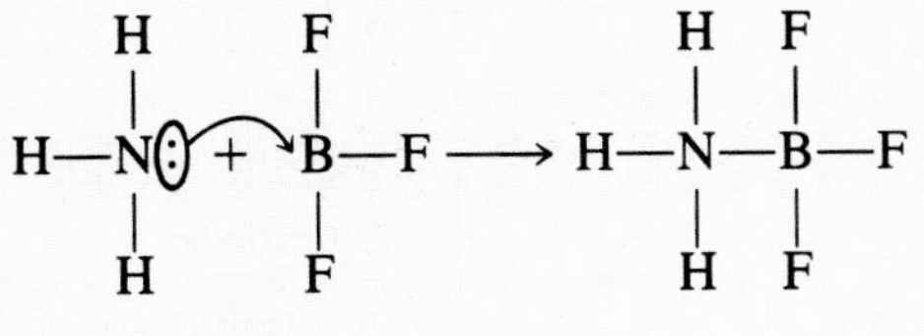

Note that this acid-base reaction does not involve the transfer of a hydrogen ion. A Lewis acid does not need to contain any hydrogen ions.

$$
\begin{array}{ccc}
& \text{H} \quad\quad \text{F} & \text{H} \quad \text{F} \\
& | \quad\quad\ \ | & | \quad\ | \\
\text{H}-\text{N}\!:\!+\ \text{B}-\text{F} & \longrightarrow & \text{H}-\text{N}-\text{B}-\text{F} \\
& | \quad\quad\ \ | & | \quad\ | \\
& \text{H} \quad\quad \text{F} & \text{H} \quad \text{F}
\end{array}
$$

Solution

Ammonia is donating a pair of electrons. Ammonia is a Lewis base. Boron trifluoride is accepting a pair of electrons. It is a Lewis acid.

12. a. H^+ is the Lewis acid; H_2O is the Lewis base.
b. $AlCl_3$ is the Lewis acid; Cl^- is the Lewis base.

A strong acid or a strong base is completely dissociated in aqueous solution.

For strong acids or bases the equilibrium favors the products. For weak acids or bases the equilibrium favors the reactants.

Problem

12. Identify the Lewis acid and Lewis base in each reaction.

a. $H^+ + H\overset{\cdot\cdot}{\underset{}{O}}H \longrightarrow H_3O^+$ **b.** $AlCl_3 + Cl^- \longrightarrow AlCl_4^-$

18·8 The Strengths of Acids and Bases

Chemists classify acids as strong or weak depending on the degree to which the acids ionize in water. For practical purposes, **strong acids** *are completely ionized in aqueous solution.* Hydrochloric acid and sulfuric acid are strong acids.

$$HCl \longrightarrow H^+ + Cl^- \text{ (100\% dissociated)}$$

Weak acids *ionize only slightly in aqueous solution.* The ionization of acetic acid, a typical weak acid, is not complete.

$$\underset{\substack{\text{Acetic} \\ \text{acid}}}{CH_3COOH} + \underset{\text{Water}}{H_2O} \rightleftharpoons \underset{\substack{\text{Hydronium} \\ \text{ion}}}{H_3O^+} + \underset{\substack{\text{Acetate} \\ \text{ion}}}{CH_3COO^-}$$

Over 99% of acetic acid molecules exist in solution as undissociated co-valent molecules (CH_3COOH). Less than 1% are ionized at any instant. Table 18·4 gives the relative strength of some common acids and bases.

Table 18·4 Relative Strengths of Common Acids and Bases		
Substance	Formula	Relative Strength
Hydrochloric acid	HCl	Strong acids
Nitric acid	HNO_3	
Sulfuric acid	H_2SO_4	
Phosphoric acid	H_3PO_4	
Acetic acid	$HC_2H_3O_2$	Increasing strength
Carbonic acid	H_2CO_3	
Hydrosulfuric acid	H_2S	
Hypochlorous acid	HClO	
Boric acid	H_3BO_3	
		Neutral solution
Sodium cyanide	NaCN	
Ammonia	NH_3	Increasing strength
Methylamine	CH_3NH_2	
Sodium silicate	NaSiO	
Calcium hydroxide	$Ca(OH)_2$	
Sodium hydroxide	NaOH	Strong bases
Potassium hydroxide	KOH	

Figure 18·18
Which of these pH test papers has been dipped into 1.0*M* hydrochloric acid and which has been dipped into 1.0*M* acetic acid?
The paper on the left has been dipped into hydrochloric acid. The paper on the right has been dipped into acetic acid.

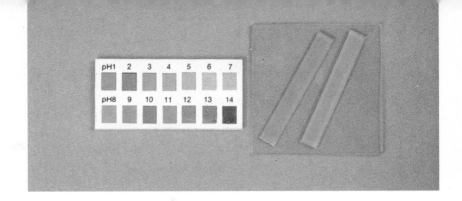

The equilibrium-constant expression for the ionization of acetic acid can be written from the preceding equation.

$$K_{eq} = \frac{[H_3O^+] \times [CH_3COO^-]}{[CH_3COOH] \times [H_2O]}$$

For dilute solutions the concentration of water is a constant. It can be combined with K_{eq} to give an acid dissociation constant. *An* **acid dissociation constant** *(K_a) is the ratio of the concentration of the dissociated form of an acid to the undissociated form.* The dissociated form includes both the H^+ and the anion.

$$K_{eq} \times [H_2O] = K_a = \frac{[H^+] \times [CH_3COO^-]}{[CH_3COOH]}$$

The acid dissociation constant, K_a, for acetic acid at 25°C is 1.8×10^{-5}.

The acid dissociation constant, K_a, reflects that fraction of an acid that is in the ionized form. For this reason dissociation constants are sometimes called ionization constants. If the value of the ionization constant, K_a, is small then the dissociation of the acid in the solution is small. Weak acids have small K_a values. A larger value of K_a means that the dissociation, or ionization, of the acid is more complete. Strong acids have large K_a values. For example, nitrous acid has a K_a of 4.4×10^{-4} whereas acetic acid has a K_a of 1.8×10^{-5}. Nitrous acid is a stronger acid than acetic acid. This means that nitrous acid is more ionized, or dissociated, in solution than acetic acid.

Diprotic and triprotic acids lose their hydrogens one at a time. Each ionization reaction has a separate ionization constant, K_a. Thus phosphoric acid, H_3PO_4, has three ionization constants to go with its three ionizable hydrogens. Table 18·5 shows the ionization reactions and ionization constants for some common acids. The acids are ranked by the value of the first ionization constant for each acid.

Problems

13. boric acid
14. strongest: oxalic acid
weakest: carbonic acid

13. Which acid in Table 18·4 would you expect to have the lowest ionization constant?

14. Based on the first ionization constant, which acid in Table 18·5 is the strongest? Which is weakest?

Table 18·5   Dissociation Constants of Weak Acids

Acid	Ionization	$K_a(25°C)$
Oxalic Acid	$H_2C_2O_4(aq) \rightleftharpoons H^+(aq) + HC_2O_4^-(aq)$	5.6×10^{-2}
	$HC_2O_4^-(aq) \rightleftharpoons H^+(aq) + C_2O_4^{2-}(aq)$	5.1×10^{-5}
Phosphoric Acid	$H_3PO_4(aq) \rightleftharpoons H^+(aq) + H_2PO_4^-(aq)$	7.5×10^{-3}
	$H_2PO_4^-(aq) \rightleftharpoons H^+(aq) + HPO_4^{2-}(aq)$	6.2×10^{-8}
	$HPO_4^{2-}(aq) \rightleftharpoons H^+(aq) + PO_4^{3-}(aq)$	4.8×10^{-13}
Formic Acid	$HCOOH(aq) \rightleftharpoons H^+(aq) + HCOO^-(aq)$	1.8×10^{-4}
Benzoic Acid	$C_6H_5COOH(aq) \rightleftharpoons H^+(aq) + C_6H_5COO^-(aq)$	6.3×10^{-5}
Acetic Acid	$CH_3COOH(aq) \rightleftharpoons H^+(aq) + CH_3COO^-(aq)$	1.8×10^{-5}
Carbonic Acid	$H_2CO_3(aq) \rightleftharpoons H^+(aq) + HCO_3^-(aq)$	4.3×10^{-7}
	$HCO_3^-(aq) \rightleftharpoons H^+(aq) + CO_3^{2-}(aq)$	4.8×10^{-11}

Just as there are strong acids and weak acids, there are also strong bases and weak bases. All the bases in Table 18·3 are classified as strong bases. **Strong bases** *dissociate completely into metal ions and hydroxide ions in aqueous solution.* (Some bases, such as calcium hydroxide and magnesium hydroxide, are not very soluble in water. The small amounts of those bases that do dissolve dissociate completely.) Unlike strong bases, **weak bases** *do not dissociate completely in aqueous solution.* The relative strengths of some bases are listed in Table 18·4.

Aqueous ammonia is an example of a weak base.

$$NH_3 + H_2O \rightleftharpoons NH_4^+ + OH^-$$

Ammonia   Water   Ammonium   Hydroxide
                            ion   ion

The equilibrium greatly favors NH_3 and H_2O. Approximately 99% of the ammonia is un-ionized, and only 1% is in the form of NH_4^+ and OH^-. Very little NH_4^+ and OH^- are available. Not even this small amount of NH_4OH can be isolated, however, because all the NH_3 and H_2O must first be removed. If the NH_3 and H_2O were removed, all the NH_4^+ and OH^- ions would revert to NH_3 and H_2O. Bottles of aqueous ammonia used in laboratories are usually labeled ammonium hydroxide, NH_4OH. Nevertheless, no chemist has ever isolated this compound.

The **base dissociation constant,** K_b, *is the ratio of the dissociated form of a base to the undissociated form.* It indicates the degree of dissociation. The base dissociation constant for ammonia is 1.8×10^{-5}.

$$K_b = \frac{[NH_4^+] \times [OH^-]}{[NH_3]} = 1.8 \times 10^{-5}$$

Weak acids and weak bases have relatively small K_a and K_b values, respectively.

Problem

15. From Table 18·4, name a weak base and a strong base.

15. Weak base: ammonia
strong base: sodium hydroxide

Figure 18·19
Which of these pH test papers has been dipped into sodium hydroxide? Which has been dipped into sodium bicarbonate?
The brown paper has been dipped into sodium hydroxide. The green paper has been dipped into sodium bicarbonate.

If a solution is a weak electrolyte, it could be a dilute solution of a strong acid (or base) or a concentrated solution of weak acid (or base).

Concentrated and dilute do not mean the same as strong and weak. For example, it is possible to have a concentrated weak acid or a dilute strong base.

The words *concentrated* and *dilute* tell how much of an acid or base is dissolved in solution. These terms refer to the number of moles of the acid or base in a given volume. The words *strong* and *weak* refer to the extent of ionization of an acid or base. They indicate how many of the molecules dissociate into ions. Hydrochloric acid, HCl, is a strong acid. Gastric juice in the stomach is a dilute solution of hydrochloric acid. A relatively small number of HCl molecules are present in a given volume of gastric juice, but they are all dissociated into ions. A sample of hydrochloric acid added to a large volume of water becomes more dilute, but it is still a strong acid. Vinegar is a dilute solution of a weak acid, acetic acid. Pure acetic acid (glacial acetic acid) is still a weak acid. Aqueous ammonia is an example of a weak base. Solutions of ammonia can be concentrated or dilute depending on the amount of ammonia dissolved in a given volume of water. Any solution of ammonia, whether concentrated or dilute, will be a weak base. This is because the amount of dissociation will be small. Table 18·6 lists the concentrations of acids and bases commonly found in the laboratory.

Safety

Glacial acetic acid is 17*M*. It causes severe chemical burns. A concentrated weak acid can be very corrosive.

Table 18·6 Concentrations of Some Common Laboratory Acids and Bases		
	Concentration	
Acid or base	Moles/liter (molarity)	Grams/liter
Concentrated hydrochloric acid	12	438
Dilute hydrochloric acid	6	219
Concentrated sulfuric acid	18	1764
Dilute sulfuric acid	6	588
Concentrated phosphoric acid	15	1470
Concentrated nitric acid	16	1008
Dilute nitric acid	6	378
Glacial acetic acid	17	1020
Dilute acetic acid	6	360
Dilute sodium hydroxide	6	240
Concentrated aqueous ammonia	15	255
Dilute aqueous ammonia	6	102

18·9 Calculating Dissociation Constants

The acid dissociation constant, K_a, of a weak acid can be calculated from experimental data. To do this, the equilibrium concentrations of all the substances present at equilibrium must be measured. For a weak acid these concentrations can be determined experimentally if we know two conditions. First, the initial molar concentration of the acid must be known. Second, the pH (or hydrogen-ion concentration) of the solution at equilibrium must be measured.

Example 7

A 0.100M solution of acetic acid is only partially ionized. Using a measure of pH, the [H^+] is calculated as $1.34 \times 10^{-3}M$. What is the acid dissociation constant of acetic acid?

Solution

Write the equation for the ionization of acetic acid.

$$HC_2H_3O_2(aq) \rightleftharpoons H^+ + C_2H_3O_2^-$$

The assumption that the hydrogen ion and acetate ion concentrations are equal is valid only in a pure solution of acetic acid, where no other source of these ions is present.

Each molecule of $HC_2H_3O_2$ that ionizes gives a H^+ and an $C_2H_3O_2^-$ ion. Therefore at equilibrium the [H^+] = [$C_2H_3O_2^-$] = $1.34 \times 10^{-3}M$. The equilibrium concentration of $HC_2H_3O_2$ is the initial concentration changed by the ionization of the acid, $(0.100 - 0.00134)M = 0.09866M$. This data is summarized in the following table.

Concentrations	$HC_2H_3O_2$ $\rightleftharpoons$	H^+ +	$C_2H_3O_2^-$
Initial	0.100	0	0
Change	-1.34×10^{-3}	$+1.34 \times 10^{-3}$	$+1.34 \times 10^{-3}$
Equilibrium	0.0987	1.34×10^{-3}	1.34×10^{-3}

(All concentrations are in mol/L.)

The equilibrium values are now substituted into the expression for K_a.

$$K_a = \frac{[H^+] \times [C_2H_3O_2^-]}{[HC_2H_3O_2]}$$

$$= \frac{(1.34 \times 10^{-3}) \times (1.34 \times 10^{-3})}{0.0987}$$

$$= 1.82 \times 10^{-5}$$

Problem

16. A 0.200M solution of a weak acid has a [H^+] of $9.86 \times 10^{-4}M$. **a.** What is the pH of this solution? **b.** What is the value of K_a for this acid?

Key Terms

acid dissociation		hydroxide ion	
constant (K_a)	*18·8*	(OH⁻)	*18·2*
acidic solution	*18·2*	ion-product constant	
alkaline solution	*18·2*	for water (K_w)	*18·2*
amphoteric	*18·6*	Lewis acid	*18·7*
base dissociation		Lewis base	*18·7*
constant (K_b)	*18·8*	monoprotic acid	*18·5*
basic solution	*18·2*	neutral solution	*18·2*
conjugate acid	*18·6*	pH	*18·3*
conjugate base	*18·6*	self-ionization	*18·2*
conjugate acid–base		strong acid	*18·8*
pair	*18·6*	strong base	*18·8*
diprotic acid	*18·5*	triprotic acid	*18·5*
hydrogen-ion		weak acid	*18·8*
acceptor	*18·6*	weak base	*18·8*
hydrogen-ion donor	*18·6*		
hydronium ion			
(H₃O⁺)	*18·2*		

Chapter Summary

Water molecules dissociate into hydrogen ions (H⁺) and hydroxide ions (OH⁻). The concentrations of these ions in pure water at 25°C are both equal to 1×10^{-7} mol/L.

The pH scale, which has a range from 0 to 14, is used to denote the hydrogen-ion concentration of a solution. On this scale 0 is strongly acidic, 14 is strongly basic, and 7 is neutral. Water at 25°C has a pH of 7. The pH of a solution is measured with acid–base indicators.

Compounds can be classified as acids or bases according to three different theories. An Arrhenius acid gives hydrogen ions in aqueous solution. An Arrhenius base gives hydroxide ions in aqueous solution. A Brønsted–Lowry acid is a proton donor. A Brønsted–Lowry base is a proton acceptor. In the

Lewis theory an acid is an electron-pair acceptor. A Lewis base is an electron-pair donor.

The strength of an acid or base is determined by the degree of ionization of the substance in solution. The acid dissociation constant, K_a, is a quantitative measure of acid strength. A strong acid has a much larger K_a than a weak acid. The K_a of a acid is determined from measured pH values.

Hydrochloric acid and sulfuric acid are completely ionized in solution and are strong acids. Acetic acid, which is only about 1% ionized, is a weak acid. Sodium hydroxide and calcium hydroxide are strong bases. Ammonia is only slightly ionized in aqueous solution and is a weak base.

Practice Questions and Problems

17. List at least three characteristic properties of acids.   *18·1*

18. List at least three characteristic properties of bases.   *18·1*

19. Write an equation showing the ionization of water.   *18·2*

20. What are the concentrations of H⁺ and OH⁻ in pure water at 25°C?   *18·2*

21. Write the expression for the ion-product constant for water. What value does it have at 25°C?   *18·2*

22. What is true about the relative concentrations of hydrogen ions and hydroxide ions in each of these solutions?   *18·2*
  a. basic   **b.** acidic   **c.** neutral

23. Calculate the hydrogen-ion concentration [H⁺] for a solution in which [OH⁻] is 1×10^{-2} mol/L. Is this aqueous solution acidic, basic, or neutral? *18·2*

24. How is the pH of a solution calculated?   *18·3*

25. Why is the pH of pure water at 25°C equal to 7.0?   *18·3*

26. Calculate the pH for the following solutions and indicate whether the solution is acidic or basic.
  a. $[H^+] = 1 \times 10^{-2}$ mol/L   *18·3*
  b. $[OH^-] = 1 \times 10^{-2}$ mol/L
  c. $[OH^-] = 1 \times 10^{-8}$ mol/L
  d. $[H^+] = 1 \times 10^{-6}$ mol/L

27. Determine the hydrogen-ion concentrations for aqueous solutions that have the following pH values.   **a.** 7.0   **b.** 13.0   **c.** 2.0   *18·3*

28. What are the hydroxide-ion concentrations for solutions that have the following pH values?
  a. 4.0   **b.** 8.0   **c.** 12.0   *18·3*

29. How did Arrhenius describe acids and bases?   *18·5*

30. Classify each of these as an Arrhenius acid or an Arrhenius base.   *18·5*
  a. HBr   **d.** HNO_3
  b. $Ca(OH)_2$ **e.** KOH
  c. H_2SO_4 **f.** C_2H_5COOH

31. Identify each of the acids in Problem 30 as monoprotic, diprotic, or triprotic.   *18·5*

32. Write balanced equations for the reaction of each of these metals with water.   *18·5*
  a. lithium   **b.** barium

33. How are acids and bases defined by the Brønsted–Lowry theory? What advantage does this theory have over the theory proposed by Arrhenius?   *18·6*

34. Identify each of the reactants in the following equations as a hydrogen-ion donor (acid) or a hydrogen-ion acceptor (base).   *18·6*
  a. $HNO_3 + H_2O \rightleftharpoons H_3O^+ + NO_3^-$
  b. $CH_3COOH + H_2O \rightleftharpoons H_3O^+ + CH_3COO^-$
  c. $H_2O + NH_3 \rightleftharpoons NH_4^+ + OH^-$
  d. $H_2O + CH_3COO^- \rightleftharpoons CH_3COOH + OH^-$

35. Label the conjugate acid–base pairs in each equation in Problem 34.   *18·6*

36. What makes a substance amphoteric?   *18·6*

37. What is a Lewis acid and a Lewis base? What advantage does this theory have over the Arrhenius and Brønsted–Lowry theories?   *18·7*

38. Write the equations for the ionization of the following acids and bases in water.   *18·8*
  a. nitric acid   **c.** ammonia
  b. acetic acid   **d.** magnesium hydroxide

39. Define strong and weak acids and bases.   *18·8*

40. Identify each of the following compounds as a strong or weak acid or base.   *18·8*
  a. NaOH   **e.** NH_3
  b. HCl   **f.** H_2SO_4
  c. $Ca(OH)_2$ **g.** H_2CO_3
  d. CH_3COOH

41. Would a stong acid have a large or a small K_a? Explain.   *18·9*

42. Why are $Mg(OH)_2$ and $Ca(OH)_2$ called strong bases even though their saturated solutions are only mildly basic?   *18·9*

43. Write the expression for K_a for each of these acids. Assume that only one hydrogen is ionized.   **a.** HI   **b.** H_2CO_3 *18·9*

Mastery Questions and Problems

44. Calculate the pH or $[H^+]$ for each solution.
  a. $[H^+] = 2.4 \times 10^{-6}$ **c.** pH = 13.2   *18·4*
  b. $[H^+] = 9.1 \times 10^{-9}$ **d.** pH = 6.7

45. Is it possible to have a concentrated weak acid? Explain.   *18·8*

46. Identify the conjugate acid–base pair in each reaction.   *18·6*
  a. $NH_4^+ + H_2O \rightleftharpoons H_3O^+ + NH_3$
  b. $HCO_3^- + H_2O \rightleftharpoons H_2CO_3 + OH^-$
  c. $CO_3^{2-} + H_2O \rightleftharpoons HCO_3^- + OH^-$
  d. $H_3PO_4 + H_2O \rightleftharpoons H_3O^+ + H_2PO_4^-$

47. Write equations that show that the hydrogen phosphate ion, HPO_4^{2-}, is amphoteric.   *18·6*

48. The pH of a 0.50M HNO_2 solution is 1.83. What is the K_a of this acid?   *18·9*

49. Write the formula and name of the conjugate base of each Brønsted–Lowry acid.
  a. HCO_3^- **b.** HI   **c.** NH_4^+ **d.** H_2SO_3 *18·6*

50. Use the Brønsted–Lowry and Lewis definitions of acids and bases to identify each reactant as an acid or a base.   *18·7*
  a. $KOH + HBr \rightarrow KBr + H_2O$
  b. $HCl + H_2O \rightarrow Cl^- + H_3O^+$

51. Write the formula and name of the conjugate acid of each Brønsted–Lowry base.   *18·6*
  a. ClO_2^- **b.** $H_2PO_4^-$ **c.** H_2O **d.** NH_3

---

52. It is determined that 1.40% of a 0.080M solution of a weak acid is ionized. Calculate the K_a for this acid. *18·9*

53. Calculate the $[OH^-]$ or the pH of each solution.
 a. pH = 4.6   **c.** $[OH^-] = 1.8 \times 10^{-2}$ *18·4*
 b. pH = 9.3   **d.** $[OH^-] = 7.3 \times 10^{-9}$

54. Write the three equations for the stepwise dissociation of phosphoric acid. *18·5*

Review Questions and Problems

55. List three ways to increase the rate at which a solid dissolves in water.

56. How would you prepare 400.0 mL of a 0.680M KOH solution?

57. How would each of the following affect the rate of most reactions?
 a. increase the temperature
 b. add a catalyst
 c. decrease the concentration of reactants
 d. increase the surface area of the reactants

58. How many liters of 8.0M HCl are needed to prepare 1.50 L of 2.5M HCl by dilution with water?

59. How would each change affect the position of equilibrium of this reaction?

$$2H_2(g) + O_2(g) \rightleftharpoons 2H_2O(g) + \text{heat}$$

 a. increasing the pressure
 b. adding a catalyst
 c. increasing the concentration of $H_2(g)$
 d. cooling the reaction mixture
 e. removing water vapor from the container

60. Write an equilibrium constant expression for each equation.
 a. $2CO_2(g) \rightleftharpoons 2CO(g) + O_2(g)$
 b. $N_2(g) + 3H_2(g) \rightleftharpoons 2NH_3(g)$

Challenging Questions and Problems

61. A bottle labeled dilute HCl in the laboratory is usually 6M. Assuming that HCl is completely ionized, calculate the $[H^+]$, $[OH^-]$, and the pH of this solution.

62. Calculate the pH of a 0.010M solution of sodium cyanide, NaCN. The K_b of CN^- is 2.1×10^{-5}.

63. Show that for any conjugate acid–base pair $K_aK_b = K_w$.

64. The K_w of water varies with the temperature. For example, at 10°C, $K_w = 2.920 \times 10^{-15}$; at 45°C, $K_w = 4.018 \times 10^{-14}$.   **a.** What is the pH of pure water at 10°C and at 45°C?   **b.** Is pure water an acid or a base at these temperatures?

Research Projects

 1. What are the steps involved in etching a silicon chip for computers? Why are scientists investigating the use of reactive ion plasmas to etch the chips?

 2. What contributions did Libavius and Blauber make to the preparation of acids?

 3. Use pH test paper to determine the pH of common substances such as orange juice, milk, shampoo, cleaning solutions, tap water, and rain water.

 4. How is sodium hydroxide manufactured? What are the major uses for this compound?

 5. Measure the acidity of rain at various points during a storm. Account for any variations.

 6. Describe the effects of acid rain on plants, animals, and stone structures.

 7. How do meteorological processes contribute to acid rain? How have local industrial pollution control measures affected the dispersion of acid rain?

Readings and References

Gay, Kathlyn. *Acid Rain*. New York: Watts, 1983.

"If You Breathe, Don't Smoke." *Science 84* (January/February 1984), pp. 83–84.

Ostmann, Robert, Jr. *Acid Rain: A Plague upon the Waters*. Minneapolis: Dillon, 1982.

Sitwell, Nigel. "Our Trees Are Dying." *Science Digest* (September 1984), pp. 39–48.

Visich, Marian, Jr. "Acid from the Sky." *Science Year* (1984), pp. 40–53.

Section			Demonstrations and Experiments	Resource Materials
19·1	Neutralization Reactions	C*	Dem 19·1 Blow Out a Light	Objectives Worksheet 19, SPB
				Skillsheet 19, SPB
			Exp 40 Neutralization Reactions, LM	Prelab 40, SPB
19·A	Soil Chemistry for Farmers	E		Agricultural Pollution, ICT 19
19·2	Titration	C	Dem 19·2 Titration	
			Exp 41 Acid–Base Titrations, LM	Prelab 41, SPB
19·3	Equivalents	O		
19·4	Normality	O		Quiz 19·1
19·5	Salt Hydrolysis	C	Exp 42 Salt Hydrolysis, LM	Prelab 42, SPB
				Beyond the Text:
				Mordants and Dyes
19·6	Buffers	H	Dem 19·3 Buffering Capacity	Quiz 19·2
			Exp 43 Buffers, LM	Prelab 43, SPB
19·7	The Solubility Product Constant	H	Exp 44 A Solubility Product Constant, LM	Prelab 44, SPB
19·B	Swimming Pool Chemistry	E		
19·8	The Common Ion Effect	H		Quiz 19·3
				Reviewsheet 19, SPB
				Chapter 19 Test
*C = Core, O = Optional			LM = Laboratory Manual	SPB = Skills Practice Book
E = Enrichment, H = Honors				ICT = Issues in Chem. Tech.

Chapter Objectives

Having studied this chapter and done the problems, the student should be able to:

1. Complete and balance a neutralization reaction. *19·1*

2. Perform calculations involving acid–base reactions. *19·1*

3. Explain the steps of a titration. *19·2*

4. Calculate the gram equivalent mass of any acid or base. *19·3*

5. Describe the procedure for preparing a dilute solution of known concentration from a more concentrated solution. *19·4*

6. Define and calculate the normality of a solution. *19·4*

7. Use the concept of hydrolysis to explain why aqueous solutions of some salts are acidic or basic. *19·5*

8. Define a buffer, and show with equations how a buffer system works. *19·6*

9. Calculate concentrations of ions of slightly soluble salts. *19·7*

10. Use Le Châtelier's principle to explain the common ion effect. *19·8*

Teaching Suggestions

19·1 Neutralization Reactions

Approach neutralization as a process which occurs whenever an acid reacts with a base, no matter what their relative amounts. For those molecules or ions that react, the distinguishing acidic and basic properties are lost in a neutralization reaction.

When equimolar amounts of a strong acid such as HCl and a strong base such as NaOH react, the resulting solution will be a neutral solution. However, it is important that the students understand that the process of neutralization does not always produce neutral solutions. As an example, consider the case in which one mole of a strong acid (HCl) is added to two moles of a strong base (NaOH). A neutralization reaction will occur between the one mole of acid and one of the moles of base. However, there will still be a mole of base left over. The solution will not be neutral.

After a discussion of neutralization, the students could do **Experiment 40** *Acid–Base Neutralization Reactions*. In this experiment they mix equimolar amounts of hydrochloric acid and sodium hydroxide to obtain a neutral product. **Demonstration 19·1** *Blow Out a Light* shows another neutralization reaction.

19·2   Titration

Of all the laboratory techniques of the chemist there are few that are more important or widely used than the technique of titration. Be sure that the students thoroughly understand how to perform titrations and how to handle the calculations that are associated with titrations.

It is best to have the students observe all of the steps that are involved in doing a titration before they actually do one themselves. **Demonstration 19·2** *Titration* can be done to accomplish this.

Once the process of titration has been introduced, the students should have some direct experience with it. Have them do **Experiment 41** *Acid–Base Titrations* before proceeding to the next section.

19·3   Equivalents

19·4   Normality

Some substances contain more than one mole of available hydrogen ion or available base in each mole of the substance. It is generally more useful (especially in titrations) to prepare solutions which have equal numbers of reacting species, rather than an equal number of moles of solute. This is accomplished through the use of equivalents and normality.

The sequence in this section is straightforward. First, the concept of equivalent mass is introduced. Show the students a few examples of how to calculate equivalent mass using the gram formula mass and the formula of a substance. They should then have little difficulty with the next step, which is to define an equivalent as one gram equivalent mass.

You can then introduce the concept of normality. Remind the students that previously we have expressed concentration in terms of moles per liter. Point out that

normality is very similar. Instead of using moles, it expresses concentration in terms of *equivalents* per liter.

Stress that calculations involving normality are very similar to calculations with molarity. When dealing with molarity we have been using the relationship that the product of volume and molarity gives the number of moles of solute. Emphasize that, in a similar fashion, the product of volume and normality gives the number of equivalents.

It may be helpful to the slower students to have the relationship between normality and molarity given in a form they can memorize. Show them that they can always obtain the normality by multiplying the molarity by the number of equivalents per mole. (Or they can obtain the molarity by dividing the normality by the number of equivalents per mole.)

19·5   Salt Hydrolysis

We have already seen in the previous chapter that a weak acid or a weak base in aqueous solution always establishes an equilibrium between the undissociated form and the ionic form. Point out that it is this very same equilibrium which is encountered in hydrolysis. The only difference is that this equilibrium is established by the ionic form reacting in such a way as to produce the acid, rather than the acid producing the ionic form.

Give the students examples that show how the salt of a weak acid or base, when dissolved in water, reacts with water to form the weak acid or weak base, and establishes an equilibrium.

Point out that this reaction always uses one part of the water molecule and leaves behind the other. Show how the salt of a weak acid will always react with water in such a way as to produce hydroxide ions. The salt of a weak base will always produce hydrogen ions. The solutions formed therefore cannot be neutral.

In **Experiment 42** *Salt Hydrolysis* students find the pH values of solutions which they make from salts of weak acids and bases. It offers reinforcement of this section.

An alternate approach is to use **Experiment 42** as a discovery experience which can serve as an introduction to this section. Have the students go through the procedure without answering the questions (or do it as a demonstration yourself). Then ask for a simple explanation of the results. This should lead nicely into the topic of hydrolysis.

19·6   Buffers

The topic of buffers shows how previously learned concepts can be applied in a practical way. As you discuss the action of buffers, point out that an effective buffer always makes use of the equilibrium established by the combination of a weak acid and its salt or a weak base and its salt. If a base is added to a buffered solution, the acidic form reacts with it. If an acid is added to a buffer, the basic form

reacts with it. Emphasize that this behavior is not unique to acids and bases, but is merely an application of Le Châtelier's principle. The addition of an acid or base to a buffered system applies a stress to it. The equilibrium system attempts to use up the added acid or base and relieve the stress. As long as the system is able to do so, the system will keep the pH reasonably constant.

The students will become aware of the effectiveness of buffers by doing **Experiment 43** *Buffers*. They will also find **Demonstration 19·3** *Buffering Capacity* to be an interesting study of the relative abilities of common medicinal products to act as buffers.

19·7 The Solubility Product Constant

Any ionic solid placed in water can establish an equilibrium between its ions and its solid form. In the case of low solubility compounds the relative amount of the ionic form may be exceedingly small. In this case of a very soluble substance, the relative quantity of the ionic form may be very large, and a great deal of solid may have to be added to establish the equilibrium. Nevertheless, an equilibrium state is always possible.

Once equilibrium is established, an equilibrium constant expression can be written. The amount of solid material is never included in an equilibrium expression. Thus, this particular constant always ends up being written as the product of the concentrations of the ionic forms. Since this constant has to do with solubility, and is written as a product, it is logically called a solubility product constant and is given the symbol, K_{sp}. It is important to note that this is just another example of equilibrium and fundamentally involves no new concepts.

It is essential that the students see the difference between the terms *solubility* and *solubility product*. Point out that solubility has to do with the amount of solid substance which can dissolve in a given amount of solute. It is usually expressed as g/100 mL, g/L, or even mol/L. The solubility product, on the other hand, is an equilibrium constant. The value of the solubility product is obtained by substituting the concentration values for each ion into an equilibrium law expression.

Be sure to allocate adequate time to work out plenty of sample problems. Those who are weaker in mathematics will experience some difficulty at first in taking square and cube roots of numbers that are written in scientific notation.

Once they have worked through the problems in this section, the students should do **Experiment 44** *A Solubility Product Constant*.

19·8 The Common Ion Effect

The common ion effect is another example of Le Châtelier's principle at work. It should not be presented as a new concept, but simply as an application of one that is very familiar to us. The students should have little difficulty in seeing that the addition of one ion to an equilibrium system which already contains that ion will cause a shift in the direction which uses up the ion. In the case of solubility equilibria, this always results in a decrease in solubility.

Demonstrations

19·1 Blow Out a Light

Concept: Carbonic acid can neutralize a base.

Materials: conductivity apparatus (with 6V power supply), 30 cm of 6-mm diameter glass tubing, 250-mL beaker, 50 mL of freshly prepared limewater ($Ca(OH)_2$), water, safety goggles.

Procedure: **Caution:** *Use only 6V power supply.* 1. Pour the limewater into the beaker. 2. Test with the conductivity apparatus. Observe that the light goes on. 3. Instruct a student to blow into the solution with the glass tubing. 4. After about a minute, the light dims. Continued blowing extinguishes it. The solution becomes cloudy. 5. Write the chemical equations for the reaction:
$$CO_2 + H_2O \longrightarrow H_2CO_3$$
$$Ca(OH)_2 + H_2CO_3 \longrightarrow CaCO_3 + 2H_2O$$
6. Ask the students to explain why the light goes out and the solution becomes cloudy.

19·2 Titration

Concept: Neutralization reactions can be used to find the concentrations of acidic and basic solutions.

Materials: 2 burets, buret clamp, ring stand, two 150-mL beakers, two 250-mL flasks, long-handled brush, detergent, 500 mL of 0.100M hydrochloric acid (HCl), 500 mL of 0.100M sodium hydroxide (NaOH), 5 mL of 1% phenolphthalein, bottle of distilled water.

Procedure: 1. Clean each buret with a mild detergent and long-handled brush. 2. Rinse with tap water. 3. Rinse with distilled water. 4. Finally, rinse with a few mL of the solution with which the buret is to be filled. Swirl to be sure the solution contacts all the interior surfaces. 5. Fill one buret with the solution of known concentration (use the acid solution), and the other with the unknown one (use the basic solution). 6. Allow the solution to run out through the buret tip. Remove any air bubbles trapped in the tip. 7. Demonstrate how to read the buret. Be sure that your eyes are level with the bottom of the meniscus. 8. Estimate the position of the meniscus *between* the smallest graduated lines to obtain precision to the nearest 0.01 mL. 9. Make a table which includes the initial and final readings of each buret. The volume is obtained by subtracting the initial

reading from the final reading. 10. Open the buret and run about 20 mL of the acid solution into a flask. Mention that it is 0.100M HCl; read its volume *exactly*. 11. Add 3 drops of phenolphthalein. 12. Add base from the buret to the flask, swirling after the addition of each drop. 13. Rinse the inside surfaces of the flask with distilled water to ensure that no unreacted solution remains. 14. The endpoint is marked by a faint pink color that persists for at least half a minute. If the color does not persist, add more base, a drop at a time. 15. As the end point is approached, allow a fraction of a drop to form on the end of the tip, and then wash it into the flask with distilled water. 16. If the endpoint is passed, add a few more drops of acid, and then continue to add base. 17. Record the final volumes of both solutions. 18. Calculate the concentration of the base.

Vol. acid $\times$ molarity acid = vol. base $\times$ molarity base
Thus, $V_a \times M_a = V_b \times M_b$.
19. Since we know the values of V_a, V_b, and M_a, we can obtain M_b. **Caution:** *Hydrochloric acid and sodium hydroxide are corrosive.*

19·3 Buffering Capacity

Concept: The neutralizing abilities of commercial buffers differ.

Materials: various commercial antacids tablets, buffered aspirin, plain aspirin, 500 mL of 0.5M hydrochloric acid (HCl), 500 mL of 0.5M sodium hydroxide (NaOH), 2 burets, ring stand, buret clamp, 5 mL of 0.1% methyl red, 5 mL of 0.1% bromthymol blue, eight 500-mL flasks, safety goggles.

Procedure: 1. For each type of tablet, set up two 500-mL flasks. In each, place one tablet dissolved in 100 mL water. 2. Put hydrochloric acid in one buret and sodium hydroxide in the other. 3. Add 3 drops of methyl red to one of the flasks and place it under the acid-containing buret. 4. Add 3 drops of bromthymol blue to the other flask and place it under the base-containing buret. 5. Add acid or base to the flasks until the endpoints are reached. 6. Explain that the buffering ability of a substance is directly related to the amount of acid or base required to produce a color change. Compare the amounts needed for the various tablets and liquids. **Caution:** *Hydrochloric acid and sodium hydroxide are corrosive.*

Audiovisual Resources

Acids, Bases, and Salts (FS) Educational Dimensions, 1978, 15–20 min. (Use with Section 19·1. Presents a concise discussion of acids, bases, and salts.

All About Acids and Bases (4 FS) Focus Media, 1981, 20–30 min. each. (Use with Section 19·1.) Explains the neutralization process.

Proton Transfer in Chemical Change (FS) Prentice-Hall Media, 1971. (Use with Sections 19·1 or 19·5.) Discusses the relative strengths of acids and bases as they apply to neutralization and hydrolysis.

Beyond the Text

Mordants and Dyes

Dyes are intensely colored compounds used to impart color in textiles, plastics, paper, cosmetics, paints and other materials. The first use of dyes predates recorded history. Red ochre has been discovered in several ancient burial sites over 15 000 years old. Pigments (insoluble dyes) found in cave drawings in Spain and southern France are even older. The earliest dyes were obtained from naturally occurring sources such as plants, insects and shellfish. Modern dyes are almost exclusively synthesized from coal tar and petroleum.

The textile industry is the predominant user of dyes. The fascination of coloring clothing is well documented in the ancient cultures of China, Egypt and India. Depending upon the fabric, the type of garment and the type of dye, the raw material used may be dyed at different stages of the manufacturing process. Thus, some clothes are dyed after assembly while others are made from dyed yarns.

Some materials resist dyeing due to complex surface chemistry interactions. For example, most naturally occurring dyes do not bind to fibers of vegetable origin. Cotton and linen cannot be effectively colored. It was discovered that if an auxiliary chemical, called a *mordant,* was added during the dyeing process, the dye would bind to the fabric. Mordants are metal salts initially derived from aluminum, iron, copper or tin. Chromium salts first appeared in the 1850s, and have dominated ever since. While not completely understood, scientists believe that mordants are first absorbed by the fiber, and then combine with the dye to form an insoluble compound.

Until the mid-19th century, the number of dyes used was small, and the number of colors available was limited. This changed quite dramatically with the discovery of mauveine, in 1856, by W. H. Perkins. While still a student at the Royal College of Chemistry in London, Perkins was experimenting with a coal tar derivative called aniline ($C_6H_5NH_2$). This aromatic compound (see Chapter 25) yielded a dye of intense color that resisted fading. He continued his experimentation, and realized the importance of his discovery. Within a year, he began the first synthetic dye manufacturing company. The quality and low price of his dyes created a huge demand around the world. It was thought that the time consuming and costly procedures of extracting natural dyes would some day come to an end, and this has indeed almost come to pass.

Manufacturing facilities sprung up in several countries at an incredible rate. Many historians credit Perkins with creating the synthetic organic chemical industry because of the interest he started in synthesizing naturally occurring and novel compounds.

Today, the chemical dye industry produces over 7 000 different dyes. They also introduce new dyes at rate of approximately 200 per year. This large number is needed because of the large number of man-made fibers created. Chemists are actively involved in designing new dyes, and increasing the effectiveness of some of the older compounds.

Answers to End of Chapter Questions and Problems

Practice Questions and Problems

19. It occurs when an acid and a base react in an aqueous solution to form water and a salt:
$$HCl + KOH \longrightarrow H_2O + KCl.$$

20. a. $H_2SO_4 + 2KOH \rightarrow 2H_2O + K_2SO_4$; potassium sulfate
b. $HCl + NH_4OH \rightarrow H_2O + NH_4Cl$; ammonium chloride
c. $2H_3PO_4 + 3Ca(OH)_2 \rightarrow 3H_2O + Ca_3(PO_4)_2$; calcium phosphate
d. $2HNO_3 + Mg(OH)_2 \rightarrow 2H_2O + Mg(NO_3)_2$; magnesium nitrate

21. a. 0.2 mol **b.** 2 mol **c.** 0.2 mol

22. Neutralization occurs.

23. a. $1.4M$ **b.** $2.61M$

24. The mass of an acid that gives one mole of hydrogen ions.

25. The mass of a base that gives one mole of hydroxide ions.

26. 32.7 g **b.** 40.0 g **c.** 29.2 g **d.** 60.0 g

27. a. 0.50 equiv **b.** 0.20 equiv **c.** 0.30 equiv **d.** 0.40 equiv **e.** 0.30 equiv

28. Number of equivalents of solute in 1 L of solution.

29. a. $1N$ **b.** $2N$ **c.** $0.2N$ **d.** $0.2N$

30. a. $1.0N$ **b.** $0.13N$ **c.** $0.074N$ **d.** $0.105N$ **e.** $0.80N$ **f.** $0.234N$

31. a. 3.2 equiv **b.** 0.46 equiv **c.** 0.031 equiv

32. 12.5 mL

33. The number of equiv of acid equals the number of equiv of base.

34. a. $0.060N$ **b.** $0.400N$ **c.** $0.171N$ **d.** $0.0752N$ **e.** $0.262N$

35. Salts with a cation from a weak base and an anion from a strong acid, or with a cation from a strong base and an anion from a weak acid.

36. Weak acid anions accept protons from water, increasing the pH of the solution. Weak base cations donate protons to water, decreasing the pH.

37. a. basic **b.** acidic **c.** basic **d.** neutral **e.** neutral **f.** basic **g.** neutral **h.** acidic

38. A solution in which the pH remains relatively constant when small amounts of acid or base are added.

39. No. HCl is a strong acid.

40. The product of the ion concentrations raised to the power of their coefficients.

41. a. $[Ni^{2+}][S^{2-}]$ **b.** $[Ba^{2+}][CO_3^{2-}]$ **c.** $[Pb^{2+}][Cl^-]^2$ **d.** $[Ag^+]^2[CrO_4]$

42. c, b, d, a.

43. Lowers the solubility.

44. The product of the concentrations of the two ions is greater than the solubility product constant of the precipitate.

Mastery Questions and Problems

45. a. $1.2N$ $Mg(OH)_2$ **b.** $0.15N$ HBr **c.** $0.80N$ H_2SO_3

46. $H_2PO_4^- + OH^- \rightleftharpoons H_2O + HPO_4^{2-}$
$HPO_4^{2-} + H^+ \rightleftharpoons H_2PO_4^-$ Added OH^- is neutralized by $H_2PO_4^-$ and added acid is neutralized by HPO_4^{2-}.

47. a. $[OH^-] = 8.4 \times 10^{-6}M$
b. $[OH^-] = 2.4 \times 10^{-2}M$ **c.** $[OH^-] = 5.5 \times 10^{-9}M$

48. a. $NH_4^+ + OH^- \rightleftharpoons NH_3 + H_2O$
b. $H_2PO_4^- + OH^- \rightleftharpoons HPO_4^{2-} + H_2O$

49. $NaC_2H_3O_2 + H_2O \rightleftharpoons Na^+ + HC_2H_3O_2 + OH^-$

50. b, d, c, e, a.

51. $[Ba^{2+}] = 2.0 \times 10^{-8}M$

52. Yes. Ion product is greater than K_{sp}.

Review Questions and Problems

53. a. ~ 8 **b.** use a pH meter

54. a. 5.34 **b.** 11.30 **c.** 0.52 **d.** 9.01

55. 2.25 g KCl

56. a.
$$:\!\overset{\displaystyle ..}{\underset{\displaystyle ..}{F}}\!:$$
$$:\!F\!:\!\overset{\displaystyle ..}{\underset{\displaystyle ..}{Si}}\!:\!F\!:$$
$$:\!\overset{\displaystyle ..}{\underset{\displaystyle ..}{F}}\!:$$

b. $:\!\ddot{C}l\!:\!\ddot{S}\!:\!\ddot{C}l\!:$

c.
$$H\!:\!\overset{\displaystyle ..}{P}\!:\!H$$
$$\overset{\displaystyle |}{H}$$

d. $H\!:\!\overset{..}{\underset{..}{O}}\!:\!\overset{..}{\underset{..}{O}}\!:\!H$

e.
$$\begin{array}{ccc} H & H & H \\ H\!:\!C\!:\!C\!:\!C\!:\!H \\ H & H & H \end{array}$$

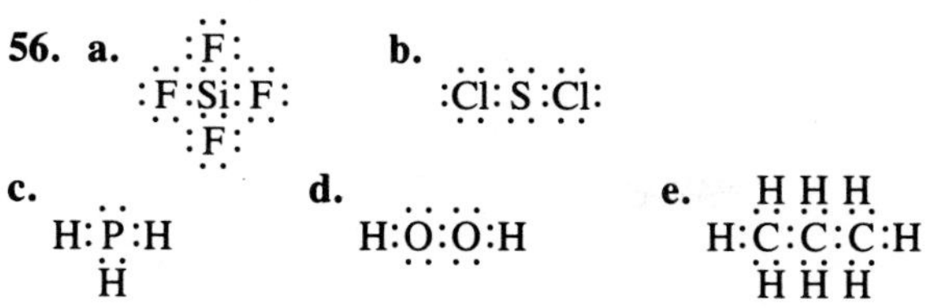

57. a. HSO_4^- **b.** CN^- **c.** OH^- **d.** NH_3

58. a. $NaCl(aq)$ **b.** $CO_2(g)$ **c.** H_2O at 60°C

59. $0.5M$ NaCl

Challenging Questions and Problems

60. Hyperventilation releases CO_2. The equilibrium shift causes H_2CO_3 and H^+ to decrease. The loss of H^+ increases the basicity of the blood and alkalosis results. Hypoventilation does not release enough CO_2. The CO_2 build-up increases H_2CO_3 and H^+. The H^+ increases the acidity of the blood and acidosis results.

61. $1.00 \times 10^{-1}N$ H_2SO_4

62. 74.4% $AgNO_3$

63. CO_2 concentration is higher in pure water. Less CO_2 becomes carbonate because pure water does not have the OH^- ions needed to reduce H^+ concentration.

19

Neutralization and Salts

Chapter Preview

The properties of acids, bases, and salts help explain many diverse phenomena. For example, the usefulness of antacids depends on the process of acid–base neutralization. Farmers use a similar process to control the pH of their soil. The formation of caves and of stalactites in caves is caused by changes in the solubilities of salts. In a similar way certain conditions lead to the formation of kidney stones from salts within the body. Neutralization reactions and the solubilities of salts are the topics of this chapter.

19·1   Neutralization Reactions

■ Acids and bases react to produce salts and water.

If a solution containing hydronium ions (an acid) is mixed with a solution that has an equal amount of hydroxide ions (a base), a neutral solution results. The final solution has properties that are not characteristic of either an acidic or a basic solution. Consider these two examples.

$$HCl + NaOH \longrightarrow NaCl + H_2O$$
$$H_2SO_4 + 2KOH \longrightarrow K_2SO_4 + 2H_2O$$

In each reaction, a strong acid reacts with a strong base. If solutions of these substances are mixed in the mole ratios specified by the balanced equation, neutral solutions will result. Similar reactions of weak acids and/or weak bases do not usually produce neutral solutions. In general, however, *reactions in which an acid and a base react in an aqueous solution to produce a salt and water are called* **neutralization reactions.** They are all double-replacement reactions (Section 7·6).

Neutralization reactions are one way that pure samples of salts can be prepared. For example, potassium chloride could be prepared by mixing together equal molar quantities of hydrochloric acid and potassium

Figure 19·1
A salt is the result of an acid–base neutralization. The white cloud of ammonium chloride seen here forms from the reaction of hydrogen chloride and ammonia gases escaping from aqueous solutions of those gases.

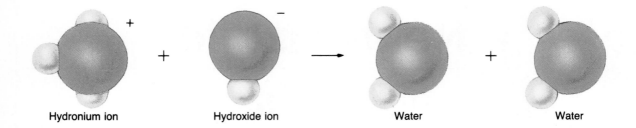

| Hydronium ion | | Hydroxide ion | | Water | | Water |

Figure 19-2
In a neutralization reaction, hydrogen ions (as hydronium ions) combine with hydroxide ions to form neutral water.

hydroxide. An aqueous solution of potassium chloride would result. The water could be removed by evaporation. Table 19·1 lists some common salts and their applications.

Problem

1. **a.** $HNO_3 + KOH \rightarrow$
$KNO_3 + H_2O$
b. $2HCl + Mg(OH)_2 \rightarrow$
$MgCl_2 + 2H_2O$
c. $H_3PO_4 + 3NH_4OH \rightarrow$
$(NH_4)_3PO_4 + 3H_2O$

1. Identify the products and write balanced equations for the following neutralization reactions.
   a. $HNO_3 + KOH \longrightarrow$
   b. $HCl + Mg(OH)_2 \longrightarrow$
   c. $H_3PO_4 + NH_4OH \longrightarrow$

Table 19·1 Some Salts and Their Applications		
Name	Formula	Applications
Ammonium sulfate	$(NH_4)_2SO_4$	Fertilizer
Barium sulfate	$BaSO_4$	Gastrointestinal studies; white pigment
Calcium chloride	$CaCl_2$	De-icing roadways and sidewalks
Calcium sulfate dihydrate (gypsum)	$CaSO_4 \cdot 2H_2O$	Plasterboard
Copper sulfate pentahydrate (blue vitriol)	$CuSO_4 \cdot 5H_2O$	Dyeing; fungicide
Calcium sulfate sesquihydrate	$(CaSO_4)_2 \cdot H_2O$	Plaster casts
Magnesium sulfate heptahydrate (Epsom salts)	$MgSO_4 \cdot 7H_2O$	Purgative
Potassium chloride	KCl	Sodium-free salt substitute
Potassium permanganate	$KMnO_4$	Disinfectant and fungicide
Silver nitrate	$AgNO_3$	Cauterizing agent
Silver bromide	$AgBr$	Photographic emulsions
Sodium bicarbonate (baking soda)	$NaHCO_3$	Antacid
Sodium carbonate decahydrate (washing soda)	$Na_2CO_3 \cdot 10H_2O$	Glass manufacture; water softener
Sodium chloride (table salt)	$NaCl$	Body electrolyte; chlorine manufacture
Sodium sulfate decahydrate (Glauber's salt)	$Na_2SO_4 \cdot 10H_2O$	Purgative
Sodium thiosulfate (hypo)	$Na_2S_2O_3$	Fixing agent in photographic process

19·A Soil Chemistry for Farmers

Soil is the complex mixture of minerals and organic matter that covers large portions of the earth's crust. It is formed from rocks and minerals weathered by wind and precipitation. Chemical and biological reactions play important secondary roles in the formation of soil. Soil is often considered lifeless and inert. Actually it undergoes constant change and is teeming with life. One square meter of soil only a few centimeters deep may contain well over one billion organisms!

Soil scientists classify soil into 10 to 16 categories depending on the history and chemistry of the soil. The soil's pH, the amount and type of clay it contains, and its nitrogen content are factors that determine its type. These are also the factors that are most important in agricultural chemistry.

Soils that contain a good deal of organic matter are generally acidic. As plants decay, acids are formed. If rainfall is frequent in the area, these acids are washed down through the soil. As they move through the soil, the hydrogen ions in the acid replace metal ions in the clay particles of the soil. Many clays are primarily silicates of aluminum. In other clays, some of the aluminum ions are replaced by sodium, magnesium, or other metals. These cations in the clay can be exchanged for other cations such as H^+, NH_4^+, and K^+. These cations are then held by the clay particles. The process of acidic water washing metal ions out of clay by replacing them with hydrogen ions is called *leaching*.

The pH of soil is a very important consideration in farming. It affects the solubilities of minerals and nutrients. It also affects the ease with which these substances reach the roots of growing plants. Most crops have adapted to grow within a specific pH range, between 5 and 7. Soils with a pH of less than 5 are suitable only for acid-tolerant plants such as those found in moist forested areas. Only a few plants are capable of surviving in soils with a pH greater than 7. Such alkaline soils are generally found in very arid regions.

If a soil is too acidic, its pH can be raised. Lime (calcium oxide or calcium hydroxide), or limestone (calcium carbonate) can be added to neutralize the soil. If the soil is too alkaline, its pH can be lowered by adding aluminum sulfate. This salt hydrolyzes to give the weak base aluminum hydroxide and hydrogen ions.

$$Al_2(SO_4)_3 + 6\ H_2O \longrightarrow 2Al(OH)_3 + 6\ H^+ + 3\ SO_4^{2-}$$

Fertilizers that contain ammonium ions increase soil acidity. So does increasing the amount of organic material in the soil by adding manure. Plowing under a plant crop also increases soil acidity.

For healthy growth, plants need a wide variety of nutrients. Nitrogen in the form of nitrate ions, phosphorus in the form of phosphate ions, and potassium ions are called macronutrients. They are needed in relatively large amounts. These materials are the three

Figure 19·3
Farmers and gardeners benefit from having their soil tested for pH and important nutrients. The appropriate fertilizers can then be chosen.

principal components of chemical fertilizers. The soil and air supply other necessary macronutrients. These are carbon, hydrogen, oxygen, sulfur, magnesium, calcium, and iron. Plants also need a number of other elements in trace amounts. Manganese, boron, copper, zinc, molybdenum and chlorine are necessary micronutrients. They are supplied by special fertilizers if they are not present in the soil in sufficient amounts. Good farming practices insure that all these nutrients are supplied to growing plants. Routine chemical tests can alert farmers if the level of any of these substances is low.

19·2   Titration

A titration is a convenient method of determining the concentration of an acid or a base.

It should be clear from the previous section that acids and bases sometimes, but not always, react in a 1:1 mole ratio.

$$HCl + NaOH \longrightarrow NaCl + H_2O$$
$$\text{1 mol} \quad \text{1 mol} \qquad \text{1 mol} \quad \text{1 mol}$$

When sulfuric acid reacts with sodium hydroxide, however, the ratio is 1:2. Two moles of base are required to neutralize one mole of H_2SO_4.

$$H_2SO_4 + 2NaOH \longrightarrow Na_2SO_4 + 2H_2O$$
$$\text{1 mol} \quad \text{2 mol} \qquad \text{1 mol} \quad \text{2 mol}$$

Even more base is required to neutralize 1 mol of H_3PO_4.

$$H_3PO_4 + 3NaOH \longrightarrow Na_3PO_4 + 3H_2O$$
$$\text{1 mol} \quad \text{3 mol} \qquad \text{1 mol} \quad \text{3 mol}$$

Safety

Strong bases like NaOH and KOH cause severe progressive burns. If they are spilled on you they should be flushed from the eye or skin with running water for 10 to 15 minutes.

Example 1

How many moles of sulfuric acid are required to neutralize 0.50 mol of sodium hydroxide?

Solution

Write a balanced equation for the reaction to find the acid–base mole ratio.

$$H_2SO_4 + 2NaOH \longrightarrow Na_2SO_4 + 2H_2O$$
$$\text{1 mol} \quad \text{2 mol} \qquad \text{1 mol} \quad \text{2 mol}$$

The ratio of H_2SO_4 to NaOH is 1:2. The necessary number of moles of H_2SO_4 is calculated using this ratio.

$$0.50 \text{ mol NaOH} \times \frac{1 \text{ mol } H_2SO_4}{2 \text{ mol NaOH}} = 0.25 \text{ mol } H_2SO_4$$

Problem

2. 0.60 mol NaOH

2. How many moles of sodium hydroxide are required to neutralize 0.20 mol of phosphoric acid?

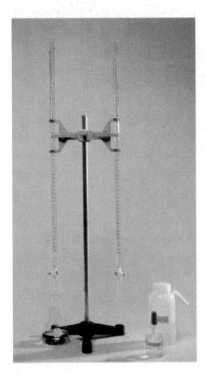

Figure 19·4
Laboratory titrations usually call for two burets, (one filled with acid, the other filled with base), a flask, and an indicator such as phenolphthalein.

The technique of titration does not only apply to neutralization reactions. It is useful in other areas as well, such as in the study of oxidation–reduction reactions.

The amount of acid (or base) in a solution is determined by carrying out a neutralization reaction. An appropriate acid–base indicator is used to show when neutralization is completed. The steps in the process are as follows. **1.** A measured amount of an acid of unknown concentration is added to a flask. **2.** An appropriate indicator (such as phenolphthalein) is added to the solution. **3.** Measured amounts of a base of known concentration are mixed into the acid. *The solution of known concentration is called the* **standard solution.** The addition is carried out using a buret. This process is continued until the indicator shows that neutralization has occurred. *The point at which neutralization is achieved is the* **end point** *of the titration.* The process just described is a **titration,** *the addition of a known amount of solution to determine the volume (or concentration) of another solution.* The unknown solution can be a base instead of an acid; the process is the same.

Example 2

A 25 mL solution of H_2SO_4 is neutralized by 18 mL of 1.0M NaOH using phenolphthalein as an indicator. What is the concentration of the H_2SO_4 solution?

Solution

Write an equation for the neutralization.

$$H_2SO_4 + 2\,NaOH \longrightarrow Na_2SO_4 + 2\,H_2O$$

The H_2SO_4 has two ionizable hydrogens. Thus it will take twice as many moles of NaOH for neutralization to occur. First calculate the moles of NaOH needed for neutralization.

$$0.018\,\text{L NaOH} \times \frac{1.0\,\text{mol NaOH}}{1\,\text{L NaOH}} = 0.018\,\text{mol NaOH}$$

Next use the equation to find the moles of H_2SO_4 neutralized.

$$0.018\,\text{mol NaOH} \times \frac{1\,\text{mol } H_2SO_4}{2\,\text{mol NaOH}} = 0.0090\,\text{mol } H_2SO_4$$

Then calculate the concentration of the acid.

$$\text{Molarity} = \frac{\text{moles}}{\text{liters}} = \frac{0.0090\,\text{mol}}{0.025\,\text{L}} = 0.36M$$

The H_2SO_4 is 0.36M.

Problems   3. 56 mL HCl   4. 0.129M

3. How many milliliters of 0.45M hydrochloric acid must be added to 25.0 mL of 1.00M potassium hydroxide to make a neutral solution?

4. What is the molarity of phosphoric acid if 15.0 mL of the solution is neutralized by 38.5 mL of 0.15M NaOH?

19·3 Equivalents

In any neutralization reaction, one mole of hydrogen ions reacts with one mole of hydroxide ions. This does not mean that one mole of any acid will neutralize one mole of any base. For some acids, one mole of the acid can give one mole of hydrogen ions. HCl and HNO_3 are such acids. For other acids, one mole of the acid can give two or more moles of hydrogen ions. For example, one mole of H_2SO_4 gives two moles of hydrogen ions. One mole of H_3PO_4 gives three moles of hydrogen ions. The same is true of bases such as $Ca(OH)_2$ and $Al(OH)_3$. They give two and three moles of hydroxide ions respectively for one mole of base.

Chemists need a unit for the amount of an acid (or base) that will give one mole of hydrogen (or hydroxide) ions. This unit is called an equivalent of the acid or base. *One **equivalent** is the amount of an acid (or base) that will give one mole of hydrogen (or hydroxide) ions.*

One mole of HCl is one equivalent of HCl. One mole of H_2SO_4 is two equivalents of H_2SO_4. One mole of NaOH is one equivalent of NaOH. One mole of $Ca(OH)_2$ is 2 equivalents of $Ca(OH)_2$. One mole of HCl will neutralize one mole of NaOH. This is because one mole of each compound is also one equivalent.

$$HCl + NaOH \longrightarrow H_2O + NaCl$$

One mole of HCl will not neutralize one mole of $Ca(OH)_2$.

$$2HCl + Ca(OH)_2 \longrightarrow 2 H_2O + CaCl_2$$

In this example, two moles of acid are required to neutralize one mole of base. Two moles of HCl contains two equivalents of acid. One mole of $Ca(OH)_2$ contains two equivalents of base. In any neutralization reaction, one equivalent of acid will neutralize one equivalent of base.

*The mass of one equivalent of a substance is called its **gram equivalent mass.*** One mole of HCl is one equivalent of HCl. Its gram equivalent mass is equal to its gram molecular mass, 36.5 grams. One mole of H_2SO_4 is two equivalents of H_2SO_4. Its gram equivalent mass is only half of its gram molecular mass, or 49.0 grams.

Figure 19·5
At the end point of a titration, the change of color by the indicator shows that equivalent amounts of acid and base are present.

Neutralization reactions require equivalent amounts of acid and base.

The equivalent mass is less than or equal to the formula mass.

Example 3

What is the mass of 1 equiv of calcium hydroxide?

Solution

The gram formula mass of $Ca(OH)_2$ is 74 g. One formula unit of $Ca(OH)_2$ has two hydroxide ions.

$$Ca(OH)_2 \longrightarrow Ca^{2+} + 2 OH^-$$

$$\text{Gram equivalent mass of } Ca(OH)_2 = \frac{74 \text{ g}}{2} = 37 \text{ g}$$

Calcium hydroxide is 2 equiv per mol and 1 equiv of $Ca(OH)_2$ is 37 g.

Example 4

How many equivalents is 4.8 g of sulfuric acid?

Solution

The gram formula mass of H_2SO_4 is 98 g. Therefore, 4.8 g of H_2SO_4 is less than 1 mol.

$$4.8 \text{ g } H_2SO_4 \times \frac{1 \text{ mol } H_2SO_4}{98 \text{ g } H_2SO_4} = 0.050 \text{ mol } H_2SO_4$$

The acid H_2SO_4 is 2 equiv per mol. Thus 0.050 mol H_2SO_4 is 0.10 equiv of H_2SO_4, and 4.8 g of H_2SO_4 is 0.10 equiv of H_2SO_4.

Problems

5. a. 56.1 g (1 equiv per mol)
b. 36.5 g (1 equiv per mol)
c. 49.0 g (2 equiv per mol)
6. a. 0.10 equiv
b. 3.86 equiv
c. 0.30 equiv
d. 0.30 equiv

5. Determine the gram equivalent mass and the equivalents per mole for each compound. **a.** KOH **b.** HCl **c.** H_2SO_4

6. How many equivalents is each of the following?
a. 3.7 g $Ca(OH)_2$ **b.** 189 g H_2SO_4 **c.** 9.8 g H_3PO_4

19·4   Normality

The concentrations of acids and bases can be stated in molarity. Chemists are usually more interested, however, in how many equivalents of acid or base a solution contains. Thus the concentrations of acids and bases are usually expressed as normalities. A solution containing 1.0 equiv of an acid or base per liter has a normality of 1.0. That is, the solution is 1.0 normal (1.0N). The **normality** of a solution is the concentration expressed as the number of equivalents of solute in 1 L of solution.

■ Concentrations of acids and bases are often expressed in normalities.

$$\text{Normality } (N) = \text{equiv/L}$$

The numerical values of normality and molarity are equal for acids and bases that give 1 equiv of H^+ or OH^- per mole. For example, a solution containing 1 mol of NaOH per liter is 1M and also 1N. A solution containing 1 mol of H_2SO_4 per liter is 1M, but it is 2N. This is because H_2SO_4 contains 2 equiv per mole.

Normality = molarity × number of ionizable hydrogens.

Problems

7. a. 2N HCl
b. 0.1N HC$_2$H$_3$O$_2$
c. 0.9N H$_3$PO$_4$
d. 0.50N H$_2$SO$_4$
8. a. 0.50N
b. 0.20N

7. What is the normality of the following solutions?
a. 2M HCl   **c.** 0.3M H_3PO_4
b. 0.1M $HC_2H_3O_2$ **d.** 0.25M H_2SO_4

8. What is the normality of the following solutions?
a. 20.0 g NaOH in 1.0 L of solution
b. 4.9 g H_2SO_4 in 500 mL of solution

The number of equivalents of an acid or base in a known volume of a solution of known normality can be calculated.

Number of equivalents = volume (liters) × normality
of solution   of solution

Equiv = $V(L) \times N$

Example 5

How many equivalents are in 2.5 L of 0.60N H_2SO_4?

Solution

Number of equivalents = $V(L) \times N$

$$= 2.5 \, \cancel{L} \times \frac{0.60 \text{ equiv}}{\cancel{L}} = 1.5 \text{ equiv}$$

Problem

9. a. 0.99 equiv
b. 0.80 equiv
c. 0.070 equiv

9. How many equivalents are in the following?
    a. 0.55 L of 1.8N NaOH
    b. 1.6 L of 0.50N H_3PO_4
    c. 250 mL of 0.28N H_2SO_4

Solutions of known normality can be made less concentrated by diluting them with water. The changes in concentration can be calculated using this relationship.

$$N_1 \times V_1 = N_2 \times V_2$$

Here N_1 and V_1 are the initial solution's normality and volume. N_2 and V_2 are the final solution's normality and volume.

Example 6

You need to make 250 mL of 0.10N sodium hydroxide from a stock solution that is 2.0N sodium hydroxide. How many milliliters of the stock solution must you dilute to 250 mL to get the required solution?

Solution

Use $N_1 \times V_1 = N_2 \times V_2$. You know that $N_1 = 2.0N$, $N_2 = 0.10N$, and $V_2 = 250$ mL. To find V_1, rearrange the equation and then insert the values of N_1, N_2, and V_2.

$$V_1 = \frac{N_2 \times V_2}{N_1} = \frac{0.10 \, \cancel{N} \times 250 \text{ mL}}{2.0 \, \cancel{N}} = 12.5 \text{ mL} = 13 \text{ mL}$$

(to two significant figures)

Dilute 13 mL of 2.0N NaOH to 250 mL to make 0.1N NaOH.

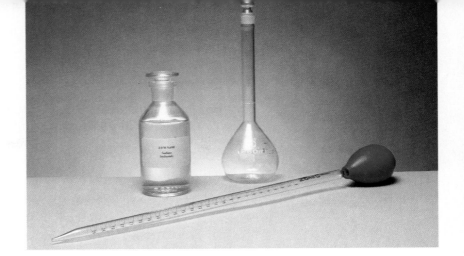

Figure 19·6
A solution with a given normality can be diluted to make a solution of a lower normality. Calculate the volume of concentrated solution needed to make the dilute solution. Then use accurate measuring devices such as a pipet and volumetric flask to make the dilution.

Problem

10. Dilute 25 mL of 4.0*N* H₂SO₄ to 500 mL.

10. How would you prepare 500 mL of 0.20*N* sulfuric acid from a stock solution of 4.0*N* sulfuric acid?

Acid–base titrations are neutralization reactions.

Titration calculations are usually done in terms of normality instead of molarity. This is because normality takes into account the number of ionizable hydrogens in an acid whereas molarity does not. *In a titration, the point of neutralization is called the* **equivalence point.** At the equivalence point, the number of equivalents of acid and base are equal. It is thus possible to calculate the number of equivalents of acid or base in an unknown sample. Let N_A and N_B be the normalities of the acid and base solutions. Let V_A and V_B be the volumes of the acid and base solutions required to give a neutral solution.

$$\text{Equivalents of acid} = N_A \times V_A$$
$$\text{Equivalents of base} = N_B \times V_B$$

At the equivalence point of a titration the equivalents of acid equals the equivalents of base.

The number of equivalents of acid and base are equal at the equivalence point.

$$N_A \times V_A = N_B \times V_B$$

The volumes of V_A and V_B may be expressed in liters or milliliters, provided the same unit is used for both. For practical reasons, milliliters are usually used for reporting solution volumes in analyses.

Example 7

If 35.0 mL of 0.20*N* hydrochloric acid is required to neutralize 25.0 mL of an unknown base, what is the normality of the base?

Solution

$$N_B = \frac{V_A \times N_A}{V_B} = \frac{35.0 \, \text{mL} \times 0.20N}{25.0 \, \text{mL}} = 0.28N$$

Example 8

How many milliliters of 0.500N sulfuric acid are required to neutralize 50.0 mL of 0.200N potassium hydroxide?

Solution

$$V_A = \frac{V_B \times N_B}{N_A}$$

$$= \frac{50.0 \text{ mL} \times 0.200 \cancel{N}}{0.500 \cancel{N}} = 20.0 \text{ mL}$$

Problems

11. 19 mL NaOH
12. 1.2N base

11. How many milliliters of 0.20N sodium hydroxide must be added to 75 mL of 0.050N hydrochloric acid to make a neutral solution?

12. What is the normality of a solution of a base if 25 mL is neutralized by 75 mL of 0.40N acid?

19·5   Salt Hydrolysis

Solutions of a salt are not neutral if the salt promotes hydrolysis.

Salts of weak acids and salts of weak bases promote hydrolysis.

A salt is made by neutralizing an acid with a base. Many solutions of salts are neutral, but some are acidic and others are basic. Solutions of sodium chloride and potassium sulfate are neutral. A solution of ammonium chloride is acidic. A solution of sodium acetate is basic. This happens because some salts promote hydrolysis. *In salt hydrolysis, the cations or anions of the dissociated salt accept hydrogen ions from water or donate hydrogen ions to water.* Depending on the direction of the hydrogen-ion transfer, solutions containing hydrolyzing salts may be either acidic or basic. Hydrolyzing salts are usually derived from a strong acid and a weak base or from a weak acid and a strong base.

Sodium acetate (CH_3COONa) is the salt of a weak acid (acetic acid, CH_3COOH) and a strong base (sodium hydroxide, $NaOH$). In solution the salt is completely ionized.

$$\underset{\text{Sodium acetate}}{CH_3COONa} \longrightarrow \underset{\text{Acetate ion}}{CH_3COO^-} + \underset{\text{Sodium ion}}{Na^+}$$

The acetate ion is a Bronsted–Lowry base. It establishes an equilibrium with water, forming un-ionized acetic acid and hydroxide ions.

$$\underset{\substack{\text{(hydrogen-ion} \\ \text{acceptor,} \\ \text{Bronsted–Lowry} \\ \text{base)}}}{CH_3COO^-} + \underset{\substack{\text{(hydrogen-ion} \\ \text{donor} \\ \text{Bronsted–Lowry} \\ \text{acid)}}}{H_2O} \rightleftharpoons CH_3COOH + \underset{\substack{\text{(makes the} \\ \text{solution basic)}}}{OH^-}$$

This process is called hydrolysis because it splits a hydrogen ion off a water molecule. The solution contains a hydroxide-ion concentration greater than the hydrogen-ion concentration. Thus the solution is basic.

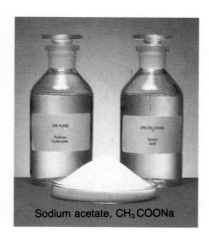

Sodium acetate, CH_3COONa

Figure 19·7
The salt of a strong base and a weak acid will form a basic solution when added to water.

Ammonium chloride, NH_4Cl

Figure 19·8
Will the solution be basic or acidic when the salt of a strong acid and weak base is dissolved in water?
Acidic.

◼ Buffers are solutions that resist changes in pH.

Ammonium chloride (NH_4Cl) is the salt of a strong acid (hydrochloric acid, HCl) and a weak base (ammonia, NH_3). It is completely ionized in solution.

$$NH_4Cl \longrightarrow NH_4^+ + Cl^-$$

The ammonium ion (NH_4^+) is a strong enough acid to donate a hydrogen ion to a water molecule, although the equilibrium is strongly to the left.

$$\underset{\substack{\text{(hydrogen-ion donor} \\ \text{Bronsted–Lowry} \\ \text{acid)}}}{NH_4^+} + \underset{\substack{\text{(hydrogen-ion} \\ \text{acceptor} \\ \text{Bronsted–Lowry} \\ \text{base)}}}{H_2O} \rightleftharpoons NH_3 + \underset{\substack{\text{(makes the} \\ \text{solution} \\ \text{acidic)}}}{H_3O^+}$$

This process is also called hydrolysis. It results in the formation of unionized ammonia and hydronium ions. The $[H_3O^+]$ is greater than the $[OH^-]$. Thus a solution of ammonium chloride is acidic.

19·6 Buffers

Buffers *are solutions in which the pH remains relatively constant when small amounts of acid or base are added.* A buffer is a solution of a weak acid and one of its salts. It could also be a solution of a weak base and one of its salts. The acetate buffer system is a typical example. A solution containing 0.20 mol/L of both acetic acid and sodium acetate has a pH of 4.76. When moderate amounts of either acid or base are added to this buffer system, the pH changes little. For example, the addition of 10 mL of 0.10*M* sodium hydroxide to 1 L of this buffer increases the pH by only 0.01 pH units (from 4.76 to 4.77). In contrast, the addition of 10 mL of 0.10*M* sodium hydroxide to 1 L of pure water increases the pH by 4.0 pH units (from 7.0 to 11.0).

The buffer solution is better able to resist drastic changes in pH than pure water. Acetic acid (CH_3COOH) and its anion (CH_3COO^-) act as reservoirs of neutralizing power. They react with any hydrogen ions or hydroxide ions that are added to the solution. For example, the sodium acetate (CH_3OONa) in the buffer solution is completely ionized.

$$\underset{\text{Sodium acetate}}{CH_3COONa} \longrightarrow \underset{\text{acetate ion}}{CH_3COO^-} + \underset{\text{Sodium ion}}{Na^+}$$

When an acid is added to the solution, the acetate ions (CH_3COO^-) act as a "hydrogen-ion sponge." This creates acetic acid, which does not dissociate extensively in water. Thus the pH does not change appreciably.

$$\underset{\text{Acetate ion}}{CH_3COO^-} + \underset{\text{Hydrogen ion}}{H^+} \longrightarrow \underset{\text{Acetic acid}}{CH_3COOH}$$

A base is a source of hydroxide ions. When a base is added to the solution, the acetic acid and the hydroxide ions react to produce water.

$$\underset{\text{Acetic acid}}{CH_3COOH} + \underset{\text{Hydroxide ion}}{OH^-} \longrightarrow \underset{\text{Acetate ion}}{CH_3COO^-} + \underset{\text{Water}}{H_2O}$$

Both the HCO_3^-/H_2CO_3 and the $HPO_4^{2-}/H_2PO_4^-$ buffers help maintain the pH of blood.

The acetate ion is not a strong enough base to accept hydrogen ions from water extensively. Again the pH changes very little.

Figure 19·9
This device measures the pH of human blood. The carbonic acid–bicarbonate buffer system is responsible for maintaining blood pH within a very narrow range.

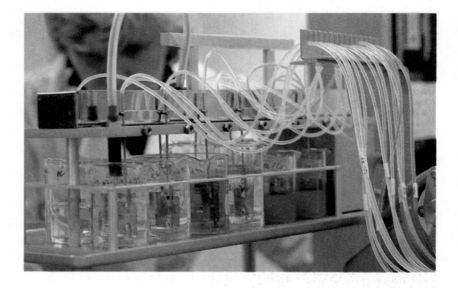

The manner in which a buffer resists changes in pH is an excellent illustration of Le Châtelier's principle.

An acetate buffer can not control the pH when too much acid is added. Then no more acetate ions are present to accept hydrogen ions. The buffer also becomes ineffective when too much base is added. Then no more acetic acid molecules are present to donate hydrogen ions. *The **buffer capacity** is the amount of acid or base that may be added to a buffer solution before a significant change in pH occurs.* When too much acid or base is added, the buffer capacity of a solution is exceeded. Two buffer systems are crucial in controlling pH in the human body. One is the carbonic acid–bicarbonate buffer. The other is the monohydrogen phosphate–dihydrogen phosphate buffer. Table 19·2 lists several buffer systems.

Example 9

Show how the carbonic acid–bicarbonate buffer can mop up hydrogen ions and hydroxide ions.

Solution

The carbonic acid–bicarbonate buffer is a solution of carbonic acid (H_2CO_3) and bicarbonate ions (HCO_3^-). When a base is added to this buffer, it reacts with H_2CO_3 to produce neutral water. The pH changes very little.

$$\underset{\substack{\text{Carbonic} \\ \text{acid}}}{H_2CO_3} + \underset{\substack{\text{Hydroxide} \\ \text{ion}}}{OH^-} \longrightarrow \underset{\substack{\text{Bicarbonate} \\ \text{ion}}}{HCO_3^-} + \underset{\text{Water}}{H_2O}$$

When an acid is added to the buffer, it reacts with HCO_3^- to produce undissociated carbonic acid. Again the pH changes very little.

$$\underset{\substack{\text{Bicarbonate} \\ \text{ion}}}{HCO_3^-} + \underset{\substack{\text{Hydrogen} \\ \text{ion}}}{H^+} \longrightarrow \underset{\substack{\text{Carbonic} \\ \text{acid}}}{H_2CO_3}$$

Table 19·2	Important Buffer Systems	
Buffer name	Buffer species	Buffer pH (components $0.1M$)
Acetic acid–acetate	CH_3COOH/CH_3COO^-	4.76
Dihydrogen phosphate ion– monohydrogen phosphate ion	$H_2PO_4^-/HPO_4^{2-}$	7.20
Carbonic acid–bicarbonate (solution saturated with CO)	H_2CO_3/HCO_3^-	6.46
Ammonium ion–ammonia	NH_4^+/NH_3	9.25

13. **a.** $HPO_4^{2-} + H^+ \longrightarrow H_2PO_4^-$
    b. $H_2PO_4^- + OH^- \longrightarrow$
        $HPO_4^{2-} + H_2O$
14. **a.** $CH_3COO^- + H^+ \longrightarrow$
        CH_3COOH
    b. $NH_3 + H^+ \longrightarrow NH_4^+$

Problems

13. Write reactions to show what happens when the following occur.
    a. Acid is added to a solution of HPO_4^{2-}.
    b. Base is added to a solution of $H_2PO_4^-$.

14. Write equations that show what happens when acid is added to the following buffers. **a.** acetic acid–acetate buffer **b.** ammonium ion–ammonia buffer

19·7 The Solubility Product Constant

Salts differ in their solubilities. In general, compounds of the alkali metals are soluble in water. For example, over 35 g of sodium chloride will dissolve in 100 mL of water. Many classes of ionic compounds, however, are insoluble. For example, many compounds that contain phosphate, sulfide, sulfite, or carbonate ions are insoluble. Exceptions are compounds in which these ions are combined with ammonium ions or alkali metal ions. Table 19·3 summarizes the solubilities of many ionic compounds in water.

Most "insoluble" salts will dissolve to some extent in water. These salts are said to be slightly or sparingly soluble in water. For example, when the "insoluble" salt silver chloride is mixed with water, a very small amount of it dissolves.

$$AgCl \rightleftharpoons Ag^+ + Cl^-$$

An equilibrium expression can be written for this process.

$$K_{eq} = \frac{[Ag^+] \times [Cl^-]}{[AgCl]}$$

As long as some undissolved (solid) AgCl is present, the concentration of the AgCl is a constant. Thus, the concentration of AgCl can be combined with the equilibrium constant.

$$K_{eq} \times [AgCl] = [Ag^+] \times [Cl^-] = K_{sp}$$

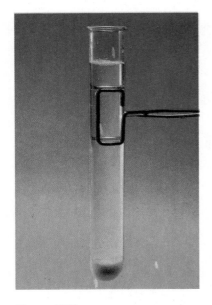

Figure 19·10
Silver chloride is slightly soluble in water.

Table 19·3   Solubilities of Ionic Compounds in Water

Compounds	Solubility	Exceptions
Compounds of Group IA metals and of ammonium ions	Soluble	A few lithium compounds
Acetates, nitrates, chlorates, and perchlorates	Soluble	Few exceptions
Sulfates	Soluble	Compounds of Pb, Ag, Hg, Ba, Sr, and Ca
Chlorides, bromides, and iodides	Soluble	Compounds of Ag and a few others of Hg and Pb
Sulfides and hydroxides	Most are insoluble	Alkali metal sulfides and hydroxides are soluble. Compounds of Ba, Sr, and Ca are slightly soluble.
Carbonates, phosphates, and sulfites	Insoluble	Compounds of the alkali metals and of ammonium ions

■ The concentration of ions of slightly soluble salts can be calculated from the solubility product, K_{sp}.

This new constant, called *the **solubility product constant**, K_{sp}, is equal to the product of the concentration terms each raised to the power of the coefficient of the substance in the dissociation equation.* The value of K_{sp} for silver chloride at 25°C is 1.8×10^{-10}.

$$K_{sp} = [Ag^+] \times [Cl^-] = 1.8 \times 10^{-10}$$

Example 10

What is the concentration of silver and chloride ions in a saturated silver chloride solution at 25°C? $K_{sp} = 1.8 \times 10^{-10}$.

Solution

The equation shows that for each Ag^+ ion formed, one Cl^- ion is formed.

$$AgCl \rightleftharpoons Ag^+ + Cl^-$$

Therefore at equilibrium $[Ag^+] = [Cl^-]$.
Write the expression for K_{sp}.

$$K_{sp} = [Ag^+] \times [Cl^-] = 1.8 \times 10^{-10}$$

Substitute for the $[Cl^-]$ then solve for the $[Ag^+]$.

$$[Ag^+] \times [Ag^+] = 1.8 \times 10^{-10}$$

$$[Ag^+]^2 = 1.8 \times 10^{-10}$$

$$[Ag^+] = 1.3 \times 10^{-5} M$$

When doing this kind of calculation be sure to express the exponent so that it will be evenly divisible when you take the square root.

The equilibrium concentration of Cl^- is also $1.3 \times 10^{-5} M$.

Table 19·4	Solubility Product Constants, K_{sp}, at 25°C		
Salt	K_{sp}	Salt	K_{sp}
Halides		**Sulfides**	
AgCl	1.8×10^{-10}	NiS	4×10^{-20}
AgBr	5.0×10^{-13}	CuS	8×10^{-37}
AgI	8.3×10^{-17}	Ag_2S	8×10^{-51}
$PbCl_2$	1.7×10^{-5}	ZnS	3×10^{-23}
$PbBr_2$	2.1×10^{-6}	FeS	8×10^{-19}
PbI_2	7.9×10^{-9}	CdS	1×10^{-27}
PbF_2	3.6×10^{-8}	SnS	1.3×10^{-26}
CaF_2	3.9×10^{-11}	PbS	3×10^{-28}
Carbonates		**Hydroxides**	
$CaCO_3$	4.5×10^{-9}	$Al(OH)_3$	3×10^{-34}
$SrCO_3$	9.3×10^{-10}	$Zn(OH)_2$	3.0×10^{-16}
$ZnCO_3$	1.0×10^{-10}	$Ca(OH)_2$	6.5×10^{-6}
Ag_2CO_3	8.1×10^{-12}	$Mg(OH)_2$	7.1×10^{-12}
$BaCO_3$	5.0×10^{-9}	$Fe(OH)_2$	7.9×10^{-16}
Sulfates		**Chromates**	
$PbSO_4$	6.3×10^{-7}	$PbCrO_4$	1.8×10^{-14}
$BaSO_4$	1.1×10^{-10}	Ag_2CrO_4	1.2×10^{-12}
$CaSO_4$	2.4×10^{-5}		

The smaller the value of K_{sp}, the lower the solubility of a salt.

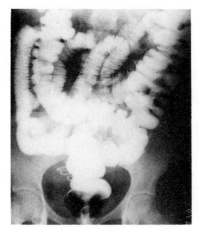

Figure 19·11
Barium sulfate is used for X-rays of the digestive tract. This relatively insoluble salt is used as a suspension. X-rays do not pass through the salt thereby producing light areas on the film.

Example 11

Calcium fluoride has a K_{sp} of 3.9×10^{-11} at 25°C. What is the fluoride ion concentration at equilibrium?

Solution

Write the equation: $CaF_2 \rightleftharpoons Ca^{2+} + 2F^-$.

Write the K_{sp} expression: $K_{sp} = [Ca^{2+}][F^-]^2 = 3.9 \times 10^{-11}$.

When the $[Ca^{2+}]$ is x, the $[F^-]$ is 2x. (There are twice as many F^- ions as Ca^{2+} ions formed when CaF_2 dissociates.) Now substitute into the K_{sp} expression and solve for x.

$$K_{sp} = (x)(2x)^2 = 3.9 \times 10^{-11}$$
$$4x^3 = 3.9 \times 10^{-11}$$
$$x^3 = 9.8 \times 10^{-12}$$
$$x = 2.1 \times 10^{-4}$$

The $[Ca^{2+}] = 2.1 \times 10^{-4} M$. The $[F^-]$ is twice the $[Ca^{2+}]$. Thus $[F^-] = 4.2 \times 10^{-4} M$.

Problems

15. $2 \times 10^{-14} M$
16. a. $2 \times 10^{-17} M$
   b. $1 \times 10^{-17} M$

15. Lead(II) sulfide, PbS, has a K_{sp} of 3×10^{-28}. What is the concentration of lead(II) ion in a saturated solution of PbS?

16. The K_{sp} of silver sulfide, Ag_2S, is 8×10^{-51}. **a.** What is the silver-ion concentration of a saturated solution of silver sulfide? **b.** What is the sulfide-ion concentration of the same solution?

19·B   Swimming Pool Chemistry

The major problem in swimming pool maintenance is preventing the growth of algae and bacteria. Algae foul the water and can clog filters. Bacteria can cause illness. Chlorine compounds are usually used to disinfect the water in pools. The "liquid chlorine" sold for use in home pools is a solution of sodium hypochlorite, NaOCl. "Dry chlorine" is solid calcium hypochlorite, $Ca(OCl)_2$. When these ionic compounds are added to water, they undergo hydrolysis to form the weak acid, hypochlorous acid, HOCl.

$$OCl^- + H_2O \longrightarrow HOCl + OH^-$$

Chlorine gas, Cl_2, also forms hypochlorous acid when added to water. This method is sometimes used in large public pools.

$$Cl_2 + H_2O \rightleftharpoons Cl^- + H^+ + HOCl$$

For proper pool maintenance enough hypochlorous acid must be present in the water. It prevents the growth of bacteria and algae. The amount of undissociated hypochlorous acid in the water depends on the pH. If the pH is too high, the hydrolysis reaction shown above will be shifted toward the reactants. Then the concentration of HOCl is reduced. This is according to LeChatelier's principle. If the pH is too low, however, the acid content of the water can cause eye and skin irritation. Too much acid can also etch the plaster and corrode the metal piping and filters in the pool.

If the pool pH is too high, it can be lowered by adding an acid. This will neutralize the excess hydroxide ions. Muriatic acid (a solution of HCl) or solid sodium hydrogen sulfate can be used.

$$HCl + OH^- \longrightarrow H_2O + Cl^-$$
$$NaHSO_4 + OH^- \longrightarrow Na^+ + SO_4^{2-} + H_2O$$

If the pool pH is too low, it can be raised by neutralizing some of the acid. Sodium carbonate (also called soda ash) or sodium bicarbonate (baking soda) can be used.

$$Na_2CO_3 + 2H^+ \longrightarrow 2Na^+ + H_2O + CO_2$$
$$NaHCO_3 + H^+ \longrightarrow Na^+ + H_2O + CO_2$$

Figure 19·12
Chemicals are used to keep the pH of a swimming pool near neutral.

19·8   The Common Ion Effect

In a saturated solution of silver chloride, an equilibrium is established between the solid silver chloride and its ions.

$$AgCl(s) \rightleftharpoons Ag^+ + Cl^- \qquad K_{sp} = 1.8 \times 10^{-10}$$

What would happen if some silver nitrate was added to this solution? Immediately after the addition, the product of the $[Ag^+]$ and the $[Cl^-]$ would be greater than K_{sp}. Le Châtelier's principle (Section 17·12) applies here. The "stress" of the additional Ag^+ could be relieved if the reaction shifted to the left. Silver ions would combine with chloride ions to form additional solid AgCl. In fact, AgCl would precipitate until the product of the $[Ag^+]$ and the $[Cl^-]$ once again equalled 1.8×10^{-10}.

In this example, the silver ion is called a common ion. *A* **common ion** *is an ion that is common to both salts.* Adding silver nitrate to a saturated solution of AgCl causes the solubility of AgCl to be decreased. The solubility of AgCl is less in the presence of $AgNO_3$ than it is in pure water. *The lowering of the solubility of a substance by the addition of a common ion is called the* **common ion effect.**

In this example, the addition of sodium chloride would also give the common ion effect. The additional chloride ion (common ion) would cause the reaction to shift to the left. More AgCl would be formed, and the solubility of AgCl would thus decrease.

■ The solubility of an ionic solid is decreased when a common ion is present in the solution.

The common ion effect is not a unique phenomenon. It is merely another example of Le Châtelier's principle.

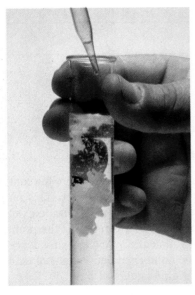

Figure 19·13
When silver nitrate is added to a saturated solution of silver chloride, additional silver chloride forms due to the common ion effect.

Example 12

The K_{sp} of silver iodide is 8.3×10^{-17}. What is the iodide ion concentration of a 1.00 L saturated solution of AgI to which 0.020 mol of $AgNO_3$ is added?

Solution

Write the equation for the equilibrium.

$$AgI(s) \rightleftharpoons Ag^+ + I^-$$

Write the expression for the solubility product.

$$K_{sp} = [Ag^+] \times [I^-] = 8.3 \times 10^{-17}$$

If the equilibrium concentration of iodide ion from the dissociation is x, then the equilibrium concentration of silver ion is x + 0.020. Because of the small value of K_{sp}, x will be small compared to 0.020. Therefore, the $[Ag^+]$ at equilibrium = x + 0.020 ≈ 0.020. Substitute these values into the K_{sp} expression.

$$K_{sp} = [Ag^+] \times [I^-] = 8.3 \times 10^{-17}$$

$$(0.020)(x) = 8.3 \times 10^{-17}$$

$$x = 4.2 \times 10^{-15}$$

The equilibrium concentration of iodide ion is $4.2 \times 10^{-15} M$.

Problem

17. $3.2 \times 10^{-6}M$

17. The K_{sp} of $SrSO_4$ is 3.2×10^{-7}. What is the equilibrium concentration of sulfate ion in a 1.0-L solution of strontium sulfate to which 0.10 mol of $Sr(C_2H_3O_2)_2$ has been added?

The K_{sp} is used to calculate whether precipitation will occur when solutions of ions are mixed.

The solubility product, K_{sp}, can be used to predict whether a precipitate will form when solutions are mixed together. If the ion product of two ions in the mixture is greater than the K_{sp} of the compound, a precipitate will form. If the ion product equals K_{sp}, the solution is saturated, and no precipitate will form. If the ion product is less than K_{sp}, no precipitate will form, and the solution will be unsaturated.

Problem

18. No.

18. A student prepares a solution by combining 0.025 mol $CaCl_2$ and 0.015 mol $Pb(NO_3)_2$ and adding water to make 1.0 L of solution. Will a precipitate of $PbCl_2$ form in this solution?

19 Neutralization and Salts

Chapter Review

Key Terms

buffer	19·6	neutralization	
buffer capacity	19·6	reaction	19·1
common ion	19·8	normality (N)	19·4
common ion effect	19·8	salt hydrolysis	19·5
end point	19·2	solubility product	
equivalence point	19·4	constant (K_{sp})	19·7
equivalent (equiv)	19·3	standard solution	19·2
gram equivalent mass		titration	19·2
of an acid	19·3		
gram equivalent mass			
of a base	19·3		

Chapter Summary

In the reaction of an acid with a base, hydrogen ions and hydroxide ions react to produce water. This reaction, called neutralization, is usually carried out by titration. The end point in a titration is the point at which the solution is neutral. At the equivalence point of a titration the number of equivalents of acid equals the number of equivalents of base.

An equivalent of an acid is the mass of the acid that provides 1 mol of hydrogen ions in solution. A solution that contains one equivalent of an acid or a base in a single liter of solution is a one normal ($1N$) solution.

A salt forms when an acid is neutralized by a base. Salts consist of an anion from the acid and a cation from the base. Salts of strong acid–strong base reactions produce neutral solutions with water. Salts formed from weak acids or weak bases hydrolyze water. They produce solutions that are acidic or basic.

Solutions that resist changes in pH are called buffer solutions. The pH of body fluids is kept within its normal range with buffers.

The solubility product constant, K_{sp}, is the equilibrium constant for the equilibrium between an ionic solid and its ions in solution. The solubility of a salt is decreased by the addition of a common ion.

Practice Questions and Problems

19. What is a neutralization reaction? Illustrate your answer by writing a balanced equation for the reaction that occurs when a solution of hydrochloric acid is added to potassium hydroxide. *19·1*

20. Write complete balanced equations for these acid–base reactions. Give the names of the salts produced. *19·1*
   a. $H_2SO_4 + KOH \longrightarrow$
   b. $HCl + NH_4OH \longrightarrow$
   c. $H_3PO_4 + Ca(OH)_2 \longrightarrow$
   d. $HNO_3 + Mg(OH)_2 \longrightarrow$

21. How many moles of hydrochloric acid are required to neutralize these bases? *19·2*
   a. 0.2 mol NaOH
   b. 2 mol NH_4OH
   c. 0.1 mol $Ca(OH)_2$

22. What is true at the end point of a titration? *19·2*

23. What is the molarity of sodium hydroxide if 20.0 mL of the solution is neutralized by the following 1.00*M* solutions? *19·2*
   a. 28.0 mL of HCl
   b. 17.4 mL of H_3PO_4

24. What is the equivalent mass of an acid? *19·3*

25. What is the equivalent mass of a base? *19·3*

26. Determine the gram equivalent mass of each compound. *19·3*
   a. H_3PO_4 **c.** $Mg(OH)_2$
   b. NaOH   **d.** CH_3COOH

27. Determine the number of equivalents in each of the following. *19·3*
   a. 20 g NaOH   **d.** 19.6 g H_2SO_4
   b. 7.4 g $Ca(OH)_2$ **e.** 12 g NaOH
   c. 9.8 g H_3PO_4

28. How is the normality of a solution usually calculated? *19·4*

29. What is the normality of each of the following solutions? *19·4*
   a. 1*M* NaOH   **c.** 0.2*M* KOH
   b. 2*M* HNO_3 **d.** 0.1*M* H_2SO_4

30. Determine the normality of each solution. *19·4*
   a. 250 mL of solution containing 10 g of NaOH
   b. 750 mL of solution containing 4.9 g of H_2SO_4
   c. 270 mL of solution containing 0.74 g of HCl
   d. 2.80 L of solution containing 18.6 g of HNO_3
   e. 7.3 g HCl in 250 mL of solution
   f. 18.4 g HNO_3 in 1250 mL of solution

31. How many equivalents are in the following solutions? *19·4*
   a. 5.8 L of 0.55*N* HCl
   b. 330 mL of 1.4*N* H_3PO_4
   c. 0.14 L of 0.22*N* KOH

32. How many milliliters of 2.00*N* NaOH would you need to dilute with water to make 250 mL of 0.100*N* NaOH? *19·4*

33. What is meant by the equivalence point of a titration? *19·4*

34. A student titrated several solutions of unknown concentration with various standard solutions to the point of neutralization. The volume of each unknown solution and the volume and normality of the standard solution used are given below. Calculate the normality for each unknown. *19·4*

   a. 25.0 mL NaOH required 15.0 mL of 0.100*N* HCl
   b. 10.0 mL H_2SO_4 required 20.0 mL of 0.200*N* HCl
   c. 17.5 mL NaOH required 25.0 mL of 0.120*N* HNO_3
   d. 50.0 mL CH_3COOH required 39.6 mL of 0.0950*N* KOH
   e. 29.2 mL $Ca(OH)_2$ required 50.0 mL of 0.152*N* HNO_3

35. What kinds of salts hydrolyze water? *19·5*

36. Explain why solutions of salts that hydrolyze water are not pH 7. *19·5*

37. Predict whether an aqueous solution of each salt will be acidic, basic, or neutral.　　*19·5*
  a. $NaHCO_3$
  b. NH_4NO_3
  c. CH_3COONa
  d. $NaCl$
  e. KCl
  f. Na_2CO_3
  g. Na_2SO_4
  h. NH_4Cl

38. What is a buffer?　　*19·6*

39. Would a solution of HCl and NaCl be a good buffer? Explain.　　*19·6*

40. What does the solubility product constant, K_{sp}, signify?　　*19·7*

41. Write the solubility product expression for each salt.　　*19·7*
  a. NiS
  b. $BaCO_3$
  c. $PbCl_2$
  d. Ag_2CrO_4

42. Use Table 19·4 to rank these salts from most soluble to least soluble.　　*19·7*
  a. CuS
  b. $BaSO_4$
  c. $SrCO_3$
  d. AgI

43. How does the addition of a common ion affect the solubility of another substance?　　*19·8*

44. What must be true about the concentration of two ions if precipitation occurs when solutions of the two ions are mixed?　　*19·8*

Mastery Questions and Problems

45. Find the normality of each solution.　　*19·4*
  a. 86.3 g $Mg(OH)_2$ in 2.5 L of solution.
  b. 5.6 g HBr in 450 mL of solution.
  c. 49.4 g H_2SO_3 in 1.5 L of solution.

46. Use the phosphate buffer ($H_2PO_4^-$/HPO_4^{2-}) to illustrate how a buffer system works. Show by means of equations how the pH of a solution can be kept almost constant when small amounts of acid or base are added.　　*19·6*

47. What is the concentration of hydroxide ions in a saturated solution of each salt?　　*19·7*
  a. $Zn(OH)_2$　　b. $Ca(OH)_2$　　c. $Al(OH)_3$

48. Give the reactions for the addition of base to these buffers.　　*19·6*
  a. ammonium ion–ammonia buffer
  b. dihydrogen phosphate ion–monohydrogen phosphate ion buffer

49. Write an equation to show that an aqueous solution of sodium acetate will be basic.　　*19·6*

50. Arrange these solutions in order of decreasing acidity.　　*19·5*
  a. 0.1*N* NaOH
  b. 0.1*N* HCl
  c. 0.1*M* NaCl
  d. 0.1*M* ammonium chloride
  e. 0.1*M* sodium acetate

51. What is the equilibrium concentration of barium ion in a 1.0-L saturated solution of barium carbonate to which 0.25 mol of K_2CO_3 has been added?　　*19·8*

52. Would precipitation occur when 500 mL of a 0.02*M* solution of $AgNO_3$ is mixed with 500 mL of a 0.001*M* solution of NaCl?　　*19·8*

Review Questions and Problems

53. A colorless solution of unknown pH turns blue when tested with the acid–base indicator bromthymol blue. It remains colorless when tested with phenolphthalein.
  a. What is the approximate pH of the solution?
  b. How could you determine the pH more accurately?

54. Calculate the pH of solutions with the following hydrogen-ion concentrations.
  a. $4.6 \times 10^{-6} M$
  b. $5.0 \times 10^{-12} M$
  c. $3.0 \times 10^{-1} M$
  d. $9.8 \times 10^{-10} M$

55. How many grams of potassium chloride are in 45.0 mL of a 5.0% (by mass) solution?

56. Draw electron dot formulas for each compound.　a. SiF_4　b. SCl_2　c. PH_3　d. H_2O_2　e. C_3H_8

57. Write the formula for the conjugate base of each acid.
  a. H_2SO_4
  b. HCN
  c. H_2O
  d. NH_4^+

58. Which of the pair has the highest entropy?
  a. $NaCl(s)$ *or* $NaCl(aq)$
  b. $CO_2(s)$ *or* $CO_2(g)$
  c. H_2O at 60°C *or* H_2O at 25°C

59. What is the molarity of the salt in the solution that results from the mixing of 200 mL of 1.00*M* NaOH and 200 mL of 1.00*M* HCl?

Challenging Questions and Problems

60. It is important for the pH of the blood to be maintained in the range of 7.35 to 7.45. The bicarbonate ion/carbonic acid buffer system is the most important of three buffer systems in the blood that help maintain this pH range. This system is represented by the following equation.

$$H_2O + CO_2 \underset{\text{lungs}}{\rightleftharpoons} H_2CO_3 \underset{\text{blood}}{\rightleftharpoons} H^+ + HCO_3^-$$

Given this equation, can you explain how abnormal breathing patterns can lead to acid–base imbalances in the blood that are called respiratory acidosis (abnormally low pH) and respiratory alkalosis (abnormally high pH)?

Too-rapid and too-deep breathing, a condition called hyperventilation, leads to respiratory alkalosis. Why? Conversely, hypoventilation, the result of too-shallow breathing, can cause respiratory acidosis. Explain.

61. What is the normality of an H_2SO_4 solution if 80.0 mL of the solution reacts completely with 0.424 g of Na_2CO_3?

$$H_2SO_4 + Na_2CO_3 \longrightarrow H_2O + CO_2 + Na_2SO_4$$

62. An impure sample of $AgNO_3$ weighing 0.340 g was dissolved in water. After the addition of 10.0 mL of 0.200N HCl, 0.213 g of AgCl was recovered. Calculate the percentage of $AgNO_3$ in the sample.

63. The following equilibria are involved in the solubility of carbon dioxide in water.

$$CO_2(g) \rightleftharpoons CO_2(aq)$$
$$CO_2(aq) + H_2O \rightleftharpoons H_2CO_3(aq)$$
$$H_2CO_3(aq) \rightleftharpoons H^+(aq) + HCO_3^-(aq)$$
$$HCO_3^-(aq) \rightleftharpoons H^+(aq) + CO_3^{2-}(aq)$$

If seawater is slightly alkaline, would you expect the concentration of dissolved CO_2 to be higher or lower than in pure water? Explain.

Research Projects

1. How do antacids work? Devise an experiment to compare and test their effectiveness.

2. Describe some common electrodes used on pH meters. How do they work?

3. How are acids neutralized in soils? What are the effects of different concentrations of metals on plant growth? Are the metals concentrated by the plant?

4. What techniques do soil chemists use to provide information about soil samples to farmers?

5. Why are salts a problem in soil? What steps are being taken to reduce this problem?

6. Trace the history of natural and synthetic dyes.

7. Are different dyes needed for different types of fabric? Describe some examples.

8. Describe the buffering action of the bicarbonate ion in the bloodstream.

Readings and References

Bolton, Ruth, Elizabeth Lamphere, and Mario Menesini. *Action Chemistry*. New York: Holt, Rinehart and Winston, 1979.

Lyttle, Richard B. *Paints, Inks and Dyes*. New York: Holiday House, 1974.

Olmert, Michael. "Genes and Viruses are Harnessed on a Farm Tended by Scientists." *Smithsonian* (March 1982), pp. 54-59.

Tanis, David. "Underground Sculpture." *ChemMatters:* American Chemical Society (February 1984), pp. 10–11.

Young, Gordon, "Salt." *National Geographic* (September 1977), pp. 381–401.

20 Oxidation–Reduction Reactions

Chapter Planning Guide

Section			Demonstrations and Experiments	Resource Materials
20·1	Oxygen in Redox Reactions	C*	Dem 20·1 Reduction of Ores Dem 20·2 Reduction of Lead Oxide Dem 20·3 Oxidation of Magnesium	Objectives Worksheet 20, SPB Skillsheet 20, SPB
20·2	Electron Transfer in Redox Reactions	C	Dem 20·4 Methylene Blue System Exp 45 Oxidation–Reduction Reactions, LM	Prelab 45, SPB
20·A	Corrosion	E	Exp 46 Corrosion, LM Dem 20·5 Oxidation of Iron	Prelab 46, SPB
20·3	Assigning Oxidation Numbers	C		Quiz 20·1
20·4	Oxidation Number Changes	C	Dem 20·6 Glycerine and Potassium Permanganate Dem 20.7 Lead Tree	
20·5	Balancing Redox Equations	C		
20·6	Identifying Redox Reactions	C	Dem 20·8 Redox Color Change	Quiz 20·2
20·B	Rocket Fuels and Household Bleach	E		Alternate Fuels, ICT 20
20·7	Using Half-Reactions to Balance Redox Equations	O	Dem 22·9 The Light Sensitivity of the Silver Halides	Quiz 20·3 Reviewsheet 20, SPB Chapter 20 Test
20·C	Photographic Chemistry	E		

*C = Core, O = Optional
E = Enrichment, H = Honors

LM = Laboratory Manual

SPB = Skills Practice Book
ICT = Issues in Chem. Tech.

Chapter Objectives

Having studied this chapter and done the problems, the student should be able to:

1. Define oxidation and reduction in terms of the loss or gain of oxygen or hydrogen. *20·1*

2. Define oxidation and reduction in terms of the loss, gain, or shift of electrons. *20·2*

3. Give the characteristics of a redox reaction. *20·2*

4. Identify the oxidizing and reducing agent in a redox reaction. *20·2*

5. Determine the oxidation number of an atom of any element in a pure substance. *20·3*

6. Define oxidation and reduction in terms of a change in oxidation number. *20·4*

7. Use the oxidation-number change method to identify atoms being oxidized or reduced in redox reactions. *20·4*

8. Use the oxidation-number change method to balance redox equations. *20·5*

9. Distinguish between redox and non-redox reactions. *20·6*

10. Break a redox reaction into oxidation and reduction half-reactions. *20·7*

11. When given an unbalanced redox equation, use the half-reaction method to balance the equation. *20·7*

Teaching Suggestions

20·1 Oxygen in Redox Reactions

Originally oxidation was a term that referred to the combination of an element with oxygen. Reduction was the reverse process. In reduction, an oxide (usually a metal ore) loses its oxygen and is reduced to its elemental state.

All students have seen examples of oxidation in their daily lives. They have seen substances burn and they have noticed the corrosion of metals. They may not have noticed reduction reactions, however. **Demonstrations 20·1** *Reduction of Ores* and **20·2** *Reduction of Lead Oxide* show two examples of the reduction of a metal from the oxide form to the elemental state. **Demonstration 20·3** *Oxidation of Magnesium* shows the oxidation of a metal.

20·2 Electron Transfer in Redox Reactions

We now know that whenever an element combines with oxygen, it loses electrons. Whenever oxygen is removed from the oxide of an element, the element gains electrons. Thus, broader definitions of oxidation and reduction are possible. Any reaction in which there is a loss of electrons, whether oxygen is involved or not, is called an oxidation reaction. Any reaction in which there is a gain of electrons is called reduction. **Demonstration 20·4** *Methylene Blue System* shows this kind of oxidation–reduction in a fascinating way.

Stress that these two kinds of reactions *always* come in pairs. A substance cannot give up electrons unless they have a place to go. Therefore, there cannot be oxidation without simultaneous reduction. A substance cannot gain electrons unless something donates them. Reduction cannot occur without simultaneous oxidation.

Spend adequate time discussing oxidizing and reducing agents. Students often have trouble identifying these. Go over examples until they have mastered the concept. Emphasize that the substance being oxidized reduces the other substance, and is therefore the reducing agent.

Before proceeding to the next sections the students should gain some first-hand experience with oxidation–reduction reactions. Have them do **Experiment 45** *Oxidation–Reduction Reactions*. Also, they will find **Experiment 46** *Corrosion* to be an interesting activity. It is a "discovery" experiment in which they explore the factors which affect the corrosion of iron. **Demonstration 20·5** *Oxidation of Iron* also shows the corrosion of iron.

20·3 Assigning Oxidation Numbers

Inform the students that in the next few sections they will be learning how to balance oxidation–reduction equations. This is more difficult than previous equation balancing efforts, since they must balance the transfer of electrons in addition to balancing the number of atoms and charge. The use of oxidation numbers provides them with one method for balancing these equations.

Go over the six rules for assigning oxidation numbers, one by one. Warn the students that they *must* memorize these rules before proceeding further. Use examples to illustrate each of these rules. Finish this section by having the students work practice problems until they are proficient in assigning oxidation numbers.

20·4 Oxidation Number Changes

When a transfer of electrons occurs, there is a change in oxidation number. The oxidation number of the oxidized substance increases while the oxidation number of the reduced substance decreases. Thus, by comparing the oxidation numbers of each of the reactants and products we can easily identify the oxidation reaction, the reduction reaction, the oxidizing agent, and the reducing agent.

If they have learned the rules of the previous section, the students will be able to find oxidation number changes in most instances without difficulty. Caution them that oxidation number refers to the apparent charge *per atom*. A change in oxidation number is calculated on a *per atom* basis. If a species has more than one atom of a particular kind, that must be taken into account. For instance, in Mn_2O_3 the oxidation number of manganese is $+3$. In $Cr_2O_7^{2-}$ the oxidation number of chromium is $+6$.

Demonstrations 20·6 *Glycerine and Potassium Permanganate* and **20·7** *Lead Tree* show redox reactions.

20·5 Balancing Redox Equations

Stress that when a redox equation is balanced, there are three requirements. The law of conservation of atoms must be satisfied. Charge must be conserved: the total electric charge on the left side of the equation must equal the total electric charge on the right side of the equation. The total number of electrons gained in reduction must equal the total number of electrons lost in oxidation.

The oxidation-number change method presented in this section is a very useful approach to balancing redox equations. Present the rules and show how they are used in several examples. Then have the students apply them to problems.

Again, caution the students about finding oxidation number changes when more than one atom is involved. When doing Step 4, they should first find the oxidation number change for one atom and then multiply by the number of atoms involved. For instance, when I_2 changes to I^-, the change in oxidation number is -1 for each atom. However, one I_2 molecule cannot produce one I^- ion. It must produce two of these ions. Therefore, the total change in oxidation number is -2 for the two atoms.

20·6 Identifying Redox Reactions

Before starting this section you may wish to refer the students back to Chapter 7 and remind them of the various types of chemical reactions. Point out that many chemical reactions do not involve a transfer of electrons and so cannot be classified as redox reactions.

The distinguishing feature of redox reactions is the change in oxidation numbers which occurs. To decide whether a given reaction is a redox reaction, we need only compare the oxidation numbers of the reactants to the oxidation numbers of the products. If a change has occurred, it is a redox reaction. If not, it is some other type of reaction. **Demonstration 20·8** *Redox Color Change* shows an oxidation–reduction compared to a precipitation.

20·7 Using Half-Reactions to Balance Redox Equations

The method of balancing redox equations presented in Section 20·5 uses changes in oxidation number to obtain electron balance. In this section an alternate method is presented. This method uses the conservation of electric charge to determine the number of electrons transferred.

The underlying assumption in this method is that any redox reaction can always be considered as two separate processes which occur simultaneously. Thus, the "whole" reaction can be thought of as the sum of two halves, an oxidation reaction and a reduction reaction. Emphasize that oxidation half-reactions are always written with the electrons on the right-hand side of the equation. Reduction half-reactions are always written with the electrons on the left-hand side of the equation.

Again, work several examples for the students, showing how the six steps are applied. Then have them balance equations themselves until proficient.

Demonstration 22·9 *The Light Sensitivity of the Silver Halides* could be done with Section 20·C.

Demonstrations

20·1 Reduction of Ores

Concept: Pure metals are obtained from their ores by reduction.

Materials: 3 g of copper(II) oxide (CuO), 3 g of charcoal, crucible with cover, crucible tongs, triangle, gas burner, matches, spatula, glass plate, safety goggles.

Procedure: 1. Mix the copper(II) oxide and charcoal. 2. Heat strongly in a covered crucible for 10 minutes. 3. When the crucible has cooled, remove the solid copper with tongs, and pass it around on the plate. 4. The reaction is:

$$2CuO + C \rightarrow 2Cu + CO_2$$

20·2 Reduction of Lead Oxide

Concept: Reduction of an oxide involves a loss of oxygen.

Materials: 20 g of lead(II) oxide (PbO), large Pyrex test tube, gas burner, clamp, ring stand, matches, safety goggles.

Procedure: 1. Place the lead(II) oxide in an unstoppered Pyrex test tube. 2. Heat for 30 minutes. 3. Note the beads of lead on the interior of the tube. The reaction is:

$$2PbO \rightarrow 2Pb + O_2$$

20·3 Oxidation of Magnesium

Concept: Magnesium is oxidized as it burns in steam.

Materials: 20 cm of magnesium ribbon, large Pyrex test tube with rubber stopper, blow pipe, wire test tube holder, gas burner, Fischer burner, water, matches, safety goggles.

Procedure: 1. Using a blow pipe and gas burner, make a 2 mm hole in a test tube at the point where the side curves into the bottom. 2. Place the magnesium ribbon in the lower third of the test tube. 3. Add 10 mL water to the tube, stopper it, and support it in the test tube holder at a 30° angle with the stopper pointing down. 5. Heat the upper portion of the water with the gas burner. 6. After the water begins to boil, heat the test tube near the magnesium ribbon with the Fischer burner. The magnesium burns in the steam. 7. Ignite the hydrogen gas that is emitted from the hole. 8. Write the equation for the reaction on the board.

$$Mg + 2H_2O \rightarrow Mg(OH)_2 + H_2$$

20·4 Methylene Blue System

Concept: Methylene blue can undergo visible redox reactions.

Materials: 500-mL flask with stopper, 1 g of iron(II) sulfate ($FeSO_4$), 8 g of potassium hydroxide (KOH), 8 g of dextrose, 0.25 g methylene blue in 1 L water, 3 small crystals of methylene blue, 50 mL of 0.1M sulfuric acid (H_2SO_4), 100-mL beaker, stirring rod, test tube, test tube holder, test tube rack, slide projector or other bright light source, water, safety goggles.

Procedure: 1. Add methylene blue to iron(II) sulfate and stir. 2. Pour some into a test tube. 3. Place the tube in front of the light. 4. The solution becomes colorless; the light reduces the methylene blue. 5. If no color change is observed, dilute the solution by one-half and try again. 6. Dissolve the potassium hydroxide and dextrose in 300 mL of water in the 500-mL flask. 7. Add 5 mL of methylene blue, stopper, and shake. 8. After about a minute, the color disappears. 9. Shake the flask again; the blue color reappears. (The blue dye loses its color when it

comes in contact with alkaline carbohydrate. Then, dissolved oxygen oxidizes it and the blue color reappears.) **Caution:** *Sulfuric acid and potassium hydroxide are corrosive.*

20·5 Oxidation of Iron

Concept: Iron can be protected from oxidation.

Materials: 1 g of agar–agar, 10 drops of $0.2M$ potassium ferricyanide ($K_3Fe(CN)_6$), 10 drops of 0.1% phenolphthalein, 6 nails, 1 cm^2 pieces of zinc, copper, and aluminum, 5 cm of magnesium ribbon, steel wool, 250-mL beaker, stirring rod, 6 large covered petri dishes, ring stand, ring, gas burner, wire gauze, pliers, matches, safety goggles.

Procedure: 1. Shine the nails with steel wool. 2. Bend a nail with pliers to form a right angle. 3. Wrap four other nails with zinc, copper, aluminum, and magnesium respectively. 4. Place one nail in each petri dish. (Don't forget the one remaining nail.) 5. Boil 100 mL water. 6. Dissolve 1 g of agar in the boiling water. 7. Remove the beaker from the heat. Add 10 drops each of potassium ferricyanide and phenolphthalein solutions and stir. 8. Pour the agar into the petri dishes to cover the nails. Cover the dishes and allow to cool. 9. Redox reactions have caused visible changes. The deep blue of ferrous ferricyanide indicates that ferrous ions have formed. The pink color of phenolphthalein indicates that hydroxide ions have formed. In the zinc wrapped nail, the zinc is oxidized first. This "sacrifice" protects the iron from oxidation. Contrast with the other nails.

20·6 Glycerine and Potassium Permanganate

Concept: A redox reaction can start a fire.

Materials: 3 g of potassium permanganate ($KMnO_4$), 0.5 mL of glycerine, paper cup, ceramic pad, dropper, safety goggles.

Procedure: **Caution:** *Potassium permanganate is an irritant and suspected mutagen. Use a fume hood and have students stand back during the demonstration.* 1. Place the potassium permanganate in a paper cup and place on the ceramic pad. 2. With the dropper, add the glycerine to the cup containing potassium permanganate. 3. After 30 seconds, a fire starts in the cup.

20·7 Lead Tree

Concept: Lead can be reduced with zinc.

Materials: 150-mL beaker, 1 cm × 3 cm zinc strip, 100 mL of 0.1 lead(II) acetate ($Pb(C_2H_3O_2)_2$).

Procedure: 1. Place the lead(II) acetate and zinc in the beaker. 2. A "tree" of lead forms over the course of a day. **Caution:** *Lead(II) acetate is a suspected animal carcinogen and mutagen.*

20·8 Redox Color Change

Concept: Redox reactions sometimes result in color changes.

Materials: 6 crystals of potassium permanganate ($KMnO_4$), 800-mL beaker, stirring rod, 1 g sodium hydrogen sulfite ($NaHSO_3$), 1 g barium chloride dihydrate ($BaCl_2 \cdot 2H_2O$), water, two 50-mL beakers, safety goggles.

Procedure: 1. Dissolve potassium permanganate in 500 mL of water in the large beaker. 2. Dissolve sodium hydrogen sulfite in 20 mL of water in a 50-mL beaker. Add to the potassium permanganate solution and stir. The red solution becomes clear. 3. Dissolve barium chloride dihydrate in 20 mL of water in another 50-mL beaker. Add to the large beaker and stir. The solution turns cloudy-white. 4. Ask the students to try to explain these color changes. **Caution:** *Potassium permanganate is an irritant and suspected mutagen. Barium chloride is toxic.*

Audiovisual Resources

Electron Transfer in Chemical Change (FS) Prentice-Hall Media, 1971. (Use with Sections 20·2, 20·5, or 20·6.) Discusses electron transfer in oxidation–reduction reactions, uses oxidation–reduction rules to identify redox reactions, and develops equation writing skills.

Answers to End of Chapter Questions and Problems

Practice Questions and Problems

8. Oxidation is the combination of an element with oxygen. Reduction is the the loss of oxygen from a compound.

9. **a.** $C_2H_4 + 3O_2 \rightarrow 2CO_2 + 2H_2O$; oxidation
b. $2KClO_3 \rightarrow 2KCl + 3O_2$; reduction
c. $CuO + H_2 \rightarrow Cu + H_2O$; reduction
d. $2H_2 + O_2 \rightarrow 2H_2O$; oxidation

10. **a.** Oxidation is the loss of electrons. Reduction is the gain of electrons. **b.** Oxidation is the loss of hydrogen by a covalent bond. Reduction is the gain of hydrogen by a covalent bond. **c.** Oxidation is the gain of oxygen. Reduction is the loss of oxygen. **d.** Oxidation is the shift in electrons away from an atom in a covalent bond. Reduction is the shift of electrons toward an atom in a covalent bond.

11. Donates electrons in a redox reaction.

12. Accepts electrons in a redox reaction.

13. a. oxidation **b.** oxidation **c.** reduction **d.** reduction

14. a. oxidizing agent **b.** oxidizing agent **c.** reducing agent **d.** reducing agent **e.** oxidizing agent

15. a. Na oxidized, Br_2 reduced
b. H_2 oxidized, N_2 reduced
c. S oxidized, O_2 reduced
d. Mg oxidized, Cu reduced

16. a. Na red. agent, Br_2 ox. agent
b. H_2 red. agent, N_2 ox. agent
c. S red. agent, O_2 ox. agent
d. Mg red. agent, Cu ox. agent

17. They represent the charge each atom would have if bonding electrons were assigned to the atom of the more electronegative element.

18. The electrons in each bond are assigned to the atom of the more electronegative element; used to balance complex redox reactions.

19. a. S, +3; O, -2 **b.** O, 0 **c.** Na, +1; O, -2; H, +1 **d.** Al, +3; S, +6; O, -2 **e.** Na, +1; O, -1 **f.** P, +5; O, -2

20. a. +2 **b.** -3 **c.** +5 **d.** +3 **e.** +5 **f.** -3

21. Oxidation is the increase in oxidation number. Reduction is the decrease in oxidation number

22. a. H_2 oxidized, O_2 reduced
b. K^+ unchanged, N reduced, O oxidized
c. N in NH_4^+ oxidized, H unchanged, N in NO_2^- reduced, O unchanged
d. Pb reduced, O unchanged, H unchanged, I oxidized

23. a. H_2 red. agent, O_2 ox. agent
b. N,+5, ox. agent, O,-2, red. agent
c. N,-3, red. agent, N,+3 ox. agent
d. Pb,+4, ox. agent, I,-1 red. agent

24. a.
$$\overbrace{\underset{2KClO_3}{\overset{+1+5-2}{}} \longrightarrow \underset{2KCl}{\overset{+1-1}{}} + \underset{3O_2}{\overset{0}{}}}^{3 \times (+2) = +6}$$
$1 \times (-6) = -6$

b.
$$\overbrace{\underset{2HNO_2}{\overset{+1+3-2}{}} + \underset{2HI}{\overset{+1-1}{}} \longrightarrow \underset{2NO}{\overset{+2-2}{}} + \underset{I_2}{\overset{0}{}} + \underset{2H_2O}{\overset{+1-2}{}}}^{2 \times (-1) = -2}$$
$2 \times (+1) = +2$

c.
$$\overbrace{\underset{As_2O_3}{\overset{+3-2}{}} + \underset{2Cl_2}{\overset{0}{}} + \underset{5H_2O}{\overset{+1-2}{}} \longrightarrow \underset{2H_3AsO_4}{\overset{+1+5-2}{}} + \underset{4HCl}{\overset{+1-1}{}}}^{4 \times (-1) = -4}$$
$2 \times (+2) = +4$

d.
$$\overbrace{\underset{Bi_2S_3}{\overset{+3-2}{}} + \underset{8HNO_3}{\overset{+1+5-2}{}} \longrightarrow \underset{2Bi(NO_3)_3}{\overset{+3+5-2}{}} + \underset{2NO}{\overset{+2-2}{}} + \underset{3S}{\overset{0}{}} + \underset{4H_2O}{\overset{+1-2}{}}}^{2 \times (-3) = -6}$$
$3 \times (+2) = +6$

e.
$$\overbrace{\underset{MnO_2}{\overset{+4-2}{}} + \underset{H_2SO_4}{\overset{+1+6-2}{}} + \underset{H_2C_2O_4}{\overset{+1+3-2}{}} \longrightarrow \underset{MnSO_4}{\overset{+2+6-2}{}} + \underset{2CO_2}{\overset{+4-2}{}} + \underset{2H_2O}{\overset{+1-2}{}}}^{2 \times (+1) = +2}$$
$1 \times (-2) = -2$

f.
$$\overbrace{\underset{SbCl_5}{\overset{+5-1}{}} + \underset{2KI}{\overset{+1-1}{}} \longrightarrow \underset{SbCl_3}{\overset{+3-1}{}} + \underset{2KCl}{\overset{+1-1}{}} + \underset{I_2}{\overset{0}{}}}^{2 \times (+1) = +2}$$
$1 \times (-2) = -2$

25. a. Cl,+5, ox. agent, O,-2, red. agent
b. N,+3, ox. agent, I,-1, red. agent
c. As,+3, red. agent, Cl_2 ox. agent
d. S,-2, red. agent, N,+5, ox. agent
e. Mn,+4, ox. agent, C,+3 red. agent
f. Sb,+5 ox. agent, I,-1, red. agent

26. a, b, c, d, e, f, g, i. redox; **h.** not redox

27. a. Li red. agent, H ox. agent
b. Cr ox. agent, Cl red. agent
c. Al red. agent, H ox. agent
d. P red. agent, S ox. agent
e. Mn red. agent, Pb ox. agent
f. Cl ox. agent, Cl red. agent
g. I ox. agent, C. red. agent
h. not redox
i. Bi ox. agent, Sn red. agent

28. a. $3Sn^{2+} + 14H^+ + Cr_2O_7^{2-} \longrightarrow$
$\qquad\qquad 3Sn^{4+} + 2Cr^{3+} + 7H_2O$
b. $CuS + 6NO_3^- + 8H^+ \longrightarrow$
$\qquad\qquad Cu^{2+} + SO_2 + 6NO_2 + 4H_2O$
c. $6I^- + 2NO_3^- + 8H^+ \longrightarrow$
$\qquad\qquad 3I_2 + 2NO + 4H_2O$

29. a. $6I^- + 2MnO_4^- + 4H_2O \longrightarrow$
$\qquad\qquad 3I_2 + 2MnO_2 + 8OH^-$
b. $S_2O_3^{2-} + 2NiO_2 + H_2O \longrightarrow$
$\qquad\qquad 2SO_3^{2-} + 2Ni^{2+} + 2OH^-$
c. $4Zn + NO_3^- + 6H_2O + 7OH^- \longrightarrow$
$\qquad\qquad 4Zn(OH)_4^{2-} + NH_3$

Mastery Questions and Problems

30. a. $2Li + 2H_2O \rightarrow 2LiOH + H_2$ (by inspection)

b.
$$\overbrace{\underset{K_2Cr_2O_7}{\overset{+1+6-2}{}} + \underset{14\,HCl}{\overset{+1-1}{}} \longrightarrow \underset{2\,KCl}{} + \underset{2\,CrCl_3}{\overset{+3-1}{}} + \underset{7\,H_2O}{\overset{+1-2}{}} + \underset{3\,Cl_2}{\overset{0}{}}}^{2 \times (-3) = -6}$$
$6 \times (+1) = +6$

c. $2Al + 6HCl \rightarrow 2AlCl_3 + 3H_2$ (by inspection)

$$16 \times (+5) = +80$$
$$\begin{array}{c} 0 \qquad 0 \qquad\quad +5-2 \\ 4P_4 + 5S_8 \longrightarrow 8P_2S_5 \end{array}$$
$$40 \times (-2) = -80$$

e. $5PbO_2 + 8H^+ + 2MnO \longrightarrow$
$5Pb^{2+} + 4H_2O + 2MnO_4^-$ (by redox half-reactions)
f. $Cl_2 + H_2O \longrightarrow HCl + HClO$
(by inspection)

g.
$$2 \times (-5) = -10$$
$$\begin{array}{c} +5-2 \quad +2-2 \qquad 0 \quad +4-2 \\ I_2O_5 + 5CO \longrightarrow I_2 + 5CO_2 \end{array}$$
$$5 \times (+2) = 10$$

h. $H_2O + SO_3 \longrightarrow H_2SO_4$
(not a redox reaction)

i.
$$1 \times (-2) = -2$$
$$\begin{array}{c} +2-2+1 \quad +1+2-2 \qquad 0 \quad +1-2 \quad +1+4-2 \\ Bi(OH)_2 + K_2SnO_2 \longrightarrow Bi + H_2O + K_2SnO_3 \end{array}$$
$$1 \times (+2) = +2$$

31. a. +4 **b.** +5 **c.** +5 **d.** +3 **e.** +5 **f.** +3

32. a. $3Sn^{2+} + 6H^+ + IO_3^- \longrightarrow$
$3Sn^{4+} + 3H_2O + I^-$
b. $Cr_2O_7^{2-} + 3H_2S + 8H^+ \longrightarrow$
$2Cr^{3+} + 3S + 7H_2O$
c. $Cr_2O_7^{2-} + 2Al + 14H^+ \longrightarrow$
$2Cr^{3+} + 2Al^{3+} + 7H_2O$

33. a. Carbon is oxidized. **b.** ClO_2 is the oxidizing agent.

34. a. Cl oxidized, Mn reduced, MnO_2 oxidizing agent, HCl reducing agent
b. Cu oxidized, N reduced, HNO_3 oxidizing agent, Cu reducing agent
c. P oxidized, N reduced, HNO_3 oxidizing agent, P reducing agent
d. Sn oxidized, Bi reduced, $Bi(OH)_3$ oxidizing agent, Na_2SnO_2 reducing agent
e. Cr oxidized, Cl reduced, NaClO oxidizing agent, $NaCrO_2$ reducing agent
f. I oxidized, V reduced, V_2O_5 oxidizing agent, KI reducing agent

35. a.
$$1 \times (-2) = -2$$
$$\begin{array}{c} +4-2 \quad +1-1 \qquad +2-1 \quad 0 \quad +1-2 \\ MnO_2 + 4 HCl \longrightarrow MnCl_2 + Cl_2 + 2 H_2O \end{array}$$
$$2 \times (+1) = +2$$

b.
$$1 \times (+2) = +2$$
$$\begin{array}{c} 0 \quad +1+5-2 \qquad +2+5-5 \quad +4-2 \quad +1-2 \\ Cu + 4 HNO_3 \longrightarrow Cu(NO_3)_2 + 2 NO_2 + 2 H_2O \end{array}$$
$$2 \times (-1) = -2$$

c.
$$3 \times (+5) = +15$$
$$\begin{array}{c} 0 \quad +1+5-2 \quad +1-2 \qquad +2-2 \quad +1+5-2 \\ 3 P + 5 HNO_3 + 2 H_2O \longrightarrow 5 NO + 3 H_3PO_4 \end{array}$$
$$5 \times (-3) = -15$$

d.
$$2 \times (-3) = -6$$
$$\begin{array}{c} +3-2+1 \quad +1+2-2 \qquad 0 \quad +1+4-2 \quad +1-2 \\ 2 Bi(OH)_3 + 3 Na_2SnO_2 \longrightarrow 2 Bi + 3 Na_2SnO_3 + 3 H_2O \end{array}$$
$$3 \times (+2) = +6$$

e.
$$2 \times (+3) = +6$$
$$\begin{array}{c} +1+3-2 \quad +1+1-2 \quad +1-2+1 \qquad +1+6-2 \quad +1-1 \quad +1-2 \\ 2 NaCrO_2 + 3 NaClO + 2 NaOH \longrightarrow 2 Na_2CrO_4 + 3 NaCl + H_2O \end{array}$$
$$3 \times (-2) = -6$$

f.
$$1 \times (-1) = -1$$
$$\begin{array}{c} +5-2 \quad +1-1 \quad +1-1 \qquad +4-2 \quad +1-1 \quad 0 \quad +1-2 \\ V_2O_5 + 2 KI + 2 HCl \longrightarrow V_2O_4 + 2 KCl + I_2 + H_2O \end{array}$$
$$1 \times (+1) = +1$$

36. a. $3ClO_2^- + 4MnO_4^- + 2H_2O \longrightarrow$
$3ClO_4^- + 4MnO_2 + 4 OH^-$
b. $2Cr^{3+} + 10OH^- + 3ClO^- \longrightarrow$
$2CrO_4^{2-} + 5H_2O + 3Cl^-$
c. $6Mn^{3+} + I^- + 6OH^- \longrightarrow$
$6Mn^{2+} + IO_3^- + 3H_2O$

Review Questions and Problems

37. a. 5 **b.** 10 **c.** 13 **d.** 6.5

38. a. acidic **b.** basic **c.** basic **d.** acidic

39. a. NH_4^+ and NH_3; H_2O and H_3O^+
b. H_2SO_3 and HSO_3^-; HN_2^- and NH_3
c. HNO_3 and NO_3^-; I^- and HI
d. H_2O and OH^-; ClO_4^- and $HClO_4$

40. 56.3 mL KOH

41. a. $1.0 \times 10^{-2}M$ **b.** $1.0 \times 10^{-11}M$
c. $1.6 \times 10^{-9}M$

42. $1.14N$ H_3PO_4

43. Solubility$_{PbBr_2} = 8.1 \times 10^{-3}$

44. Dilute 110 mL of $6.0M$ HCl to 440 mL total volume.

45. When Na_2SO_4 is added, the SO_4^{2-} concentration increases. To restore equilibrium, $BaSO_4$ precipitates, removing excess SO_4^{2-}. As a result, the Ba^{2+} concentration decreases.

Challenging Questions and Problems

46. 0.406 g Cu

47. 104 mL $K_2Cr_2O_7$

48. a. $5CO + I_2O_5 \longrightarrow I_2 + 5 CO_2$
b. C is oxidized. I is reduced.
c. 0.22 g CO

20 Oxidation–Reduction Reactions

Chapter Preview

The *chemical changes that occur when electrons are transferred between reactants are known as* **oxidation–reduction reactions.** Oxidation reactions are the principal source of energy on earth. The combustion of gasoline in an automobile engine and the burning of wood in a fireplace are oxidation reactions. So is the "burning" of food by our bodies. All oxidation reactions are accompanied by reduction reactions. *Oxidation–reduction reactions are also called* **redox reactions.**

20·1 Oxygen in Redox Reactions

■ Elements and compounds combine with oxygen in oxidation reactions.

Oxidation *originally meant the combination of an element with oxygen to give oxides.* When iron slowly turns to rust, it oxidizes to iron(III) oxide (Fe_2O_3). When carbon burns in air, it oxidizes to carbon dioxide.

$$4Fe + 3O_2 \longrightarrow 2Fe_2O_3$$

$$C + O_2 \longrightarrow CO_2$$

Compounds can also be oxidized. Methane gas (CH_4) burns in oxygen. It oxidizes to form oxides of carbon and hydrogen.

$$CH_4 + 2O_2 \longrightarrow CO_2 + 2H_2O$$

Over the years, **reduction** *has meant the loss of oxygen from a compound.* The reduction of iron ore to metallic iron causes the removal of oxygen from iron(III) oxide. It is done by heating the ore with charcoal.

$$\underset{\text{Iron(III) oxide}}{2Fe_2O_3} + \underset{\text{Carbon}}{3C} \longrightarrow \underset{\text{Iron}}{4Fe} + \underset{\text{Carbon dioxide}}{3CO_2}$$

Figure 20·1
The corrosion of iron is an oxidation–reduction reaction that causes the formation of rust.

Figure 20·2
The iron in this piece of steel wool burns brightly in oxygen. The iron is oxidized to iron(III) oxide.

As iron oxide loses oxygen, it is reduced to metallic iron. The term *reduction* refers to the fact that when a metal oxide is reduced to the metal, there is a considerable decrease in volume. In other words, the amount of solid material has been reduced.

Oxidation and reduction occur simultaneously. As iron oxide is reduced to iron by losing oxygen, carbon is oxidized to carbon dioxide by gaining oxygen. No oxidation occurs without reduction and no reduction occurs without oxidation. This is true of all redox reactions.

20·2   Electron Transfer in Redox Reactions

■ In an oxidation–reduction reaction, electrons are transferred from one reactant to another.

Today, chemists have extended the concepts of oxidation and reduction to include all transfers or shifts of electrons. The advantage of the new definition is that it has much wider application than the old. Hence *oxidation is complete or partial loss of electrons or gain of oxygen. Reduction is complete or partial gain of electrons or loss of oxygen.*

Oxidation	**Reduction**
Loss of electrons or gain of oxygen	Gain of electrons or loss of oxygen

Some examples will show what this means. In the reactions between a metal and nonmetal, electrons are transferred from atoms of the metal to atoms of the nonmetal. An ionic compound such as magnesium sulfide is produced.

It may be helpful to remember that "LEO the lion goes GER," where LEO = Losing Electrons in Oxidation and GER = Gaining Electrons in Reduction.

$$\odot Mg \odot \;+\; \cdot \ddot{S} \colon \longrightarrow \; Mg^{2+} \;+\; \colon \ddot{S} \colon^{2-}$$

Magnesium atom	Sulfur atom		Magnesium ion	Sulfide ion

The net result of this reaction is a transfer of two electrons from a magnesium atom to a sulfur atom. The magnesium atom loses two electrons and is oxidized to a magnesium ion. Simultaneously the sulfur atom gains two electrons and is reduced to a sulfide ion.

Oxidation: $\cdot Mg \cdot \longrightarrow Mg^{2+} + 2e^-$ (loss of electrons)

Reduction: $\cdot \ddot{S} \colon + 2e^- \longrightarrow \colon \ddot{S} \colon^{2-}$ (gain of electrons)

The substance in a redox reaction that donates electrons is a **reducing agent.** *By losing electrons,* magnesium reduces sulfur. Magnesium is a

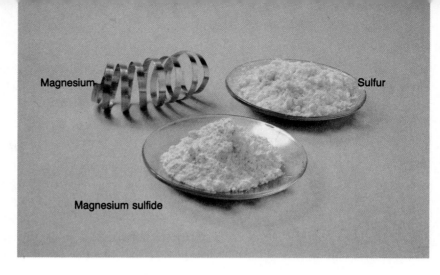

Figure 20·3
When magnesium and sulfur are heated together they undergo an oxidation–reduction reaction and form magnesium sulfide. Magnesium becomes more stable by losing electrons (oxidation). Sulfur becomes more stable by gaining electrons (reduction).

Reducing agents are themselves oxidized. Oxidizing agents are themselves reduced.

reducing agent. *The substance in a redox reaction that accepts electrons is an* **oxidizing agent.** By *accepting electrons,* sulfur oxidizes magnesium. Sulfur is an oxidizing agent.

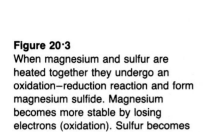

Example 1

What is oxidized and what is reduced in this single replacement reaction?

$$2AgNO_3(aq) + Cu(s) \longrightarrow Cu(NO_3)_2(aq) + 2Ag(s)$$

Solution

Begin by rewriting the equation and showing the ions.

$$2Ag^+ + 2NO_3^- + Cu \longrightarrow Cu^{2+} + 2NO_3^- + 2Ag$$

What has happened in this reaction? Two electrons have been transferred from a copper atom (Cu) to two silver ions (Ag^+).

Oxidation: $Cu \longrightarrow Cu^{2+} + 2e^-$ (loss of electrons)

Reduction: $2Ag^+ + 2e^- \longrightarrow 2Ag$ (gain of electrons)

The Ag^+ gains electrons and is reduced; Cu loses electrons and is oxidized. Hence Ag^+ is the oxidizing agent and Cu is the reducing agent.

Problem

1. **a.** Na: oxidized (reducing agent)
   S: reduced (oxidizing agent)
   b. K: oxidized (reducing agent)
   Cl_2: reduced (oxidizing agent)
   c. Al: oxidized (reducing agent)
   O_2: reduced (oxidizing agent)

1. Determine what is oxidized and what is reduced in each reaction. Identify the oxidizing agent and reducing agent in each case.
   a. $2Na + S \longrightarrow Na_2S$
   b. $2K + Cl_2 \longrightarrow 2KCl$
   c. $4Al + 3O_2 \longrightarrow 2Al_2O_3$

Figure 20·4
An oxyhydrogen torch can be used to weld metals like aluminum and iron. When hydrogen burns in oxygen, the redox reaction generates temperatures of about 2600°C.

Complete transfers of electrons are easy to see in ionic reactions such as those just examined. What about reactions that produce covalent compounds? Consider the reaction of hydrogen and oxygen.

$$2H_2 + O_2 \longrightarrow 2H_2O$$

The old definition of oxidation says that hydrogen is oxidized to water when it combines with oxygen. Electron transfer can also explain this process. Consider what happens to the bonding electrons in the reactants and in the products. The bonding electrons in the hydrogen molecule are shared equally between the hydrogens. In water, however, the bonding electrons are not shared equally between hydrogen and oxygen. (Recall that oxygen is much more electronegative than hydrogen.) The net result is a shift of bonding electrons away from hydrogen.

H—H electrons shared equally   H—O shift of bonding electrons away from hydrogen
                                      |
                                      H

Hydrogen is oxidized because it experiences a partial loss of electrons.

What about oxygen, the other reactant? The bonding electrons are shared equally between oxygens in the oxygen molecule, but they shift closer to oxygen in water.

O＝O electrons shared equally   H—O shift of bonding electrons toward oxygen
                                      |
                                      H

Oxygen is therefore reduced because there is a partial gain of electrons.

There is always an oxidizing agent and a reducing agent in every redox reaction. In the reaction of hydrogen and oxygen to produce water, hydrogen is the reducing agent and oxygen is the oxidizing agent.

To summarize, oxidation–reduction reactions can be described on the basis of the addition or removal of oxygen. They can also be described on the basis of electron transfer. With compounds of carbon, the addition of oxygen or the removal of hydrogen is always oxidation. Conversely, the removal of oxygen or the addition of hydrogen is always reduction. Table 20·1 lists the various processes that constitute oxidation and reduction. The last entry in the table mentions oxidation numbers, another way that oxidation and reduction can be described.

2. a. H_2: oxidized (reducing agent)
   Cl: reduced (oxidizing agent)
b. H_2: oxidized (reducing agent)
   N_2: reduced (oxidizing agent)
c. S: oxidized (reducing agent)
   Cl_2: reduced (oxidizing agent)
d. N_2: oxidized (reducing agent)
   O_2: reduced (oxidizing agent)
e. Li: oxidized (reducing agent)
   F_2: reduced (oxidizing agent)
f. H_2: oxidized (reducing agent)
   S: reduced (oxidizing agent)

Problem

2. In each of the following reactions decide which reactant is oxidized and which reactant is reduced. Which reactant is the reducing agent and which is the oxidizing agent? (To determine this, use the electronegativity values in Table 12·3.)

a. $H_2 + Cl_2 \longrightarrow 2HCl$ **d.** $N_2 + 3H_2 \longrightarrow 2NH_3$
b. $S + Cl_2 \longrightarrow SCl_2$ **e.** $N_2 + 2O_2 \longrightarrow 2NO_2$
c. $2Li + F_2 \longrightarrow 2LiF$ **f.** $H_2 + S \longrightarrow H_2S$

Table 20·1	Processes Leading to Oxidation and Reduction	
Oxidation		**Reduction**
Complete loss of electrons (ionic reactions)		Complete gain of electrons (ionic reactions)
Shift of electrons away from an atom in a covalent bond		Shift of electrons toward an atom in a covalent bond
Gain of oxygen		Loss of oxygen
Loss of hydrogen by a covalent compound		Gain of hydrogen by a covalent compound
An increase in oxidation number		A decrease in oxidation number

20·A   Corrosion

Billions of dollars are spent worldwide each year to prevent and clean up after a special family of redox reactions, the corrosion of metals. Iron and steel, common construction metals, can be oxidized to metallic ions by water and oxygen in the environment. Oxygen is reduced by the reaction to the oxide or hydroxide ion. The corrosion of iron is described by these equations.

$$2Fe + O_2 + 2H_2O \longrightarrow 2Fe(OH)_2$$

$$4Fe(OH)_2 + O_2 + 2H_2O \longrightarrow 4Fe(OH)_3$$

Corrosion occurs more easily in the presence of salts or acids. These substances combine with the water present to make conducting solutions. This makes electron transfer easier.

Not all metals corrode easily. Gold and platinum are called the noble metals because they are very resistant to losing their electrons by corrosion. Other metals lose electrons easily but are protected by an oxide coating on their surface. Aluminum, for example, corrodes quickly in air to form a coating of very tightly packed aluminum oxide particles. This coating protects the aluminum object from any further corrosion. When iron corrodes, the coating of iron oxide is not tightly packed. Water and air can penetrate it and attack more of the iron metal below the coating. The corrosion continues until the iron object is only a pile of rust.

The corrosion of a shovel or a knife is a common but relatively small problem. By contrast, the corrosion of the support pillar of a bridge or the hull of an oil tanker is much more serious and costly to repair! Methods for controlling and preventing corrosion fall into two categories: surface protection and electrochemical protection.

Surface protection involves coating the metal surface with oil, paint, plastic, or another metal. These coatings exclude air and water,

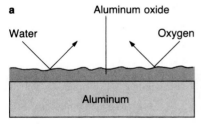

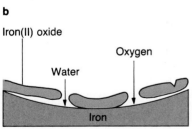

Figure 20·5
Oxidation causes the corrosion of some metals and not of others. How does aluminum oxide differ from iron(III) oxide?
Aluminum oxide adheres to and protects its parent metal from further oxidation whereas iron(III) oxide does not.

a

b

Figure 20·6
a Painting a metal surface protects it from the corrosive effects of chemicals in the environment.
b Chromium metal also serves as a protective coating on automobile parts, while imparting an attractive, mirror-like finish. Like aluminum, chromium forms a corrosion-resistant oxide film on its surface.

and so prevent the corrosion reaction. If the coating is scratched or worn away, however, the bare metal will begin to corrode.

Electrochemical protection involves "sacrificing" one metal to save another. To protect an iron object, for example, a piece of magnesium or zinc is placed in electrical contact with it. Magnesium and zinc are more easily oxidized than iron, but they resist corrosion by oxygen and water because of oxide coatings. When oxygen and water attack an iron object, iron atoms lose electrons. Immediately, the magnesium or zinc transfers electrons to the iron ions, reducing them to neutral iron metal once again. This transfer is not prevented by the oxide coating, because electrical contact between the metals has been established. Plates of magnesium are bolted to bridge pillars and ship hulls. Underground pipelines and storage tanks are protected by a block of magnesium buried nearby. It is connected to the pipe or tank by a conducting cable. Obviously, it is much easier to replace a block or plate of magnesium than to replace a bridge or pipeline. Galvanzied iron is iron coated with zinc. It is used for roofing, plumbing, and large and small items made from sheet metal. The sacrificial metal is slowly consumed, but the iron object is protected.

20·3 Assigning Oxidation Numbers

Each atom in a substance can be assigned an oxidation number.

Oxidation numbers are a bookkeeping concept devised by chemists. *An* **oxidation number** *is a positive or negative number assigned to an atom according to a set of arbitrary rules*. As the next section will show, complex redox equations can be balanced by using oxidation-number changes. As a general rule, an oxidation number is the charge that an atom would have if the electrons in each bond were assigned to the atom of the more electronegative element. In binary ionic compounds such as NaCl and $CaCl_2$ the oxidation numbers of the atoms are equal to their ionic charges. The compound sodium chloride is composed of sodium ions, Na^{1+}, and chloride ions, Cl^{1-}. Thus, the oxidation number of

sodium is $+1$, and that of chlorine is -1. Notice that when writing oxidation numbers, the sign is put before the number. Sodium has an ionic charge of $1+$ and an oxidation number of $+1$. In calcium fluoride, CaF_2, the oxidation number of calcium is $+2$, and that of fluorine, -1.

Because water is a molecular compound, no ionic charges are associated with its atoms. As was shown in the last section, however, oxygen is considered to be reduced in the formation of water. Oxygen is the more electronegative element. In water, the shared electrons in the bond are shifted closer to oxygen and away from hydrogen. Imagine that the two electrons contributed by the hydrogen atoms were completely transferred to the oxygen. The charges that would result from this transfer are the oxidation numbers of the elements. The oxidation number of oxygen is -2. The oxidation number of each hydrogen is $+1$.

Rules for Assigning Oxidation Numbers

1. The oxidation number of a monatomic ion is equal in magnitude and sign to its ionic charge. For example, the oxidation number of the bromide ion, Br^{1-}, is -1; that of the Fe^{3+} ion is $+3$.

2. The oxidation number of hydrogen in a compound is always $+1$ except in metal hydrides, for example, NaH, where it is -1.

3. The oxidation number of oxygen in a compound is always -2 except in peroxides, for example, H_2O_2, where it is -1.

4. The oxidation number of an uncombined element is zero. For example, the oxidation number of the potassium atoms in potassium metal, K, and of the nitrogen atoms in nitrogen gas, N_2, is zero.

5. For any neutral compound, the sum of the oxidation numbers of the atoms in the compound must equal zero.

6. For a polyatomic ion, the sum of the oxidation numbers must equal the ionic charge of the ion.

These last two rules can be used to determine the oxidation number of elements not covered in the first four rules.

Figure 20·7
Oxidation–reduction reactions cause corrosion. The copper on this roof reacted with carbon dioxide and water vapor in the air to form a pale green film of copper carbonate.

Example 2

What is the oxidation number of each element in the following?
a. SO_2 **b.** CO_3^{2-} **c.** K_2SO_4

Solution

a. The oxidation number of oxygen is -2. There are two oxygens, and the sum of the oxidation numbers must be zero. Thus the oxidation number of sulfur is $+4$.

$$\overset{+4-2}{SO_2}$$

b. The oxidation number of oxygen is -2.

$$\overset{?\ -2}{CO_3^{2-}}$$

The sum of the oxidation numbers of the carbon and oxygen atoms must equal the ionic charge, $2-$. The oxidation number of carbon must be $+4$.

$$\overset{+4-2}{CO_3^{2-}}$$

c. The oxidation number of the potassium ion is $+1$, the same as its ionic charge. The oxidation number of oxygen is -2.

$$\overset{+1\ ?-2}{K_2SO_4}$$

For the sum of the oxidation numbers in the compound to be zero, the oxidation number of sulfur must be $+6$.

$$\overset{+1\ +6-2}{K_2SO_4}$$

Problem

3. Find the oxidation number of each element in these formulas.
a. P_2O_5 **b.** NH_4^+ **c.** $Na_2Cr_2O_7$ **d.** $Ca(OH)_2$.

3. a. $\overset{+5-2}{P_2O_5}$ **b.** $\overset{-3+1}{NH_4^+}$
c. $\overset{+1\ +6\ -2}{Na_2Cr_2O_7}$ **d.** $\overset{+2\ -2+1}{Ca(OH)_2}$

20·4 Oxidation Number Changes

Oxidation numbers allow chemists to keep track of electrons during chemical reactions.

An *increase* in the oxidation number of an atom signifies *oxidation*. A *decrease* in the oxidation number of an atom signifies *reduction*. Look again at the equation in Example 1 to identify what is being oxidized and reduced on the basis of oxidation-number changes. Oxidation numbers have been added to this equation.

$$\overset{+1\ -5-2}{2AgNO_3}(aq) + \overset{0}{Cu}(s) \longrightarrow \overset{+2\ +5-2}{Cu(NO_3)_2}(aq) + \overset{0}{2Ag}(s)$$

The change in oxidation number is used to identify the substance being oxidized and the substance being reduced.

In this reaction, the oxidation number of silver decreases from $+1$ to 0. This is reduction. Silver is reduced from Ag^{+1} to Ag^0. On the other hand, copper is oxidized in this reaction. Its oxidation number increases from 0 to $+2$. Copper is oxidized from Cu^0 to Cu^{2+}. These results agree with those obtained by analyzing the reaction by using electron transfer.

Figure 20·8
When a copper wire is placed in a colorless silver nitrate solution **(a)**, crystals of silver coat the wire **(b)**. The solution slowly turns blue, as a result of copper(II) nitrate formation. What change occurs in the oxidation number of the silver? How does the oxidation number of the copper change?
The silver changes from +1 to 0; the copper changes from 0 to +2.

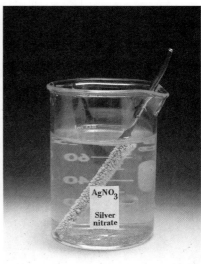

a   b

Safety

Many substances that are harmless in their reduced form may be toxic or corrosive in their oxidized form, or vice versa. Do not assume that all forms of a chemical are harmless just because one form is harmless.

Example 3

Use the change in oxidation number to identify which elements are oxidized and reduced in each of these reactions.
a. $Cl_2(g) + 2HBr(aq) \longrightarrow 2HCl(aq) + Br_2(l)$
b. $C(s) + O_2(g) \longrightarrow CO_2(g)$
c. $Zn(s) + 2MnO_2(s) + 2NH_4Cl(aq) \longrightarrow$
$$ZnCl_2(aq) + Mn_2O_3(s) + 2NH_3(g) + H_2O(l)$$

Solution

Assign oxidation numbers to each element. A decrease in oxidation number indicates reduction. An increase in oxidation number indicates oxidation.

a. $\overset{0}{Cl_2}(g) + 2\overset{+1-1}{HBr}(aq) \longrightarrow 2\overset{+1-1}{HCl}(aq) + \overset{0}{Br_2}(l)$

The element chlorine is reduced ($0 \rightarrow -1$). The element bromine is oxidized ($-1 \rightarrow 0$).

b. $\overset{0}{C}(s) + \overset{0}{O_2}(g) \longrightarrow \overset{+4-2}{CO_2}(g)$

The element carbon is oxidized ($0 \rightarrow +4$). The element oxygen is reduced ($0 \rightarrow -2$).

c. $\overset{0}{Zn}(s) + 2\overset{+4\ -2}{MnO_2}(s) + 2\overset{-3+1\ -1}{NH_4Cl}(aq) \longrightarrow$
$$\overset{+2\ -2}{ZnCl_2}(aq) + \overset{+3\ -2}{Mn_2O_3}(s) + 2\overset{-3+1}{NH_3}(g) + \overset{+1\ -2}{H_2O}(l)$$

The element zinc is oxidized ($0 \rightarrow +2$). The element manganese is reduced ($+4 \rightarrow +3$).

A reducing agent is an electron donor. An oxidizing agent is an electron acceptor.

Example 4

Identify the oxidizing agent and reducing agent in each of the equations in Example 3.

Solution

Recall from Section 20·2 that the oxidizing agent is reduced in the reaction and the reducing agent is oxidized.

a. Since chlorine is reduced, Cl_2 is the oxidizing agent. Since bromine (in HBr) is oxidized, Br^{1-} is the reducing agent.

b. Carbon is the reducing agent. Oxygen is the oxidizing agent.

c. Zinc is the reducing agent. Manganese (in MnO_2) is the oxidizing agent.

4. a. Na: oxidized
      (reducing agent)
   Cl_2: reduced
      (oxidizing agent)
b. I: oxidized
   N: reduced
   HNO_3: oxidizing agent
   HI: reducing agent
c. S: oxidized
   N: reduced
   HNO_3: oxidizing agent
   H_2S: reducing agent
d. Pb: oxidized and reduced
   $PbSO_4$: oxidizing and
      reducing agent

Problem

4. In each of the following reactions identify the element oxidized; the element reduced, the oxidizing agent, and the reducing agent.

a. $2Na(s) + Cl_2(g) \longrightarrow 2NaCl(s)$

b. $2HNO_3(aq) + 6HI(g) \longrightarrow 2NO(g) + 3I_2(s) + 4H_2O(l)$

c. $3H_2S(aq) + 2HNO_3(aq) \longrightarrow 3S(s) + 2NO(g) + 4H_2O(l)$

d. $2PbSO_4(s) + 2H_2O(l) \longrightarrow Pb(s) + PbO_2(s) + 2H_2SO_4(aq)$

20·5 Balancing Redox Equations

Simple redox equations can be balanced by inspection or by trial and error. Many other oxidation–reduction reactions are too complex, however, to balance in this way. Fortunately, two systematic methods are available. These are the oxidation–number change method and the half-reaction method. These methods are based on the fact that *the total number of electrons gained in reduction must equal the total number of electrons lost in oxidation.* The oxidation-number change method will be described in this section. The half-reaction method will be described in Section 20·7.

The change in the oxidation numbers of atoms in a chemical reaction can be used to balance redox equations.

With the **oxidation-number change method,** *a redox equation is balanced by comparing the increases and decreases in oxidation numbers.* To use this method, start with a skeleton equation for a redox reaction. We will use the reduction of iron ore as an example.

$$Fe_2O_3 + CO \longrightarrow Fe + CO_2$$

Step 1: Assign oxidation numbers to all the atoms in the equation. Write the number *above* the appropriate atoms.

$$\overset{+3 \; -2}{Fe_2O_3} + \overset{+2-2}{CO} \longrightarrow \overset{0}{Fe} + \overset{+4-2}{CO_2}$$

Note that the oxidation number is stated as the charge *per atom.* In Fe_2O_3 the total positive charge is +6, but the oxidation number of Fe is +3.

Figure 20·9
Iron ore, Fe_2O_3, (on the left) is converted to metallic iron (on the right) by an oxidation–reduction process involving carbon monoxide, CO. What is oxidized and what is reduced?

Iron is reduced and carbon monoxide is oxidized.

In every oxidation–reduction reaction the total increase in oxidation number must equal the total decrease in oxidation number.

Step 2: Identify which atoms are oxidized and which are reduced. In this reaction, iron decreases in oxidation number from +3 to 0, a change of −3. Therefore iron is reduced. Carbon increases in oxidation number from +2 to +4, a change of +2. Thus carbon is oxidized. Oxygen does not change in oxidation number (because neither elemental oxygen nor peroxides are involved).

Step 3: Use a line to connect the atoms that undergo oxidation and those that undergo reduction. Write the oxidation-number change at the mid-point of each line.

$$\overset{+3\ -2}{Fe_2O_3} + \overset{+2-2}{CO} \longrightarrow \overset{0}{Fe} + \overset{+4\ -2}{CO_2}$$

with +2 change (oxidation) shown above CO to CO_2 and −3 change (reduction) shown below Fe_2O_3 to Fe.

Step 4: Make the total increase in oxidation number equal to the total decrease in oxidation number by using appropriate coefficients. In this example, the oxidation number increase should be multiplied by 3 and the oxidation number decrease should be multiplied by 2. This gives an increase of +6 and a decrease of −6. This can be done in the equation by placing the coefficient 2 in front of Fe and the coefficient 3 in front of both CO and CO_2. The formula Fe_2O_3 does not need a coefficient because the formula indicates 2Fe.

$$3 \times (+2) = +6$$
$$Fe_2O_3 + 3CO \longrightarrow 2Fe + 3CO_2$$
$$2 \times (-3) = -6$$

Step 5: Finally, check to be sure that the equation is balanced for both atoms and charge. If necessary, the remainder of the equation is balanced by inspection.

$$Fe_2O_3 + 3CO \longrightarrow 2Fe + 3CO_2$$

Example 5

Balance this redox equation by using the oxidation-number change method.

$$K_2Cr_2O_7(aq) + H_2O(l) + S(s) \longrightarrow$$
$$KOH(aq) + Cr_2O_3(aq) + SO_2(g)$$

Solution

Step 1: Assign oxidation numbers.

$$\overset{+1\ +6\ -2}{K_2Cr_2O_7}(aq) + \overset{+1\ -2}{H_2O}(l) + \overset{0}{S}(s) \longrightarrow$$
$$\overset{+1-2+1}{KOH}(aq) + \overset{+3\ -2}{Cr_2O_3}(aq) + \overset{+4-2}{SO_2}(g)$$

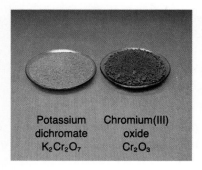

Potassium   Chromium(III)
dichromate   oxide
$K_2Cr_2O_7$ Cr_2O_3

Figure 20·10
Potassium dichromate is a red crystalline substance. It reacts with water and sulfur to form chromium(III) oxide, the green compound shown here. What are the other products? Potassium hydroxide, KOH, and sulfur dioxide, SO_2.

Steps 2 and 3: Connect the atoms that change in oxidation number. Indicate the sign and magnitude of the change.

$$\overset{+6}{K_2Cr_2O_7}(aq) + H_2O(l) + \overset{0}{S}(s) \longrightarrow$$
$$KOH(aq) + \overset{+3}{Cr_2O_3}(aq) + \overset{+4}{S}O_2(g)$$

with -3 change connecting Cr, and $+4$ change connecting S.

Step 4: Balance the increase and decrease in oxidation numbers. Four chromium atoms must be reduced $[4 \times (-3) = -12$ decrease] for each three sulfur atoms that are oxidized $[3 \times (+4) = +12$ increase]. Put the coefficient 3 in front of S and SO_2 and the coefficient 2 in front of $K_2Cr_2O_7$ and Cr_2O_3.

$$(4)(-3) = -12$$
$$2\overset{+6}{K_2Cr_2O_7}(aq) + H_2O(l) + 3\overset{0}{S}(s) \longrightarrow$$
$$KOH(aq) + 2\overset{+3}{Cr_2O_3}(aq) + 3\overset{+4}{S}O_2(g)$$
$$(3)(+4) = +12$$

Step 5: Now finish balancing by inspection. The coefficient 4 in front of KOH balances potassium. The coefficient 2 in front of H_2O balances the hydrogen and oxygen.

$$2K_2Cr_2O_7(aq) + 2H_2O(l) + 3S(s) \longrightarrow$$
$$4KOH(aq) + 2Cr_2O_3(aq) + 3SO_2(g)$$

Problems

5. a. $2Al(s) + 3Cl_2(g) \rightarrow 2AlCl_3(s)$
b. $2KClO_3(s) \rightarrow$
$\qquad 2KCl(s) + 3O_2(g)$
c. $PH_3(g) + 2I_2(s) + 2H_2O(l)$
$\qquad \rightarrow H_3PO_2(aq) + 4HI(aq)$
d. $3Cl_2(g) + 6KOH(aq) \rightarrow$
$\qquad KClO_3(aq) + 5KCl(aq)$
$\qquad\qquad + 3H_2O(l)$
e. $2HNO_3(aq) + 3H_2S(aq) \rightarrow$
$\qquad 3S(s) + 2NO(g) + 4H_2O(l)$
f. $KIO_4(aq) + 7KI(aq)$
$\qquad + 8HCl(aq) \rightarrow 8KCl(aq)$
$\qquad\qquad + 4I_2(s) + 4H_2O(l)$

5. Balance each of these redox equations.
    a. $Al(s) + Cl_2(g) \longrightarrow AlCl_3(s)$
    b. $KClO_3(s) \longrightarrow KCl(aq) + O_2(g)$
    c. $PH_3(g) + I_2(s) + H_2O(l) \longrightarrow H_3PO_2(aq) + HI(aq)$
    d. $Cl_2(g) + KOH(aq) \longrightarrow KClO_3(aq) + KCl(aq) + H_2O(l)$
    e. $HNO_3(aq) + H_2S(g) \longrightarrow S(s) + NO(g) + H_2O(l)$
    f. $KIO_4(aq) + KI(aq) + HCl(aq) \longrightarrow KCl(aq) + I_2(s) + H_2O(l)$

20·6   Identifying Redox Reactions

In general, all chemical reactions can be assigned to one of two classes. In oxidation–reduction reactions electrons are transferred from one reacting species to another. In all other reactions electrons are not transferred. A majority of the reactions presented prior to this chapter do not involve electron transfer and are not redox reactions. Double-replacement reactions, and acid–base reactions are not redox reactions. Many single-replacement reactions, combination reactions, decomposition reactions, and combustion reactions are redox reactions.

An equation in which the oxidation numbers of at least two elements change is a redox reaction.

How can you determine if a reaction is a redox reaction? Use oxidation numbers. If the oxidation number of an element in a reacting species changes, then that element has undergone either oxidation or reduction. The reaction is part of a redox reaction.

Example 6

Use the change in oxidation number to identify which of these reactions are redox reactions. If a reaction is a redox reaction, name the element reduced, the element oxidized, the reducing agent, and the oxidizing agent.

a. $N_2O_4(g) \longrightarrow 2NO_2(g)$
b. $Cl_2(g) + 2NaBr(aq) \longrightarrow 2NaCl(aq) + Br_2(g)$
c. $PbCl_2(s) + K_2SO_4(aq) \longrightarrow 2KCl(aq) + PbSO_4(s)$
d. $2NaOH(aq) + H_2SO_4(aq) \longrightarrow Na_2SO_4(aq) + 2H_2O(l)$
e. $2K(s) + 2H_2O(l) \longrightarrow 2KOH(aq) + H_2(g)$

Solution

Assign oxidation numbers to each element. A decrease in oxidation number indicates reduction. An increase indicates oxidation.

a. $\overset{+4\ -2}{N_2O_4}(g) \longrightarrow 2\overset{+4\ -2}{NO_2}(g)$

This is a decomposition reaction. Neither oxygen nor nitrogen changes in oxidation number. Therefore it is not a redox reaction.

b. $\overset{0}{Cl_2}(g) + 2\overset{+1\ -1}{NaBr}(aq) \longrightarrow 2\overset{+1\ -1}{NaCl}(aq) + \overset{0}{Br_2}(l)$

This is a single-displacement reaction. The element chlorine is reduced ($0 \rightarrow -1$). The element bromine is oxidized ($-1 \rightarrow 0$). This is a redox reaction. Chlorine is the oxidizing agent; bromine is the reducing agent.

c. $\overset{+2\ -1}{PbCl_2}(s) + \overset{+1\ +6\ -2}{K_2SO_4}(aq) \longrightarrow 2\overset{+1\ -1}{KCl}(aq) + \overset{+2\ +6\ -2}{PbSO_4}(s)$

This is a double-replacement reaction. None of the elements changes in oxidation number. This is not a redox reaction.

d. $2\overset{+1\ -2+1}{NaOH}(aq) + \overset{+1\ +6\ -2}{H_2SO_4}(aq) \longrightarrow \overset{+1\ +6\ -2}{Na_2SO_4}(aq) + 2\overset{+1\ -2}{H_2O}(l)$

This is an acid–base reaction. None of the elements changes in oxidation number. This is not a redox reaction.

e. $2\overset{0}{K}(s) + 2\overset{+1\ -2}{H_2O}(l) \longrightarrow 2\overset{+1\ -2+1}{KOH}(aq) + \overset{0}{H_2}(g)$

The element potassium is oxidized ($0 \rightarrow +1$). The element hydrogen is reduced ($+1 \rightarrow 0$). This is a redox reaction. Potassium is the reducing agent; hydrogen is the oxidizing agent. (Note that not all the hydrogens are reduced. Some of them do not change in oxidation number.)

Yes. Potassium is oxidized and hydrogen (from the water) is reduced.

Figure 20·11
Potassium reacts violently with water. Is this a redox reaction?

6. The following are redox reactions.

   c. Mg: oxidized
       (reducing agent)
     Br$_2$: reduced
       (oxidizing agent)

   d. Nitrogen in NO$_2^-$ is oxidized.
     Nitrogen in NH$_4^+$ is reduced.
     NH$_4^+$ is the oxidizing agent.
     NO$_2^-$ is the reducing agent.

   e. Oxygen is oxidized;
     it is the reducing agent.
     Chlorine is reduced;
     it is the oxidizing agent.

   g. Hydrogen is oxidized.
     Copper is reduced.
     CuO is the oxidizing agent.
     H$_2$ is the reducing agent.

   i. Antimony is oxidized.
     Nitrogen is reduced.
     HNO$_3$ is the oxidizing agent.
     Sb is the reducing agent.

Figure 20·12
Oxidation–reduction reactions provide the energy to launch space vehicles.

Problem

6. Identify which of these are oxidation–reduction reactions. If a reaction is a redox reaction, name the element oxidized, the element reduced, the oxidizing agent, and the reducing agent.

  a. $BaCl_2(aq) + 2KIO_3(aq) \longrightarrow Ba(IO_3)_2(s) + 2KCl(aq)$

  b. $H_2CO_3(aq) \longrightarrow H_2O(l) + CO_2(g)$

  c. $Mg(s) + Br_2(l) \longrightarrow MgBr_2(s)$

  d. $NH_4NO_2(s) \longrightarrow N_2(g) + 2H_2O(l)$

  e. $2KClO_3(s) \longrightarrow 2KCl(s) + 3O_2(g)$

  f. $CaCO_3(s) + 2HCl(aq) \longrightarrow CaCl_2(aq) + H_2O(l) + CO_2(g)$

  g. $CuO(s) + H_2(g) \longrightarrow Cu(s) + H_2O(l)$

  h. $CaCO_3(s) \longrightarrow CaO(s) + CO_2(g)$

  i. $2Sb(s) + HNO_3(aq) \longrightarrow Sb_2O_5(s) + NO(g) + H_2O(l)$

20·B Rocket Fuels and Household Bleach

What could laundry bleach and rocket fuels have in common? Both do their work through oxidation–reduction reactions. Bleaches work by producing very reactive substances that are strong oxidizing agents. The most common household bleach is a solution of sodium hypochloride. It decomposes to produce atomic oxygen.

$$NaClO \longrightarrow NaCl + O$$

Hydrogen peroxide is used commercially for bleaching. It also produces atomic oxygen.

$$H_2O_2 \longrightarrow H_2O + O$$

Atomic oxygen is a very strong oxidizing agent. It reacts with the organic molecules that give color to cloth and paper. The oxidized forms of these molecules are colorless.

    The power of a rocket is also the result of oxidation–reduction reactions. Some fuels are mixtures of two liquids: a fuel and an oxidizer. Liquid hydrogen, for example, can be oxidized by liquid oxygen. They combine to form water.

$$2H_2(l) + O_2(l) \longrightarrow 2H_2O(g)$$

Hydrogen is oxidized, and oxygen is reduced in this reaction. The thrust of a rocket increases as the molecular mass of the exhaust gas decreases. Water vapor has a low molecular mass. The fuel gases also occupy a small volume. These facts make this cryogenic hydrogen/oxygen mixture the most commonly used fuel in space launch vehicles.

    Some rocket fuels are self-oxidizing. The oxidation–reduction reactions of hydrogen peroxide and hydrazine are decompositions rather than combustion reactions. Hydrazine decomposes to molecular nitrogen and hydrogen.

$$N_2H_4 \longrightarrow N_2 + 2H_2$$

20·7 Using Half-Reactions to Balance Redox Equations

The half-reaction method involves balancing and adding oxidation and reduction half-reactions to obtain a balanced equation.

Electron-transfer reactions can be separated into two half-reactions.

Another method can be used to balance redox equations. *The* **half-reaction method** *is used to balance redox equations by balancing the oxidation and reduction half-reactions*. The procedure is different but the outcome is the same as with the oxidation-number change method. The first step in the half-reaction method is to divide the overall reaction into two parts. *A* **half-reaction** *is an equation showing either the reduction or the oxidation of a species in an oxidation–reduction reaction*. Then each half-reaction is balanced. The number of electrons gained by the reduction half-reaction must be equal to the number of electrons lost by the oxidation half-reaction. Finally, the two half-reactions are added to give a balanced equation. The half-reaction method is particularly useful for balancing equations for ionic reactions.

The oxidation of sulfur with nitric acid in aqueous solution can be our example.

$$S + HNO_3 \longrightarrow SO_2 + NO + H_2O$$

Step 1: Write the equation in ionic form. (Hint: Only HNO_3 is ionized. The products are covalent compounds.)

$$S + H^+ + NO_3^- \longrightarrow SO_2 + NO + H_2O$$

Step 2: Write separate half-reactions for the oxidation and reduction processes. (Hint: Sulfur is oxidized because its oxidation number increases from 0 to 4. Nitrogen is reduced because its oxidation number decreases from +5 to +2.)

Oxidation: $S \longrightarrow SO_2$ Reduction: $NO_3^- \longrightarrow NO$

Step 3: Balance the atoms in the half-reactions.

a. *Balance the oxidation half-reaction.* Since this reaction takes place in acid solution, H_2O and H^+ can be used to balance oxygen and hydrogen as needed. Sulfur is already balanced. Two molecules of H_2O can be added to balance the oxygen.

$$2H_2O + S \longrightarrow SO_2$$

Oxygen is now balanced, but four hydrogens must be added to the right to balance those on the left.

$$2H_2O + S \longrightarrow SO_2 + 4H^+$$

This half-reaction is now balanced in terms of atoms.

b. *Balance the reduction half-reaction.* Nitrogen is already balanced. Two molecules of H_2O can be added to balance the oxygen.

$$NO_3^- \longrightarrow NO + 2H_2O$$

Oxygen is balanced, but four hydrogens ($4H^+$) must be added to the left to balance hydrogen.

$$4H^+ + NO_3^- \longrightarrow NO + 2H_2O$$

This half-reaction is now balanced in terms of atoms.

Electrons are as much a part of a half-reaction as the atoms themselves. They must be written into the equation.

Step 4: *Add sufficient electrons to one side of each half-reaction to balance the charges.* Four electrons are needed on the right side in the oxidation half-reaction. Three electrons are needed on the left side in the reduction half-reaction.

$$\text{Oxidation: } 2H_2O + S \longrightarrow SO_2 + 4H^+ + 4e^-$$

$$\text{Reduction: } 4H^+ + NO_3^- + 3e^- \longrightarrow NO + 2H_2O$$

Each half-reaction is now balanced with respect to both atoms and charge.

In every oxidation–reduction reaction the total number of electrons gained is equal to the total number of electrons lost.

Step 5: *Multiply each half-reaction by an appropriate number to make the electron changes equal.* In any redox reaction, the electrons lost in oxidation must be equal to the electrons gained in reduction. If the oxidation half-reaction is multiplied by 3 and the reduction half-reaction by 4, the number of electrons lost in oxidation and the number of electrons gained in reduction both equal 12.

$$\text{Oxidation: } 6H_2O + 3S \longrightarrow 3SO_2 + 12H^+ + 12e^-$$

$$\text{Reduction: } 16H^+ + 4NO_3^- + 12e^- \longrightarrow 4NO + 8H_2O$$

Step 6: *Add the half-reactions and subtract terms that appear on both sides of the equation.*

$$\overset{4}{\cancel{16H^+}} + \cancel{6H_2O} + 4NO_3^- + 3S + \cancel{12e^-} \longrightarrow$$

$$3SO_2 + 4NO + \cancel{12H^+} + \cancel{12e^-} + \overset{2}{\cancel{8H_2O}}$$

The final equation should be checked to be sure that atoms are conserved, charge is conserved, and electrons have cancelled.

Now the balanced equation can be written.

$$4H^+ + 4NO_3^- + 3S \longrightarrow 3SO_2 + 4NO + 2H_2O$$

or

$$4HNO_3 + 3S \longrightarrow 3SO_2 + 4NO + 2H_2O$$

Example 7

Balance the reaction that occurs between permanganate ions, MnO_4^-, and chloride ions, Cl^-, in acid solution. The products are manganese (II) ions, Mn^{2+}, and chlorine gas, Cl_2.

Solution

Step 1: Write the unbalanced reaction in ionic form.

$$MnO_4^- + Cl^- \longrightarrow Mn^{2+} + Cl_2$$

Step 2: Write the half-reactions for oxidation and reduction. (Use oxidation numbers to determine the oxidation process and the reduction process.)

$$\text{Oxidation: } Cl^- \longrightarrow Cl_2$$

$$\text{Reduction: } MnO_4^- \longrightarrow Mn^{2+}$$

Figure 20·13
a A redox reaction occurs when hydrochloric acid, HCl, is added to potassium permanganate, KMnO₄.
b The products of this reaction are manganese(II) chloride, chlorine gas, water, and potassium chloride. Why should this reaction be done only in a fume hood?
Poisonous chlorine gas is produced.

a   b

Step 3: Balance the atoms. Because the solution is acidic, use H_2O and H^+ to balance the hydrogen and oxygen if necessary.

Oxidation: $2Cl^- \longrightarrow Cl_2$ (atoms balanced)

Reduction: $MnO_4^- + 8H^+ \longrightarrow Mn^{2+} + 4H_2O$
                                (atoms balanced)

Step 4: Balance the charges. Add electrons as needed.

Oxidation: $2Cl^- \longrightarrow Cl_2 + 2e^-$ (charges balanced)

Reduction: $MnO_4^- + 8H^+ + 5e^- \longrightarrow Mn^{2+} + 4H_2O$
                               (charges balanced)

Step 5: Make the electron charges equal. Multiply the oxidation half-reaction by 5 and the reduction half-reaction by 2. Ten electrons are lost in oxidation, and 10 electrons are gained in reduction.

Oxidation: $10Cl^- \longrightarrow 5Cl_2 + 10e^-$

Reduction: $2MnO_4^- + 16H^+ + 10e^- \longrightarrow 2Mn^{2+} + 8H_2O$

Step 6: Add the half-reactions and subtract terms that appear on both sides of the equation.

$2MnO_4^- + 10Cl^- + 16H^+ + \cancel{10e^-} \longrightarrow$
$$2Mn^{2+} + 5Cl_2 + 8H_2O + \cancel{10e^-}$$

The balanced ionic equation is the net equation.

$$2MnO_4^- + 10Cl^- + 16H^+ \longrightarrow 2Mn^{2+} + 5Cl_2 + 8H_2O$$

In this example, the permanganate ions could come from potassium permanganate, KMnO₄. The chloride ions were from HCl. As an additional step the spectator ions should be added to the equation.

Step 7: *Add the spectator ions and balance.* **Spectator ions** *are those which do not change oxidation number or composition during a reaction.* The K^+ and Cl^- ions can now be added.

$2K^+ + 2MnO_4^- + 16H + 16Cl^- \longrightarrow$
$$2Mn^{2+} + 4Cl^- + 5Cl_2 + 8H_2O + 2K^+ + 2Cl^-$$
or
$$2KMnO_4 + 16HCl \longrightarrow 2MnCl_2 + 5Cl_2 + 8H_2O + 2KCl$$

a **b**

Figure 20·14
a A redox reaction occurs when potassium chlorate is added to potassium iodide in acid solution. The chlorate ion is the oxidizing agent and the iodide ion is the reducing agent.
b The resulting solution is yellow due to dissolved iodine, a product of the reaction. See Problem **7.a.**

As a quick review, here is a summary of the steps for balancing redox equations by the ion–electron method.

Step 1: Write the equation in ionic form.

Step 2: Write separate half-reactions for the oxidation and reduction processes.

Step 3: Balance the atoms in the half-reactions. Use H_2O and H^+ to balance oxygen and hydrogen in an acid solution. Use H_2O and OH^- for reactions in a basic solution.

Step 4: Add electrons to one side of each half-reaction to balance the charges.

Step 5: Multiply each half-reaction by an appropriate number to make the electron changes equal.

Step 6: Add the half-reactions and subtract terms that appear on both sides of the equation.

Step 7: The final equation should be checked to be sure that atoms are conserved, charge is conserved, and all electrons have cancelled. If spectator ions are known, add them now and the equation will be balanced.

Problem

Balanced equations are given in the Appendix.

7. Balance each of these redox equations by the ion-electron method.
  a. $ClO_3^-(aq) + I^-(aq) \longrightarrow Cl^-(aq) + I_2(aq)$ [acid solution]
  b. $C_2O_4^{2-}(aq) + MnO_4^-(aq) \longrightarrow$
$$Mn^{2+}(aq) + CO_2(aq) \text{ [acid solution]}$$
  c. $Br_2(l) + SO_2(g) \longrightarrow Br^-(aq) + SO_4^{2-}(aq)$ [acid solution]
  d. $MnO_2(s) + H^+(aq) + NO_2^-(aq) \longrightarrow$
$$NO_3^-(aq) + Mn^{2+}(aq) + H_2O(l)$$
  e. $MnO_4(aq) + NO_2^-(aq) \longrightarrow$
$$MnO_2(s) + NO_3^-(aq) \text{ [basic solution]}$$
  f. $Cl_2(g) \longrightarrow ClO_3^-(aq) + Cl^-(aq)$ [basic solution]

20·C Photographic Chemistry

Photographs, too, depend on oxidation–reduction reactions. Black-and-white photographic film is an emulsion of gelatin and fine silver bromide crystals. (Color film is more complex.) The emulsion is spread in a very thin layer on paper or clear plastic. The silver bromide crystals are sensitive to certain colors (wavelengths) of light. Small amounts of compounds that are sensitive to other colors are added to the emulsion. This produces a film that will react to all colors of light. When the film is exposed to light, the silver bromide crystals become activated. The effect is not yet visible, however, on the film.

When film is developed, the changes in the silver bromide become visible. This process must be done in darkness. First the film is placed in a solution of an organic chemical that is a reducing agent. This chemical is called the developer. It reduces the silver ions in the activated silver bromide grains to silver. (It does not reduce the grains that have not been activated by the light.) The silver produced is dark in color.

$$AgBr + C_6H_4(OH)_2 \longrightarrow 2Ag + C_6H_4O_2 + 2HBr$$

Where the film has been exposed to more light, more grains of silver bromide are reduced. This makes the film darker. For this reason, the lightest parts of the photographed image will be dark on the film.

The developed film is next placed in a solution of "fixer." This chemical can dissolve away the silver bromide that has not been reduced. Sodium thiosulfate, which is commonly called "hypo," is used for this purpose.

$$AgBr + 2Na_2S_2O_3 \longrightarrow NaBr + Na_3Ag(S_2O_3)_2$$

After a bath in fixer, the film is clear wherever it was not exposed to light. It is dark where it was exposed. This creates an image that reverses the light and dark of the original scene. For this reason, this initial film image is called a negative.

To make a positive print of black and white film, the negative is placed over photographic paper. Like the film, this paper is coated with a light-sensitive emulsion of a silver halide. Light goes through the negative in the area where silver bromide was washed away by the fixer. Wherever light strikes the paper the silver halide grains on the paper will be reduced to silver. When the print is developed, those areas will be black. What was dark in the original scene is clear in the negative. The same area is dark again in the printed picture. This is all due to redox reactions.

The process by which silver bromide grains are "activated" by exposure to light is not well understood. Light sensitive chemical reactions are the subject of a special branch of chemistry, called photochemistry.

Figure 20·15
On a developed negative, the light and developer have caused silver bromide to be reduced and deposited as dark metallic silver. Areas of the film that received less light appear clear. The unchanged silver bromide crystals were dissolved by the fixer.

Figure 20·16
A positive print reverses the areas of light and dark that are recorded on a film negative.

Key Terms

half-reaction	20·7	oxidation–reduction	
half-reaction		reaction	20·0
method	20·7	oxidizing agent	20·2
oxidation	20·1	redox reaction	20·0
oxidation number	20·3	reducing agent	20·2
oxidation-number		reduction	20·1
change method	20·5	spectator ion	20·7

The half-reaction method is another way to write a balanced equation for a redox reaction. In this method the net ionic equation is first divided into two half-reactions. One is for the oxidation and the other is for the reduction. Each half-reaction is balanced independently for mass. H^+, OH^-, or H_2O are added as needed. The net charge on both sides is balanced by adding electrons. The half-reactions are then multiplied by factors to make the number of electrons the same in each. Finally the half-reactions are added.

Chapter Summary

Oxidation–reduction, or redox, reactions are an important category of chemical reactions. The original meaning of oxidation was the chemical combination of a substance with oxygen. Reduction was originally the loss of oxygen. These definitions have long since been expanded. Oxidation is now considered to be any shift of electrons away from an atom. Reduction now includes any shift of electrons toward an atom. An oxidation reaction is always accompanied by a reduction reaction. The substance that does the oxidizing is called an oxidizing agent. It is reduced. The substance that does the reducing is called a reducing agent. It is oxidized.

An oxidation number can be assigned to an element in a substance according to a set of rules. The oxidation number of an element in an uncombined state is zero. The oxidation number of a monatomic ion is the same in magnitude and sign as its ionic charge. The sum of the oxidation numbers of the elements in a neutral compound is zero. In a polyatomic ion, however, the sum is equal to the charge of the ion. Oxidation numbers help us keep track of electrons in redox reactions. An oxidation number increase is oxidation. A decrease is reduction.

One method for balancing redox equations involves determining the change in oxidation number of the substances that are oxidized and reduced. Coefficients are then used to make the increase in oxidation-number equal to the decrease.

Practice Questions and Problems

8. Define the processes of oxidation and reduction in terms of the loss or gain of oxygen. *20·1*

9. Balance each equation. Then classify each reaction as oxidation or reduction based on the loss or gain of oxygen. *20·1*
 a. $C_2H_4 + O_2 \longrightarrow CO_2 + H_2O$
 b. $KClO_3 \longrightarrow KCl + O_2$
 c. $CuO + H_2 \longrightarrow Cu + H_2O$
 d. $H_2 + O_2 \longrightarrow H_2O$

10. Define oxidation and reduction in these terms.
 a. Gain or loss of electrons. *20·2*
 b. Gain or loss of hydrogen by a covalent bond.
 c. Gain or loss of oxygen.
 d. The shift of electrons in a covalent bond.

11. What is a reducing agent? *20·2*

12. What is an oxidizing agent? *20·2*

13. Identify these reactions as either oxidation or reduction. *20·2*
 a. $Li \longrightarrow Li^+ + e^-$
 b. $2I^- \longrightarrow I_2 + 2e^-$
 c. $Zn^{2+} + 2e^- \longrightarrow Zn$
 d. $Br_2 + 2e^- \longrightarrow 2Br^-$

14. Which of the following would most likely be oxidizing agents and which would most likely be reducing agents? **a.** Mn^{4+} **b.** Cl_2 **c.** K
 d. O^{2-} **e.** K^+ *20·2*

15. Use electron transfer or electron shift to identify what is oxidized and what is reduced in each of these reactions. Use electronegativity values for molecular compounds. *20·2*

  a. $2Na + Br_2 \longrightarrow 2NaBr$
  b. $N_2 + 3H_2 \longrightarrow 2NH_3$
  c. $S + O_2 \longrightarrow SO_2$
  d. $Mg + Cu(NO_3)_2 \longrightarrow Mg(NO_3)_2 + Cu$

16. Identify the oxidizing agent and the reducing agent in each reactant in Problem 15. *20·2*

17. What are oxidation numbers? *20·3*

18. How are oxidation numbers determined and used? *20·3*

19. Determine the oxidation number of each element in these substances. *20·3*

  a. S_2O_3 **d.** $Al_2(SO_4)_3$
  b. O_2 **e.** Na_2O_2
  c. $NaOH$ **f.** PO_4^{3-}

20. Determine the oxidation number of nitrogen in each of these substances. *20·3*

  a. NO **d.** $NaNO_2$
  b. NH_4Cl **e.** N_2O_5
  c. NO_3^- **f.** NH_3

21. Define oxidation and reduction in terms of a change in oxidation number. *20·4*

22. Use the oxidation-number to identify which elements are oxidized and which are reduced in each of these reactions. *20·4*

  a. $2H_2(g) + O_2(g) \longrightarrow 2H_2O(l)$
  b. $2KNO_3(s) \longrightarrow 2KNO_2(s) + O_2(g)$
  c. $NH_4NO_2(s) \longrightarrow N_2(g) + 2H_2O(g)$
  d. $PbO_2(aq) + 4HI(aq) \longrightarrow$
               $I_2(aq) + PbI_2(aq) + 2H_2O(l)$

23. Identify the oxidizing agent and reducing agent in each equation in Problem 22. *20·4*

24. Balance each of these redox equations using the oxidation-number change method. *20·5*

  a. $KClO_3 \longrightarrow KCl + O_2$
  b. $HNO_2 + HI \longrightarrow NO + I_2 + H_2O$
  c. $As_2O_3 + Cl_2 + H_2O \longrightarrow H_3AsO_4 + HCl$
  d. $Bi_2S_3 + HNO_3 \longrightarrow$
               $Bi(NO_3)_3 + NO + S + H_2O$
  e. $MnO_2 + H_2SO_4 + H_2C_2O_4 \longrightarrow$
                 $MnSO_4 + CO_2 + H_2O$
  f. $SbCl_5 + KI \longrightarrow SbCl_3 + KCl + I_2$

25. Identify the oxidizing agent and the reducing agent in each reaction in Problem 24. *20·5*

26. Identify which of these equations represent redox reactions. *20·6*

  a. $Li(s) + H_2O(l) \longrightarrow LiOH(aq) + H_2(g)$
  b. $K_2Cr_2O_7(aq) + HCl(aq) \longrightarrow$
       $KCl(aq) + CrCl_3(aq) + H_2O(l) + Cl_2(g)$
  c. $Al(s) + HCl(aq) \longrightarrow AlCl_3(aq) + H_2(g)$
  d. $P_4(s) + S_8(s) \longrightarrow P_2S_5(s)$
  e. $MnO(s) + PbO_2(s) \longrightarrow$
             $MnO_4^-(aq) + Pb^{2+}(aq)$ [acidic]
  f. $Cl_2(g) + H_2O(l) \longrightarrow HCl(aq) + HClO(aq)$
  g. $I_2O_5(s) + CO(g) \longrightarrow I_2(s) + CO_2(g)$
  h. $H_2O(l) + SO_3(g) \longrightarrow H_2SO_4(aq)$
  i. $Bi(OH)_3 + K_2SnO_2(aq) \longrightarrow$
             $Bi(s) + H_2O(l) + K_2SnO_3(aq)$

27. For each redox equation in Problem 26, identify the oxidizing agent and reducing agent. *20·6*

28. Write balanced ionic equations for the following reactions which occur in acid solution. Use the half-reaction method. *20·7*

  a. $Sn^{2+}(aq) + Cr_2O_7^{2-}(aq) \longrightarrow$
                 $Sn^{4+}(aq) + Cr^{3+}(aq)$
  b. $CuS(s) + NO_3^-(aq) \longrightarrow$
          $Cu(NO_3)_2(aq) + NO_2(g) + SO_2(g)$
  c. $I^-(aq) + NO_3^-(aq) \longrightarrow I_2(s) + NO(g)$

29. The following reactions take place in basic solution. Use the half-reaction method to write a balanced ionic equation for each. *20·7*

  a. $MnO_4^-(aq) + I^-(aq) \longrightarrow MnO_2(s) + I_2(aq)$
  b. $NiO_2(s) + S_2O_3^{2-}(aq) \longrightarrow$
              $Ni(OH)_2(s) + SO_3^{2-}(aq)$
  c. $Zn(s) + NO_3^-(aq) \longrightarrow$
              $NH_3(aq) + Zn(OH)_4^{2-}(aq)$

Mastery Questions and Problems

30. Balance the equations in Problem 26 by the most appropriate method. *20·6*

31. Determine the oxidation number of phosphorus in each substance. *20·3*

  a. P_4O_8 **d.** P_4O_6
  b. PO_4^{3-} **e.** $H_2PO_4^-$
  c. P_2O_5 **f.** PO_3^{3-}

32. Write balanced ionic equations for the following reactions, which occur in acid solution. Use the half-reaction method. *20·7*

  a. $Sn^{2+}(aq) + IO_3^-(aq) \longrightarrow$
                $Sn^{4+}(aq) + I^-(aq)$

b. $Cr_2O_7^{2-}(aq) + H_2S(g) \longrightarrow Cr^{3+}(aq) + S(s)$

c. $Cr_2O_7^{2-}(aq) + Al(s) \longrightarrow$
$$Cr^{3+}(aq) + Al^{3+}(aq)$$

33. Sodium chlorite is a powerful bleaching agent that is used in the paper and textile industries. It is prepared by this reaction.   *20·4*

$$4NaOH(aq) + Ca(OH)_2(aq) + C(s) + 4ClO_2(g)$$
$$\longrightarrow 4NaClO_2(aq) + CaCO_3(s) + 3H_2O(l)$$

a. Identify the element oxidized in this reaction.
b. What is the oxidizing agent?

34. Identify the element oxidized, the element reduced, the oxidizing agent, and the reducing agent in each of these redox reactions.   *20·4*
a. $MnO_2 + HCl \longrightarrow MnCl_2 + Cl_2 + H_2O$
b. $Cu + HNO_3 \longrightarrow Cu(NO_3)_2 + NO_2 + H_2O$
c. $P + HNO_3 + H_2O \longrightarrow NO + H_3PO_4$
d. $Bi(OH)_3 + Na_2SnO_2 \longrightarrow$
$$Bi + Na_2SnO_3 + H_2O$$
e. $NaCrO_2 + NaClO + NaOH \longrightarrow$
$$Na_2CrO_4 + NaCl + H_2O$$
f. $V_2O_5 + KI + HCl \longrightarrow$
$$V_2O_4 + KCl + I_2 + H_2O$$

35. Balance each of the redox equations shown in Problem 34 by using the oxidation-number change method.   *20·6*

36. The following oxidation-reduction reactions take place in basic solution. Use the half-reaction method to write a balanced ionic equation for each reaction.   *20·7*
a. $MnO_4^-(aq) + ClO_2^-(aq) \longrightarrow$
$$MnO_2(s) + ClO_4^-(aq)$$
b. $Cr^{3+}(aq) + ClO^-(aq) \longrightarrow$
$$CrO_4^{2-}(aq) + Cl^-(aq)$$
c. $Mn^{3+}(aq) + I^-(aq) \longrightarrow Mn^{2+}(aq) + IO_3^-(aq)$

Review Questions and Problems

37. Calculate the pH of solutions with the following hydrogen-ion or hydroxide-ion concentrations.
a. $[H^+] = 0.00001M$
b. $[OH^-] = 1 \times 10^{-4}M$
c. $[OH^-] = 1 \times 10^{-1}M$
d. $[H^+] = 3 \times 10^{-7}M$

38. Classify each of the solutions in the previous problem as acidic, basic, or neutral.

39. Identify the conjugate acid–base pairs in each of these equations.
a. $NH_4^+ + H_2O \rightleftharpoons NH_3 + H_3O^+$
b. $H_2SO_3 + NH_2^- \rightleftharpoons HSO_3^- + NH_3$
c. $HNO_3 + I^- \rightleftharpoons HI + NO_3^-$
d. $H_2O + ClO_4^- \rightleftharpoons HClO_4 + OH^-$

40. How many milliliters of $4.00M$ KOH are needed to neutralize 45.0 mL of $2.5M$ H_2SO_4?

41. What is the hydrogen-ion concentration of solutions with the following pH? **a.** 2.0 **b.** 11.0 **c.** 8.8

42. What is the normality of the solution prepared by dissolving 46.4 g of H_3PO_4 in enough water to make 1.25 L of solution?

43. The K_{sp} of lead(II) bromide at 25°C is 2.1×10^{-6}. What is the solubility of $PbBr_2$ in mol/L at this temperature?

44. How would you prepare 440 mL of $1.5M$ hydrochloric acid from a stock solution of $6.0M$ HCl?

45. Use LeChatelier's principle to explain what happens to the concentration of barium ions in a saturated solution of $BaSO_4$ ($K_{sp} = 1.1 \times 10^{-10}$) when a few drops of dilute Na_2SO_4 are added.

Challenging Questions and Problems

46. How many grams of copper are needed to completely reduce the silver in 85.0 mL of $0.150M$ $AgNO_3(aq)$?

47. How many milliliters of $0.280M$ $K_2Cr_2O_7(aq)$ are needed to reduce 1.40 g of sulfur. First balance the equation.

$$K_2Cr_2O_7(aq) + H_2O(l) + S(s) \longrightarrow$$
$$SO_2(g) + KOH(aq) + Cr_2O_3(aq)$$

48. Carbon monoxide can be removed from the air by passing it over solid diiodine pentoxide.

$$CO(g) + I_2O_5(s) \longrightarrow I_2(s) + CO_2(g)$$

a. Balance the equation.
b. Identify the element being oxidized and the element being reduced.
c. How many grams of carbon monoxide can be removed from the air by 0.55 g of I_2O_5?

Research Projects

1. What did George Ernst Stahl contribute to corrosion science? Why did his phlogiston theory fail to account for mass changes in rusting?

2. What techniques are used to prevent corrosion in industrial pipes carrying gas, oil, or water?

3. What substances are used to make corrosion resistant coatings such as underbody rust protection for automobiles?

4. When is liquid metal corrosion a problem? What can be done to prevent it?

5. What causes corrosion fatigue? When is it a problem?

6. What is hydrogen embrittlement?

7. Describe the oxidation–reduction reactions involved in rotting fruit.

8. Trace the development of rocket fuels. Why was the change from solid to liquid fuels significant?

9. What substances are used as flame retardants for cloth? How do they prevent cloth from burning?

10. Trace the history of photography beginning with the work of Joseph Niepce and Louis Daguerre.

11. What are some recent improvements in the chemicals used in photography?

Readings and References

Collins, Dennis. "The Rockettes." *Science 85* (March 1985), pp. 90–91.

Conkling, John A. "Chemistry of Fireworks." *Chemical and Engineering News* (June 29, 1981), pp. 24–32.

Hedgecoe, John. *The Photographer's Handbook,* 2nd ed. New York: Knopf, 1982.

Horenstein, Henry. *Black and White Photography; a Basic Manual,* 2nd ed. Boston: Little, Brown, 1983.

Light and Film. Alexandria, VA: Time-Life, 1981. Low, Betty-Bright. "Pyrotechnic Paeans Have Been Flying High for 600 Years." *Smithsonian* (July 1980), pp. 84–92.

Chapter Planning Guide

Section		Demonstrations and Experiments	Resource Materials
21·1 Electrochemical Processes	C*	Dem 21·1 An Electrochemical Reaction of Silver	Objectives Worksheet 21, SPB Skillsheet 21, SPB
21·A Michael Faraday	E		
21·2 Voltaic Cells	C	Dem 21·2 Electrochemical Cells Dem 21·3 Fruit and Vegetable Batteries	Teaching Diagram 26
21·3 Dry Cells	C	Dem 21·4 The Dry Cell	
21·4 Lead Storage Batteries	C	Dem 21·5 The Lead Cell	Beyond the Text: Batteries
21·5 Fuel Cells	O		Quiz 21·1
21·6 Half-Cells	H		
21·7 Standard Reduction Potentials	H		Teaching Diagram 27
21·8 Calculating Cell Potentials	H		
21·9 Electrolytic Cells	O	Dem 21·6 Electrolysis of Water Dem 21·7 Migration of Ions Exp 47 Electrochemistry, LM	Quiz 21·2 Reviewsheet 21, SPB Prelab 47, SPB Chapter 21 Test
21·C Electroplating and Related Processes	E		Chemical Dentistry, ICT 21
*C = Core, O = Optional E = Enrichment, H = Honors		LM = Laboratory Manual	SPB = Skills Practice Book ICT = Issues in Chem. Tech.

Chapter Objectives

Having studied this chapter and done the problems, the student should be able to:

1. Describe the nature of electrochemical processes. *21·1*

2. Sketch a voltaic cell, labeling the cathode, the anode, and the direction of flow of the electrons. *21·2*

3. Describe how a battery produces electrical energy. *21·2*

4. Identify the substance oxidized and the substance reduced in a dry cell. *21·3*

5. Describe the reaction that occurs when a lead storage battery is recharged. *21·4*

6. Explain how a fuel cell produces electrical energy. *21·5*

7. Given a voltage cell, identify the half-cell in which oxidation occurs and the half-cell in which reduction occurs. *21·6*

8. Define cell potential, and describe how it is determined. *21·6*

9. Define the standard electrode potential of an electrode. *21·7*

10. Use standard electrode potentials to calculate the standard *emf* of a cell. *21·8*

11. Distinguish between electrolytic and voltaic cells. *21·9*

12. List some of the possible uses of an electrolytic cell. *21·9*

Teaching Suggestions

21·1 Electrochemical Processes

As seen in the previous chapter, a redox reaction involves a transfer of electrons. Point out that this chapter will look at ways to make use of this transfer of electrons. In the case of an electrochemical cell, a flow of electrons can be produced from a chemical reaction and directed to do useful work. In an electrolytic cell, a flow of electrons causes a desired chemical reaction to occur. In both instances, electron flow is linked with chemical changes. These are called electrochemical processes.

In **Demonstration 21·1** *An Electrochemical Reaction of Silver*, copper metal reacts with a solution containing silver ion. A redox reaction takes place in which crystalline blades of metallic silver are produced. This reaction can be used as the basis for discussing electrochemical processes.

Show the students how Table 21·2 can be used to predict whether or not a given metal will react with the ion of another metal. **Experiment 48** *Reactivity of Metals* is designed for Chapter 22 but could also be done now.

21·2 Voltaic Cells

You can introduce the topic of voltaic cells with **Demonstration 21·2** *Electrochemical Cells*. While discussing the processes which occur within these cells, you can introduce and define the relevant terms. **Demonstration 21·3** *Fruit and Vegetable Batteries* shows how voltaic cells can be constructed from common fruits and vegetables.

21·3 Dry Cells

Dry cells are of interest to nearly every student since they are used to power so many electrical devices. Rather than just discussing these cells as a theoretical topic, show them a functioning model of a dry cell and the internal construction of a real cell. See **Demonstration 21·4** *The Dry Cell*.

21·4 Lead Storage Batteries

A demonstration lead storage cell can be easily constructed from lead sheet and sulfuric acid and can serve as the basis for discussion of lead storage batteries. See **Demonstration 21·5** *The Lead Cell*.

21·5 Fuel Cells

Stress the fact that dry cells and storage batteries can only produce electrical energy for a finite amount of time. When one of the reactants is consumed, the cell stops functioning. The advantage of a fuel cell is that it can produce a continuous flow of energy, since its reactants are constantly being replenished. Their construction is much more complex and bulky than dry cells. They are not as suitable for applications where portability is important.

21·6 Half-Cells
21·7 Standard Reduction Potentials

Emphasize that a half-cell can never function by itself. It must be connected to another half-cell. As one of them undergoes oxidation, the other undergoes reduction. Nevertheless, it is often useful to consider each half-cell as a separate entity.

The approach developed in these sections is to consider the two half-cells in an electrochemical cell as competing for electrons. As set up, each cell could undergo either oxidation or reduction. However, the one with the higher reduction potential will win the competition and undergo reduction. The other half-cell will be forced to undergo oxidation. The potential produced by the cell is the *difference* in the potentials of the two half-reactions.

Stress that the potential of a half-cell can never be found independently. A given half-cell must always be connected to another to produce a potential. The value of that potential is determined by the nature of that other cell. Thus, some standardization is necessary. Emphasize that all half-cell potentials are determined by connecting the given half-cell to the standard hydrogen half-cell. This is strictly an arbitrary (but useful) decision. Theoretically, any half-cell could have been chosen for the standard. If a different half-cell had been chosen as the standard, all of the potentials listed in Table 21·2 would have been different. However, since these are all relative values, *the values of the whole cell potentials would still be the same*.

21·8 Calculating Cell Potentials

A new consideration is brought up in this section. We now must take the *sign* of the cell potential into account.

So far we have considered electrochemical cells as consisting of standard half-cells. These standard half-cells are so constituted that their reactions can always go in the spontaneous direction. For instance we know that a cell which consists of Cu/Cu^{2+} and Ag/Ag^+ standard half-cells will proceed in a direction in which copper oxidizes and silver ion reduces. The potential for this cell is positive.

However, if these cells are constructed in such a fashion that the only substance available for oxidation is silver metal and the only substance available for reduction is copper ion, a negative value will be obtained when the potential for the oxidation reaction is subtracted from the potential for the reduction reaction. Stress that the negative sign is important. It is an indication that this reaction will not occur spontaneously.

21·9 Electrolytic Cells

Emphasize that an electrolytic cell is the reverse of a voltaic cell. In an electrolytic cell electrical energy is used to produce a chemical change. Electrolysis and electroplating are examples of useful chemical changes produced by electric currents.

Stress that the reactions in electrolytic cells have negative potentials and so are not spontaneous. They are *forced* to occur by an outside electric potential.

Do **Demonstration 21·6** *Electrolysis of Water*, if you have not yet done it. As you do, discuss the half-reactions which are occurring at each electrode. **Demonstration 21·7** *Migration of Ions* proves that the ions move.

Experiment 47 *Electrochemistry* is a fitting conclusion to this chapter. It provides experience with and review of both voltaic cells and electrolytic cells.

Demonstrations

21·1 An Electrochemical Reaction of Silver

Concept: Copper reduces silver ions.

Materials: 200 mL of 0.1*M* silver nitrate ($AgNO_3$), copper strip, 250-mL beaker, stirring rod, steel wool, metal-cutting scissors, copper wire, petri dish.

Procedure: 1. Place the silver nitrate in the beaker. 2. Polish the copper strip with steel wool to form a fresh reacting surface. 3. Place a stirring rod across the top of a beaker. Suspend the copper strip from the rod so that it hangs into the solution. 4. The metal surface darkens and then appears "fuzzy" as silver metal is deposited. 5. If the metal is left undisturbed, a layer of silver about 1 cm thick forms. 6. The solution turns blue, indicating the formation of copper(II) ion. 7. This reaction can also be done on an overhead projector. Place a piece of clean copper wire across the bottom of a petri dish. 8. Fill the dish with silver nitrate solution. 9. Blades of silver will form rapidly on the copper wire. 10. Point out that this is an electochemical reaction involving a transfer of electrons from copper atoms to silver ions. The copper is oxidized and the silver ions are reduced. The net reaction is as follows.

$$2Ag^+(aq) + Cu(s) \rightarrow 2Ag(s) + Cu^{2+}(aq)$$

Caution: *Silver nitrate is a suspected mutagen.*

21·2 Electrochemical Cells

Concept: A cell is made of two half-cells.

Materials: 1 cm × 5 cm strips of copper, zinc, iron, lead, aluminum, and tin, 150 mL each of 1*M* solutions of the nitrates (—NO_3^-) of the 6 metals, 500 mL of saturated

potassium nitrate (KNO_3), six 250-mL beakers, steel wool, 6 U-tubes, 12 cotton balls, 3 voltmeters, 6 wires with clips at both ends.

Procedure: 1. Polish the metal strips with the steel wool. 2. Set-up six half-cells, each consisting of a metal electrode and its nitrate solution in a 250-mL beaker. 3. Construct salt bridges from the U-tubes by filling each tube with a saturated solution of potassium nitrate and then stoppering both ends with cotton plugs. 4. Arrange the half cells in pairs: copper/lead, copper/zinc, and zinc/lead. 5. Invert the U-tubes and lower into the two beakers of each pair. 6. Connect a voltmeter to the metal electrodes of each pair of half-cells. 7. Note the voltage produced by each pair. 8. Remove the salt bridge from one pair of half-cells. The voltage of that cell drops to zero. Explain that the salt bridge prevents the accumulation of any net charge on either side by allowing ions to diffuse in both directions. 9. Use the copper/zinc pair to illustrate the principles of the voltaic cell:
  a. Zinc is the anode and copper is the cathode.
  b. Electrons flow through the external circuit from the anode to the cathode.
  c. Positive ions migrate in the salt bridge from the zinc cell to the copper cell. Negative ions move in the opposite direction.
  d. Zinc is the reducing agent. Cu^{2+} ion is the oxidizing agent.
  e. The oxidation half-reaction is:
$$Zn(s) \rightarrow Zn^{2+}(aq) + 2e^-$$
  f. The reduction half-reaction is:
$$Cu^{2+}(aq) + 2e^- \rightarrow Cu(s)$$
  g. The overall reaction is:
$$Zn(s) + Cu^{2+}(aq) \rightarrow Zn^{2+}(aq) + Cu(s)$$
  h. Eventually, the zinc dissolves completely and copper is deposited on the copper electrode.
10. After this example, have the students explain the copper/lead and zinc/lead reactions. **Caution:** *Copper nitrate is an irritant.*

21·3 Fruit and Vegetable Batteries

Concept: Voltaic cells require two metals and a solution to react with the metals and transfer electrons.

Materials: 1 cm × 3 cm strips of zinc, copper, aluminum, iron, tin, and lead, voltmeter, 2 connecting wires with clips at both ends, grapefruit, orange, lemon, potato or other firm vegetables, knife.

Procedure: 1. Cut the grapefruit in half. 2. Insert the zinc and copper strips into the same section of the grapefruit. 3. Connect the strips to the voltmeter with the wires. 4. Record the potential on the blackboard. 5. Insert the metal strips into different sections and test the potential. 6. Try other fruits or vegetables with the same metal strips. 7. Repeat using other metal strips. 8. The potentials

do not equal standard potentials because we are not using standard $1M$ solutions. The half-reactions are the same, however. Using the tables, the students can predict which of the electrodes in any pair is negative.

21·4 The Dry Cell

Concept: Dry cells have a paste electrolyte.

Materials: an ignition battery (zinc–carbon dry cell), hacksaw, 20 mL of manganese dioxide (MnO_2), 50 mL of saturated ammonium chloride (NH_4Cl), 2 cm × 5 cm zinc strip, carbon rod*, 100-mL beaker, voltmeter. (*A carbon rod can be made by carefully stripping the wood from a pencil. This will work well as an electrode.)

Procedure: 1. Before class, saw the battery from the top down to the right of the central carbon electrode. 2. Show that the battery consists of three parts: the central carbon electrode, the zinc container which serves as the other electrode, and the manganese dioxide/ammonium chloride paste. 3. Point out that the dry cell is not really dry. The paste is moist enough to react. 4. A dry cell can be constructed by placing a zinc electrode and a carbon electrode into a manganese dioxide/ammonium chloride paste. 5. Add saturated ammonium chloride solution to powdered manganese dioxide until thick. 6. Clean the zinc strip with the steel wool. 7. Insert the carbon electrode. 8. Connect the dry cell to a voltmeter to demonstrate that it works. 9. The half-reactions are:
$$Zn(s) \rightarrow Zn^{2+}(aq) + 2e^-$$
$$2MnO_2(s) + 2NH_4^+(aq) + 2e^- \rightarrow$$
$$Mn_2O_3(s) + 2NH_3(aq) + H_2O(l)$$

21·5 The Lead Cell

Concept: A reversible reaction takes place in a lead cell.

Materials: two 2 cm × 10 cm lead strips, 200 mL of $6M$ sulfuric acid (H_2SO_4), 250-mL beaker, wooden rod, 6 V DC power supply, two wires with clips, electric doorbell, safety goggles.

Procedure: 1. Attach the lead strips to the wooden rod so that they hang vertically in the beaker 4 cm apart. 2. Pour sufficient sulfuric acid into the beaker to cover 2/3 of each strip. 3. Connect the power supply to the strips and charge for a few minutes. 4. The cell will operate the doorbell when attached. 5. Discuss the electrochemical reactions taking place. **Caution:** *Sulfuric acid is corrosive.*

21·6 Electrolysis of Water

Concept: Water can decompose into its elements.

Materials. 500 mL of $1M$ sulfuric acid (H_2SO_4), Hoffman apparatus (or two test tubes, iron nails, 500 mL of $6M$ sodium hydroxide (NaOH), and wire), 6 V power supply, safety goggles.

Procedure: 1. Use a Hoffman apparatus or construct a substitute. Use iron nails as the electrodes, sodium hydroxide as the electrolyte, and two test tubes to collect the hydrogen (at the negative electrode) and oxygen (at the positive electrode). 2. Fill the test tubes with sodium hydroxide solution. 3. Invert them in a beaker that is one-third filled with sodium hydroxide solution. 4. Insert the iron electrodes into the lower end of the test tubes. The wire leads connected to the nails should be insulated where they come in contact with the electrolyte. 5. Connect to the power supply. Oxygen and hydrogen bubble off as in the Hoffman apparatus. **Caution:** *Sulfuric acid and sodium hydroxide are corrosive.*

21·7 Migration of Ions

Concept: In the presence of an electric field, ions migrate through a solution.

Materials: 100 mL of 5% agar with $0.1M$ copper sulfate ($CuSO_4$), 100 mL of $0.1M$ potassium nitrate (KNO_3), 100 mL of $0.1M$ barium chloride ($BaCl_2$), U-tube, charcoal powder, two electrodes with connecting wires, 110 volt DC power source, safety goggles.

Procedure: 1. Half fill the U-tube with warm agar/copper sulfate. 2. Sprinkle charcoal on both surfaces of liquid. Allow to cool and set. 3. Add potassium nitrate to fill the tube on both sides. 4. Insert the electrodes and pass current through for 30 minutes. 5. The blue copper ions have visibly migrated. 6. The sulfate ions can be detected by adding barium chloride to the other side to form a white precipitate. **Caution:** *Copper sulfate is an irritant.*

Audiovisual Resources

Classification of Electrodes, the Hydrogen Electrode and Standard Potentials (FS) Prentice-Hall Media, 1975. (Use with Sections 21·6, 21·7, and 21·8.) Presents a discussion of metal–metal ion, redox, and reference electrodes and illustrates the calculation of electrode potentials using the Nernst equation.

Electrical Units, Definitions, and Faraday's Laws of Electrolysis (FS) Prentice-Hall Media, 1976. (Use with Sections 21·1 or 21·9.) Compares electroiytic conduction with electronic conduction, explains electrolysis, and illustrates Faraday's laws of electrolysis.

Electrochemical Cells (F, V) Chem Study, 1963, 22 min. (Use with Sections 21·1 and 21·2.) Describes electron flow and ion migration, explains the role of equilibrium at the electrodes and shows the effect of changing concentrations in an electrochemical cell.

Beyond the Text

Batteries

Both single cells and groups of cells are commonly called batteries. They range from the tiny cells that power hearing aids and wristwatches to submarine batteries in which each cell weighs more than a ton. All of these batteries convert chemical energy into electricity in a convenient package.

Batteries that cannot be recharged are called primary batteries. The most common primary battery is the zinc/manganese dioxide battery discussed in Section 21·3. This battery runs down even when it is not in use. The zinc electrode may corrode, and the liquid electrolyte may leak or evaporate. A newer battery is the lithium/thionyl chloride cell. This battery has a longer shelf-life, and a higher voltage. If your wristwatch battery was advertised to last three years, it is probably a lithium battery.

Secondary batteries can be recharged. The lead/lead oxide/sulfuric acid battery used in automobiles is a secondary battery. The nickel/cadmium alkaline battery is also rechargable. It is a variation of the nickel/iron battery invented by Thomas Edison at the start of the 20th century. The nickel/cadmium battery is used in portable electronic devices like calculators and personal tape recorders. The reaction in this battery is:

$$2NiO(OH) \cdot H_2O + Cd \rightarrow 2Ni(OH)_2 + Cd(OH)_2$$

The nickel compound in this battery is not a stoichiometric compound, that is, its formula is not exact. The oxidation number of nickel is changing from +3 to +2; nickel is being reduced in the reaction. The oxidation number of cadmium is changing from 0 to +2; cadmium is being oxidized. This battery produces 1.3 volts and can be completely sealed. It can produce a large current, and can be charged very quickly.

Another secondary battery is the silver oxide/zinc battery, developed in the 1940s. The reaction is:

$$Ag_2O + Zn + H_2O \rightarrow 2Ag + Zn(OH)_2$$

This battery is lighter and produces more power than the nickel/cadmium battery. Because of the high cost of silver, this battery is mainly used for special military applications.

Answers to End of Chapter Questions and Problems

Practice Questions and Problems

5. The copper does not become iron-plated.

6. The conversion of chemical energy into electrical energy or vice-versa.

7. a. Cu **b.** Ca **c.** Mg **d.** Sn **e.** Zn **f.** Al

8. The oxidation or reduction in a redox reaction.
Oxidation: $Al(s) \rightarrow Al^{3+}(aq) + 3e^-$
Reduction: $Cu^{2+}(aq) + 2e^- \rightarrow Cu(s)$

9. $Mg(s) + Cu^{2+}(aq) \rightarrow Mg^{2+}(aq) + Cu(s)$

10. A metal rod or strip immersed in a solution of its ions in which oxidation or reduction occurs.

11. A voltaic cell has two half-cells connected by a porous partition or a salt bridge.

12. The salt bridge allows ions to pass from one half-cell to the other but prevents the solutions from mixing.

13. The anode.

14. Negative.

15. a. zinc **b.** carbon (graphite)

16. Water is produced by the redox reaction and sulfuric acid is used up.

17. Lead sulfate produced during discharge falls off the lead plates.

18. The anode is spongy lead. The cathode is lead(IV) oxide. The electrolyte is sulfuric acid.

19. A voltaic cell with a continuous supply of fuel to oxidize for electrical energy.

20. Needs no recharging, does not produce toxic wastes if the fuel is hydrogen gas, lighter.

21. The standard cell potential (E° cell) is the cell potential under standard state conditions. The standard reduction potential (E° red) is the reduction potential of the half-cell under standard conditions.

22. A reference potential measures half-cell potentials; it can be used for both oxidation and reduction.

23. The cell potential is the sum of the reduction potential of the half-cell where reduction occurs, and the negative of the reduction potential of the half-cell where oxidation occurs.

24. The cell potential can be measured under any conditions; the standard cell potential is measured under standard conditions.

25. The ability of a voltaic cell to produce a current.

26. The cathode.

27. The cadmium half-cell has a tendency to oxidize.

28. The aluminum half-cell is connected to a standard hydrogen half-cell and a voltmeter is used. The aluminum half-cell has the indicated voltage.

29. a. $E^{\circ}_{cell} = E^{\circ}_{red} - E^{\circ}_{oxid}$
$$= 1.36\ V - (-0.25\ V) = 1.61\ V$$
b. $E^{\circ}_{cell} = 0.80\ V - (-0.14\ V) = 0.94\ V$
c. $E^{\circ}_{cell} = 1.07\ V - (-0.76\ V) = 1.83\ V$

30. Oxidation at the anode; reduction at the cathode.

31. A direct current flows in one direction only.

32. The teaspoon is the cathode in an electrolytic cell with silver cyanide as the electrolyte. When the DC current flows, the silver ions deposit on the teaspoon.

33. The cathode.

Mastery Questions and Problems

34. Voltaic cells convert chemical energy into electrical energy. Electrolytic cells use electrical energy to cause a chemical reaction.

35. Two half-cells are needed. One gains electrons and one loses them, producing an electric current.

36. The anode and cathode grids are both packed with $PbSO_4$. The electrolyte is very dilute sulfuric acid.

37. Some of the iron dissolves and the nail becomes coated with copper.
$$Fe(s) + CuSO_4 \rightarrow FeSO_4 + Cu(s)$$
Oxidation: $Fe \rightarrow Fe^{2+} + 2e^-$
Reduction: $Cu^{2+} + 2e^- \rightarrow Cu$

38. a. $Sn(s) + Pb^{2+}(aq) \rightarrow Sn^{2+}(aq) + Pb(s)$
$E^{\circ}_{cell} = +0.01\ V$
b. $H_2(g) + Br_2(l) \rightarrow 2H^+(aq) + 2Br^-(aq)$
$E^{\circ}_{cell} = +1.07\ V$
c. $Cl_2(g) + 2I^-(aq) \rightarrow 2Cl^-(aq) + I_2(s)$
$E^{\circ}_{cell} = +0.82\ V$

39. Lead(II) sulfate and lead dioxide are very insoluble in sulfuric acid.

Review Questions and Problems

40. a. $3H_2S + 2HNO_3 \rightarrow 3S + 2NO + 4H_2O$
b. $2AgNO_3 + Pb \rightarrow Pb(NO_3)_2 + 2Ag$
c. $3Cl_2 + 6NaOH \rightarrow 5NaCl + NaClO_3 + 3H_2O$
d. $3CuO + 2NH_3 \rightarrow N_2 + 3Cu + 3H_2O$
e. $Mg(OH)_2 + 2HBr \rightarrow MgBr_2 + 2H_2O$
f. $Al_2O_3 + 3H_2SO_4 \rightarrow Al_2(SO_4)_3 + 3H_2O$

41. Dilute 31 mL of $16M$ acid to 500 mL total volume.

42. a. $+4$ **b.** $+6$ **c.** $+7$ **d.** $+5$ **e.** $+3$ **f.** $+7$
g. $+5$ **h.** $+3$

43. 550 mL O_2

44. 0.82 g/cm³

Challenging Questions and Problems

45. a. $2AgCl + Ni \rightarrow 2Ag + NiCl_2$
$E^{\circ}_{cell} = +0.47\ V$
b. $3Cl_2 + 2Al \rightarrow 2AlCl_3$
$E^{\circ}_{cell} = +3.02\ V$

46.

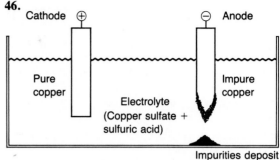

Oxidation: $2Cu + 2H_2SO_4 \rightarrow 2Cu^{2+} + 2H_2 + SO_4^{2-}$
Reduction: $2Cu^{2+} + 2SO_4^{2-} + 2H_2O \rightarrow$
$$2Cu + 2H_2SO_4 + O_2$$
$2Cu(impure) + 2Cu^{2+} + 2SO_4^{2-} + 2H_2SO_4 + 2H_2O \rightarrow$
$2Cu(pure) + 2Cu^{2+} + 2SO_4^{2-} + 2H_2SO_4 + 2H_2 + O_2$

47. Anode: $Pb(s) \rightarrow Pb^{2+}(aq) + 2e^-$
Cathode: $Cu^{2+}(aq) + 2e^- \rightarrow Cu(s)$
$Pb(s) + Cu^{2+}(aq) \rightarrow Pb^{2+}(aq) + Cu(s)$
Electrons leave the anode and travel in the external circuit to the cathode where they are picked up by copper ions to form copper metal.

48. a.

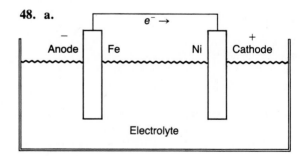

b. Anode: $Fe(s) \rightarrow Fe^{2+}(aq) + 2e^-$
Cathode: $Ni^{2+}(aq) + 2e^- \rightarrow Ni(s)$
c. The anode is the iron electrolyte and the cathode is the nickel electrolyte.   **d.** The anode is negative, and the cathode is positive.   **e.** Electrons flow from the anode through the wire in the external circuit to the cathode.   **f.** $E^{\circ}_{cell} = +0.19\ V$

21

Electrochemistry

Chapter Preview

Sections 21·6, 21·7, and 21·8 are appropriate for honors students.

Electrochemistry has many applications in the home as well as in industry. Flashlight and automobile batteries are familiar examples. Others are the manufacture of sodium and aluminum metals and the silver plating of tableware. Biological systems also use electrochemistry to carry out nerve-impulse conduction. This chapter starts with a discussion of the relationship between redox reactions and electrochemistry.

21·1 Electrochemical Processes

The conversion of chemical energy into electrical energy and the conversion of electrical energy into chemical energy are **electrochemical processes.** All electrochemical processes involve redox reactions. The conversion of chemical energy into electrical energy will be discussed first.

Redox reactions allow chemical energy to be converted into electrical energy and electrical energy into chemical energy.

When a strip of zinc metal is dipped into a aqueous solution of copper sulfate, the zinc becomes copper-plated (Figure 21·2). The net ionic equation involves only zinc and copper.

$$Zn(s) + Cu^{2+}(aq) \longrightarrow Zn^{2+}(aq) + Cu(s)$$

In electrochemical reactions metal atoms are oxidized by ions of other metals.

Electrons are transferred from zinc atoms to copper ions. This is a *redox reaction* and it occurs *spontaneously*. As the reaction proceeds, zinc atoms lose electrons as they are oxidized to zinc ions. The zinc metal slowly dissolves. At the same time, copper ions in solution gain electrons. They are reduced to copper atoms and deposit as metallic copper. As the copper ions are gradually replaced by zinc ions, the blue color of the solution fades. Balanced half-reactions for this redox reaction can be written as follows.

Figure 21·1
Electroplating utilizes electrochemical processes to protect and beautify metal surfaces.

a

b

Figure 21·2
a A spontaneous redox reaction occurs when a zinc strip is immersed in a solution of copper(II) sulfate. **b** If the zinc remains in solution for a long time, the blue color of the solution fades and the zinc strip is badly corroded. What substance is oxidized? What is reduced?
Zinc metal is oxidized; copper ions are reduced.

Oxidation: $Zn(s) \longrightarrow Zn^{2+}(aq) + 2e^-$

Reduction: $Cu^{2+}(aq) + 2e^- \longrightarrow Cu(s)$

If you look at the activity series of metals (Table 21·1), you will see that zinc is above copper. This table is very useful in electrochemistry. For any two metals in the table, the metal that is the higher of the two is the most readily oxidized. As Figure 21·2 shows, when zinc is dipped in a copper sulfate solution the zinc becomes copper-plated. By contrast, when a copper rod is dipped into a solution of zinc sulfate, the copper does not become zinc-plated. This is because copper metal is not oxidized by zinc ions. Zinc is above copper in the activity series. Zinc plating on copper is a nonspontaneous process.

An electric current is a flow of electrons. When a zinc rod is dipped into a copper sulfate solution, electrons are transferred from zinc metal to copper ions. If a redox reaction is to be used as a source of electrical energy, however, the two half-reactions must be physically separated. That is, the electrons released by zinc must pass through an external circuit to reach the copper ions. Electrical energy is produced in an electrochemical cell. Alternatively, an electric current can also be used to produce a chemical change. *An* **electrochemical cell** *is any device that converts chemical energy into electrical energy or electrical energy into chemical energy.* Redox reactions occur in electrochemical cells.

Table 21·1	Activity Series of Metals, with Half-Reactions for Oxidation Processes	
	Element	Oxidation half-reactions
Most active and most easily oxidized	Lithium	$Li(s) \longrightarrow Li^+(aq) + e^-$
	Potassium	$K(s) \longrightarrow K^+(aq) + e^-$
	Barium	$Ba(s) \longrightarrow Ba^{2+}(aq) + 2e^-$
	Calcium	$Ca(s) \longrightarrow Ca^{2+}(aq) + 2e^-$
	Sodium	$Na(s) \longrightarrow Na^+(aq) + e^-$
	Magnesium	$Mg(s) \longrightarrow Mg^{2+}(aq) + 2e^-$
	Aluminum	$Al(s) \longrightarrow Al^{3+}(aq) + 3e^-$
	Zinc	$Zn(s) \longrightarrow Zn^{2+}(aq) + 2e^-$
	Iron	$Fe(s) \longrightarrow Fe^{2+}(aq) + 2e^-$
	Nickel	$Ni(s) \longrightarrow Ni^{2+}(aq) + 2e^-$
	Tin	$Sn(s) \longrightarrow Sn^{2+}(aq) + 2e^-$
	Lead	$Pb(s) \longrightarrow Pb^{2+}(aq) + 2e^-$
	Hydrogen*	$H_2(g) \longrightarrow 2H^+(aq) + 2e^-$
	Copper	$Cu(s) \longrightarrow Cu^{2+}(aq) + 2e^-$
	Mercury	$Hg(s) \longrightarrow Hg^{2+}(aq) + 2e^-$
Least active and least easily oxidized	Silver	$Ag(s) \longrightarrow Ag^+(aq) + e^-$
	Gold	$Au(s) \longrightarrow Au^{3+}(aq) + 3e^-$

*Hydrogen is included for reference purposes.

21·A Michael Faraday

Unquenchable enthusiasm for reading and the habit of taking careful notes launched the career of one of the greatest chemists of all time. Michael Faraday (1791–1867) was the son of a poor English blacksmith. He had little formal education and was apprenticed to a bookbinder when he was 14. Faraday first learned about the phenomenon of electricity from an article in an encyclopedia that was brought to his employer for rebinding. His interest in science was born, and he pursued it against all odds. He joined a group of young men in London who attended lectures on science. He persuaded one of this group to help him improve his writing to make up for his lack of schooling. He read everything he could find on electricity and science. Furthermore, he wrote complete notes on every book he read and every lecture he heard.

Eventually Faraday won a job at the prestigious Royal Institution by sending in the notes he had taken at one of the director's lectures. The job was menial, but Faraday advanced quickly for he soon became known for his careful laboratory work. He went on to become the principal lecturer at the Institution. In this role he did much to popularize science among the English upper class.

Faraday began working in analytical chemistry. He discovered benzene in 1825 and was the first person to produce compounds of carbon and chlorine in the laboratory. He is most famous for his work with electricity. Faraday gave the world electricity when he discovered that an electric current was induced in a coil of wire rotating in a magnetic field. He went on to prove that electricity generated in this way is identical to electricity produced by an electrochemical

Figure 21·3
Faraday began his work at the Royal Institution under Sir Humphrey Davy. In 1807 and 1808 Davy was the first to isolate several alkali metals. This was accomplished with a "trough battery." Troughs of baked wood held partitions of copper and zinc plates, soldered in pairs, with ammonium chloride solution filling the compartments between the plates.

cell. He performed many experiments measuring the changes that take place in such cells. His work established these laws of electrochemistry.

1. The amount of material decomposed or synthesized in an electrochemical cell is proportional to the amount of electricity that passes through the cell.

2. The amounts of substances deposited and dissolved in such a cell are proportional to their molecular masses.

Other scientists realized that these results showed that electricity must be made of particles. The amount of charge carried by one mole of electrons is called a faraday in honor of this great chemist.

21·2 Voltaic Cells

■ Voltaic cells produce electrical energy from redox reactions.

The voltaic cell is also called a galvanic cell after Luigi Galvani (1737–1798), an Italian anatomist who discovered that the contraction of muscles is caused by electrochemical processes.

The passage of ions through the salt bridge is necessary to maintain electrical neutrality between the half-cells.

Figure 21·4
A voltaic cell can be constructed without a salt bridge. It will not function long, however, because one electrode will become plated.

The first electrochemical cell was invented by the Italian physicist Alessandro Volta (1745–1827). He designed a cell that can be used to generate a direct electric current (DC current). **Voltaic cells** *are electrochemical cells that are used to convert chemical energy into electrical energy.* The energy is produced by *spontaneous* redox reactions.

A **half-cell** *is one part of a voltaic cell in which either oxidation or reduction occurs.* A half-cell consists of a metal rod or strip immersed in a solution of its ions. In a typical voltaic cell, one half-cell is a zinc rod immersed in a solution of zinc sulfate. The other half-cell is a copper rod immersed in a solution of copper sulfate. The two half-cells are separated by a porous partition. *A* **salt bridge,** *which is a tube containing a conducting solution,* may also be used. These dividers allow the passage of ions from one compartment to the other but prevent the solutions from mixing completely. A wire carries the electrons in the external circuit from zinc to copper. A voltmeter or light bulb can be connected in the circuit. The driving force of such a voltaic cell is the spontaneous redox reaction between zinc metal and copper(II) ions in solution.

The zinc and copper rods in a voltaic cell are the electrodes. *An* **electrode** *is a conductor in a circuit that carries electrons to or from a substance other than a metal.* The type of electrode reaction determines whether an electrode is labeled as a cathode or an anode. Note that the name of the electrode is *not* determined by its charge. *The electrode at which oxidation occurs is the* **anode.** Electrons are produced here. Thus the anode is labeled the *negative* electrode. *The electrode at which reduction occurs is the* **cathode.** Electrons are consumed at the cathode. As a result, it is labeled the *positive* electrode. Neither electrode is really charged. All parts of the voltaic cell remain balanced in terms of charge at all times. The moving electrons balance any charge that might build up as oxidation and reduction occur.

The electrochemical process that occurs in a zinc–copper voltaic cell can best be described in a number of steps. These steps all occur at the same time.

Figure 21·5
In all electrochemical cells, oxidation occurs at the anode and reduction occurs at the cathode. In this voltaic cell which electrode is positive and which is negative?
The anode is negative and the cathode is positive.

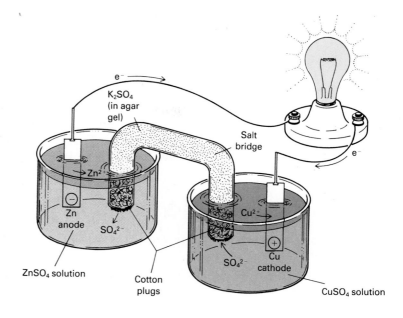

Safety

Even a low voltage source can have a dangerously high current if the resistance is very low. Treat all sources of electricity with care.

As far as the *external* circuit is concerned, the anode is producing electrons and is therefore negatively charged.

As far as the *external* circuit is concerned, the cathode is attracting electrons and therefore it is positively charged.

Oxidation and reduction reactions always accompany each other. An oxidation half-cell cannot function apart from a reduction half-cell.

1. Electrons are produced at the zinc rod according to the *oxidation* half-reaction.

$$Zn(s) \longrightarrow Zn^{2+}(aq) + 2e^-$$

Because it is oxidized, the zinc rod is the anode, or negative electrode.

2. The electrons leave the zinc anode and pass through the external circuit to the copper rod. (If a bulb is in the circuit, it will light. If a voltmeter is present, it will indicate a voltage.)

3. Electrons enter the copper rod and pass to copper ions in solution. There the following *reduction* half-reaction occurs.

$$Cu^{2+}(aq) + 2e^- \longrightarrow Cu(s)$$

4. At the copper rod, copper ions are reduced. The copper rod is the cathode, or positive electrode. To complete the circuit, ions (both positive and negative) move through the aqueous solutions via the salt bridge. The two half-reactions can be summed to get the overall cell reaction. The electrons must cancel.

$$Zn(s) + Cu^{2+}(aq) \longrightarrow Zn^{2+}(aq) + Cu(s)$$

Chemists use a shorthand method to represent an electrochemical cell. The zinc–copper voltaic cell can be written as follows.

$$Zn(s) \mid ZnSO_4(aq) \parallel CuSO_4(aq) \mid Cu(s)$$

The half-cell which undergoes oxidation (the anode) is written first at the left. The double vertical lines represent the salt bridge or porous partition that separates the anode compartment from the cathode compartment. The single vertical lines indicate boundaries of phases that are in contact. For example, the zinc rod, $Zn(s)$, and the zinc sulfate solution, $ZnSO_4(aq)$, are separate phases in physical contact. When the solutions in the voltaic cells are both $1.0M$, the cell generates an electrical

potential of 1.10 volts (1.10 V). If different metals are used for the electrodes in the cell, the voltage will change. Different solution concentrations will also affect the voltage.

The zinc–copper voltaic cell is of great historical importance, but it is no longer used commercially. Nevertheless, this cell is a convenient model to use when describing the production of electrical energy from a chemical change. Today, the more practical and compact "dry" cell is usually chosen when a portable electrical energy source is required.

The purpose of a voltaic cell is to *produce* electrical energy on demand. Electrical energy cannot be stored.

21·3   Dry Cells

■ The *dry* cell is a voltaic cell that is filled with a *moist* paste.

A voltaic cell in which the electrolyte is a paste is known as a **dry cell.** The most commonly used dry cell is usually referred to as a flashlight battery. A zinc container is filled with a thick moist paste of manganese(IV) oxide (MnO_2), zinc chloride ($ZnCl_2$), ammonium chloride (NH_4Cl), and water. A graphite rod is embedded in the paste (Figure 21·6). The zinc container is the anode and the graphite rod is the cathode. The thick paste prevents the contents of the cell from freely mixing so that a salt bridge is not needed. The half-reactions for this cell are as follows.

Oxidation: $Zn(s) \longrightarrow Zn^{2+}(aq) + 2e^-$ (anode reaction)

Reduction: $2MnO_2(s) + 2NH_4^+(aq) + 2e^- \longrightarrow$
$$Mn_2O_3(s) + 2NH_3(aq) + H_2O(l) \text{ (cathode reaction)}$$

In this cell the graphite rod serves only as a conductor and does not undergo reduction, even though it is the cathode. The manganese in MnO_2 is the species that is reduced. The electrical potential of this cell usually begins at 1.5 V but falls steadily during use to about 0.8 V. Dry cells of this construction are not rechargeable. A voltaic cell that is rechargeable is the lead storage battery.

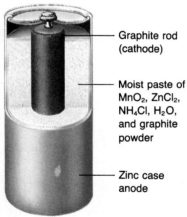

Positive (+) terminal

Graphite rod (cathode)

Moist paste of MnO_2, $ZnCl_2$, NH_4Cl, H_2O, and graphite powder

Zinc case anode

Negative (−) terminal (bottom of case)

Figure 21·6
A flashlight battery is a single electrochemical cell. It produces about 1.5 V. What is oxidized in this cell and what is reduced?
Zinc is oxidized. Manganese dioxide is reduced.

21·4   Lead Storage Batteries

A **battery** *is a group of cells that are connected together.* Lead storage batteries are used in automobiles. A 12-V storage battery consists of six voltaic cells connected together (Figure 21·7). Each cell, which produces about 2 V, contains two lead electrodes or grids. One of the grids, the anode, is packed with spongy lead. The other grid, the cathode, is packed with lead(IV) oxide, PbO_2. The grids are immersed in dilute sulfuric acid and are separated by a perforated plate. The half-reactions are as follows.

Oxidation: $Pb + SO_4^{2-} \longrightarrow PbSO_4 + 2e^-$

Reduction: $PbO_2 + 4H^+ + SO_4^{2-} + 2e^- \longrightarrow PbSO_4 + 2H_2O$

■ A 12-volt lead storage battery is composed of six voltaic cells connected in series.

When a lead storage battery discharges, it produces the electric power to start the car. The overall spontaneous redox reaction is the sum of the oxidation and reduction half-reactions.

Figure 21·7
A 12 V lead storage battery consists of six 2-V cells in series. The cells do not need to be in separate compartments, but this improves performance. While the battery is producing a current, lead at the anode and lead(IV) oxide at the cathode are both converted to lead sulfate. This decreases the sulfuric acid concentration in the battery. Recharging the battery reverses these reactions. This occurs whenever the engine in a car is running.

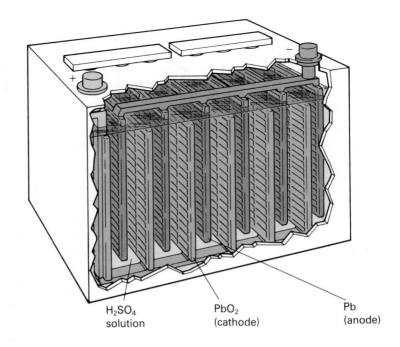

H_2SO_4
solution

PbO_2
(cathode)

Pb
(anode)

Safety

The sulfuric acid in a lead storage battery is about $5M$ and is very corrosive. Handle with care.

The newer lead storage batteries are sealed. The specific gravity of the electrolyte cannot be measured in these batteries.

The purpose of a lead storage battery is to *convert* chemical potential energy to electrical energy. Its advantage is that it can be recharged: electrical energy can be used to restore a supply of chemical potential energy.

■ A voltaic cell in which a fuel is oxidized is known as a fuel cell.

$$Pb(s) + PbO_2(s) + 2H_2SO_4(aq) \longrightarrow 2PbSO_4(s) + 2H_2O(l)$$

This reaction shows that during discharge, lead sulfate slowly builds up on the plates, and the concentration of sulfuric acid decreases. The condition of a lead storage battery can be checked by measuring the specific gravity of the electrolyte, sulfuric acid. If it is much below 1.25, the battery should be recharged.

When a storage battery is recharged, the reverse reaction occurs.

$$2PbSO_4(s) + 2H_2O(l) \longrightarrow Pb(s) + PbO_2(s) + 2H_2SO_4(aq)$$

This reaction is *nonspontaneous*. To make it go, a direct current must be passed through the cell in the reverse direction. In theory, a lead storage battery can be recharged indefinitely, but in practice its life span is limited. This is because small amounts of lead sulfate continually fall from the electrodes and collect on the bottom of the cell. Eventually the electrodes lose so much lead sulfate that the recharging process is ineffective or the cell is shorted out. To help overcome this problem, fuel cells with renewable electrodes have been developed in recent years.

21·5　Fuel Cells

Fuel Cells *are voltaic cells in which a fuel substance undergoes oxidation and from which electrical energy is obtained continuously.* Fuel cells do not have to be recharged. They can be designed to emit no air pollutants and to operate more quietly and more cheaply than a conventional electrical generator.

Perhaps the simplest fuel cell to visualize is the hydrogen–oxygen fuel cell. In this cell three compartments are separated from one another by two electrodes made of porous carbon (Figure 21·8). Oxygen (the oxidizer) is fed into the cathode compartment. Hydrogen (the fuel) is fed

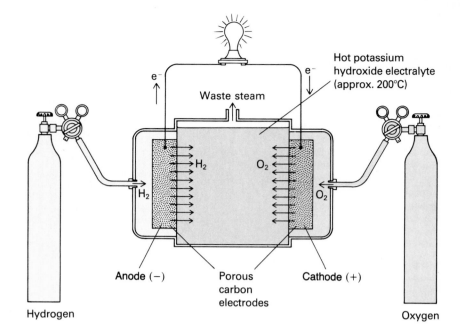

Figure 21·8
The hydrogen–oxygen fuel cell is a clean source of power. What "waste" products are produced?
Pure water (steam).

into the anode compartment. The gases diffuse slowly through the electrodes. The electrolyte in the central compartment is a hot concentrated solution of potassium hydroxide. Electrons from the oxidation reaction at the anode pass through an external circuit to enter the reduction reaction at the cathode.

Oxidation: $2H_2(g) + 4OH^-(aq) \longrightarrow 4H_2O(l) + 4e^-$ (anode)

Reduction: $O_2(g) + 2H_2O(l) + 4e^- \longrightarrow 4OH^-(aq)$ (cathode)

The equation for the overall reaction is the oxidation of hydrogen to form water.

$$2H_2(g) + O_2(g) \longrightarrow 2H_2O(l)$$

Other fuels, such as methane, CH_4, and ammonia, NH_3, can be used in place of hydrogen. Other oxidizers, such as chlorine, Cl_2, and ozone, O_3, can be used in place of oxygen. Fuel cells are currently being built as auxiliary power sources for submarines and other military vehicles. At present, however, they are too expensive for general use. Hydrogen–oxygen fuel cells, weighing approximately 100 kg each, were used in the Apollo spacecraft missions. Instead of producing toxic wastes like an internal combustion engine, these cells produce drinkable water.

Appropriate for honors students.

21·6   Half-Cells

*The **electrical potential** of a voltaic cell is the ability of the cell to produce an electric current.* Electrical potential is usually measured in volts (V). The potential of an isolated half-cell cannot be measured. For example, we cannot measure the electrical potential of a zinc half-cell or of a copper half-cell separately. When these two half-cells are connected to form a voltaic cell, however, the difference in potential can be measured. The electrical potential of a $1.0M$ zinc–copper cell is $+1.10$ V.

The electrical potential of a cell results from a competition between the two half-cells for electrons. The half-cell with the greater tendency to acquire electrons will do so and will undergo reduction. The other half-cell loses electrons and is oxidized. The half-cell in which reduction occurs has a greater reduction potential than the half-cell in which oxidation occurs. *The **reduction potential** of a half-cell is a measure of the tendency of a given half-reaction to occur as a reduction. The difference between the reduction potentials of the two half-cells is called the* **cell potential.**

$$\text{Cell potential} = \left(\begin{array}{c} \text{reduction potential} \\ \text{of half-cell in which} \\ \text{reduction occurs} \end{array} \right) - \left(\begin{array}{c} \text{reduction potential} \\ \text{of half-cell in which} \\ \text{oxidation occurs} \end{array} \right)$$

or $\quad E^0_{cell} = E^0_{red} - E^0_{oxid}$

The **standard cell potential** *(E^0_{cell}) is the measured cell potential when the ion concentrations in the half-cells are 1.00M, gases are at a pressure of 1 atm, and the temperature is 25°C.* The symbols E^0_{red} and E^0_{oxid} are the standard reduction potentials for the reduction and oxidation half-cells respectively. Because half-cell potentials cannot be measured, scientists have chosen an arbitrary reference electrode. *The* **standard hydrogen electrode** *is used with other electrodes so that the reduction potentials of those cells can be measured.* The standard reduction potential of the hydrogen electrode has been assigned a value of 0.00 V.

The standard hydrogen electrode (Figure 21·9) consists of a platinum electrode immersed in a solution with a hydrogen ion concentration of 1.00M. The solution is at 25°C. The platinum electrode is a small square of platinum foil coated with finely divided platinum (known as *platinum black*). Hydrogen gas, at a pressure of 1 atm, is bubbled around the platinum electrode. The half-cell reaction that occurs at the platinum black surface is as follows.

$$2H^+(aq, 1M) + 2e^- \rightleftharpoons H_2(g, 1 \text{ atm}) \quad E^0_{H^+} = 0.00 \text{ V.}$$

The symbol $E^0_{H^+}$ represents the standard reduction potential of H^+. The double arrows mean that the reaction is reversible. Whether this half-cell reaction occurs as a reduction or as an oxidation is determined by the reduction potential of the half-cell to which it is connected.

21·7 Standard Reduction Potentials

A voltaic cell can be constructed by connecting a standard hydrogen half-cell to a standard zinc half-cell (Figure 21·10). The first step in determining the overall reaction for this cell is to identify in which half-cell reduction takes place. Reduction takes place at the cathode and oxidation takes place at the anode in all electrochemical cells. A voltmeter gives a reading of +0.74 V when the zinc electrode is connected to the negative terminal and the hydrogen electrode is connected to the positive terminal. Thus, the zinc electrode must be the anode. Zinc is oxidized. The hydrogen electrode must be the cathode. Hydrogen ions are reduced. The half-reactions and cell reaction can now be written.

A half-cell with a greater tendency to acquire electrons (than another half-cell) has the greater reduction potential.

Standard reduction potentials are measured at 25°C when the concentrations are 1*M* and the pressure is 1 atm.

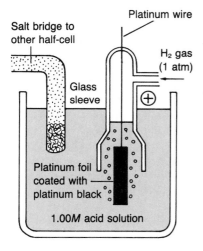

Figure 21·9
The standard hydrogen electrode is arbitrarily assigned a standard reduction potential of 0.00 V at 25°C.

Appropriate for honors students.

Safety

When running an electrochemical cell, always consider whether any of the products is a flammable or toxic gas.

Figure 21·10
This voltaic cell consists of zinc and
hydrogen half-cells. What is the
measured cell potential?
0.76 V

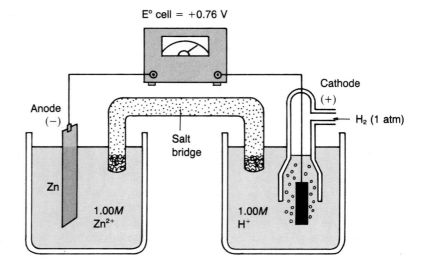

Oxidation: $Zn(s) \longrightarrow Zn^{2+}(aq) + 2e^-$

Reduction: $2H^+(aq) + 2e^- \longrightarrow H_2(g)$

Cell reaction: $Zn(s) + 2H^+(aq) \longrightarrow Zn^{2+}(aq) + H_2(g)$

The use of a standard hydrogen electrode allows us to calculate the standard reduction potential for the zinc half-cell.

$$E^0_{cell} = E^0_{red} - E^0_{oxid}$$

$$E^0_{cell} = E^0_{H^+} - E^0_{Zn^{2+}}$$

The cell potential was measured: $E^0_{cell} = +0.76$ V. The reduction potential of the hydrogen half-cell is a known standard: $E^0_{H^+} = 0.00$ V.

$$+0.76 \text{ V} = 0.00 \text{ V} - E^0_{Zn^{2+}}$$

$$E^0_{Zn^{2+}} = -0.76 \text{ V}$$

The standard reduction potential for the zinc half-cell is -0.76 V. The value is negative because the tendency for zinc ions to be reduced in this cell is less than that of hydrogen ions (H^+). Consequently, zinc metal is oxidized.

Many different half-cells can be paired with the hydrogen half-cell in a similar manner. The standard reduction potential for each half-cell can be obtained. With a standard copper half-cell, for example, the measured standard cell potential is $+0.34$ V. Copper is the cathode (the positive electrode) and Cu^{2+} is reduced to Cu when the cell operates. The hydrogen half-cell is the anode (the negative electrode) and H_2 is oxidized to H^+. The standard reduction potential for copper is calculated as follows.

$$E^0_{cell} = E^0_{red} - E^0_{oxid}$$

$$= E^0_{Cu^{2+}} - E^0_{H^+}$$

$$+0.34 \text{ V} = E^0_{Cu^{2+}} - 0.00$$

$$E^0_{Cu^{2+}} = +0.34 \text{ V}$$

The reduction potential of a half-cell can be calculated even though a half-cell cannot operate independently.

These calculations show that the standard reduction potential of copper is +0.34 V. The value is positive because the tendency for copper ions to be reduced in this cell is greater than that of hydrogen ions.

Table 21·2 lists some standard reduction potentials at 25°C. These are arranged in increasing order. The half-reactions at the top of the table have the least tendency to occur as reductions. The half-reactions at the bottom of the table have the greatest tendency to occur as reductions.

Appropriate for honors students.

21·8 Calculating Cell Potentials

In order to function, a cell must be constructed of two half-cells. The half-cell reaction having the *more positive* reduction potential occurs as a reduction in the cell. With this in mind it is possible to calculate cell potentials and write cell reactions for cells before they have been assembled. Standard reduction potentials for the various half-cells are used for this purpose.

Example 1

Calculate the standard cell potential of a cell composed of the half-cells Zn/Zn^{2+} and Cu/Cu^{2+}. Write the half-cell reactions for the anode and cathode processes and the cell reaction.

Solution

Table 21·2 gives the following standard reaction potentials.

$$Zn^{2+}(aq)\,2e^- \longrightarrow Zn(s) \qquad E^0_{Zn^{2+}} = -0.76 \text{ V}$$

$$Cu^{2+}(aq) + 2e^- \longrightarrow Cu(s) \qquad E^0_{Cu^{2+}} = +0.34 \text{ V}$$

Because Cu^{2+} has the more positive reduction potential, it occurs as a reduction in the cell. The zinc is oxidized.

When two half-cells are connected, the one with the larger reduction potential acquires electrons from the half-cell with the smaller reduction potential.

The standard cell potential is the reduction potential of the reduction half-cell minus the reduction potential of the oxidation half-cell.

$$E^0_{cell} = E^0_{red} - E^0_{oxid}$$

$$= E^0_{Cu^{2+}} - E^0_{Zn^{2+}}$$

$$= +0.34 \text{ V} - (-0.76 \text{ V})$$

$$= +1.10 \text{ V}$$

In this cell Zn is oxidized at the anode and Cu^{2+} is reduced at the cathode. The standard cell potential is 1.10 V. The half-reactions are as follows.

$$\text{Oxidation: } Zn(s) \longrightarrow Zn^{2+}(aq) + 2e^- \text{ (anode)}$$

$$\text{Reduction: } Cu^{2+}(aq) + 2e^- \longrightarrow Cu(s) \text{ (cathode)}$$

The cell reaction is the sum of the half-reactions.

$$Cu^{2+}(aq) + Zn(s) \longrightarrow Cu(s) + Zn^{2+}(aq)$$

Table 21·2   Reduction Potentials at 25° C

Electrode	Half-Reaction	E^0 (V)
Li^+/Li	$Li^+ + e^- \longrightarrow Li$	-3.05
K^+/K	$K^+ + e^- \longrightarrow K$	-2.93
Ba^{2+}/Ba	$Ba^{2+} + 2e^- \longrightarrow Ba$	-2.90
Ca^{2+}/Ca	$Ca^{2+} + 2e^- \longrightarrow Ca$	-2.87
Na^+/Na	$Na^+ + e^- \longrightarrow Na$	-2.71
Mg^{2+}/Mg	$Mg^{2+} + 2e^- \longrightarrow Mg$	-2.37
Al^{3+}/Al	$Al^{3+} + 3e^- \longrightarrow Al$	-1.66
H_2O/H_2	$2H_2O + 2e^- \longrightarrow H_2 + 2OH^-$	-0.83
Zn^{2+}/Zn	$Zn^{2+} + 2e^- \longrightarrow Zn$	-0.76
Cr^{3+}/Cr	$Cr^{3+} + 3e^- \longrightarrow Cr$	-0.74
Fe^{2+}/Fe	$Fe^{2+} + 2e^- \longrightarrow Fe$	-0.44
H_2O/H_2 (pH 7)	$2H_2O + 2e^- \longrightarrow H_2 + 2OH^-$	-0.42
Cd^{2+}/Cd	$Cd^{2+} + 2e^- \longrightarrow Cd$	-0.40
$PbSO_4/Pb$	$PbSO_4 + 2e^- \longrightarrow Pb + SO_4^{2-}$	-0.36
Co^{2+}/Co	$Co^{2+} + 2e^- \longrightarrow Co$	-0.28
Ni^{2+}/Ni	$Ni^{2+} + 2e^- \longrightarrow Ni$	-0.25
Sn^{2+}/Sn	$Sn^{2+} + 2e^- \longrightarrow Sn$	-0.14
Pb^{2+}/Pb	$Pb^{2+} + 2e^- \longrightarrow Pb$	-0.13
Fe^{3+}/Fe	$Fe^{3+} + 3e^- \longrightarrow Fe$	-0.036
H^+/H_2	$2H^+ + 2e^- \longrightarrow H_2$	0.000
$AgCl/Ag$	$AgCl + e^- \longrightarrow Ag + Cl^-$	$+0.22$
Hg_2Cl_2/Hg	$Hg_2Cl_2 + 2e^- \longrightarrow 2Hg + 2Cl^-$	$+0.27$
Cu^{2+}/Cu	$Cu^{2+} + 2e^- \longrightarrow Cu$	$+0.34$
O_2/OH^-	$O_2 + 2H_2O + 4e^- \longrightarrow 4OH^-$	$+0.40$
Cu^+/Cu	$Cu^+ + e^- \longrightarrow Cu$	$+0.52$
I_2/I^-	$I_2 + 2e^- \longrightarrow 2I^-$	$+0.54$
Fe^{3+}/Fe^{2+}	$Fe^{3+} + e^- \longrightarrow Fe^{2+}$	$+0.77$
Hg_2^{2+}/Hg	$Hg_2^{2+} + 2e^- \longrightarrow 2Hg$	$+0.79$
Ag^+/Ag	$Ag^+ + e^- \longrightarrow Ag$	$+0.80$
O_2/H_2O (pH 7)	$O_2 + 4H^+ + 4e^- \longrightarrow 2H_2O$	$E0.82$
Hg^{2+}/Hg	$Hg^{2+} + 2e^- \longrightarrow Hg$	$+0.85$
Br_2/Br^-	$Br_2 + 2e^- \longrightarrow 2Br^-$	$+1.07$
O_2/H_2O	$O_2 + 4H^+ + 4e^- \longrightarrow 2H_2O$	$+1.23$
MnO_2/Mn^{2+}	$MnO_2 + 4H^+ + 2e^- \longrightarrow Mn^{2+} + 2H_2O$	$+1.28$
$Cr_2O_7^{2-}/Cr^{3+}$	$Cr_2O_7^{2-} + 14H^+ + 6e^- \longrightarrow 2Cr^{3+} + 7H_2O$	$+1.33$
Cl_2/Cl^-	$Cl_2 + 2e^- \longrightarrow 2Cl^-$	$+1.36$
PbO_2/Pb^{2+}	$PbO_2 + 4H^+ + 2e^- \longrightarrow Pb^{2+} + 2H_2O$	$+1.46$
MnO_4^-/Mn^{2+}	$MnO_4^- + 8H^+ + 5e^- \longrightarrow Mn^{2+} + 4H_2O$	$+1.51$
$PbO_2/PbSO_4$	$PbO_2 + 4H^+ + SO_4^{2-} + 2e^- \longrightarrow PbSO_4 + 2H_2O$	$+1.69$
F_2/F^-	$F_2 + 2e^- \longrightarrow 2F^-$	$+2.87$

Example 2

What is the cell reaction and the standard cell potential for a voltaic cell composed of the following half-cells?

$$Fe^{3+}(aq) + e^- \longrightarrow Fe^{2+}(aq) \quad E^0_{Fe^{3+}} = +0.77 \text{ V}$$

$$Ni^{2+}(aq) + 2e^- \longrightarrow Ni(s) \quad E^0_{Ni^{2+}} = -0.25 \text{ V}$$

Which half-cell is the cathode?

Solution

The half-cell with the more positive reduction potential occurs as a reduction. In this cell Fe^{3+} is reduced and Ni is oxidized. Because reduction takes place at the Fe^{3+} half-cell, this half-cell is the cathode. The half-cell reactions are as follows.

$$\text{Oxidation: } Ni(s) \longrightarrow Ni^{2+}(aq) + 2e^- \text{ (anode)}$$

$$\text{Reduction: } Fe^{3+}(aq) + e^- \longrightarrow Fe^{2+}(aq) \text{ (cathode)}$$

Before the half-reactions are added, care must be taken that the electrons cancel.

$$Ni(s) \longrightarrow Ni^{2+}(aq) + 2e^-$$
$$\underline{2[Fe^{3+}(aq) + e^- \longrightarrow Fe^{2+}(aq)]}$$
$$Ni(s) + 2Fe^{3+}(aq) \longrightarrow Ni^{2+}(aq) + 2Fe^{2+}(aq)$$

The standard cell potential can now be calculated.

$$
\begin{aligned}
E^0_{cell} &= E^0_{red} - E^0_{oxid} \\
&= E^0_{Fe^{3+}} - E^0_{Ni^{2+}} \\
&= +0.77 \text{ V} - (-0.25 \text{ V}) \\
&= +1.02 \text{ V}
\end{aligned}
$$

Note that the E^0 of a half-cell is not multiplied by any number even if one of the equations was multiplied by a coefficient to make the electrons cancel.

Problems

1. A voltaic cell is constructed using electrodes with the following half-reactions.

$$Cu^{2+}(aq) + 2e^- \longrightarrow Cu(s) \quad E^0_{Cu^{2+}} = +0.34 \text{ V}$$

$$Al^{3+}(aq) + 3e^- \longrightarrow Al(s) \quad E^0_{Al^{3+}} = -1.66 \text{ V}$$

What is the overall cell reaction and the standard cell potential?

2. From these half-reactions determine the cell reaction and the standard cell potential.

$$Ag^+(aq) + e^- \longrightarrow Ag(s) \quad E^0_{Ag^+} = +0.80 \text{ V}$$

$$Cu^{2+}(aq) + 2e^- \longrightarrow Cu(s) \quad E^0_{Cu^{2+}} = +0.34 \text{ V}$$

1. $2Al(s) + 3Cu^{2+}(aq) \longrightarrow$
   $2Al^{3+}(aq) + 3Cu(s) + 2.00 \text{ V}$
2. $Cu(s) + 2Ag^+(aq) \longrightarrow$
   $Cu^{2+}(aq) + 2Ag(s) + 0.46 \text{ V}$

The use of standard reduction potentials makes it possible to predict whether or not a redox reaction will take place. The reactants do not need to be paired in a voltaic cell. The half-reaction with the more positive reduction potential always undergoes reduction. Therefore, the other half-reaction has to undergo oxidation.

If the cell potential for the redox reaction, as written, is positive, then the reaction is spontaneous. If the cell potential is negative, then the reaction is nonspontaneous. It will be spontaneous in the reverse direction and the cell potential will be equally positive.

Example 3

Is the following redox reaction spontaneous as written?

$$Ni(s) + Fe^{2+}(aq) \longrightarrow Ni^{2+}(aq) + Fe(s)$$

Solution

The half-reactions are as follows.

$$\text{Oxidation: } Ni(s) \longrightarrow Ni^{2+}(aq) + 2e^-$$

$$\text{Reduction: } Fe^{2+}(aq) + 2e^- \longrightarrow Fe(s)$$

The standard reduction potentials are found in Table 21·2.

$$Ni^{2+}(aq) + 2e^- \longrightarrow Ni(s) \quad E^0_{Ni^{2+}} = -0.25 \text{ V}$$

$$Fe^{2+}(aq) + 2e^- \longrightarrow Fe(s) \quad E^0_{Fe^{2+}} = -0.44 \text{ V}$$

The standard cell potential is the difference of the potentials of the nickel half-cell and the iron half-cell.

$$E^0_{cell} = E^0_{red} - E^0_{oxid}$$

$$= E^0_{Fe^{2+}} - E^0_{Ni^{2+}}$$

$$= -0.44 \text{ V} - (-0.25 \text{ V})$$

$$= -0.19 \text{ V}$$

Since the standard cell potential is a negative number, the redox equation is nonspontaneous as written. Energy would have to be applied in order to make this reaction occur.

Problems

3. +0.16 V
4. a. nonspontaneous, −0.34 V
   b. nonspontaneous, −1.24 V
   c. nonspontaneous, −0.02 V

3. Calculate the cell potential for this spontaneous redox reaction.

$$Co^{2+}(aq) + Fe(s) \longrightarrow Fe^{2+}(aq) + Co(s)$$

4. Determine which of these redox reactions will occur spontaneously and calculate the standard cell potential in each case.
   a. $Cu(s) + 2H^+(aq) \longrightarrow Cu^{2+}(aq) + H_2(g)$
   b. $2Ag(s) + Fe^{2+}(aq) \longrightarrow 2Ag^+(aq) + Fe(s)$
   c. $3Zn^{2+}(aq) + 2Cr(s) \longrightarrow 3Zn(s) + 2Cr^{3+}(aq)$

Figure 21·11
In cells like these, magnesium metal and chlorine gas are produced by the electrolysis of magnesium chloride.

21·9 Electrolytic Cells

Electrolysis is the use of electrical energy to make a nonspontaneous chemical change occur.

The section on voltaic cells described how a spontaneous chemical reaction can be used to generate a flow of electrons (an electric current). This section will show how an electric current can be used to make a nonspontaneous redox reaction go. *The process in which electrical energy is used to bring about a chemical change is called* **electrolysis.** The apparatus in which electrolysis is carried out is an electrolytic cell.

The reaction in an electrolytic cell is always nonspontaneous as written. Thus a potential must be applied which is greater and opposite in sign to make it go.

Electrolytic cells *are electrochemical cells used to cause a chemical change through the application of electrical energy.* An electrolytic cell is any cell that uses electrical energy (DC current) to make a nonspontaneous redox reaction go to products.

In both voltaic and electrolytic cells, electrons flow from the anode to the cathode in the external circuit. In both types of cells, the electrode at which the reduction reaction occurs is the cathode. The electrode at which oxidation occurs is the anode. In an electrolytic cell, however, the flow of electrons is being "pushed" by an outside source such as a battery. The cathode is called the negative electrode of the electrolytic cell. This is because it is connected to the negative electrode of the battery, the anode. (Remember that in a voltaic cell, the anode is the *negative* electrode and the cathode is the *positive* electrode.) The anode in the electrolytic cell is called the positive electrode. This is because it is connected to the positive electrode of the battery (the battery's cathode). It is important to remember this difference in convention.

Pure water cannot be electrolyzed.

Electrolysis of Water. When a current is applied via two electrodes in pure water nothing happens. There is no current flow and no electrolysis. When an electrolyte is added, such as H_2SO_4 or KNO_3 in low concentration, the solution conducts, and electrolysis takes place (Figure 21·12). The products of the electrolysis of water are hydrogen and oxygen. Water is reduced to hydrogen at the cathode.

$$2H_2O(l) + 2e^- \longrightarrow H_2(g) + 2OH^-(aq)$$

Water is oxidized at the anode.

$$2H_2O(l) \longrightarrow O_2(g) + 4H^+(aq) + 4e^-$$

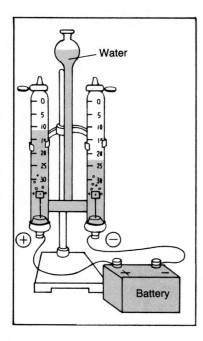

Figure 21·12
When an electric current is passed through water, it decomposes into oxygen and hydrogen. Which tube contains hydrogen gas and which tube contains oxygen gas? Hint: Note from the equation how many moles of hydrogen are produced for each mole of oxygen.

Oxygen is on the left and hydrogen is on the right.

The region around the cathode turns basic due to an increase in OH^- ions. The region around the anode turns acidic due to an increase in H^+ ions. The overall cell reaction is obtained by adding the half-reactions.

$$2[2H_2O(l) + 2e^- \longrightarrow H_2(g) + 2OH^-(aq)]$$
$$\frac{2H_2O(l) \longrightarrow O_2(g) + 4H^+(aq) + 4e^-}{6H_2O(l) \longrightarrow 2H_2(g) + O_2(g) + 4H^+(aq) + 4OH^-(aq)}$$

Some of the ions produced re-form into reactants. These are not included in the net reaction.

$$4H^+(aq) + 4OH^-(aq) \longrightarrow 4H_2O(l)$$

$$2H_2O(l) \xrightarrow{\text{electrolysis}} 2H_2(g) + O_2(g)$$

In some cases, the electrolyte will be more easily oxidized or reduced than water. Then the products of electrolysis will be substances other than hydrogen and oxygen. An example is the electrolysis of brine.

Electrolysis of Brine. Chlorine gas, hydrogen gas, and sodium hydroxide are three important industrial chemicals. They are produced simultaneously by electrolysis of a concentrated aqueous sodium chloride solution (brine). The electrolytic cell for this process is shown in Figure 21·13. During electrolysis, chloride ions are oxidized to produce chlorine gas at the anode. Water is reduced to produce hydrogen gas at the cathode. Sodium ions are not reduced to sodium metal in this process because water molecules are more easily reduced than sodium ions. The reduction of water produces hydroxide ions as well as hydrogen gas. Thus the electrolyte in solution becomes sodium hydroxide.

Oxidation: $2Cl^-(aq) \longrightarrow Cl_2(g) + 2e^-$
(anode)

Reduction: $2H_2O(l) + 2e^- \longrightarrow H_2(g) + 2OH^-(aq)$
(cathode)

Figure 21·13
The electrolysis of a concentrated solution of sodium chloride produces which two gases?

Hydrogen and chlorine.

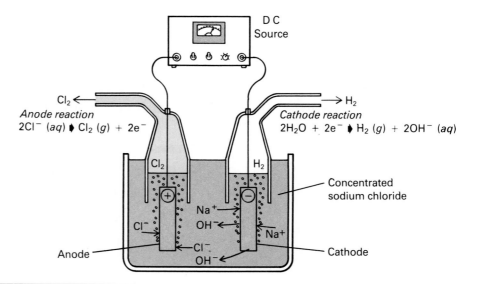

The overall ionic equation is the sum of the two half-reactions.

$$2Cl^-(aq) + 2H_2O(l) \longrightarrow Cl_2(g) + H_2(g) + 2OH^-(aq)$$

The spectator ion, Na^+, can be included in the equation to show the formation of sodium hydroxide.

$$2NaCl(aq) + 2H_2O(l) \longrightarrow Cl_2(g) + H_2(g) + 2NaOH(aq)$$

Chloride ions are eliminated from solution and hydroxide ions are formed. The electrolyte gradually changes from sodium chloride to sodium hydroxide. When the sodium hydroxide solution is about 10%, it is removed from the cell and processed further.

Electrolysis of brine is a very important industrial process. It is used to produce chlorine gas, hydrogen gas, and sodium hydroxide.

Electrolysis of Molten Sodium Chloride. Sodium and chlorine are both of commercial importance. Sodium is used in sodium vapor lamps and as the coolant in some nuclear power reactors. Chlorine, a toxic greenish–yellow gas, is used to sterilize drinking water and is important in the manufacture of polyvinyl chloride and various pesticides. These two elements are produced when molten sodium chloride is electrolyzed. Chlorine gas comes off at the anode and molten sodium collects at the cathode. The electrolytic cell in which this process is carried out commercially is called the Down's cell (Figure 21·14). Its design allows fresh sodium chloride to be added as required. The design also keeps the products apart so that they will not react to re-form sodium chloride. The half-reactions and overall cell reaction are as follows.

Oxidation: $2Cl^-(l) \longrightarrow Cl_2(g) + 2e^-$
(anode)

Reduction: $2Na^+(l) + 2e^- \longrightarrow 2Na(l)$
(cathode)

Cell reaction: $2NaCl(l) \longrightarrow 2Na(l) + Cl_2(g)$

Figure 21·14
The Down's cell is constructed to prevent sodium and chlorine from recombining after they are separated from molten sodium chloride by electrolysis. A Down's cell operates at about 600°C to maintain the salt in a molten state.

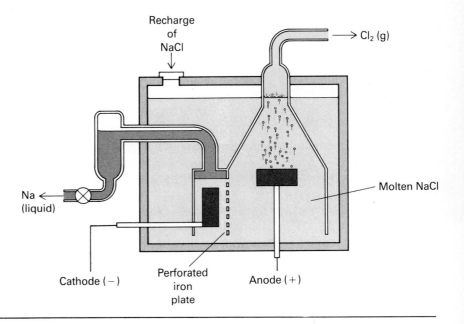

Recharge of NaCl

$\longrightarrow Cl_2$ (g)

Na (liquid)

Molten NaCl

Cathode (−)

Perforated iron plate

Anode (+)

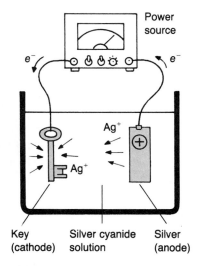

Power
source

e^-

e^-

Ag$^+$

Ag$^+$

Key
(cathode)

Silver cyanide
solution

Silver
(anode)

Figure 21·15
Electroplating is the coating of an object with a thin layer of metal. It is done in an electrolytic cell. The electrolyte contains ions of the metal that will be plated on the object that is made the cathode in the cell.

Figure 21·16
Aluminum is anodized to produce construction materials such as aircraft body parts, window frames, and rain gutters.

21·B Electroplating and Related Processes

Electroplating is the deposition of a thin layer of a metal on an object in an electrolytic cell. It has many important applications. An object may be electroplated to protect the surface of the base metal from corrosion or to make it more attractive. The layer of the deposited metal is very thin, usually from 5×10^{-5} cm to 1×10^{-3} cm thick. Metals commonly used for electroplating include gold, silver, copper, nickel, and chromium. An object that is to be silver-plated, for example, is made the cathode in a cell (Figure 21·15), and the anode is metallic silver. A silver cyanide solution is the electrolyte. When a DC current is applied, silver ions move to the object to be plated. They pick up electrons and are deposited as silver atoms.

$$\text{Cathode reaction: } Ag^+(aq) + e^- \longrightarrow Ag(s)$$

The net result is that silver is transferred from the silver electrode to the object being plated. Controlling this reaction is a fine art.

Many factors contribute to the quality of the metal coating that is formed. In the plating solution, the concentration of the cations to be reduced is carefully controlled. The solution must contain compounds to control the acidity, and to increase the conductivity. Some solutions contain compounds that form complex ions with the cation to be reduced. Other compounds make the metal coating brighter or smoother. In many plating cells, the anode must be shaped like the object at the cathode in order to plate all parts of the cathode evenly!

Several techniques involve the depositing of metal at the cathode of a cell. In *electroforming,* an object is reproduced by making a metal "mold" of it at the cathode. A phonograph record, for example, can be coated with metal so that it will conduct electricity. It is then electroplated to get a thick coating. This coating can be stripped off and used as a mold to produce copies of the record.

Impure metals can be purified in electrolytic cells. In *electrowinning,* the cations of molten salts or aqueous solutions are reduced at the cathode to give very pure metals. Electrowinning from molten salt is the only method for obtaining pure sodium and other very reactive metals. In *electrorefining,* a piece of impure metal is made the anode of the cell. It is oxidized to the cation, and then reduced to the pure metal at the cathode. This technique is used for obtaining ultrapure silver, lead, and copper.

Other electrolytic processes are centered on the anode rather than the cathode. In *electropolishing,* an object at the anode is selectively dissolved to give it a high polish. In *electromachining* a piece of metal at the anode dissolves to give an exact copy of the object that is made at the cathode. In *anodizing,* the metal object at the anode is oxidized to create an oxide deposit on its surface.

Key Terms

Chapter Summary

Spontaneous redox reactions can be used to generate electrical energy in voltaic cells. Conversely, electrical energy can be used to make nonspontaneous reactions go in electrolytic cells. In either type of electrochemical cell, the electrode at which oxidation occurs is the anode, and the electrode at which reduction occurs is the cathode.

In a voltaic cell the half-reactions take place in half-cells. The half-cells are separated by a porous plate or salt bridge. This barrier prevents the contents of the two half-cells from mixing but permits the passage of ions between the half-cells. Reduction occurs at the cathode (the positively-charged electrode) and oxidation occurs at the anode (the negatively-charged electrode). Electrons transfer in the external circuit from the anode to the cathode. The half-cell with the higher reduction potential undergoes reduction, the other half-cell undergoes oxidation. The cell potential is the difference between the reduction potentials of the half-cells.

The reduction potential of an isolated half-cell cannot be measured. Values can be assigned, however, by comparing them to a reference electrode. The reference used is the standard hydrogen electrode which is given a reduction potential of 0.00 volts. Half-cells more easily reduced than the reference electrode have positive reduction potentials. Half-cells less easily reduced have negative reduction potentials.

Using our knowledge of electrochemistry we can design cells and batteries to provide electrical energy for specific purposes. The dry cell, the battery commonly used in flashlights, is not rechargeable. The lead storage battery, as used in automobiles, is rechargeable. Fuel cells do not have to be recharged. The fuels that they consume are fed into the cell continuously.

In electrolysis, a flow of electrons causes reduction at the cathode (the negatively-charged electrode) and oxidation at the anode (the positively-charged electrode). In an electrolytic cell electrical energy is used to bring about desirable redox reactions. Electrolytic cells are used in electroplating, in the refining of metals, and in the production of such important chemicals as sodium hydroxide, aluminum and sodium metals, and chlorine gas.

Practice Questions and Problems

5. Predict the result when a strip of copper is dipped into a solution of iron(II) sulfate. *21·1*

6. What is an *electrochemical process*? *21·1*

7. For each of the pairs of metals listed below decide which metal is the more readily oxidized. *21·1*
a. Hg and Cu   **c.** Ni and Mg   **e.** Pb and Zn
b. Ca and Al   **d.** Sn and Ag   **f.** Cu and Al

8. What is meant by the term "half-reaction"? Write the half-reactions that occur when a strip of Al is dipped into a solution of copper sulfate. *21·1*

9. When a bar of magnesium metal is immersed in a solution of copper ions the magnesium dissolves to give Mg^{2+} and copper metal is deposited. Write the net ionic equation for this reaction. *21·1*

10. What is a half-cell? *21·2*

11. Describe briefly the construction of a voltaic cell. *21·2*

12. Explain the function of the salt bridge in a voltaic cell. *21·2*

13. At which electrode does oxidation occur in the voltaic cell? *21·2*

14. In the voltaic cell what charge is assigned to the anode? *21·2*

15. What material is **a.** the anode and **b.** the cathode made of in the flashlight battery? *21·3*

16. Explain why the specific gravity of the electrolyte in a lead storage battery decreases during the discharge process. *21·4*

17. Why is it not possible to recharge a lead storage battery an infinite number of times? *21·4*

18. Describe the composition of the anode, cathode, and electrolyte in a fully charged lead storage battery. *21·4*

19. What is a fuel cell? *21·5*

20. List the advantages of a fuel cell over a lead storage battery. *21·5*

21. Explain the terms *standard cell potential* and *standard reduction potential*. Give the symbols that are used for these terms. *21·6*

22. What is the purpose of using the standard hydrogen electrode as a reference electrode? *21·6*

23. How is a cell potential derived from the reduction potentials of the two half-cells? *21·6*

24. What is the difference between a *cell potential* and a *standard cell potential*? *21·6*

25. What is the electric potential of a cell? *21·6*

26. At which electrode does reduction occur in all electrochemical cells? *21·7*

27. The standard reduction potential for the cadmium half-cell is -0.40 volts. What does this mean? *21·7*

28. Explain how you would determine the standard reduction potential for the aluminum half-cell. *21·7*

29. Use the information in Table 21·2 to calculate standard cell potentials for these voltaic cells. *21·8*
  a. $Ni \mid Ni^{2+} \parallel Cl_2 \mid Cl^-$
  b. $Sn \mid Sn^{2+} \parallel Ag^+ \mid Ag$
  c. $Zn \mid Zn^{2+} \parallel Br_2 \mid Br^-$

30. What processes occur at the anode and cathode in an electrolytic cell? *21·9*

31. Why is a *direct current* and not an *alternating current* used in the electroplating of metals? *21·9*

32. Describe briefly how you would electroplate a teaspoon with silver. *21·9*

33. At which electrode does reduction take place in an electrolytic cell? *21·9*

Mastery Questions and Problems

34. Distinguish between voltaic and electrolytic cells. *21·9*

35. Why is it not possible to measure the potential of an isolated half-cell? *21·6*

36. Describe the composition of the anode, cathode, and electrolyte of a fully discharged lead storage battery. *21·4*

37. Predict what will happen, if anything, when an iron nail is dipped into a solution of copper sulfate. Write the oxidation and reduction half-reactions for this process and the balanced equation for the overall reaction. *21·2*

38. Calculate E^0_{cell} and write the overall cell reaction for these cells: *21·8*
  a. $Sn \mid Sn^{2+} \parallel Pb^{2+} \mid Pb$
  b. $H_2 \mid H^+ \parallel Br_2 \mid Br^-$
  c. $I^- \mid I_2 \parallel Cl_2 \mid Cl^-$
  d. $Mg \mid Mg^{2+} \parallel Zn^{2+} \mid Zn$

39. What property of lead(II) sulfate and lead dioxide makes it unnecessary to have salt bridges in a lead storage battery? *21·4*

Review Questions and Problems

40. Balance these equations:
  a. $H_2S + HNO_3 \longrightarrow S + NO + H_2O$
  b. $AgNO_3 + Pb \longrightarrow Pb(NO_3)_2 + Ag$
  c. $Cl_2 + NaOH \longrightarrow NaCl + NaClO_3 + H_2O$
  d. $CuO + NH_3 \longrightarrow N_2 + Cu + H_2O$
  e. $Mg(OH)_2 + HBr \longrightarrow MgBr_2 + H_2O$
  f. $Al_2O_3 + H_2SO_4 \longrightarrow Al_2(SO_4)_3 + H_2O$

41. Concentrated nitric acid is $16M$. How would you prepare 500 mL of $1.0M$ HNO_3?

42. What is the oxidation number of the italicized element in each of these formulas?

a. $Pb O_2$
b. $K_2 Cr_2 O_7$
c. $K Cl O_4$
d. $K I O_3$
e. $N O_2^-$
f. $Mn O_4^-$
g. $Na N O_3$
h. $Fe Cl_3$

43. A sample of oxygen gas has a volume of 500 mL at 30°C. What is the new volume of the gas if the temperature is raised to 60°C while the pressure is kept constant?

44. A 2.50-L sample of kerosene has a mass of 2.05 kg. What is the density of kerosene in g/cm^3?

Challenging Questions and Problems

45. Write the overall cell reactions and calculate E_{cell}^0 for voltaic cells composed of the following sets of half-reactions.

a. $AgCl + e^- \rightleftharpoons Ag + Cl^-$
$Ni^{2+} + 2e^- \rightleftharpoons Ni$

b. $Al^{3+} + 3e^- \rightleftharpoons Al$
$Cl_2(g) + 2e^- \rightleftharpoons 2Cl^-$

46. Impure copper is purified in an electrolytic cell. Design an electrolytic cell that will allow you to carry out this process. Give the oxidation and reduction half-reactions and a balanced equation for the overall reaction.

47. A voltaic cell is made of two half-cells separated by a porous plate. One is a piece of lead in a solution of lead nitrate and the other is a strip of copper in a solution of copper nitrate. Determine which half-cell is the anode and which is the cathode. Write the two half-cell reactions and the overall reaction for the cell. Describe the flow of electrons as the cell operates.

48. This spontaneous redox reaction occurs in a voltaic cell.

$$Ni^{2+}(aq) + Fe(s) \longrightarrow Ni(s) + Fe^{2+}(aq)$$

a. Sketch the cell.
b. Write the half-reactions.
c. Label the anode and cathode.
d. Assign charges to the electrodes.
e. Indicate the direction of electron flow.
f. Calculate the standard cell potential when the half-cells are at standard conditions.

Research Projects

1. What contributions did Luigi Galvani make to the discovery of electric current? How is his name used to describe electrochemical processes?

2. How did Humphry Davy use electricity to identify elements?

3. Construct a simple voltage cell.

4. What contributions did William Nicholson make to the field of electrochemistry? How did his work relate to Alessandro Volta's work?

5. Measure the rate of movement of various ions in an agar salt bridge.

6. Why do some batteries last longer than others? Test several common batteries to see which lasts the longest under various conditions.

7. What did John Daniell do to improve the quality of batteries? What are some recent improvements in batteries?

8. Compare the voltage produced by a pure metal to the voltage produced by an alloy of the metal.

9. How do electrostatic precipitators in industrial smokestacks work? Draw a diagram of this device.

10. How are fuel cells used? What are the prospects for widespread use? Describe the commerical production of sodium and chlorine.

11. Study the effects of various conditions on electroplating. Examples include: concentration of electrolyte, distance between electrodes, temperature, presence of other substances, preparation of the surface to be plated, and voltage.

12. Make a diagram of a silver plating apparatus. How do the properties of a silver-plated object differ from a sterling silver object?

13. How can hot brines be used commercially?

Readings and References

Bockris, J. O'M., and Z. Nagy. *Electrochemistry for Ecologists*. New York: Plenum, 1974.

McDougall, Angus. *Fuel Cells*. New York: Halsted/Wiley, 1977.

22 The Chemistry of Metals

Chapter Planning Guide

Section			Demonstrations and Experiments	Resource Materials
22·1	The Alkali Metals	C*		Objectives Worksheet 22, SPB Skillsheet 22, SPB
22·2	The Alkaline Earth Metals	C	Dem 12·2 The Alkaline Earth Metals Dem 11·3 Emission Spectra Dem 22·1 Magnesium from Sea Water	
22·A	The Solvay Process	E	Dem 22·2 The Solvay Process	
22·3	Aluminum for the Masses	C	Dem 22·3 The Reaction of Aluminum with Water	
22·4	Tin and Lead	C	Dem 20·1 Reduction of Ores	Quiz 22·1
22·5	The Transition Metals	C	Dem 22·4 Colorful Copper Compounds Dem 22·5 Colorful Silicates Dem 22·6 Silver Chloride and Silver Chromate	Beyond the Text: Deep Sea Mining
22·5	Iron, Cobalt, and Nickel	C	Exp 48 Reactivity of Metals, LM Dem 22·7 Blueprinting	Prelab 48, SPB
22·7	Copper, Silver, and Gold	C	Dem 20·1 Reduction of Ores Dem 22·8 The Light Sensitivity of the Silver Halides	Quiz 22·2
22·B	Toxic Metals	E		Toxic Metals, ICT 22
22·8	Metal Ores	O	Dem 22·9 Separation of Ores	
22·9	The Blast Furnace	O		
22·10	Steelmaking	O		Quiz 22·3 Reviewsheet 22, SPB Chapter 22 Test
*C = Core, O = Optional E = Enrichment, H = Honors			LM = Laboratory Manual	SPB = Skills Practice Book ICT = Issues in Chem. Tech.

Chapter Objectives

Having studied this chapter and done the problems, the student should be able to:

1. Explain why alkali metals are not found in the free state in nature. *22·1*

2. Describe the methods of preparation of alkali metal and alkaline earth metals. *22·1, 22·2*

3. Explain the differences in densities and ionization energies between the alkali metals and the alkaline earth metals. *22·1, 22·2*

4. Describe the preparation and commercial uses of aluminum. *22·3*

5. List important uses of tin and lead. *22·4*

6. Identify some uses of the common transition metals. *22·5*

7. List important uses of nickel and cobalt. *22·6*

8. Name some metals which are found in an uncombined state in nature. *22·7*

9. List some properties of gold which help explain its commercial value. *22·7*

10. Describe some methods of recovering metals from their ores. *22·8*

11. Write the overall reaction for the reduction of iron ore in a blast furnace. *22·9*

12. Explain the process and purpose of making steel. *22·10*

Teaching Suggestions

This chapter is purely descriptive. Information is given about the sources, properties, and uses of some of the more important metallic elements.

You will probably wish to present this material in lecture fashion. Whenever possible, try to add interest by giving the students direct visual experience with these elements, either through displays or demonstrations. Have samples of each element on hand, and pass them among the students as you discuss the properties of that element. When possible, show samples of the common ores of the element as well.

Many of these elements have already been discussed. If you have not already done so, you may wish to perform some of the earlier demonstrations in which the elements were involved. Some of these are suggested below.

22·1 The Alkali Metals

22·2 The Alkaline Earth Metals

Demonstration 12·2 shows the reaction of the alkaline earth metals with acids. It is appropriate here.

If the students have not done **Experiment 21,** you could demonstrate the variety of colors produced when alkali or alkaline earth metals are heated. See also **Demonstration 11·3. Demonstration 22·1** *Magnesium from Sea Water* shows how magnesium is obtained. **Demonstration 22·2** *The Solvay Process* shows how sodium bicarbonate is made.

22·3 Aluminum for the Masses

Aluminum is one of the most useful metals. It is abundant, relatively inexpensive, and is apparantly corrosion resistant. Actually, aluminum is very reactive. It is prevented from showing this reactivity by a protective oxide layer which forms as soon as a fresh surface is exposed to the air. The reactivity of aluminum is shown in **Demonstration 22·3** *The Reaction of Aluminum with Water*.

22·4 Tin and Lead

The production of tin and lead from their ores is a reduction process. This is shown in **Demonstration 20·1.**

22·5 The Transition Metals

A characteristic of the transition metals is that they form so many brightly colored compounds. As the oxidation state of the element varies, so does the color. Locate some examples of these compounds and display them. **Demonstrations 22·4** *Colorful Copper Compounds,* **22·5** *Colorful Silicates,* and **22·6** *Silver Iodide and Silver Chromate* show such colors.

22·6 Iron, Cobalt, and Nickel

Magnetism is a property which is unique to these three elements. Many students are surprised to learn that magnetic materials can be found in nature. One naturally magnetic compound of iron is magnetite, commonly called lodestone. Obtain a piece of lodestone (perhaps from your physics instructor) and pass it among your students. Point out that it will pick up tiny iron objects, such as paper clips.

Blueprinting is illustrated in **Demonstration 22·8** *Blueprinting.* It shows the reactions of two iron-containing compounds.

22·7 Copper, Silver, and Gold

The reduction of copper ore is shown in **Demonstration 20·1.** Silver halides are important to photography because they are affected by light. This is seen in **Demonstration 22·9** *The Light Sensitivity of Silver Halides.*

22·8 Metal Ores

22·9 The Blast Furnace

22·10 Steelmaking

Few metals are found in nature in the elemental state. Most are refined from ores. **Demonstration 22·10** *Separation of Ores* shows one step of the process. Emphasize that, whatever the process, the production of a metal from an ore is an example of reduction.

Spend some time discussing the ecological aspects of the production of metals. The mining of ores can have a devastating effect on the environment, especially in the case of strip mining. The separation of metals from their ores *always* involves the production of waste products. We are seeing the effects of some of the gaseous wastes as "acid rain" becomes more and more noticeable. The solids (gangue and slag) and liquids that are by-products of ore processing present disposal problems.

Demonstrations

22·1 Magnesium from Sea Water

Concept: Sea water has a high concentration of magnesium ions.

Materials: 250 mL of sea water ($0.1M$ magnesium chloride ($MgCl_2$)) in a 500-mL beaker, 250 mL of $0.1M$ calcium hydroxide ($Ca(OH)_2$), stirring rod.

Procedure: 1. Add the calcium hydroxide to the sea water and stir. 2. Magnesium hydroxide is precipitated. Point out that it could be reduced to obtain magnesium.

22·2 The Solvay Process

Concept: Sodium bicarbonate precipitates out in the Solvay process.

Materials: 100 mL of a concentrated aqueous ammonia ($NH_3(aq)$) saturated with sodium chloride ($NaCl$) in a 250-mL beaker, dry ice, hammer, tongs, insulated gloves, safety goggles.

Procedure: 1. Break off chips of dry ice using the hammer and gloves. 2. With tongs, add dry ice chips to the contents of the beaker. 3. The sodium bicarbonate precipitates. **Caution:** *Dry ice can cause frostbite. Do not touch.*

22·3 The Reaction of Aluminum with Water

Concept: Mercury breaks down the protective oxide coating of aluminum, making it reactive.

Materials: 3-cm square of aluminum sheet, 1 drop of mercury, rubber gloves, 500-mL beaker of water, safety goggles.

Procedure: 1. Point out that the protective oxide on aluminum makes it unreactive. 2. Using rubber gloves, rub mercury on the surface of the metal until it is coated evenly. 3. Immerse the aluminum in a beaker of water. 4. Bubbles of hydrogen gas form on the surface of the metal. 5. Eventually, the aluminum will appear corroded. 6. A jelly-like precipitate of aluminum hydroxide forms
$$2Al(s) + 6H_2O(l) \rightarrow 2Al(OH)_3(aq) + 3H_2(g)$$
Caution: *Mercury is poisonous in all its states. Use a fume hood and handle only with rubber gloves. Use a mercury sponge to clean up spills.*

22·4 Colorful Copper Compounds

Concept: Copper compounds exist in many colors; the copper(II) ion, however, is blue.

Materials: 4 watch glasses, 2 g each of white copper(II) sulfate ($CuSO_4$), brown copper(II) bromide ($CuBr_2$), green copper(II) chloride ($CuCl_2$), and blue copper(II) nitrate ($Cu(NO_3)_2$), water, safety goggles.

Procedure: 1. Place the compounds in the watch glasses and observe the variety of colors. 2. Add water to each and note the blue color as ions form. **Caution:** *Copper bromide is corrosive. Copper sulfate, copper chloride, and copper nitrate are irritants.*

22·5 Colorful Silicates

Concept: Colorful silicate crystals form when sodium silicate is mixed with various transition metal chlorides.

Materials: 100 mL of waterglass (a concentrated solution of sodium silicate (Na_2SiO_3)) in 200 mL of water in a 600-mL beaker with a thin layer of sand on the bottom, 5 crystals each of cobalt(II) chloride ($CoCl_2$), copper(II) chloride ($CuCl_2$), lead(II) chloride ($PbCl_2$), iron(III) chloride ($FeCl_3$), nickel(II) chloride ($NiCl_2$), manganese(II) chloride ($MnCl_2$), and calcium chloride ($CaCl_2$), safety goggles.

Procedure: 1. Spread the crystals into the beaker. 2. Colorful silicate crystals form over several days. **Caution:** *Iron(III) chloride is an irritant.*

22·6 Silver Chloride and Silver Chromate

Concept: Transition metals such as silver form numerous colorful compounds.

Materials: 250 mL of $0.1\,M$ potassium chromate (K_2CrO_4), 250 mL of $0.1M$ sodium chloride ($NaCl$), 250 mL of $0.1M$ silver nitrate ($AgNO_3$), three 500-mL beakers.

Procedures: 1. Mix the potassium chromate and sodium chloride. 2. Slowly add the silver nitrate solution. White silver chloride forms. 3. Add additional silver nitrate. Red silver chromate forms. **Caution:** *Potassium chromate and silver nitrate are suspected mutagens.*

22·7 Blueprinting

Concept: Blueprinting involves compounds of iron.

Materials: floodlight, 0.1 g of iron(III) oxalate ($Fe_2(C_2O_4)_3 \cdot 5H_2O$), 10 mL of $0.1M$ potassium ferricyanide ($K_3Fe(CN)_6$), blueprint paper, two 100-mL graduated cylinders, three 600-mL beakers, key, gas burner, stirring rod, safety goggles.

Procedure: 1. Dissolve the iron oxalate in 200 mL of water and boil. 2. Place 100 mL of the solution in each of two beakers. 3. Place one beaker under a floodlight for 5 minutes. 4. Compare the colors of the two beakers. 5. Add 400 mL water to each beaker and stir. 6. Add 5 mL of potassium ferricyanide to each beaker. 7. The solution in the beaker lit by the floodlight appears blue-green. 8. Place a key on the blueprint paper. 9. Shine the floodlight on the key for 1 minute. 10. Dip the paper into water to reveal the print of the key. **Caution:** *Potassium ferricyanide and iron(II) oxalate are toxic.*

22·8 The Light Sensitivity of the Silver Halides

Concept: Photography involves the reduction of silver.

Materials: 300 mL of $1M$ silver nitrate ($AgNO_3$), 100 mL of each of: $1M$ sodium chloride ($NaCl$), $1M$ sodium bromide ($NaBr$), and $1M$ sodium iodide (NaI), three 500-mL beakers, gas burner, ring, ring stand, wire gauze, matches, spatula, filter funnel, filter paper, funnel holder, tongs, bright lamp, safety goggles.

Procedure: 1. In three separate beakers, boil 100 mL of silver nitrate with 100 mL each of sodium chloride, bromide, and iodide. 2. When cool, filter each precipitate and spread the precipitates on the filter paper. 3. Shine a bright light on each of the three precipitates. (Direct sunlight works extremely well.) 4. The precipitates will darken. 5. This effect occurs only on the surface. This can be seen by scraping off some of the darkened material. Light-colored precipitate will be visible underneath. 6. Explain that halides of silver are reduced when they are exposed to certain wavelengths of light and are therefore very useful in photography. **Caution:** *Silver nitrate is a suspected mutagen.*

22·9 Separation of Ores

Concept: Waste is separated from ores by physical means.

Materials: 5 g of lead(II) oxide (PbO), 5 g sand, large test tube, 10 mL of water, 10 mL of mineral oil, rubber stopper.

Procedure: 1. Mix the lead(II) oxide and sand in the test tube. 2. Add water and mineral oil. 3. Stopper and shake well. 4. The sand separates from the lead oxide.

Audiovisual Resources

Chemistry of Iron (FS) Educational Dimensions, 1978, 15–20 min. (Use with Sections 22·6, 22·9, or 22·10.)

Lead in Motion (F) Lead Industries Association, 1975, 21 min. (Use with Section 22·4.) Presents the mining and the extraction of lead and discusses its properties and many uses.

Of Metal and Men (F, V) Media Guild, 1982, 25 min. (Use with Sections 22·1, 22·2, 22·3, 22·4, 22·6, 22·7, or 22·9.) Classifies elements according to the ease with which they can be extracted from their ores and relates this to their chemical reactivity.

Steel: The Metal Giant (F, V) Centron, 1981, 12 min. (Use with Sections 22·9 and 22·10.) Presents good visual imagery of the steelmaking process.

Beyond the Text

Deep Sea Mining

The world's need for minerals and metals grows dramatically every year. Most rich mineral deposits on the land surface have been found and exploited. The mining industry is now turning to the oceans.

Ocean waters contain large amounts of dissolved metals and their compounds. The metals include sodium, potassium, magnesium, calcium, strontium, and uranium. In addition, large amounts of manganese, copper, nickel, and cobalt are dissolved. This second group of metals and their compounds are also deposited as sediment on the sea floor. These minerals enter the sea from hot springs along the mid-ocean ridges. They precipitate slowly, often growing as nodules around a piece of rock or fish bone. These round crystalline clumps form at the rate of about one molecular layer a day. A deposit one millimeter in diameter may take 1 000 000 years to precipitate!

The nodules are mostly oxides of manganese and iron. Some are rich in cobalt, copper, and nickel. Of course, mining from the deep sea floor is expensive and complicated. The mineral deposit must be considerably richer than deposits on land if mining it is to be worthwhile. In some areas of the Pacific Ocean the sea floor at a depth of 3 to 5 kilometers is dotted with nodules containing 32% manganese. At depths of 1 kilometer near Western Samoa, the sea floor crust contains up to 2% cobalt. These concentrations are more than high enough to make mining economical.

Ships can be used to dredge minerals from the bottom of the ocean. A "chain" of buckets is dragged along the sea floor, then raised to the surface again. Another method uses a powerful pump that is dragged along the ocean floor. It sucks in the nodules and pumps them to the surface. Dissolved minerals can also be recovered from sea water by evaporation and/or precipitation. This type of mining may become more feasible if desalinization plants are built to recover fresh water from the ocean.

The top meter of sea floor sediment in the Pacific Ocean is estimated to contain 400 billion metric tons of manganese and 9 billion tons of copper. It is thought that 16 billion metric tons of nickel and 6 billion tons of cobalt are also present.

Answers to End of Chapter Questions and Problems

Practice Questions and Problems

3. Deposits of alkali metal salts.

4. Their large atomic diameters.

5. $Na_2O_2 + 2H_2O \rightarrow 2NaOH + H_2O_2$
$2Na + 2H_2O \rightarrow 2NaOH + H_2$

6. NaOH

7. Sodium vapor lamps, the production of chemicals, nuclear reactors.

8. Group 1A: alkali metals. Group 2A: alkaline earth metals.

9. Calcium oxide, CaO; in a kiln at 900°C.

10. Calcium is made by the electrolysis of molten calcium chloride. Magnesium is precipitated from sea water as magnesium hydroxide by reaction with lime. Hydrochloric acid converts it to magnesium chloride. Magnesium metal is then made by electrolysis of molten magnesium chloride.

11. Calcium, strontium, and barium react with cold water. Beryllium and magnesium react only with hot water or steam.
$$Ca + 2H_2O \rightarrow Ca(OH)_2 + H_2$$

12. Their atomic diameters are smaller.

13. Group 2A metals are less reactive.

14. $Ca + 2H_2O \rightarrow Ca(OH)_2 + H_2$
$CaO + H_2O \rightarrow Ca(OH)_2 + heat$

15. $Ca(OH)_2 + CO_2 \rightarrow CaCO_3 + H_2O$

16. $2Ca + O_2 \rightarrow 2 CaO$
$CaO + H_2O \rightarrow Ca(OH)_2 + heat$
$Ca + 2H_2O \rightarrow Ca(OH)_2 + H_2$

17. Bauxite.

18. Melted cryolite dissolves aluminum oxide.

19. Low density, good electrical conductivity, high corrosion resistance.

20. Cathode reaction: $Al^{3+} + 3e^- \rightarrow Al$
Anode reaction: $2O^{2-} \rightarrow O_2 + 4e^-$

21. Tin is used as a protective coating on iron or steel, in some types of fluoride toothpastes, and in the alloys bronze and solder. Lead is used in lead storage batteries, as an additive to gasoline, and in solder.

22. $2PbS + 3O_2 \rightarrow 2PbO + 2SO_2$
$2PbO + C \rightarrow 2Pb + CO_2$

23. +2, +3, +6

24. Titanium dioxide; half as dense as iron, strong, corrosion resistant.

25. Coating for iron and steel, stainless steel.

26. The most common iron minerals.

27. Fe_2O_3 (hematite); Fe_3O_4 (magnetite)

28. +2, +3

29. **a.** 72.3% Fe **b.** 69.9% Fe **c.** 35.5% Co

30. Nickel is used to electroplate iron and steel and to catalyze industrial reactions. Monel metal is a strong, corrosion-resistant alloy of nickel and copper.

31. Cobalt is corrosion resistant and can be magnetized. It is used in the alloy stellite and as an industrial catalyst.

32. They occur in the free state and were collected by the ancients.

33. Contain silver and gold.

34. Copper: electrical wiring, copper plumbing. Silver: mirrors, photography. Gold: gold leaf, contacts of microcircuits, cover for satellites.

35. A mineral used for the commercial production of metals.

36. **a.** argentite, Ag_2S **b.** chalcopyrite, chalcocite, and cuprite

37. Involves the various procedures used to separate metals from their ores.

38. Froth flotation uses detergent and oil in agitated ore. The oil sticks to the sulfide but not to the sand and rock. Air blown into the mixture forms bubbles that rise to the surface. Oil and sulfide stick to them. The sulfides are skimmed off while impurities settle to the bottom.

39. The worthless sand and rock in ore.

40. To form the oxide and drive off volatile sulfide impurities.

41. The fused waste material from a smelting process.

42. Reduction converts positively charged metal ions in a compound to the free metal.

43. Concentrating the ore removes the sand and rock. Chemically reducing the ore to the metal frees the metal from its compound. Refining and purifying the metal removes other compounds and metals until the desired pure metal is obtained.

44. A blast of hot air blows up through the charge of iron ore, coke, and limestone from the bottom of the furnace.

45. Iron ore, coke, limestone.

46. $Fe_2O_3 + 3CO \rightarrow 2Fe + 3CO_2$

47. Calcium oxide released from the limestone reacts with the sand in the ore to form a slag which trickles down through the charge to float on the surface of the molten iron.

48. Steel is iron with a carbon content of 0.02% to 2.0%. Impurities are removed. It is not brittle and has high tensile strength. Pig iron has 3% to 5% carbon and impurities. It is brittle with low tensile strength. Cast iron is pig iron melted with scrap iron. It is less impure than pig iron.

49. A shallow lined vessel is used to hold the iron. Hot air and burning gases melt the iron and react with it. The lining of the vessel helps remove impurities, while other impurities leave as gases.

50. Nickel steel: 3.5% nickel, tough and hard, used in crankshafts. Chrome steel: 1.0% chromium, tough and strong, used in springs. Manganese steel: 12-14% manganese, holds a temper, used in safes. Tungsten steel: 5% tungsten, maintains its hardness when hot, used in high-speed cutting tools. Stainless steel: 12-30% chromium, hard and resists corrosion, used in surgical implements.

Mastery Questions and Problems

51. 12.9% Al

52. 55% Fe

53. **a.** $2Na + O_2 \rightarrow Na_2O_2$
b. $2Na + 2H_2O \rightarrow 2NaOH + H_2$
c. $2Cs + O_2 \rightarrow Cs_2O_2$

54. When free metal is made from its ion, reduction occurs at the cathode.

55. The basic oxygen process converts pig iron and scrap iron, mixed with powdered limestone, into steel. Pure oxygen is injected under pressure into the molten mixture to oxidize impurities. No external heat source is required. The oxygen process is also much faster.

56. The alkali metals have lower densities than the alkaline earth metals. The diameter of the alkali metal atoms is greater because the nucleus has one fewer proton for the two groups in one period.

57. 31.6% Ti

58. Blister copper from the final reduction is used as the anode of a cell containing a strong acid to dissolve the copper. The dissolved copper is reduced at the cathode and plated out.

59. 35.5% Co in CoAsS; 258 kg Co

60. **a.** Aluminum is electrolytically refined from bauxite ore. **b.** Copper is obtained from chalcopyrite, chalcocite, and cuprite by concentrating the ore by flotation. Then smelting reduces copper(I) sulfide and copper(I) oxide to copper. Finally, the impure copper is electrolytically refined. **c.** Magnesium is extracted from sea water. It is precipitated by lime as magnesium hydroxide. Hydrochloric acid converts $Mg(OH)_2$ to magnesium chloride. Molten magnesium chloride is electrolytically treated to reduce the magnesium ions to magnesium metal.

61. 128 kg ore

Review Questions and Problems

62. **a.** K_2S **b.** $BaBr_2$ **c.** AlF_3 **d.** NaI **e.** CaO

63. **a.** $1s^2\, 2s^2\, 2p^6\, 3s^2\, 3p^6\, 3d^6\, 4s^2$
b. $1s^2\, 2s^2\, 2p^6\, 3s^2\, 3p^6\, 3d^3\, 4s^2$
c. $1s^2\, 2s^2\, 2p^6\, 3s^2\, 3p^6\, 3d^{10}\, 4s^2\, 4p^6\, 4d^{10}\, 5s^1$
d. $1s^2\, 2s^2\, 2p^6\, 3s^2\, 3p^6\, 3d^3\, 4s^2$
e. $1s^2\, 2s^2\, 2p^6\, 3s^2\, 3p^6\, 3d^{10}\, 4s^1$
f. $1s^2\, 2s^2\, 2p^6\, 3s^2\, 3p^6\, 3d^6\, 4s^2$
g. $1s^2\, 2s^2\, 2p^6\, 3s^2\, 3p^6\, 3d^{10}\, 4s^2$
h. $1s^2\, 2s^2\, 2p^6\, 3s^2\, 3p^6\, 3d^{10}\, 4s^2\, 4p^6\, 4d^{10}$

64. **a.** 1 **b.** 7 **c.** 4 **d.** 3

65. **a.** $0.0019M$ Mg^{2+} **b.** 526 L

66. **a.** Li^+ Br^- **b.** Ca^{2+} OH^- **c.** K^+ I^- **d.** Cd^{2+} Br^-

67. **a.** nonelectrolyte **b.** nonelectrolyte **c.** weak electrolyte **d.** strong electrolyte **e.** strong electrolyte **f.** strong electrolyte

68. $2Cr(OH)_4^- + 2OH^- + IO_3^- \rightarrow 2CrO_4^{2-} + 5H_2O + I^-$

69. **a.** 0 **b.** +5 **c.** +4 **d.** +1 **e.** +3

70. Oxidation: $Ti^{2+} \rightarrow Ti^{3+} + e^-$
Reduction: $Co^{2+} + 2e^- \rightarrow Co$

71. I_2O_5 oxidizing agent, CO reducing agent.

72. **a.** $CuBr$ **b.** Zn_3N_2 **c.** CdS **d.** AgI

Challenging Questions and Problems

73. 31 kg SO_2

74. 0.27 L Cl_2

75. $Cu_3C_2O_8H_2$

76. $Mg(OH)_2 + 2HCl \rightarrow MgCl_2 + 2H_2O$
a. 0.110 mol H^+ **b.** 36.6 mL

77. 1.45 atm

78. 908 g Co_3O_4

22 The Chemistry of Metals

Chapter Preview

Approximately 75 of the more than one hundred known elements are metals. These elements exhibit a wide range of properties. They have common physical and chemical characteristics, however, that distinguish them from nonmetals. This chapter describes some of the distinctive properties of metals and their practical applications.

22·1   The Alkali Metals

The alkali metals and their compounds show a striking similarity. For this reason, sodium will be discussed as a typical member of the group. Table 22·1 lists some physical properties of alkali metals. Along with their Group 2A neighbors, alkali metal atoms are among the largest atoms known. Even though their atoms are closely packed, these metals have low densities because of their large atomic sizes. Atomic size also

The physical properties of the alkali metals follow definite trends. As atomic number increases, their melting points, boiling points, hardnesses, specific heats, and ionization energies all decrease, while their densities increase.

Figure 22·1
Molten metals are poured into molds in which they will solidify into ingots.

Table 22·1	Some Physical Properties of the Alkali Metals			
Element	Melting Point (°C)	Boiling Point (°C)	Density (g/cm³)	Atomic Radius (nm)
Lithium	179	1336	0.53	0.123
Sodium	98	883	0.97	0.157
Potassium	64	758	0.86	0.203
Rubidium	39	700	1.53	0.216
Cesium	28	670	1.90	0.235

Alkali metals should not be used except under the direct supervision of the teacher.

Because the alkali metals are so reactive they occur in nature as salts instead of as the free metals.

helps explain the low ionization energies of these elements. Because they lose a single valence electron so easily, alkali metals are powerful reducing agents.

Although sodium is the best known alkali metal, few people are familiar with its appearance. It is so active chemically that it never occurs in nature as the free metal. As a group, the 1A elements are the most reactive metals known. Within the group, the larger atoms, cesium and rubidium, are the most reactive.

A lump of sodium has the consistency of stiff modeling clay and is easily cut (Figure 12·14). When freshly cut, it has the typical silvery luster of a metal, but it tarnishes quickly in air. Like most metals, sodium is a good conductor of heat and electricity.

Rich deposits of alkali metal salts are found all over the world. The Bonneville Salt Flats in Utah and deposits at Searles Lake, California contain huge quantities of sodium chloride and other alkali salts. The evaporation of ancient seas left large deposits which are now underground near the Gulf Coast shores of Texas and Louisiana.

Alkali metal salts are very soluble in water. Rainwater leaches them out of the soil, and rivers carry them to the sea. Seawater is about 3% (by mass) alkali salts.

Sodium is the only alkali metal produced on a large scale. In most industrial processes it serves as well as the more expensive members of the group. To produce the free metal, sodium ions must be reduced. This is usually done by electrolysis. Production of metallic sodium by the electrolysis of molten sodium chloride is described in Section 21·9. Chlorine gas is a valuable by-product of this process.

Sodium is used in sodium vapor lamps and in the production of many chemicals. Liquid sodium is an excellent conductor of heat. It is often used in nuclear reactors to remove heat from the reactor core.

Figure 22·2
Large amounts of sodium chloride are produced by the evaporation of sea water.

Sodium reacts vigorously with most nonmetals. When sodium burns in a stream of dry oxygen, sodium peroxide, Na_2O_2, forms.

$$2Na(s) + O_2(g) \longrightarrow Na_2O_2(s)$$

In water, metal peroxides are powerful oxidizing agents used in bleaching and disinfecting. The reaction between sodium peroxide and water produces sodium hydroxide and hydrogen peroxide.

$$Na_2O_2(s) + 2H_2O(l) \longrightarrow 2NaOH(aq) + H_2O_2(aq)$$

The freshly formed hydrogen peroxide decomposes rapidly in the strongly basic solution to yield oxygen and water.

Sodium metal reacts violently with cold water, forming sodium hydroxide (lye) and releasing hydrogen gas.

$$2Na(s) + 2H_2O(l) \longrightarrow 2NaOH(aq) + H_2(g)$$

The reactions of the alkali metals with water are so rapid and exothermic that the hydrogen burns as it is produced (Figure 7·12).

Sodium hydroxide is one of the most widely produced strong bases. It is used in the production of soap, petroleum, synthetic textiles, and paper pulp. The electrolysis of brine (a concentrated aqueous solution of sodium chloride) is the major source of sodium hydroxide for the chemical industry. Chlorine and hydrogen gases are also produced.

$$2NaCl(aq) + 2H_2O(l) \xrightarrow{\text{electrical energy}} 2NaOH(aq) + H_2(g) + Cl_2(g)$$

Problem

1. $2K(s) + 2H_2O(l) \rightarrow$ $2KOH(aq) + H_2(g)$

1. Write a balanced equation for the reaction of potassium with water.

22·2 The Alkaline Earth Metals

Calcium and magnesium are the most abundant metals of Group 2A.

The alkaline earth metals are also highly reactive and are not found free in nature. They are less reactive, however, than the alkali metals. Barium is the most reactive element in the group. Group 2A metals are somewhat harder than those in Group 1A. Some physical properties of the alkaline earth metals are listed in Table 22·2.

Alkaline earth salts are less soluble than the corresponding alkali salts. Nevertheless, the sea is a rich source of magnesium and calcium ions. Calcium ions in seawater are used by shellfish in building their calcium carbonate shells. Coral animals carry out a similar process in forming reefs.

Some of the alkaline earth carbonates and sulfates are insoluble enough to resist weathering and the leaching action of rainwater. Limestone is the most common mineral form of calcium carbonate (Figure 22·3). It is often made up of compressed layers of seashells. The White Cliffs of Dover on the southern coast of England are another form of calcium carbonate. Shells of microscopic marine animals have been pressed

Figure 22·3
Calcium carbonate occurs naturally in several forms. The rectangular slab is marble. Continuing clockwise, calcite, limestone, and a cross-section of a stalactite are shown.

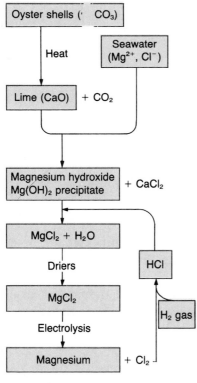

Figure 22·4
Sea water is the main source of magnesium compounds. Most commercial magnesium is prepared electrolytically from magnesium chloride. Each ton of sea water yields about 3 kg of magnesium.

into a natural chalk. Marble is limestone that has been transformed to metamorphic rock by the action of heat and pressure deep within the earth. Another important calcium mineral is the hydrate gypsum, $CaSO_4 \cdot 2H_2O$, from which plaster of Paris is made.

Igneous rocks such as granite and basalt are composed of insoluble silicate salts of almost all the Group 1A and 2A metals. The slow weathering of these rocks is responsible for the presence of alkali and alkaline earth metal ions in fertile soil.

Calcium and magnesium are the most important alkaline earth metals. Calcium is produced by the electrolysis of molten calcium chloride in a reaction similar to that used to produce sodium. By contrast, magnesium is prepared from seawater (Figure 22·4). Lime is added to precipitate the magnesium as magnesium hydroxide. Then hydrochloric acid is added to convert the hydroxide to magnesium chloride. Magnesium metal is recovered from molten magnesium chloride by electrolysis.

Magnesium is the only Group 2A metal widely used in the free state. It is an important structural material and is the chief component in a number of high tensile-strength, low-density alloys. These properties make these alloys valuable in aircraft and spacecraft construction. Magnesium ribbon or powder is used in photoflash bulbs.

With the exception of beryllium and magnesium, the alkaline earth metals tarnish quickly in air. They may continue to corrode until completely converted to the oxide, hydroxide, or carbonate. Beryllium and magnesium also oxidize readily. They form a tough oxide film, however, that prevents further reactions at room temperature.

Calcium, strontium, and barium react with cold water but more slowly than Group 1A metals do (Figure 22·5). Beryllium and magnesium react only with hot water or steam.

$$Ca(s) + 2H_2O(l) \longrightarrow Ca(OH)_2(aq) + H_2(g)$$

Table 22·2	Some Physical Properties of the Alkaline Earth Metals			
Element	Melting Point (°C)	Boiling Point (°C)	Density (g/cm³)	Atomic Radius (nm)
Beryllium	1280	1500	1.86	0.089
Magnesium	651	1107	1.75	0.136
Calcium	851	1487	1.55	0.174
Strontium	800	1366	2.60	0.191
Barium	850	1537	3.59	0.198

Note that there are no clear-cut trends in the melting points, boiling points, and densities of the alkaline earth metals. They have higher melting points and are harder, however, than the alkali metals.

Alkaline earth oxides are used more widely than the pure metals. They are white solids with very high melting points. They react with water to form hydroxides and with carbon dioxide to produce carbonates. The reaction with water, called slaking, is exothermic.

$$CaO(s) + H_2O(l) \longrightarrow Ca(OH)_2(aq) + heat$$
Lime   Slaked lime

$$CaO(s) + CO_2(s) \longrightarrow CaCO_3(s)$$

When heated with an intense flame, lime will produce a very bright white light. This was used in early theaters and has given rise to the term, "in the limelight."

Calcium oxide, commonly called **lime,** or quicklime, is an important industrial chemical. It is made by the high-temperature decomposition of limestone in a lime kiln.

$$CaCO_3(s) \xrightarrow{900°C} CaO(s) + CO_2(g)$$
Limestone   Lime

Water is added to quicklime to get **slaked lime,** *calcium hydroxide.* It is used to make plaster and mortar and to neutralize acid soils. Mortar is a mixture of slaked lime, sand, and water. The setting process involves drying and crystallization. These processes are followed by slow conversion of the slaked lime to calcium carbonate by the action of atmospheric carbon dioxide. Magnesium oxide is manufactured from magnesium car-

Magnesium oxide is manufactured from magnesium carbonate in a process that is similar to the manufacture of lime. Magnesium oxide is used for making firebrick and for insulating steam pipes.

Group 2A hydroxides are strong bases similar to those of Group 1A, although less soluble in water. Calcium hydroxide is used in large quantities in the manufacture of building mortar and bleaching powder, and in water softening. A suspension of magnesium hydroxide, $Mg(OH)_2$, in water is known as milk of magnesia. It is used as a laxative.

Safety

Calcium oxide should be kept in air-tight and waterproof containers when not in use. Large amounts of heat are released when it reacts with water.

Calcium hydroxide and hydrogen gas.

Figure 22·5
Alkaline earth metals are less reactive than the alkali metals. Here, calcium reacts with water. What are the products of the reaction?

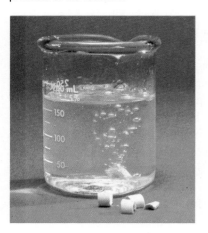

Problem

2. $MgO + CO_2 \rightarrow MgCO_3$

2. Write a balanced equation for the reaction between magnesium oxide and carbon dioxide.

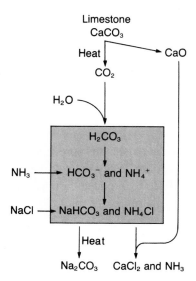

Limestone
CaCO₃

Heat → CaO

CO₂

H₂O

H₂CO₃

NH₃ → HCO₃⁻ and NH₄⁺

NaCl → NaHCO₃ and NH₄Cl

Heat

Na₂CO₃   CaCl₂ and NH₃

Figure 22·6
Large amounts of sodium carbonate are manufactured by the Solvay process. This material is used in the manufacture of glass, soap, and paper, in cleaning compounds, and for water softening.

22·A The Solvay Process

Sodium carbonate, Na_2CO_3, is an important industrial chemical used in the manufacture of glass, soap, and paper. Commonly called soda ash, it is also an ingredient in cleaning compounds and water softeners. Sodium carbonate is obtained commercially from natural salt lakes. The demand for it outstrips this supply. Thus more than five million metric tons are produced in North America each year by the Solvay process.

The Belgian chemist Ernest Solvay (1838–1922) invented the ammonia–soda process around 1860. It uses sodium chloride, calcium carbonate, and ammonia as raw materials (Figure 22·6). Limestone is heated to produce calcium oxide and carbon dioxide, as described in Section 22·2. The carbon dioxide is then bubbled into a cold aqueous solution of sodium chloride and ammonia. In the solution, carbonic acid is formed in equilibrium with the dissolved carbon dioxide. The carbonic acid reacts with ammonia. Ammonium and bicarbonate ions are produced.

$$CO_2(aq) + H_2O(l) \rightleftharpoons H_2CO_3(aq)$$
$$NH_3(aq) + H_2CO_3(aq) \longrightarrow NH_4^+(aq) + HCO_3^-(aq)$$

At the low reaction temperature, sodium bicarbonate precipitates from the solution and is filtered off. When heated, it yields sodium carbonate. Carbon dioxide from the reaction is recycled.

$$NH_4^+(aq) + HCO_3^-(aq) + Na^+(aq) + Cl^-(aq) \longrightarrow$$
$$NaHCO_3(s) + NH_4Cl(aq)$$
$$2NaHCO_3(s) \xrightarrow{\text{heat}} Na_2CO_3(s) + CO_2(g) + H_2O(g)$$

Ammonium chloride is also recovered from the reaction liquor. It is combined with lime to give a second major product, calcium chloride. The ammonia that forms is recycled.

$$2NH_4Cl(s) + CaO(s) \longrightarrow CaCl_2(s) + 2NH_3(g) + H_2O(g)$$

22·3 Aluminum for the Masses

Aluminum is refined electrolytically from bauxite by the Hall–Heroult process.

Aluminum is present in many rocks and minerals and is the most abundant metal in the earth's crust. As a pure metal it has a low density, good electrical conductivity, and corrosion resistance. These properties make it valuable as a structural metal, as well as in the manufacture of many essential products. Freshly formed aluminum is highly reactive. It will react with oxygen, water, acids, and bases. Fortunately, when aluminum is exposed to air, an adherent film of oxide quickly forms, protecting it from further chemical reactions. Until the end of the last century, however, aluminum sold for the same price as silver. At that time only the rich could afford aluminum items.

Figure 22·7
Our chief source of aluminum is bauxite, a reddish-brown ore. When this ore is heated with coke (the black substance), aluminum oxide (the white powder) is formed. Aluminum metal is obtained from aluminum oxide by electrolysis.

Aluminum was expensive because chemists were unable to produce it by the electrolysis of molten aluminum halides. These compounds have relatively low boiling points. They distill out of the electrolyzing baths at the high operating temperatures necessary. The melting point of another potential raw material, aluminum oxide, was over 2000°C. No practical way of melting it was available.

The first commercial process for the production of aluminum was invented almost simultaneously by Paul Heroult, a Frenchman, and Charles Hall, an American. Hall's chemistry professor at Oberlin College challenged class members to develop a cheap way to produce aluminum. After graduation, Hall set up a laboratory in a woodshed to tackle this problem. Within a year, he discovered that cryolite, Na_3AlF_6, would dissolve aluminum oxide. A low-melting solution formed, from which aluminum could be obtained by electrolysis.

This process is essentially the method used for aluminum production today. Modern production is a continuous process, however, using long lines of electrolytic cells connected in series. The structure of an individual cell is shown in Figure 22·8. In a cell, cryolite is melted in a large iron tank lined with carbon. The carbon is the cathode of the cell. Refined bauxite, an aluminum ore rich in Al_2O_3, is dissolved in the melted cryolite at a temperature slightly below 1000°C. Large carbon rods serve as the anode. When a current passes through the cell, aluminum ions are reduced at the cathode. Molten aluminum sinks to the bottom of the tank where it is periodically drawn off. Oxygen is liberated at the anode. It reacts with the carbon, producing carbon dioxide. Thus the anodes must be replaced at regular intervals.

$$\text{Cathode reaction: } Al^{3+} + 3e^- \longrightarrow Al$$

$$\text{Anode reaction: } 2O^{2-} \longrightarrow O_2 + 4e^-$$

$$\text{Net cell reaction: } 4Al^{3+} + 6O^{2-} \longrightarrow 4Al + 3O_2$$

To make 1 kg of aluminum metal requires 2 kg of aluminum oxide and 0.5 kg of carbon anode. Eight to ten kilowatt hours of electricity are needed per kilogram of product. Aluminum plants are often located near hydroelectric power plants where the cost of electricity is relatively low.

Figure 22·8
In the Hall–Heroult process, aluminum is produced by passing an electric current through an electrolyte of fused cryolite and aluminum oxide. The molten aluminum is withdrawn from the bottom of the tank.

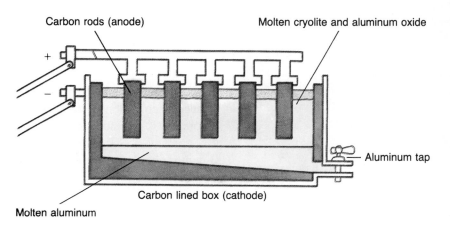

Carbon rods (anode)

Molten cryolite and aluminum oxide

Aluminum tap

Carbon lined box (cathode)

Molten aluminum

Figure 22·9
Fusible alloys that have melting points lower than the boiling point of water are used in automatic sprinkling systems for buildings. These alloys are usually made of lead, tin, cadmium, and bismuth.

Tin and lead are components of many alloys.

The transition metals have typical metallic properties.

22·4 Tin and Lead

Tin and lead are the metals of Group 4A. Tin is usually found in nature as its oxide, SnO_2. The mineral is reduced to the free metal by heating with coke.

$$SnO_2(s) + C(s) \longrightarrow Sn(s) + CO_2(g)$$

Lead is found chiefly as the sulfide ore galena, PbS. The ore is roasted in air to to produce the oxide, which is then reduced to metallic lead by heating with carbon.

$$2PbS(s) + 3O_2(g) \longrightarrow 2PbO(s) + 2SO_2(g)$$

$$2PbO(s) + C(s) \longrightarrow 2Pb(s) + CO_2(g)$$

Because tin and lead are not very reactive, they have many uses as the free metal. Both are widely utilized in alloys. **Bronze** *is an alloy of tin, copper and zinc.* Solder is an alloy of lead and tin.

Tin is applied as a thin coating to iron or steel to make tin cans. The tin protects the iron against corrosion, particularly that caused by acidic foods. A tin compound, stannous fluoride (SnF_2), is an important ingredient in some toothpastes.

Since Roman times lead has been used in plumbing. It is also used to make lead storage batteries and in the manufacture of tetraethyl lead, $Pb(C_2H_5)_4$. In small quantities this compound improves the octane rating of gasoline. The current switch to lead-free gasolines began when scientists discovered the toxic effects of lead from exhaust gases.

22·5 The Transition Metals

The transition metals exhibit typical metallic properties. In general, they are ductile, malleable, and good conductors of heat and electricity. With the exception of copper and gold, they have a silvery luster. Some important uses of these metals are shown in Table 22·3.

Titanium is an important structural metal. It is strong and corrosion resistant. Moreover, its density is about half that of iron. Titanium alloys are used in high performance aircraft engines and missiles.

The most important compound of titanium is its white dioxide, TiO_2, commonly used as a pigment in white paint. Titanium tetrachloride, $TiCl_4$, is a clear, colorless liquid. Because of its rapid reaction with damp air, it is employed by the military to make dense smoke screens.

$$TiCl_4(l) + 2H_2O(l) \longrightarrow TiO_2(s) + 4HCl(g)$$

Chromium is a hard, brittle metal with a white luster. Its extreme resistance to corrosion makes it an ideal coating for iron and steel objects. Chromium is an important ingredient in stainless steel. Typical stainless steel contains about 18% chromium and 10% nickel, with trace amounts of carbon, manganese, and phosphorous.

Like most transition metals, chromium has more than one oxidation state. The most common oxidation states of chromium are +2, +3, and +6. The metal has an oxidation number of +6 in two polyatomic ions:

Figure 22·10
Many jet engine parts are made from hard, corrosion-resistant titanium alloys.

Table 22·3	Common Transition Metals and Their Uses
Metal	Uses
Cadmium (Cd)	Batteries; control rods for nuclear reactors
Chromium (Cr)	Plating; making stainless steel
Cobalt (Co)	Alloys; treatment of cancer (Co-60 only)
Copper (Cu)	Electrical wiring; plumbing; coinage
Gold (Au)	Jewelry; ornaments; standard of wealth
Iron (Fe)	Steel; magnets
Manganese (Mn)	Steel; nonferrous alloys
Mercury (Hg)	Lamps; switches; thermometers; barometers
Nickel (Ni)	Hardens steel; plating; catalyst
Platinum (Pt)	Catalyst; electronics; lab-ware; jewelry
Silver (Ag)	Mirrors; jewelry; photography; coins
Tantalum (Ta)	Surgery; corrosion resistant equipment
Titanium (Ti)	Combustion chambers for rockets and jets
Tungsten (W)	Filaments for light bulbs; alloys
Vanadium (V)	Shock resistant steel alloys; catalyst
Zinc (Zn)	Galvanized iron; brass; dry cells

The compounds of chromium are colored in all of its oxidation states. Its name is derived from the Greek word for color, *chroma*.

chromate, CrO_4^{2-}, and dichromate, $Cr_2O_7^{2-}$. All compounds in which chromium is in the +6 oxidation state are powerful oxidizing agents, particularly in acid solution.

Zinc is one of industry's most useful metals. It is obtained from the oxide ore zinc blende. Large amounts of zinc are used to produce galvanized iron. This is iron coated with a thin layer of zinc to protect it from corrosion. Zinc is also a component of several alloys. Brass is an alloy of copper and zinc; bronze is an alloy of tin, copper, and zinc. In ordinary dry cell batteries the zinc lining acts as the anode.

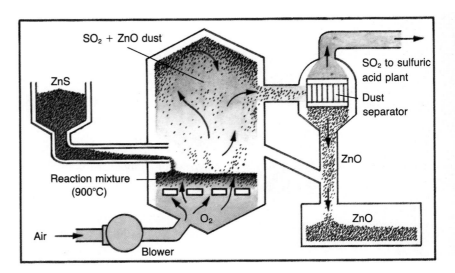

Figure 22·11
When hot zinc sulfide is treated with compressed air, it reacts to form zinc oxide dust and sulfur dioxide. Later carbon monoxide is used to reduce the zinc oxide to zinc metal.

Figure 22·12
Strong permanent magnets are made from alloys of iron with nickel, cobalt, and small amounts of other metals.

22·6 Iron, Cobalt, and Nickel

Iron, cobalt, and nickel share a number of common properties. Their densities are similar, as are their melting and boiling points. Their most striking physical property, however, is magnetism. Iron is the most strongly magnetic, and nickel is the least magnetic of the three metals.

Making up about 5% of the earth's crust, iron is the second most abundant metal. (Aluminum is the most abundant.) Common iron minerals are Fe_2O_3 (the red oxide, hematite) and Fe_3O_4 (magnetite).

The world's largest nickel and cobalt deposits are in Ontario, Canada. The two metals occur as sulfide ores, together with copper, silver, iron, platinum, paladium, and iridium. Most of the nickel and cobalt produced today is used in the manufacture of steels. Nickel makes steel more ductile and corrosion resistant.

Unlike iron, nickel and cobalt are resistant to atmospheric corrosion. Nickel is often used to electroplate iron and steel objects before they are plated with chromium. **Monel metal,** *a strong, corrosion-resistant alloy of nickel and copper,* is used for propeller shafts of seagoing vessels. Stellite, an alloy of cobalt, chromium, and tungsten, retains its hardness when hot. It is useful for high-speed cutting tools and drill bits. Both cobalt and nickel are used as catalysts in industrial processes. For example, finely divided nickel catalyzes the hydrogenation of vegetable oils.

■ Iron, cobalt, and nickel are the magnetic metals.

22·7 Copper, Silver, and Gold

Copper, silver, and gold have low chemical activities and often occur naturally in the free state. They were the first metals collected and worked by humans. In the Middle East, copper and gold artifacts dating back to about 7,000 B.C. have been found.

Copper was probably the first metal to be reduced from its ore. Some of the most important copper ores are chalcopyrite, $CuFeS_2$, chalcocite, Cu_2S, and cuprite, Cu_2O. Low grade sulfide ores are processed into copper of high purity by reduction and electrolytic refining. The crushed ore, which may be less than 1% copper, is concentrated by flotation (Figure 22·19). In the smelter furnaces, oxygen-enriched air converts some of the sulfide to the oxide.

$$2Cu_2S(s) + 3O_2(g) \longrightarrow 2Cu_2O(s) + 2SO_2(g)$$

The mixture of copper(I) sulfide and copper(I) oxide reacts, forming copper and sulfur dioxide.

$$2Cu_2O(s) + Cu_2S(s) \longrightarrow 6Cu(s) + SO_2(g)$$

The molten copper is poured into slabs called "blister copper" with 98.5% to 99.5% purity. The final step is electrolytic refining, which produces 99.99% pure copper.

Copper is the most widely-used metal for electrical wiring. Only silver is a better conductor of electricity. Copper is also widely used in plumbing for pipes that carry hot or cold water.

■ Copper, silver, and gold are less reactive than most other metals.

These three metals have similar electron configurations. Each has one s^1 electron just outside a complete d^{10} sublevel.

Figure 22·13
Turquoise is one of the many beautiful copper-containing ores.

a

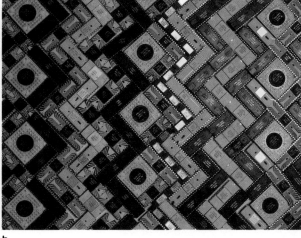

b

Figure 22·14
Copper, silver, and gold are excellent conductors. **a** Copper tubing is also used for plumbing. **b** Gold is often used for the contacts on computer chips.

The tarnish on silverware is a thin coating of black Ag_2S.

Gold slowly dissolves in *aqua regia,* a mixture of concentrated hydrochloric and nitric acids.

Silver occurs as the free metal and as the sulfide ore argentite, Ag_2S. Today, however, most commercial silver is produced as a by-product in the processing of copper, lead, and zinc ores. The muddy layers that collect on the bottom of electrolysis tanks in copper refining are the best source of silver. The mud is treated with sulfuric acid, forming silver sulfate. Then copper rods are dipped into the solution and silver deposits form on the copper.

$$Ag_2SO_4(aq) + Cu(s) \longrightarrow CuSO_4(aq) + 2Ag(s)$$

Because of its high luster, silver reflects light extremely well and has long been used to coat the backs of mirrors. The light-sensitive silver halides are utilized in photographic processes.

Gold occurs chiefly as small particles of the free metal in veins of quartz. About 5 g of gold is produced from a metric ton of gold-bearing rock. Gold is also recovered as a by-product of copper refining. It is the most malleable and ductile of all metals and can be pounded into sheets so thin that they transmit light. Gold leaf, as it is called, is used in decorative lettering and other forms of ornamentation. Corrosion resistance coupled with high electrical and thermal conductivity makes gold valuable in the high-tech industries. It is used to plate the contacts in microcircuits and to cover the external surfaces of satellite components.

Figure 22·15
The last step in producing copper is electrolysis. Blister copper is placed at the anode. Pure copper accumulates at the cathode. About six metric tons of rock is mined to produce ten kilograms of copper metal.

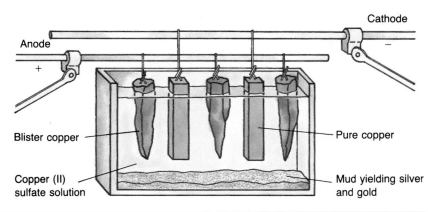

Cathode

Anode

+ −

Blister copper

Pure copper

Copper (II) sulfate solution

Mud yielding silver and gold

Figure 22·16
Mercury pollution has forced the
closing of many waterways to fishing.

22·B Toxic Metals

Metals are among the industrial waste products that contaminate the environment. Some of these elements are essential for human nutrition in trace amounts. Nevertheless, higher concentrations are toxic (Table 22·4). Others belong to a group of heavy metals that have no known biological function in humans. For example, low concentrations of lead, cadmium, and mercury produce toxic effects. Within the body, heavy-metal ions eventually cause irreversible damage to the central nervous system (Table 22·5).

Metals vary greatly in their toxic properties. Copper, for example, has a relatively low toxicity. A deficiency of copper in the diet causes anemia and nerve cell degeneration. Only 2 mg ingested daily prevents these effects. If the copper intake is increased to 50 mg, however, vomiting and diarrhea occur.

By contrast, mercury is highly toxic and is a serious environmental pollutant. Scientists have only recently discovered that bacteria convert insoluble forms of mercury, once thought harmless, into highly toxic dimethyl mercury, $(CH_3)_2Hg$. This volatile liquid can enter the body through the skin or via the lungs.

For decades mercury and mercury salts have been used in industrial processes. As a result, large quantities of these substances have been discarded into the environment. Much of this mercury has collected in lake and river sediments. Here, dimethyl mercury accumulates in the tissues of aquatic plants and small animals. Like other heavy metals, it is eliminated from living tissues very slowly. It moves up the food chain, becoming more concentrated with each step (Figure 22·17). This sequence makes some fish unfit for human consumption and creates a long-term environmental hazard.

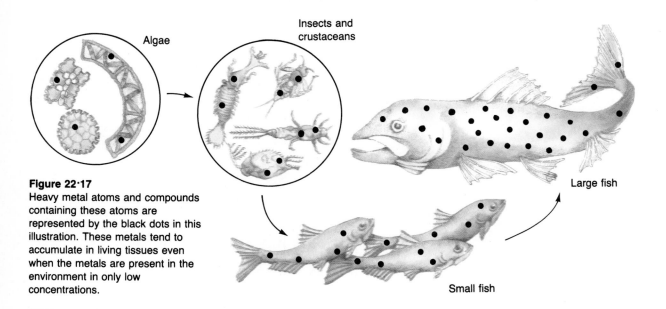

Algae

Insects and
crustaceans

Large fish

Small fish

Figure 22·17
Heavy metal atoms and compounds containing these atoms are represented by the black dots in this illustration. These metals tend to accumulate in living tissues even when the metals are present in the environment in only low concentrations.

Table 22·4	Some Essential Elements that Produce Toxic Effects		
Element	Required for	Toxic effect	Recommended limit in drinking water (mg/L)
Arsenic	Reproduction	Mental disturbance, kidney failure	0.05
Copper	Component of several enzymes, formation of hemoglobin	Liver damage	1.0
Selenium	Normal liver function	Mental disturbance, liver damage	0.01

Figure 22·18
Most metals are refined from ores. Those shown here (clockwise from the upper left) are: cinnabar (mercury), sphalerite (zinc), wulfenite (lead, molybdenum), malachite (copper), and rutile (titanium) in the center.

Most metals are obtained from ore deposits.

Table 22·5	Toxic Metals	
Element	Toxic effect	Recommended limit in drinking water (mg/L)
Cadmium	Kidney damage, loss of red blood cells	0.01
Lead	Mental retardation in children, convulsions, kidney failure	0.05
Mercury	Birth defects, nerve damage, paralysis, brain damage	0.002

22·8 Metal Ores

Although some metals are extracted from seawater, most come from mineral deposits in the earth. *Minerals that are used for the commercial production of metals are called* **ores.** Some common metal ores are listed in Table 22·6.

Metallurgy *involves the various procedures used to separate metals from their ores.* Many of these techniques were developed over the centuries by trial and error. Separating metals from their ores requires three steps.

1. concentrating the ore
2. chemically reducing the ore to the metal
3. refining and purifying the metal

Freshly mined ore contains various amounts of worthless sand and rock called **gangue.** If the quantity of gangue is high, the ore is crushed and ground to separate the mineral and gangue. The ore is then enriched by physical processes such as washing, froth flotation, or magnetic separation. These processes remove the gangue. Washing the crushed ore with a turbulent stream of water removes lighter gangue from a mineral.

a

b

Figure 22·19
a An entire mountain has been dug away to get copper out of the world's largest open pit copper mine in Bingham Canyon, Utah.
b Finely crushed copper ore is agitated with detergent and oil in the copper flotation process. Oil-coated ore particles stick to air bubbles rising to the surface where they can be skimmed off.

Washing helps enrich some iron ores. *The* **froth flotation** *method is commonly used to enrich the sulfide ores of copper and lead* (Figure 22·19). Finely crushed ore is agitated with a detergent and oil. The oil sticks to the particles of sulfide, but not to the gangue. When air is blown into the mixture, oil-coated ore particles stick to the bubbles, and rise to the surface where they can be skimmed off. The gangue settles to the bottom and is removed at intervals.

Many ores need a second pretreatment. **Roasting** *is used to purify ores by heating the ore with air*. Enriched sulfide ores are usually roasted to drive off volatile impurities. Roasting converts the sulfides to oxides.

$$2PbS(s) + 3O_2(g) \longrightarrow 2PbO(s) + 2SO_2(g)$$

$$2ZnS(s) + 3O_2(g) \longrightarrow 2ZnO(s) + 2SO_2(g)$$

The sulfur dioxide formed is a serious air pollutant. It is removed from exhaust gases by reacting it with calcium oxide to form calcium sulfite.

$$CaO(s) + SO_2(g) \longrightarrow CaSO_3(s)$$

Smelting *involves melting an ore to remove impurities*. It is another type of refining process. During smelting, metal ions in an ore are reduced at a high temperature to the molten metal. A **flux** *can be added to a furnace to combine with undesired material in an ore*. The flux (usually lime) combines with the gangue (usually sand) at high temperatures. A molten material called slag is formed. **Slag** *is the fused waste material from a smelting process*.

$$\underset{\text{Flux}}{CaO(s)} + \underset{\text{Gangue}}{SiO_2(s)} \longrightarrow \underset{\text{Slag}}{CaSiO_3(s)}$$

The less dense slag floats on the surface and is removed. Slag helps prevent contact between the molten metal and oxygen in the air.

Table 22·6	Metal Ores	
Metal	Ore	Process
Chromium	chromite, $FeCr_2O_4$	reduction, electrolysis
Cobalt	cobalite, $CoAsS$	roasting, reduction
Copper	chalcopyrite, $CuFeS_2$ chalcocite, Cu_2S cuprite, Cu_2O	flotation, reduction, electrolysis
Lead	galena, PbS	flotation, roasting, reduction
Nickel	pentlandite, NiS	flotation, roasting, reduction
Tin	cassiterite, SnO_2	flotation, reduction
Titanium	rutile, TiO_2	convert to $TiCl_4$, reduction
Zinc	spahlerite, ZnS	roasting, reduction

Figure 22·20
The refining of iron is an important
industrial process.

22·9 The Blast Furnace

The metals in most ores have positive oxidation numbers. Thus production of the free metal from an ore requires reduction. Oxides of many metals can be reduced by carbon. *A* **blast furnace** *is a towerlike furnace in which carbon is used to reduce iron ores to metallic iron.* Once fired up, these huge vessels may operate continuously for several years.

The **charge** *is a load of material added to a furnace.* A mixture of iron ore, limestone, and coke enters the top of the blast furnace through a hopper. A typical ore contains iron oxide (Fe_2O_3) and gangue (sand). When heated, the limestone produces a flux (CaO) which reacts with the sand to form a slag (Section 22·8). Coke is almost pure carbon that is produced when coal is heated and the volatile matter is driven off. In the blast furnace, coke reduces the iron ore to the free metal.

To get the reaction going, a blast of hot air is blown up through the furnace. Rapid combustion of coke with the hot air occurs first.

$$C(s) + O_2(g) \longrightarrow CO_2(g) + \text{heat}$$

This reaction is very exothermic. It raises the temperature to about 2000°C. As the carbon dioxide rises up through the furnace, it is reduced by the hot coke to carbon monoxide.

$$CO_2(g) + C(s) \longrightarrow 2CO(g)$$

This reaction is endothermic and causes the temperature in the upper part of the furnace to drop to about 1300°C. As the carbon monoxide rises through the charge, it reacts with the iron oxide to form metallic iron. A series of redox reactions occurs in which the iron compounds are reduced and carbon monoxide is oxidized.

$$3Fe_2O_3(s) + CO(g) \longrightarrow 2Fe_3O_4(s) + CO_2(g)$$

$$Fe_3O_4(s) + CO(g) \longrightarrow 3FeO(s) + CO_2(g)$$

$$FeO(s) + CO(g) \longrightarrow Fe(s) + CO_2(g)$$

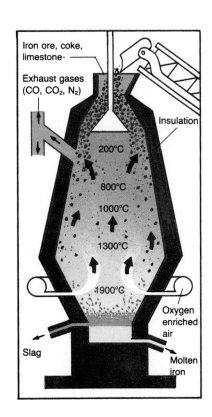

Iron ore, coke, limestone·

Exhaust gases (CO, CO₂, N₂)

Insulation

200°C

800°C

1000°C

1300°C

1900°C

Oxygen enriched air

Slag

Molten iron

Figure 22·21
A blast furnace is about 30 m high and 10 m in diameter. Iron ore, limestone, and coke (a form of carbon) are added at the top. During the process, carbon, the reducing agent, is oxidized to CO_2. The limestone converts sand in the ore to silicate slag.

The reduction of iron ore to iron takes place in the middle and upper portions of the furnace. It is often summarized as a single equation.

$$Fe_2O_3(s) + 3CO(g) \longrightarrow 2Fe(s) + 3CO_2(g)$$

The molten iron trickles down through the charge and collects in a well at the bottom of the furnace. About every six hours, the furnace must be tapped to drain off the iron. The molten slag also trickles down through the charge and collects on the surface of the iron. It is drawn off periodically when the furnace is tapped.

Some blast furnaces produce up to 2500 tons of pig iron a day. *This* **pig iron** *still contains impurities and usually undergoes further treatment to produce steel.* To produce a ton of pig iron requires two tons of iron ore, one ton of coke, 0.3 ton of limestone, and four tons of air. Besides the iron, 0.6 ton of slag and six tons of flue gas are produced. The slag is a valuable by-product, used in the manufacture of Portland cement.

Pig iron is crude iron as it comes from a blast furnace. The molten metal is cast in sand molds which resemble a pig feeding her litter.

22·10 Steelmaking

Pig iron has little practical use. The impurities make it brittle and reduce its tensile strength. These impurities include 3%–5% carbon and smaller amounts of phosphorus, manganese, silica, and sulfur. *When pig iron is melted with scrap iron, the product is called* **cast iron.** Cast iron cannot be rolled, forged, or welded, but articles can be made from it by casting them in a mold. Cast iron has limited value as a structural material.

Most pig iron is converted to steel. This requires decreasing the carbon content (to 0.02%–2.0%) and the removal of other impurities. At the same time, specific amounts of other metals are added to produce a steel with the desired qualities (Table 22·7).

Steel has a much lower carbon content than cast iron.

One of the first methods of making steel was invented in England in 1856 by Sir Henry Bessemer. *In the* **Bessemer process,** *a blast of hot air is bubbled through molten pig iron in a huge egg-shaped converter.* The hot air oxidizes the excess carbon in each batch of about 25 tons of iron. A vigorous reaction between the carbon and air takes place. Because of this, careful adjustment of the percentages of carbon and other alloying elements is not possible.

Table 22·7	The Composition of Some Alloy Steels*		
Name	Composition	Characteristics	Uses
Nickel steel	Ni 3.5%	Tough, hard	Crankshafts
Chrome steel	Cr 1.0%	Tough, strong	Springs
Stainless steel	Cr 12% − 30%	Hard, resists corrosion	Surgical implements
Manganese steel	Mn 12% − 14%	Holds temper	Safes
Tungsten steel	W 5%	Maintains hardness when hot	High speed cutting tools

*The carbon content is typically 0.1 to 1.0 percent.

Figure 22·22
In an open hearth furnace two burners
alternate to produce bursts of hot air
and burning gases. The chambers on
each side of the hearth store the heat.

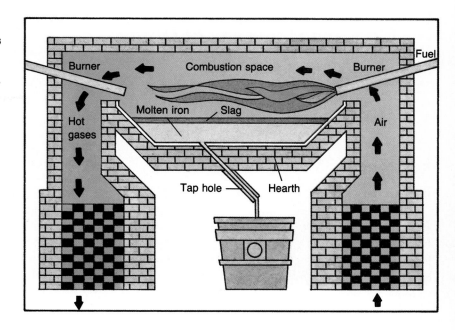

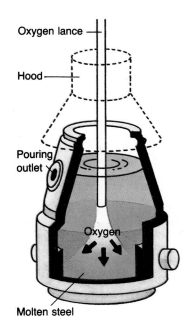

Figure 22·23
In a basic oxygen furnace, scrap steel
is mixed with molten iron from a blast
furnace. Oxygen is introduced through
the lance to oxidize the impurities in
the charge.

The **open-hearth method** *uses a shallow lined vessel to produce high quality steel in a five to eight hour process.* The hearth, or floor of the open hearth furnace, is a shallow vessel. It is approximately 13 m long, 7 m wide, and 1 m deep. The hearth is lined with a basic or an acidic lining, depending on the type of pig iron being purified. In North America, iron ores usually have acid impurities (sulfur or phosphorus). Therefore basic linings of calcium oxide and magnesium oxide are used. An arched roof of firebrick covers the hearth. The floor of the hearth is exposed to the blast of hot air and the burning gases used to heat the steel. Charges of 100 tons or more include pig iron, rusty scrap iron or smaller amounts of iron ore, and materials for special alloys. As the charge melts, chemical reactions convert the molten mass into steel. Carbon dioxide gas bubbles out of the melt, and the oxides of sulfur and phosphorus combine with the basic oxides of the lining to form slag. Since the process is slow, each batch of steel can be analyzed as needed to ensure quality control. This is the chief advantage of this method over the Bessemer process. Alloying metals such as manganese, nickel, chromium, molybdenum, tungsten, and vanadium may be added as needed before the charge is poured. When the steel is ready, the furnace is tapped and the steel is ready for fabrication.

The **basic oxygen process** *uses calcium oxide and pressurized oxygen to produce high quality steel.* Most steel today is made by this process which usually takes about one hour per batch (Figure 22·23). A batch of steel is about 300 metric tons. Molten pig iron, scrap iron, and powdered limestone are placed in a converter lined with a basic oxide such as calcium oxide. Pure oxygen, blown through a narrow tube called a lance at about 10 atmospheres pressure, oxidizes the impurities in the charge. No external heat source is required. The rapid, highly exothermic reactions cause the contents to remain mixed and molten.

The Chemistry of Metals

Chapter Review

Key Terms

basic oxygen process	22·10	metallurgy	22·8
Bessemer process	22·10	Monel metal	22·6
blast furnace	22·9	open-hearth method	22·10
bronze	22·4	ore	22·8
cast iron	22·10	pig iron	22·9
charge	22·9	roasting	22·8
froth flotation	22·8	slag	22·8
flux	22·8	slaked lime	22·2
gangue	22·8	smelting	22·8
lime	22·2		

Chapter Summary

The alkali metals have large atomic radii. This helps explain their low densities, low ionization energies, and high reactivities. Because they ionize so readily, the alkali metals do not occur naturally as free metals. Important sodium compounds are sodium hydroxide and sodium carbonate.

The alkaline earth metals are also not found free in nature. They are less reactive, however, than the alkali metals. Calcium and magnesium are the two most important alkaline earth metals. Alkaline earth oxides and hydroxides such as calcium oxide (lime) and calcium hydroxide (slaked lime) have many industrial uses.

Aluminum, in Group 3A, is the most abundant metal in the earth's crust. It is not found as a free metal. Its value in industry derives from its corrosion-resistance and good electrical conductivity.

Tin and lead are the metals of Group 4A. They have numerous uses as both the free metal and in alloys such as bronze and solder. Tin is used in plating "tin cans," and lead is used in plumbing.

Many transition metals, such as titanium, chromium, and zinc, are used to make alloys. Iron, cobalt, and nickel are also prized for their magnetic

properties. Monel metal is a corrosion-resistant alloy of copper and nickel. Copper, silver, and gold are excellent conductors.

Ores are minerals used for the commercial production of metals. Metallurgy involves various procedures used to separate metals from their ores. In the purifying of metals the worthless gangue must be removed from the ore.

A blast furnace is used to reduce iron ore contained in the charge to metallic iron. This smelting process produces pig iron, which is further refined into steel.

Practice Questions and Problems

3. What are the sources of the Group 1A metals? *22·1*

4. Why do the alkali metals have low densities and low ionization energies? *22·1*

5. When sodium is exposed to oxygen, it forms a peroxide. When this compound is added to water, it gives a solution of sodium hydroxide. The same solution can be obtained by adding sodium to water. Write balanced equations for these reactions. *22·1*

6. What is the chemical formula for lye? *22·1*

7. What are some uses of sodium metal? *22·1*

8. What are the group names for the elements in Group 1A and Group 2A? *22·2*

9. What is lime? How is lime made from calcium carbonate, $CaCO_3$? *22·2*

10. How are the alkaline earth metals calcium and magnesium prepared? *22·2*

11. Which alkaline earth metals react with cold water and which do not? Write a typical equation that shows such a reaction. *22·2*

12. Why do the alkaline earth metals as a group have higher densities than the alkali metals? *22·2*

13. How does the reactivity of the Group 2A metals compare to that of the Group 1A metals? *22·2*

14. Give two reactions by which $Ca(OH)_2$ can be made. *22·2*

15. Write the equation that represents the setting of mortar. *22·2*

16. When calcium metal is exposed to air, it forms an oxide. This oxide reacts with water to form calcium hydroxide. Calcium hydroxide can also be made by adding calcium metal to water. Write a balanced equation for each reaction. *22·2*

17. Name an aluminum ore rich in Al_2O_3. *22·3*

18. Aluminum oxide must be dissolved in melted cryolite before it can be electrolyzed. Why? *22·3*

19. Describe the physical properties of aluminum that make it a commercially valuable metal. *22·3*

20. Aluminum is produced by electrolysis. Write the electrode reactions for the process. *22·3*

21. What are some uses for tin and lead? *22·4*

22. Write equations for the preparation of lead from galena, its sulfide ore. *22·4*

23. What are the common oxidation states of chromium? *22·5*

24. What is the most important compound of titanium? Why is titanium a commercially useful metal? *22·5*

25. Give two uses of chromium metal. *22·5*

26. What are hematite and magnetite? *22·6*

27. Write formulas for the oxides of iron. *22·6*

28. What are the two most common oxidation states of iron? *22·6*

29. Calculate the mass percent of metal in each of the following mineral compounds.
  a. Fe_3O_4 **b.** Fe_2O_3 **c.** $CoAsS$ *22·6*

30. Nickel is an important metal. Why? What is *monel* metal? *22·6*

31. What are the properties of cobalt and how is it used? *22·6*

32. Copper, silver, and gold are among the few metals that have been used for thousands of years. Explain. *22·7*

33. The mud that deposits during the electrolysis of copper has great commercial value. Why? *22·7*

34. Give examples of practical applications of the metals copper, silver, and gold. *22·7*

35. What is an ore? *22·7*

36. Name an ore that contains each element.
  a. silver **b.** gold *22·7*

37. Explain the term *metallurgy*. *22·8*

38. How does froth flotation separate an ore mineral from its impurities? *22·8*

39. What is *gangue?* *22·8*

40. Why is zinc ore roasted? *22·8*

41. What is slag? *22·8*

42. Reduction and not oxidation is required to convert the metal in a compound to the free metal. Why? *22·8*

43. List the steps involved in extracting a metal from its ore. Briefly describe the significance of each step. *22·8*

44. How does the blast furnace get its name? *22·9*

45. Describe the composition of the charge added to a blast furnace. *22·9*

46. Write an equation that summarizes the reactions that take place in the upper regions of a blast furnace. *22·9*

47. How is slag formed in a blast furnace? *22·9*

48. What is steel? How does steel differ from pig iron and from cast iron? *22·10*

49. Describe the open hearth method for making steel. *22·10*

50. Name three different types of steel. Comment on their composition, characteristics, and use. *22·10*

Mastery Questions and Problems

51. Calculate the mass percent of aluminum in cryolite, Na_3AlF_6. *22·3*

52. A sample of magnetite contains Fe_3O_4 76.0%, sand (SiO_2) 11.0%, and other impurities 13.0%. Calculate the percent by mass of iron in the ore. *22·9*

53. Complete and balance each of the following equations. *22·1*
  a. $Na + O_2 \longrightarrow$
  b. $Na + H_2O \longrightarrow$
  c. $Cs + O_2 \longrightarrow$

54. At which electrode is the free metal produced in the electrolysis of a metal compound? Explain your answer. *22·3*

55. Describe the *basic oxygen* process. Why has this process largely replaced the open hearth method for steel production? *22·10*

56. Compare the alkali metals with the alkaline earth metals with respect to their densities. Explain the comparisons. *22·2*

57. A commercially important source of titanium is ilmenite, $FeTiO_3$. Calculate the mass percent of titanium in ilmenite. *22·5*

58. Describe and illustrate the electrolytic refining of copper. *22·7*

59. Calculate the percentage of cobalt in cobaltite containing 72.6% CoAsS by mass. How many kilograms of cobalt would be contained in 1000 kg of the ore? *22·6*

60. Describe the processes used to obtain the following elements from their natural sources.
  a. Al   **b.** Cu   **c.** Mg   *22·7*

61. A copper ore contains 7.2% Cu_2S by mass. The ore is concentrated by flotation and 18% of the Cu_2S is lost. If 17% of the Cu_2S that remains is lost during copper production, how much ore will be needed to produce 5.00 kg of copper? *22·7*

Review Questions and Problems

62. Write the chemical formula for each of the following ionic compounds.
  a. potassium sulfide   **d.** sodium iodide
  b. barium bromide   **e.** calcium oxide
  c. aluminum fluoride

63. Write complete electron configurations for the following.
  a. Fe   **e.** Cu
  b. V   **f.** Ni^{2+}
  c. Ag   **g.** Zn
  d. Fe^{3+} **h.** Ag^+

64. How many outer-shell d electrons are in each of these transitions metal ions?
  a. Mo^{3+} **c.** Ir^{3+}
  b. Cu^{2+} **d.** Fe^{3+}

65. A sample of spring water contains 46.0 mg of magnesium ions per liter.
  a. What is the molarity of Mg^{2+} in the sample?
  b. What volume of this water contains 1.00 mol Mg^{2+}?

66. What are the ions produced when the following substances are dissolved in water?
  a. LiBr   **c.** KI
  b. $Ca(OH)_2$ **d.** $CdBr_2$

67. Classify each of the following compounds as a nonelectrolyte, a weak electrolyte, or a strong electrolyte.
  a. CH_3COCH_3 (acetone)   **d.** KNO_3
  b. C_2H_5OH (ethyl alcohol)   **e.** Na_2SO_3
  c. $C_2H_4O_2$ (acetic acid)   **f.** $CaCl_2$

68. Balance the following equation.
$$IO_3^-(aq) + Cr(OH)_4^-(aq) \longrightarrow$$
$$I^-(aq) + CrO_4^{2-}(aq) \text{ (basic)}$$

69. Determine the oxidation of nitrogen in each of the following.   **a.** N_2 **b.** NO_3^- **c.** NO_2 **d.** N_2O **e.** NO_2^-

70. Identify the oxidation and reduction half-reactions in the following equation.
$$2Ti^{2+}(aq) + Co^{2+}(aq) \longrightarrow 2Ti^{3+}(aq) + Co(s)$$

71. Identify the oxidizing agent and the reducing agent in the following reaction.
$$I_2O_5(s) + 5CO(g) \longrightarrow 5CO_2(g) + I_2(s)$$

72. Give the chemical formula for each of these compounds.
  a. copper(I) bromide   **c.** cadmium sulfide
  b. zinc nitride   **d.** silver iodide

Challenging Questions and Problems

73. Calculate the mass in kilograms of sulfur dioxide produced in the roasting of one thousand kilograms of chalcocite ore containing Cu_2S 7.2%, Ag_2S 0.6%, and no other sulfur compounds.

74. A 0.50 g sample of metallic sodium is converted to NaCl by reaction with chlorine gas. What volume of Cl_2 at 20°C and 740 mm Hg will be required to react completely with the sodium?

75. Azurite, a dark blue copper mineral, has the following composition: Cu 55.3%, C 6.97%, O 37.1%, H 0.585%. Determine the simplest formula of this mineral.

76. Write the equation for the reaction that occurs when $Mg(OH)_2$ dissolves in hydrochloric acid. Use this equation to answer the following questions.
  a. How many moles of H^+ are required to react with 3.20 g $Mg(OH)_2$?
  b. Calculate the volume of 3.00 M HCl required to react with 3.20 g $Mg(OH)_2$?

77. Barium peroxide decomposes above 700°C according to this equation.

$$2BaO_2(s) \longrightarrow 2BaO(s) + O_2(g)$$

The oxygen liberated when 20.0 g of barium peroxide is heated, is collected in a 1-L flask at 25°C. Calculate the pressure in the flask.

78. How many grams of Co_3O_4 must react with an excess of aluminum to produce 500 g of cobalt metal, assuming 75% yield? The equation for the reaction is as follows.

$$3Co_3O_4 + 8Al \xrightarrow{heat} 9Co + 4Al_2O_3$$

Research Projects

1. How do growing plants use potassium? Why is it that other alkali metals cannot be substituted?

2. How is sodium hydroxide used in the production of paper pulp?

3. How did Charles Hall and Paul Heroult improve on the work of Henri Sainte Claire Deville?

4. How is aluminum recycled? What proportion of the aluminum used today is recycled aluminum?

5. How can rare metals be produced in space? How does this compare with their production on earth?

6. How has the search for gold been significant in history?

7. How are silver mirrors made?

8. Make a diagram of how mercury gets into the food chain.

9. How were iron tools developed in the Iron Age?

10. Make a timeline of the historical developments in metallurgy.

11. Describe Henry Bessemer's experimentation with steel manufacture. How did he become involved in this area? Why was his work significant for manufacturers?

12. Why were the nineteenth century advances in metallurgy important?

13. How does water pollution occur from mining mineral deposits? What can be done to prevent it?

14. Report on a land reclamation project in a strip-mined area.

Readings and References

Coombs, Charles. *Gold and Other Precious Metals.* New York: Morrow, 1981.

Hartmann, William R. "Mines in the Sky Promise Riches, a Greener Earth." *Smithsonian* (September 1982), pp. 70–77.

Kerrod, Robin. *Metals.* Morristown, NJ: Silver Burdett, 1982.

Orna, Mary Virginia. "Paintmaking Adventures." *ChemMatters:* American Chemical Society, (December 1984), pp. 12–13.

Page, Jake. "Moly Be-Damned." *Science 84* (July/August 1984), pp. 48–51.

Petit, Charles. "Neptune's Fortune." *Science 83* (January/February 1983), pp. 60–64.

Wertime, Theodore A., and James D. Muhly, eds. *The Coming of the Age of Iron.* New Haven, CT: Yale University Press, 1980.

23 The Chemistry of Nonmetals

Chapter Planning Guide

Section			Demonstrations and Experiments	Resource Materials
23·1	Hydrogen and Its Compounds	C*	Dem 23·1 Hydrogen	Objectives Worksheet 23, SPB Skillsheet 23, SPB
23·A	Reaction Alternatives: Preparing Hydrogen	E		
23·2	Oxygen	C	Dem 21·6 Electrolysis of Water	
23·3	Compounds of Oxygen	C	Dem 12·1 The Properties of the Elements Dem 23·2 Oxygen from Sodium Peroxide	
23·B	The Frasch Process	E		
23·4	Sulfur and Its Compounds	C	Dem 23·3 Sulfur Dioxide Exp 49 Allotropic Forms of Sulfur, LM	Quiz 23·1 Prelab 49, SPB
23·C	Sulfuric Acid	E		Indoor Air Pollution, ICT 23
23·5	Nitrogen	C		

23·6	Compounds of Nitrogen	C	Dem 23·4 Making Ammonia	Beyond the Text:
				   The Nitrogen Cycle and
				   Nitrogen Fixation

23·7	Preparation of the Halogens	C	Dem 23·5 Preparation of the Halogens	
23·8	Properties of the Halogens	C	Dem 23·6 Sublimation of Iodine Dem 23·7 Bleaching	Quiz 23·2 Reviewsheet 23, SPB Chapter 23 Test
*C = Core, O = Optional E = Enrichment, H = Honors			LM = Laboratory Manual	SPB = Skills Practice Book ICT = Issues in Chem. Tech.

Chapter Objectives

Having studied this chapter and done the problems, the student should be able to:

1. List some important commercial uses of hydrogen.
   23·1

2. Write a balanced chemical equation for photosynthesis.
   23·2

3. Use oxygen or sulfur to define allotropes.
   23·2, 23·4

4. Distinguish between an oxide and a peroxide. *23·3*

5. List some manufactured products which contain sulfur.
   23·4

6. Write representative equations for the formation of oxides and sulfides.
   23·3, 23·4

7. Describe the preparation of nitrogen and oxygen.
   23·2, 23·5

8. Explain the unreactive nature of elemental nitrogen.
   23·5

9. List some commercially important compounds of nitrogen.
   23·6

10. Describe the preparation of the halogens. *23·7*

11. Relate the properties of the halogens to their important commercial uses.
    23·8

Teaching Suggestions

Like the previous chapter, this chapter is descriptive in nature. There are few principles to explain. The content is mostly a statement of the facts relevant to the elements hydrogen, oxygen, sulfur, and nitrogen.

As with the previous chapter, you will probably wish to present these facts in lecture fashion. Again, try to add interest through demonstrations whenever possible.

23·1 Hydrogen and Its Compounds

Hydrogen is involved in many reactions and is found in many of the compounds encountered in this course so far. So most students are now quite familiar with this gas. To demonstrate the laboratory preparation of hydrogen and show its rapid combination with oxygen, do **Demonstration 23·1** *Hydrogen.*

23·2 Oxygen

23·3 Compounds of Oxygen

Like hydrogen, the chemistry of oxygen has already appeared in many places in this course. The students may wish to see some of its reactions again. If so, repeat **Demonstrations 1·12, 12·1, 12·2** and **17·1. Demonstrations 23·2** *Oxygen from Sodium Peroxide* show how to form oxygen.

23·4 Sulfur and Its Compounds

Sulfur is a unique element because it exists in so many forms. As a solid it appears as the monoclinic, rhombic, or amorphous forms. As a liquid, it can exist as S_8 rings, short chains, or long chains. **Experiment 49** *Allotropic Forms of Sulfur* shows these forms.

Demonstration 23·3 *Sulfur Dioxide* uses chemical "magic" to show the preparation of sulfur dioxide and some of its properties. The strong affinity of sulfuric acid for water can be shown by repeating **Demonstration 1·15** in which sugar is decomposed by sulfuric acid.

23·5 Nitrogen

23·6 Compounds of Nitrogen

The students should be reminded that our atmosphere is mostly nitrogen, not oxygen. The nitrogen molecule is stable and chemically unreactive. Yet, nitrogen compounds make up an important part of chemistry and are essential to living systems, both plant and animal. The reactions which "fix" nitrogen and change it from elemental to compound form are therefore very important.

Ammonia is one of the more useful nitrogen compounds. It displays an extraordinary solubility in water. **Demonstration 23·4** *Making Ammonia* shows its preparation from ammonium chloride.

23·7 Preparation of the Halogens

Demonstration 23·5 *Preparation of the Halogens* shows how they can be obtained from the halides.

23·8 Properties of the Halogens

The halogens have been discussed in nearly every chapter. Some of the experiments have included halogen compounds. You may need to do little more than remind the students of their previous experiences with the halogens.

Demonstration 23·6 *Sublimation of Iodine* shows its change from a solid to a gas. **Demonstration 23·7** *Bleaching* shows the oxidizing power of some of the halogen compounds.

Demonstrations

23·1 Hydrogen

Concept: Hydrogen can be liberated from water.

Materials: 5 g of mossy zinc, large test tube, test tube holder, one-hole stopper with a glass tube attached to a rubber tube, two small collection test tubes with stoppers, pneumatic trough, 10 mL of 6M sulfuric acid (H_2SO_4), safety goggles, wood splints, burning splint, matches.

Procedure: 1. Place the zinc in the large test tube and place in the holder. 2. Put water in the trough. 3. Fill a collection test tube with water and invert in the trough. 4. Place the open end of the rubber tube from the stopper assembly into the inverted collection tube. 5. Pour sufficient sulfuric acid into the large test tube to cover the zinc. 6. Once the solution starts to bubble vigorously, insert the stopper assembly into the mouth of the larger test tube and collect the hydrogen gas in the collection tube. 7. When the tube fills with hydrogen (when all the water has been displaced from the tube), insert a stopper, and set the tube aside. 8. Repeat the procedure with the other collection tube. 9. Invert one of the tubes and remove the stopper. Hydrogen is lighter than air and should remain in the test tube. 10. Insert a *glowing* wooden splint into the test tube. The splint is extinguished; hydrogen does not support combustion. 11. Remove the stopper from another inverted tube. 12. Bring a *burning* wood splint to the mouth of the tube. The hydrogen burns rapidly. 13. After the tube cools, observe the condensation of water on the walls. **Caution:** *Mixtures of hydrogen gas with air or oxygen are explosive. Wear goggles and keep students back.*

23·2 Oxygen from Sodium Peroxide

Concept: Water liberates oxygen from sodium peroxide.

Materials: 3 g of sodium peroxide (Na_2O_2), dropper pipet, water, test tube, test tube rack, wood splint, matches, safety goggles.

Procedure: 1. Place the sodium peroxide in the test tube. 2. Add water, drop by drop, to liberate oxygen. 3. Test for oxygen with a glowing splint. The presence of sodium is indicated by a yellow flame. **Caution:** *Sodium peroxide reacts violently with water.*

23·3 Sulfur Dioxide

Concept: Sulfur dioxide can be produced from sulfuric acid.

Materials: 0.25 g of sodium bisulfite ($NaHSO_3$), 3 mL of 6M sulfuric acid (H_2SO_4), 300 mL of 0.01M potassium permanganate ($KMnO_4$), 1-L Erlenmeyer flask, 500-mL glass cylinder, safety goggles.

Procedure: 1. Place the sodium bisulfite in the flask. 2. Pour in the sulfuric acid. 3. Sulfur dioxide is produced by the reaction:

$$HSO_3^-(aq) + H^+(aq) \rightarrow SO_2(g) + H_2O(l)$$

4. Pour the sulfur dioxide gas into a 500-mL glass cylinder. This gas pours easily because it is heavier than air. 5. Slowly pour the potassium permanganate solution into the cylinder containing the sulfur dioxide. 6. The purple color disappears. The reaction is:

$$2MnO_4(aq) + 5SO_2(g) + 2H_2O(l)$$
$$2Mn^{2+}(aq) + 5SO_4^{2-}(aq) + 4H^+(aq)$$

Caution: *Sulfur dioxide is an irritating gas. Avoid inhalation of fumes. Use a fume hood. Potassium permanganate is an irritant. Sulfuric acid is corrosive.*

23·4 Making Ammonia

Concept: Ammonia gas forms from ammonium chloride.

Materials: 30 g of ammonium chloride (NH_4Cl), 15 g of sodium hydroxide ($NaOH$), 10 mL of water, 500-mL Erlenmeyer flask, one-hole stopper with glass tube and rubber tube attached, 250-mL beaker, water, 3 drops of 0.1% phenolphthalein, safety goggles.

Procedure: 1. Mix the ammonium chloride and the sodium hydroxide in the flask. 2. Add 10 mL water and stopper the flask with the one-hole stopper. 3. Pour 10 mL of water into the beaker and add phenolphthalein. 4. Position the open end of the rubber tube into the beaker. 5. Ammonia gas bubbles into the water, turning the indicator red. 6. After about 10 minutes, the water from the beaker is pulled back into the flask. The ammonia has dissolved in the water and lowered the pressure in the flask. **Caution:** *Sodium hydroxide is corrosive.*

23·5 Preparation of the Halogens

Concept: Halogen gas or vapor can be produced by oxidizing a halide.

Materials: 5 g each of sodium iodide (NaI), sodium bromide (NaBr), and sodium chloride (NaCl), 30 mL of concentrated sulfuric acid (H_2SO_4), 15 mL of water, 15 g of manganese dioxide (MnO_2), 3 flasks, 3 hot plates, safety goggles.

Procedure: 1. Place 10 mL of sulfuric acid, 5 mL of water, and 5 g of manganese dioxide in each flask. 2. Gently swirl the flasks to mix and place on the hot plates. 3. Add one halide to each flask and swirl. 4. The halogen gases or vapors are evolved. Note the color of each. **Caution:** *Use a fume hood. The halogen gases are irritants.*

23·6 Sublimation of Iodine

Concept: Iodine can pass directly from a solid to gaseous state.

Materials: 2 g of iodine (I_2), large test tube, test tube holder, gas burner, matches, safety goggles.

Procedure: 1. Place a few iodine crystals in a large test tube in a holder. 2. **Caution:** *Use a fume hood. Iodine is an irritant and is toxic!* Heat gently with a gas burner. The crystals give off a purple gas. Remove from heat as soon as the gas is halfway up the tube. 4. On cooling, the iodine recrystallizes on the sides of the tube.

23·7 Bleaching

Concept: Bleaching is an oxidation reaction.

Materials: 2 strips of colored cloth, 2 beakers, 10 g of dry bleach, 10 mL of liquid bleach, 2 stirring rods, safety goggles.

Procedure: 1. Place the dry bleach in one beaker and the liquid bleach in the other. 2. Drop one cloth into each beaker and stir. 3. The liquid bleach removes color from the cloth, but the dry bleach does not. 4. Add water to the dry bleach to bleach the cloth. 5. Ask the students to explain how oxidation is involved in this reaction.

Audiovisual Resources

Bromine — Element from the Sea (F, V) Chem Study, 1963, 22 min. (Use with Sections 23·7 and 23·8.) Develops the procedure for extraction of bromine from sea water and shows its reactivity with metals and nonmetals.

Sulfur and Its Compounds (F) Coronet, 1962, 14 min. (Use with Sections 23·B and 23·4.) Demonstrates the

physical and chemical properties of sulfur, describes the Frasch process, and discusses uses of sulfur and its compounds.

The Earth: Resources in Its Crust (F, V) Coronet, 1982, 9 min. (Use with Sections 23·4, 23·7, and 23·8.) Discusses briefly the chemistry, mining, and uses of earth resources including sulfur and salt.

The Halogens (F) Coronet, 1966, 17 min. (Use with Sections 23·7 and 23·8.) Shows the relationship between the structure of the halogens and their reactivity, describes the formation of ionic and covalent compounds, and discusses current uses.

Beyond the Text

The Nitrogen Cycle and Nitrogen Fixation

Although nitrogen is an essential element, it cannot be used in its free state by most forms of life. For life processes, nitrogen must be "fixed"; that is, free nitrogen must be converted to nitrogen compounds such as ammonia and nitrates. Several of the nitrogen-fixation processes occur naturally.

Lightning converts some of the atmospheric nitrogen and oxygen in its path into nitric oxide. The nitric oxide then reacts with other oxygen molecules in the air to form nitrogen dioxide. This dissolves in rainwater, forming a very dilute nitric acid solution. When it reaches the soil, the nitric acid is converted into compounds that can be used by plants. It is estimated that a region with moderate rainfall receives from 2 to 4 kg of nitrogen, as nitric acid, annually.

A second, and more important nitrogen-fixation process involves microorganisms. Certain bacteria (and several types of blue–green algae) reduce atmospheric nitrogen to ammonia and other nitrogen compounds. Nitrogen-fixing bacteria are of two types: free-living and symbiotic. Colonies of symbiotic bacteria live in nodules on the roots of certain plants. The most common hosts are legumes, a plant family that includes alfalfa, clover, peas, and beans. Symbiotic bacteria can convert atmospheric nitrogen into organic nitrogen compounds that pass directly into the plant host. Soil fertility can be increased by plowing nitrogen-rich legumes back into the ground instead of harvesting them.

Proteins and other nitrogen compounds are usually produced first in green plants, which then make them available to animals. Thus nitrogen passes from organism to organism along the food chain. All these organisms eventually die and decay. This process, accomplished by decay bacteria and other decomposers, returns nitrogen to the soil as nitrate or nitrite ions, and ammonia. It also releases some free nitrogen to the atmosphere. The flow of nitrogen between the earth, the atmosphere, and living creatures is the nitrogen cycle, shown in the diagram below. The daily amount of atmospheric nitrogen currently fixed by industrial processes actually exceeds the amount fixed by living organisms.

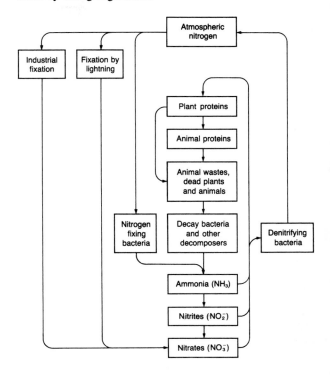

Answers to End of Chapter Questions and Problems

Practice Questions and Problems

1. To manufacture ammonia.

2. Colorless, odorless, gaseous, low freezing and boiling point, low density.

3. Protium (hydrogen-1), $_1^1H$, mass number = 1. Deuterium (hydrogen-2), $_1^2H$, mass number = 2. Tritium (hydrogen-3), $_1^3H$, mass number = 3.

4. It easily loses its single electron.

5. A catalyst speeds up a reaction but does not change the equilibrium and is not consumed; nickel or platinum.

6. Atmospheric gas, in water molecules, in compounds found in rocks and soils.

7. 21%. Nitrogen gas, water vapor, carbon dioxide, and small amounts of other gases.

8. Oxygen molecule: $:\overset{..}{O}:\overset{..}{O}:$ in liquid form, $:\overset{..}{O}::\overset{..}{O}:$ in gaseous form.
Ozone molecule: $:\overset{..}{O}:\overset{..}{O}::\overset{..}{O}:$

9. Paramagnetism is the magnetic attraction caused by unpaired electrons. Liquid oxygen has two unpaired electrons, one on each atom, and is attracted to a magnet.

10. The manufacture of steel.

11. a. colorless, odorless, gaseous **b.** pale blue, odorous, gaseous

12. The earth's upper atmosphere.

13. a. silicon dioxide **b.** hydrogen peroxide
c. sulfur trioxide **d.** iron(III) oxide **e.** barium peroxide **f.** carbon dioxide

14. a. CaO **b.** HgO **c.** CO **d.** Al_2O_3 **e.** SO_2
f. Na_2O_2

15. a. $2Mg(s) + O_2(g) \rightarrow 2MgO(s)$
b. $2H_2(g) + O_2(g) \rightarrow 2H_2O(g)$
c. $S(s) + O_2(g) \rightarrow SO_2(g)$

16. A bleach and an antiseptic.

17. Pale yellow, tasteless, odorless, brittle, solid.

18. Rhombic sulfur has cubelike S_8 units.

19. The vulcanization of rubber, the manufacture of paper from wood pulp, the preparation of fungicides, fertilizers, matches, fireworks, insecticides, explosives, drugs, paints, plastics, and dyes.

20. Pour molten sulfur near its boiling point into cold water. Plastic sulfur is elastic and rubber-like when fresh, but converts to rhombic crystals within hours.

21. a. $Mg + S \rightarrow MgS$ **b.** $2Al + 3S \rightarrow Al_2S_3$
c. $H_2 + S \rightarrow H_2S$ **d.** $2Na + S \rightarrow Na_2S$

22. By fractional distillation of liquid air or by passing air over red-hot coke to remove oxygen (as carbon dioxide) and leave nitrogen gas.

23. Air, nitrates, and ammonium compounds.

24. Liquid nitrogen has a lower boiling point. Nitrogen gas can be fractionally distilled from liquified air.

25. Fertilizer, refrigerant, cleaning products, the manufacture of nitric acid.

26. Colorless, strong odor, gaseous, high boiling and melting point, high heat of vaporization, very soluble in water.

27. $4NH_3(g) + 5O_2(g) \xrightarrow{600°C/Pt} 4NO(g) + 6H_2O(l)$
$2NO(g) + O_2 \longrightarrow 2NO_2(g)$
$3NO_2(g) + H_2O(l) \longrightarrow 2HNO_3(aq) + NO(g)$

28. Ammonia, NH_3; ammonium sulfate, $(NH_4)_2SO_4$; ammonium nitrate, NH_4NO_3.

29. Etching processes, the production of fertilizers and dyes, the manufacture of explosives.

30. Nitrocellulose (gun cotton), nitroglycerine, trinitrotoluene (TNT).

31. The electrolysis of an aqueous sodium chloride solution.

32. $2NaBr(aq) + Cl_2(g) \longrightarrow 2NaCl(aq) + Br_2(l)$; single-replacement and redox reaction.

33. By reacting sodium iodate with sodium hydrogen sulfite solution to precipitate iodine crystals.

34. By electrolyzing an ice-cold solution of potassium fluoride dissolved in hydrogen fluoride.

35. Fluoride, F_2; chlorine, Cl_2; bromine, Br_2; iodine, I_2; astatine, At_2.

36. Halogens are extremely reactive because they easily gain a single electron. As a result, they readily form compounds by gaining or sharing electrons.

37. $Cl_2(g) + H_2O(l) \rightleftharpoons HClO(aq) + HCl(aq)$
$Br_2(l) + H_2O(l) \rightleftharpoons HBrO(aq) + HBr(aq)$

38. $2F_2(g) + 2H_2O(l) \longrightarrow O_2(g) + 4HF(g)$

39. $Cl_2(g) + CaO(s) \longrightarrow Ca(ClO)Cl(s)$

40. Chlorine in solution is a strong oxidizing agent that kills disease-causing bacteria.

Mastery Questions and Problems

41. Oxygen gas is obtained from liquid air by fractional distillation. Ozone is made by passing an electrical discharge through oxygen gas.

42. Sulfur is not mined because it is found under quicksand. Superheated water and compressed air are sent down two tubes into the sulfur beds. A third tube brings sulfur froth to the surface.

43. $MnO_2 + 4HCl \longrightarrow$
$\qquad\qquad Cl_2 + MnCl_2 + 2H_2O$; 146 g HCl

44. a. +4 **b.** +1 **c.** +5 **d.** 0 **e.** +5 **f.** −3
g. +2 **h.** +3 **i.** −3 **j.** +3

45. In hydrogenation, oil is treated with hydrogen gas at a high temperature and pressure in the presence of a catalyst. This process converts liquid oils into solid fats.

46. Fluorine and chlorine are yellow-green gases with a sharp odor. Bromine is a dark red liquid with a strong odor. Iodine is a shiny purple-blue crystal with no odor.

47. a. 88.9%　**b.** 48.0%　**c.** 53.2%　**d.** 47.0%

48. Oxygen, O_2, is stable, odorless, and colorless. Ozone, O_3, is unstable, has odor, and is pale blue.

49. a. N_2O　**b.** O_3　**c.** $Ca(ClO)Cl$　**d.** $HClO$
e. $NaIO_4$　**f.** $CH_2{=}CHCl$

50. Iodine is prepared from a mixture of KI and MnO_2 solids, which are reacted with hot concentrated sulfuric acid.

51. a. $3H_2 + N_2 \longrightarrow 2NH_3$
b. $H_2 + Cl_2 \longrightarrow 2HCl$
c. $H_2 + Ca \longrightarrow CaH_2$

52. I, Br, Cl, F

53. To prepare fertilizers, pickle iron and steel, refine petroleum, and in a variety of other industries.

54. It is a small, polar molecule with hydrogen bonding. It is covalently bonded with bond angles similar to those in water.

55. $[\ddot{\underset{..}{O}}\,]^{2-}$ oxide; $[\ddot{\underset{..}{O}}\ddot{\underset{..}{O}}\,]^{2-}$ peroxide ion

56. a. N_2, O_2, F_2, Cl_2, H_2　**b.** Br_2　**c.** I_2

57. Nitrogen dioxide:
$3NO_2 + H_2O \longrightarrow 2HNO_3 + NO$.
Calcium oxide: $CaO + H_2O \longrightarrow Ca(OH)_2 + heat$.

Review Questions and Problems

58. a. Group 1 metals have a single electron in their outermost orbitals. This electron is easily lost, forming 1+ ions.　**b.** The atoms have an increasing number of quantum levels of electrons.

59. a. cement, plaster　**b.** paint pigment, heavy filler, medicine　**c.** antacid, baking powder, filler.
d. medicine, tanning, fertilizer

60. a. $6p^2$　**b.** $6p^3$　**c.** $5p^5$　**d.** $6s^2$

61. $Ag^+ + Cl^- \longrightarrow AgCl(s)$
$Ag^+ + Br^- \longrightarrow AgBr(s)$

62. $CaCO_3 + 2HCl \longrightarrow CaCl_2 + H_2O + CO_2$

63. a. Be^{2+} $\ddot{\underset{..}{O}}{:}^{2-}$　**b.** Ca^{2+} $\ddot{\underset{..}{S}}{:}^{2-}$
c. $\ddot{\underset{..}{Cl}}{:}^-$ Al^{3+} $\ddot{\underset{..}{Cl}}{:}^-$
　　$\ddot{\underset{..}{Cl}}{:}^-$

64. a. -4　**b.** 0　**c.** -4　**d.** -4　**e.** $+4$　**f.** $+2$

65. a. Mg^{2+} $2Br^-$　**b.** Ca^{2+} $2Br^-$　**c.** $2Cs^+$ Se^{2-}

66. It reacts to remove oxygen from metal oxides and generates heat. Coke is made when coal is heated and the volatile matter driven off.

67. a. $Mg + 2H_2O \longrightarrow Mg(OH)_2 + H_2$
b. $CaSO_4 \cdot 2H_2O + heat \longrightarrow CaSO_4 + 2H_2O$
c. $CaCO_3 + heat \longrightarrow CaO + CO_2$

Challenging Questions and Problems

68. 2.8×10^8 kg Br^-

69. 400 g SO_2; 140 L SO_2

70. Hydrogen gas is produced by steam reforming.
$\overset{-4+1}{CH_4} + \overset{+1}{H_2O} \xrightarrow{\ Ni\ } \overset{+2}{CO} + \overset{0}{3H_2}$
a. methane, CH_4　**b.** H_2O　**c.** hydrogen　**d.** carbon

71. $S + O_2 \longrightarrow SO_2$
$2SO_2 + O_2 \longrightarrow 2SO_3$
$SO_3 + H_2O \longrightarrow H_2SO_4$
6.09×10^4 kg H_2SO_4

72. 14.2 L O_2

23 The Chemistry of Nonmetals

Chapter Preview

The nonmetallic elements are found in the upper right corner of the periodic table. Unlike metals, nonmetals are poor conductors of heat and electricity. Bonding between nonmetal atoms is primarily covalent. Pairs of electrons are shared and the compounds formed consist of molecules. The electronegativities of nonmetals are high. Compounds formed between metals and nonmetals tend to be ionic, with metals as cations and nonmetals as anions.

23·1   Hydrogen and Its Compounds

Hydrogen is a common component of many compounds.

Hydrogen and helium are the most abundant elements in the universe. Free, or elemental, hydrogen is very rare on Earth, but compounds of hydrogen are common. They account for about one percent of the earth's crust. Water is the most abundant hydrogen compound. Combined with carbon and oxygen, hydrogen is present in all sugars, starches, fats, and proteins. These complex compounds are abundant in living tissues. Coal, natural gas, and petroleum products such as gasoline, kerosene, and lubricating oils also contain hydrogen.

Alchemists undoubtedly produced hydrogen long ago when they reacted certain metals with acids and obtained a colorless, odorless gas. Sir Henry Cavendish is generally given credit, however, for the discovery of hydrogen in 1766. At that time, he thought hydrogen came from the metal rather than from the acid. Cavendish called the gas "inflammable air." He recognized that it burned in air to produce water. Antoine Lavoisier showed that hydrogen is a component of water. He named it *hydrogen* from the Greek words *hydro*, water, and *genes*, forming.

Figure 23·1
The halogens have many similar chemical properties. From left to right are chlorine, bromine, and iodine.

Figure 23·2

Hydrogen is seldom found free in nature but is present in a large number of compounds. All these items contain compounds of hydrogen.

Hydrogen exhibits a double nature in its chemical behavior. In some reactions it loses one electron as if it belongs in Group 1A. In other reactions it gains one electron and so behaves as if it belongs in Group 7A.

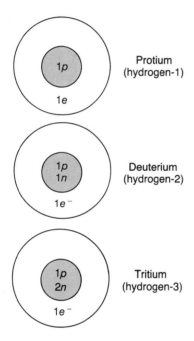

Protium (hydrogen-1)

Deuterium (hydrogen-2)

Tritium (hydrogen-3)

Figure 23·3

Most naturally occurring hydrogen atoms are hydrogen-1 or protium. About one in every 6,000 hydrogen atoms in sea water is deuterium. Tritium is rarely found in nature but can be produced artificially by certain nuclear reactions. How do these three isotopes differ?

Protium has no neutrons, deuterium has one neutron, and tritium has two neutrons. This difference affects their atomic mass, but not their chemical behavior.

Naturally occurring hydrogen is composed of three isotopes (Figure 23·3). Protium (hydrogen-1) and deuterium (hydrogen-2) account for 99.98% and 0.02% of a sample, respectively. The most abundant isotope is protium. It is commonly called hydrogen. Tritium, an unstable form of hydrogen, is present in extremely small amounts.

Hydrogen burns readily in oxygen with a hot, colorless flame. A mixture of hydrogen and air in a test tube produces a small explosion when brought near an open flame. This result confirms the presence of hydrogen gas in a laboratory experiment.

Hydrogen combines directly with a number of metallic and nonmetallic elements. With nitrogen, it forms ammonia (NH_3); with chlorine, hydrogen chloride (HCl); with calcium, calcium hydride (CaH_2). Because it loses its single electron easily, hydrogen is a good reducing agent. When passed over heated calcium oxide, for example, it reduces the metal oxide to the free metal.

$$CaO(s) \ + \ H_2(g) \xrightarrow{\Delta} Ca(s) \ + \ H_2O(g)$$

The major use of hydrogen is in the manufacture of ammonia. It is also used to reduce certain metal oxides to the free metal. Metals that can be produced from their oxide by hydrogen reduction include copper, silver, tungsten, and iron.

Large volumes of hydrogen are used in the conversion of vegetable oils such as peanut and coconut oil into solid fats. This process, called **hydrogenation,** *involves treating an oil with hydrogen at high temperature and pressure in the presence of a catalyst.* Finely divided nickel or platinum is commonly used. Solid shortenings and margarine are produced in this way.

Liquid hydrogen has become an important rocket fuel because of its high energy and light weight. Hydrogen gas was once used to fill lighter-than-air balloons and dirigibles. Helium, a nonflammable gas, is now used instead. The oxyhydrogen torch is used to cut and weld metals. It utilizes the intense heat produced when hydrogen burns in oxygen.

Safety

Do not ignite any quantity of hydrogen larger than the volume of a small test tube. If oxygen has mixed with the hydrogen, the explosion could shatter the container, particularly if it is scratched or weakened from use.

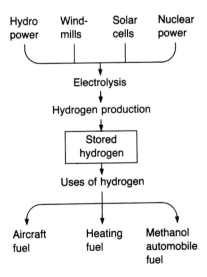

Figure 23·5
Hydrogen could become a more widely used source of energy if cheaper methods of producing it are devised. It could be produced during off-peak periods of electricity generation.

23·A Reaction Alternatives: Preparing Hydrogen

Supplies of hydrogen compounds are almost limitless. The gas can be produced from water, natural gas, coal, crude oil, and many other substances. The cost of production usually determines the method to be used commercially.

The electrolysis of water can produce very pure hydrogen. This method is only practical, however, in small scale operations. The raw material is cheap and plentiful, but the cost of electricity makes the process expensive. The apparatus is shown in Figure 21·12. A small amount of acid or base is added to the water to make it an electrical conductor. When the current flows, bubbles of hydrogen gas collect at the cathode and oxygen collects at the anode.

$$2H_2O(l) \xrightarrow{\text{electrical energy}} 2H_2(g) + O_2(g)$$

The volume of hydrogen produced is slightly more than twice that of oxygen. A little less oxygen than expected is produced because oxygen is more soluble in water than hydrogen.

Hydrogen can be prepared commercially from water by the Bosch process. In this method, steam is passed over red hot iron filings. The iron combines with the oxygen in steam and hydrogen gas is liberated.

$$3Fe(s) + 4H_2O(g) \longrightarrow Fe_3O_4(s) + 4H_2(g)$$

Hydrogen has great potential as a non-polluting fuel. Thus a great deal of research is being directed toward finding a cheaper method of producing hydrogen from water.

More than half of the hydrogen produced in North America is produced by the reaction between steam and natural gas. This method is known as steam reforming. It is the least expensive method to produce large volumes of this gas. The raw material is

methane, the chief component of natural gas. It is reacted with steam over a finely divided nickel catalyst at 700°C to 1000°C.

$$CH_4(g) + H_2O(g) \xrightarrow{\text{catalyst}} CO(g) + 3H_2(g)$$

The carbon monoxide is removed by cooling and compressing the mixture of gases. Hydrogen remains a gas after the carbon monoxide liquifies out of the mixture.

The first commercial process developed for hydrogen production involved passing steam over white-hot coke. This method also produces a mixture of carbon monoxide and hydrogen known as water gas.

$$C(s) + H_2O(g) \xrightarrow{\Delta} CO(g) + H_2(g)$$

The carbon monoxide is removed by oxidizing it to carbon dioxide, using steam and a catalyst. Additional hydrogen is formed.

$$CO(g) + H_2O(g) \xrightarrow{\text{catalyst}} CO_2(g) + H_2(g)$$

The mixture passes through a cold-water scrubber, which dissolves the carbon dioxide in water under moderate pressure. Production of hydrogen from coke declined as natural gas became readily available. Today, the process is more expensive than steam reforming and is practical only in small scale operations.

Small quantities of hydrogen are prepared in the laboratory by the reaction between certain metals and an acid. The apparatus for this method is shown in Figure 23·6. Dilute sulfuric acid is poured down the thistle tube onto pieces of zinc in the flask. Hydrogen gas bubbles off as long as the metal and acid are in contact. The gas is usually collected over water.

$$Zn(s) + H_2SO_4(aq) \longrightarrow H_2(g) + ZnSO_4(aq)$$

Hydrogen is also produced in the laboratory when very active metals such as sodium and potassium react with water. In these reactions, the metal hydroxide is formed in addition to hydrogen gas.

$$2Na(s) + 2H_2O(l) \longrightarrow 2NaOH(aq) + H_2(g)$$

Safety

A hydrogen generator flask should be wrapped in a towel to contain the glass in case of an explosion. Never ignite hydrogen coming from a generator.

Safety

The production of hydrogen by the reaction of alkali metals with water is not recommended as a student experiment. Sodium can spatter when it contacts water. The oxide coating on potassium that has been stored for a long time may contain very explosive peroxides.

Zinc sulfate.

Figure 23·6
Hydrogen is prepared in the laboratory by adding zinc to dilute sulfuric acid. Bubbles of hydrogen displace water in the collecting bottle. What is the other product of the reaction?

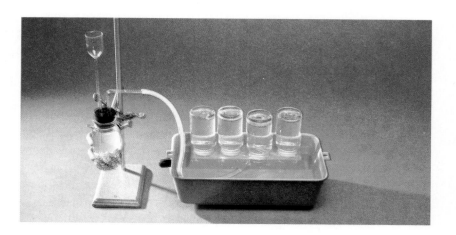

23·2 Oxygen

Of the elements that make up the earth's crust, oxygen is by far the most abundant. Its total mass is nearly equal to all of the other elements combined. Free oxygen exists as diatomic covalent molecules, O_2. The gas is a major component of the atmosphere, accounting for 21% of the air, by volume. Most of this oxygen is the product of photosynthesis. In this process, green plants manufacture carbohydrates by combining carbon dioxide and water with the aid of sunlight. Glucose, a simple sugar, is one product; oxygen is the other.

$$6CO_2(g) + 6H_2O(l) \xrightarrow{\text{light energy}} C_6H_{12}O_6(aq) + 6O_2(g)$$

Most of the oxygen on earth, however, is in compounds that are the constituents of rocks and soils. Quartz and sand (SiO_2), limestone and marble ($CaCO_3$), and gypsum ($CaSO_4$) are common oxygen-containing minerals. Clay has a complex composition of aluminum, silicon, and oxygen. Water and the organic molecules that make up living tissues also contain oxygen.

Karl Wilhelm Scheele, a Swedish pharmacist, and Joseph Priestly, an English clergyman, carried out early experiments with oxygen. In 1771, Scheele prepared oxygen by heating a mixture of concentrated sulfuric acid and manganese dioxide.

$$2MnO_2(s) + 2H_2SO_4(l) \longrightarrow 2MnSO_4(aq) + 2H_2O(l) + O_2(g)$$

Priestly decomposed mercury(II) oxide by heating it, in 1774 (Figure 2·4). When the French chemist Antoine Lavoisier learned of their work, he carried out further experiments (Section 2·A). Lavoisier gave oxygen its name, which means "acid forming."

Small quantities of oxygen can be generated in the laboratory by heating unstable oxygen-containing compounds. These include mercury(II) oxide and potassium chlorate (Figure 23·8).

$$2KClO_3(s) \xrightarrow{\Delta} 2KCl(s) + 3O_2(g)$$

Figure 23·8
When potassium chlorate is heated, it decomposes to yield potassium chloride and oxygen. Manganese dioxide is used as a catalyst.

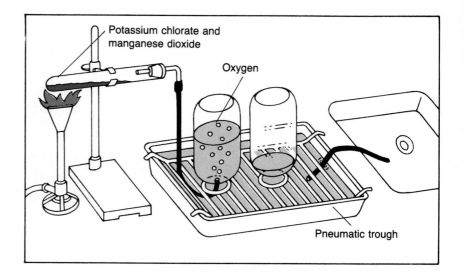

Potassium chlorate and manganese dioxide

Oxygen

Pneumatic trough

Such methods are unsuitable for large scale oxygen production because the starting materials are expensive. The primary source of commercial oxygen is air. Relatively pure oxygen is separated from the other gases present by liquefying air and then fractionally distilling the liquid. Nitrogen (b.p. $-196°C$) comes off first, followed by the noble gas argon (b.p. $-186°C$). Oxygen distills off at $-183°C$.

LOX is the trade name for liquid oxygen.

When cooled, oxygen condenses to a clear blue liquid that freezes at $-218°C$. In liquid form, oxygen is attracted to a magnet. This property, called paramagnetism, is caused by the presence of unpaired electrons in the oxygen molecule.

$$:\overset{..}{O}:\overset{..}{O}:$$

The major commercial use of oxygen is in the basic oxygen process for the manufacture of steel. Oxygen is also used in oxyhydrogen and oxyacetylene torches for welding metals and glassworking. Fuels burn in oxygen at a higher temperature than they do in air. The flame temperature in an oxyacetylene torch is about $2500°C$. The fuel and oxygen are brought together in a specially designed torch (Figure 20·4). Acetylene is a clean fuel because it burns to produce carbon dioxide and water.

$$2C_2H_2(g) + 5O_2(g) \longrightarrow 4CO_2(g) + 2H_2O(g) + \text{heat}$$

Oxygen tanks are carried in airplanes for use at high altitudes. Medical emergency teams administer oxygen to victims of smoke inhalation, electrical shock, or drowning. For certain medical conditions such as pneumonia, emphysema, or gas poisoning, a patient may need to breathe air enriched with oxygen for long periods of time.

Oxygen exists in two allotropic forms.

Oxygen exists in a second form, ozone, which has the molecular formula O_3. The two forms are referred to as allotropes of oxygen. **Allotropes** *of an element are two or more different molecular forms in the same physical state.* Ozone is formed in the earth's upper atmosphere by the action of ultraviolet light on oxygen. This decreases the amount of ultraviolet light which penetrates the atmosphere. Without this process,

Figure 23·9
Large quantities of ozone are produced for industrial use. This form of oxygen is used as a bleaching agent and as a sterilizing agent.

living things would be damaged by the additional ultraviolet light that would reach the earth's surface. The process of ozone formation occurs in two stages.

$$O_2 \xrightarrow{\text{ultraviolet light}} 2O$$

$$O_2 + O \longrightarrow O_3$$

Ozone is also produced near high-voltage generators and during electrical storms.

Ozone is a pale blue gas with a characteristic odor. When cooled to $-112°C$, it condenses into a deep blue, explosive liquid. Ozone is a strong oxidizing agent. It is used commercially to bleach flour, oil, and delicate fabrics. It is also used to sterilize water, and to destroy odors.

Because ozone is unstable, it must be generated where it will be used. It is prepared by passing oxygen through an electrical discharge. The structure of an industrial ozonator is shown in Figure 23·10. Air is passed through glass tubes partially covered with metal foil. The tubes are placed one within the other, and the pieces of foil are connected to a high-voltage source. When the current is on, electrical discharges pass between the layers of foil. Some of the oxygen moving through the generator is converted to ozone.

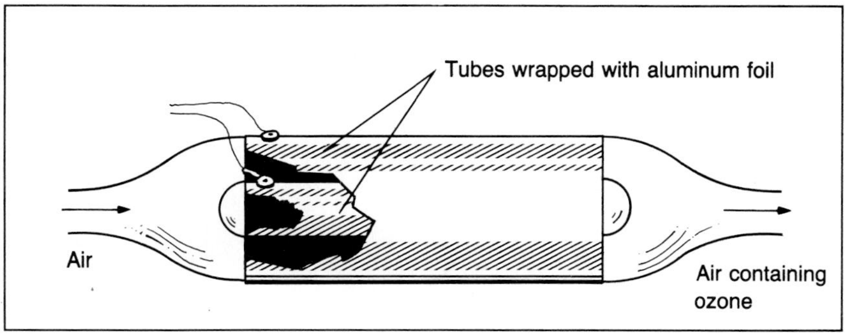

Ozone is an extremely powerful oxidant.

Tubes wrapped with aluminum foil

Air

Air containing ozone

Figure 23·10
Ozone is produced by passing air through concentric tubes that are covered with aluminum foil. High voltage discharges between the tubes convert some of the oxygen to ozone.

23·3 Compounds of Oxygen

■ Most elements will form oxides when heated in the presence of oxygen.

Bonding in the metallic oxides is predominately ionic. Bonding in the nonmetallic oxides is predominately covalent.

Oxides of many metals are *basic* oxides, whereas oxides of many nonmetals are *acidic* oxides.

When substances combine chemically with oxygen, the process is called oxidation and the substance is oxidized. Substances oxidize at different rates. A lighted candle oxidizes rapidly, but iron oxidizes (rusts) slowly. The product of an oxidation reaction is called an oxide. In general, oxides of metals are solids while oxides of nonmetals may be solid, liquid, or gas. The oxides of metals and nonmetals differ chemically from each other in one important respect. Many metallic oxides react with water to form bases. Many nonmetallic oxides, however, react with water to form acids.

Oxides of all elements, except the noble gases and a few inactive metals, can be prepared simply by heating the element with oxygen. Here are some examples.

$$2Hg(l) + O_2(g) \longrightarrow 2HgO(s)$$

$$3Fe(s) + 2O_2(g) \longrightarrow Fe_3O_4(s)$$

$$S(s) + O_2(g) \longrightarrow SO_2(g)$$

A few oxides such as mercury(II) oxide are easily decomposed by heating. Others like calcium oxide are stable even at a temperature of 3000°C.

While most metals yield oxides in reaction with oxygen, a few also yield peroxides. Peroxides are compounds that contain the peroxide ion, O_2^{2-}. For example, barium reacts with oxygen to form barium peroxide.

$$Ba(s) + O_2(g) \longrightarrow BaO_2(s)$$

Hydrogen peroxide, H_2O_2, is one of the most important peroxides. It is a colorless, viscous, highly unstable liquid. Dilute aqueous solutions of hydrogen peroxide, usually 3% by volume, are used in homes as a bleach and antiseptic. The Lewis structure of hydrogen peroxide is shown here.

Safety

Laboratories often use 30% m/m hydrogen peroxide. This concentrated solution can cause serious burns. Containers should be vented to prevent pressure buildup as oxygen gas forms from the decomposition of the peroxide.

Many common substances (including human tissue) act as catalysts for the rapid decomposition of hydrogen peroxide to form oxygen. This free oxygen works well as a bleaching and disinfecting agent.

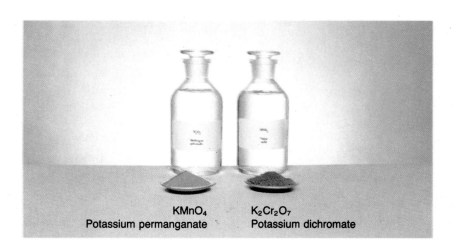

Figure 23·11
Oxygen-rich compounds like those shown here are good oxidizing agents.

KMnO₄
Potassium permanganate

K₂Cr₂O₇
Potassium dichromate

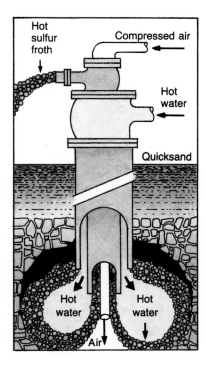

Figure 23·12
Sulfur deposits deep within the earth are mined by the Frasch process. The sulfur, melted by hot water and whipped into a froth by compressed air, rises to the surface.

A metric ton is 1000 kg.

23·B The Frasch Process

Some of the world's richest deposits of elemental sulfur are on the Gulf Coast in Louisiana and Texas. These deposits are not easily mined because they are buried under several hundred feet of quicksand. A German–American engineer, Herman Frasch (1851–1914), devised a clever method for getting this sulfur out of the ground. The method takes advantage of sulfur's low melting point (119°C). Eighty percent of the world's sulfur output is produced by the Frasch process.

Wells are drilled into the sulfur bed. Then an arrangement of three concentric tubes (with 2.5 cm, 7.5 cm, and 15 cm diameters) is installed (Figure 23·12). Superheated water (180°C) under pressure is pumped down the outside tube to melt the sulfur. Compressed air is pumped down the center tube. A frothy mixture of air, water, and molten sulfur rises up the third tube. The molten sulfur, 99.5% pure, is pumped into large storage vats where it cools and solidifies into huge blocks. These blocks may be as much as 130 m long, 70 m wide, and 30 m high. For shipping, the sulfur is loosened by dynamite blasting and loaded into freight cars.

Large amounts of sulfur are also obtained from hydrogen sulfide gas, a product of petroleum refining. Some of the hydrogen sulfide is burned in air to produce sulfur dioxide. The sulfur dioxide is then treated with more hydrogen sulfide. This can be summarized in a single reaction.

$$2H_2S(g) + SO_2(g) \longrightarrow 2H_2O(g) + 3S(s)$$

The annual production of sulfur in North American is more than ten million metric tons.

Figure 23·13
After being mined, sulfur is dried and stored in huge blocks until it is shipped.

Figure 23·14

Figure 23·14
Crystalline sulfur exists as S_8 molecules. Above the melting point, the S_8 rings of sulfur break and form chains of sulfur. Near the boiling point the chains break into smaller groups and individual atoms.
Students may associate sulfur with unpleasant odors. Pure sulfur itself is odorless. Some of its *compounds* have very bad odors.

Sulfur occurs in three allotropic forms.

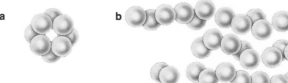

a

b

Crystalline sulfur

Molten sulfur

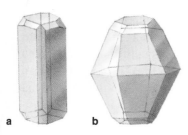

Figure 23·15
As sulfur cools, the needlelike monoclinic crystals (**a**) gradually change to the rhombic form (**b**).

Dark brown, rubbery, elastic.

Figure 23·16
This sulfur is the amorphous form. What are its properties?

23·4   Sulfur and Its Compounds

Sulfur has been known since ancient times to be a pale yellow, tasteless, odorless, brittle solid. It is insoluble in water, but dissolves in carbon disulfide. Today, sulfur is an extremely important raw material in the chemical industry. Large amounts of sulfur are used in the vulcanization of rubber and the manufacture of paper from wood pulp. It is also used in the preparation of fungicides, fertilizers, matches, fireworks, insecticides, explosives, drugs, paints, plastics, and dyes.

Sulfur occurs in several allotropic forms. When molten sulfur cools below 119°C, it forms needle-like crystals of *monoclinic* sulfur. In this allotrope, eight-membered rings of covalently bonded sulfur atoms (S_8) are arranged in monoclinic crystals (Figure 23·15). Below 95.5°C, the sulfur changes to *rhombic* sulfur, another allotrope. Rhombic sulfur is also composed of S_8 units, but it has orthorhombic crystals. Rhombic sulfur is stable at ordinary temperatures.

As molten sulfur is heated, it becomes a deep red-brown color and its viscosity increases. At about 160°C, it is so thick it cannot be poured. The viscosity decreases, however, as the temperature nears the boiling point (445°C). Apparently, as sulfur melts, the S_8 rings begin to break, producing short chains. With continued heating, they join to produce longer chains. The longer chains become entangled so that the viscosity increases, reaching a maximum at 160°C. Above this temperature, the long chains begin to break up and the viscosity decreases.

A third form of sulfur is the dark brown rubber-like allotrope known as amorphous or "plastic sulfur." This can be produced by pouring molten sulfur into cold water when the sulfur is near its boiling point. Amorphous solids do not have a distinct crystal form. Within hours, the amorphous sulfur loses its elasticity as it converts to rhombic crystals.

Sulfur can be purified by boiling it and condensing the vapor. Tiny rhombic crystals form in flower-like patterns on the walls of the condensation chamber. This sulfur powder is called "flowers of sulfur."

Sulfur is a reactive element. When heated, it burns readily in air or oxygen, producing an irritating, toxic gas, sulfur dioxide. In the laboratory, sulfur dioxide is prepared by the action of an acid on a sulfite.

$$Na_2SO_3(aq) + 2HCl(aq) \longrightarrow 2NaCl(aq) + H_2O(l) + SO_2(g)$$

Sulfur dioxide will combine with more oxygen in the presence of a catalyst to form sulfur trioxide.

$$2SO_2(g) + O_2(g) \xrightarrow{\text{catalyst}} 2SO_3(g)$$

Figure 23·17
Sulfur dioxide can be prepared by the action of hydrochloric acid on sodium sulfite. Sulfurous acid, H_2SO_3, is formed when the SO_2 dissolves in water.

Sulfuric acid is the most important manufactured chemical.

Safety

Never add water to concentrated sulfuric acid. The heat generated may cause the water to boil, spattering the acid.

This reaction of sulfur dioxide with oxygen is the basis for the manufacture of sulfuric acid. Sulfur dioxide is also used as a bleaching agent and a fumigant.

When heated with metals (except gold and platinum), sulfur forms compounds called sulfides.

$$Fe(s) + S(s) \longrightarrow \underset{\text{iron(II) sulfide}}{FeS(s)}$$

$$2Cu(s) + S(s) \longrightarrow \underset{\text{copper(I) sulfide}}{Cu_2S(s)}$$

With active metals like magnesium and zinc, the reaction is highly exothermic.

Hydrogen combines with sulfur to form hydrogen sulfide, a poisonous gas that smells like rotten eggs. In the laboratory, hydrogen sulfide is prepared by the action of an acid on a sulfide.

$$FeS(s) + 2HCl(aq) \longrightarrow FeCl_2(aq) + H_2S(g)$$

23·C Sulfuric Acid

The principal use of sulfur is in the manufacture of sulfuric acid. In North America alone, more than 8×10^7 metric tons of sulfuric acid are produced annually. The two main methods of making sulfuric acid are the lead chamber process and the contact process. Both processes convert sulfur dioxide to sulfur trioxide. The latter forms sulfuric acid when dissolved in water. Most of the sulfuric acid produced in this country is made by the contact process, described in Section 17·A. The product from the lead chamber process is less pure, but satisfactory for some commercial uses.

Pure, anhydrous sulfuric acid is a dense, colorless, oily liquid. The concentrated acid used in laboratories is 98% H_2SO_4 and 2% H_2O. Sulfuric acid has the chemical properties of a typical acid. The dilute acid reacts with metals, oxides, hydroxides, or carbonates to form salts called sulfates. The reaction with metals also releases hydrogen gas. Sulfuric acid displaces other acids from their salts. For example, hydrogen chloride can be produced from sulfuric acid and sodium chloride. When dissolved in water it forms hydrochloric acid.

$$H_2SO_4(l) + 2NaCl(s) \longrightarrow Na_2SO_4(s) + 2HCl(g)$$

Concentrated sulfuric acid dissolves readily in water, liberating a large amount of heat. This strong affinity for water makes sulfuric acid a powerful dehydrating agent. Thus it must be handled with great care. For example, when the concentrated acid is added to sugar, a vigorous reaction takes place. A large volume of charred material is produced as the acid removes water, leaving only carbon.

$$C_{12}H_{22}O_{11}(s) + 11H_2SO_4(l) \longrightarrow 12C(s) + 11H_2SO_4 \cdot H_2O(aq)$$

Figure 23·18
Sulfuric acid was used to manufacture
the paper of this book and many other
objects you use daily.

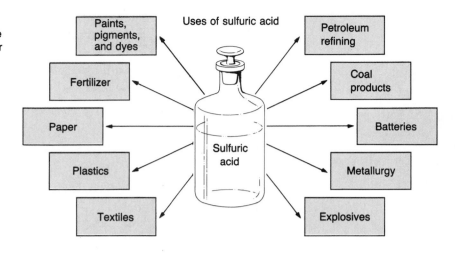

Uses of sulfuric acid

Paints, pigments, and dyes

Fertilizer

Paper

Plastics

Textiles

Sulfuric acid

Petroleum refining

Coal products

Batteries

Metallurgy

Explosives

Hot concentrated sulfuric acid is an oxidizing agent. It reacts with certain metals to generate sulfur dioxide.

$$2H_2SO_4(l) + Cu(s) \longrightarrow CuSO_4(aq) + SO_2(g) + 2H_2O(l)$$

Practically every industry uses some sulfuric acid. Almost half the world's production goes into the manufacture of fertilizers such as ammonium sulfate and superphosphate. Large amounts of sulfuric acid are used in the metal industry for pickling iron and steel. *Pickling* involves putting a metal in a chemical bath to remove oxides on the metal surface. Sulfuric acid is also essential in petroleum refining. Other uses are shown in Figure 23·18.

Nitrogen cannot exist as a liquid above about −174°C no matter how much pressure is applied. Therefore, cylinders of nitrogen contain the highly compressed gas, rather than the liquid.

23·5 Nitrogen

Air is about 80% elemental nitrogen by volume. Nitrogen is isolated commercially by two processes. In one method, nitrogen is fractionally distilled from liquefied air. Since liquid nitrogen boils at a lower temperature than liquid oxygen, nitrogen distills off first. In the second method, air is passed over red-hot coke. The carbon combines with oxygen to form carbon dioxide, while the nitrogen remains unchanged.

Free nitrogen is a colorless, odorless, tasteless gas, composed of diatomic molecules, N_2. It is slightly soluble in water. Its melting point is −210°C and its boiling point is −196°C.

Molecular nitrogen is extremely stable. With an electronegativity of 3.0, we would expect nitrogen to be a reactive element. Molecular nitrogen resists reaction, however, because of the strong attraction nitrogen atoms have for each other. In a molecule of elemental nitrogen, the two atoms share three pairs of electrons, forming a triple covalent bond. The bond energy is very large: 226 kcal/mol.

Despite the stability of atmospheric nitrogen, numerous nitrogen compounds are found in nature. Large deposits of sodium nitrate (Chile saltpeter) and potassium nitrate (saltpeter) exist, and soils may contain ammonium compounds. In addition, nitrogen is an essential component

Figure 23·19
Liquid nitrogen boils away quickly when poured from an insulated flask into a beaker at room temperature. The smoke-like effect in the beaker is caused by the condensation of water vapor from the air.

of many organic compounds found in both plants and animals. These organic compounds include amino acids, proteins and nucleic acids.

In the laboratory, nitrogen can be prepared by heating certain unstable nitrogen compounds. When an aqueous solution of ammonium nitrate is carefully heated, it decomposes, yielding nitrogen gas and water.

$$NH_4NO_2(aq) \xrightarrow{\Delta} N_2(g) + 2H_2O(l)$$

Ammonium nitrate is a potentially explosive solid. It should not be heated in the dry state.

23·6   Compounds of Nitrogen

The most important use of atmospheric nitrogen is in the manufacture of nitrogen compounds. Two important industrial processes use nitrogen: the Haber–Bosch process for making ammonia (Section 17·C) and the Ostwald process for preparing nitric acid.

Ammonia is a colorless gas with a strong odor. The gas is extremely soluble in water. At room temperature, about 700 volumes of ammonia dissolve in one volume of water! The resulting solution is called aqueous ammonia. Ammonia is easily liquefied by cooling. Liquid ammonia boils at -33°C and it solidifies at -78°C. Liquid ammonia exhibits many water-like properties because ammonia molecules are polar. Hydrogen bonds can form between the hydrogen atoms of one ammonia molecule and the nitrogen atoms of a nearby molecule. Evidence of this hydrogen bonding is ammonia's high boiling and melting points and its high heat of vaporization for such a small molecule.

Liquid ammonia, aqueous ammonia, and several ammonium salts are used as fertilizers. Liquid ammonia is also called anhydrous ammonia. It is sometimes applied under pressure directly to the soil, or it may be bubbled into irrigation water. Ammonium sulfate is the most important solid fertilizer in the world today.

Figure 23·20
Pure, liquid ammonia is called anhydrous ammonia and is used extensively as a fertilizer. The ammonia, normally a gas, is kept under pressure in a tank.

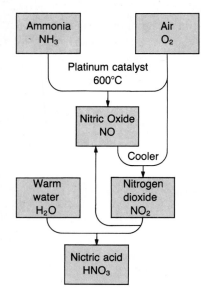

Figure 23·21
The Ostwald process produces nitric acid by a two-stage oxidation of ammonia to nitrogen dioxide. In the third step, the nitrogen dioxide is passed through warm water, forming nitric acid.

Liquid ammonia is used as a refrigerant, particularly in the frozen food industry. Aqueous ammonia is weakly basic and is a component of many cleaning products. Household ammonia is approximately a two molar aqueous solution of ammonia with detergent added. About one-quarter of all the ammonia produced is made into nitric acid. This acid is used in etching processes and the production of fertilizers and dyes. It is also an important raw material in the manufacture of explosives. Nitro-cellulose (gun cotton), nitroglycerine, and trinitrotoluene (TNT) are all made from nitric acid.

Nitric acid is made in the laboratory by the action of hot concentrated sulfuric acid on sodium nitrate.

$$NaNO_3(s) + H_2SO_4(l) \longrightarrow NaHSO_4(s) + HNO_3(g)$$

Large amounts of nitric acid are made commercially by the Ostwald method. The process was invented by a German chemist, Wilhelm Ostwald (1854–1932). It involves three steps (Figure 23·21).

1. Ammonia is oxidized by air in the presence of a catalyst to form nitric oxide (nitrogen monoxide). The mixture of air and ammonia is heated to about 600°C before contact with the catalyst, a cylinder of platinum gauze.

$$4NH_3(g) + O_2(g) \xrightarrow{600°C/Pt} 4NO(g) + 6H_2O(g)$$

2. More air is introduced into the system. It oxidizes the nitric oxide to nitrogen dioxide.

$$2NO(g) + O_2(g) \longrightarrow 2NO_2(g)$$

3. After cooling, the nitrogen dioxide is passed through water, forming a solution of nitric acid.

$$3NO_2(g) + H_2O(l) \longrightarrow 2HNO_3(aq) + NO(g)$$

The nitric oxide, a by-product of this third reaction, is recycled.

23·7 Preparation of the Halogens

The halogens form a large number of widely distributed compounds. Most of these compounds are soluble in water. Thus halide ions are abundant in seawater and in salt beds formed by the evaporation of salt water (Table 23·1).

Fluorine is the most electronegative element. Although it had long been known in its combined form, the free element was not isolated until 1886. French chemist Henri Moissan made it by electrolyzing an ice-cold solution of potassium fluoride in hydrogen fluoride. Fluorine is still made this way today. The electrolytic cell is made of a Monel metal and steel with carbon electrodes.

Chlorine gas is made commercially by the electrolysis of a sodium chloride solution (see Section 21·9). In a separate process, the hydrogen also produced is burned in the chlorine to make hydrogen chloride gas.

■ Except for fluorine, the halogens are prepared from the salts of sea water or salt beds.

Table 23·1
Concentration of Halide Ions in Seawater

Ion	g/L
F^-	1.3×10^{-3}
Cl^-	1.9×10^{1}
Br^-	6.5×10^{-2}
I^-	5.0×10^{-5}

This is an important source of hydrochloric acid. In the laboratory, chlorine is made by heating concentrated hydrochloric acid and manganese dioxide (Figure 23·22).

$$MnO_2(s) + 4HCl(aq) \longrightarrow MnCl_2(s) + 2H_2O(l) + Cl_2(g)$$

Bromine is obtained commercially from seawater and salt-well brines. Sodium chloride in the water is allowed to crystallize out, leaving a solution that contains the more soluble bromides. Chlorine gas, more electronegative than bromine, is then used to displace bromide ions from the solution.

$$2NaBr(aq) + Cl_2(g) \longrightarrow 2NaCl(aq) + Br_2(l)$$

In the laboratory, bromine is prepared by adding hot concentrated sulfuric acid to a mixture of potassium bromide and manganese dioxide (Figure 23·22). Hydrogen bromide is produced, then oxidized to bromine.

$$KBr(s) + H_2SO_4(l) \longrightarrow KHSO_4(s) + HBr(aq)$$

$$4HBr(aq) + MnO_2(s) \longrightarrow MnBr_2(aq) + 2H_2O(l) + Br_2(aq)$$

At one time, iodine was extracted from the ashes of certain seaweeds, which concentrate iodine from seawater. Now it is produced commercially from sodium iodate, which occurs as an impurity in deposits of sodium nitrite.

$$2NaIO_3(aq) + 5NaHSO_3(aq) \longrightarrow$$
$$2Na_2SO_4(aq) + 3NaHSO_4(aq) + H_2O(l) + I_2(s)$$

The laboratory preparation of iodine is similar to that of bromine. A mixture of potassium iodide and manganese dioxide is treated with hot concentrated sulfuric acid.

$$2NaI(s) + MnO_2(s) + 2H_2SO_4(l) \longrightarrow$$
$$Na_2SO_4(s) + MnSO_4(s) + 2H_2O(l) + I_2(g)$$

The iodine vapor condenses on a cold surface, forming black crystals.

It is denser than air.

Figure 23·22
The preparation of both chlorine and bromine should be carried out in a hood. The chlorine is collected by upward displacement of air. What does this tell you about the density of chlorine compared to that of air?

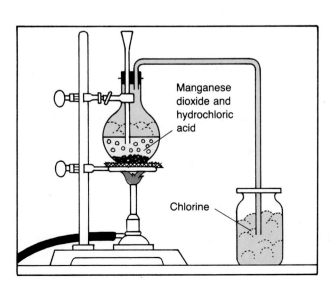

Manganese dioxide and hydrochloric acid

Chlorine

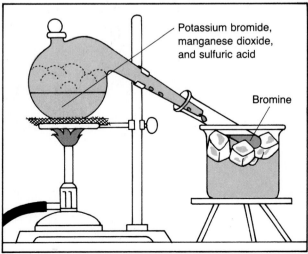

Potassium bromide, manganese dioxide, and sulfuric acid

Bromine

Figure 23·23
A heated piece of steel wool reacts vigorously in chlorine gas. The "smoke" is actually fine particles of the iron(III) chloride which form. Would the reaction be more or less vigorous in bromine? in fluorine?
Less vigorous in bromine, more vigorous in fluorine.

The halogens are very reactive. Their reactivities decrease as the atomic mass increases.

23·8 Properties of the Halogens

Although the halogens are similar in many ways, their appearances vary considerably (Figure 23·1). Bromine and iodine are not gases at room temperature, but they vaporize easily. When heated, iodine crystals sublime: they change directly from a solid to a gas, forming a dense cloud of purple vapor. Bromine is slightly soluble in cold water and is often available in the laboratory as bromine water. Iodine is only slightly soluble in water, but dissolves readily in alcohol, forming a dark brown solution.

The halogens are among the most reactive nonmetals. They are always found combined with other elements in nature. Fluorine is the most electronegative and chemically reactive of all the nonmetals. It is also the strongest elemental oxidizing agent known. Fluorine forms compounds with all elements except helium, neon, and argon. The reactivity of the other halogens decreases as their size and mass increase. Thus iodine is the least reactive of the common halogens.

Halogens react readily with most metals to form ionic salts. For example, copper is oxidized by chlorine to form copper(II) chloride.

$$Cu(s) + Cl_2(g) \longrightarrow Cu^{2+} + 2Cl^- \qquad (CuCl_2(s))$$

With nonmetals the halogens bond covalently to form molecules.

Halogens react with hydrogen to form the corresponding hydrogen halides. All of these compounds are colorless gases.

$$H_2(g) + Br_2(g) \longrightarrow 2HBr(g)$$

The reaction with fluorine and chlorine is explosive; bromine and iodine react more slowly. With the exception of hydrogen fluoride, the hydrogen halides are highly ionized in water, forming strong acids. Hydrofluoric acid is a weak acid because it is weakly ionized in water. The large electronegativity difference between hydrogen and fluorine $(4.0 - 2.1 = 1.9)$ explains why. Hydrogen fluoride molecules are very polar and strongly hydrogen-bonded to one another. The other hydrogen halides exhibit this effect to a much lesser degree.

Solutions of chlorine or bromine in water contain hypochlorous and hypobromous acids, respectively.

$$Cl_2(g) + H_2O(l) \rightleftharpoons HClO(aq) + HCl(aq)$$

$$Br_2(l) + H_2O(l) \rightleftharpoons HBrO(aq) + HBr(aq)$$

In solution, these acids act as oxidizing agents. The active ingredient in chlorine bleach is hypochlorous acid. By contrast, fluorine liberates oxygen gas when it reacts with water.

$$2F_2(g) + 2H_2O(l) \longrightarrow O_2(g) + 4HF(aq)$$

Elemental fluorine is seldom used because of its extreme reactivity, but many fluorine compounds have commercial applications. Hydrogen fluoride is used to etch designs in glass and to frost light bulbs. For many years, it had to be stored in wax containers. Today, plastic bottles are used instead.

Figure 23·24
What happens to cloth when it is placed in a bottle of chlorine gas? Much of the color disappears due to the bleaching action of chlorine.

Teflon (polytetrafluoroethylene) is a heat-resistant plastic used in electrical insulators and for coating non-stick cookware. It is a polymer made up of fluorine and carbon. The volatile liquids used as coolants in most household refrigerators are fluorine compounds like dichloro-difluoromethane, CCl_2F_2. Unlike most fluorine compounds, they are non-toxic.

The enrichment of uranium is another important use of fluorine. In the process for separating the isotopes of uranium, the metal is converted to uranium hexafluoride (UF_6), a gas. The diffusion of this gas allows the separation of U-235, the fissionable isotope, from the nonfissionable isotope, U-238.

This concentration is about 1 part per million of fluorine in water.

Small quantities of sodium fluoride are added to drinking water to reduce tooth decay. The concentration is very low, about $5 \times 10^{-5} M$. Fluorides are also added to toothpaste to make teeth more decay resistant.

Large amounts of chlorine are used in the purification of city water supplies, swimming pools, and sewage. Because chlorine in solution is a powerful oxidizing agent, it kills disease-causing bacteria. Hypochlorous acid and its salts, the hypochlorites, are strong disinfectants and bleaches. Chlorine reacts with lime to produce a white compound known as *bleaching powder,* or chlorinated lime. It is a mixture of calcium chloride and calcium hypochlorite, $Ca(OCl)_2$, usually assigned the formula $Ca(ClO)Cl$. In the presence of dilute acid, bleaching powder releases chlorine gas. Thus it is frequently used for bleaching cloth.

An important use of chlorine is in the synthesis of vinyl chloride, $CH_2{=}CHCl$, which reacts to form polyvinyl chloride (PVC). PVC, a plastic, is used for floor coverings, phonograph records, and other "vinyl" products. With hot, concentrated alkalis, chlorine forms chlorates, which are used in making matches and as a weed-killer.

$$6KOH(aq) + 3Cl_2(g) \longrightarrow 5KCl(aq) + KClO_3(aq) + 3H_2O(l)$$

Chlorine gas was used in World War I, the first poisonous gas to be used in modern warfare.

Iodine is essential for the correct functioning of the thyroid gland. Small amounts of potassium iodide are added to table salt to insure adequate iodine in the diet. Silver iodide, like silver bromide, is used in making photographic film. Tincture of iodine, a solution of iodine in alcohol, is a well-known antiseptic.

Figure 23·25
Teflon is the trade name for a heat resistant plastic composed of fluorine and carbon. It is used as a non-stick coating.

Key Terms

allotrope   23·2
hydrogenation   23·1

and salt beds. Fluorine, the most electronegative element, reacts with nearly all of the other elements. Its uses include the enrichment of uranium and the inhibition of tooth decay. Chlorine, a powerful oxidizing agent, is used in disinfectants and the manufacture of "vinyl" products. It is also used to make hydrochloric acid. Iodine and bromine are two other halogens with numerous uses.

Chapter Summary

The nonmetallic elements are found in the upper right corner of the periodic table. They have very high electronegativities. Bonding between nonmetal atoms is primarily covalent. By contrast, compounds formed between metals and nonmetals are usually ionic.

Free hydrogen is rare on earth. Hydrogen containing compounds, however, such as water, are abundant. The three isotopes of hydrogen are protium, deuterium, and tritium. Hydrogen is used as a reducing agent, in ammonia production, and in the hydrogenation of vegetable oils.

Oxygen is the most abundant element on the earth's crust. It exists freely in the atmosphere as O_2. Most of the earth's oxygen, however, is found in numerous compounds. Ozone, O_3, is an allotrope of oxygen formed in the upper atmosphere. Oxygen's primary industrial use is in the production of steel.

Elemental sulfur occurs in several allotropic forms, including monoclinic and rhombic sulfur. Sulfur readily forms compounds with most metals and nonmetals. Some uses of sulfur are the manufacture of sulfuric acid, rubber, and paper.

Nitrogen is found in the free state as N_2. It comprises 80% of the air by volume. Two important nitrogen compounds are ammonia and nitric acid. Ammonia is used to make cleaning products and fertilizers. Nitric acid is used to make fertilizers and explosives.

The halogens do not occur in the free state. They exist in nature as halide ions found in seawater

Practice Questions and Problems

1. What is the largest industrial use of hydrogen?
   23·1

2. Give four physical properties of hydrogen. 23·1

3. What are the names, atomic symbols, and mass numbers of the isotopes of hydrogen?   23·1

4. Why is hydrogen a good reducing agent? 23·1

5. What is a catalyst? Name one of the catalysts used in hydrogenation.   23·1

6. In what three major forms is oxygen present on earth?   23·2

7. What is the volume precentage of oxygen in the earth's atmosphere? What are the other components of air?   23·2

8. Draw electron dot structures for the oxygen molecule and the ozone molecule.   23·2

9. Explain the term paramagnetism. Use liquid oxygen as your example.   23·2

10. What is the largest industrial use of oxygen?
    23·2

11. Give three physical properties of each substance. **a.** oxygen **b.** ozone   23·2

12. Where is ozone produced naturally?   23·2

13. Write the name of each compound.   23·3
    a. SiO_2 **d.** Fe_3O_4
    b. H_2O_2 **e.** BaO_2
    c. SO_3 **f.** CO_2

14. Write the formula of each compound.   *23·3*
  a. calcium oxide   **d.** aluminum oxide
  b. mercury(II) oxide   **e.** sulfur dioxide
  c. carbon monoxide   **f.** sodium peroxide

15. Complete and balance these equations   *23·3*
  a. $Mg(s) + O_2(g) \longrightarrow$
  b. $H_2(g) + O_2(g) \longrightarrow$
  c. $S(s) + O_2(g) \longrightarrow$

16. List some uses of hydrogen peroxide.   *23·3*

17. Name four physical properties of sulfur.   *23·4*

18. Describe the common allotrope of sulfur that is stable at room temperature.   *23·4*

19. What are some uses of sulfur?   *23·4*

20. Describe how to make a sample of *plastic* sulfur. How do the physical properties of freshly prepared and day-old plastic sulfur compare?   *23·4*

21. Complete and balance these equations.   *23·4*
  a. $Mg + S \longrightarrow$ **c.** $H_2 + S \longrightarrow$
  b. $Al + S \longrightarrow$ **d.** $Na + S \longrightarrow$

22. How is elemental nitrogen prepared for industrial use?   *23·5*

23. In what two major forms is nitrogen present on Earth?   *23·5*

24. Compare the boiling points of liquid nitrogen and liquid oxygen. How is the difference in boiling points put to practical use?   *23·5*

25. List major uses of ammonia in industry.   *23·6*

26. Give four physical properties of ammonia.   *23·6*

27. Nitric acid is produced commercially from ammonia by the Ostwald process. Write equations for the individual steps in this process.   *23·6*

28. Give the names and formulas of two substances that are used as fertilizers.   *23·6*

29. What are three uses of nitric acid?   *23·6*

30. Name two nitrogen-containing explosives. *23·6*

31. How is chlorine gas normally prepared for commercial use?   *23·7*

32. Bromine is extracted from seawater. Write an equation for the reaction and identify the reaction type.   *23·7*

33. Describe how iodine is obtained commercially.   *23·7*

34. By what process is fluorine made?   *23·7*

35. Give the names and molecular formulas of the halogens.   *23·8*

36. The halogens do not exist in nature in the free state. Explain.   *23·8*

37. How do chlorine and bromine react with water? Write equations.   *23·8*

38. Write the chemical equation to show how fluorine reacts with water.   *23·8*

39. How would you make *bleaching powder?* Give equations.   *23·8*

40. Why is chlorine added to drinking water and swimming pools?   *23·8*

Mastery Questions and Problems

41. Name the two allotropic forms of the element oxygen. Describe one method of preparation for each.   *23·2*

42. Explain why superheated water and compressed air are used in sulfur recovery by the Frasch process. What conditions do not allow sulfur to be mined, like coal, for example?   *23·4*

43. Give the equation for the laboratory preparation of chlorine from manganese dioxide and hydrochloric acid. What mass of HCl is required for the production of 1 mol of Cl_2?   *23·7*

44. What is the oxidation state (number) of nitrogen in each form?   *23·6*
  a. NO_2 **f.** NH_3
  b. N_2O **g.** NO
  c. NO_3^- **h.** N_2O_3
  d. N_2 **i.** NH_4^+
  e. HNO_3 **j.** NO_2^-

45. Large volumes of hydrogen are used in the hydrogenation of vegetable oils. Describe the process and comment on its commercial value.   *23·1*

46. Give three important physical properties of each of the halogens.   *23·8*

47. Calculate the mass percent of oxygen in these compounds.   *23·3*
  a. H_2O **c.** SiO_2
  b. $CaCO_3$ **d.** $CaSO_4$

48. Distinguish between oxygen and ozone. *23·2*

49. Write formulas for these substances. *23·8*
a. nitrous oxide   **d.** hypochlorous acid
b. ozone   **e.** sodium periodate
c. bleaching powder   **f.** vinyl chloride

50. Describe how iodine can be prepared in the laboratory. *23·7*

51. Write a balanced equation for the reaction of hydrogen with these elements.
a. nitrogen   **b.** chlorine   **c.** calcium   *23·1*

52. List all of the halogens in order of increasing electronegativity. *23·8*

53. List some of the major uses of sulfuric acid in industry. *23·6*

54. Explain why ammonia exhibits many water-like properties. *23·6*

55. Draw Lewis structures for the oxide ion, O^{2-}, and the peroxide ion, O_2^{2-}. *23·3*

56. List the nonmetals that occur as diatomic molecules. *23·8*
a. gases   **b.** liquids   **c.** solids

57. Name a nonmetallic oxide that reacts with water to form a base and a metallic oxide that reacts with water to form an acid. Write a balanced equation for each reaction. *23·3*

Review Questions and Problems

58. Explain these statements.
a. Group 1 metals form 1+ ions.
b. The atomic radius increases going down a group in the Periodic Table.

59. Give uses for these compounds.
a. $CaSO_4 \cdot 2H_2O$ **c.** $CaCO_3$
b. $BaSO_4$ **d.** $MgSO_4 \cdot 7H_2O$

60. State the outer electron configuration.
a. Pb   **b.** Bi   **c.** I   **d.** Ba

61. Give chemical equations for the reactions involved in the analytical test for Ag^+

62. Calcium carbonate is used as an antacid to neutralize HCl in the stomach. Write the equation for the neutralization reaction.

63. Use Lewis dot structures to predict the products of the following reactions.
a. beryllium and oxygen gas
b. calcium and sulfur
c. aluminum and chlorine gas

64. Determine the oxidation state of carbon in each of the following compounds.
a. CH_3OH **d.** $HCHO_2$
b. H_2CO **e.** CO_2
c. CH_4 **f.** CO

65. Using electron configurations, predict the product of the reaction between each of the following pairs of elements.
a. magnesium and bromine
b. calcium and bromine
c. cesium and selenium

66. Why is carbon such a useful industrial reducing agent? How is *coke* made?

67. Write a balanced equation for each reaction.
a. magnesium is exposed to steam
b. $CaSO_4 \cdot 2H_2O$ is heated
c. calcium carbonate is heated

Challenging Questions and Problems

68. How many kilograms of Br^- are there in a cubic mile of seawater?

69. How many grams of sulfur dioxide are produced when 200 g of sulfur is burned in oxygen? What volume would the sulfur dioxide occupy at STP?

70. What is the principal commercial method for producing hydrogen gas? Write a balanced chemical equation for the process. Identify each species.
a. the reducing agent
b. the oxidizing agent
c. the substance reduced
d. the substance oxidized
Use the changes in oxidation state to illustrate your answer.

71. Give the reactions for the production of sulfuric acid from elemental sulfur by the contact process. How many kilograms of H_2SO_4 will be obtained from 2.00×10^4 kg of sulfur if its purity is 99.6%?

72. Hydrogen peroxide decomposes according to this equation.

$$2H_2O_2 \longrightarrow 2H_2O + O_2$$

A solution is 3.00% H_2O_2 by volume. The density of H_2O_2 is 1.44 g/cm^3. How many liters of oxygen gas, measured at STP, is produced when 1 L of 3.00% H_2O_2 is decomposed?

Research Projects

1. How did Henry Cavendish discover hydrogen?

2. How is deuterium used in scientific research?

3. Report on the discoveries of Joseph Priestly and the results of his collaborations with Benjamin Franklin and Antoine Lavoisier.

4. Compare the reactivities of various allotropic forms of sulfur.

5. Make a diagram of the lead chamber process for sulfuric acid production.

6. What is "nitrogen fixation"? Describe one natural and one industrial process of nitrogen fixation.

7. Why was Fritz Haber's method of nitrogen fixation important? How did his work with gases change the course of history? Why was his Nobel prize denounced by some other scientists?

8. Devise a method to detect halide ions in seawater.

9. Describe the commercial production method for one of the halogens.

10. How is freon used to keep food cold in modern refrigerators?

11. What are some of the most commonly used propellants in aerosols? How do they compare to chlorofluorocarbon?

Readings and References

Asimov, Isaac. *Building Blocks of the Universe.* New York: Abelard-Schuman, 1974.

Renmore, C. D. *Silicon Chips and You: The Magical Mineral in Your Telephone, Calculator, Toys, Automobile, Hospital, Air Conditioning, Factory, Furnace, Sewing Machine, and Countless Other Future Inventions.* New York: Beaufort, 1980.

24 Nuclear Chemistry

Chapter Planning Guide

Section		Demonstrations and Experiments	Resource Materials
24·1 Radioactivity	C*	Dem 24·1 Geiger Counter	Objectives Worksheet 24, SPB Skillsheet 24, SPB
24·2 Types of Radiation	C	Dem 24·2 Radioactivity and Distance Dem 24·3 Radioactivity and Shielding Exp 50 Radioactivity and Radiation, LM Dem 24·4 Electroscope and Radioactivity	Prelab 50, SPB
24·3 Nuclear Stability	H		Teaching Diagram 28 Beyond the Text: Nuclear Energy
24·4 Half-Life	C		Quiz 24·1 Teaching Diagram 29
24·A Carbon-14 Dating	E		
24·5 Transmutation Reactions	C		
24·B Particle Accelerators	E		

24·6 Nuclear Fission	C	Dem 24·5 Chain Reaction with
		    Matchsticks
		Dem 24·6 Chain Reaction with
		    Mousetraps
			Teaching Diagram 30
			
			Nuclear Waste Disposal, ICT 24

24·7 Nuclear Fusion	C		Beyond the Text: Radioactive Wastes

24·8 Detecting Radiation	O	Dem 24·7 Radioactive Exposure of Film
		Dem 24·8 The Cloud Chamber
			Quiz 24·2
			Beyond the Text:
			    Units of Radiation
			    Background Radiation
			Reviewsheet 24, SPB
			Chapter 24 Test

24·C Radioisotopes in Research and Medicine	E		
*C = Core, O = Optional E = Enrichment, H = Honors		LM = Laboratory Manual	SPB = Skills Practice Book ICT = Issues in Chem. Tech.

Chapter Objectives

Having studied this chapter and done the problems, the student should be able to:

1. Define radioisotope, radioactive decay, and transmutation.   *24·1*

2. Characterize alpha, beta, and gamma radiation by composition and penetrating power.   *24·2*

3. Write balanced nuclear equations for alpha and beta decay processes.   *24·3*

4. Use the half-life to calculate the amount of radioisotope remaining at a given time.   *24·4*

5. Explain how radioisotopes can be used to date objects.   *24·4*

6. Use equations to show how transuranium elements are synthesized by transmutation.   *24·5*

7. Describe how a nuclear power plant operates.   *24·6*

8. Compare nuclear fission and nuclear fusion.   *24·6, 24·7*

9. Write an equation for solar fusion.   *24·7*

10. Describe three methods of detecting radiation, and state each method's limitations. *24·8*

11. List the effects of various types of radiation on a living organism. *24·8*

Teaching Suggestions

24·1 Radioactivity

As you start this unit, make the students aware that they are encountering a kind of chemistry that is entirely different from the chemistry they have studied previously. Emphasize that in all of the topics that we have considered so far, we always assumed that the nuclei of atoms were inviolate. That is, all chemical changes, reactions, and processes, involved only the outer portions (orbitals) of the atoms. In this unit we now focus on the changes which can occur within the nucleus of the atom.

Demonstration 24·1 *Geiger Counter* shows the level of natural radioactivity. Stress that this radiation is always present, although the *amount* of background radiation varies from place to place.

24·2 Types of Radiation

Radioactivity is the result of the attempts by atomic nuclei to attain stability. Stress that all such readjustments involve giving off energy. In some cases the energy is lost as electromagnetic radiation (gamma ray or X-ray). In other cases it is carried away by high-speed electrons. In still other cases an entire "chunk" of nuclear material (alpha particle) carries it. Be sure that your students realize that any time a nucleus emits a particle (alpha or beta), the number of protons in the nucleus has changed and therefore an isotope of a different element results. Remind them that in chemical reactions nuclear changes *never* occur.

As you introduce the three main types of radiation and give examples of their production, be sure to write balanced equations. Point out that the sum of the superscripts of the reactants always equals the sum of superscripts of the products, and the sum of the subscripts of the reactants always equals the sum of the subscripts of the products.

The students will understand radioactivity and its detection more thoroughly if they can get some direct experience. Have them do **Experiment 50** *Radioactivity,* or do **Demonstrations 24·2** *Radioactivity and Distance* and **24·3** *Radioactivity and Shielding* for them. Both deal with the detection of radiation, the concept of background radiation, and the comparison of various substances as shielding materials. **Demonstration 24·4** *Electroscope and Radioactivity* shows that some radioactivity consists of charged particles.

24·3 Nuclear Stability

There is a single underlying concept which allows us to explain the manner in which atomic nuclei change their composition. For each element there exists only a small range in which the numbers of neutrons and protons are correct for the existence of a stable isotope. If an isotope does not possess a stable ratio to neutrons to protons, then it must change.

There are three processes available. A nucleus can increase the number of protons and decrease the number of neutrons by beta emission. This results in a decrease in the neutron to proton ratio. A nucleus can decrease the number of protons and increase the number of neutrons by positron emission. This increases the neutron to proton ratio.

In the case of the very heavy elements, the nucleus loses both neutrons and protons by emitting a helium nucleus (alpha particle emission). This results in a slight increase in the ratio of neutrons to protons.

Try to get across the point that all of these changes are predictable, and can be related to Figure 24·7, in which neutron number is plotted against proton number.

24·4 Half-Life

The rate of disintegration of a nuclear isotope is constant. It is unaffected by external influences such as heat, pressure, or chemical reactions.

This rate is also independent of the number of atoms which are present. Thus, it is stated in terms of the *fraction* of the sample which will decay in a certain time period. The time required for exactly half of the radioactive atoms in a given sample to decay is convenient to use, and is called the half-life. Be sure that the students realize that after each half-life, exactly one-half of the atoms present initially will have decayed. After each half-life, the amount of radioactive element remaining is exactly one-half the amount present at the start of the half-life period.

Refer the students to Table 24·2 and have them note the tremendous range in possible values for half-lives. Remind them that these numbers do not tell us how long a given isotope will last, but how long it takes for *half* of the material to convert.

24·5 Transmutation Reactions

One of the main goals of the alchemists was the conversion of low cost metals to precious metals. No chemical reaction can make that possible. However, in transmutation reactions chemists are able to accomplish what the early alchemists were not. Through transmutation reactions chemists are able to change one element into another.

Point out that with transmutation reactions chemists not only can make isotopes of elements which already exist on earth, but also can produce many which do not exist on earth, such as the transuranium elements.

24·6 Nuclear Fission

Be sure to emphasize that the production of energy by fission is a different process than that which occurs in chemical reactions. In fission, matter is converted to energy as the heavy nuclei split, releasing a tremendous amount of energy. The amount of energy given off during fission makes even the most energetic of chemical reactions seem insignificant by comparison.

An important feature of nuclear fission is the chain reaction. Be sure that the students are aware of how a single neutron can trigger a chain reaction in a fissionable material. It might be helpful to show them an example of a chain reaction. See **Demonstrations 24·5** *Chain Reaction with Matchsticks* and **24·6** *Chain Reaction with Mousetraps* for two possibilities.

Stress that the main factor in the control of nuclear fission reactions is the control of the neutrons. The reaction cannot be sustained unless the neutrons are moving at the proper speed, and thus a moderator is needed. If the reaction proceeds too rapidly, it can be slowed simply by absorbing free neutrons. This is the function of the control rods in a nuclear reactor.

Most students are aware of the controversy which surrounds the use and construction of nuclear reactors. Point out that the control of nuclear fission reactions is not the main issue, except for fears of meltdowns. The basic problem with the fission of heavy elements is that radioactive products are *always* produced. Some of these products have very long half-lives. The methods of containment and disposal of these products are problems which have not yet been solved.

24·7 Nuclear Fusion

As you discuss this section, compare and contrast fission and fusion. Point out that both produce energy by the conversion of matter to energy. In fission very heavy nuclei are split into lighter nuclei. In fusion very light nuclei combine to produce heavier nuclei. Fission reactions are relatively easy to control but produce radioactive waste. Our technology has still not been able to control large-scale fusion reactions, since they require such extraordinarily high temperatures and pressures. Fusion reactions produce little radioactive waste.

24·8 Detecting Radiation

This section describes some of the basic methods for detecting the various forms of radiation. **Demonstration 24·7** *Radioactive Exposure of Film* shows this effect of radioactivity. Another method which had wide application in the past is the cloud chamber. These are easily constructed. See **Demonstration 24·8** *The Cloud Chamber* for details.

Demonstrations

24·1 Geiger Counter

Concept: Natural background radiation is detectable.

Materials: Geiger counter with meter and/or loudspeaker.

Procedure: 1. Keep a Geiger counter turned on for the duration of the class. Be sure no radioactive sources are nearby. The students will notice a random clicking as background radiation is being recorded. 2. Point out that this radiation is *always* present. The amount may vary from location to location, but it is inescapable. To make an accurate count of the radiation from a given source, we must take this background into account.

24·2 Radioactivity and Distance

Concept: Distance from the source affects radioactivity levels.

Materials: Geiger counter with loudspeaker and rate meter or a Geiger tube connected to a scaler, sources of beta and/or gamma radiation (embedded in plastic for safety in handling), ruler, forceps.

Procedure: 1. Discuss the fact that the relationship between the distance from a radioactive source and the radiation received obeys the inverse square law. 2. To show this, arrange a radioactive source so that it is opposite the window of the Geiger tube. 3. Measure the rate of radiation detected at various distances from the source. 4. Record the results in counts per minute. 5. Subtract the background count from each of these measurements. 6. Make plots of corrected radiation readings versus distance and of corrected radiation readings versus the reciprocal of the square of the distance. 7. The latter plot should produce a straight line, indicating an inverse square relationship. For example, the radiation received will be only one-fourth as great if the distance from the source is doubled. **Caution:** *Use only safely packaged radiation sources. Do not directly touch any radioactive material.*

24·3 Radioactivity and Shielding

Concept: The effectiveness of a radiation shield is proportionate to its density.

Materials: Geiger counter with loudspeaker and rate meter, sources of beta and/or gamma radiation (embedded in plastic for safety in handling), ruler, 5-cm square pieces of aluminum, lead, and cardboard, forceps.

Procedure: 1. Point out that the ability of a substance to act as a radiation shield is generally proportionate to its density. 2. Mount the beta source 10–30 cm from the

window of a Geiger counter. 3. Measure the radiation received. 4. Place pieces of the shielding material, one at a time, between the Geiger counter and radiation source. 5. Note the radiation received each time. 6. A convenient way to compare shielding abilities is to find the *half-thickness* of a material. This is the thickness of material needed to reduce the radiation to exactly one half of its original value. For each material, add layers of the material until the radiation drops to half of its original value. Then measure the total thickness of all of the layers. **Caution:** *Use only safely packaged radiation sources. Do not directly touch any radioactive material.*

24·4 Electroscope and Radioactivity

Concept: Charged radioactive particles can discharge electroscopes.

Materials: electroscope, rubber rod, cat fur, radioactive source, forceps.

Procedure: 1. Rub the rod with fur and touch the top of the electroscope with the rod. 2. The gold leaves spread apart. 3. Bring the radioactive source close to the top of the electroscope. 4. The gold leaves fall back together as the radioactive charges cancel the added charges. **Caution:** *Use only safely packaged radioactive sources. Do not directly touch any radioactive substance.*

24·5 Chain Reaction with Matchsticks

Concept: Chain reactions require products that initiate a new reaction.

Materials: wooden matchsticks, glass or metal plate, matches, fire extinguisher, safety goggles.

Procedure: 1. Cut the matchsticks in half and arrange the heads in branching chains on a noncombustible surface. 2. Construct the chains so that the end of each matchstick is touching the heads of two other matchsticks to form a "Y" shape. 3. Ignite the first match. Flames will spread in a chain reaction. **Caution:** *Keep all flammable materials away from the demonstration. Have a fire extinguisher ready.*

24·6 Chain Reaction with Mousetraps

Concept: Chain reactions require products that initiate a new reaction.

Materials: 16 mousetraps, 32 cork stoppers, cardboard cover (.5m × .5m).

Procedure: 1. Arrange the mousetraps in four rows of four traps each. 2. Set each trap, and place two cork stoppers on the loop of each. 3. Support the cardboard about 30 cm above the traps to deflect the stoppers back toward the mousetraps. It should be the same shape and size as the mousetrap grid. 4. Toss in a stopper to set off one of the traps. 5. A chain reaction results.

24·7 Radioactive Exposure of Film

Concept: Radioactivity reduces silver in photographic film.

Materials: unexposed photographic film wrapped in black paper, key, radiation source, forceps.

Procedure: 1. Place a key on top of photographic film on a desktop. 2. Place the radiation source on top of the key. 3. After one week, develop the film. The key area is unexposed, but the rest of the film has been exposed. **Caution:** *Use only a safely packaged radiation source. Do not directly touch any radioactive substance.*

24·8 The Cloud Chamber

Concept: The path of ionizing radiation is visible in a cloud chamber.

Materials: cloud chamber*, ethanol, dry ice, tongs, radiation source, strong light, forceps, safety goggles. (*A cloud chamber may be purchased from a scientific supply company, or constructed as follows: Paint the bottom of a 2″ × 4″ plastic box black. Glue blotter paper to the inside of the lid of the box.)

Procedure: 1. Place the box on a slab of dry ice. **Caution:** *Dry ice can cause frostbite. Use tongs.* 2. Saturate the blotter paper with ethanol. 3. Place a source of radiation in the box and put on the lid. 4. Allow a few minutes for equilibrium to be established. 5. Darken the room and shine a strong light through the side of the box. 6. Vapor tracks should be visible. 7. If the chamber does not work right away, try gently warming the top of the chamber to increase the rate of evaporation of the ethanol. **Caution:** *Use only a safely packaged radiation source. Do not directly touch any radioactive substance.*

Audiovisual Resources

Energy: The Nuclear Alternative (F) Churchill Films, 1980, 22 min. (Use with Section 24·6.) Presents both sides of the nuclear energy issue in terms of two major concerns: reactor safety and the management of radioactive wastes.

Fission and Fusion Reactions (FS) Prentice-Hall Media, 1980. (Use with Sections 24·A, 24·4, 24·5, 24·6, 24·7, or 24·C.) Explains principles of accelerator design, describes nuclear reactions, and discusses production of artificial elements, radiochemical tracer methods, radiometric analysis, and carbon-14 dating.

Fusion: The Ultimate Energy Answer? (FS) Knowledge Unlimited, 1983, 60 min. (Use with Section 24·7.) Describes three current lines of fusion research and discusses future prospects.

Fusion: The Ultimate Fire (F) BFA Educational Media, 1976, 14 min. (Use with Section 24·7.) Provides a quick overview of thermonuclear fusion research with animated depiction of the fusion of hydrogen nuclei.

Nuclear Energy (F, V) National Geographic, 1981, 23 min. (Use with Section 24·6.) Discusses a wide range of issues relating to the future of nuclear power.

Nuclear Energy: Too Hot to Handle? (FS) Carolina Biological Supply, 1980, 17 min. (Use with Section 24·6.) Discusses three key issues: consequences of a major nuclear accident, effects of low-level radiation, and radioactive waste disposal.

Nuclear Radiation (6 FS) Eyegate, 1968, 15–25 min. each. (Use with Sections 24·1, 24·2, 24·8, or 24·C.) Illustrates basic nuclear principles, explains the use of radiation detectors, and presents applications in medicine, industry, earth science, and other areas.

Radiation and Your Environment (V) EME, 1983, 25 min. (Use with Sections 24·1 and 24·2.) Introduces types of radiation and describes their sources, characteristics, uses, and hazards.

Radiation . . . Naturally (F, V) Atomic Industrial Forum, 1981, 29 min. (Use with Sections 24·2 and 24·C.) Explains the sources and levels of background radiation and describes risks from background and medical exposures.

Radioactive Dating (F) Coronet, 1981, 13 min. (Use with Sections 24·4 and 24·A.) Introduces some of the principles of radiocarbon and potassium–argon dating methods.

Transuranium Elements (F, V) Chem Study, 1963, 23 min. (Use with Section 24·5.) Reviews methods and techniques used in discovering and identifying transuranium elements.

The Atom and Archeology (F) ERDA, 1975, 25 min. (Use with Sections 24·4, 24·A, or 24·8.) Explains the use of carbon-14 dating, thermoluminescence measurement, neutron activation, and radiography by archeologists.

The Breeder (F) Stuart Finley, 1978, 23 min. (Use with Section 24·6.) Presents a comprehensive description of the scientific and technical aspects of nuclear reactors and discusses related social and environmental issues.

The Nucleus: Composition, Stability, and Decay (FS) Prentice-Hall Media, 1980. (Use with Sections 24·2

and 24·3.) Introduces nuclear theory, reviews nuclear symbols, describes decay pathways, and examines the stability of isotopes.

The Ultimate Energy (F) ERDA, 1976, 28 min. (Use with Section 24·7.) Describes the conversion of hydrogen to helium in the sun and reviews government-sponsored nuclear fusion research.

Beyond the Text

Nuclear Energy

If two protons and two neutrons were brought together the positively charged protons would repel each other. By contrast, the nucleus of helium has two protons and two neutrons but is extremely stable. What allows these particles to stay together in the helium nucleus? A clue to the answer lies in the nuclear mass defect and the binding energy of the nucleus.

The total mass of the protons and neutrons in the helium nucleus is *less than* the total mass of the same particles when they are separated. The difference in mass between the separate and united nuclear particles is called the *nuclear mass defect*. Some of the mass of the separated particles is converted to energy when the nucleus is formed. This energy becomes lost (dissipated) to the surroundings.

Suppose that the nuclear particles could be separated. The energy that was dissipated when they came together must now be restored and turned into mass. If this doesn't happen, the nucleus remains intact. The energy that is required to separate the nuclear particles is called the *binding energy*. It holds the nuclear particles together.

The nuclear mass defect for the helium nucleus is calculated as follows. (Units are in atomic mass units, amu.)

Mass of two protons (2 × 1.0073 amu) = 2.0146 amu
Mass of two neutrons (2 × 1.0087 amu) = 2.0174 amu
Combined mass of separated particles = 4.0320 amu
Mass of helium nucleus = 4.0015 amu
Difference in mass (nuclear mass defect) = 0.0305 amu

Albert Einstein (1879–1955) showed with his famous equation that mass and energy are interchangeable.

$$E = mc^2$$

Here E is energy (joules), m is mass (kilograms), and c is the speed of light (3.00×10^8 m/s). The square of the speed of light is an enormous number. It follows that when even a very small mass is converted to energy, the energy production is considerable.

Einstein's equation can be used to convert this nuclear mass defect for the helium nucleus into its energy equivalent. The mass difference between $^4_2$He and its constituent particles is 0.0305 amu. Since 1 amu = 1.66×10^{-27} kg

and $c = 3.00 \times 10^8$ m/s, this mass corresponds to an energy of 4.46×10^{-12} J.

$$E = 0.305 \text{ amu} \times \frac{1.66 \times 10^{-27} \text{ kg}}{\text{amu}} \times \left(\frac{3.00 \times 10^8 \text{ m}}{\text{s}}\right)^2$$

$$= 0.035 \text{ amu} \times \frac{1.66 \times 10^{-27} \text{ kg}}{\text{amu}} \times \frac{9.00 \times 10^{16} \text{ m}^2}{\text{s}^2}$$

$$= \frac{4.46 \times 10 \text{ kg m}^2}{\text{s}^2}$$

This number can be converted to Joules: 1 kg m²/s² = 1 J.

$$4.46 \times \frac{10 \text{ kg m}^2}{\text{s}^2} \times \frac{1 \text{ J}}{\text{kg m}^2/\text{s}^2} = 4.46 \times 10^{-12} \text{ J}$$

The binding energy of the $^4_2$He nucleus is 4.46×10^{-12} J.

The nuclear particles, protons and neutrons, are collectively called *nucleons*. (The total number of nucleons in the nucleus of an atom is the mass number of that atom.) There are four nucleons in $^4_2$He. *The binding energy per nucleon in helium is, therefore, calculated by dividing the total binding energy by four.*

$$\frac{4.46 \times 10^{-12} \text{ J}}{4 \text{ nucleons}} = \frac{1.11 \times 10^{-12} \text{ J}}{\text{nucleon}}$$

The highest binding energies per nucleon occur with atoms of intermediate mass numbers 40 to 70. Nuclei of these atoms have the greatest stability of all the elements. Iron has the most stable nucleus of all.

For elements with a smaller mass number than iron, *fusion* is a favorable process. In fusion, heavier nuclei with greater binding energy per nucleon are produced. Energy is released in the process (Section 24·7).

In contrast, *fission* is an energetically favorable process for atoms with a greater mass number than iron. In fission, atoms with intermediate masses and greater binding energies per nucleon are formed from larger unstable nuclei. Energy is also released in fission (Section 24·6).

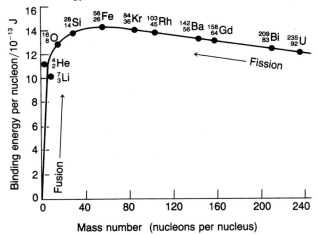

Mass number (nucleons per nucleus)

Radioactive Wastes

One of the major problems facing the nuclear industry is the disposal of radioactive wastes. As fission reactors operate, fission products accumulate in the fuel rods. In addition, some of the uranium-238 in the rods is converted to plutonium. These materials are highly radioactive. They are dangerous to handle and extremely harmful to living organisms.

As fission products accumulate in the fuel rods, the fission reaction slows down. This effect occurs even though a large amount of usable fuel still remains in the rods. Periodically, approximately once a year, the fuel rods must be removed from the reactor and replaced by new ones. The nuclear industry hopes eventually to reprocess these rods. This would involve removing the useful fuel and recovering the plutonium in the rods. Plutonium-239 is fissionable and can be used as fuel in breeder reactors. The technology of reprocessing these highly radioactive fuel assemblies is very complex and expensive. Commercial reprocessing plants have not yet begun operation in North America. The spent fuel rods are now stored under pools of very pure water, generally at the reactor site. Some engineers believe that reprocessing the fuel will always remain prohibitively expensive. In their view, the used fuel rods should simply be permanently disposed of.

Spent fuel rods account for the largest part of high level radioactive waste. Several plans for disposing of this waste have been proposed. Ideally, the disposal system should insure that the wastes remain isolated from the biosphere and the ground water for as long as they might be harmful to living organisms. The generally accepted isolation time is 10 to 20 half-lives. In the case of fission products, this is 300 to 600 years. Plutonium, with a half-life of 24 000 years, should be isolated from the biological environment for more than 250 000 years.

Most of the plans proposed for permanent disposal of radioactive wastes involve several steps. First the wastes need to be concentrated. Then they must be combined with a ceramic material that will be very resistant to corrosion. Finally they must be buried in a stable geological formation. Abandoned salt mines, if they can be proven free of all water seepage, are one possibility. Holes drilled deep into bedrock are another. Rocketing the wastes into space, letting them melt their way down through polar ice caps, or burying them on the edge of a descending continental plate are other proposals. These ideas may seem extreme, but they do point out the magnitude and seriousness of the problem.

The temporary disposal methods now in use are far from satisfactory. Tens of thousands of fuel rod assemblies already await burial in North America. Four thousand more are added each year. Large quantities of solutions of radioactive waste have leaked from storage tanks. These tanks have been kept in service decades longer than their intended lifetime. Above-ground storage at reactor sites or other facilities does not guarantee that the wastes can be kept out of the biosphere. Some people feel that no system of disposal can remain secure for 500 years, given the political and social history of our world. Radioactive waste disposal is a serious problem that remains to be solved.

Units of Radiation

It is often necessary to measure radiation accurately. Several units of measurement that describe specific features about a radiation source and its radiation are discussed in the following paragraphs.

The curie. We have learned that radioisotopes decay at specific rates called half-lives. Intensity of radiation depends on the number of atoms that decay in a given period of time; this breakdown is called the *rate of decay*. The *curie* (named after Madame Curie) is the unit used to measure the rate of radioactive decay. One curie (Ci) is 3.7×10^{10} disintegrations per second (dps); this number is the measured activity in disintegrations per second of 1 g of pure radium. The curie measures only the activity of a radiation source; it does not describe the source or type of radiation emitted. Any source that gives 3.7×10^{10} dps is by definition 1 Ci. When smaller units are needed the *millicurie,* mCi (10^{-3} Ci or 3.7×10^{7} dps), or the *microcurie*, μCi (10^{-6} Ci or 3.7×10^{4} dps), is used.

Cobalt-60 sources are gamma emitters used in many hospitals for radiation therapy. These source are rated in curies. Used under the same conditions and in a given period of time, a 1-Ci source delivers two times as much radiation to a patient as a 0.5-Ci source.

The roentgen. Like the curie, the *roentgen* (R) (named for Wilhelm Roentgen, 1845–1923, the German physicist who discovered X-rays in 1895) is a measure of the output from a radiation source. However, the roentgen measures the capacity of the source to cause ionization, not the rate at which the source disintegrates. One roentgen is the amount of X-rays or gamma radiation that produces ions carrying 2.1×10^{9} units of electrical charge in 1 cm^3 of dry air at 0°C and 1 atm pressure. This definition is rather long-winded, perhaps, but we can see that the roentgen unit is a measure of a radiation beam's capacity for causing ionization in air.

The roentgen is used to measure the radiation output from a radiation source. For example, when an object is placed for 1 min in front of a radiation source emitting 1 R/min, we say that the object receives an exposure (an exposed dose) of 1 R. Ionization of body tissue is proportional to radiation exposure measured in roentgens. The greater the number of ionizations in body tissue, the greater the damage. A person receiving a single dose of about 600 R to the entire body (a total body dose) will die within three weeks.

The rad. The *rad* (radiation *a*bsorbed *d*ose) is a measure of the energy absorbed by an object exposed to a radiation source. One rad is the quantity of ionizing radiation which delivers 100 erg of energy to 1 g of a substance. (The erg is a very small unit of energy; 4.2×10^{7} erg is equivalent to only 1 cal.) When we are dealing with soft tissue, the rad and the roentgen are equivalent; the delivery of 1 R to soft tissue results in the absorption of 1 rad, so a single total body dose of 600 rads will also kill a human being.

The rem. The *rem* (*r*oentgen *e*quivalent *m*edical) is a measure of a quantity of radiation. The quantity differs with the type of radiation exposure. The absorption of 1 rem of *any* ionizing radiation produces the same biologic effects as the absorption of 1 R (1 rad) of gamma rays of X-rays. Since biologic damage caused by 1 rad of alpha particles differs from that caused by 1 rad of gamma rays or X-rays, the rem measure is used to compensate. For example, 1 rad of alpha radiation causes about 15 times more radiation damage than 1 rad of X-rays; a 1-rem dose of alpha radiation is therefore 15 times less radiation than a 1-rem dose of X-rays.

Background Radiation

No matter who we are or where we live, we cannot escape exposure to ionizing radiation. Radioisotopes are present in soil and rocks, in the air we breathe, in the water we drink, in the food we eat. Of the 350 or so naturally occurring isotopes, about 50 are radioactive. Natural *background radiation* consists almost entirely of cosmic rays and gamma rays from potassium-40, thorium-232, and the decay of uranium-238.

Natural background radiation exposes us to about 120 millirem per year or about 10 rem in a lifetime. There are a few places on earth (the monazite sand areas of India and Brazil) with soils so rich in thorium that people living there receive natural background radiation of about 2 rem per year.

Average Annual Per Capita Radiation Received in the United States

Source	Average dose per year (mrem)
Natural background (soil, air, water, food)	120
Fallout from atmospheric testing and pollutants from nuclear power plants	4
Medical	
Diagnostic (chest)	50
Diagnostic (dental)	20
Therapeutic	5
Other (air travel, television)	3
Total radiation exposure	202

Besides naturally occurring background radiation, amounts occur through the atmospheric testing of nuclear devices and as environmental pollutants from nuclear power station wastes. The detonation of a nuclear weapon spreads radioactive isotopes worldwide. These isotopes include plutonium-239, cesium-137, strontium-90, and iodine-131. During the mid-1960s the average dose from fallout in the United States was less than 15 millirem per year (about 10% of natural background).

Because of the widespread use of X-rays and radioisotopes in medicine, we are also subjected to what we might call medical background radiation. The amount of radiation used for medical purposes varies widely. Some people never have a dental or chest X-ray. But at the other end of the scale, a cancer patient might receive a dose of 6000 rem concentrated at a small region where a tumor is located. On the average, each of us receives about 70 millirem per year from dental and medical X-rays.

The human body incorporates a selection of radioisotopes that produce a measurable, *internal* background radiation. The predominant isotope is potassium-40, a gamma emitter; there are lesser amounts of carbon-14, thorium-232, and uranium-238. Radium-226, which is an alpha and gamma emitter, chemically resembles calcium. (Both are in Group 2A in the periodic table.) Since it tends to accumulate in the skeleton, radium-226 is called a bone-seeker. The major danger from these isotopes is that they are incorporated into the tissues and skeleton after ingestion. Strontium-90, which resembles calcium, is incorporated into bones; iodine-131, like the nonradioactive isotope iodine-127, concentrates in the thyroid. Young children are at a far greater risk from accumulation of the artificially produced background radioisotopes than adults. Adults use strontium-90 only for bone repair, but young children use it to build bones. Each person in the United States receives a radiation dose of about 202 millirems each year from a variety of sources. A person who is employed to handle radioisotopes or who operates radiation-emitting devices is permitted to receive up to 5000 millirem of radiation per year.

Any exposure to ionizing radiation is potentially harmful. Having an occasional diagnostic X-ray is not likely to cause harm, but any exposure to ionizing radiation should be avoided if at all possible. No dose of ionizing radiation, however small, is completely safe.

Symptoms of Radiation Sickness in Humans			
Time after exposure	Sublethal dose (100–200 R)	Median lethal dose (300–400 R)	Lethal dose (500 R)
First week	Nausea, vomiting possible; no definite symptons	Nausea, vomiting after 2 hr; no definite symptoms	Nausea, vomiting within 2 hr, diarrhea; reddening of throat and mouth
Second week		Loss of hair, loss of appetite, general discomfort, sore throat, bleeding	Fever, rapid weight loss, death
Third week	Loss of hair, loss of appetite, general discomfort, sore throat, bleeding	Diarrhea, death (50% mortality rate)	
Fourth week	Diarrhea; survival probable	Short-term survival possible	Survival improbable

Answers to End of Chapter Questions and Problems

Practice Questions and Problems

6. A nuclear reaction changes the nucleus. A chemical reaction changes the electron configuration.

7. Each *isotope* of an element has the same atomic number but a different atomic mass. A *radioisotope* is an isotope that is radioactive.

8. The nucleus.

9. a. α, +2 **b.** β, −1 **c.** γ, 0

10. a. a sheet of aluminum or other metal foil, or thin pieces of wood **b.** several feet of concrete or inches of lead **c.** a sheet of paper

11. a. $^{238}_{92}U \rightarrow ^{234}_{90}Th + ^{4}_{2}He$; thorium-234
b. $^{230}_{90}Th \rightarrow ^{226}_{88}Ra + ^{4}_{2}He$; radium-226
c. $^{235}_{92}U \rightarrow ^{231}_{90}Th + ^{4}_{2}He$; thorium-231
d. $^{222}_{86}Rn \rightarrow ^{218}_{84}Po + ^{4}_{2}He$; polonium-218

12. a. $^{14}_{6}C \rightarrow ^{14}_{7}N + ^{0}_{-1}e$ **b.** $^{90}_{38}Sr \rightarrow ^{90}_{39}Y + ^{0}_{-1}e$
c. $^{40}_{19}K \rightarrow ^{40}_{20}Ca + ^{0}_{-1}e$ **d.** $^{13}_{7}N \rightarrow ^{13}_{8}O + ^{0}_{-1}e$

13. Alpha radiation is a helium nucleus. Beta radiation is an electron. Gamma radiation is high energy electromagnetic radiation.

14. a. atomic mass: decreases by four; atomic number: decreases by two **b.** atomic mass: unchanged; atomic number: increases by one **c.** atomic mass and atomic number: unchanged

15.

	Alpha	Beta	Gamma
a. Mass:	4 amu	1/1837 amu	0
b. Charge:	2+	1−	0
c. Penetrating power:	low	moderate	very high

16. a. $^{234}_{92}U$ **b.** $^{206}_{81}Tl$ **c.** $^{170}_{70}Yb$ **d.** $^{206}_{82}Pb$ **e.** $^{226}_{88}Ra$

17. Stable nuclei are located in a band of stability when the number of neutrons is plotted vs. the number of protons. The nuclei outside the band of stability undergo spontaneous radioactive decay.

18. a. $^{14}_{6}C$ **b.** $^{1}_{1}H$ **c.** $^{16}_{8}O$ **d.** $^{14}_{7}N$

19. Platinum (**a.**), thorium (**b.**), technetium (**d.**), xenon (**e.**), vanadium (**g.**), and palladum (**h.**) have some stable isotopes. Francium (**c.**) and californium (**f.**) have no stable isotopes.

20. The time required for one-half of the atoms of a radioisotope to emit radiation and decay.

21. 2.5×10^{-2} g $^{59}_{26}Fe$

22. 5.25 years

23. 6.3×10^{-1} mg $^{131}_{53}I$

24. 1.6×10^{4} atoms $^{133}_{54}Xe$

25. The conversion of an atom of one element to an atom of another element:
$^{238}_{92}U \rightarrow ^{234}_{90}Th + ^{4}_{2}He$ (alpha emission)
$^{14}_{7}N + ^{4}_{2}He \rightarrow ^{18}_{9}F$ (alpha bombardment)
$^{239}_{93}Np \rightarrow ^{239}_{94}Pu + ^{0}_{-1}e$ (beta emission)

26. The elements with atomic number greater than 92; none occur in nature and all are radioactive.

27. Natural radioactivity comes from radioactive elements present in nature. Artificial radioactivity comes from elements created in nuclear reactors and accelerators.

28. a. $^{27}_{13}Al + ^{4}_{2}He \rightarrow ^{30}_{14}Si + ^{1}_{1}H$
b. $^{214}_{83}Bi \rightarrow ^{4}_{2}He + ^{210}_{81}Tl$ **c.** $^{27}_{14}Si \rightarrow ^{0}_{-1}e + ^{27}_{15}P$
d. $^{66}_{29}Cu \rightarrow ^{66}_{30}Zn + ^{0}_{-1}e$

29. The nuclei of certain isotopes are bombarded with neutrons. The nuclei break into two and release more neutrons. The released neutrons hit other nuclei to start a chain reaction that releases large amounts of energy.

30. The control rods absorb neutrons to prevent further reactions. They are made of cadmium.

31. A nuclear chain reaction involves the splitting of atomic nuclei that release energetic neutrons that split more nuclei.

32. By using neutron moderation or neutron absorption.

33. Uranium-235 is one natural fissionable material. Plutonium-239 is one artificially produced fissionable material. Answers will vary.

34. Two nuclei combine to produce a nucleus of heavier mass.

35. Fusion requires a temperature of at least 4×10^{7} °C. At that temperature, the fuel is a plasma that destroys any container.

36. Ionizing radiation, like X-rays and radioactivity, has sufficient energy to remove electrons from the atoms it hits.

37. An exposed film badge indicates how much radiation a worker has received.

38. A Geiger counter is a gas-filled metal tube with a central wire electrode. A potential is kept between the electrode and the tube. When ionizing radiation enters the tube, the ionized gas allows a current to flow. This

current is registered on a meter or by a speaker. A Geiger counter mainly detects beta radiation. It does not usually detect alpha particles or gamma rays.

Mastery Questions and Problems

39. a. $^{30}_{15}P + ^{0}_{-1}e \rightarrow ^{30}_{14}Si$ **b.** $^{13}_{6}C + ^{1}_{0}n \rightarrow ^{14}_{6}C$

40. Nuclear *fusion* takes place in the sun. A nuclear reactor utilizes nuclear *fission*.

41. a. $^{32}_{16}S$ **b.** $^{14}_{6}C$ **c.** $^{4}_{2}He$ **d.** $^{141}_{57}La$

42. a. $^{90}_{38}Sr \rightarrow ^{90}_{39}Y + ^{0}_{-1}e$ **b.** $^{14}_{6}C \rightarrow ^{14}_{7}N + ^{0}_{-1}e$
c. $^{137}_{55}Cs \rightarrow ^{137}_{56}Ba + ^{0}_{-1}e$ **d.** $^{239}_{93}Np \rightarrow ^{239}_{94}Pu + ^{0}_{-1}e$

43. A radioisotope could be put in the water supply and a Geiger counter used to detect where it escaped from the pipe.

44. a. $^{222}_{86}Rn \rightarrow ^{218}_{84}Po + ^{4}_{2}He$ **b.** $^{234}_{90}Th \rightarrow ^{230}_{88}Ra + ^{4}_{2}He$
c. $^{210}_{84}Po \rightarrow ^{206}_{82}Pb + ^{4}_{2}He$

45. a. named radioactivity and discovered several radioactive elements. **b.** discovered natural radioactivity from uranium ores **c.** discovered the neutron **d.** transmuted elements

Review Questions and Problems

46. The Pauli exclusion principle states that no two electrons in an atom can have the same quantum numbers. Hund's rule states that electrons that occupy orbitals of equal energy distribute with unpaired spins as much as possible.

47. a. $Ca(OH)_2 + 2HCl \rightarrow CaCl_2 + 2H_2O$
b. $Fe_2O_3 + 3H_2 \rightarrow 2Fe + 3H_2O$
c. $2NaHCO_3 + H_2SO_4 \rightarrow Na_2SO_4 + 2CO_2 + 2H_2O$
d. $2C_2H_6 + 7O_2 \rightarrow 4CO_2 + 6H_2O$

48. 6.7 mL

49. a. $26p, 26e^-, 33n$ **b.** $92p, 92e^-, 143n$
c. $24p, 24e^-, 28n$

50. a. covalent **b.** ionic **c.** covalent **d.** ionic

51. 9218 cm^3 H$_2$; 0.4115 mol H$_2$

Challenging Questions and Problems

52. 2135

53. $^{211}_{83}Bi \rightarrow ^{207}_{81}Tl + ^{4}_{2}He$; thallium-207
$^{207}_{81}Tl \rightarrow ^{207}_{82}Pb + ^{0}_{-1}e$; lead-207

54. Bismuth-214 remains.

Nuclear Chemistry

Chapter Preview

Section 24·3 is appropriate for honors students.

Figure 24·1
Nuclear reactions release tremendous amounts of energy. Nuclear reactors are designed to control these reactions so that the energy can be used safely.

Atoms with unstable nuclei are radioactive.

Figure 24·2
Radiation caused the exposure of this film. Becquerel's accidental discovery of this phenomenon was the first time anyone observed the effects of radioactivity.

In the preceding chapters the focus has been on chemical reactions. In such reactions atoms gain stability by attaining stable electron configurations. This chapter deals with nuclear reactions. In nuclear reactions certain isotopes called radioisotopes gain stability by making changes within their nuclei. These changes are accompanied by the emission of large amounts of radiation energy. Unlike a chemical reaction, a nuclear reaction is not affected by changes in temperature or pressure, and it cannot be turned off.

24·1   Radioactivity

In 1896 the French chemist Antoine Becquerel (1852–1908) accidentally discovered that uranium ores emit invisible rays. Becquerel had left some ore on top of photographic plates that were wrapped with light-tight paper. The plates became fogged. At that time two of his graduate students were Marie Curie (1867–1934) and Pierre Curie (1859–1906). They pursued this research and showed that uranium was the element emitting these rays. Marie named *the property by which uranium gives off rays* **radioactivity.** *The penetrating rays emitted by a radioactive source are called* **radiation.** Pierre assisted his wife in the isolation of several radioactive elements. Together with Becquerel in 1903, they won the Nobel prize in physics for this work.

Becquerel's discovery of radioactivity was the deathblow to Dalton's theory of an indivisible atom. A radioactive atom undergoes drastic changes as it emits radiation. *Certain isotopes, called* **radioisotopes,** *are radioactive because they have unstable nuclei.* The stability of the nucleus depends on its ratio of protons to neutrons. Too many or too few neutrons lead to an unstable nucleus. *An unstable nucleus loses energy by*

Figure 24·3
An electric field has different effects on the three types of radiation. Alpha particles and beta particles are deflected in opposite directions. Gamma rays are undeflected.

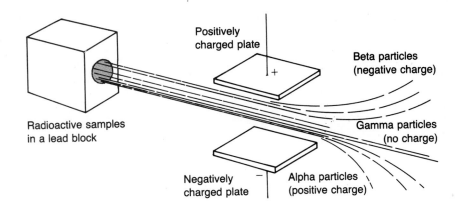

Positively charged plate

Beta particles (negative charge)

Radioactive samples in a lead block

Gamma particles (no charge)

Negatively charged plate

Alpha particles (positive charge)

TV waves, radio waves, microwaves, light waves, and X-rays are all forms of electro-magnetic radiation. They are not necessarily associated with radioactivity.

Radioisotopes decay by emitting alpha radiation, beta radiation, and/or gamma radiation.

Safety

Substances that emit alpha particles are very dangerous if ingested. Never eat, drink, chew gum, etc. when handling any radioisotopes.

emitting radiation during the process of **radioactive decay.** Eventually unstable nuclei achieve a more stable state when they are transformed into atoms of a different element. Radioactive decay is spontaneous and does not require any input of energy.

24·2 Types of Radiation

Several types of radiation can be emitted during radioactive decay. They include alpha radiation (Greek α), beta radiation (Greek β), and gamma radiation (Greek γ). Table 24·1 summarizes the properties of different types of radiation. The different types of radiation from a radioactive source can be separated by an electric or magnetic field (Figure 24·3).

Alpha radiation *consists of helium nuclei that have been emitted from a radioactive source.* **Alpha particles** *contain two protons and two neutrons and have a double positive charge.* In writing nuclear chemical reactions, an alpha particle is written as $^4_2$He or α. The charge is omitted.

Table 24·1	Characteristics of Some Ionizing Radiations		
Property	Alpha radiation	Beta radiation	Gamma radiation
Composition	Alpha particle (helium nucleus)	Beta particle (electron)	High-energy electromagnetic radiation
Symbol	α, $^4_2$He	β, $^0_{-1}e$	γ
Charge	2+	1−	0
Mass (amu)	4	1/1837	0
Common source	Radium-226	Carbon-14	Cobalt-60
Approximate energy	5MeV*	0.05 to 1 MeV	1 MeV
Penetrating power	Low (0.05 mm body tissue)	Moderate (4 mm body tissue)	Very high (penetrates body easily)
Shielding	Paper, clothing	Metal foil	Lead, concrete (incompletely shields)

*(1 MeV = 1.60×10^{-13} J)

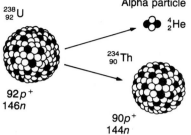

$^{238}_{92}U$

Alpha particle

$^{4}_{2}He$

$^{234}_{90}Th$

$92p^+$
$146n$

$90p^+$
$144n$

Figure 24·4
What particle is emitted when uranium-238 decays to thorium-234?
An alpha particle.

1. $^{226}_{88}Ra \longrightarrow {}^{222}_{86}Rn + {}^{4}_{2}He$

Beta particle

$^{14}_{6}C$

$^{0}_{-1}e$

$^{14}_{7}N$

$6p^+$
$8n$

$7p^+$
$7n$

Figure 24·5
What particle is emitted when carbon-14 decays to nitrogen-14?
A beta particle.

2. $^{210}_{82}Pb \longrightarrow {}^{210}_{83}Bi + {}^{0}_{-1}e$

The radioisotope uranium-238 releases alpha radiation. The more stable (but still radioactive) isotope thorium-234 is produced.

$$^{238}_{92}U \xrightarrow{\text{radioactive decay}} {}^{234}_{90}Th + {}^{4}_{2}He \qquad (\alpha \text{ emission})$$

Uranium-238   Thorium-234   Alpha particle

When an atom loses an alpha particle, the atomic number of the product atom is lower by two and its mass number is lower by four. Because of their large mass and charge, alpha particles do not travel very far and are not very penetrating. They are easily stopped by a sheet of paper. They are unable to penetrate even the dead cells on the surface of the skin.

Problem

1. The disintegration of the radioisotope radium-226 produces an isotope of the element radon and alpha radiation. The atomic number of radium (Ra) is 88; the atomic number of radon (Rn) is 86. Write a balanced equation for this transmutation.

Beta radiation *consists of fast-moving electrons formed by the decomposition of a neutron of an atom.* The neutron breaks into a proton and an electron. *These fast-moving electrons are called* **beta particles.**

$$^{1}_{0}n \longrightarrow {}^{1}_{1}H + {}^{0}_{-1}e$$

Neutron   Proton   Electron
(beta particle)

The proton stays in the nucleus and the electron is ejected from the atom. Carbon-14 emits a beta particle as it undergoes radioactive decay to form nitrogen-14.

$$^{14}_{6}C \longrightarrow {}^{14}_{7}N + {}^{0}_{-1}e \qquad (\beta \text{ emission})$$

Carbon-14   Nitrogen-14   Beta
(radioactive)   (stable)   particle

The mass number of the nitrogen-14 that is produced is the same as that of carbon-14. Meanwhile the atomic number has increased by 1. The nucleus now contains an additional proton and one less neutron.

Beta particles are much smaller than alpha particles, and they have half as much charge. Consequently, they are much more penetrating. Beta particles are stopped by aluminum foil or thin pieces of wood.

Problem

2. A radioisotope of the element lead (Pb) decays to an isotope of the element bismuth (Bi) by emission of a beta particle. Complete the equation for the decay process.

$$^{210}Pb \longrightarrow {}_{83}Bi + {}^{0}_{-1}e$$

Figure 24·6
Alpha particles have the least pene-trating power because they have a large mass and charge. Gamma rays have no mass or charge and are very penetrating.

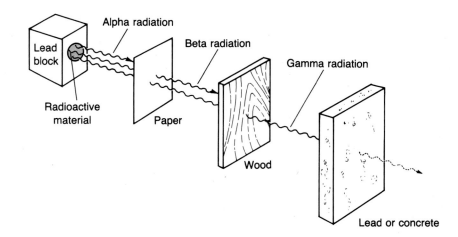

Gamma rays travel at the speed of light.

Gamma radiation *is electromagnetic radiation.* Visible light (the light we see) is also electromagnetic radiation but of much lower energy. Gamma rays are often emitted by the nuclei of disintegrating radioactive atoms along with alpha or beta radiation.

$$^{226}_{88}\text{Ra} \longrightarrow {}^{222}_{86}\text{Rn} + {}^{4}_{2}\text{He} + \gamma$$

Radium-226   Radon-222   Alpha   Gamma
                                       particle   ray

$$^{234}_{90}\text{Th} \longrightarrow {}^{234}_{91}\text{Pa} + {}^{0}_{-1}e + \gamma$$

Thorium-234   Protactinium-234   Beta   Gamma
                                        particle   ray

Gamma rays have no mass and no electrical charge. Thus the emission of only gamma radiation does not alter the atomic number or mass number of an atom.

X-radiation is produced by the decay of excited electrons in atoms. (It is not emitted during radioactive decay.) Except for their origins, gamma rays and X-rays are essentially the same. They are extremely penetrating and potentially very dangerous. Both gamma rays and X-rays pass easily through paper, wood, and the human body. They can be stopped (though not completely) by several feet of concrete or several inches of lead (Figure 24·6).

Safety

It is easier to prevent spills than to decontaminate a spill area. Keep radioisotope containers in secondary containers to prevent spills. Work in trays rather than directly on the lab bench.

3. alpha radiation
    beta radiation
    gamma radiation

Problem

3. List the three types of radiation in order of their penetrating power.

24·3 Nuclear Stability

About 1500 different nuclei are known. Of these only 264 are stable. Stable nuclei do not decay or change with time. The stability of a nucleus depends on its neutron-to-proton ratio. For elements of low atomic number, below about 20, this ratio is 1. This means that the nuclei have equal numbers of neutrons and protons. For example, the isotopes $^{12}_{6}\text{C}$, $^{14}_{7}\text{N}$,

■ The neutron-to-proton ratio determines the stability of a nucleus.

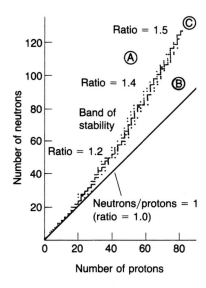

Figure 24·7
On a neutron versus proton plot, stable nuclei form a pattern known as a band of stability. For isotopes of small atomic number, the stable ratio is 1.0; for the heavier isotopes it increases to about 1.5. In region A unstable nuclei undergo beta decay. In region B they convert a neutron to a proton. In region C they undergo alpha particle emission. (The solid line is a reference line for a neutron-to-proton ratio equal to 1.0.)

A positron is a particle of antimatter. It has a charge and a spin which is opposite to that of the electron. When a positron and an electron meet, they annihilate each other. That is, they disappear and are totally converted to energy.

and $^{16}_{8}O$ are stable. Above atomic number 20 the stable nuclei have more neutrons than protons. The neutron-to-proton ratio reaches about 1.5 with heavy elements. The lead isotope $^{206}_{82}Pb$, for example, with 124 neutrons and 82 protons, is stable. Its ratio is $\frac{206}{82} \approx 1.5$.

A plot of the number of neutrons versus the number of protons for the known stable nuclei is given in Figure 24·7. *The stable nuclei on a neutron-vs-proton plot are located in a* **band of stability.** The nuclei that fall outside the band of stability undergo spontaneous radioactive decay. The type of decay that occurs depends upon the position of the nucleus with respect to the band of stability.

Nuclei in *region A,* to the left of the band of stability, have too many neutrons. They turn a neutron into a proton by emitting a beta particle or electron from the nucleus.

$$^{1}_{0}n \longrightarrow ^{1}_{1}H + ^{0}_{-1}e$$

This process is known as *beta decay* or *beta emission*. It produces a simultaneous increase in the number of protons and decrease in the number of neutrons.

$$^{66}_{29}Cu \longrightarrow ^{66}_{30}Zn + ^{0}_{-1}e$$

$$^{14}_{6}C \longrightarrow ^{14}_{7}N + ^{0}_{-1}e$$

Nuclei in *region B,* to the right of the band of stability, have too many protons. They increase their stability by converting a proton to a neutron. An electron is captured in this process.

$$^{59}_{28}Ni + ^{0}_{-1}e \longrightarrow ^{59}_{27}Co$$

$$^{37}_{18}Ar + ^{0}_{-1}e \longrightarrow ^{37}_{17}Cl$$

A **positron** *is a particle with the mass of an electron but a positive charge,* $^{0}_{+1}e$. A positron may be emitted as a proton changes to a neutron.

$$^{8}_{5}B \longrightarrow ^{8}_{4}Be + ^{0}_{+1}e$$

$$^{15}_{8}O \longrightarrow ^{15}_{7}N + ^{0}_{+1}e$$

When a neutron is converted to a proton the atomic number decreases by one, the number of neutrons increases by one, and the mass number remains the same.

Region C is above the upper end of the band of stability. The nuclei in this region are especially heavy. They have both too many neutrons and too many protons. They emit alpha particles. Alpha emission results in an increase in the neutron-to-proton ratio. This is a favorable change and increases nuclear stability.

$$^{204}_{82}Pb \longrightarrow ^{200}_{80}Hg + ^{4}_{2}He$$

In alpha emission, the mass number decreases by four and the atomic number decreases by two. *All* nuclei with atomic number greater than 82 are radioactive. A majority of these undergo alpha emission.

$$^{226}_{88}Ra \longrightarrow ^{222}_{86}Rn + ^{4}_{2}He$$

$$^{232}_{90}Th \longrightarrow ^{228}_{88}Ra + ^{4}_{2}He$$

24·4 Half-Life

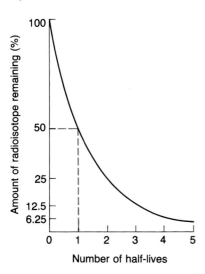

Figure 24·8
This decay curve for a radioactive element shows that after each half-life, one-half of the remaining original radioactive atoms have decayed into atoms of a new element.

Every radioisotope has a characteristic rate of decay measured by its half-life. *A* **half-life** ($t_{1/2}$) *is the time required for one-half of the atoms of a radioisotope to emit radiation and to decay to products.* After one half-life, one-half of the original radioactive atoms have decayed into atoms of a new element. The other one-half remain unchanged (Figure 24·8). After a second half-life only one-quarter of the original radioactive atoms remain. If the masses of the reactants and products of a nuclear reaction were determined with a sensitive balance, it would appear that the mass was conserved. However, nuclear reactions differ from ordinary chemical reactions. An infinitesimally small quantity of mass is lost. The lost mass is converted to radiation energy.

The stability of a radioisotope is indicated by its half-life. The longer the half-life, the more stable the isotope. Half-lives may vary from fractions of a second to millions of years (Table 24·2). Many artificially produced radioisotopes are highly unstable and have very short half-lives. This feature is a great advantage in nuclear medicine. This is because rapidly decaying isotopes are not long-term biological radiation hazards.

One isotope, uranium-238, decays through a complex series of radioactive intermediates to the stable isotope lead-206 (Figure 24·9). The age of certain rocks is determined by measuring the ratio of uranium-238 to lead-206. The half-life of uranium-238 is 4.5×10^9 years. Thus it is possible to use this method to date rocks as old as our solar system (4.6×10^9 years).

Lead-206.

Figure 24·9
Uranium-238 decays through a complex series of radioactive intermediates. What is the stable end product of this series?

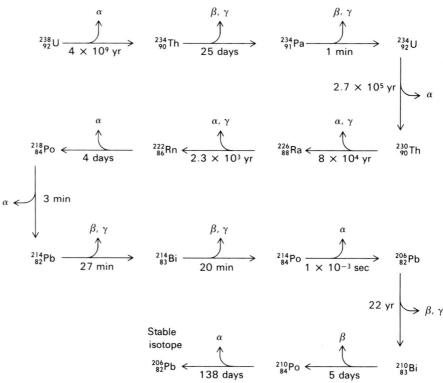

Table 24·2	Half-lives and Radiation of Some Naturally Occurring Radioisotopes		
Isotope	Half-life	Radiation emitted
Carbon-14	5.73×10^3 yr	β
Potassium-40	1.28×10^9 yr	β, γ
Radon-222	3.8 days	α
Radium-226	1.6×10^3 yr	α, γ
Thorium-230	8.0×10^4 yr	α, γ
Thorium-234	25 days	β, γ
Uranium-235	7.1×10^8 yr	α, γ
Uranium-238	4.5×10^9 yr	α

Half-life values are determined experimentally.

Safety

All radioisotopes must be isolated from living systems until their radio-activity has been reduced to safe levels. For rapidly decaying isotopes this time will be relatively short.

Example 1

Nitrogen-13 emits beta radiation and decays to carbon-13 with $t_{1/2} = 10$ min. Assume a starting mass of 2 g of nitrogen-13.
a. How long is four half-lives?
b. How many grams of that iostope will remain after four half-lives?

Solution

a. One half-life is 10 min. Four half-lives is 4×10 min. $= 40$ min.

b. After four half-lives, 0.0625 g remains out of each initial gram.

$$2\cancel{g} \times \frac{0.0625 \text{ g}}{1\cancel{g}} = 0.125 \text{ g}$$

Problem

4. 0.0625 mg Mn-56

4. Manganese-56 is a beta emitter with a half-life of 2.6 hr. What is the mass of manganese-56 in a 1-mg sample of the isotope after 10.4 hr?

24·A   Carbon-14 Dating

Archaeologists use the half-lives of naturally occurring radioisotopes to establish the ages of fossils and other ancient artifacts. Carbon-14, with a half-life of 5730 years, has been used most extensively. When cosmic rays in the upper atmosphere strike atoms, the atoms disinte-grate into electrons, protons, neutrons, and other particles. Some-times a free neutron collides with a nitrogen atom and causes it to lose a proton. The radioactive product is carbon-14.

$$\underset{\text{Nitrogen-14}}{^{14}_{7}\text{N}} + \underset{\text{Neutron}}{^{1}_{0}n} \longrightarrow \underset{\text{Carbon-14}}{^{14}_{6}\text{C}} + \underset{\text{Proton}}{^{1}_{1}\text{H}}$$

Carbon-14 combines with oxygen, just as carbon-12 does, to form carbon dioxide.

$$^{14}C \quad + \quad O_2 \quad \longrightarrow \quad ^{14}CO_2$$

Carbon-14   Oxygen   Carbon dioxide
(radioactive)

$$^{12}C \quad + \quad O_2 \quad \longrightarrow \quad ^{12}CO_2$$

Carbon   Oxygen   Carbon dioxide
(nonradioactive)

Plants use carbon dioxide to make carbon-containing compounds. Animals eat plants containing these compounds. Thus, all living organisms contain carbon-12 and carbon-14. The carbon-14 slowly decays in the organism's tissues. It is continuously replaced, however, by more carbon-14. Therefore, while the organism is alive, its ratio of carbon-12 to carbon-14 is constant. After the organism dies, however, it does not incorporate any new carbon. The carbon-12 to carbon-14 ratio changes as the carbon-14 decays to nitrogen-14.

$$^{14}_{6}C \longrightarrow \, ^{14}_{7}N + \, ^{0}_{-1}e$$

In the 1940s, the American chemist Willard Libby developed a method using carbon-14 to determine the age of an artifact. He measured the ratio of carbon-14 to carbon-12 in wood and textile samples from parchments and mummies. Then, he compared this ratio with the carbon-14 to carbon-12 ratio in recently-dead samples of similar materials. Using the half-life of carbon-14, he was able to calculate the age of the artifacts. For example, an object that had once been living might now have a carbon-14 concentration of one-half its original value. This object must therefore be about 5730 years old (one half-life). This technique can be used to determine the ages of objects between 200 and 50 000 years old. The accuracy of this method is good. For example, the Dead Sea Scrolls were determined to be 1940 ± 70 years old. This compares well with the historical record. Libby was awarded the 1960 Nobel Prize in chemistry for his work.

One of two techniques is used to measure the carbon-14 in an object. The most traditional method involves burning a small sample of the object to convert all the carbon to carbon dioxide. The carbon dioxide is trapped and frozen with liquid air. The carbon-14 present is determined by measuring the radioactivity of the carbon dioxide with a radiation counter. A newer technique involves ionizing the sample and passing it through a particle accelerator. The isotopes are separated by a magnetic field and counted directly by a detector.

Carbon-14 dating is a good example of how chemistry helps researchers in other areas. Before this technique was used, archaeologists had to use time-consuming and sometimes imprecise methods to date objects. With carbon-14 dating, they have been able to accurately determine the age of objects. This assists in dating significant events, such as the initial migration of people to this continent.

Figure 24·10
The age of ancient artifacts such as the Dead Sea scrolls can be determined by carbon-14 dating. The half-life of carbon-14 is 5730 years. Scientists can date objects up to 40 000 years old by using this system.

24·5 Transmutation Reactions

■ A nuclear reaction transforms an isotope of one element to an isotope of another.

The conversion of an atom of one element to an atom of another element is called **transmutation.** Radioactive decay (Figure 24·4) is one way in which transmutations occur. A transmutation can also occur when high-energy particles bombard the nucleus of an atom. The high-energy particles may be protons, neutrons, or alpha particles. Some transmutations occur in nature. For example, the production of carbon-14 from nitrogen-14 occurs in the upper atmosphere. Many other transmutations are done in laboratories or in nuclear reactors. The earliest artificial transmutation was performed in 1919 by Ernest Rutherford. He bombarded nitrogen gas with alpha particles to produce an unstable isotope of fluorine.

$$\underset{\text{Nitrogen-14}}{^{14}_{7}\text{N}} \quad + \quad \underset{\substack{\text{Alpha}\\\text{particle}}}{^{4}_{2}\text{He}} \quad \longrightarrow \quad \underset{\text{Fluorine-18}}{^{18}_{9}\text{F}}$$

The fluorine isotope quickly decomposes to a stable isotope of oxygen and a proton. This experiment eventually led to the discovery of the proton.

$$\underset{\text{Fluorine-18}}{^{18}_{9}\text{F}} \quad \longrightarrow \quad \underset{\text{Oxygen-17}}{^{17}_{8}\text{O}} \quad + \quad \underset{\text{Proton}}{^{1}_{1}\text{H}}$$

James Chadwick's discovery of the neutron in 1932 also involved a transmutation experiment. The neutrons were produced when beryllium-9 was bombarded with alpha particles.

$$\underset{\text{Beryllium-9}}{^{9}_{4}\text{Be}} \quad + \quad \underset{\substack{\text{Alpha}\\\text{Particle}}}{^{4}_{2}\text{He}} \quad \longrightarrow \quad \underset{\text{Carbon-12}}{^{12}_{6}\text{C}} \quad + \quad \underset{\text{Neutron}}{^{1}_{0}n}$$

The elements in the periodic table with atomic numbers above 92 are called the **transuranium elements.** None of them occur in nature and all of them are radioactive. These elements have been synthesized in nuclear reactors and nuclear accelerators, which accelerate the bombarding particles to very high speeds.

All the transuranium elements are synthetic. They have been produced in nuclear reactors and particle accelerators.

Figure 24·11
In 1919, Ernest Rutherford carried out the first artificial transmutation when he bombarded nitrogen gas with alpha particles. What particles were formed?
Protons and atoms of oxygen-17.

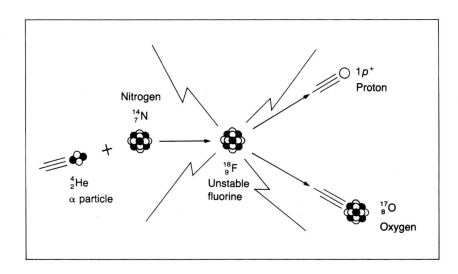

When uranium-238 is bombarded with slow neutrons from a nuclear reactor, some uranium nuclei capture neutrons to produce uranium-239.

$$^{238}_{92}U + ^{1}_{0}n \longrightarrow ^{239}_{92}U$$

Uranium-239 is radioactive and emits a beta particle. The product isotope is the artificial, radioactive element neptunium with atomic number 93.

$$^{239}_{92}U \longrightarrow ^{239}_{93}Np + ^{0}_{-1}e$$

Neptunium is unstable and emits a beta particle to produce a second artificial element, plutonium. Plutonium has an atomic number of 94.

$$^{239}_{93}Np \longrightarrow ^{239}_{94}Pu + ^{0}_{-1}e$$

Plutonium and neptunium are both transuranium elements. They do not occur in nature. Each has an atomic number greater than 92. Neptunium and plutonium, the first artificial elements ever made, were synthesized in 1940. Since that time 15 more transuranium elements, atomic numbers 95 through 109, have been synthesized.

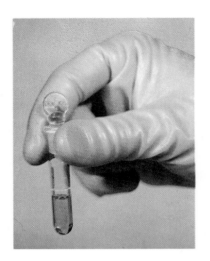

Figure 24·12
All of the elements with atomic numbers above 92 are synthetic. These elements are prepared by bombarding nuclei of uranium or more complex atoms with neutrons, alpha particles, or other nuclear "bullets". Plutonium, shown here, and neptunium were the first elements to be produced artificially. They are both transuranium elements.

24·B Particle Accelerators

Since the 1930s, physicists have used particle accelerators to probe the mysteries of the atom. In a particle accelerator, sub-atomic particles, usually electrons or protons, travel at close to the speed of light. A beam of these particles has enough energy to smash a nucleus into fragments (hence the name "atom smashers"). The relativity effect at such high energies results in the conversion of energy into matter. As a result, new particles are created. These particles leave a trail of bubbles in a detection device called a bubble chamber. Electronic detectors may also be used in conjunction with a computer that records the event on a printout.

Accelerators use electric fields and electromagnetic guides to accelerate charged particles to very high speeds. The simplest accelerators use a steady electric field. The field is created by mounting a metal sphere on a long pipe and charging it to a very high voltage. This causes a beam of particles to move faster and faster down the

Figure 24·13
A linear accelerator is made up of a long series of tubes connected to a source of high-frequency alternating current. As the charge on the tubes alternates, a particle is repelled by the tube it is leaving and attracted to the next tube. A high vacuum reduces collisions that would slow down the particles.

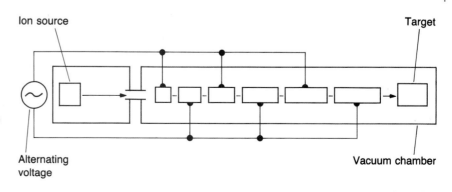

Ion source

Target

Alternating voltage

Vacuum chamber

length of the pipe and to strike a target. This design is capable of energies of up to 10 million electron volts (1×10^7 eV). The linear accelerator, or linac, later improved on this design. It uses an alternating electric field to reach energies of up to 5×10^{10} eV. A linac boosts an electron's speed to nearly the speed of light. Large magnets keep the electrons from veering off course. The two mile long Stanford Linear Accelerator in California is currently the largest linac in North America.

The cyclotron is another kind of accelerator. Protons enter the center of a spiral shaped vacuum chamber. They are accelerated at each turn of the spiral by an electrical jolt, while an electromagnet guides them. The largest cyclotron has reached an energy of 7.2×10^8 eV. Synchrotrons accelerate particles in an oval shaped pathway resembling a race track. A linac in one or more of the straight sections increases the particles' speed. Particles can also be sent in opposite directions to produce high-speed collisions. The synchrotron's unique design has made energies of 1×10^{12} eV possible.

Today's giant accelerators have opened the door to new research. They have revealed, for example, that protons and neutrons consist of even smaller particles called quarks (Section 4·C). Quarks are thought to be held together by other particles called gluons. Accelerator research has had practical benefits as well. Particle beams are being used by medical researchers to destroy tumors and create radioactive tracers. These tracers can be used instead of exploratory surgery. Accelerator technology is also being applied in the development of superspeed trains.

Figure 24·14
Scientists use huge particle accelerators to produce high energy particles for bombardment. The cyclotron (cyclic accelerator) at Fermi National Accelerator laboratory near Chicago has a circumference of 6.3 km.

Figure 24·15
In nuclear fission, uranium-235 breaks
into two fragments. Energy and more
neutrons are released. The released
neutrons can cause other uranium-
235 atoms to split.

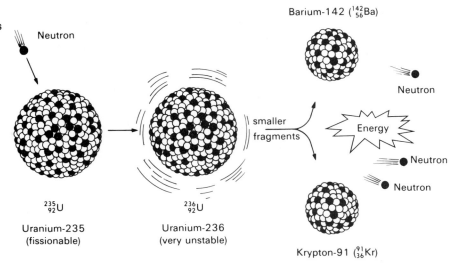

Barium-142 ($^{142}_{56}$Ba)

Neutron

Neutron

smaller
fragments

Energy

Neutron

Neutron

$^{235}_{92}$U
Uranium-235
(fissionable)

$^{236}_{92}$U
Uranium-236
(very unstable)

Krypton-91 ($^{91}_{36}$Kr)

The nucleus of an atom splits on
nuclear fission.

24·6 Nuclear Fission

When the nuclei of certain isotopes are bombarded with neutrons, they
undergo **fission** *which is the splitting of a nucleus into smaller fragments.*
Uranium-235 and plutonium-239 are fissionable materials. A fissionable
atom such as uranium-235 breaks into two fragments of roughly the same
size when it is struck by a slow-moving neutron. At the same time, more
neutrons are released (Figure 24·15). These neutrons react with the nuclei of other uranium-235 atoms, continuing fission by a chain reaction.
In a chain reaction, some of the neutrons produced react with other
atoms, producing more neutrons that react with still more atoms.

Einstein stated the relationship between the mass lost and the energy
released. $E = mc^2$

Here c is the speed of light. The loss
of only 1 gram of mass will produce
9×10^{10} kilojoules of energy.

Fission unleashes enormous amounts of energy. The fission of 1 kg
of uranium-235 releases an amount of energy equal to that generated in
the explosion of 20000 tons of dynamite. If a nuclear chain reaction is
uncontrolled, the energy release is nearly instantaneous. Atomic bombs
are devices that start uncontrolled nuclear chain reactions.

Fission can be controlled so that energy is released more slowly. Nuclear reactors use controlled fission to produce useful energy (Figure
24·16). In the controlled fission reaction within the nuclear reactor, much
of the energy generated appears as heat. The heat is removed from the
reactor core by a suitable coolant fluid (usually liquid sodium or water).
The heat is used to generate steam to drive a turbine. The spinning
turbine generates electricity.

The control of fission in a nuclear reactor involves two steps.

Moderators and control rods are used
to regulate the fission process in a
nuclear reactor.

1. Neutron moderation *slows down the neutrons so that they can be
captured by the reactor fuel to continue the chain reaction.* The reactor
fuel is usually uranium-235. Most of the neutrons produced by uranium
are moving so fast that they will pass right through the nucleus without
being absorbed. Water and carbon are good moderators. They slow down
the neutrons so that the chain reaction can be sustained.

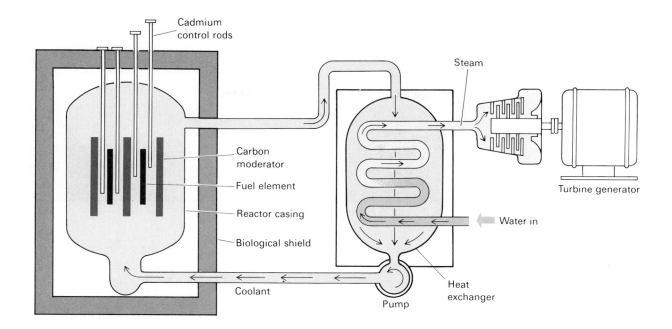

Figure 24·16
All nuclear reactors have five basic components: fuel, moderator, control rods, coolant, and shielding. Electrical energy is generated by the controlled fission process. The energy is removed from the reactor as heat. A steam drive turbine is used to generate electricity.

A nuclear reactor that produces more fuel than it consumes is known as a breeder reactor. For example, fissionable plutonium-239 could be produced from nonfissionable uranium-238 (Section 24·5).

■ Fusion unites the nuclei of small atoms.

Fusion reactions release more energy than fission reactions.

2. Neutron absorption *decreases the number of slow neutrons.* To prevent the chain reaction from going too fast, some of the slowed neutrons must be trapped before they hit fissionable atoms. Neutron absorption is carried out by the use of control rods made of a material such as cadmium which absorbs neutrons. When the control rods extend all the way into the reactor core, they absorb many neutrons and fission occurs slowly. As the rods are pulled out, they absorb fewer neutrons and the fission process speeds up. If the chain reaction were to go too fast, heat might be produced faster than it could be removed by the coolant. In that case, the reactor core would overheat. This could lead to mechanical failures and a release of radioactive materials into the atmosphere. Ultimately, a meltdown of the reactor core may occur. The fuel in a reactor is never concentrated enough, however, to produce a nuclear explosion.

Once a nuclear reactor is started, it remains highly radioactive for many generations. Shields are used to protect the reactor structure from radiation damage. Walls of high-density concrete are designed to protect the operating personnel.

24·7 Nuclear Fusion

The sun is an extraordinary energy source. The energy released from the sun is the result of a nuclear fusion, or thermonuclear, reaction. **Fusion** *occurs when two nuclei combine to produce a nucleus of heavier mass.* In solar fusion, hydrogen nuclei (protons) are fused to make helium nuclei. The reaction requires two beta particles.

$$4\,^1_1\text{H} + 2\,^0_{-1}e \longrightarrow \,^4_2\text{He} + \text{energy}$$

Fusion takes place only at temperatures that exceed 40 000 000°C. It releases an even greater amount of heat!

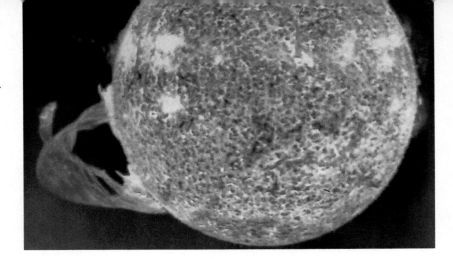

Figure 24·17
Thermonuclear fusion reactions occurring in the sun have provided the earth with energy for billions of years.

There is enough deuterium and tritium in the water in our oceans to fill virtually any future energy need we could imagine.

Controlled nuclear fusion is appealing as an energy source on earth. The potential fuels are inexpensive and readily available, and fusion products are usually not radioactive. The problems with fusion are in achieving the high temperatures necessary to start the reaction and in containing the reaction. One reaction scientists are studying is the combination of a deuterium nucleus and a tritium nucleus to form a helium nucleus.

$$^2_1H + ^3_1H \longrightarrow ^4_2He + ^1_0n + \text{energy}$$

The high temperatures required to initiate fusion reactions have been achieved by using an atomic bomb. It is the triggering device for setting off the hydrogen bomb, which is an uncontrolled fusion device. It is clearly of no use, however, as a controlled generator of power.

To date, no large scale controlled fusion reactions have been achieved. At the high temperatures involved, matter exists as a *plasma*. Containing the plasma is a formidable task. No known structural material can withstand the high temperatures and corrosive effects of plasmas.

Figure 24·18
This experimental tokamak is a nuclear reactor in which magnets are used to confine a hydrogen plasma within a doughnut-shaped torus. Thirty-two D-shaped coils create a magnetic field that holds the hot corrosive plasma away from the walls of the vacuum vessel. The inner and outer field coils are used to adjust the shape of the plasma.

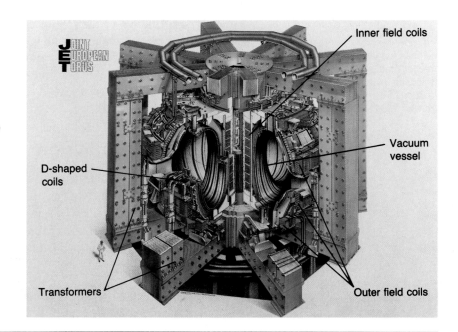

Figure 24·19
We cannot see, hear, feel, or smell radiation. Thus we must depend on detection instruments and signs to alert us of the presence of radiation and to monitor its levels.

■ Radiation can be detected with Geiger counters, scintillation counters, and film badges.

The most commonly used home smoke detector contains a radioisotope which produces ionizing radiation in a chamber. When smoke enters the chamber, ions are produced. The formation of these ions causes a current to flow between oppositely charged plates within the chamber. This current is detected, and an alarm is set off.

Figure 24·20
The Geiger counter is widely used to detect beta radiation.

Some success has been achieved with magnetic confinement using "magnetic bottles". In this approach, specially shaped magnets keep the reacting nuclei trapped in dense free-flowing plasma. Use of powerful lasers to generate the temperatures required for fusion has also been the subject of much recent research. Tremendous technical difficulties will have to be resolved, however, before fusion becomes a practical source of energy.

24·8   Detecting Radiation

The radiation emitted by radioisotopes (and X-rays) is ionizing radiation. **Ionizing radiation** *knocks electrons off some atoms of the bombarded substance to produce ions*. Ionizing radiation cannot be detected with any of our senses. Instead, various instruments and devices are used to do the job.

A **Geiger counter** *uses a gas-filled metal tube to detect radiation* (Figure 24·20). The tube is connected to a power supply and has a central wire electrode. When ionizing radiation penetrates the thin window at one end of the tube, the gas inside becomes ionized. When charged ions and free electrons are produced, the gas becomes an electrical conductor. Each time a Geiger tube is exposed to radiation, a current flows. The bursts of current drive electronic counters or cause audible clicks from a built-in speaker. Geiger counters are used primarily to detect beta radiation. Alpha particles cannot pass through the end window. Most gamma rays and X-rays pass through the gas, causing few ionizations.

A **scintillation counter** *uses a phosphor to detect radiation*. Ionizing radiation striking the specially coated surface, or phosphor, produces bright flashes of light (scintillations). (This device is similar to a television screen coated with zinc sulfide, ZnS, as the phosphor. The electrons from the TV gun striking the phosphor of the screen also produce scintillations. The pattern of scintillations is the TV picture.) The number of flashes and their respective energies are detected electronically. They are then converted into electronic pulses that are measured and recorded. Scintillation counters have been designed to detect all types of ionizing radiation.

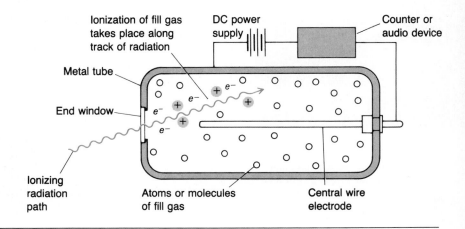

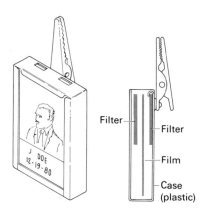

Filter — Filter

— Film

— Case (plastic)

Figure 24·21
The film badge detector is worn by people who work with radiation. The film must be developed to be read. It darkens in proportion to the amount of radiation it receives.

5. No, because a Geiger counter cannot detect alpha radiation.

Film badges are the most important radiation detectors for persons near radiation sources. *A* **film badge** *consists of several layers of photographic film covered with black lightproof paper encased in a plastic or metal holder* (Figure 24·21). It is worn all the time a person is at work. At frequent specific intervals, depending on the type of work involved, the film is removed and developed. The strength and type of radiation exposure are determined from any darkening of the film. Records are kept of the results. Film badges do not protect a person from radiation exposure. They merely serve as precautionary monitoring devices. The only protection against radiation is to keep a safe distance away and use adequate shielding.

Problem

5. A radioactive solution containing an alpha emitter accidentally gets on your hands. You wash them with soap and water and then check them with a Geiger counter for residual radioactive contamination. The Geiger counter does not register any radioactivity. Are your hands positively free from radioactive contamination? Explain.

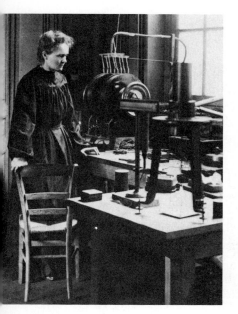

Figure 24·22
Both Marie Curie (shown here) and her daughter, Irene, died of leukemia. This was probably the result of overexposure to radiation.

24·C   Radioisotopes in Research and Medicine

Although radiation can be harmful and should be handled with care, it can be used safely and is important in many scientific procedures.

Neutron activation analysis is used to detect trace amounts of elements in samples. In this technique, a sample is bombarded with neutrons from a radioactive source. This causes the atoms in the sample to become radioactive. The half-life and type of radiation emitted by the radioisotopes is detected and processed by a computer. Since this information is characteristic for each element, scientists can tell what radioisotopes are produced and what elements were originally present in the sample. This is one of the most sensitive techniques for detecting trace amounts of elements. It is capable of measuring 10^{-9} g of an element in a sample. Neutron activation analysis is used by museums to detect art forgeries and by crime laboratories to analyze gunpowder residues.

Radioisotopes called tracers are used by chemists and biochemists to study chemical reactions and molecular structures. One of the reactants, labeled with a radioisotope, is added to the reaction mixture. After the reaction is over, the radiation of the product is measured to determine the uptake of the tracer. By comparing this amount with the amount originally added, scientists can learn much about the reaction mechanism. Reactions with many steps can be studied using this method.

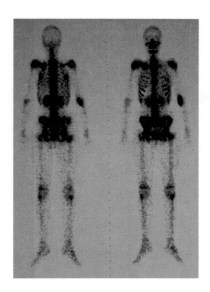

Figure 24·23
A radioisotope scan can be used to diagnose some suspected diseases without using exploratory surgery.

Agricultural researchers use radioisotopes to test the effects of herbicides, pesticides, and fertilizers. The tracer is introduced into the substance being tested to make it radioactive. Next, the plants are treated with the radioactive substance. Then, the radioactivity of the plants is measured to determine the location of the substance. Often the tracer is also monitored in animals that consume the plants, in water, and in soil. This information helps scientists determine the effects of using the substance.

Radioisotopes are used to diagnose some diseases. Iodine-131 is used to detect thyroid problems. The thyroid gland extracts iodide ions from the bloodstream and uses them to make thyroxine. To diagnose thyroid disease, the patient is given a small amount of iodine-131 in a liquid. After about two hours, the amount of iodide uptake is measured by scanning the patient's throat with a radiation detector. In a similar way, technetium-99^m is used to detect brain tumors, and phosphorus-32 is used to detect skin cancer.

Radiation is used to treat some cancers. This group of diseases is characterized by rapidly dividing abnormal cells. These cells are more sensitive to radiation than are normal cells. The cancerous area can be treated with radiation to kill the cancer cells. Some normal cells are also killed, however, and cancer cells at the center of the tumor may be radiation resistant. Therefore, the benefits of killing the cancer cells and the risks to the patient must be evaluated.

In teletherapy, a narrow beam of high intensity gamma radiation is directed at the cancerous tissue. Cobalt-60 and cesium-137 are commonly used as radiation sources. To minimize damage to healthy tissue, the patient is positioned so that only the cancerous region is within the radiation beam at all times. The unit rotates so that the radiation dose to the skin and surrounding normal tissue is distributed in a belt all the way around the patient.

Radioisotope seeds are radioisotope salts that are sealed in gold tubes and directly implanted in tumors. The radioisotopes emit beta

Figure 24·24
Radiation therapy is a commonly used method for treating cancer. This cobalt-60 unit emits a narrow, intense beam of radiation that destroys the ability of cells to reproduce. Cancer cells are more sensitive to radiation than normal cells because they divide more rapidly. Cells are most vulnerable when they are dividing.

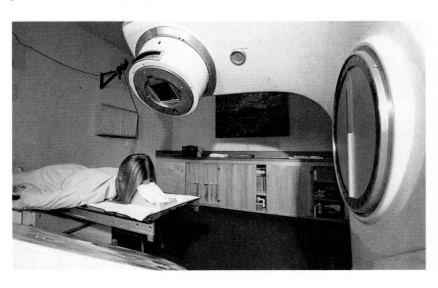

and gamma rays which kill the surrounding cancer cells. Since the radioisotope is in a sealed container, the excretions of patients undergoing this therapy are not radioactive.

Radioactive pharmaceuticals containing radioisotopes of gold, iodine, or phosphorus are sometimes given in radiation therapy. A larger dose of iodine-131 than that given to detect thyroid disease can be given to treat the disease. The radioactive iodine collects in the thyroid and emits beta and gamma rays to provide therapy. Since the radioisotope is not sealed, the patient's excretions are radioactive and must be specially handled.

24 Nuclear Chemistry

Chapter Review

Key Terms

alpha particle	24·2	neutron	
alpha radiation	24·2	moderation	24·6
band of stability	24·3	positron	24·3
beta particles	24·2	radiation	24·1
beta radiation	24·2	radioactive decay	24·1
film badge	24·8	radioactivity	24·1
fission	24·6	radioisotopes	24·1
fusion	24·7	scintillation	
gamma radiation	24·2	counter	24·8
Geiger counter	24·8	transmutation	24·5
half-life ($t_{1/2}$)	24·4	transuranium	
ionizing radiation	24·8	element	24·5
neutron absorption	24·6		

Chapter Summary

Isotopes with unstable nuclei are radioactive and are called radioisotopes. The nuclei of radioisotopes decay to stable nuclei plus radiation. The radiation may be alpha, beta, or gamma. Alpha radiation consists of alpha particles (positively charged helium nuclei) that are easily stopped by a sheet of paper. Beta radiation is composed of fast-moving beta particles, which are electrons. Beta radiation is more penetrating than alpha radiation; it is stopped by aluminum foil. Gamma radiation is electromagnetic radiation similar to visible light, but much more energetic. Gamma radiation has no mass or charge. It is extremely penetrating. Lead bricks and concrete reduce the intensity of gamma radiation but do not completely stop it. Specially built instruments produce X-radiation, which is essentially the same as gamma radiation.

Every radioisotope decays at a characteristic rate. A half-life is the time required for one-half of the nuclei in a radioisotope to decay. The product nuclei may or may not be radioactive. Half-lives vary from fractions of a second to millions of years.

The decay of radioisotopes is represented by nuclear equations. When a radioactive nucleus emits an alpha particle, its atomic number decreases by 2 and its mass number decreases by 4. When a beta particle is emitted, the atomic number increases by 1, and the mass number stays the same. When a gamma ray is emitted, the atomic number and the mass number stay the same.

Nuclear fission occurs when fissionable isotopes are bombarded with neutrons. The isotopes split into two fragments of about the same size, and in the process they release more neutrons. Some of

these neutrons strike other nuclei, releasing more neutrons, which split more nuclei. This is called a chain reaction. Fission releases enormous amounts of energy. Controlled fission is the energy source in every nuclear power plant. In nuclear fusion small nuclei fuse to make heavier nuclei. The sun's energy is released when hydrogen nuclei fuse to make helium nuclei. Fusion releases even more energy than fission.

Radiation may be detected with a Geiger counter or a scintillation counter. The film badge is the most important personnel radiation detector. The radiation its wearer receives is detected by darkening of the encased film.

Practice Questions and Problems

6. In what way does a nuclear reaction differ from a chemical reaction? *24·1*

7. Explain the difference between the terms *isotope* and *radioisotope*. *24·1*

8. What part of an atom undergoes change during radioactive decay? *24·1*

9. Write a symbol and state the charge for each.
a. an alpha particle
b. a beta particle
c. a gamma ray *24·2*

10. Describe the type of shielding required for protection against these types of radiation. *24·2*
a. beta radiation
b. gamma radiation
c. alpha radiation

11. Alpha radiation is emitted during the disintegration of the following isotopes. Write balanced nuclear equations for their decay processes. Name the element produced in each case. *24·2*
a. uranium-238 ($^{238}_{92}U$)   **c.** uranium-235 ($^{235}_{92}U$)
b. thorium-230 ($^{230}_{90}Th$)   **d.** radon-222 ($^{222}_{86}Rn$)

12. The following radioisotopes are beta emitters. Write balanced nuclear equations for their decay processes. *24·2*
a. carbon-14 ($^{14}_{6}C$)   **c.** potassium-40 ($^{40}_{19}K$)
b. strontium-90 ($^{90}_{38}Sr$)   **d.** nitrogen-13 ($^{13}_{7}N$)

13. Describe three kinds of radiation that are products of radioactive decay. *24·2*

14. How are the atomic number and mass of a nucleus affected by the loss of the following? *24·2*
a. a beta particle
b. an alpha particle
c. a gamma ray

15. Tell how alpha, beta, and gamma radiation are distinguished on the basis of the following. *24·2*
a. mass **b.** charge **c.** penetrating power

16. The following radioactive nuclei decay by emitting alpha particles. Write the product of the decay process for each. *24·2*
a. $^{238}_{94}Pu$ **d.** $^{210}_{84}Po$
b. $^{210}_{83}Bi$ **e.** $^{230}_{90}Th$
c. $^{174}_{72}Hf$

17. How does the *band of stability* help you to predict the stability of any given isotope? *24·3*

18. Identify the most stable isotope in each of the following pairs. *24·3*
a. $^{14}_{6}C$, $^{13}_{6}C$ **c.** $^{16}_{8}O$, $^{18}_{8}O$
b. $^{3}_{1}H$, $^{1}_{1}H$ **d.** $^{14}_{7}N$, $^{15}_{7}N$

19. Name the elements represented by the following symbols and indicate which of them would have *no* stable isotopes. *24·3*
a. Pt   **e.** Xe
b. Th   **f.** Cf
c. Fr   **g.** V
d. Tc   **h.** Pd

20. Explain the term *half-life*. *24·4*

21. Iron-59 has a half-life of 45 days. How much of the iron-59 will remain in a 0.2-g sample after 135 days? *24·4*

22. The mass of cobalt-60 in a sample is found to have decreased from 0.8 g to 0.2 g in a period of 10.5 years. From this information, calculate the half-life of cobalt-60. *24·4*

23. A patient is administered 20 mg of iodine-131. How much of this isotope will remain in the body after 40 days if the half-life for iodine-131 is 8 days? *24·4*

24. The half-life of xenon-133 is 5 days. If you start with 2×10^6 atoms of this isotope today, how many would remain after 5 weeks? *24·4*

25. Explain the process of transmutation. Write at least three nuclear equations to illustrate your answer. *24·5*

26. What are the transuranium elements? Why are they unusual? *24·5*

27. What are the differences between natural and artificial radioactivity? *24·5*

28. Complete and balance the equations for the following nuclear reactions. *24·5*
  a. $^{27}_{13}Al + ^{4}_{2}He \longrightarrow ^{30}_{14}Si +$
  b. $^{214}_{83}Bi \longrightarrow ^{4}_{2}He +$
  c. $^{27}_{14}Si \longrightarrow ^{0}_{-1}e +$
  d. $^{66}_{29}Cu \longrightarrow ^{66}_{30}Zn +$

29. Describe the process of nuclear fission. *24·6*

30. What is the function of the control rods in a nuclear reactor? What are they made of? *24·6*

31. Explain the term *nuclear chain reaction*. *24·6*

32. How is the chain reaction in a nuclear reactor controlled? *24·6*

33. Name one fissionable material that occurs in nature and one that is artificial. *24·6*

34. What happens in nuclear fusion? *24·7*

35. Fusion reactions produce enormous amounts of energy. Why don't we see power stations operating fusion devices? *24·7*

36. Why are X-rays and the radiations emitted by radioisotopes called *ionizing radiation?* *24·8*

37. What is the purpose of wearing a film badge when working with radiation sources? *24·8*

38. Explain how a Geiger counter works. State its limitations. *24·8*

Mastery Questions and Problems

39. Write nuclear equations for these conversions.
  a. $^{30}_{15}P$ to $^{30}_{14}Si$ **b.** $^{13}_{6}C$ to $^{14}_{6}C$ *24·5*

40. What is the difference between the nuclear reactions taking place in the sun and the nuclear reactions taking place in a nuclear reactor? *24·7*

41. Complete these nuclear reactions. *24·5*
  a. $^{32}_{15}P \longrightarrow$ ____ $+ ^{0}_{-1}e$
  b. ____ $\longrightarrow ^{14}_{7}N + ^{0}_{-1}e$
  c. $^{238}_{92}U \longrightarrow ^{234}_{90}Th +$ ____
  d. $^{141}_{56}Ba \longrightarrow$ ____ $+ ^{0}_{-1}e$

42. Write nuclear equations for the beta decay of the following isotopes. *24·2*
  a. $^{90}_{38}Sr$ **c.** $^{137}_{55}Cs$
  b. $^{14}_{6}C$ **d.** $^{239}_{93}Np$

43. An underground water pipe develops a leak. How might a radioisotope be used to locate the break? *24·8*

44. Write a nuclear reaction for each of these word equations. *24·5*
  a. Radon-222 emits an alpha particle to form polonium-218.
  b. Radium-230 is produced when thorium-234 emits an alpha particle.
  c. When polonium-210 emits an alpha particle the product is lead-206.

45. Describe the various contributions the following people made to the fields of nuclear and radiation chemistry. *24·5*
  a. Marie Curie   **c.** James Chadwick
  b. Antoine Becquerel   **d.** Ernest Rutherford

Review Questions and Problems

46. What is the Pauli exclusion principle? What is Hund's rule?

47. Balance the following equations.
  a. $Ca(OH)_2 + HCl \longrightarrow CaCl_2 + H_2O$
  b. $Fe_2O_3 + H_2 \longrightarrow Fe + H_2O$
  c. $NaHCO_3 + H_2SO_4 \longrightarrow$
  $$Na_2SO_4 + CO_2 + H_2O$$
  d. $C_2H_6 + O_2 \longrightarrow CO_2 + H_2O$

48. You have a 0.30*M* solution of sodium sulfate. What volume in milliliters must be measured to give 0.0020 mol of sodium sulfate?

49. How many protons, neutrons, and electrons are in an atom of each isotope?
  a. iron-59   **b.** uranium-235   **c.** chromium-52

50. Identify the bonds between the following pairs of atoms as ionic or covalent.
  a. carbon and silicon   **c.** sulfur and nitrogen
  b. calcium and fluorine   **d.** bromine and cesium

51. How many cm^3 of hydrogen gas, at STP, will be produced when 10.00 g of magnesium metal reacts with an excess of sulfuric acid? How many moles is this?

Challenging Questions and Problems

52. The radioisotope cesium-137 has a half-life of 30 years. A sample decays at the rate of 544 counts/min (544 cpm) in 1985. In what year will the decay rate be 17 cpm?

53. Bismuth-211 is a radioisotope. It decays by alpha emission to yield another radioisotope which emits beta radiation as it decays to a stable isotope. Write equations for the nuclear reactions and name the decay products.

54. What isotope remains after three beta particles and five alpha particles are lost from the thorium-234 isotope. (Refer to the uranium-238 decay series to check your answer.)

Research Projects

1. Why is it said that the atomic age began with Enrico Fermi?

2. How did Marie Curie's discovery of radium affect science and industry?

3. How did the Curies obtain large quantities of radium?

4. What were Otto Hahn's contributions to nuclear science?

5. How has nuclear science helped scientists produce elements?

6. What safeguards exist at nuclear power plants?

7. Make a diagram of what happens in a nuclear meltdown.

8. Report on the Three Mile Island incident. What steps should have been taken to prevent the incident? How likely are the prospects for a similar incident in the future?

9. What are some of the technical difficulties in using nuclear fusion as an energy source? Do you believe it should be developed? Why or why not?

10. What are the environmental hazards of fast breeder reactors?

11. What is radioactive fallout? How is it measured? What are its effects?

12. What precautions should be followed in shipping, using, and disposing of radioisotopes?

13. Measure background radiation at various sites in your community and under various weather conditions.

Readings and References

Frisch, Otto R. *What Little I Remember*. New York: Cambridge University Press, 1979.

Gold, Michael. "To Breed or Not to Breed." *Science 82* (May 1982), pp. 35–42.

Kidder, Tracy. "Taming a Star." *Science 82* (March 1982), pp. 50–64.

Kunetka, James W. *City of Fire: Los Alamos and the Birth of the Atomic Age, 1943–1945*. Englewood Cliffs, NJ: Prentice-Hall, 1978.

Murray, Raymond L. *Understanding Radioactive Waste*. Columbus, OH: Battelle Press, 1982.

Olsen, Steve. "Nuclear Undertakers." *Science 84* (September 1984), pp. 50–59.

Patterson, Walter C. *Nuclear Power,* 2nd ed. New York: Penguin, 1983.

Reid, Robert. *Marie Curie*. New York: Saturday Review Press/Dutton, 1974.

Romer, Alfred. *The Restless Atom: The Awakening of Nuclear Physics*. New York: Dover, 1982.

Walker, Charles A., Leroy C. Gould, and Edward J. Woodhouse, eds. *Too Hot To Handle? Social and Policy Issues in the Management of Radioactive Wastes*. New Haven, CT: Yale University Press, 1983.

West, Susan. "Hot." *Science 84* (December 1984), pp. 28–37.

25 Hydrocarbon Compounds

Chapter Planning Guide

Section			Demonstrations and Experiments	Resource Materials
25·1	Hydrocarbon Bonds	C*		Objectives Worksheet 25, SPB Skillsheet 25, SPB
25·2	Continuous-Chain Alkanes	C	Dem 25·1 Methane Bubbles	Teaching Diagram 31
25·3	Branched-Chain Alkanes	C		
25·4	Properties of Alkanes	C		
25·5	Alkenes and Alkynes	C	Dem 25·2 Detecting Multiple Bonds	Quiz 25·1
25·A	Goodyear's Discovery	E		
25·6	Geometric Isomers	H		
25·7	Stereoisomers	H		
25·8	Cyclic and Aromatic Hydrocarbons	C	Exp 51 Hydrocarbons: A Structural Study, LM	Prelab 51, SPB Beyond the Text: Nuclear Magnetic Resonance Oil Spills, ICT 25
25·9	Petroleum and Natural Gas	O		Quiz 25·2 Reviewsheet 25, SPB Chapter 25 Test
25·B	Coal	E		
*C = Core, O = Optional E = Enrichment, H = Honors			LM = Laboratory Manual	SPB = Skills Practice Book ICT = Issues in Chem. Tech.

Chapter Objectives

Having studied this chapter and done the problems, the student should be able to:

1. Characterize a hydrocarbon.   25·1

2. Draw electron dot structures of simple alkanes.
                                                        25·1

3. Recognize structural, condensed, and molecular formulas of the continuous-chain hydrocarbons containing up to ten carbons.   25·2

4. Given the structural formula of an alkane, alkene, or alkyne, name it according to IUPAC rules.
                                                        25·2–25·5

5. Given the IUPAC name of an alkane, alkene, or alkyne, draw its structural formula.   25·2–25·5

6. Distinguish between structural isomers and geometric isomers.   25·4–25·6

7. Identify the asymmetric carbon in a stereoisomer.
                                                        25·7

8. Describe the bonding and structure of benzene.
                                                        25·8

9. Name and draw the structures of simple cyclic and aromatic compounds.   25·8

10. Describe the formation of petroleum and natural gas deposits.   25·9

Teaching Suggestions

25·1 Hydrocarbon Bonds

The next two chapters discuss the chemistry of carbon compounds. Remind the students that the carbon atom is unique in that each atom can form four bonds to other atoms. These can be single, double, or triple bonds. The

multiple bonding of carbon allows it to form chains, branched structures, and rings. Thus, carbon is able to form a nearly limitless variety of compounds. The study of carbon chemistry is called *organic chemistry*.

Suggest that even though organic chemistry is unique and complex, it is not all that different from "regular" chemistry. Stress that organic chemistry uses the same basic principles that have been used throughout this course. Present the reactions and structures of carbon compounds as examples of concepts already encountered, not as new material to be memorized.

It is important that the students visualize the various organic compounds in these two chapters. Unfortunately, the formulas given in the text are, by necessity, two-dimensional. Where possible, show them diagrams and models of the important structures. Better yet, have them examine and construct models themselves.

25·2   Continuous-Chain Alkanes

The continuous chain alkanes provide a good starting point for the study of organic chemistry. Use them to illustrate the idea of a homologous series. Show how the structures of methane, ethane, propane, butane, and so on, are similar and how one can be built from the previous one by the addition of $-CH_2-$ groups. **Demonstration 25·1** *Methane Bubbles* can be done at this point to pique student interest.

After working out the complete structural formulas for some of the alkanes, introduce examples of the use of condensed structural formulas. Warn the students that a condensed structural formula is a shorthand notation. It does not represent the true structure.

Go over the names listed in Table 25·1. Impress upon the students the importance of memorizing them, since these names are the basis of much of the nomenclature in organic chemistry.

25·3   Branched-Chain Alkanes

Using models, show how alkanes which have more than three carbon atoms can form branched chains. Be sure the students understand that each arrangement of atoms represents a different kind of molecule with different properties. Spend some time discussing the rules for naming the alkanes. Work out examples, step by step. Then give them plenty of practice.

Not only should the students be able to name compounds when given the structural formulas, but they should also be able to draw structural formulas when given the names. You might suggest the following sequence for accomplishing this. First, draw the main skeleton of carbon atoms suggested by the name. Then attach the substituent groups in the places suggested by the numbers. As a final step add hydrogen atoms to all of the unfilled bonding sites.

25·4   Properties of Alkanes

The main point here is that molecules can have identical molecular formulas and yet be different. The *arrangement* of atoms in a molecule is as important as the *number* of atoms. Each different way of arranging the atoms imparts a slightly different set of properties. We call these different arrangements of atoms *structural isomers*.

25·5   Alkenes and Alkynes

When discussing alkenes and alkynes, note that the addition of a double or triple bond to an alkane does not change its physical properties much, but does affect its chemical properties. **Demonstration 25·2** *Detecting Multiple Bonds* shows the increased reactivity which results from the presence of multiple bonds.

Using models, show that the presence of a double or triple bond prevents rotation of the molecule about that bond. As a result the molecule loses some of its flexibility.

Allocate plenty of time to show how the naming rules are applied to the naming of the alkenes and the alkynes.

25·6   Geometric Isomers

The concept of isomers is difficult for many students since it involves the visualization of abstract three-dimensional figures. Give students the opportunity to see models of typical structures. Construct ball and stick models of *cis*- and *trans*-2-pentene. Show how the presence of the double bond prevents one form from becoming the other.

Construct a ball and stick model of 2-methyl-1-butene as well. Point out that 2-methyl-1-butene, *cis*-2-pentene, and *trans*-2-pentene are all *structural* isomers, with the same molecular formula. Only *cis*-2-pentene and *trans*-2-pentene are *geometrical* isomers. Emphasize that geometrical isomerism has to do with the positions of identical groups in relation to the double bond.

25·7   Stereoisomers

Stress that the key to the existence of stereoisomers is the presence of a carbon atom with four different groups attached to it. Such an atom is called *asymmetric*. If a carbon atom is asymmetric, stereoisomers *must* exist. Construct models of the stereoisomers of a simple compound, such as CHFClBr. Show that these two forms can never be held or viewed so that one is identical to the other.

25·8   Cyclic and Aromatic Hydrocarbons

The flexibility of a carbon chain makes it possible for the ends of the chain to come around upon themselves, attach, and form a ring. The geometry of five- and six-carbon

chains is the best for ring formation. Demonstrate the formation of rings by constructing ball and stick models.

Discuss the benzene structure as being a particularly unique and useful ring structure. Stress that its properties are not exactly those which would be predicted by simple alternating double bonds. Thus a resonance structure is proposed for it. Point out that benzene is important because it is the beginning molecule for a whole class of chemical compounds, the aromatic compounds.

Having finished this section, the students should apply and review the principles they have learned with regard to hydrocarbons. They should now do **Experiment 51** *Hydrocarbons: A Structural Study.*

25·9 Natural Gas and Petroleum

Petroleum deposits are essentially a collection of aliphatic hydrocarbons, ranging from simple molecules of methane to the high molecular mass molecules which make up asphalt. They also include a small percentage of cyclic compounds.

Point out that it is the task of the petroleum industry to extract these molecules from the ground and then separate them into useful compounds. The separation is done by a distillation process.

Mention that the low molecular mass compounds are of the most use. Compounds like methane, propane, butane, and octane are useful as fuels.

An examination of Table 25·3 shows that the boiling points of hydrocarbons rise as the molecular mass increases. This holds true of melting points as well. The higher molecular mass compounds are thick liquids or solids at room temperature and are poor fuels. Therefore, another task of the petroleum industry is to transform the higher molecular mass compounds into lower molecular mass compounds. Point out that this is why the cracking process is necessary.

Demonstrations

25·1 Methane Bubbles

Concept: Methane is a flammable gas.

Materials: methane gas outlet, small funnel with 1 m length of rubber tube, 10 mL of glycerine mixed with 10 mL of liquid detergent in a 100-mL beaker, candle attached to the end of a meter stick, matches, safety goggles.

Procedure: 1. Connect the tubing to a natural gas outlet. 2. Dip the funnel in the beaker and form a bubble by opening the gas tap slightly. Turn off the gas. 3. Right the funnel, and shake it gently to allow the bubble to rise.

4. Light the candle and touch it to the bubble. 5. Observe the reaction. Ask the students to name the products. **Caution:** *Methane is a flammable gas. Make sure that students stand back during the demonstration, and that the gas is shut off after the demonstration.*

25·2 Detecting Multiple Bonds

Concept: Multiple bonds give the alkenes and alkynes more reactivity than the alkanes.

Materials: 4 test tubes and stoppers, 400-mL beaker, 1 mL of liquid bromine, 20 mL of trichlorotrifluoroethane (CCl_2FCClF_2), 20 mL of cyclohexane (C_6H_{12}), 20 mL of cyclohexene (C_6H_{10}), 0.1 g of potassium permanganate ($KMnO_4$), 15 g of sodium hydroxide (NaOH) in 100 mL of water, safety goggles.

Procedure: **Caution:** *Use a fume hood. Bromine is corrosive. Potassium permanganate is a suspected mutagen. Alkaline potassium permanganate solution is extremely corrosive to the skin. Cyclohexane is extremely flammable.* 1. Prepare the bromine solution by adding bromine to trichlorotrifluoroethane or paint thinner. 2. Place 10 mL of the cyclohexane and cyclohexene in two separate test tubes. 3. Add 5 mL of bromine solution to each. 4. Stopper and shake gently. **Caution:** *Be careful when shaking a stoppered test tube in which heat is evolved. Pressure can build up.* 5. Note that the characteristic color of bromine has disappeared from the cyclohexene solution. Point out that cyclohexane has no double bond, but cyclohexene does. The general equation for the reaction of bromine with an unsaturated hydrocarbon is:

$$R-CH=CHR + Br_2 \rightarrow R-CHBr=CHBrR$$

6. Put 10 mL of cyclohexane and cyclohexene in two separate test tubes. 7. Add 5 ml of alkaline potassium permanganate solution to each. 8. Stopper and shake. 9. Note that the characteristic purple permanganate color disappears from the cyclohexene solution and is replaced by the brown color of manganese dioxide. The general equation for the reaction of permanganate with an unsaturated hydrocarbon is:

$$R-CH=CH-R + MnO_4^- \rightarrow$$
$$R-CHOH-CHOH-R + MnO_2$$

10. Have students bring in samples of organic liquids for testing. Decolorization indicates the presence of double or triple bonds.

Audiovisual Resources

A Well in West Virginia (F) Stuart Finley, 1974, 15 min. (Use with Section 25·9.) Describes geological exploration and shows natural gas drilling equipment and techniques.

Chemistry: **Organic Chemistry** (7 FS) Charles Clark, 1978, 12–17 min. (Use with Sections 25·2, 25·3, 25·4, 25·5, 25·6, and 25·7.) Introduces saturated and unsaturated hydrocarbons and discusses isomerism.

Chemistry: **The Quest for Synthetic Fuels** (F, V) Sterling Educational Films, 1983, 12 min. (Use with Sections 25·9 and 25·B.) Discusses conversion of biomass into ethyl alcohol and methane, coal liquefaction and gasification, and shale oil extraction.

Hydrocarbons and Their Structures (F) Coronet, 1962, 14 min. (Use with Sections 25·1, 25·2, 25·3, or 25·5.) Describes the bonding properties of the carbon atom, illustrates five homologous series of hydrocarbons, and discusses some hydrocarbon compounds and their uses.

Beyond the Text

Nuclear Magnetic Resonance

How do chemists learn about the structure of complex molecules which cannot be seen? Nuclear magnetic resonance (NMR) is a tool for solving this and other chemical problems. In NMR, radio waves and strong magnetic fields are used to determine the composition of molecules. Unlike some other techniques, NMR can examine molecules without removing them from their surroundings or altering them chemically. The nuclei of many elements can be detected by NMR, but proton NMR is the most common. In proton NMR of hydrocarbons, for example, each hydrogen nucleus (proton) in a C—H grouping produces a distinct NMR signal. Chemists use this information to obtain structures of organic compounds. The distinction between structural isomers, usually a difficult task, is easy with proton NMR.

To do proton NMR the substance being studied is placed in a strong magnetic field. The hydrogen nuclei behave as tiny magnets. A few of them line up in the direction of the applied field. The sample is then scanned with radio waves of various frequencies. When a hydrogen nucleus aligned with the field and the radio wave have the same frequency, they are said to be "in resonance". The energy of the resonant wave is absorbed by the nucleus. Hydrogen nuclei in dissimilar environments in the molecule absorb energy from waves of different frequency. These NMR absorption frequencies are detected and recorded to produce an NMR absorption spectrum. The nuclei of the hydrogens in CH_3— are in a different molecular environment than the hydrogen nuclei in $-CH_2-$. Thus a CH_3— group is distinguished from a $-CH_2-$ or other groups containing hydrogen by the different resonance frequencies of their hydrogen nuclei. Information about the number of protons in the molecule is obtained from the strength of the absorptions in the NMR spectrum. The stronger the absorption, the greater the number of hydrogens in the same molecular environment. For example, the absorption of energy by three hydrogen nuclei of CH_3— is three times greater than the absorption by one one of the nuclei, and 1.5 times greater than the absorption by the two hydrogen nuclei of $-CH_2-$. The characteristic NMR absorption spectrum serves as a "fingerprint" to identify the compound.

NMR is now being used as a medical diagnostic tool. It can be used to take pictures of soft body tissues which do not show up well on X-rays. It does this by monitoring the signals of hydrogen nuclei in the body's water molecules. Because the water content varies in different body tissues, such as fat or bone, a contrasting image is formed. This has made exploratory surgery unnecessary in many instances. NMR can also locate tiny tumors that even CAT scans, a computerized X-ray procedure, cannot detect. In other conditions NMR can be used to detect blood clots. Changes caused by an impaired oxygen flow can also be detected.

Answers to End of Chapter Questions and Problems

Practice Questions and Problems

11. Four.

12. See Table 25·1.

13. a. propane **b.** octane **c.** pentane **d.** propane **e.** pentane

14.

H—C— methyl

H—C—C— ethyl

H—C—C—C— propyl

15. Branched-chain alkanes are named by the IUPAC rules: 1. Find the longest continuous chain of carbons. 2. Number the carbons so that the groups attached to the chain have the lowest numbers. 3. Put that number before the name of the substituent group. 4. Use prefixes to show the number of substituent groups of the same kind. 5. List the names of the alkyl substituents in alphabetical order. 6. Use proper punctuation.

16. a. 2,2-dimethylpentane **b.** pentane **c.** 2-methylbutane **d.** 3-methylpentane

17. a.

$$CH_3-CH-CH-CH_3$$
with CH_3 and CH_3 substituents on the two central carbons

b.

$$CH_3-\underset{\underset{CH_3}{|}}{\overset{\overset{CH_3}{|}}{C}}-CH_2-CH_3$$

c.

$$CH_3-\underset{\underset{CH_3}{|}}{\overset{\overset{CH_3}{|}}{C}}-\overset{\overset{CH_3}{|}}{CH}-CH_3$$

d.

$$CH_3-CH_2-CH-\underset{\underset{CH_2}{|}}{\overset{\overset{CH_3}{|}}{C}}-\underset{\underset{CH_2}{|}}{\overset{\overset{CH_3}{|}}{CH}}-CH_2-CH_2-CH_3$$
with CH_3 and CH_3 at the ends of the CH_2 branches

18. a. $CH_3-CH_2-CH_2-CH_2-CH_3$

b. $CH_3-CH_2-\underset{\underset{CH_3}{|}}{\overset{\overset{|}{CH_2}}{CH}}-CH_2-CH_3$

c.

$$CH_3-\overset{\overset{CH_3}{|}}{CH}-\overset{\overset{CH_3}{|}}{CH}-\underset{\underset{CH_3}{|}}{\overset{\overset{CH_3}{|}}{C}}-CH_2-CH_2-CH_2-CH_3$$
with CH_2–CH_3 branch

d.

$$CH_3-\overset{\overset{CH_3}{|}}{CH}-\underset{\underset{CH_3}{|}}{\overset{\overset{CH_3}{|}}{C}}-CH_2-\underset{\underset{CH_3}{|}}{\overset{\overset{CH_2}{|}}{C}}-CH_2-CH_2-CH_2-CH_2-CH_3$$

19. a. 2-methylpropane **b.** 3-ethyl-2,5-dimethyl-hexane **c.** 2-methylhexane **d.** 3-methylheptane

20. a. 2-methylbutane **b.** 2,3-dimethylbutane
c. 3-methylhexane

21. Compounds that have the same molecular formula but different molecular structures.

22. a. Any isomer with 5 carbons and 12 hydrogens.
b. Any isomer with 7 carbons and 16 hydrogens.
c. Any isomer with 11 carbons and 24 hydrogens.

23. a. and **c.**; **b.** and **d.**

24. Saturated: contain the maximum number of hydrogen atoms (alkanes). Unsaturated: some hydrogen atoms have been replaced by double or triple carbon-carbon bonds (alkenes and alkynes).

25. a. propene **b.** *trans*-2-pentene
c. 4-methyl-1-pentene **d.** 3-ethyl-2-methyl-2-pentene
e. 1-hexene

26. $CH_2{=}CH-CH_2-CH_2-CH_3$ 1-pentene
$CH_3-CH{=}CH-CH_2-CH_3$ 2-pentene
$CH_2{=}C-CH_2-CH_3$ 2-methyl-1-butene
with CH_3 branch

$CH_2{=}CH-CH-CH_3$ 3-methyl-1-butene
with CH_3 branch

$CH_3-C{=}CH-CH_3$ 2-methyl-2-butene
with CH_3 branch

27. $CH_2{=}CH-CH_2-CH_3$ 1-butene
$CH_3-CH{=}CH-CH_3$ 2-butene (*cis* and *trans*)
$CH_2{=}C-CH_3$ methylpropene
with CH_3 branch

28.

trans-2-pentene $\qquad$ cis-2-pentene

Since no rotation can occur around the double bond, these two compounds are geometric isomers.

29. a.

trans-2-pentene $\qquad$ *cis*-2-pentene

b.

2-methyl-2-pentene

c.

trans-3-methyl-2-pentene $\qquad$ *cis*-3-methyl-2-pentene

30. Parts **a, b,** and **c:** no mirror image (symmetric).
Part **d:** mirror image (asymmetric carbon).

31. a. CH_2CH_3 (benzene ring) CH_2CH_3

b.

$$CH_3-\overset{\overset{CH_3}{|}}{CH}-CH-CH_2-CH_3$$
with phenyl group

c. CH_3—(ring)—CH_3 **d.** (ring)—CH_3

32. Two different structural formulas are possible. This compound exhibits resonance. The pi electrons are evenly distributed around the ring.

33. Aliphatic.

34. Petroleum refining: the distillation of crude oil to separate it into fractions. Cracking: the breaking down and rearranging of hydrocarbon chains into smaller molecules.

35. $C_5H_{12} + 8O_2 \rightarrow 5CO_2 + 6H_2O$

Mastery Questions and Problems

36. a. consists of hydrogen and carbon
b. a hydrocarbon with no double or triple bonds
c. an unsaturated, cyclic hydrocarbon with resonance
d. a hydrocarbon with one or more triple bond
e. a hydrocarbon with one or more double bond
f. a hydrocarbon containing a benzene ring

37. a.
$$H:\overset{\textstyle H}{\underset{}{C}}::\overset{\textstyle H}{\underset{}{C}}:H$$
b.
$$H:\overset{\textstyle H}{\underset{\textstyle H}{C}}:\overset{\textstyle H}{\underset{\textstyle H}{C}}:\overset{\textstyle H}{\underset{\textstyle H}{C}}:H$$

c. $H:C:::C:H$ **d.**
$$\begin{array}{c} H \quad H \\ H:\overset{}{\underset{}{C}}:\overset{}{\underset{}{C}}:H \\ H:\overset{}{\underset{}{C}}:\overset{}{\underset{}{C}}:H \\ H \quad H \end{array}$$

38. a. $CH{\equiv}C{-}CH_3$ **b.**

c. $CH_3{-}CH{-}CH_3$

d.
$$CH_3{-}\overset{\textstyle CH_3}{\underset{\textstyle CH_3}{CH}}{-}CH_2{-}\overset{\textstyle CH_3}{\underset{}{CH}}{-}CH_3$$

e.
$$CH_3{-}\overset{\textstyle CH_3}{\underset{}{CH}}{-}\overset{\textstyle CH_3}{\underset{}{CH}}{-}CH_2{-}CH_3$$

f. $H{-}\overset{}{\underset{}{C}}{-}CH_2{-}CH_2{-}CH_2{-}CH_2{-}CH_3$

39. a. 3,4-dimethyl-3-heptane **b.** 2-phenylbutane
c. 3-ethyl-2,2,3-trimethylhexane

40. Propane, butane, pentane.

41. The middle structure is most stable due to resonance within its benzene ring. The double bonds of the other structures are reactive.

Review Questions and Problems

42. a. 10.0 **b.** 7.59 **c.** 12 **d.** 11.7

43. a. Ca, +2; C,+4; O,−2 **b.** Cl, O
c. Li, +1; I, +5; O, −2 **d.** Na, +1; S, +4; O, −2

44. a. $K_{eq} = \dfrac{[ICl]^2}{[Cl_2][I_2]}$ **b.** $K_{eq} = \dfrac{[H_2][Br_2]}{[HBr]^2}$

c. $K_{eq} = \dfrac{[HCl]^4[S]^3[SO_2]}{[S_2Cl_2]^2[H_2O]^2}$ **d.** $K_{eq} = \dfrac{[NH_3]^2}{[N_2][H_2]^3}$

45. a. $H:\overset{\textstyle }{\underset{\textstyle H}{P}}:H$ pyramidal **b.** $:C:::O:$ linear

c. $:S::C::S:$ linear **d.**
$$\begin{array}{c} :\ddot{F}: \\ :\ddot{F}:C:\ddot{F}: \\ :\ddot{F}: \end{array} \quad \text{tetrahedral}$$

46. d. CaS **f.** Ba(OH)$_2$

Challenging Questions and Problems

47.

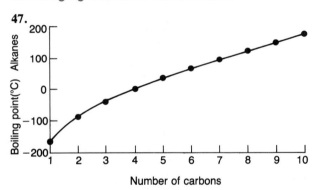

The graph is not a straight line. The predicted boiling point of undecane is 200°C. Its actual b.p. is 196°C.

48. Typical octane numbers are: 87 (unleaded regular), 88 (leaded regular), 92 (super-unleaded), 94 (super-leaded). The octane number is the % of 2,2,4-trimethyl-pentane in heptane. (% = g solute per 100 g solution.) Octane numbers greater than 100 are possible with fuels such as xylene. The 2,2-dimethylpropane molecule is less linear and therefore has superior antiknocking properties.

25 Hydrocarbon Compounds

Chapter Preview

Sections 25·6 and 25·7 are appropriate for honors students.

The element carbon comprises only two-tenths of 1% of the elements found in the earth's crust. Oxygen, silicon, aluminum, and iron are much more abundant, but carbon is the basis of life on earth.

Scientists of 150 years ago believed the ability to produce carbon compounds rested exclusively with living things. The creation of carbon compounds was thought to be directed by a mysterious "vital force." Vitalism was rudely shattered in 1828 by a German chemist named Friedrich Wöhler (1800–1882). Wöhler discovered one way to make urea in the absence of any living agent. Urea is a carbon-containing compound found in urine.

Since Wöhler's day the definition of organic chemistry has been extended to include the study of all carbon compounds, regardless of their origin. Organic chemists have discovered how carbon compounds can be synthesized, or built, from simpler materials by ordinary chemical reactions. *Organic compounds that contain only carbon and hydrogen are called* **hydrocarbons.** They provide a logical introduction to organic chemistry.

25·1 Hydrocarbon Bonds

The simplest organic molecules are the **alkanes** *which are hydrocarbons that contain only single covalent bonds.* Methane is the simplest alkane. It is a gas at standard temperature and pressure. Methane is the major component of natural gas. It is sometimes called "marsh gas" because it is formed by the action of bacteria on decaying vegetation in swamps and other marshy areas. The methane molecule, which contains four hydrogens and one carbon, is a good example of carbon–hydrogen bonding.

Figure 25·1
In a petroleum refinery, useful hydrocarbons such as gasoline, kerosene, and heating oil are distilled from crude oil.

Figure 25·2
In this painting by Ford Madox Brown, John Dalton is collecting "marsh gas" (methane), which he used in many of his experiments. Methane is one product of the decomposition of plant materials by decay bacteria.

■ The covalent bonding in alkanes involves the sharing of valence electrons between carbon and hydrogen or between two carbons.

A carbon atom has four valence electrons. Four hydrogen atoms, each with one valence electron, form four covalent carbon–hydrogen bonds. This combination is a molecule of methane.

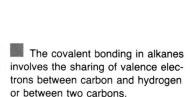

This illustrates an important principle. *Because a carbon atom contains four valence electrons, it always forms four covalent bonds.* Remembering this principle will help you write complete and correct structures for organic molecules.

For simplicity, organic chemists often abbreviate bonding electron pairs as short lines. The line between the atomic symbols represents two bonding electrons.

H
|
H—C—H   Line represents
| shared electron pair
H

Methane
molecule

Structural formulas are convenient to write on a page. Keep in mind though that they are only two-dimensional representations of three-dimensional molecules. Molecular models represent the shapes of molecules more accurately. These shapes are predicted by VSEPR theory and hybrid orbital theory (Sections 14·8 and 14·9). For example, methane has a tetrahedral shape (Figure 25·3).

Carbon has the unique ability to make stable carbon–carbon bonds and to form chains. This is the major reason for the vast number of

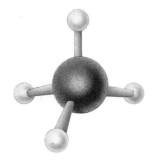

Figure 25·3
This three dimensional model shows the tetrahedral shape of the methane molecule.

organic molecules. Silicon also forms short chains, but they are unstable in an oxygen environment.

Ethane, C_2H_6, is the simplest alkane containing a carbon–carbon bond. Like methane, ethane is a gas at standard temperature and pressure. When ethane is formed from carbon and hydrogen, two carbon atoms share a pair of electrons. A carbon-carbon covalent bond is formed. The remaining six valence-shell electrons form bond pairs with the electrons from six hydrogen atoms.

$$2 \cdot \dot{C} \cdot \; + \; 6H \cdot \; \longrightarrow \; \cdot \dot{C} \text{---} \dot{C} \cdot \; + \; 6H \cdot \; \longrightarrow \; H \text{---} \underset{\underset{H}{|}}{\overset{\overset{H}{|}}{C}} \text{---} \underset{\underset{H}{|}}{\overset{\overset{H}{|}}{C}} \text{---} H$$

Ethane

25·2 Continuous-Chain Alkanes

■ Continuous-chain alkanes are hydrocarbons with the general formula C_nH_{2n+2}.

Continuous-chain alkanes *contain any number of carbon atoms in a straight chain*. They are similar to ethane. To draw a structural formula, just write the symbol for carbon as many times as necessary to get the proper chain length. Then fill in with hydrogens and lines representing covalent bonds. Remember that carbon has four covalent bonds. Table 25·1 shows the continuous-chain alkanes containing up to ten carbons. Note that the names of alkanes always end with *-ane*.

The continuous-chain alkanes are an example of a homologous series. *A group of compounds forms a* **homologous series** *if there is a constant increment of change in molecular structure from one compound in the series to the next*. The increment of change in the continuous-chain

—CH_2— is shorthand notation for —$\overset{\overset{H}{|}}{\underset{\underset{H}{|}}{C}}$—

alkanes is the —CH_2— group. For example, propane and butane are *homologs* of each other. Note that as the number of carbons in this series increases, so does the boiling point. This is also true of the melting point.

Table 25·1	Structural Formulas of the First Ten Continuous-Chain Alkanes		
Name	Molecular formula	Structural formula	Boiling point (°C)
Methane	CH_4	CH_4	−161.0
Ethane	C_2H_6	CH_3CH_3	−88.5
Propane	C_3H_8	$CH_3CH_2CH_3$	−42.0
Butane	C_4H_{10}	$CH_3CH_2CH_2CH_3$	0.5
Pentane	C_5H_{12}	$CH_3CH_2CH_2CH_2CH_3$	36.0
Hexane	C_6H_{14}	$CH_3CH_2CH_2CH_2CH_2CH_3$	68.7
Heptane	C_7H_{16}	$CH_3CH_2CH_2CH_2CH_2CH_2CH_3$	98.5
Octane	C_8H_{18}	$CH_3CH_2CH_2CH_2CH_2CH_2CH_2CH_3$	125.6
Nonane	C_9H_{20}	$CH_3CH_2CH_2CH_2CH_2CH_2CH_2CH_2CH_3$	150.7
Decane	$C_{10}H_{22}$	$CH_3CH_2CH_2CH_2CH_2CH_2CH_2CH_2CH_2CH_3$	174.1

Figure 25·4
The structure of butane can be represented in a variety of ways.

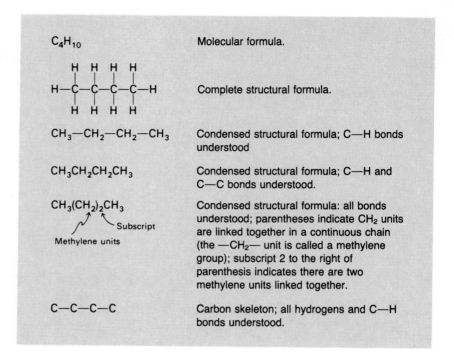

C_4H_{10}	Molecular formula.
H—C—C—C—C—H	Complete structural formula.
CH_3—CH_2—CH_2—CH_3	Condensed structural formula; C—H bonds understood
$CH_3CH_2CH_2CH_3$	Condensed structural formula; C—H and C—C bonds understood.
$CH_3(CH_2)_2CH_3$	Condensed structural formula: all bonds understood; parentheses indicate CH_2 units are linked together in a continuous chain (the —CH_2— unit is called a methylene group); subscript 2 to the right of parenthesis indicates there are two methylene units linked together.
C—C—C—C	Carbon skeleton; all hydrogens and C—H bonds understood.

By custom we draw the structural formulas of continuous chain alkanes so that the carbon atoms form a straight line. In reality, the atoms are connected in a zig-zag manner because of the tetrahedral bonding of carbon. Since rotation can occur about the carbon–carbon single bond, a long chain will take a random shape. It may even curve back upon itself.

Complete structural formulas show all the atoms and bonds in a molecule. Sometimes, however, shorthand or condensed structural formulas work just as well. **Condensed structural formulas** *leave out some bonds and/or atoms from the structural formula.* The reader must understand that these bonds and atoms are there. Figure 25·4 shows several ways to draw condensed structural formulas for butane.

Example 1

Draw complete structural formulas for the continuous-chain alkanes that have three and four carbons.

Solution

H—C—C—C—H   H—C—C—C—C—H

Problems

1. Draw complete structural formulas for the continuous-chain alkanes with five and six carbons.

2. Draw condensed structural formulas for pentane and hexane. Assume that the C—H and C—C bonds are understood.

1. H—C—C—C—C—C—H

   H—C—C—C—C—C—C—H

2. $CH_3CH_2CH_2CH_2CH_3$
   $CH_3CH_2CH_2CH_2CH_2CH_3$

Figure 25·5
Pressurized tanks of propane and butane are used as heating and cooking fuels for campers. They are also used in rural areas where gas pipelines are not available.

The names listed in Table 25·1 are recommended by the International Union of Pure and Applied Chemistry (IUPAC). You should memorize these names. They are the basis of *a precise, internationally accepted system of naming organic compounds called the* **IUPAC system.** Note, however, that organic chemists still rely on a mixture of systematic, semisystematic, and common names. This is in spite of the precision of the IUPAC system.

Problem   **3. a.** propane   **b.** pentane   **c.** hexane

3. Name the following alkanes.

a.
$$H-\overset{\displaystyle H}{\underset{\displaystyle H}{\overset{|}{\underset{|}{C}}}}-\overset{\displaystyle H}{\underset{\displaystyle H}{\overset{|}{\underset{|}{C}}}}-\overset{\displaystyle H}{\underset{\displaystyle H}{\overset{|}{\underset{|}{C}}}}-H$$

c.
$$H-\overset{\displaystyle H}{\underset{\displaystyle H}{\overset{|}{\underset{|}{C}}}}-\overset{\displaystyle H}{\underset{\displaystyle H}{\overset{|}{\underset{|}{C}}}}-\overset{\displaystyle H}{\underset{\displaystyle H}{\overset{|}{\underset{|}{C}}}}-\overset{\displaystyle H}{\underset{\displaystyle H}{\overset{|}{\underset{|}{C}}}}-\overset{\displaystyle H}{\underset{\displaystyle H}{\overset{|}{\underset{|}{C}}}}-\overset{\displaystyle H}{\underset{\displaystyle H}{\overset{|}{\underset{|}{C}}}}-H$$

b.
$$H-\overset{\displaystyle H}{\underset{\displaystyle H}{\overset{|}{\underset{|}{C}}}}-\overset{\displaystyle H}{\underset{\displaystyle H}{\overset{|}{\underset{|}{C}}}}-\overset{\displaystyle H}{\underset{\displaystyle H}{\overset{|}{\underset{|}{C}}}}-\overset{\displaystyle H}{\underset{\displaystyle H}{\overset{|}{\underset{|}{C}}}}-\overset{\displaystyle H}{\underset{\displaystyle H}{\overset{|}{\underset{|}{C}}}}-H$$

Many organic compounds are best known by their common names. These names bear no relation to the IUPAC name or to the molecular structure of the compounds. Nevertheless, these names have been used for a long time. Many organic compounds isolated from nature have common names that reflect their origin. For example, penicillin is named from the mold *Penicillium notatum*. In most instances, common names are simpler than IUPAC names, which can become long and cumbersome. Scientists also use semisystematic names which mix IUPAC and common names. This is similar to the way that immigrants lapse into their native tongue when they have an important idea to express. Like any living language, the language of science is constantly changing. IUPAC, semisystematic, and common names are used in this book.

25·3   Branched-Chain Alkanes

One or more hydrogens on a continuous-chain alkane can be substituted by other hydrocarbon groups to form branched-chain hydrocarbons.

An atom or group of atoms, called a **substituent,** *can take the place of a hydrogen atom on a parent hydrocarbon molecule.* Common substituents are the halogens and groups of atoms including carbon, hydrogen, oxygen, nitrogen, sulfur, or phosphorus.

$$\overset{\text{Substituent}}{\underset{\text{Parent alkane (propane)}}{\overset{C}{\underset{C-C-C}{|}}}} \qquad \overset{\text{Substituents}}{\underset{\text{Parent alkane (hexane)}}{\overset{C \quad C \quad C}{\underset{C-C-C-C-C-C}{|\quad|\quad|}}}}$$

A hydrocarbon substituent is called an **alkyl group.** It can be one or several carbons long. Three common alkyl groups are the methyl group (CH_3—), the ethyl group (CH_3CH_2—), and the propyl group ($CH_3CH_2CH_2$—). As you can see, an alkyl group consists of an alkane with one terminal hydrogen removed. Alkyl groups are sometimes referred to as radicals. They are named by removing the *-ane* ending from the parent hydrocarbon name and adding *-yl*.

An alkane with one or more alkyl groups is a **branched-chain alkane.** The IUPAC rules for naming branched-chain alkanes are quite straightforward. The following compound can be used as an example.

$$\overset{7}{C}H_3\overset{6}{-CH_2}\overset{5}{-CH_2}\overset{4}{-CH}\overset{3}{-CH}\overset{2}{-CH}\overset{1}{-CH_3}$$

$$| \qquad | \qquad |$$
$$CH_2 \quad CH_3 \quad CH_3$$
$$|$$
$$CH_3$$

1. *Find the longest continuous chain of carbons in the molecule.* This chain is used as the parent structure. In the example, the longest continuous chain contains seven carbons. Therefore the parent hydrocarbon structure is heptane.

2. *Number the carbons in the main chain in sequence.* In doing this start at the end that will give the groups attached to the chain the *smallest numbers.* This has already been done in the preceding example. In this instance the numbers go from right to left, which places the substituent groups at carbon atoms 2, 3, and 4. If the chain were numbered from left to right, the groups would be at positions 4, 5, and 6. These are higher numbers and therefore violate the rule.

3. *Add numbers to the names of the substituent groups to identify their positions on the chain.* These numbers become prefixes to the name of the parent alkane. In this example the substituents and positions are 2-methyl, 3-methyl, and 4-ethyl.

4. *Use prefixes to indicate the appearance of a group more than once in the structure.* Common prefixes are *di* (twice), *tri* (three times), *tetra* (four), and *penta* (five). This example has two methyl substituents. Thus the word *dimethyl* will be part of the complete name.

5. *List the names of alkyl substituents in alphabetical order.* For purposes of alphabetizing, the prefixes *di, tri,* and so on are ignored. In this example, the 4-ethyl group is listed before the 2-methyl and 3-methyl groups (which are combined as 2, 3-dimethyl in the name).

6. *Use proper punctuation.* This is very important in writing the names of organic compounds in the IUPAC system. Commas are used to separate numbers. Hyphens are used to separate numbers and words. *The name of the alkane is written as one word.* The demonstration compound, then, would be written as dimethylheptane, *not* dimethyl heptane.

According to the IUPAC rules, the name of this compound is 4-ethyl-2,3-dimethylheptane.

Figure 25·6
This is a ball and stick model of 4-ethyl-2,3, dimethylheptane. The parent structure forms a diagonal zig-zag chain from the lower right to the upper left.

Example 2

Name these compounds using the IUPAC system. (Note: The longest continuous chain is *not* written in a straight line in molecule **a.**)

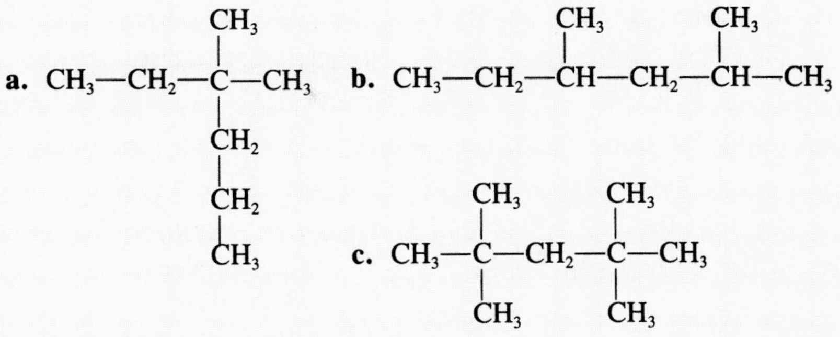

a.
$$CH_3-CH_2-\underset{\underset{\underset{\underset{CH_3}{|}}{CH_2}}{\overset{\overset{CH_3}{|}}{\underset{|}{C}}}}{}-CH_3$$

b.
$$CH_3-CH_2-\overset{\overset{CH_3}{|}}{CH}-CH_2-\overset{\overset{CH_3}{|}}{CH}-CH_3$$

c.
$$CH_3-\overset{\overset{CH_3}{|}}{\underset{\underset{CH_3}{|}}{C}}-CH_2-\overset{\overset{CH_3}{|}}{\underset{\underset{CH_3}{|}}{C}}-CH_3$$

Solution

a. 3,3-dimethylhexane   **b.** 2,4-dimethylhexane
c. 2,2,4,4-tetramethylpentane

With an alkane name and knowledge of the IUPAC rules, it is easy to reconstruct the structural formula.

1. *Find the root word* (ending in *-ane*) *in the hydrocarbon name.* Then write the longest carbon chain to create the parent structure.

2. *Number the carbons on this parent carbon chain.*

3. *Identify the substituent groups.* Attach the substituents to the numbered parent chain at the proper positions.

4. *Add hydrogens as needed.*

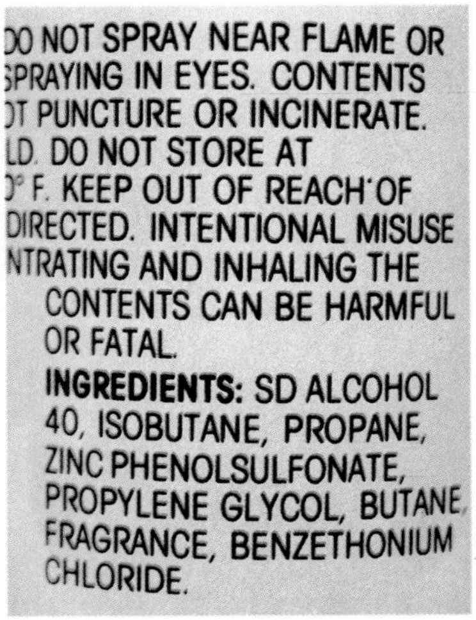

Example 3

Draw complete structural formulas for the following compounds.
a.   3,3-dimethyl-pentane   **c.** 2,2,4-trimethylpentane
b.   3-ethylhexane

Solution

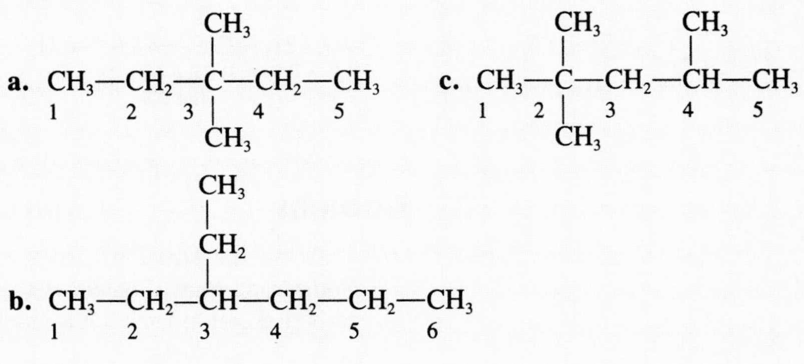

a.
$$\underset{1}{CH_3}-\underset{2}{CH_2}-\underset{3}{\overset{\overset{CH_3}{|}}{\underset{\underset{CH_3}{|}}{C}}}-\underset{4}{CH_2}-\underset{5}{CH_3}$$

c.
$$\underset{1}{CH_3}-\underset{2}{\overset{\overset{CH_3}{|}}{\underset{\underset{CH_3}{|}}{C}}}-\underset{3}{CH_2}-\underset{4}{\overset{\overset{CH_3}{|}}{CH}}-\underset{5}{CH_3}$$

b.
$$\underset{1}{CH_3}-\underset{2}{CH_2}-\underset{3}{\overset{\overset{\overset{CH_3}{|}}{CH_2}}{\underset{|}{CH}}}-\underset{4}{CH_2}-\underset{5}{CH_2}-\underset{6}{CH_3}$$

Figure 25·7
Alkanes such as isobutane, propane, and butane are commonly used as propellants in aerosol sprays.

4. a. 2-methylbutane
b. 3-methylpentane
c. 3-ethyhexane

5. a. 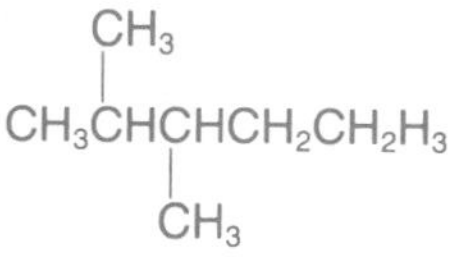
2,3-dimethylhexane

b. 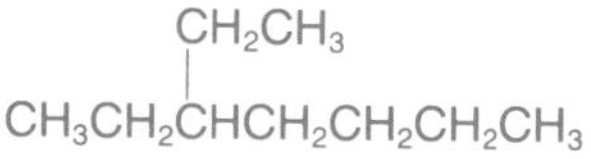
3-ethylheptane

c. 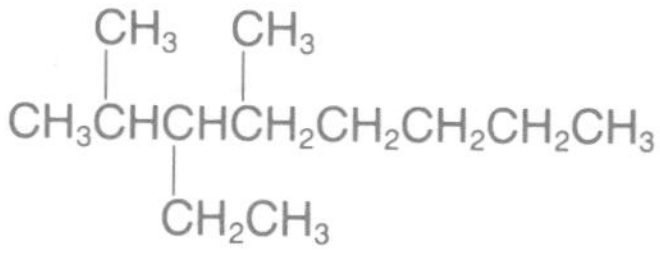
3-ethyl-2,4-dimethyloctane

Problems

4. Name the following compounds according to the IUPAC system.

a. 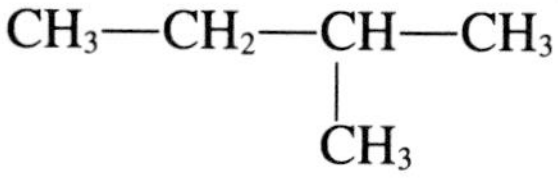

b. 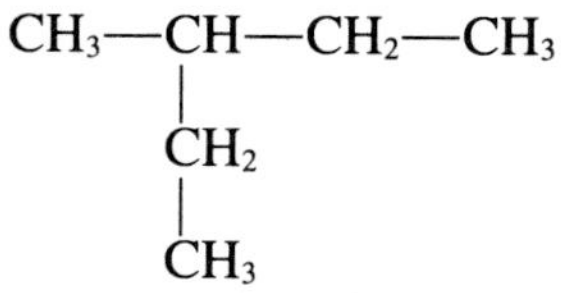

c. 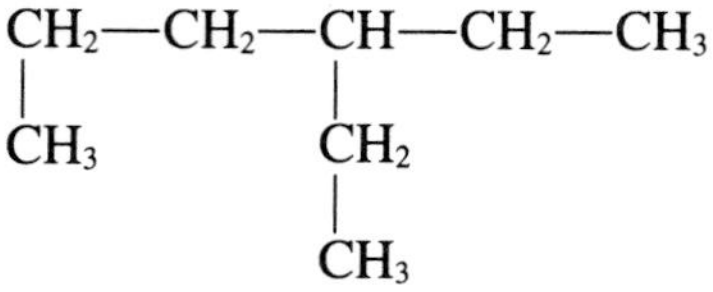

5. Draw a structural formula for each of the following compounds.
a. 2,3-dimethylhexane
b. 3-ethylheptane
c. 3-ethyl-2,4-dimethyloctane

25·4 Properties of Alkanes

■ The alkanes are gases or low-boiling, greasy liquids which are insoluble in water.

The electron pair in a carbon–hydrogen or a carbon–carbon bond is about equally shared by the nuclei of the elements involved. Therefore hydrocarbon molecules such as the alkanes are nonpolar. The nonpolar attractions that hold hydrocarbon molecules together are the very weak van der Waals forces. Thus hydrocarbons of low formula weight tend to be gases or low-boiling liquids.

Nonpolar organic molecules such as the hydrocarbons are not attracted to water. For example, oil and water do not mix. A good rule of thumb is that "like dissolves like." That is, two nonpolar compounds will form a solution as will two polar compounds. By contrast, a nonpolar compound and a polar compound will not form a solution.

It is possible to draw the structures of two or more alkanes that have the same molecular formula but different molecular structures. *Compounds that have the same molecular formula but different molecular structures are called* **structural isomers.** For example, two different molecules have the formula C_4H_{10}: butane and 2-methylpropane. They are isomers of each other.

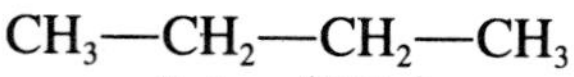
Butane (C_4H_{10})
(bp 0°C)

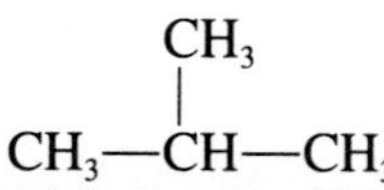
2-Methylpropane (C_4H_{10})
(bp −10.2°C)

6. Five structural isomers of molecular formula C_6H_{14} exist.

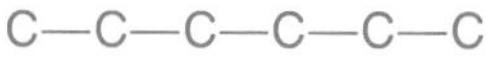
hexane

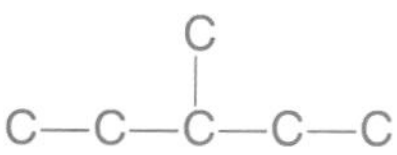
3-methylpentane

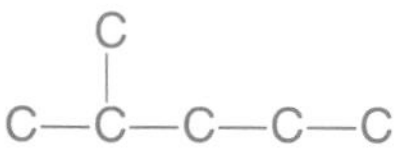
2-methylpentane

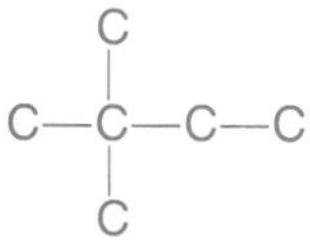
2,2-dimethylbutane

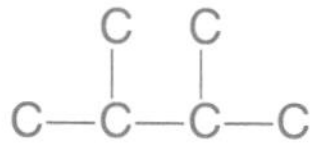
2,3-dimethylbutane

Problem

6. Draw all the structural isomers with the molecular formula C_6H_{14}. Name each one. (For convenience, you may wish to draw only the carbon skeleton for each structure.)

The physical properties of structural isomers are different.

Structural isomers differ in their physical properties such as boiling points and melting points. They also have different chemical reactivities. In general, the more highly branched the hydrocarbon structure, the lower its boiling point compared with its other structural isomers. For example, 2-methylpropane has a lower boiling point than butane.

25·5 Alkenes and Alkynes

■ The alkenes have the general formula C_nH_n, and they contain carbon–carbon double bonds.

The carbon–carbon bonds in alkanes are examples of single bonds. Multiple bonds between carbons also exist. *Organic compounds containing carbon–carbon double bonds are called* **alkenes.** This is the carbon–carbon double bond found in alkenes.

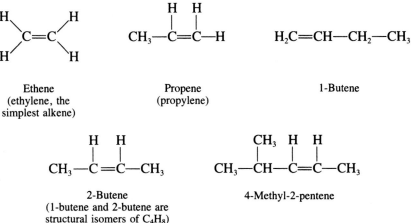

Organic compounds that contain double and triple carbon–carbon bonds are called **unsaturated compounds.** This is because they contain fewer than the maximum number of hydrogens in their structure. *The alkanes (which contain the maximum number of hydrogens) are called* **saturated compounds.**

To name an alkene by the IUPAC system, find the longest continuous chain in the molecule that contains the double bond. This chain is the parent alkene. It gets the root name of the alkane with the same number of carbons plus the ending *-ene*. The chain is numbered so that the carbon atoms of the double bond get the lowest possible numbers. Substituents on the chain are named and numbered the same way as for the alkanes. Ethene and propene are the simplest alkenes. They are often called by the common names ethylene and propylene. Here are some examples of the structures and IUPAC names of simple alkenes.

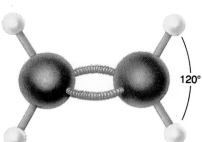

Figure 25·8
Plants produce ethene, which plays a vital role in their growth and development. Farmers treat tomato plants with a compound that breaks down into ethene inside the plants. This makes the tomatoes ripen at the same time so they can be harvested more efficiently.

Ethene
(ethylene, the simplest alkene)

Propene
(propylene)

1-Butene

2-Butene
(1-butene and 2-butene are structural isomers of C_4H_8)

4-Methyl-2-pentene

Figure 25·9
The six atoms of ethene lie in one plane. Rotation does not occur about the double bond.

120°

No rotation occurs about a carbon–carbon double bond. The four hydrogens that project from the double-bonded carbons in ethene lie in a plane and are 120° apart (Figure 25·9). This is the maximum separation of atoms that can be attained without breaking bonds.

Figure 25·10
This is a ball-and-stick model of ethyne, the simplest alkyne. Rotation about the triple bond does not occur.

Organic compounds containing carbon–carbon triple bonds are called **alkynes.** Like alkenes, alkynes are unsaturated compounds. This is the carbon–carbon triple bond found in alkynes.

$$-C\equiv C-$$

Alkynes are not plentiful in nature. The simplest alkyne is the gas ethyne, C_2H_2. The common name for ethyne is acetylene. It is the fuel burned in oxyacetylene torches used in welding. In open flame lamps that were used for mining, acetylene was produced by reacting calcium carbide with water.

$$CaC_2(s) + 2H_2O(l) \longrightarrow C_2H_2(g) + Ca(OH)_2(aq)$$

The single bonds that extend from the carbons involved in the carbon–carbon triple bond of ethyne are separated by the maximum angle of 180° (Figure 25·10). Thus ethyne is a linear molecule.

The major attractions between alkanes, alkenes, or alkynes are weak van der Waals forces. As a result, the introduction of a double or triple bond into a hydrocarbon does not have a dramatic effect on physical properties such as the boiling point (Table 25·2).

Safety

Alkenes and alkynes are very reactive because of the presence of double and triple bonds.

The physical properties of alkanes and alkenes of similar molecular mass are similar.

Table 25·2	Boiling Points of Homologous Alkanes, Alkenes, and Alkynes	
Name	Molecular structure	Boiling Point(°C)
C_2		
Ethane	CH_3-CH_3	−88.5
Ethene	$CH_2=CH_2$	−103.9
Ethyne	$CH\equiv CH$	−81.8
C_3		
Propane	$CH_3CH_2CH_3$	−42.0
Propene	$CH_3CH=CH_2$	−47.0
Propyne	$CH_3C\equiv CH$	−23.3
C_4		
Butane	$CH_3CH_2CH_2CH_3$	0.5
1-Butene	$CH_3CH_2CH=CH_2$	−6.3
1-Butyne	$CH_3CH_2C\equiv CH$	8.6
C_5		
Pentane	$CH_3CH_2CH_2CH_2CH_3$	36.0
1-Pentene	$CH_3CH_2CH_2CH=CH_2$	30.0
1-Pentyne	$CH_3CH_2CH_2C\equiv CH$	40.0

25·A Goodyear's Discovery

Natural rubber comes from rubber trees found in moist, tropical climates. Rubber's usefulness derives mostly from its excellent elasticity, or ability to stretch. It is also airtight, water resistant, and shock absorbing. Natural rubber, however, has its limitations. It becomes sticky in hot weather and brittle in cold weather. The solution to this problem was accidentally discovered in 1839 by the American inventor Charles Goodyear. While conducting an experiment, Goodyear spilled a mixture of rubber and sulfur on a hot stove. He was surprised to find that the rubber had been improved by the accident. It could now keep its shape and elasticity even in extreme heat and cold. This method of heating a sulfur–rubber mixture became known as vulcanization. It is named after Vulcan, the Roman god of fire.

A look at the chemistry of rubber reveals why vulcanization strengthens rubber. In natural rubber, thousands of isoprene (C_5H_8) molecules link to form giant polymers. In unstretched rubber, the polymers fold back on each other much like an accordion. Stretching the rubber straightens the chain. It returns to its folded position when released. In vulcanization, sulfur chemically combines with the rubber to form cross-links between the polymers. This binds the chain more firmly, giving the rubber greater elasticity and strength. If harder rubber is desired, more sulfur is added.

Many improvements have been made in rubber since Goodyear's time. Synthetic rubber is more widely used now than natural rubber. Synthetic rubber has hydrocarbons other than isoprene as its building blocks. Some compounds used are butadiene (C_4H_6), styrene ($C_6H_5CHCH_2$), and chloroprene (C_4H_5Cl). All of these substances are easier to polymerize than isoprene. Other forms of synthetic rubber are being made from silicon rather than carbon compounds.

Current research is focused on the production of synthetic rubbers that can withstand greater temperature extremes. This has become critical in the age of nuclear plants and space travel. Other researchers are looking for new ways to break down and recycle rubber. Mounds of abandoned tires are a monument to rubber's durability. They are also eyesores. At present, some used rubber is digested in a bath of zinc chloride. This removes all nonrubber components. The reclaimed rubber can then be used for new products.

Figure 25·11
The vulcanization of rubber was accidentally discovered by Charles Goodyear. It gives automobile tires and other rubber products strength, durability, and weather-resistance.

Figure 25·12
The isoprene unit of natural rubber is shown here in blue. When a mixture of sulfur and rubber is heated, sulfur atoms form bonds between the isoprene units, strengthening the rubber.

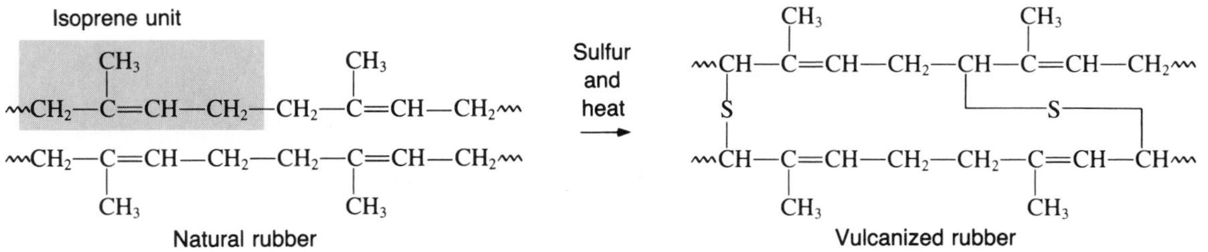

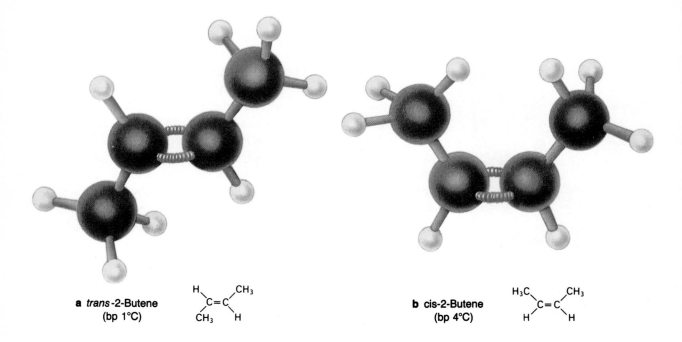

a *trans*-2-Butene
(bp 1°C)

b cis-2-Butene
(bp 4°C)

Figure 25·13
These are the two geometric isomers of 2-butene. How does the *trans* configuration differ from the *cis* configuration?
The methyl groups are on opposite sides of the double bond in the *trans* configuration. They are on the same side of the double bond in the *cis* configuration.

■ Stable geometric isomers exist because there is no rotation about carbon–carbon double bonds.

Note that a *fourth* isomer possible is: 1-pentene

CH₃CH₂CH₂   H
         C=C
       H   H

However, there are only two *geometric* isomers, the *cis*- and *trans*- forms.

Answers are shown in Appendix C.

25·6   Geometric Isomers

Appropriate for honors students.

The lack of rotation around carbon–carbon double bonds has an important structural implication. Look at the structure of 2-butene in Figure 25·13. Two arrangements are possible for the methyl groups with respect to the rigid double bond. *In the* **trans** **configuration** *the substituted groups are on opposite sides of the double bond. In the* **cis** **configuration** *the substituted groups are on the same side of the double bond. Trans*-2-butene and *cis*-2-butene are geometric isomers. **Geometric isomers** *differ only in the geometry of their substituted groups.* Like other structural isomers, isomeric 2-butenes are distinguishable by their different physical and chemical properties. The groups on the carbons of the double bond need not be the same. Geometric isomerism is possible whenever each carbon of the double bond has at least one substituent.

CH₃   H
     C=C
H   CH₂CH₃
trans-2-Pentene

CH₃   CH₂CH₃
     C=C
H   H
cis-2-Pentene

CH₃   H
     C=C
CH₃CH₂   H
2-Methyl-1-butene
(no *cis*, *trans* isomers)

Problem

7. Draw structural formulas for the following alkenes. If a compound has geometric isomers, draw both the *cis* and *trans* forms.
   a. 1-pentene   **c.** 2-methyl-2-hexene
   b. 2-hexene   **d.** 2,3-dimethyl-2-butene

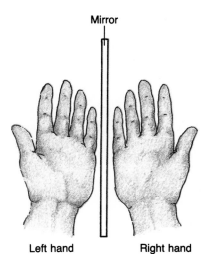

Mirror

Left hand   Right hand

Figure 25·14
The reflected image of a right hand in a mirror is a left hand. Note the position of the thumb relative to the other fingers.

■ Many objects in nature, including molecules, exist in right-handed and left-handed forms.

8. Nonsuperimposable mirror images are given by **a, d, e, f.**

Stereoisomers are also called enantiomers. Stereoisomers are optically active. That is, they have the ability to rotate plane polarized light which is passed through them. One isomer will rotate it in one direction, the other isomer will rotate it in the opposite direction.

Figure 25·15
Stereoisomers are mirror image molecules that cannot be superimposed on each other.

25·7 Stereoisomers   Appropriate for honors students.

Placing an object in front of a mirror can give two different results. If the object is symmetrical, like a ball, then its mirror image is superimposable. That is, the appearance of the ball and its reflection are indistinguishable. By contrast, a pair of hands are distinguishable even though they consist of identical parts. The right hand reflects as a left hand and the left hand reflects as a right hand (Figure 25·14). Your hands are examples of nonsuperimposable mirror images. They are mirror images which cannot be placed on top of each other to obtain a match. Many pairs of ordinary objects like ears, feet, shoes, and bird wings are similarly related.

Recall that four groups attached to a carbon by single covalent bonds form a tetrahedron with the carbon at the center. In Figure 25·15 the carbon has four *different* groups attached: —F, —H, —Cl, and —Br. *A carbon with four different groups attached is called an* **asymmetric carbon.** Compounds whose molecules contain an asymmetric carbon have handedness. For these compounds, two kinds of molecules exist that are related to one another in much the same way as a pair of hands. Figure 25·15 shows the mirror images of CHFClBr. Like hands, these mirror images are nonsuperimposable. Unless bonds are broken, these molecules cannot be superimposed. The four atoms attached to the carbon will not all match at once. **Stereoisomers** *are molecules of the same molecular structure that differ only in the arrangement of the atoms in space.* The mirror images of CHFClBr are stereoisomers.

Problem

8. Which of the following objects would have a nonsuperimposable mirror image? (Ignore designs or other markings.)
   a. clam shell   **b.** cup   **c.** ball   **d.** car   **e.** wood screw
   f. fingerprint   **g.** baseball bat

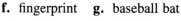

Mirror

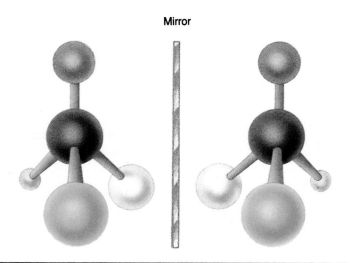

Example 4

Which of the following compounds have an asymmetric carbon?

a. CH_3CHCH_3 **b.** $CH_3CHCH_2CH_3$ **c.** CH_3CHCHO **d.** CH_3CHOH
       | | | |
       OH   OH   OH   OH

Solution

An asymmetric carbon has four different groups attached. It may help to draw the structures in a more complete form.

a. The central carbon has one H, one OH, and two CH_3 groups attached. It is not asymmetric.

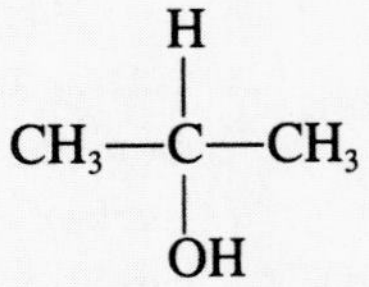

$$CH_3 \overset{\overset{\displaystyle H}{|}}{\underset{\underset{\displaystyle OH}{|}}{C}} CH_3$$

b. The central carbon has one H, one OH, one CH_3, and one CH_2CH_3 group attached. Because these four groups are different, the central carbon is asymmetric. It can be marked with an asterisk. None of the other carbons in this molecule is asymmetric (check to be sure).

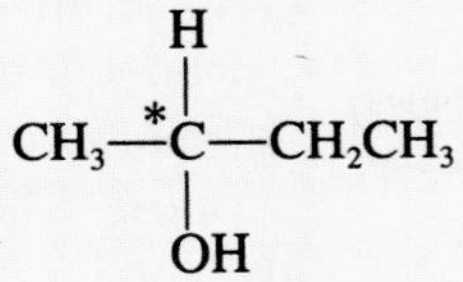

$$CH_3 \overset{\overset{\displaystyle H}{|}}{\underset{\underset{\displaystyle OH}{|}}{\overset{*}{C}}} CH_2CH_3$$

c. This molecule also has an asymmetric carbon. It is marked with an asterisk.

$$CH_3 \overset{\overset{\displaystyle H}{|}}{\underset{\underset{\displaystyle OH}{|}}{\overset{*}{C}}} CHO$$

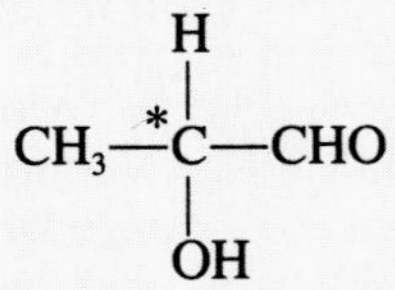

d. This molecule does not have an asymmetric carbon.

$$CH_3 \overset{\overset{\displaystyle H}{|}}{\underset{\underset{\displaystyle OH}{|}}{C}} OH$$

9. The asymmetric carbon(circled) is found in **c.** and **d.**

c. $CH_3 \overset{\overset{\displaystyle H}{|}}{\underset{\underset{\displaystyle Cl}{|}}{\boxed{C}}} OH$

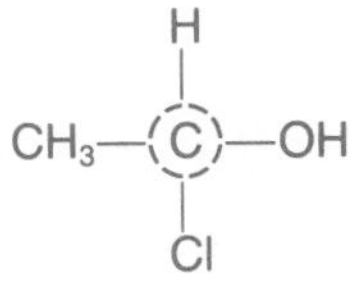

d. $CH_3 \overset{\overset{\displaystyle H}{|}}{\underset{\underset{\displaystyle CH_2CH_3}{|}}{\boxed{C}}} CHO$

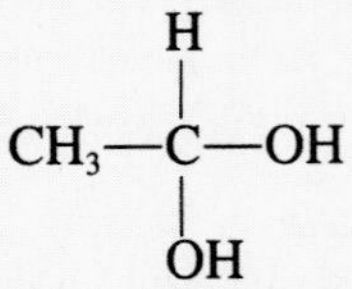

Problem

9. Identify the asymmetric carbon, if there is one, in each of the following structures.

a. CH_3CH_2CHO **b.** CH_3CHCHO **c.** CH_3CHOH
                         | |
                         CH_3 Cl

d. CH_3CHCHO
       |
      CH_2CH_3

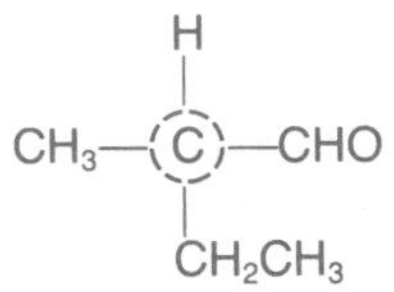

25·8 Cyclic and Aromatic Hydrocarbons

Carbon forms rings as well as open-chain molecules.

Cyclopropane (bp −34.4°C)

CH_2
H_2C——CH_2

Cyclobutane (bp −13°C)

H_2C——CH_2
H_2C——CH_2

Cyclopentane (bp 49.5°C)

H_2
C
H_2C CH_2
H_2C—CH_2

Cyclohexane (bp 81.4°C)

H_2
C
H_2C CH_2
H_2C CH_2
C
H_2

Cycloheptane (bp 118°C)

H_2
C
H_2C CH_2
H_2C CH_2
C—C
H_2 H_2

Cyclooctane (bp 149°C)

H_2 H_2
C—C
H_2C CH_2
H_2C CH_2
C—C
H_2 H_2

Figure 25·16
Cycloalkanes are named after the parent alkane. Cycloalkenes are similar but are not shown here.

A more satisfactory model is provided by modern bonding theory. It is thought that each carbon atom forms three sigma bonds, one to a hydrogen atom and two to neighboring carbon atoms. The remaining six electrons are spread evenly over the entire molecule to form pi bonds.

In some hydrocarbon compounds, the two ends of a carbon chain are attached to form a ring. *Compounds that contain a hydrocarbon ring are* **cyclic hydrocarbons.** The structures of some cyclic hydrocarbons are shown in Figure 25·16. Rings containing from 3 to 20 carbons are found in nature. Five- and six-membered rings are the most abundant. *All hydrocarbon compounds which do not contain rings are known as* **aliphatic compounds.** They include compounds with both short and long carbon chains.

A special group of unsaturated cyclic hydrocarbons are known as **arenes.** These compounds contain single rings or groups of rings. The arenes were originally called aromatic compounds because many of them have pleasant odors. Benzene, C_6H_6, is the simplest arene. *Today the term* **aromatic compound** *is applied to any substance in which the bonding is like that of benzene.*

The benzene molecule has a six-membered carbon ring with a hydrogen attached to each carbon. This leaves one electron from each carbon free to participate in a double bond. Two different structures with double bonds can be written for benzene.

These structural formulas show only the extremes in electron sharing between any two adjacent carbons in benzene. One extreme is a normal single bond. The other extreme is a normal double bond. *Resonance occurs when two or more equally valid structures can be drawn for a molecule.* The benzene molecule exhibits resonance. Benzene and other molecules that exhibit resonance are more stable than similar molecules that do not exhibit resonance. Thus benzene is not as reactive as six-carbon alkenes.

Because of resonance, the bonding in benzene and related arenes is unique. The benzene molecule is perfectly flat. Bending or twisting would disrupt the electron sharing and the molecule's stability. Some chemists use a circle to show the presence of resonance in a benzene ring.

The inscribed circle is a good way to represent the nature of resonance bonding. However, it does not show the number of electrons involved. For this reason, the traditional structure (shown on the right) will be used.

Safety

Benzene is a known carcinogen and is not recommended for use in schools. Several of its derivatives are also suspected carcinogens or are highly toxic.

Compounds containing substituents attached to the benzene ring are named as derivatives of benzene. Sometimes the benzene ring is named as a substitutent on an alkane. In such instances the C_6H_5— group is called a phenyl group.

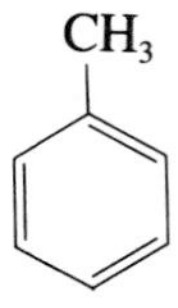
CH₃
Methylbenzene (toluene)

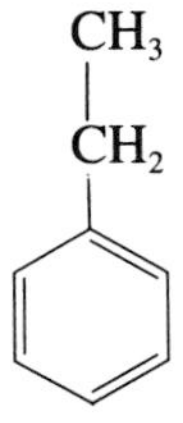
CH₃
CH₂
Ethylbenzene

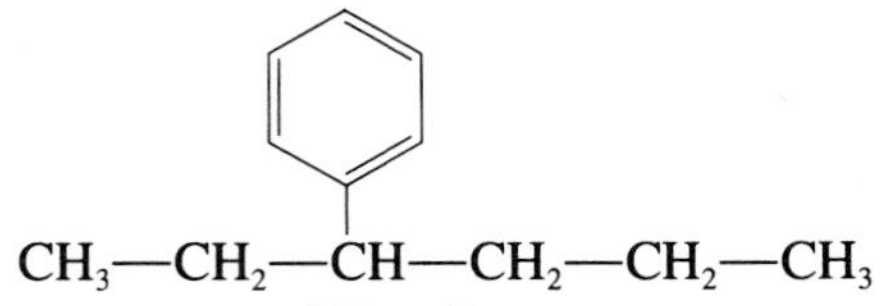
CH₃—CH₂—CH—CH₂—CH₂—CH₃
3-Phenylhexane

Problem

10. a. 1-phenylpropane
b. 2, 5-dimethyl-3-phenylhexane
c. 2-phenylpropane

10. Name the following compounds.

a. 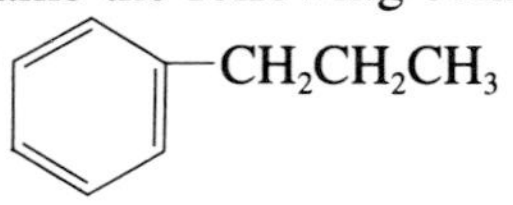
CH₂CH₂CH₃

c. 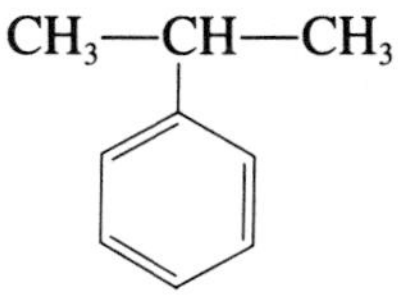
CH₃—CH—CH₃

b. 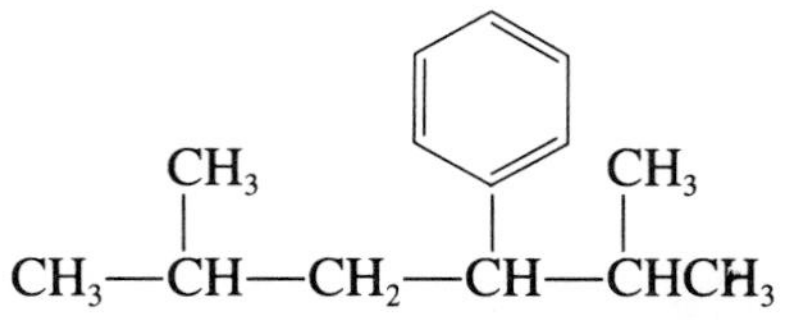
CH₃
CH₃
CH₃—CH—CH₂—CH—CHCH₃

Some derivatives of benzene have two substituents. Such derivatives are called *disubstituted* benzenes. Three different structural isomers occur for the liquid aromatic compound dimethylbenzene, $C_6H_4(CH_3)_2$. Once again, the physical properties of structural isomers are different, as indicated by their boiling points.

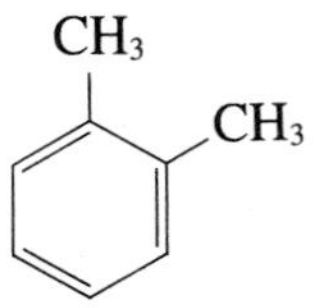
CH₃
CH₃
1,2-Dimethylbenzene (*o*-dimethylbenzene, *o*-xylene) (bp 144°C)

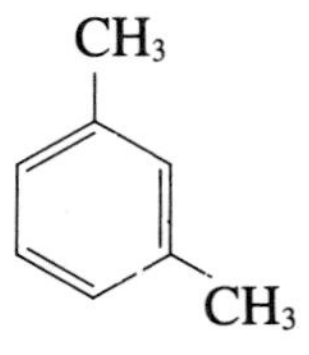
CH₃
CH₃
1,3-Dimethylbenzene (*m*-dimethylbenzene, *m*-xylene) (bp 139°C)

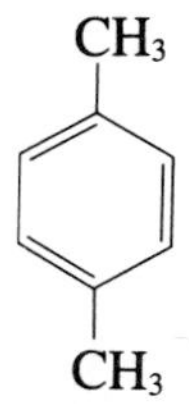
CH₃
CH₃
1,4-Dimethylbenzene (*p*-dimethylbenzene, *p*-xylene) (bp 138°C)

In the IUPAC naming system, the possible positions of two substituents in disubstituted benzene are designated as 1,2; 1,3; or 1,4. Common names for disubstituted benzenes use the terms *ortho, meta,* and *para* (abbreviated *o, m,* and *p*) in place of numbers. The dimethylbenzenes are also called xylenes.

25·9 Natural Gas and Petroleum

Much of the world's need for energy is supplied by burning fossil fuels. These fuels are organic in nature because they are derived from the decay of organisms in geologic history. Natural gas and petroleum are two important fossil fuels. They contain mostly aliphatic, or open-chain, hydrocarbons.

Petroleum, or crude oil, was first discovered seeping out of rocks. Petroleum and natural gas had their origin in marine life buried in the sediments of the oceans millions of years ago. Heat, pressure, and the action of bacteria changed this residue into petroleum and natural gas. The natural gas is often found overlying the oil deposits or in separate pockets in rock (Figure 25·18).

Natural gas is an important source of alkanes of low molecular mass. Typically, natural gas is composed of about 80% methane, 10% ethane, 4% propane, and 2% butane. The remaining 4% consists of nitrogen and higher molecular mass hydrocarbons. Natural gas also contains a small amount of the noble gas helium, and is one of its major sources. Methane is the major constituent of natural gas. It is especially prized for combustion because it burns with a hot, clean flame.

$$CH_4 + 2O_2 \longrightarrow CO_2 + 2H_2O + heat$$

■ Petroleum, formed from the effects of heat and pressure on decaying vegetation over time, is an important source of energy and organic chemicals.

Figure 25·17
Chemicals derived from petroleum and natural gas are called petrochemicals. They are the raw materials from which literally millions of essential products are made. Petrochemicals were used in the production of all of these items.

It is primarily methane, mixed with ethane, propane, and butane. Small amounts of nitrogen and helium are also present.

Figure 25·18
Natural gas and oil are typically found in dome-shaped geological formations. Sometimes the gas is under pressure and will force the oil up the well pipe, but pumping is usually required. What are the components of natural gas?

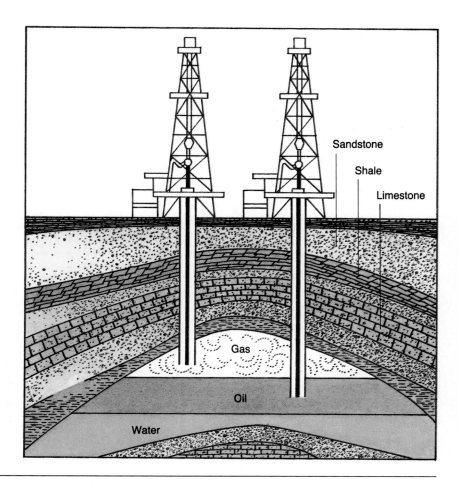

Sandstone
Shale
Limestone
Gas
Oil
Water

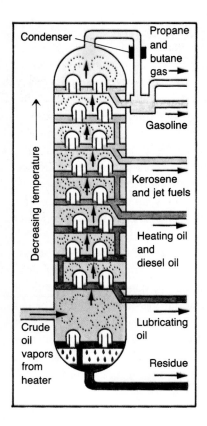

Figure 25·19
Petroleum is refined by fractional distillation. First the crude oil is heated so that it vaporizes and rises through the column. Compounds with the highest boiling points condense first near the bottom. Compounds with the lowest boiling points condense last near the top.

Propane and butane are also good heating fuels. They are separated from the other gases by liquefaction. They are sold in liquid form in pressurized tanks as liquid petroleum gas (LPG).

A sufficient supply of oxygen is necessary to oxidize a hydrocarbon fuel completely and to obtain the greatest amount of heat. Complete combustion of a hydrocarbon gives a blue flame. Incomplete combustion gives a yellow flame. This is due to the formation of small, glowing carbon particles that are deposited as soot when they cool. Carbon monoxide, a toxic gas, is also formed along with carbon dioxide and water during incomplete combustion.

$$6CH_4 + 9O_2 \longrightarrow 2C + 2CO + 2CO_2 + 12H_2O$$

The organic compounds found in petroleum are more complex than those in natural gas. Most of its hydrocarbons are continuous-chain and branched-chain alkanes. Petroleum also contains small amounts of aromatic compounds, and small amounts of sulfur-, oxygen-, and nitrogen-containing organic compounds.

Vast deposits of petroleum were discovered in the United States in 1859, and in the Middle East in 1908. It has since been found in other parts of the world as well. Crude oil must be refined before it is commercially useful. Petroleum refining consists of distilling crude oil to divide it into fractions according to boiling point (Figure 25·19). Each fraction contains several different hydrocarbons. The fractions, which have a variety of uses, are shown in Table 25·3.

The fractions containing compounds of higher molecular mass can be "cracked" to produce the more useful short chain components of gasoline and kerosene. **Cracking** *is a controlled process by which hydrocarbons are broken down or rearranged into smaller, more useful molecules.* Hydrocarbons are cracked with the aid of a catalyst or with heat. By this process, petroleum is the principal source of raw materials for the organic chemicals industry. For example, the low molecular mass alkanes are starting materials for the manufacture of paints and plastics.

Table 25·3 Fractions Obtained from Crude Oils			
Fraction	Composition of carbon chains	Boiling range (°C)	Percent of crude oil
Natural gas	C_1 to C_4	Below 20	
Petroleum ether (solvent)	C_5 to C_6	30 to 60	10%
Naphtha (solvent)	C_7	60 to 90	
Gasoline	C_6 to C_{12}	75 to 200	40%
Kerosene	C_{12} to C_{15}	200 to 300	10%
Fuel oils, mineral oil	C_{15} to C_{18}	300 to 400	30%
Lubricating oil, petroleum jelly, greases, paraffin wax, asphalt	C_{16} to C_{24}	Over 400	10%

Figure 25·20
Peat and three forms of coal are shown here. They are arranged clockwise, starting from the top: peat, lignite, bituminous or soft coal, and anthracite or hard coal.

Figure 25·21
Coal is chemically similar to both natural gas and crude oil. All three are composed chiefly of hydrocarbons. When heat and pressure are applied in the right way, coal can be converted into synthetic gas and crude oil. This two kilogram chunk of coal will yield about one liter of synthetic crude oil or about one cubic meter of synthetic gas.

25·B Coal

Geologists believe that coal had its origin some 300 million years ago. At that time, huge tree ferns and mosses grew abundantly in swampy tropical regions. When the plants died, they formed thick layers of decaying vegetation. They were eventually covered by layer after layer of soil and rock, which caused a build-up of intense pressure. This pressure together with the heat from the interior of the earth slowly turned these plant remains into coal.

The first stage in the formation of coal is an intermediate material know as *peat*. Peat is a soft, brown, spongy, fibrous material rather like decayed and compressed garden refuse. It has a very high water content when first dug out of a "peat bog." After it has been allowed to dry, it produces a low cost but smoky fuel. If peat is left in the ground, it continues to change. After a long period of time it loses most of its fibrous texture and becomes *lignite,* or brown coal. Lignite is much harder than peat and has a higher carbon content (about 50%). The water content, however, is still high. Continued pressure and heat slowly change lignite to *bituminous,* or soft coal. Bituminous coal has a lower water content and higher carbon content (70–80%) than lignite. In some regions of the earth's crust, even greater pressures have been exerted. In those places, such as in eastern Pennsylvania, coal has been changed into *anthracite,* or hard coal. Anthracite has a carbon content that exceeds 80%, making it an excellent fuel source.

Coal is obtained from both underground and surface mines. It is usually found in seams from one to three meters thick. In North America, coal mines are usually less than 100 meters underground. Much of the coal is so close to the surface that it is strip-mined. By contrast, many coal mines in Europe and other parts of the world go down 1000 to 1500 meters.

Coal consists largely of condensed ring compounds of very high molecular mass. These compounds have a very high proportion of carbon compared with hydrogen. Due to the high proportion of these aromatic compounds, coal leaves more soot upon burning than do the more aliphatic fuels obtained from petroleum. The majority of the coal burned in North America contains about 7% sulfur which burns to form SO_2 and SO_3, which are major pollutants.

Coal may be distilled to obtain a variety of products: coal gas, coal tar, ammonia, and coke. Coal gas consists mainly of hydrogen, methane, and carbon monoxide. All of these are flammable. Coal tar can be distilled further into benzene, toluene, naphthalene, phenol, and pitch. Coke is used as a fuel in many industrial processes. Because it is almost pure carbon coke produces intense heat and little or no smoke when it burns. The ammonia from distilled coal is converted to ammonium sulfate for use as a fertilizer.

Key Terms

aliphatic		cracking	25·9
compound	25·8	cyclic hydrocarbon	25·8
alkane	25·1	geometric isomer	25·6
alkene	25·5	hydrocarbon	25·0
alkyl group	25·3	homologous series	25·2
alkyne	25·5	IUPAC system	25·2
arene	25·8	saturated	
aromatic		compound	25·5
compound	25·8	stereoisomer	25·7
asymmetric carbon	25·7	structural isomer	25·4
branched-chain		substituent	25·3
alkane	25·3	*trans* configuration	25·6
cis configuration	25·6	unsaturated compound	
condensed structural			25·5
formula	25·2		
continuous-chain			
alkane	25·2		

Chapter Summary

The branch of chemistry that deals with carbon compounds is called organic chemistry. Carbon makes stable covalent bonds with other carbons to form chain and ring compounds. Hydrocarbons are compounds containing only carbon and hydrogen. Many hydrocarbons exhibit structural isomerism. Structural isomers have the same molecular formula but different molecular structures.

Alkanes contain only carbon–carbon single bonds. The groups attached to single bonds in continuous-chain alkanes rotate freely about the bonds at room temperature. Alkenes are unsaturated hydrocarbons. That is, they contain one or more carbon–carbon double bonds. Alkenes may exhibit geometric isomerism. Geometric isomers are *cis* or *trans* according to whether substituent groups are on the same side or on opposite sides of the double bond. Alkynes are also unsaturated compounds. They contain one or more carbon–carbon triple

bonds. Rotation about the multiple bonds of alkenes and alkynes does not occur at ordinary conditions. Some organic molecules exhibit stereoisomerism. Stereoisomers are related in much the same way that the right hand is related to the left. Stereoisomerism can occur if four different groups are attached to carbon.

Aromatic hydrocarbons or arenes are related to the hydrocarbon benzene. Benzene is rather unusual among hydrocarbons. As a result of resonance, the interior bonds of the benzene ring are somewhere between ordinary single bonds and double bonds. Benzene is less reactive than ordinary alkenes because of this unusual bonding.

Aliphatic, or open-chain, hydrocarbons come mainly from petroleum. Aromatic hydrocarbons come mainly from coal. Many hydrocarbons are obtained directly from crude petroleum by distillation. The molecular structures of the hydrocarbons present in natural petroleum can be reorganized into other useful products by the cracking process.

Practice Questions and Problems

11. What is the number of covalent bonds formed by carbon? *25·1*

12. Draw complete and condensed structural formulas, and give the correct names for the first ten continuous-chain alkanes. (Do not look at Table 25·1!) *25·2*

13. Name the alkanes that have the following formulas. *25·2*

  a. $CH_3CH_2CH_3$ **d.** C_3H_8

  b. $CH_3(CH_2)_6CH_3$ **e.** $CH_3CH_2CH_2CH_2CH_3$

  c.

$$\begin{array}{ccccccccc} & H & & H & & H & & H & & H \\ & | & & | & & | & & | & & | \\ H- & C & - & C & - & C & - & C & - & C & -H \\ & | & & | & & | & & | & & | \\ & H & & H & & H & & H & & H \end{array}$$

14. Write structures for the alkyl groups derived from methane, ethane, and propane. *25·3*

15. What system is used for naming branched-chain alkanes? Briefly state the rules. *25·3*

16. Why are the following names incorrect? What are the correct names? *25·3*
a. 2-dimethylpentane **c.** 3-methylbutane
b. 1,3-dimethylpropane **d.** 3,4-dimethylbutane

17. Draw structural formulas for the following branched-chain alkanes. *25·3*
a. 2,3-dimethylbutane
b. 2,2-dimethylbutane
c. 2,2,3-trimethylbutane
d. 3,4-diethyl-4,5-dimethyloctane

18. Draw structural formulas for these compounds.
a. pentane *25·3*
b. 3-ethylpentane
c. 4-ethyl-2,3,4,-trimethylnonane
d. 3,5-diethyl-2,3-dimethyl-5-propyldecane

19. Give the IUPAC name for each compound. *25·3*

a. CH$_3$—CH with CH$_3$ above and CH$_3$ below

b. CH$_3$—CH—CH$_2$—CH—CH—CH$_3$ with CH$_3$ below first CH, and CH$_2$/CH$_3$ below the other two CH groups, CH$_3$ below the CH$_2$

c. CH$_3$—CH—CH$_2$ with CH$_3$ above, CH$_2$ below, then CH$_3$—CH$_2$

d. CH$_3$—CH—CH$_2$ with CH$_2$CH$_3$ above, CH$_2$ below, then CH$_3$—CH$_2$

20. Give the IUPAC name for each compound. *25·3*

a. CH$_3$—CH—CH$_2$ with CH$_3$ and CH$_3$ below

b. CH$_3$—CH—CH—CH$_3$ with CH$_3$ and CH$_3$ below

c. CH$_3$—C—CH—CH$_2$ with CH$_2$ and CH$_3$ below, and CH$_3$ below the CH$_2$

21. What are structural isomers? *25·4*

22. Draw one structural isomer of each of the following compounds. *25·4*

a. CH$_3$—C—CH$_3$ with CH$_3$ above and CH$_3$ below

b. CH$_3$—CH—CH—CH$_3$ with CH$_3$ above first CH, CH$_2$/CH$_3$ below second CH

c. CH$_3$—CH—CH$_2$—CH—CH with CH$_3$ above first CH and CH$_3$ above last CH; CH$_2$/CH$_2$ then CH$_3$/CH$_3$ below

23. Which of these are structural isomers? *25·4*

a. CH$_3$CH with CH$_3$ above and CH$_3$ below

b. CH$_3$—CH—CH$_3$ with CH$_3$—CH$_2$ below

c. CH$_3$—CH$_2$ with CH$_2$—CH$_3$ below

d. CH$_3$—C—CH$_3$ with CH$_3$ above and CH$_3$ below

e. CH$_3$—C—CH$_2$—CH$_3$ with CH$_3$ above and CH$_3$ below

f. CH$_3$—CH$_2$ with CH$_3$ below

24. Explain the difference between saturated and unsaturated hydrocarbons. *25·5*

25. Give a systematic name for these alkenes. *25·5*

a. CH$_3$CH=CH$_2$

b. CH$_3$ and H on left carbon, H and CH$_2$CH$_3$ on right carbon of C=C

c. CH$_3$CHCH$_2$CH=CH$_2$ with CH$_3$ below the CH

d. CH$_2$ and CH$_3$ on left carbon, CH$_2$CH$_3$ and CH$_2$CH$_3$ on right carbon of C=C

e. CH$_2$=CHCH$_2$CH$_2$ with CH$_2$CH$_3$ below

26. Draw a structural formula for each alkene with the molecular formula C_5H_{10}. Name each of these compounds. *25·5*

27. Draw all the alkenes with the molecular formula C_4H_8. Name each compound. *25·5*

28. Show how lack of rotation about a carbon–carbon double bond leads to geometric isomerism. Use the isomers of 2-pentene to illustrate your answer. *25·6*

29. Draw a structural formula or carbon skeleton for each of the following alkenes. Include both *cis* and *trans* forms if the compound has geometric isomers. **a.** 2-pentene **b.** 2-methyl-2-pentene **c.** 3-methyl-2-pentene *25·6*

30. For which of the following structural formulas can mirror image molecules be drawn? Why? *25·7*

  a. CH_2Cl_2 **c.** $CH_3CF_2CH_3$

  b.
$$HS-\underset{\underset{F}{|}}{\overset{\overset{F}{|}}{C}}-OH$$

  d.
$$CH_3CH_2-\underset{\underset{F}{|}}{\overset{\overset{CH_3}{|}}{C}}-Br$$

31. Draw a structure for each compound. *25·8*
  a. *p*-diethylbenzene   **c.** *p*-xylene
  b. 2-methyl-3-phenylpentane   **d.** toluene

32. Explain why both of these structures represent 1,2-diethylbenzene. *25·8*

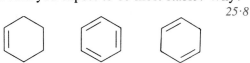

33. Does crude oil contain mostly aliphatic or aromatic hydrocarbons? *25·9*

34. Define *petroleum refining* and *cracking*. *25·9*

35. Write a balanced equation for the complete combustion of pentane. *25·9*

Mastery Questions and Problems

36. Briefly describe. *25·8*
  a. hydrocarbon   **d.** alkyne
  b. alkane   **e.** alkene
  c. arene   **f.** aromatic compound

37. Draw electron dot structures for each of these compounds. **a.** ethene **b.** propane **c.** ethyne **d.** cyclobutane *25·8*

38. Write structural formulas for each of the following compounds. *25·8*
  a. propyne   **d.** 2,2,4-trimethylpentane
  b. cyclohexane   **e.** `2,3-dimethylpentane
  c. 2-phenylpropane   **f.** 1,1-diphenylhexane

39. Give the IUPAC name for each compound. *25·8*

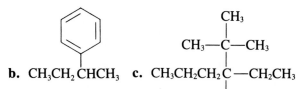

b. $CH_3CH_2CHCH_3$ **c.** $CH_3CH_2CH_2\underset{\underset{CH_3}{|}}{\overset{\overset{CH_3}{|}}{C}}-CH_2CH_3$

40. Name the next three higher homologs of ethane. *25·2*

41. Compare these three molecular structures. Which would you expect to be most stable? Why? *25·8*

42. What are the pH values for aqueous solutions containing each of the following hydroxide ion concentrations?
  a. $1.00 \times 10^{-4}M$ **c.** $0.01M$
  b. $3.92 \times 10^{-7}M$ **d.** $0.005M$

43. Give the oxidation number of each element in the following compounds.
  a. $CaCO_3$ **c.** $LiIO_3$
  b. Cl_2 **d.** Na_2SO_3

44. Write equilibrium constant expressions for the following reactions.
  a. $Cl_2(g) + I_2(g) \rightleftharpoons 2ICl(g)$
  b. $2HBr(g) \rightleftharpoons H_2(g) + Br_2(g)$
  c. $2S_2Cl_2(g) + 2H_2O(g) \rightleftharpoons$
$$4HCl(g) + 3S(g) + SO_2(g)$$
  d. $N_2(g) + 3H_2(g) \rightleftharpoons 2NH_3(g)$

Review Questions and Problems

45. Draw electron dot structures and predict the shapes of the following molecules.

a. PH_3 **b.** CO **c.** CS_2 **d.** CF_4

46. Identify any incorrect formulas among the following compounds.

a. H_2O_2 **d.** CaS_2
b. $NaIO_4$ **e.** $CaHPO_4$
c. SrO **f.** BaOH

Challenging Questions and Problems

47. Use the data of Table 25·1 to make a graph of boiling point versus number of carbons for the first ten continuous-chain alkanes. Does the graph describe a straight line? On the basis of this graph, what would you predict to be the boiling point of undecane, the continuous-chain alkane containing 11 carbons? Use a chemistry handbook to find the actual boiling point of undecane. Compare the boiling point found by experiment with your prediction.

48. The knocking properties of fuels for gasoline engines are based on standards of heptane, which causes severe engine knocking, and 2,2,4-trimethylpentane ("isooctane"), which is better than most other fuels. The *octane number* of gasoline is the percentage of 2,2,4-trimethylpentane in heptane that is required to match the knocking properties of the fuel. What are the octane numbers of gasolines available in your neighborhood? To what percentages of 2,2,4-trimethylpentane in heptane do they correspond? How might it be possible to achieve octane numbers greater than 100? On the basis of the behavior of 2,2,4-trimethylpentane and heptane, would you expect pentane or 2,2-dimethylpropane to give the best performance as a fuel in a gasoline engine?

Research Projects

1. How did Friedrich Wöhler refute the vitalism theory?

2. What contributions did Jean Dumas and Auguste Laurent make to the classification of organic compounds? Why was it difficult for their ideas to gain acceptance?

3. What was Friedrich Beilstein's major contribution to organic chemistry? How is his work used today?

4. Trace the history of the rubber industry. Compare the production and uses of natural and synthetic rubber.

5. Devise a method to distinguish two geometric isomers. How would you distinguish stereoisomers?

6. How did Friedrich Kekulé discover the structure of benzene? What are some commercial uses for this compound?

7. What environmental problems are associated with petroleum drilling and refining?

8. Do you believe it is wise to remain dependent on fossil fuels? Support your position with statistics and projections.

9. Describe some uses of chemicals derived from coal. What contributions did John Kidd make in this area?

10. Make a diagram of a coal distillation process. How does this process compare to petroleum refining?

11. What are the advantages and disadvantages of using coal gasification as an energy source?

12. What are the prospects for the widespread use of alternative fuels?

Readings and References

Kaplan, William A., and Melvyn Lebowitz. *The Student Scientist Explores Energy and Fuels.* New York: Rosen, 1981.

Kieffer, William F. *Chemistry: A Cultural Approach.* New York: Harper & Row, 1971.

Lyttle, Richard B. *Shale Oil and Tar Sands: The Promises and Pitfalls.* New York: Watts, 1982.

Maugh, Thomas H. "Digging for Black Gold." *Science Year* (1981), pp. 182–195.

Stine, William R. *Chemistry for the Consumer.* Boston: Allyn and Bacon, 1978.

Tver, David F., and Richard W. Berry. *The Petroleum Dictionary.* New York: Van Nostrand Reinhold, 1980.

26 Functional Groups and Organic Reactions

Chapter Planning Guide

Section		Demonstrations and Experiments	Resource Materials
26·1 Functional Groups	C*		Objectives Worksheet 26, SPB
			Skillsheet 26, SPB
			Teaching Diagram 32
26·2 Halocarbons	C		
26·3 Substitution Reactions	C		
26·4 Alcohols	C	26·1 Burning Kerchief	
26·5 Properties of Alcohols	C		Quiz 26·1
26·A Percy Julian and Natural Product Chemistry	E		
26·6 Addition Reactions	C		
26·7 Ethers	O		
26·8 Aldehydes and Ketones	O	Dem 26·2 Fehling's Test	
26·9 Carboxylic Acids	C	Dem 26·3 Insect Sting	Quiz 26·2
26·10 Oxidation–Reduction Reactions	C	Dem 26·4 The Oxidation of an Alcohol to an Aldehyde	
26·11 Esters	C	Dem 26·5 Esters	
		Exp 52 Esters of Carboxylic Acids, LM	Prelab 52, SPB
26·12 Polymerization	C	Dem 26·6 Rayon	Quiz 26·3
		Dem 26·7 Dyeing	
		Dem 26·8 Lye and Textiles	
26·B Synthetic Fibers	E		
26·13 Carbohydrates	O	Dem 26·9 The Starch Test	
26·14 Lipids	O	Exp 53 Preparation of Soap, LM	Prelab 53, SPB
26·15 Amino Acids, Peptides, and Proteins	O		Alternatives to Broad Spectrum Pesticides, ICT 26
26·C Enzymes	E		
26·16 Nucleic Acids	O		Quiz 26·4
			Beyond the Text: Discovering The Double Helix
			Reviewsheet 26, SPB
			Chapter 26 Test
*C = Core, O = Optional		LM = Laboratory Manual	SPB = Skills Practice Book
E = Enrichment, H = Honors			ICT = Issues in Chem. Tech.

Chapter Objectives

Having studied this chapter and done the problems, the student should be able to:

1. Recognize and identify a molecule's functional groups.   *26·1*

2. Relate differences in physical properties of classes of organic compounds to molecular structure.
26·2, 26·5, 26·7-26·9, 26·11, 26·13

3. Characterize a substitution reaction.   *26·3*

4. Identify an alcohol or an amine as primary, secondary, or tertiary.   *26·4, 26·13*

5. Write the structures for the products of an addition reaction.   *26·6*

6. Show how alcohols, aldehydes and ketones, and acids are related by oxidation and reduction reactions.
26·10

7. Predict the products of the hydrolysis of an ester.
26·11

8. Characterize the formation of a polymer.   *26·12*

9. Distinguish between common mono-, di-, and polysaccharides.   *26·14*

10. Explain the physical properties of the different kinds of lipids.   *26·15*

11. Describe the bonding that takes place in a protein molecule.   *26·16*

12. Relate the role of nucleic acids in cellular reproduction to their chemical structure.   *26·17*

Teaching Suggestions

26·1 Functional Groups

The last chapter introduced organic chemistry through the study of the hydrocarbons. Students became aware of the large number of compounds available as carbon atoms form linear chains, branching chains, and ring structures. In this chapter they will see how the addition of functional groups increases the variety of compounds even more. Stress that although the hydrocarbons form the "backbones" of organic molecules, functional groups are responsible for most of the reactions in organic chemistry. Discuss Table 26·1. Mention that each of these functional groups imparts a unique set of properties to the molecule that possesses it.

26·2 Halocarbons

In this section the idea is introduced that any hydrogen atom on a hydrocarbon can be replaced with a halogen atom. This substitution produces a halogenated hydrocarbon, called a *halocarbon*. Note the wide variety of compounds that can be produced as the number and placement of substituting halogen atoms is changed. This is illustrated well by Table 26·3, in which the four different chloro- compounds of methane are shown.

The term *alkyl group* is also introduced in this section. Point out that an alkyl group is a hydrocarbon with a bonding site made available by the removal of a hydrogen atom from the hydrocarbon molecule. Go over the name and structure of each alkyl group shown in Table 26·2.

The students should practice naming typical halocarbons when given their structural formulas, and writing structural formulas when given the names. They should get comfortable with both the common and the IUPAC names of these compounds.

26·3 Substitution Reactions

Substitution reactions enable the organic chemist to add functional groups to simple hydrocarbon molecules. They can also replace one functional group with another. Using the examples given in this section, show how the chemist can start with a simple alkane, change it to an alkyl halide, and then change the alkyl halide to an alcohol. This illustrates how organic chemists are able to alter molecules to produce the ones they want.

26·4 Alcohols
26·5 Properties of Alcohols

Of all the organic compounds the student is likely to encounter, the alcohols are among the most common. Alcohols are present in foods, cosmetics, and many other useful substances. Emphasize this class of compounds.

The presence of the $-OH$ functional group on a hydrocarbon skeleton is common to all alcohols. Stress that the $C-O-H$ bonding in alcohols is entirely covalent. In this case the $-O-H$ group does not act as the hydroxide ion. An alcohol has no basic properties. As in the previous sections, spend time with both the common and IUPAC systems of nomenclature.

Demonstration 26·1 *A Burning Kerchief* shows that alcohols are combustible.

26·6 Addition Reactions

Remind the students that a double or triple bond is more reactive than a single covalent bond. When a molecule containing a double bond reacts, one of the two bonds in the double bond is broken. This makes two bonding sites

available, one on each of the carbon atoms that were at the ends of the double bond. Thus, in an addition reaction *two* atoms are added to a molecule at a time.

Using the reactions given in this section, point out that the two atoms can be the same, as in the case of hydrogenation. They can also be different, as in the case of HCl producing an alkyl chloride, or H_2O producing an alcohol.

26·7 Ethers

26·8 Aldehydes and Ketones

Ethers, aldehydes, and ketones are all compounds in which the distinguishing atom is oxygen. The main structural difference between these is the placement of the oxygen atom. Point out that all ether molecules have an oxygen atom which is bonded to two different carbon atoms. (This gives the molecule a bent shape). Also, aldehydes and ketones possess an oxygen atom in each molecule, but it is *double* bonded to a carbon atom, forming the carbonyl group. The difference between an aldehyde and ketone lies in the position of the carbonyl group. Again, take time to go over the two systems of naming as applied to ethers, aldehydes, and ketones.

Demonstration 26·2 *Fehling's Test* is a test for the presence of aldehydes.

26·9 Carboxylic Acids

Structurally, a carboxylic acid looks as if it has characteristics of both an alcohol and an aldehyde, since it appears to have both a hydroxide group and a carbonyl group. Emphasize that it does not have the properties of either. The presence of the double-bonded oxygen weakens the bond between the other oxygen atom and the hydrogen atom attached to it. Since the hydrogen atom can be easily ionized, these substances have very definite acidic properties.

The importance of the carboxylic acids to us can be illustrated by asking the students to look on the labels of common prepared foods and cosmetics for any carboxylic acids (such as propionic acid, stearic acid, etc.) They will find a surprisingly large number.

Demonstration 26·3 *Insect Sting* simulates an insect sting with a carboxylic acid.

26·10 Oxidation–Reduction Reactions

In Chapter 20 the transfer of electrons in oxidation–reduction reactions was relatively easy to follow. When these reactions occur with organic compounds, the transfer of electrons is less obvious. This can be frustrating for the student.

In this case, it is perhaps best to use alternative definitions of oxidation and reduction. Suggest that, when dealing with organic reactions, oxidation can be defined as either the *gain* of oxygen or the *loss* of hydrogen. Reduction is the loss of oxygen or the gain of hydrogen.

Take time to go through the series of changes described in this section. Discuss each step as being an example of oxidation or reduction.

Demonstration 26·4 *The Oxidation of an Alcohol to an Aldehyde* shows the role of oxidation in some organic reactions.

26·11 Esters

Esters are of particular interest since they contribute to so many of the pleasant odors and fragrances we encounter in our world. Point out that esters are formed by the reaction of a carboxylic acid with an alcohol. In the process, a water molecule forms from the −OH of the carboxylic acid and the H of the alcohol.

The formation of esters from a carboxylic acid and an alcohol is an excellent illustration of equilibrium. Under the proper conditions, the equilibrium can be shifted greatly in favor of the products. Other conditions favor the decomposition of the ester into the carboxylic acid and alcohol. It might be worthwhile to review Le Châtelier's principle. Then use it to predict those conditions which would favor the reactants and those which would favor the products.

Give the students exposure to the ester-forming reactions in **Experiment 52** *Esters of Carboxylic Acids*. As an alternative, do **Demonstration 26·5** *Esters*.

26·12 Polymerization

The key to polymerization reactions is the ability of molecules to form nearly endless repeating chains. In order for this to happen, the reacting molecules must each have at least *two* reacting sites. Point out to your students that in an addition polymerization reaction the two sites become available as double bonds are opened up. In the case of condensation polymerization reactions the sites become available as two groups (such as −H and −OH) are split off the molecules.

You can illustrate the relationship between monomers and polymers with clothes pins. Consider each clothes pin as a monomer. The jaws are one reacting site, one leg the other. You can connect the clothes pins in chains of ever increasing length by successively clipping the jaws of one to the leg of another. The chain formed is analogous to a polymer. Point out that the only difference between one polymer and another is the type of monomer used to form the chains.

The formation of rayon polymers can be shown by doing **Demonstration 26·6** *Rayon*. The students can prepare polymers themselves by doing parts of **Experiment 53** *Preparation of Soap*. **Demonstrations 26·7** *Dyeing* and **26·8** *Lye and Textiles* compare synthetic polymers to natural ones.

26·13 Carbohydrates

An approach to take when discussing the various carbo-hydrates is that they are examples of molecules which are combinations of the kinds of compounds which have been discussed in previous sections.

If possible, construct ball and stick models of glucose and fructose. Point out the functional groups on each and how they can lose water to make the cyclic form.

Connect two together to form a disaccharide. Point out that this is a condensation reaction. If the condensation reaction is allowed to continue, many monosaccharide units could join to form a polysaccharide, such as starch or cellulose. **Demonstration 26·9** *The Starch Test* shows how starch affects iodine.

26·14 Lipids

Stress that lipids are substances which are biologically very important. This class of compounds includes waxes, fats, oils, some vitamins, and steroids.

The feature lipids share in common is that they are not water soluble. There is no particular functional group which is common to all lipids.

Fatty acids are particularly important because they are our source of soaps. The preparation of soap is easily performed. Have the students do it as part of **Experiment 53,** or do that part as a demonstration.

26·15 Amino Acids, Peptides, and Proteins

A new functional group is introduced in this section, the amino group. It consists of a nitrogen atom with two at-tached hydrogen atoms. Take a moment with the students to help them distinguish this term from the terms amine and amide.

Show the students how the feature that all amino acids share in common is the presence of *both* an amino group and a carboxylic acid group.

Demonstrate (with models, if possible) how amino acids can link through amide bonds to form peptides. Point out that this is just another example of a condensation polymerization. Have them imagine continuing this pro-cess until first polypeptides and finally protein molecules are formed.

26·16 Nucleic Acids

Approach the topic of nucleic acids as another example of polymerization. In this case, rather than the monomers that make up polynucleotides being identical, there are three main types. Each of these nucleotides in turn can consist of other monomers. For instance the base monomer could be adenine, guanine, thymine, or cytosine.

Demonstrations

26·1 A Burning Kerchief

Concept: Alcohols are combustible.

Materials: 100 mL of 50% (v:v) 2-propanol in water, lighter, kerchief, crucible tongs, candle, matches, 500-mL beaker, forceps, safety goggles.

Procedure: 1. Pour the propanol solution in the beaker. 2. Soak the kerchief in the solution. 3. Squeeze it to pre-vent dripping. 4. Holding it with tongs, light the kerchief. 5. Snap it to extinguish the flame. 6. Note that the kerchief is not burned in the fire. Explain that there is a chemical change of the alcohol to carbon dioxide and water. Energy is released as heat and light. The water absorbs heat as it vaporizes (a physical change), preventing the burning of the kerchief. **Caution:** *Have students stand back when the kerchief is ignited.*

26·2 Fehling's Test

Concept: Fehling's test detects aldehydes.

Materials: 35 g of copper sulfate pentahydrate ($CuSO_4 \cdot 5H_2O$) in water to make 500 mL of solution, 173 g potassium sodium tartrate ($KNaC_4H_4O_6$) and 50 g of sodium hydroxide (NaOH) in water to make 500 mL of solution, 400-mL beaker, three 800-mL beakers, two stir-ring rods, 2 mL each of methanol, glucose, formaldehyde, acetone, and any other organic substances, water, 4 me-dium test tubes, hot plate, safety goggles.

Procedure: 1. Place one of the organic samples in a test tube and add 2 mL each of copper sulfate solution and potassium sodium tartrate solution. 2. In the fume hood, heat in a boiling water bath for 5 minutes. 3. The formation of a red precipitate indicates the presence of an aldehyde. 4. Repeat with other organic samples, keeping a chart on the board. Formaldehyde and glucose will test positive; methanol and acetone will not. **Caution:** *Formaldehyde is a suspected animal carcinogen and mutagen. Use a fume hood and avoid breathing vapors. Sodium hydroxide is corrosive. Copper sulfate is an irritant.*

26·3 Insect Sting

Concept: A carboxylic acid can be used to simulate an insect sting.

Materials: bowl of gelatin, pasteur pipet, 1 mL of con-centrated formic acid (HCOOH), safety goggles.

Procedure: 1. Inject the gelatin with formic acid. 2. The gelatin swells at the site of the injection. **Caution:** *Formic acid is corrosive.*

26·4 The Oxidation of an Alcohol to an Aldehyde

Concept: An alcohol can be converted to an aldehyde by oxidation.

Materials: a penny, 30 cm of copper wire, 10 mL of methanol, 50-mL beaker, glass stirring rod, gas burner, matches, safety goggles.

Procedure: 1. Wrap the coin with a few turns of copper wire and wrap the other end of the wire around the middle of the glass rod. 2. Pour methanol in the beaker. 3. Place the rod across the top of the beaker so that the coin is suspended 1 cm above the methanol in the beaker. 4. Lift the coin by the glass rod and heat until it turns a dull red. Do not burn through the wire. 5. While the coin is still hot, re-suspend it above the methanol. 6. At the surface of the coin, the heat produced by the oxidation of methanol vapor keeps the coin glowing red. The surface of the coin turns black as it also is oxidized. 7. Carefully wave your hand to waft a *minute* amount of vapor to detect the formaldehyde odor. **Caution:** *Formaldehyde is a suspected animal carcinogen and mutagen. Use a fume hood and minimize contact with the vapors. Methanol is flammable.*

26·5 Esters

Concept: Esters are formed from a carboxylic acid and an alcohol.

Materials: 5 mL each of the carboxylic acids and alcohols listed below, 5 g of anhydrous calcium sulfate ($CaSO_4$), 20 mL of concentrated sulfuric acid (H_2SO_4), 6 droppers, 6 test tubes, test tube rack, test tube holder, hot plate, 400-mL beaker, 100 mL of water, filter paper, watch glass, safety goggles.

Acid	Alcohol	Odor of Ester
acetic	ethyl	apple
acetic	isoamyl	banana
acetic	amyl	apricot
acetic	octyl	orange
butyric	ethyl	pineapple
salicylic	methyl	wintergreen

Procedure: 1. Place each carboxylic acid and the corresponding alcohol (see chart above) in the six test tubes. 2. Add a granule of calcium sulfate and 3 drops of sulfuric acid to each tube. 3. Heat in a boiling water bath for a few minutes. 4. Dip a piece of filter paper into each tube and place it on a clean watch glass. 5. Have the students try to identify the odors of each of the esters. 6. Write the equation for a typical esterification reaction on the board. 7. Point out that the only difference in these reactions is in the "R" group attached to the carboxyl and alcohol functional groups. **Caution:** *Acetic and sulfuric acids are corrosive. Butyric acid is an irritant.*

26·6 Rayon

Concept: Rayon is a polymer of cellulose.

Materials: 40 g of copper(II) sulfate pentahydrate ($CuSO_4 \cdot 5H_2O$) in 150 mL water in a 400-mL beaker, 30 mL of concentrated ammonia solution ($NH_3(aq)$), 100 mL of $1M$ hydrochloric acid (HCl), 100-mL beaker of water, two 250-mL beakers, filter funnel, filter paper, funnel holder, stand, 2 g filter paper, stirring rod, hypodermic syringe with no needle, safety goggles, tongs.

Procedure: 1. Before class, add 20 mL of ammonia solution to the copper sulfate solution. 2. Filter the precipitate, using the funnel and filter paper. 3. Wash the precipitate several times with cold water. 4. During class, add 10 mL of concentrated ammonia solution to dissolve the precipitate. A dark blue solution results. 5. Tear about 2 g of filter paper into small pieces and add to the dark blue solution. 6. Stir occasionally for about one-half hour to dissolve the paper. 7. Fill a hypodermic syringe (with no needle) with the solution. 8. Inject the solution under the surface of the hydrochloric acid solution in a 250-mL beaker. 9. When the solution contacts the acid, cellulose is regenerated and forms a thread. 10. Repeat to form several threads. 11. Remove the threads from the acid with tongs and rinse. **Caution:** *Use a fume hood and wear goggles. Ammonia solution and copper sulfate are irritants.*

26·7 Dyeing

Concept: Organic dyes are polymers that can bind to cloth.

Materials: 5 g each of Sudan red, sulfanil blue, and aniline yellow, three 3″ squares of each of cotton, silk, and wool, three 3″ squares of either rayon, nylon, or polyester, three 400-mL beakers, three 500-mL beakers of water, three hot plates, tongs, 3 stirring rods, safety goggles.

Procedure: 1. Boil 100 mL water in each of the 400-mL beakers. 2. Place one dye in each beaker and stir. 3. Drop the four types of cloth into each beaker, stir, and wait five minutes. 3. Using the tongs, remove the cloths and drop each group of four into a separate rinse beaker. 4. Display how the cloth has been dyed. Compare the colors of different cloths from the same dye. **Caution:** *The dyes stain skin and clothing. Handle only with tongs.*

26·8 Lye and Textiles

Concept: Sodium hydroxide decomposes the polymers of natural and man-made textiles.

Materials: 200 mL of $10M$ sodium hydroxide (NaOH) in a 400-mL beaker, glass plate to cover beaker, hot plate, 3″ squares of cotton, wool, nylon, and silk, safety goggles, tongs.

Procedure: 1. Heat the sodium hydroxide until it approaches boiling. 2. Drop the cloths into the solution, using the tongs. Cover the beaker with the glass plate. 3. After 5 minutes, only the cotton has not decomposed. **Caution:** *Sodium hydroxide is corrosive.*

26·9 The Starch Test

Concept: Starch reacts with iodine.

Materials: high-carbohydrate foods (e.g. potato, bread, pasta, corn), other foods for comparison (e.g. milk, margarine, cauliflower), knife, 800-mL beaker, 5 mL of 1% tincture of iodine, 100 mL water.

Procedure: 1. Pour water in the beaker and add iodine. 2. Slice food samples and add to the beaker. 3. Swirl the beaker. 4. After 5 minutes, the starchy foods turn blue. **Caution:** *Iodine is an irritant and stains the skin and clothing.*

Audiovisual Resources

Atoms and Molecules: Building Blocks of Matter (6 FS) Science and Mankind, 1981, 12–18 min. each. (Use with Sections 26·14–26·17.) Introduces the structures of carbohydrates, lipids, proteins, and nucleic acids.

Fields of Fuel: The Ethanol Debate (F, V) International Film Bureau, 1980, 28 min. (Use with Section 26·4.) Examines the use of alcohol as an alternative fuel and raises related economic questions.

Functional Chemistry in Living Cells (4 FS) Human Relations Media, 1984, 14–21 min. each. (Use with Sections 26·14–26·17.) Shows how sugars, fatty acids, amino acids, and nucleic acid bases form biochemical compounds and discusses the functions of these substances.

Man-Made Macromolecules: Polymers (F, V) Media Guild, 1982, 25 min. (Use with Sections 26·12 and 26·B.) Describes laboratory and industrial processes for making polyethylene, polypropylene, and nylon.

New Forms of Life: Gene Splicing and Genetic Engineering (FS) Knowledge Unlimited, 1983, 60 min. (Use with Sections 26·16 and 26·17.) Discusses the scientific and social implications of genetic engineering. (Available in two levels: introductory and advanced.)

Pure Organic Compounds (F, V) Media Guild, 1982, 24 min. (Use with Sections 26·4 and 26·14.) Presents procedures used to prepare pure organic compounds in the research laboratory and industry, including crystallization, extraction, thin-layer and column chromatography, and distillation.

Beyond the Text

Discovering the Double Helix

Deoxyribonucleic acid, DNA, is the large molecule found in chromosomes. The nitrogen bases in DNA are adenine, cytosine, thymine, and guanine. The sequence of these bases acts as a code for protein synthesis. Protein synthesis, in turn, dictates cell growth, differentiation, enzyme production, and many other biological processes. Because of DNA's role in directing these processes, DNA is sometimes referred to as "the blueprint of life."

In 1953 an American scientist, James Watson, and his British colleague Francis Crick, published their theory of the structure of DNA. Their theory was based on evidence collected by different researchers shortly following World War II. The earlier development of paper chromatography allowed scientists to separate large molecules such as DNA into their components. Erwin Chargraff showed that there were consistent relationships between the four nucleic acid components of DNA. He found that the amount of adenine was equal to the amount of thymine and that the amount of guanine was equal to the amount of cytosine.

X-ray crystallography allowed researchers to discover repeating units in large molecules. Maurice Wilkins used this technique to study DNA. He found regular repeating structures in the molecule. Rosalind Franklin, who worked for Wilkins, found that DNA could assume a helical shape. She thought the molecule only assumed this shape, or conformation, under certain conditions.

Watson and Crick pieced together this evidence and proposed that the DNA molecule existed as two coiled strands held together by hydrogen bonds. They predicted that the sugar–phosphate groups on the nucleic acids formed the backbone of each coil. They proposed that the carbon and nitrogen-containing rings extended perpendicular to the coil. These portions of the molecule would form the hydrogen bonds between strands. More specifically, they proposed that an adenine of one strand would form hydrogen bonds with a thymine of the other strand. Also, the guanine of one strand would form hydrogen bonds with a cytosine of the other strand. These pairings would account for the equal amounts of the nucleotides and for the repeating structures discovered by Wilkins.

This equal but opposite relationship between strands helped explain how genetic information could be passed along when chromosomes duplicated. Each nucleic acid has only one partner. Thus the double helix could unwind and reproduce an exact copy of a strand using the opposite strand as a guide.

After Watson and Crick proposed their model of DNA, researchers verified the structure with experiments. They found that the geometries of the nucleic acid partners agreed with the proposed structure. In 1962, Watson, Crick and Wilkins shared the Nobel Prize in medicine for

their work. Their discoveries opened the door for genetic research. Soon after the Watson–Crick model was proposed, scientists succeeded in cracking the genetic code. In other words, they discovered the relationship between the nucleic acid sequence in DNA and the amino acid sequence in proteins.

Today, scientists are still trying to understand how the genetic code operates. Genetic engineering has allowed scientists to produce new and better vaccines, and grow higher-yielding and disease-resistant crops. This is a very active area of research.

Answers to End of Chapter Questions and Problems

Practice Questions and Problems

12. a. R—X (X = F, Cl, Br, I)

b. $R-\overset{\overset{O}{\|}}{C}-R$ **c.** $R-\overset{\overset{O}{\|}}{C}-O-R$

d. $R-\overset{\overset{O}{\|}}{C}-\overset{\overset{H}{|}}{N}-R$

13. a. aldehyde **b.** ketone **c.** ester **d.** alcohol

14. a. $\overset{\overset{Cl}{|}}{CH_2}-\overset{\overset{Cl}{|}}{\underset{\underset{Cl}{|}}{C}}-CH_2-CH_3$ **b.**

c.

15. a. 3-chloropropene **b.** 1,2-dichloro-4-methylpentane **c.** 1,3-dibromobenzene

16. a. $\overset{\overset{Cl}{|}}{\underset{\underset{Cl}{|}}{CH}}-CH_2-CH_3$ 1,1-dichloropropane

$\overset{\overset{Cl}{|}}{CH_2}-\overset{\overset{Cl}{|}}{CH}-CH_3$ 1,2-dichloropropane

$\overset{\overset{Cl}{|}}{CH_2}-CH_2-\overset{\overset{Cl}{|}}{CH_2}$ 1,3-dichloroproane

$\overset{\overset{Cl}{|}}{CH_3}-\overset{\overset{|}{\underset{\underset{Cl}{|}}{C}}}{}-CH_3$ 2,2-dichloropropane

b. $CH_3-CH_2-CH_2-\overset{\overset{Br}{|}}{CH_2}$ 1-bromobutane

$CH_3-CH_2-\overset{\overset{Br}{|}}{CH}-CH_3$ 2-bromobutane

$\overset{\overset{CH_3}{|}}{CH_3}-\overset{}{CH}-\overset{\overset{Br}{|}}{CH_2}$ 1-bromo-2-methylpropane

$\overset{\overset{CH_3}{|}}{CH_3}-\overset{\overset{|}{\underset{\underset{Br}{|}}{C}}}{}-CH_3$ 2-bromo-2-methylpropane

17. a.

b.

c. $CH_3-\overset{\overset{CH_3}{|}}{CH}-O-CH_2-CH_3$ **d.**

18. a. 2-butanol or sec-butyl alcohol **b.** 2-methyl-1-propanol **c.** 3-methyl-1-butanol **d.** 3-methyl-3-pentanol

19. a. secondary **b.** primary **c.** primary **d.** tertiary

20. Ethanol is a small molecule with a polar hydroxyl group that interacts with water molecules. Decanol is a large molecule with a polar hydroxyl group, but it is a relatively small part of the molecule. Water molecules do not interact with the hydrocarbon portion of decanol.

21. a.

b.

c.

22. a. $\overset{\overset{H}{|}}{CH_2}-\overset{\overset{Br}{|}}{CH_2}$ **b.** $\overset{\overset{Cl}{|}}{CH_2}-\overset{\overset{Cl}{|}}{CH_2}$

bromoethane   1,2-dichlorethane

c. CH_2-CH_2 (with H and OH)
ethanol

d. CH_2-CH_2 (with H and H)
ethane

e. CH_2-CH_2 (with H and Cl)
chlorethane

23. a. ethylmethyl ether   **b.** ethylphenyl ether
c. ethylisopropyl ether   **d.** diisopropyl ethyl or
isopropyl ether   **e.** divinyl ether of vinyl ether

24. The oxygen atom in diethyl ether polarizes the
small molecule. This enables diethyl ether to dissolve in
polar water. The large dihexyl ether molecule has large
nonpolar parts and does not dissolve. Propane is less
soluble in water than is diethyl ether because it is
nonpolar.

25. A carbonyl group is a carbon atom double bonded
to an oxygen atom. A carbon–carbon double bond is
between two atoms with the same electronegativity and
has no polarity. A carbon–oxygen double bond is polar
because oxygen is much more electronegative than
carbon.

26. a. propanone or acetone   **b.** 3-methylbutanal
c. 2-phenylethanal   **d.** diphenylmethanone or diphenyl
ketone or benzophenone   **e.** ethanal or acetaldehyde
f. 3-hexanone or ethylpropyl ketone

27. Acetaldehyde is polarized by the carbonyl oxygen,
forming stronger intermolecular attractions. Nonpolar
propane has weak intermolecular attractions.

28. a. formic acid   **b.** acetic acid   **c.** propionic acid
d. stearic acid

29. a. $HCOOH + KOH \longrightarrow HCOOK + H_2O$
b. $CH_3CH_2COOH + NaOH \longrightarrow$
$CH_3CH_2COONa + H_2O$

30. a. $CH_3CH_2OH \xrightarrow{K_2Cr_2O_7} CH_3-C-H$ (with =O)

b. $CH_3CH_2CHO \xrightarrow{K_2Cr_2O_7} CH_3-CH_2-C-OH$ (with =O)

c. CH_3CH_2CHOH (with CH_3) $\xrightarrow{K_2Cr_2O_7} CH_3-CH_2-C-CH_3$ (with =O)

d. (benzene ring)$-CH_2CHO \xrightarrow{K_2Cr_2O_7}$
(benzene ring)$-CH_2-C-OH$ (with =O)

e. no reaction

31. a. no product   **b.** $CH_3-CH_2-C-CH_2-CH_3$ (with =O)
3-pentanone

c.
cyclohexanone

d. CH_3-C-CH_3 (with =O)
propanone or acetone

32. a. $H-C-OH$ (with H above and H below)
methanol

b. $CH_3-CH-CH_3$ (with OH above)
propanol

c. $CH_3-CH-C-OH$ (with CH_3 and H above, H below)
2-methyl-1-propanol

d. (cyclohexane structure with OH and H)
cyclohexanol

33. a. $CH_3COOCH_3 + H_2O \xrightarrow{HCl}$
methyl ethanoate   water
(methyl acetate)

$CH_3-C-OH + CH_3OH$ (with =O)
ethanoic acid   methanol
(acetic acid)

b. $CH_3CH_2CH_2COOCH_2CH_2CH_3 + H_2O \xrightarrow{NaOH}$
propyl butanoate   water
(propyl butyate)

$CH_3CH_2CH_2-C-O^- Na^+ + CH_3CH_2COH$ (with =O, and H's)
sodium butanoate   1-propanol
(sodium butyate)

c. $HCOOCH_2CH_3 + H_2O \xrightarrow{KOH}$
ethyl methanoate   water
(ethyl formate)

$H-C-O^- Na^+ + CH_3-C-OH$ (with =O, and H's)
sodium methanoate   ethanol
(sodium formate)

34. a. $H-C-O-CH_3$ (with =O)   methyl methanoate
(methyl formate)

b. $CH_3-CH_2-CH_2-C-O-CH_2-CH_3$ (with =O)
ethyl butanoate (ethyl butyrate)

c. $CH_3-C-O-CH_2-CH_2-CH_3$ (with =O)
propyl ethanoate (propyl acetate)

35. a.

$$-CH_2-CH- $$
$$\qquad\quad | $$
$$\qquad\quad CH_2 $$
$$\qquad\quad | $$
$$\qquad\quad CH_3 $$

b.

$$-CH-CH- $$
$$\;\; | \quad\;\; | $$
$$\;\; Cl \quad\; Cl $$

36. A disaccharide is formed by linking two monosaccharides, with the loss of a water molecule.

37. a. Starch comes from plants such as corn; used for food and to "starch" clothing.
b. Cellulose comes from plant cell walls; used as a structural material, in paper, and in clothing.
c. Glycogen comes from the livers of animals; used for food.

38. Glucose is an aldehyde and turns Benedict's solution into a bright red precipitate.

39. Long-chain fatty acids and long-chain alcohols.

40.

$$CH_2-O-\overset{\displaystyle O}{\overset{\|}{C}}\!\!\left(CH_2\right)_{\overline{16}}-CH_3$$
$$|\qquad\qquad\quad O$$
$$CH_2-O-\overset{\displaystyle O}{\overset{\|}{C}}\!\!\left(CH_2\right)_{\overline{16}}-CH_3$$
$$|\qquad\qquad\quad O$$
$$CH_2-O-\overset{\displaystyle O}{\overset{\|}{C}}\!\!\left(CH_2\right)_{\overline{16}}-CH_3$$

41. The alkali metal salt of a fatty acid.

Sodium stearate: $CH_3(CH_2)_{16}\overset{\displaystyle O}{\overset{\|}{C}}O^-Na^+$

42.

$$CH_2-OH$$
$$|$$
$$CH\;-OH \qquad CH_3(CH_2)_{14}\overset{\displaystyle O}{\overset{\|}{C}}O^-Na^+$$
$$|\qquad\qquad\qquad\qquad \text{sodium palmitate}$$
$$CH_2-OH$$
$$\text{glycerol}$$

$$CH_3(CH_2)_{10}\overset{\displaystyle O}{\overset{\|}{C}}O^-Na^+$$
$$\text{sodium laurate}$$

$$CH_3(CH_2)_7CH=CH(CH_2)_7\overset{\displaystyle O}{\overset{\|}{C}}O^-Na^+$$
$$\text{sodium oleate}$$

43. a.

$$\qquad\quad CH_3$$
$$\qquad\quad |$$
$$H_2N-C-COOH \quad \text{The R group is}$$
$$\qquad\quad | \qquad\qquad\quad \text{methyl: } -CH_3$$
$$\qquad\quad H$$

b.

$$\qquad\quad OH$$
$$\qquad\quad |$$
$$\qquad\quad CH_2$$
$$\qquad\quad |$$
$$H_2N-C-COOH \quad \text{The R group is hydroxyl: } -OH$$
$$\qquad\quad |$$
$$\qquad\quad H$$

c.

$$\qquad\quad CH_2$$
$$\qquad\quad |$$
$$H_2N-C-COOH \quad \text{The R group is phenyl:}$$
$$\qquad\quad |$$
$$\qquad\quad H$$

44. A zwitterion is the internal salt of an amino acid.

$$\qquad\quad H$$
$$\qquad\quad |$$
$$H_3N^+-C-COO^-$$
$$\qquad\quad |$$
$$\qquad\quad H$$

45. Peptide bond.

46. Two.

47. The order in which the amino acids are linked.

48. Ribonucleic acid (RNA) and deoxyribonucleic acid (DNA).

49. The sugar unit in RNA has an additional oxygen on the $-OH$ group attached to the second carbon.

50. A five-carbon sugar, phosphate group, and nitrogen-containing base.

51. A nucleic acid is a polymer of nucleotides.

52. Hydrogen bonding between the nitrogen-containing bases.

53. b, c, and **d.**

Mastery Questions and Problems

54. Addition of water to an alkene, (reduction of aldehydes or ketones, hydrolysis of esters, or substitution reactions.)

55. a.

$$\qquad H \quad\; OH$$
$$\qquad | \qquad |$$
$$H-C-C-H$$
$$\qquad | \qquad |$$
$$\qquad H \quad\; H$$
$$\text{ethanol}$$

b.

$$\qquad\qquad H \quad\; OH$$
$$\qquad\qquad | \qquad |$$
$$CH_3-C-C-CH_3$$
$$\qquad\qquad | \qquad |$$
$$\qquad\qquad H \quad\; H$$
$$\text{2-butanol}$$
$$(\textit{sec}\text{-butanol})$$

c.

$$\qquad\qquad OH$$
$$\qquad\qquad |$$
$$CH_3-C-CH_3$$
$$\qquad\qquad |$$
$$\qquad\qquad H$$
$$\text{2-propanol (isopropyl alcohol)}$$

d.

$$\qquad\qquad\qquad H \quad\; OH$$
$$\qquad\qquad\qquad | \qquad |$$
$$CH_3-CH_2-C-C-CH_2-CH_3$$
$$\qquad\qquad\qquad | \qquad |$$
$$\qquad\qquad\qquad CH_3 \;\; CH_3$$
$$\text{3,4-dimethyl-3-hexanol}$$

56. a. phenol **b.** ether **c.** alcohol **d.** alcohol **e.** phenol

57. b. $CH_3CH_2OH(46)$ has the highest boiling point.

58. a.

$$CH_3\overset{\overset{\displaystyle O}{\|}}{C}CH(CH_3)_2$$

methylisopropyl ketone
(3-methyl-2-butanone)

b.

$$CH_3CH_2\overset{\overset{\displaystyle CH_3}{|}}{CH}\overset{\overset{\displaystyle O}{\|}}{C}-H$$

2-methylbutanal

c.

$$CH_3\overset{\overset{\displaystyle CH_3}{|}}{CH}CH_2-\overset{\overset{\displaystyle O}{\|}}{C}-O^-$$

3-methylbutanoate ion

59. a.

$$CH_3-CH_2-\overset{\overset{\displaystyle Cl}{|}}{\underset{\underset{\displaystyle H}{|}}{C}}-\overset{\overset{\displaystyle Cl}{|}}{\underset{\underset{\displaystyle H}{|}}{C}}-H$$

b.

$$CH_3-CH_2-\overset{\overset{\displaystyle Br}{|}}{\underset{\underset{\displaystyle H}{|}}{C}}-\overset{\overset{\displaystyle Br}{|}}{\underset{\underset{\displaystyle H}{|}}{C}}-H$$

c.

d.

$$CH_3CH_2-\overset{\overset{\displaystyle H}{|}}{\underset{\underset{\displaystyle H}{|}}{C}}-\overset{\overset{\displaystyle H}{|}}{\underset{\underset{\displaystyle CH_3}{|}}{C}}-CH_3$$

60. a.

$$CH_3-\overset{\overset{\displaystyle O}{\|}}{C}-O-CH_3 + H_2O$$

methyl ethanoate   water
(methyl acetate)

b.

$$CH_3-CH_2-CH_2-\overset{\overset{\displaystyle O}{\|}}{C}-O^-Na^+$$

sodium butanoate
(sodium butyrate)

$$+ CH_3-\overset{\overset{\displaystyle H}{|}}{\underset{\underset{\displaystyle H}{|}}{C}}-O-H$$

ethanol

c.

$$CH_3-\overset{\overset{\displaystyle O}{\|}}{C}-H$$ ethanal
(acetaldehyde)

d.

$$CH_3-CH_2-CH_2-\overset{\overset{\displaystyle O}{\|}}{C}-O^-Na^+ + H_2O$$

sodium butanoate   water
(sodium butyrate)

Review Questions and Problems

61. $0.117M$ $Ca(NO_3)_2$

62. 16% K_2SO_4

63. At any given moment, the rate of dissolving of solute is equal to the rate of precipitation of solute. As a result, the concentration of the solution remains constant.

64. b. 3

65. $:\!\overset{..}{\underset{..}{F}}\!: \xrightarrow{e^-} :\!\overset{..}{\underset{..}{F}}\!:^- \qquad H^. + \cdot\overset{..}{\underset{..}{O}}\!: \xrightarrow{e^-} \left(:\!\overset{..}{\underset{..}{O}}\!: \ H\right)^-$

66. 3 g SO_2

67. a. nitric acid **b.** sulfurous acid **c.** nitrous acid **d.** calcium hydroxide **e.** perchloric acid **f.** phosphoric acid

68. a. +7 **b.** +3 **c.** +3 **d.** +3

Challenging Questions and Problems

69. Cholesterol is an alcohol with a hydroxyl group on a cycloalkane. It has four nonaromatic rings. It has a double bond on one of the rings, as well as a large alkyl group, making it nonpolar.

70. $H_2C\!=\!CH_2 \xrightarrow[\text{KMnO}_4]{\text{alkaline}} H-\overset{\overset{\displaystyle H}{|}}{\underset{\underset{\displaystyle OH}{|}}{C}}-\overset{\overset{\displaystyle H}{|}}{\underset{\underset{\displaystyle OH}{|}}{C}}-H$

ethene   ethylene glycol

26 Functional Groups and Organic Reactions

Chapter Preview

The previous chapter introduced hydrocarbon chains and rings. These are essential components of every organic compound. Yet in most chemical reactions involving organic molecules, the hydrocarbon skeletons of the molecules are chemically inert. Thus the chemistry of the alkanes is very limited. Most organic chemistry involves substituents attached to hydrocarbon chains. This chapter discusses some of these substituents and their chemical reactions.

26·1   Functional Groups

The substituents of organic molecules often contain oxygen, nitrogen, sulfur, or phosphorus. They are called functional groups because they are the chemically functional parts of the molecules. *A* **functional group** *is a specific arrangement of atoms in an organic compound that is capable of characteristic chemical reactions.* Most organic chemistry is functional group chemistry. Thus organic chemists classify organic compounds into categories according to their functional groups. The symbol R is used to represent any carbon chains or rings attached to the functional group. The double and triple bonds of alkenes and alkynes are chemically reactive and are considered functional groups. Table 26·1 lists the other functional groups covered in this book. You can refer to this table when you encounter a non-familiar group.

■ A functional group is the chemically reactive part of an organic molecule.

Figure 26·1
Nylon forms at the interface between the two organic liquids in this beaker: a dicarboxylic acid and a diamine.

Table 26·1 Organic Compounds Classified by Functional Group

Compound type	Compound structure	Functional group
Halocarbon	R—X (X = F, Cl, Br, I)	Halogen
Alcohol	R—OH	Hydroxyl
Ether	R—O—R	Ether
Aldehyde	$R—\overset{\displaystyle O}{\overset{\|}{C}}—H$	Carbonyl
Ketone	$R—\overset{\displaystyle O}{\overset{\|}{C}}—R$	Carbonyl
Carboxylic acid	$R—\overset{\displaystyle O}{\overset{\|}{C}}—OH$	Carboxylic acid
Ester	$R—\overset{\displaystyle O}{\overset{\|}{C}}—O—R$	Ester
Amine	$R—NH_2$	Amino

Problem

1. Identify the functional group in each of the following structures.

   a. $CH_3—OH$

   b. $CH_3—CH_2—NH_2$

   c. 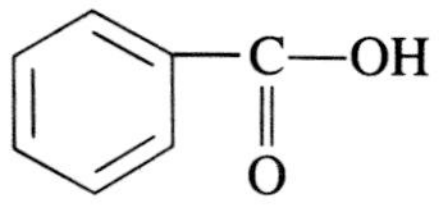 $—C—OH$ ‖ O

   d. $CH_3—CH_2—CH_2—Br$

   e. $CH_3—CH_2—O—CH_2—CH_2—CH_3$

   f. $C_6H_{13}—\overset{}{\underset{\displaystyle O}{\overset{\|}{C}}}—C_3H_7$

26·2 Halocarbons

Halocarbons *are a class of organic compounds containing covalently bonded fluorine, chlorine, bromine, or iodine.* Very few halocarbons are found in nature. Nevertheless they are readily prepared and used for many purposes. For example, they are widely used as anesthetics and insecticides.

The IUPAC rules for naming halocarbons are based on the name of the parent hydrocarbon. The halogen groups are simply added as substituents. Here are some examples of IUPAC names for simple halocarbons. (Common names are in parentheses.)

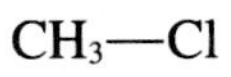

CH₃—Cl

Chloromethane
(methyl chloride)

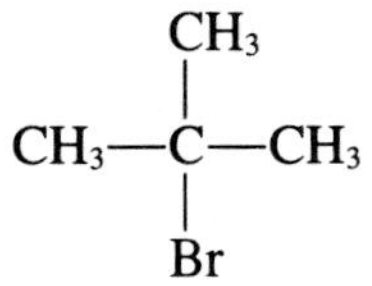

$$CH_3-\underset{\underset{Br}{|}}{\overset{\overset{CH_3}{|}}{C}}-CH_3$$

2-Bromo-2-methylpropane
(*tert*-butyl bromide)

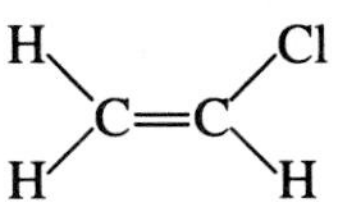

$$\underset{H}{\overset{H}{>}}C=C\underset{H}{\overset{Cl}{<}}$$

Chloroethene
(vinyl chloride)

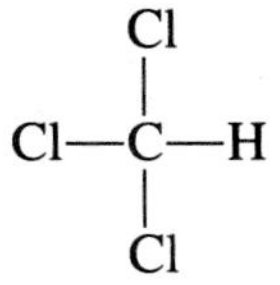

$$\underset{\underset{Cl}{|}}{\overset{\overset{Cl}{|}}{Cl-C}}-H$$

Trichloromethane
(chloroform)

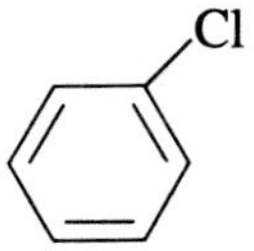

Cl (on benzene ring)

Chlorobenzene
(phenyl chloride)

Common names of halocarbons consist of two parts. The first part names the hydrocarbon part of the molecule as an alkyl group, such as methyl or ethyl. The second part gives the halogen an *-ide* ending. Methyl chloride, CH_3Cl, is an example. Remember, however, that the bonding in a halocarbon is covalent, not ionic.

On the basis of their common names, *halocarbons in which a halo-gen is attached to a carbon of an aliphatic chain are called* **alkyl halides.** Table 26·2 gives names for alkyl groups besides those of methyl, ethyl, and propyl. *Halocarbons in which a halogen is attached to a carbon of an arene ring are called* **aryl halides.**

Table 26·2   Names of Some Common Alkyl Groups

Name	Alkyl group	Remarks
Isopropyl	$CH_3-\underset{\underset{H}{|}}{\overset{\overset{CH_3}{|}}{C}}-$	The prefix *iso*- is reserved for carbon chains that are continuous except for the presence of a methyl group on the carbon second from the unsubstituted end of the longest chain.
Isobutyl	$CH_3-\underset{}{\overset{\overset{CH_3}{|}}{CH}}-CH_2-$ (primary carbon)	Note the use of the prefix *iso*-. The carbon joining this alkyl group to another group is bonded to one other carbon; it is a *primary carbon*.
Secondary butyl (*sec*-butyl)	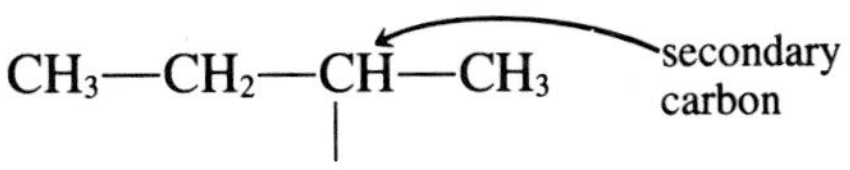 $CH_3-CH_2-\underset{}{\overset{}{CH}}-CH_3$ (secondary carbon)	The carbon joining this alkyl group to another group is bonded to two other carbons; it is a *secondary carbon*.
Tertiary butyl (*tert*-butyl)	$CH_3-\underset{\underset{CH_3}{|}}{\overset{\overset{CH_3}{|}}{C}}-$ (tertiary carbon)	The carbon joining this alkyl group to another group is bonded to three carbons; it is a *tertiary carbon*.
Vinyl	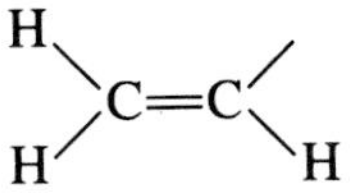 $\underset{H}{\overset{H}{>}}C=C\underset{H}{\overset{}{<}}$	When used as an alkyl group in giving compounds common names, this group, derived from ethene, is called *vinyl*.
Phenyl	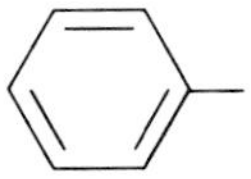 (benzene ring)	This group is derived from benzene.

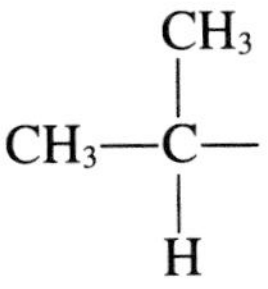

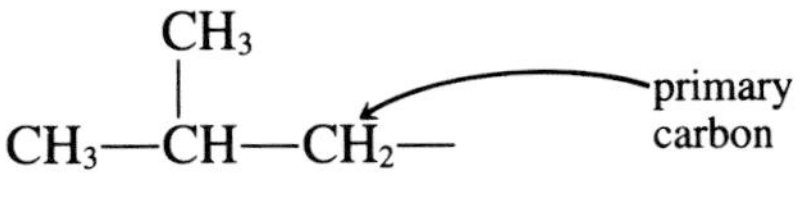

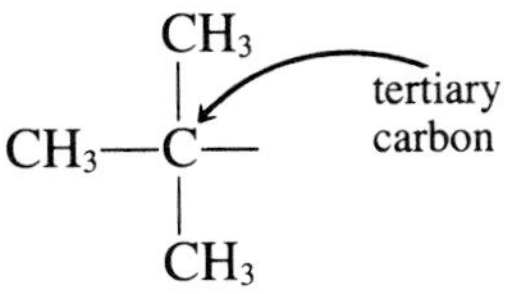

Table 26·3   Some Halocarbons and Their Uses

Halocarbon	Use
CH_3-CH_2-Cl Chloroethane (ethyl chloride)	A local anesthetic. Its rapid evaporation on the skin (bp 13°C) cools nerve endings and cuts down transmission of pain.
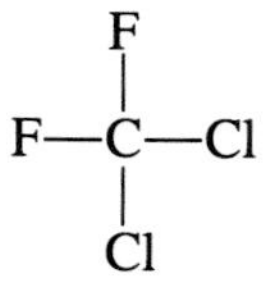 Dichlorodifluoromethane (Freon 12) and 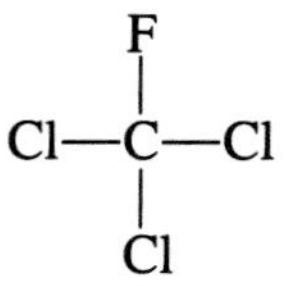 Fluorotrichloromethane (Freon 11)	Freon is the Dupont trade name for fluorinated compounds of this type. They are used as refrigerants. Freons are nontoxic, odorless, and nonflammable. Some are also used in specialized fire extinguishers.
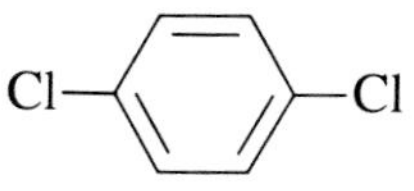 p-Dichlorobenzene	Used as a moth repellent.
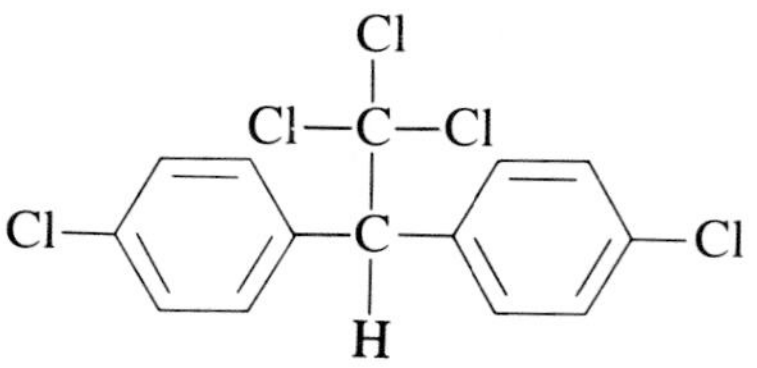 Dichlorodiphenyltrichloroethane (DDT)	A persistent pesticide. DDT was widely used as an insecticide from about 1950 to 1970. Its use is now limited because of its persistence in the environment. It is nonbiodegradable.

Table 26·3 gives the structures and uses of some halocarbons. The attractions between halocarbon molecules are primarily the result of the weak van der Waals interactions called dispersion forces. These attractions increase with the degree of halogen substitution. More highly halogenated organic compounds therefore have higher boiling points, as shown for the chloromethanes in Table 26·4.

Problems

2. Write IUPAC and common names for each of these halocarbons.

a. 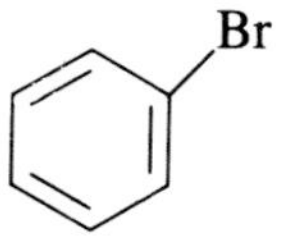 (bromobenzene structure) Br   **b.** CH_3CH_2Cl **c.** 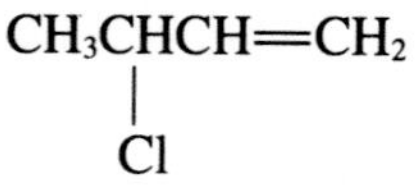 $CH_3CHCH{=}CH_2$ with Cl

3. Give the structural formula for each of the following compounds.
a. isopropyl chloride   **b.** 1-iodo-2,2-dimethylpentane
c. *p*-bromotoluene

2. a. bromobenzene
b. chloroethane
c. 3-chloro-1-butene

3. a. 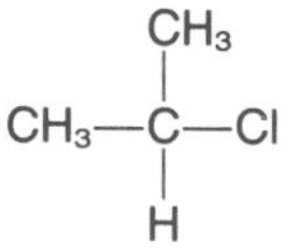 $CH_3-\overset{CH_3}{\underset{H}{C}}-Cl$ **c.** (p-bromotoluene structure with CH₃ and Br)

b. $ICH_2\overset{CH_3}{\underset{CH_3}{C}}CH_2CH_2CH_3$

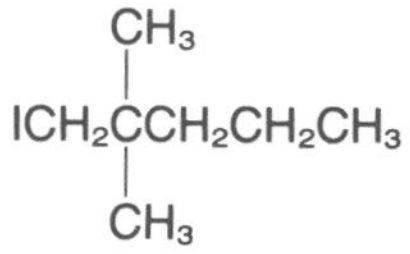

Table 26·4	Molecular Masses and Boiling Points of the Chloromethanes		
Molecular structure	Name	Formula mass	Boiling point(°C)
CH_4^*	Methane	16	−161
CH_3Cl	Chloromethane (methyl chloride)	50.5	−24
CH_2Cl_2	Dichloromethane (methylene chloride)	85.0	40
$CHCl_3$	Trichloromethane (chloroform)	129.5	61
CCl_4	Tetrachloromethane (carbon tetrachloride)	154	74

*Included for purposes of comparison.

26·3 Substitution Reactions

Organic substitution reactions involve the replacement of hydrogen or a functional group by another functional group.

The most common substitution reaction is the replacement of a hydrogen atom by a functional group.

Organic reactions often proceed more slowly than the reactions of inorganic molecules and ions. This is because reactions of organic molecules commonly involve the breaking of relatively strong covalent bonds. Chemists are therefore constantly seeking new catalysts and improved procedures for conducting organic reactions. Many organic reactions are complex. They often produce a mixture of products. The desired product must then be separated by distillation, crystallization, or other means. A common type of organic reaction is **substitution,** *the replacement of an atom or group of atoms by another atom or group of atoms.*

A halogen can replace the hydrogen on an alkane to produce a halocarbon. The symbol X stands for a halogen in this generalized equation.

$$R\!-\!H \quad + \quad X_2 \quad \longrightarrow \quad R\!-\!X \quad + \quad HX$$

Alkane   Halogen   Halocarbon   Hydrogen halide

Figure 26·2
Some halocarbons are used as pesticides. Short lived pesticides break down within about a week. They are preferred over pesticides which break down slowly.

Sunlight or another source of ultraviolet radiation is usually a sufficient catalyst for this reaction. From the generalized equation, a specific one can be written.

$$CH_4 + Cl_2 \longrightarrow CH_3Cl + HCl$$

Methane   Chlorine   Chloromethane   Hydrogen chloride

Even under controlled conditions, this simple halogenation reaction produces a mixture of the mono-, di-, tri-, and tetrachloromethanes.

If benzene is treated with a halogen in the presence of a catalyst, substitution of a ring hydrogen occurs. Iron compounds are often used as catalysts for aromatic substitution reactions. A rusty nail dropped in the reaction flask works fine.

Benzene   Bromine   Bromobenzene   Hydrogen
                 (phenyl bromide)   bromide

Halogens on carbon chains are readily displaced by hydroxide ions to produce an alcohol and a salt. The general reaction is as follows.

$$R\text{—}X + OH^- \xrightarrow[100°C]{H_2O} R\text{—}OH + X^-$$

Halocarbon   Hydroxide   Alcohol   Halide
          ion   ion

Chemists usually use aqueous solutions of sodium or potassium hydroxide as the source of hydroxide ions. Fluoro groups are not easily diplaced. Hence fluorocarbons are seldom, if ever, used to make alcohols. Here are two specific examples.

$$CH_3\text{—}I + KOH \xrightarrow[100°C]{H_2O} CH_3\text{—}OH + KI$$

Iodomethane   Potassium   Methanol   Potassium
(methyl iodide)   hydroxide   iodide

$$CH_3CH_2Br + NaOH \xrightarrow[100°C]{H_2O} CH_3CH_2OH + NaBr$$

Bromoethane   Sodium   Ethanol   Sodium
(ethyl bromide)   hydroxide   bromide

26·4 Alcohols

Alcohols are organic compounds in which a hydrogen in H_2O has been replaced by an R group.

Alcohols *are organic compounds with an —OH group.*

Alcohol molecule

The oxygen atom is held so tightly to the carbon atom, and the hydrogen atom is held so strongly to the oxygen atom, that an alcohol does not display acidic or basic properties even though an —OH group is present.

The —OH functional group in alcohols is called a **hydroxyl group** *or* hydroxy function. It is not a hydroxide ion because the oxygen is covalently bonded to carbon. Chemists often arrange aliphatic alcohols into structural categories according to the number of R groups attached to the carbon with the hydroxyl group.

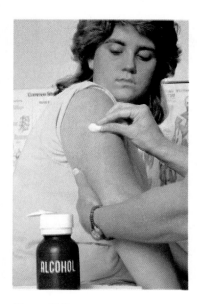

Figure 26·3
Isopropyl alcohol is an effective disinfectant.

| Primary alcohol | R—CH$_2$—OH | Only one R group is attached to C—OH of a primary (abbreviated 1°) alcohol. |

$$\text{Secondary alcohol} \quad R\!-\!\overset{\displaystyle R}{\underset{|}{C}}\!H\!-\!OH$$

Two R Groups are attached to C—OH of a secondary (2°) alcohol.

$$\text{Tertiary alcohol} \quad R\!-\!\overset{\displaystyle R}{\underset{\underset{\displaystyle R}{|}}{\overset{|}{C}}}\!-\!OH$$

Three R groups are attached to C—OH of a tertiary (3°) alcohol.

Both IUPAC and common names are used for alcohols. To name continuous-chain and substituted alcohols by the IUPAC system, drop the *-e* ending of the parent alkane name and add the ending *-ol*. The parent alkane is the longest continuous chain of carbons that includes the carbon attached to the hydroxyl group. In numbering the longest continuous chain, the position of the hydroxyl group is given the lowest possible number. Alcohols containing two, three, and four —OH substituents are named diols, triols, and tetrols.

Common names of aliphatic alcohols are written in the same way as those for the halocarbons. The alkyl group methyl, for example, is named and followed by the word alcohol, as in methyl alcohol. Compounds with more than one —OH substituent are called glycols. Here are some simple aliphatic alcohols along with their IUPAC and common names.

The common names of some diols have an *-ene* ending but the molecules contain no double bond.

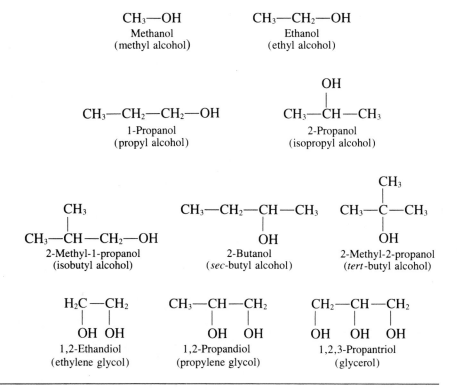

Cresols have the odor of
creosote.

Phenols are compounds in which a hydroxyl group is attached directly to an aromatic ring. Phenol is the parent compound. Cresol is the common name for the *o, m,* and *p* structural isomers of methylphenol.

OH	OH CH_3	OH CH_3	OH CH_3
Phenol	2-Methylphenol (*o*-cresol)	3-Methylphenol (*m*-cresol)	4-Methylphenol (*p*-cresol)

Problems

4. Give the following alcohols IUPAC names.

a. $CH_3CH_2CH_2CH_2OH$ **b.** $CH_3\overset{\underset{\displaystyle |}{CH_3}}{C}HOH$ **c.** $CH_3CH_2\overset{\underset{\displaystyle |}{CH_3}}{C}HCH_2OH$

5. Classify each of the alcohols in Problem 4 as primary, secondary, or tertiary.

4. a. butanol
   b. 2-propanol
   c. 2-methyl-1-butanol
5. a. primary
   b. secondary
   c. primary

26·5 Properties of Alcohols

The relatively high boiling points and high water solubility of alcohols are the result of intermolecular hydrogen bonding.

Like water, alcohols are capable of intermolecular hydrogen-bonding. Alcohols therefore boil at a higher temperature than alkanes and halocarbons containing comparable numbers of atoms.

Since alcohols are derivatives of water, you might expect them to be soluble in water. To a point that is correct. Alcohols of up to four carbons are soluble in water in all proportions. The solubility of alcohols with four or more carbons in the chain is usually much less. The reason is that alcohols consist of two parts: the carbon chain and the hydroxyl

Figure 26·4
The main ingredient in many antifreezes is 1,2-ethandiol (common name, ethylene glycol). It has a higher boiling point and lower freezing point than water.

group. These parts are in opposition to each other. The carbon chain is nonpolar and is not attracted to water. The polar hydroxyl group, however, strongly interacts with water through hydrogen-bonding.

Many aliphatic alcohols are used in laboratories, clinics, and industry. Isopropyl alcohol, a colorless, nearly odorless liquid (bp 82°C), is called rubbing alcohol. It is used for massages and as a base for perfumes, creams, lotions, and other cosmetics. Ethylene glycol (bp 197°C) is the principal ingredient of certain antifreezes. Its advantages over other high-boiling liquids are its solubility in water and a freezing point of −17.4°C. If water is added to ethylene glycol, the mixture freezes at an even lower temperature. A 50% (v/v) aqueous solution of ethylene glycol freezes at −36°C. Glycerol is a viscous, sweet-tasting, water-soluble liquid. It is used as a moistening agent in cosmetics, foods, and drugs. Glycerol is also an important component of fats and oils.

Ethyl alcohol, which has a boiling point of 78.5°C, is also called grain alcohol. It is an important industrial chemical. Some ethyl alcohol is still produced by yeast fermentation of sugar. **Fermentation** *is the production of ethanol from sugars by the action of yeast or bacteria.* The enzymes of the yeast or bacteria serve as catalysts for the transformation. The breakdown of the sugar glucose, $C_6H_{12}O_6$, is an important fermentation reaction.

$$C_6H_{12}O_6 \longrightarrow 2CH_3CH_2OH + 2CO_2$$

Glucose   Ethanol   Carbon
(Ethyl alcohol)   Dioxide

The primary source of industrial ethanol is the reaction of ethylene (a by-product of the cracking of crude oil) with water, at 200 atm. and 300°C.

Ethyl alcohol is the intoxicating substance in alcoholic beverages. It damages the liver and causes behavior changes.

In order to protect its revenues, the government demands that ethyl alcohol for industrial use be denatured. **Denatured alcohol** *is ethanol with an added substance to make it toxic.* Methyl alcohol is often the denaturant. It is sometimes called wood alcohol because before 1925 it was prepared by the distillation of wood. Wood alcohol is extremely toxic. As little as 10 mL has been reported to cause permanent blindness and as little as 30 mL, death.

Figure 26·5
Ethanol is prepared commercially by the hydration of ethene or by the fermentation of sugars.

Figure 26·6
Julian's work with soybeans provided many useful substances, including hormones. His discovery of an inexpensive way to produce cortisone, a hormone used in treating rheumatoid arthritis, made this drug available to many people.

26·A   Percy Julian and Natural Product Chemistry

Percy Julian was an important contributor to natural products chemistry. Natural products are organic substances derived from plants and animals. They are processed and used in substances such as flavors, fragrances, resins, and pharmaceuticals. Julian, an industrial research chemist, was granted over 100 patents, many of them for substances he extracted from soybeans.

Perhaps Julian's most important contribution was the inexpensive method he developed for isolating sterols from soybeans. Sterols are unsaturated cyclic alcohols. Cortisone, a sterol derivative, is used by arthritis sufferers. As a result of Julian's research, cortisone became more widely available.

In 1935, Julian synthesized physostigmine, a drug used to treat glaucoma. A fire-fighting solution Julian developed from a soybean protein is credited with saving many lives during World War II. Julian also synthesized the hormones progesterone and testosterone. He did research on amino acids, indoles, and anti-fatigue drugs. In 1947, he was awarded the NAACP Spingarn Award, for outstanding achievement by a Black American.

26·6   Addition Reactions

Carbon–carbon single bonds are not easy to break. One of the bonds in an alkene double bond is somewhat weaker, however, than a carbon–carbon single bond. Thus, it is sometimes possible for a compound of general structure X–Y to add to a double bond. *In an* **addition reaction** *a substance is added at the double or triple bond of an alkene or alkyne.* Addition reactions are an important method of introducing new functional groups into organic molecules. In this general reaction, X and Y stand for the two parts of the compound which are added.

▧ Addition reactions are the most important method of introducing a functional group into a hydrocarbon.

The breaking of a double bond opens two *sites where addition occurs.*

$$\diagdown \!\!\!\! \diagup \!\! C \!=\! C \!\! \diagup \!\!\!\! \diagdown \;+\; X\!-\!Y \longrightarrow \; -\underset{\displaystyle |}{\overset{\displaystyle \overset{X}{|}}{C}}-\underset{\displaystyle |}{\overset{\displaystyle \overset{Y}{|}}{C}}-$$

The addition of water to an alkene is a **hydration reaction.** Hydration reactions usually occur when the alkene and water are heated to about 100°C in the presence of a trace of strong acid. The acid serves as a catalyst for the reaction. Hydrochloric or sulfuric acid is generally used. The addition of water to ethene is a typical hydration reaction.

$$\underset{\text{Ethene}}{\overset{H}{\underset{H}{\diagdown}}\!\!C\!=\!C\!\!\overset{H}{\underset{H}{\diagup}}} \;+\; \underset{\text{Water}}{H\!-\!OH} \xrightarrow{H^+} \underset{\text{Ethanol}}{H\!-\!\overset{\overset{H}{|}}{\underset{\underset{H}{|}}{C}}\!-\!\overset{\overset{OH}{|}}{\underset{\underset{H}{|}}{C}}\!-\!H}$$

When the reagent X–Y is a halogen molecule like chlorine or bromine, the product of the reaction is a disubstituted halocarbon.

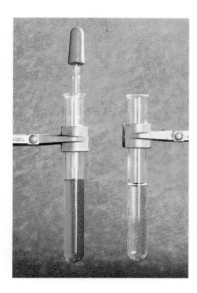

Figure 26·7
When a few drops of bromine solution (test tube on left) are added to an unsaturated organic compound, the bromine becomes colorless (right). This forms the basis of a test for unsaturated compounds.

Ethene
(colorless)

Bromine
(brownish
orange)

1,2-Dibromoethane
(colorless)

The addition of bromine to carbon–carbon multiple bonds is often used as as a chemical test for unsaturation in an organic molecule. Bromine has a brownish-orange color, but most organic compounds of bromine are colorless. The test for unsaturation is done by adding a few drops of a 1% solution of bromine in carbon tetrachloride (CCl_4) to the suspected alkene. Loss of the orange color is a positive test for unsaturation.

Hydrogen halides such as HBr or HCl can also add to a double bond. The product contains only one substituent. It is called a monosubstituted halocarbon. The addition of hydrogen chloride to ethene is an example.

Ethene
(ethylene)

Hydrogen
chloride

Chloroethane
(ethyl chloride)

In a **hydrogenation reaction,** *hydrogen is added to a carbon–carbon double bond to give an alkane.* A hydrogenation reaction usually requires a catalyst. Finely divided platinum (Pt) or palladium (Pd) is often used. Such a process is used to hydrogenate unsaturated oils to make margarine.

Ethene

Hydrogen

Ethane

Cyclohexene

Hydrogen

Cyclohexane

The hydrogenation of a double bond is a reduction reaction. Ethene is reduced to ethane, for example, and cyclohexene is reduced to cyclohexane.

Benzene resists hydrogenation. It also resists the addition of a halogen or a hydrogen halide. At high temperatures and high pressures of hydrogen, however, three molecules of hydrogen reduce one molecule of benzene to cyclohexane.

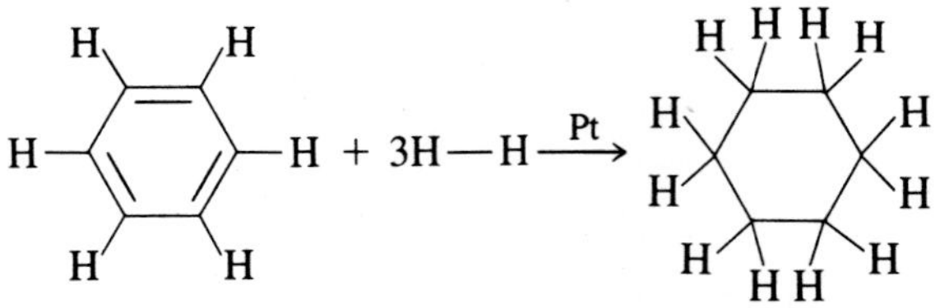

Benzene   Hydrogen   Cyclohexane

6. a. 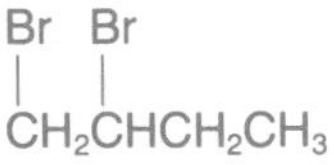 CH$_2$CHCH$_2$CH$_3$ (with Br Br above the first two carbons)

b.  CH$_3$CHCHCH$_3$

c.  CH$_3$CHCHCH$_3$ (with H H above)

d.

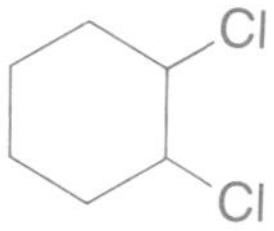

7. a. 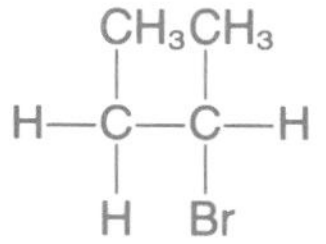 H—C—C—H (with CH$_3$ CH$_3$ above and H Br below)

b.

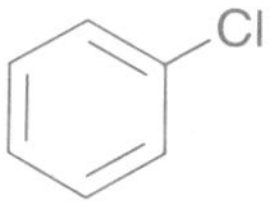

c.

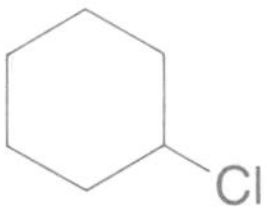

Problems

6. Write the structure for the expected product from each reaction.

    a. CH$_2$=CHCH$_2$CH$_3$ + Br$_2$ $\longrightarrow$

    d. + Cl$_2$ $\longrightarrow$

    b. CH$_3$CH=CHCH$_3$ + I$_2$ $\longrightarrow$

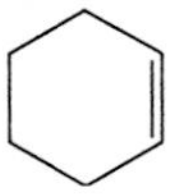

    c. CH$_3$CH=CHCH$_3$ + H$_2$ $\xrightarrow{Pt}$

7. Give the structure for the expected organic product from each of these reactions.

    a. 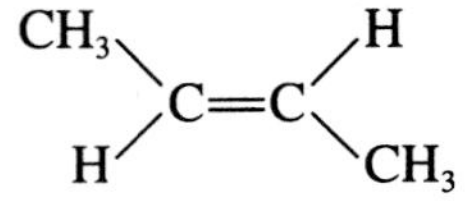 + HBr $\longrightarrow$

    b.  + Cl$_2$ $\xrightarrow{\text{catalyst}}$

    c. 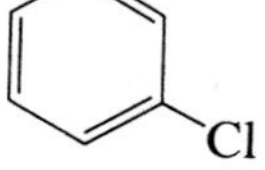 + 3H$_2$ $\xrightarrow{\text{catalyst}}$

26·7 Ethers

Ethers *are compounds in which oxygen is bonded to two carbon groups:* R—O—R. Ethers are easy to name. The alkyl groups attached to the ether linkage are named in alphabetical order and are followed by the word *ether*.

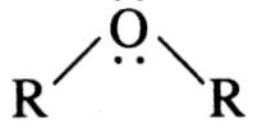

Ether molecule   CH$_3$CH$_2$—O—CH$_3$
                     Ethylmethyl ether

Ethylmethyl ether and methylphenyl ether are nonsymmetric. The R groups attached to the ether oxygen are different. When both R groups are the same, the ether is symmetric. Symmetric ethers are named by using the prefix *di-*. Sometimes, however, the prefix *di-* is dropped and a compound such as diethyl ether is simply called ethyl ether.

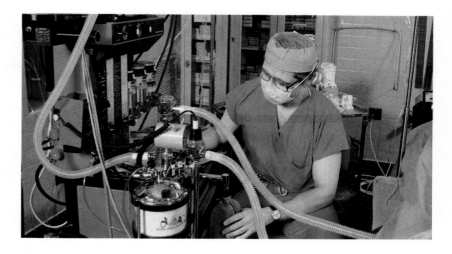

The structural formulas of ether molecules are usually written in linear fashion. However, because the central atom in an ether molecule is an oxygen atom, ether molecules are bent to form an angle that is nearly 105°.

Safety

Diethyl ether is highly flammable, and when old it may contain explosive peroxides. It is not recommended for use in schools.

$$CH_3CH_2—O—CH_2CH_3 \qquad CH_3—O—\langle \rangle \qquad \langle \rangle—O—\langle \rangle$$

Diethyl ether   Methylphenyl ether   Diphenyl ether
(ethyl ether)   (anisole)   (phenyl ether)

Diethyl ether, a volatile liquid (bp 35°C), was the first reliable general anesthetic. Originally reported in 1842 by Crawford W. Long, an American physician, diethyl ether was used by doctors for over a century. It has been replaced by other anesthetics because it is highly flammable and often causes nausea.

Ethers are usually lower-boiling than alcohols of comparable formula mass. They are higher-boiling than comparable hydrocarbons and halocarbons. Ethers are more soluble than hydrocarbons and halocarbons but less soluble than alcohols. The reason is that the oxygens in ethers are hydrogen acceptors, but ethers have no hydroxyl hydrogens to donate in hydrogen-bonding.

26·8   Aldehydes and Ketones

A double-bonded oxygen atom has a high electronegativity, and thus electrons are displaced toward it.

A carbonyl group *consists of a carbon atom and an oxygen atom joined by a double bond.* It is found in two groups of compounds called aldehydes and ketones.

Aldehydes *are organic compounds in which the carbon of the carbonyl group is always joined to at least one hydrogen.* The general formula for an aldehyde is RCHO.

Ketones *are organic compounds in which the carbon of the carbonyl group is joined to two other carbons.* The abbreviated form for a ketone is RCOR.

■ Because their carbonyl functional groups are identical, aldehydes and ketones have similar chemical and physical properties.

$$\begin{array}{cc} O & O \\ \parallel \leftarrow \text{Carbonyl group} & \parallel \leftarrow \text{Carbonyl group} \\ R—C—H & R—C—R \\ \text{Aldehyde} & \text{Ketone} \end{array}$$

The IUPAC system may be used for naming aldehydes and ketones. For either class, the longest hydrocarbon chain that contains the carbonyl group must first be identified. The *-e* ending of the hydrocarbon is replaced by *-al* to designate an aldehyde. In the IUPAC system, the continuous-chain aldehydes are named methanal, ethanal, propanal, butanal, and so forth.

Ketones are named by changing the ending of the longest continuous carbon chain that contains the carbonyl group from *-e* to *-one*. Table 26·5 demonstrates this. If the carbonyl group could occur at several places on the chain, then its position is designated by the lowest possible number.

Problem

8. a. propanal
   b. 3-hexanone
   c. 3-methylpentanal
   d. butanone

8. Give the IUPAC name for each of the following aldehydes and ketones.

a. CH_3CH_2CHO

c. $CH_3CH_2\overset{\overset{\displaystyle CH_3}{|}}{C}HCH_2CHO$

b. $CH_3CH_2CH_2\overset{\overset{\displaystyle O}{\|}}{C}CH_2CH_2$

d. $CH_3\overset{\overset{\displaystyle O}{\|}}{C}CH_2CH_3$

Aldehydes and ketones can form weak hydrogen bonds between the carbonyl oxygen and the hydrogens of water. The lower members of the series (formaldehyde, acetaldehyde, and acetone) are soluble in water in all proportions. As the length of the hydrocarbon chain increases, water solubility decreases. When the carbon chain exceeds five or six carbons, solubility of both aldehydes and ketones is very low. As might be expected, all aldehydes and ketones are soluble in nonpolar solvents.

Aldehydes and ketones cannot form intermolecular hydrogen bonds because they lack hydroxyl (—OH) groups. Consequently, they have boiling points lower than those of the corresponding alcohols. The aldehydes and ketones can attract one another, however, through polar-polar interactions of their carbonyl groups. Consequently, their boiling points are higher than those of the corresponding alkanes. These attractive forces account for the fact that nearly all aldehydes and ketones are either liquids or solids at room temperature. The exception is formaldehyde, which is an irritating pungent gas. Table 26·6 compares the boiling points of alkanes, aldehydes, and alcohols of similar formula mass.

A wide variety of aldehydes and ketones have been isolated from plants and animals. Many of them, particularly those with high formula masses, have fragrant or penetrating odors. They are usually known by their common names, which indicate their natural sources or perhaps a characteristic property. Aromatic aldehydes are often used as flavoring agents. Benzaldehyde is the simplest aromatic aldehyde. Also known as "oil of bitter almond," benzaldehyde is a constituent of the almond. It is a colorless liquid with a pleasant almond odor. Cinnamaldehyde imparts

Figure 26·9
The seeds from this orchid are the source of natural vanilla flavor for ice cream and many other foods. Vanillin is also produced synthetically.

Table 26·5 Some Common Aldehydes and Ketones

Condensed formula	Structural formula	IUPAC name	Common name
Aldehydes			
HCHO	H—C—H with O double bond	Methanal	Formaldehyde
CH_3CHO	CH_3—C—H with O double bond	Ethanal	Acetaldehyde
C_6H_5CHO	(benzene ring)—C—H with O double bond	Benzaldehyde	Benzaldehyde
$C_6H_5CH{=}CHCHO$	(benzene ring)—CH=CH—C—H with O double bond	3-Phenyl-2-propenal	Cinnamaldehyde
$CH_3O(OH)C_6H_3CHO$	(benzene ring) with C=O, HO, OCH_3	2-hydroxy-3-methoxybenzaldehyde	Vanillin
Ketones			
CH_3COCH_3	CH_3—C—CH_3 with O double bond	Propanone	Acetone (dimethyl ketone)
$C_6H_5COC_6H_5$	(two benzene rings)—C— with O double bond	Diphenylmethanone	Benzophenone (diphenyl ketone)

Table 26·6 Boiling Points of Some Compounds with One and Two Carbons

Compound	Formula	Formula Mass	Boiling Point (°C)	Comments
One carbon				
Methane	CH_4	16	−161	No hydrogen-bonding or polar-polar interactions
Formaldehyde	HCHO	26	−21	Polar-polar interactions
Methanol	CH_3OH	32	65	Hydrogen-bonding
Two carbons				
Ethane	C_2H_6	30	−89	No hydrogen-bonding or polar-polar interactions
Acetaldehyde	CH_3CHO	44	20	Polar-polar interactions
Ethanol	CH_3CH_2OH	46	78	Hydrogen-bonding

the characteristic odor of oil of cinnamon. Vanillin, which is responsible for the popular vanilla flavor, was at one time obtainable only from the podlike capsules of certain climbing orchids. Today much vanillin is synthetically produced.

The simplest aldehyde, formaldehyde, is very important industrially but inconvenient to handle in the gaseous state. Formaldehyde is usually available as a 40% aqueous solution, known as formalin. Formalin is used to preserve biological specimens. The formaldehyde in solution combines with protein in tissues to make them hard and insoluble in water. This process prevents the specimen from decaying. The greatest use of formaldehyde is in the manufacture of synthetic resins.

The most important industrial ketone is acetone. It is a colorless volatile liquid that boils at 56°C. It is used as a solvent for resins, plastics, and varnishes, and is often found in nail polish removers. Moreover, it is miscible with water in all proportions.

26·9 Carboxylic Acids

A **carboxyl group** *consists of a carbonyl group attached to a hydroxyl group.*

Carbonyl group
Hydroxyl group
Carboxyl group
(also written —CO$_2$H or —COOH)

Carboxylic acids *are compounds with a carboxyl group.* The general formula of a carboxylic acid is RCOOH. Carboxylic acids are weak acids because they ionize slightly in solution to give a carboxylate ion and a proton.

Carboxylate ion   Proton

In the IUPAC system for naming carboxylic acids, the *-e* ending of the parent alkane is replaced by the ending *-oic acid.* The parent alkane is the hydrocarbon with the longest continous carbon chain containing the carboxyl group. Table 26·7 lists the names and formulas of some common aliphatic carboxylic acids.

Carboxylic acids are abundant and widely distributed in nature. Many have common names derived from a Greek or Latin word describing their natural sources. For example, the common name for ethanoic acid is acetic acid. Acetic acid is produced when wine turns sour and becomes vinegar. The pungent aroma of vinegar comes from its acetic acid. *Many continuous-chain carboxylic acids were first isolated from fats and are called* **fatty acids.** Propionic acid, the three-carbon acid, literally means "first fatty acid". Common names are used more often than IUPAC names for carboxylic acids.

■ The presence of the carboxyl group in an organic compound makes it behave as a weak acid.

Because of the presence of the double-bonded oxygen atom, the bond between the oxygen atom and the hydrogen atom in the —OH group is weakened. The hydrogen atom can be dislodged, and the substance can behave as an acid.

Latin: *acetum* = vinegar

Greek: *protos* = first
pion = fat

Figure 26·10
These candles are being hand-dipped to give them a final coating of colored wax. Standard commercial candles are a mixture of 60% paraffin, 35% stearic acid, and 5% beeswax.

Latin: *butyrum* = butter

Greek: *stear* = tallow

Latin: *formica* = ant

The low-formula-mass members of the aliphatic carboxylic acid series are colorless, volatile liquids. They have sharp, unpleasant odors. The smells of rancid butter and dirty feet are due in part to butyric acid. The higher members of the series are nonvolatile, low-melting, waxy solids. Stearic acid (C–18) is obtained from beef fat. It is used to make cheap wax candles. Stearic acid and other long-chain fatty acids have very little odor.

Like alcohols, carboxylic acids can form intermolecular hydrogen bonds. Because of this, carboxylic acids are higher boiling and higher melting than other compounds of similar formula mass. All aromatic carboxylic acids are crystalline solids at room temperature.

The carboxyl group in carboxylic acids is polar, and it readily forms hydrogen-bonds with water molecules. Formic, acetic, propionic, and butyric acids are completely miscible with water. The solubility of carboxylic acids of higher formula mass drops off sharply. Most carboxylic acids dissolve in organic solvents like ethanol or acetone.

Table 26·7 Saturated Aliphatic Carboxylic Acids

Formula	Carbon atoms	IUPAC name	Common name	Melting point (°C)
$HCOOH$	1	Methanoic acid	Formic acid	8
CH_3COOH	2	Ethanoic acid	Acetic acid	17
CH_3CH_2COOH	3	Propanoic acid	Propionic acid	−22
$CH_3(CH_2)_2COOH$	4	Butanoic acid	Butyric acid	−6
$CH_3(CH_2)_4COOH$	6	Hexanoic acid	Caproic acid	−3
$CH_3(CH_2)_6COOH$	8	Octanoic acid	Caprylic acid	16
$CH_3(CH_2)_8COOH$	10	Decanoic acid	Capric acid	31
$CH_3(CH_2)_{10}COOH$	12	Dodecanoic acid	Lauric acid	44
$CH_3(CH_2)_{12}COOH$	14	Tetradecanoic acid	Myristic acid	58
$CH_3(CH_2)_{14}COOH$	16	Hexadecanoic acid	Palmitic acid	63
$CH_3(CH_2)_{16}COOH$	18	Octadecanoic acid	Stearic acid	70

26·10   Oxidation–Reduction Reactions

Remember that oxidation is the gain of oxygen, loss of hydrogen, or loss of electrons. Reduction is just the reverse: loss of oxygen, gain of hydrogen, or gain of electrons. Oxidation and reduction reactions are coupled. One does not occur without the other.

In organic chemistry, the number of oxygens and hydrogens attached to carbon indicates the degree of oxidation of a compound. The fewer the number of hydrogens on a carbon-carbon bond, the more oxidized the bond. For example, ethane (an alkane) can be oxidized to ethene (an alkene) and then to ethyne (an alkyne). *The loss of hydrogen is a* **dehydrogenation reaction.** Strong heating and a catalyst are usually necessary to make dehydrogenation reactions occur. The loss of each molecule of hydrogen involves the loss of two electrons.

■ Many organic oxidation–reduction reactions involve a change in the degree of unsaturation of a carbon–carbon bond or the oxidation state of an oxygen-containing functional group.

Increasing oxidation: alkane, alkene, alkyne.

These reactions can be reversed. Alkynes can be reduced to alkenes, and alkenes can be reduced to alkanes by the addition of hydrogen to a double bond.

Oxidation in organic chemistry also involves the number and degree of oxidation of the oxygens attached to carbon. For example, methane, a saturated hydrocarbon, may be oxidized in steps to carbon dioxide. This occurs if it alternately gains oxygens and loses hydrogens. Methane is oxidized to methanol, then to formaldehyde, then to formic acid, and finally to carbon dioxide. The same sequence of oxidations occurs for other alkanes. Each series of compounds consists of an alkane, alcohol, aldehyde (or ketone), carboxylic acid, and carbon dioxide. The carbon dioxide is most oxidized or least reduced, and the alkane is least oxidized or most reduced.

Oxidation reactions are energy-releasing. *The more reduced a carbon compound, the more energy it can release upon its complete oxidation to carbon dioxide.* The energy-releasing properties of oxidation

reactions are extremely important for energy production in living systems. This is also why the combustion of hydrocarbons such as methane is a good source of energy.

Primary alcohols can be oxidized to aldehydes and secondary alcohols can be oxidized to ketones.

Increasing oxidation: alcohol, aldehyde or ketone, carboxylic acid.

Primary alcohol   Aldehyde   Secondary alcohol   Ketone

Tertiary alcohols cannot be oxidized because no hydrogen is present on the carbon bearing the hydroxyl group.

The primary alcohols methanol and ethanol can be oxidized to aldehydes by warming them at about 50°C with acidified potassium dichromate ($K_2Cr_2O_7$). In these reactions, methanol produces formaldehyde and ethanol produces acetaldehyde.

Methanol   Methanal   Ethanol   Ethanal
(methyl alcohol)   (formaldehyde)   (ethyl alcohol)   (acetaldehyde)
(bp 65°C)   (bp −21°C)   (bp 78°C)   (bp 21°C)

The preparation of an aldehyde by this method is often a problem because aldehydes are easily oxidized to carboxylic acids.

Aldehyde   Carboxylic acid

Further oxidation is not a problem, however, with aldehydes that have low boiling points, such as acetaldehyde. This is because the product can be distilled from the reaction mixture as it is formed.

Oxidation of the secondary alcohol 2-propanol by warming it with acidified potassium dichromate produces acetone.

2-Propanol   Propanone
(isopropyl alcohol)   (acetone)

Ketones are resistant to further oxidation. There is no need to remove them from the reaction mixture during the course of the reaction.

9. a. $CH_3CH_2CH_2COOH$

b. no reaction

c. $CH_2CH_2\overset{\overset{O}{\|}}{C}CH_3$

d. 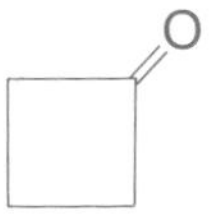

10. a. propanol, $CH_3CH_2CH_2OH$

b. 2-butanol, $CH_3CH_2\overset{\overset{OH}{|}}{C}HCH_3$

c. 2-methyl-1-butanol,
$CH_3CH_2\overset{\overset{CH_3}{|}}{C}HCH_2OH$

Problems

9. What products are expected when these compounds are oxidized?

a. $CH_3CH_2CH_2CH_2OH$

b. $CH_3CH_2\overset{\overset{OH}{|}}{\underset{\underset{CH_3}{|}}{C}}CH_3$

c. $CH_3CH_2\overset{\overset{OH}{|}}{C}HCH_3$

d. 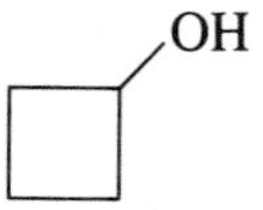

10. Give the name and structure of the alcohol that must be oxidized to make the following compounds.

a. CH_3CH_2CHO **b.** $CH_3CH_2\overset{\overset{O}{\|}}{C}CH_3$ **c.** $CH_3CH_2\overset{\overset{CH_3}{|}}{C}HCHO$

Chemists have taken advantage of the ease with which an aldehyde can be oxidized to develop several tests for their detection. **Benedict's** and **Fehling's tests** *are commonly used for aldehyde detection.* Benedict's and Fehling's reagents are deep blue alkaline solutions of copper sulfate of slightly differing composition. When an aldehyde is oxidized with Benedict's or Fehling's reagent, a bright red precipitate of cuprous oxide (Cu_2O) is obtained.

$$\underset{\text{Acetaldehyde}}{CH_3{-}\overset{\overset{O}{\|}}{C}{-}H} + \underset{\substack{\text{Cupric ion}\\\text{complex}\\\text{(blue solution)}}}{2Cu^{2+}} + 5OH^- \longrightarrow \underset{\substack{\text{Acetic acid}\\\text{(as acetate}\\\text{ion)}}}{CH_3{-}\overset{\overset{O}{\|}}{C}{-}O^-} + \underset{\substack{\text{Cuprous}\\\text{oxide (red}\\\text{precipitate)}}}{Cu_2O(s)} + 3H_2O$$

The aldehyde is oxidized to acetic acid. Cupric ions (Cu^{2+}) are reduced to cuprous ions (Cu^+).

Figure 26·11
When an aldehyde is mixed with Fehling's reagent (left) and heated, a brick-red precipitate forms (right). The blue copper(II) ions in Fehling's reagent are reduced to copper(I) ions in the red precipitate of copper(I) oxide, Cu_2O.

26·11 Esters

■ An ester is produced from the combination of a carboxylic acid and an alcohol.

Esters *are derivatives of carboxylic acids in which the —OH of the carboxyl group has been replaced by an —OR from an alcohol.* They contain a carbonyl group and an ether link to the carbonyl carbon.

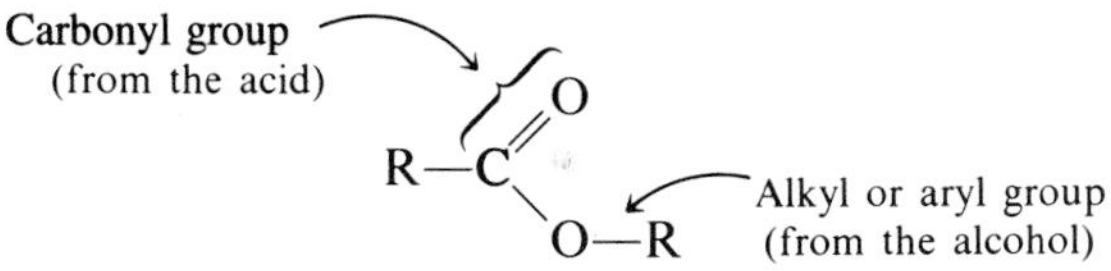

Carbonyl group
(from the acid)

$$R—C\!\!\begin{smallmatrix}O\\ \\O—R\end{smallmatrix}$$

Alkyl or aryl group
(from the alcohol)

The abbreviated formula for a carboxylate ester is RCOOR. The R group can be short chains or long chains, aliphatic (alkyl) or aromatic (aryl), saturated or unsaturated.

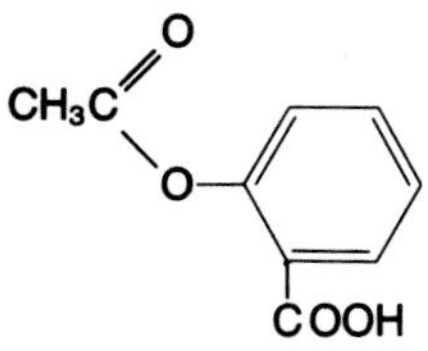

Simple esters are neutral substances. The molecules are polar but cannot form hydrogen bonds with one another. This is because they contain no hydrogen attached to oxygen or another electronegative atom. As a result, only weak attractions hold ester molecules to each other. They are much lower boiling than the strongly hydrogen-bonded carboxylic acids from which they are derived. The low-formula-mass esters are somewhat soluble in water. Esters containing more than four or five carbons have very limited solubility.

If an ester is heated with water for several hours, usually very little happens. In strong acid or base solutions, however, the ester breaks down. An ester is hydrolyzed by the addition of water to produce a carboxylic acid and an alcohol. The reaction is rapid in acidic solution because it is catalyzed by hydrogen ions.

$$CH_3—\!\!\overset{O}{\overset{\|}{C}}\!\!—OCH_2CH_3 + H—OH \overset{H^+}{\rightleftharpoons} CH_3—\!\!\overset{O}{\overset{\|}{C}}\!\!—OH + HOCH_2CH_3$$

Ethyl acetate   Acetic acid   Ethanol

Hydroxide ions also catalyze this reaction. The usual agent for ester hydrolysis is an aqueous solution of sodium hydroxide or potassium hydroxide. Because many esters do not dissolve in water, a solvent like ethanol is added to make the solution homogeneous. The reaction mixture is usually heated. All the ester is converted to products. The carboxylic acid product is in solution as its sodium or potassium salt.

$$CH_3—\!\!\overset{O}{\overset{\|}{C}}\!\!—OCH_2CH_3 + H_2O \overset{NaOH}{\longrightarrow} CH_3—\!\!\overset{O}{\overset{\|}{C}}\!\!—O^-Na^+ + HOCH_2CH_3$$

Ethyl acetate   Sodium acetate   Ethanol

If the reaction mixture is acidified, the carboxylic acid is formed.

$$CH_3—\!\!\overset{O}{\overset{\|}{C}}\!\!—O^-Na^+ + HCl \longrightarrow CH_3—\!\!\overset{O}{\overset{\|}{C}}\!\!—OH + NaCl$$

Sodium acetate   Acetic acid

Figure 26·12
An ester of great commercial importance is acetyl salicylic acid, commonly called aspirin. The R groups in its structure are a methyl group and a benzoic acid group.

The pleasant fragrances of fruits, flowers, and perfumes are due in large part to esters.

Figure 26·13
Esters give fruits their characteristic flavors and odors.

Problem

11. Write the structures of the expected products for these reactions.

a. $CH_3CH_2COOCH_2CH_3 \xrightarrow{\text{NaOH}}$

b. CH_3COO-$\xrightarrow{\text{KOH}}$

c. $CH_3CH_2COOCH_2\underset{\underset{\textstyle CH_3}{|}}{C}HCH_3 \xrightarrow{\text{HCl}}$

a. CH_3CH_2COOH, CH_3CH_2OH

b. CH_3COOH, —OH

c. CH_3CH_2COOH, $CH_3\underset{\underset{\textstyle CH_3}{|}}{C}HCH_2OH$

Figure 26·14
To create new flavors for food products a flavor chemist can select from a large number of natural and synthetic raw materials.

Giant molecules called polymers result from either addition polymerization or condensation polymerization.

Esters may be prepared from an acid and an alcohol. Esterification is the formation of an ester from a carboxylic acid and a primary or secondary alcohol. The reactants are heated with a trace of mineral acid as a catalyst. The reaction is reversible.

$$R-\overset{\displaystyle O}{\underset{\displaystyle OH}{C}} + RO-H \underset{}{\overset{H^+}{\rightleftharpoons}} R-\overset{\displaystyle O}{\underset{\displaystyle OR}{C}} + H-OH$$

Carboxylic acid	Alcohol	Carboxylate ester	Water

For example, acetic acid and ethanol react to form ethyl acetate, an ester.

$$CH_3-\overset{\displaystyle O}{\underset{\displaystyle OH}{C}} + CH_3CH_2O-H \overset{H^+}{\rightleftharpoons} CH_3-\overset{\displaystyle O}{\underset{\displaystyle OCH_2CH_3}{C}} + H_2O$$

Acetic acid	Ethanol	Ethyl Acetate	Water

Chapter 17 showed how the equilibrium in a reversible reaction can be disturbed to improve the product yield. Esterification reactions can be pushed to completion in two different ways. An excess of one of the reactants (acid or alcohol) can be used. Alternatively, the water from the reaction mixture can be removed as it is produced.

26·12 Polymerization

Most of the reactions that have been examined so far have involved reactants and products of low molecular mass. Some of the most important organic compounds made by chemists, however, are giant molecules called polymers. *A* **polymer** *is a large molecule formed by the covalent bonding of repeating smaller molecules.* Most polymerization reactions require a catalyst.

Monomers *are molecules that combine to form the repeating unit of a polymer.* Some polymers contain only one type of monomer. Others contain two or more types of monomers. The two most common ways for monomers to be joined are addition polymerization and condensation polymerization.

Figure 26·15
Polyvinyl chloride (PVC) is one of the
most versatile polymers. It is used to
make all of the items shown here, and
many more.

The substances we call "plastics" consist of polymers.

$$x \, CH_3CH{=}CH_2 \longrightarrow \underset{\substack{CH_3 \\ |}}{(CH{-}CH_2)_x}$$

Propene
(propylene)

Polypropylene

$$x \, CH_2{=}\underset{\substack{Cl \\ |}}{CH} \longrightarrow \underset{\substack{Cl \\ |}}{(CH_2{-}CH)_x}$$

Chloroethene
(vinyl chloride)

Polyvinyl chloride
(PVC)

$$x \, CF_2{=}CF_2 \longrightarrow (CF_2{-}CF_2)_x$$

Tetrafluoroethene

Teflon

$$x \, CH_2{=}CH \longrightarrow (CH_2{-}CH)_x$$

Vinyl benzene
(styrene)

Polystyrene

Figure 26·16
The structures and uses of some important addition polymers of alkenes are shown here.

Addition polymerization occurs when unsaturated monomers react to form a polymer. It is a specific type of addition reaction. Ethene undergoes addition polymerization. The molecules bond one to another to form the long-chain polymer polyethylene.

$$\overbrace{x}^{\substack{x \text{ is number of} \\ \text{ethylene units} \\ \text{that combine to} \\ \text{form long chain}}} \underset{\substack{H \\ H}}{\overset{\substack{H \\ H}}{C{=}C}} \longrightarrow H(CH_2{-}CH_2)_x H$$

x is number of repeating $-CH_2-CH_2-$ units in polymer; parentheses identify the repeating unit

Ethene
(ethylene)

Polyethylene

Polyethylene is an important industrial product because it is chemically resistant and easy to clean. It is used to make refrigerator dishes, plastic milk bottles, laboratory wash bottles, and many other familiar items found in homes and laboratories. By shortening or lengthening the carbon chains, chemists can control the physical properties of polyethylene. Polyethylene containing relatively short chains ($x = 100$) has the consistency of paraffin wax. Polyethylene with long chains ($x = 1000$) is harder and more rigid.

Polymers of substituted ethenes can also be prepared. Many of these polymers have useful properties (Figure 26·16).

Condensation polymers are formed by the head-to-tail joining of monomer units. This is usually accompanied by the loss of a small molecule, such as water. The formation of polyesters is an example of condensation. Polyesters are high-formula-mass polymers consisting of many repeating units of dicarboxylic acids and dihydroxy alcohols joined by ester bonds. The formation of a polyester is represented by a block diagram. Note that condensation polymerization always requires that there be *two* functional groups on each molecule.

$$x\,HO{-}\overset{O}{\overset{\|}{C}}{-}\square{-}\overset{O}{\overset{\|}{C}}{-}OH + x\,HO{-}\bigcirc{-}OH \longrightarrow \left(\overset{O}{\overset{\|}{C}}{-}\square{-}\overset{O}{\overset{\|}{C}}{-}O{-}\bigcirc{-}O\right)_x + 2x\,H_2O$$

Dicarboxylic acid   Dihydroxy alcohol   Representative polymer unit of a polyester

26·B Synthetic Fibers

In 1883 the Englishman Joseph Swan discovered that nitrocellulose could be made into silk-like filaments. He used these filaments in electric lamps. One year later, Louis Chardonnet, a Frenchman, produced similar material when he forced nitrocellulose through tiny holes. At the 1891 Paris Exposition, Chardonnet's synthetic material was called "rayon". The shiny fibers seemed to produce rays of light.

The widespread production of synthetic material began in the 1930s with Wallace Carothers, an American chemist. He made a polymer of diamines and dicarboxylic acids. The fibers he produced from this polymer had many of the properties of silk but were much stronger. This material, called nylon, was first used for toothbrush bristles. During World War II, nylon was reserved exclusively for parachutes. After the war, nylon became a popular material for women's hosiery.

Although there are many different synthetic fibers today, the production methods for most of these materials are similar. First the polymer is either melted or dissolved in a solvent. Then, the melted or dissolved polymer is forced through holes in a device called a spinneret. The fibers are solidified by cooling the mixture or evaporating the solvent. Finally, the fibers are stretched to make the polymer molecules lie parallel to each other. This increases the strength of the fibers.

Synthetic fibers can be divided into two groups depending on the starting materials. Cellulosic fibers use cellulose derived from wood pulp or cotton as starting material. Rayon and acetate are cellulosic fibers. Noncellulosic fibers are manufactured from petrochemicals. Nylon, polyester, and acrylic are noncellulosic polymers.

Figure 26·17
Synthetic fibers are now more widely used than natural fibers.

26·13 Carbohydrates

Carbohydrates are naturally occurring polyhydroxy aldehydes and ketones.

Carbohydrates abound in nature. Among the many forms are starch, table sugar, cotton, and wood. **Carbohydrates** *are monomers and polymers of aldehydes and ketones that have numerous hydroxy groups attached.* The name carbohydrate comes from the early observation that many of these compounds have the general formula $C_n(H_2O)_n$. As a result they appear to be "hydrates of carbon." An examination of the molecular structures will show that this is erroneous. Nevertheless, the name has stuck.

The simplest carbohydrate molecules are simple sugars called **monosaccharides.** These names are used interchangeably. Glucose and fructose are examples of simple sugars. They are structural isomers because they both have the molecular formula $C_6H_{12}O_6$. Glucose has an aldehyde functional group. Fructose has a ketone functional group. They undergo many of the same reactions as ordinary aldehydes and ketones.

Because of the tetrahedral bonding of carbon atoms and the bent bonding of oxygen atoms, saccharides do not form flat rings. It is convenient, however, to show these rings as being flat.

CHO
|
H—C—OH
|
HO—C—H
|
H—C—OH
|
H—C—OH
|
CH₂OH

⇌

Glucose and its cyclic form

CH₂OH
|
C=O
|
HO—C—H
|
H—C—OH
|
H—C—OH
|
CH₂OH

⇌

Fructose and its cyclic form

In aqueous solution, sugars such as glucose and fructose exist in dynamic equilibrium in both the cyclic and straight chain forms. The cyclic form predominates. Glucose is abundant in plants and animals. Depending on the source, it has been called corn sugar, grape sugar, and blood sugar. Fructose occurs in a large number of fruits and in honey.

The cyclic forms of two simple sugars can be linked together with the loss of water. The linkage of glucose and fructose by means of a condensation reaction gives sucrose, common table sugar. *Sugars which are formed from two monosaccharides are known as* **disaccharides.** Sucrose is a disaccharide.

a

b

Figure 26·18
Carbohydrates are the most abundant and least expensive sources of energy in food. **a** These foods all contain natural sugars. **b** These foods are good sources of starch.

Glucose

Fructose

$-H_2O$ →

Sucrose

Sucrose is obtained mainly from the juice of sugar cane and sugar beets. The world's production from these sources exceeds 7×10^9 metric tons per year.

The formation of a disaccharide is sometimes the first step in a condensation polymerization. *The linkage of many monosaccharide monomers produces* **polysaccharides.** Starches, the major storage form of glucose in plants, are polymers consisting of glucose monomers. A typical linear starch molecule contains hundreds of the glucose monomers (Figure 26·19). Some starches are branched molecules, with each branch containing about a dozen glucose units. Glycogen is the animal form of starch. It is more highly branched than plant starches.

26·13 Carbohydrates **639**

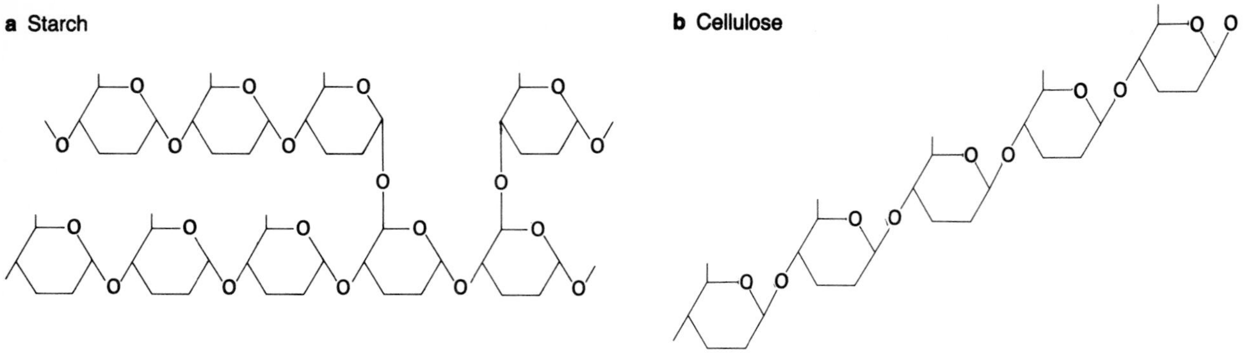

a Starch

b Cellulose

Figure 26·19
Starch and cellulose are similar polymers made up of hundreds of glucose monomers. They differ in the orientation of the bond between the glucose units. This causes starch to be readily digestible and cellulose to be nondigestible by most organisms.

Cellulose is probably the most abundant biological molecule. As shown in Figure 26·19, cellulose is also a polymer of glucose. The orientation of the bond linking the glucose monomers is different than it is in starch. Starch is edible and partially soluble in water. Cellulose can be digested by only a few microorganisms such as those that live in the digestive tract of cattle and termites. It is insoluble in water and forms rigid structures with other cellulose molecules. Cellulose is therefore an important structural polysaccharide. Plant cell walls, as in wood, are made of cellulose. Cotton is about 80% pure cellulose.

26·14   Lipids

■ Lipids are the major organic components of waxes, fats, and oils.

Compounds that are classified as lipids are generally found in living systems.

Lipids *are a large class of relatively water-insoluble compounds that includes fats, oils, and waxes.* As a group, lipids tend to dissolve in organic solvents like ether and chloroform. This property sets them apart from carbohydrates, proteins, and nucleic acids, the other great classes of biological molecules.

Waxes are part of the lipid family. **Waxes** *are esters of long-chain fatty acids and long-chain alcohols.* The hydrocarbon chains for both the acid and the alcohol usually contain from 10 to 30 carbons. Waxes are low-melting, stable solids which appear in nature in both plants and animals. A wax coat protects the surfaces of many plant leaves from water loss and attack by microorganisms. Carnauba wax is a major ingredient in car wax and floor polish. It comes from the leaves of a South American palm tree. Other waxes coat skin, hair, and feathers and help keep them pliable and waterproof. Beeswax is largely myricyl palmiate. It is the ester of myricyl alcohol and palmitic acid.

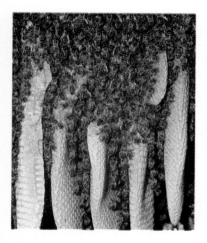

Figure 26·20
Bees construct their honeycomb from beeswax, myricyl palmitate. Waxes are esters of a long-chain fatty acid and a long-chain alcohol.

$$CH_3(CH_2)_{14}-\overset{\displaystyle O}{\overset{\displaystyle \|}{C}}-O-(CH_2)_{29}CH_3$$
Myricyl palmitate

Natural **triglycerides** *are triesters of long-chain fatty acids* (C_{12} *through* C_{24}) *and glycerol.* They are the major components of animal fats and oils. Triglycerides are simple lipids. They are important as the storage form of fat in the human body. The following equation shows the general reaction for the formation of triglycerides.

$$\text{Glycerol} \quad + \quad \text{3 Fatty acid molecules} \quad \longrightarrow \quad \text{Triglyceride (triester of glycerol)} \quad + \quad 3H_2O$$

Glycerol: CH_2OH — $CHOH$ — CH_2OH

3 Fatty acid molecules: $HO\!-\!\overset{\displaystyle O}{\overset{\|}{C}}\!-\!R$ (three of them)

Triglyceride: $CH_2\!-\!O\!-\!\overset{\displaystyle O}{\overset{\|}{C}}\!-\!R$, $CH\!-\!O\!-\!\overset{\displaystyle O}{\overset{\|}{C}}\!-\!R$, $CH_2\!-\!O\!-\!\overset{\displaystyle O}{\overset{\|}{C}}\!-\!R$

From the organic chemist's point of view, fats and oils are simply esters. Like other esters, they are easily hydrolyzed in the presence of acids and bases (Section 26·11). *The hydrolysis of oils or fats by boiling them with aqueous sodium hydroxide is called* **saponification.** This process is used to make soap. Soaps are the alkali metal (Na, K, or Li) salts of fatty acids.

$$
\begin{aligned}
&CH_2\!-\!O\!-\!\overset{O}{\overset{\|}{C}}\!-\!(CH_2)_{16}CH_3 \\
&CH\!-\!O\!-\!\overset{O}{\overset{\|}{C}}\!-\!(CH_2)_{16}CH_3 \; + \; 3NaOH \longrightarrow \; CH\!-\!OH \; + \; 3CH_3(CH_2)_{16}\overset{O}{\overset{\|}{C}}\!-\!O^-Na^+ \\
&CH_2\!-\!O\!-\!\overset{O}{\overset{\|}{C}}\!-\!(CH_2)_{16}CH_3
\end{aligned}
$$

Tristearin (a triester)   Glycerol ($CH_2\!-\!OH$, $CH\!-\!OH$, $CH_2\!-\!OH$)   Sodium stearate (soap)

Soap is made by heating beef tallow or coconut oil in large kettles with an excess of sodium hydroxide. When sodium chloride is added to the saponified mixture, the sodium salts of the fatty acids separate as a thick curd of crude soap. Glycerol is an important by-product of the reaction. It is recovered by evaporating the water layer. The crude soap is then purified. Coloring agents and perfumes are added according to market demands.

Figure 26·21
Soap molecules dissociate in water. The anionic end of the soap molecule (the carboxylate ion, —COO⁻) becomes hydrogen bonded to water molecules. The long nonpolar hydrocarbon chain of the soap molecule dissolves in organic materials such as oils. The soap-oil mixture forms droplets that disperse in water and are readily washed away.

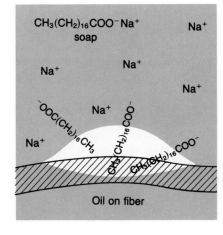
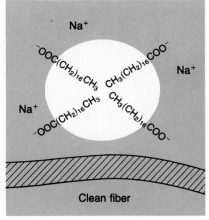

26·15   Amino Acids, Peptides, and Proteins

*An **amino acid** is a compound which contains amino ($-NH_2$) and carboxylic acid ($-COOH$) groups in the same molecule.* To most chemists and biochemists, however, the term is usually reserved for amino acids which are formed and used in living organisms. All 20 amino acids common in nature have a skeleton consisting of a carboxylic acid group and an amino group covalently bonded to a central atom. The remaining two groups on the central carbon are hydrogen and an R group which constitutes the amino acid side chain.

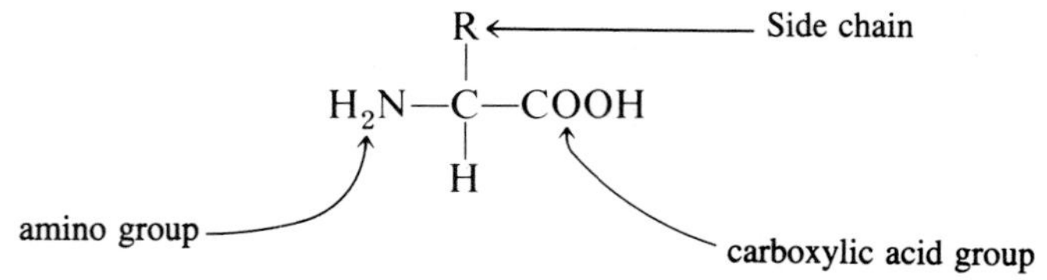

The chemical natures of the side-chain groups account for differences in amino acid properties. Some side chains are aliphatic or aromatic hydrocarbons. Others are acidic or basic. Still others are neutral but polar. Figure 26·21 shows some of these amino acid structures. Table 26·8 gives all of the names with three-letter abbreviations.

The structures of the amino acids shown in Figure 26·22 are not actually correct. The acid–base properties of carboxylic acids and amino

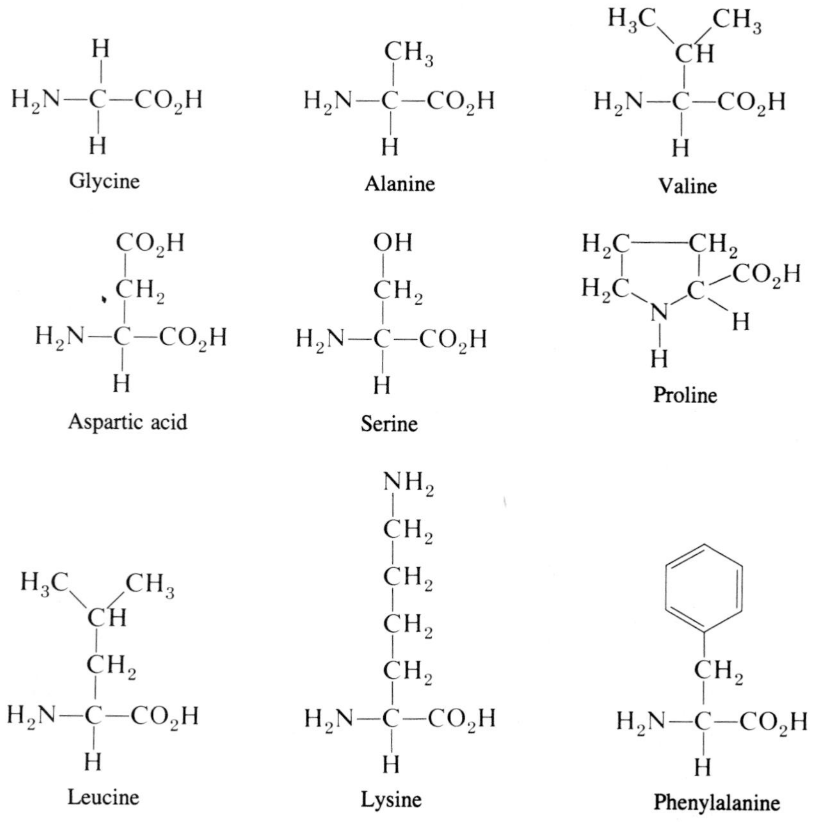

Table 26·8 Abbreviations for Amino Acids	
Amino acid	Abbreviation
alanine	Ala
arginine	Arg
asparagine	Asn
aspartic acid	Asp
cysteine	Cys
glutamine	Gln
glutamic acid	Glu
glycine	Gly
histidine	His
isoleucine	Ile
leucine	Leu
lysine	Lys
methionine	Met
phenylalanine	Phe
proline	Pro
serine	Ser
threonine	Thr
tryptophan	Try
tyrosine	Tyr
valine	Val

Figure 26·22
These are some of the 20 naturally-occurring amino acids.

groups alter these structures. The weakly acidic proton of the carboxylic acid group easily transfers to the amino group to form an internal salt. Thus amino acids are really ionic compounds. As previously discussed, ionic compounds generally have much higher melting points than molecular compounds. *The internal salts of amino acids are called* **zwitterions.** In the pure solid state and in aqueous solution near neutral pH, the amino acids exist almost completely as zwitterions.

$$\underset{\text{Amino acid}}{\underset{H_2N}{\overset{R}{\diagdown}}\overset{H}{\underset{CO_2H}{\diagup}}C} \longrightarrow \underset{\text{Zwitterion}}{\underset{H_3N^+}{\overset{R}{\diagdown}}\overset{H}{\underset{CO_2^-}{\diagup}}C}$$

A **peptide** *is any combination of amino acids in which the amino group of one acid is united with the carboxylic acid group of another.* The bonds between the amino acids always involve the central amino and central carboxylic acid groups. The side chains are not involved.

$$\underset{\text{Amino acid}}{H_2N-\overset{\overset{R}{|}}{\underset{\underset{H}{|}}{C}}-\overset{\overset{O}{\|}}{C}-OH} + \underset{\text{Amino acid}}{H-\overset{\overset{R}{|}}{\underset{\underset{H}{|}}{\underset{H}{N}}}-\overset{\overset{O}{\|}}{C}-OH} \longrightarrow \underset{\text{Peptide}}{H_2N-\overset{\overset{R}{|}}{\underset{\underset{H}{|}}{C}}-\overset{\overset{O}{\|}}{C}-\overset{}{\underset{\underset{H}{|}}{N}}-\overset{\overset{R}{|}}{\underset{\underset{H}{|}}{C}}-\overset{\overset{O}{\|}}{C}-OH} + H_2O$$

More amino acids may be added in the same fashion to form long chains. This is another example of condensation polymerization. *The bond between the carbonyl group of one amino acid and the nitrogen of the next amino acid in the peptide chain is called a* **peptide bond**. It is also called a peptide link.

As more amino acids are added, a backbone common to all peptide molecules is formed. *Any peptide with more than ten amino acid residues is called a* **polypeptide.** In theory, the process of adding amino acids to a peptide chain may be continued indefinitely. *A peptide with more than about 100 amino acids is called a* **protein.** On the average, a molecule of 100 amino acids has a molecular mass of 10 000 amu.

The order in which the amino acids of a peptide or protein molecule are linked is the amino acid sequence of that molecule. Differences in the chemical and physiological properties of peptides and proteins result from differences in the amino acid sequence. The number of ways in which 20 amino acids can be linked in a protein molecule is very large. For example 20^{100} amino acid sequences are possible for a protein of 100 amino acids containing all 20 amino acids.

The long peptide chains of proteins are folded into relatively stable shapes. Sections of chain may coil into a regular spiral known as a helix. Peptide chains may also be arranged side by side to form a wavy sheet. Much irregular folding of the chains also occurs. Protein shape is maintained by hydrogen bonds between adjacent parts of the folded chains. Covalent bonds also form between sulfur atoms in cysteine amino acids that are folded near each other. In this way separate polypeptide chains may be joined into a single protein.

■ Proteins and peptides are condensation polymers of the 20 naturally occurring amino acids.

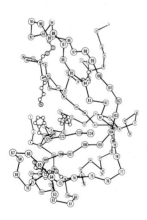

Figure 26·23
Each protein has a specific amino acid sequence. The order of the 124 amino acids in ribonuclease and the folding of the polypeptide chain are shown here.

26·C Enzymes

Enzymes are biological catalysts. They increase the rates of chemical reactions in living things. In 1926, the American chemist James B. Sumner reported the first isolation and crystallization of an enzyme. The enzyme he isolated was urease. It is able to hydrolyze urea, a constituent of urine, into ammonia and carbon dioxide. (The strong smell of dirty diapers allowed to stand for a time is the result of the action of bacteria that contain this enzyme.)

$$\underset{\text{Urea}}{NH_2{-}\overset{\overset{\displaystyle O}{\|}}{C}{-}NH_2} + \underset{\text{Water}}{H_2O} \xrightarrow{\text{urease}} \underset{\text{Ammonia}}{2NH_3} + \underset{\substack{\text{Carbon} \\ \text{dioxide}}}{CO_2}$$

Sumner demonstrated that urease is a protein. The idea that a protein could be a catalyst was disputed initially. Since then, hundreds of enzymes have been isolated and structurally characterized as proteins.

Besides being able to promote reactions, enzymes have two other properties of true catalysts. First they are unchanged by the reaction they catalyze. Second, enzymes do not change the normal position of chemical equilibrium. The same amount of product is eventually formed whether or not an enzyme is present. Few reactions in cells ever reach equilibrium, however. The products are rapidly converted to another substance in a further enzyme-catalyzed reaction. According to Le Châtelier's principle, the removal of a reaction product pulls the reaction toward completion.

Most of the chemical changes that occur in the cell are catalyzed by enzymes. *Substrates* are the molecules on which an enzyme acts. As in other reactions, substrates are transformed into products by bond-making and bond-breaking processes. In an enzymatic reaction, the substrate interacts with side chains of the amino acids on the enzyme. These interactions cause the making and breaking of bonds.

Figure 26·24
An enzyme speeds up a chemical reaction. Each enzyme has a distinctively shaped active site. Only molecules with complementary shapes can attach to the enzyme. Some enzymes catalyze decomposition reactions. Others catalyze combination reactions.

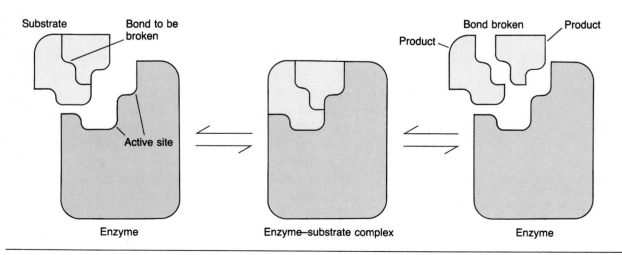

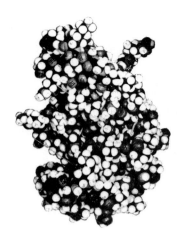

Figure 26·25
This is a space-filling model of the enzyme ribonuclease. The distinctive shape of the enzyme is important for its function as a biological catalyst.

To get some idea of the tremendous efficiency of enzymes, consider carbonic anhydrase. This enzyme catalyzes only one reversible reaction. It breaks down carbonic acid to water and carbon dioxide.

$$H_2CO_3 \underset{}{\overset{\substack{\text{carbonic} \\ \text{anhydrase}}}{\rightleftharpoons}} CO_2 + H_2O$$

A single molecule of carbonic anhydrase can catalyze the breakdown of about 36 million molecules of carbonic acid in one minute!

A substrate molecule must contact an enzyme molecule before it can be transformed into product. Once the substrate has made contact, it must bind to the enzyme. The *active site* is the place on an enzyme where processes that convert substrates to products can take effect. The active site is usually a pocket or crevice formed by folds in the peptide chains of the protein. The active site of each enzyme has a distinctive shape. Only the substrate molecule for that enzyme will fit into it, much as only one key will fit into a certain lock. Thus each enzyme catalyzes only one chemical reaction with only one substrate. An *enzyme–substrate complex* is formed when an enzyme molecule and substrate molecule are joined.

Some enzymes can catalyze the transformation of biological substrates without assistance. Other enzymes need nonprotein coenzymes, also called cofactors, to assist the transformation. *Coenzymes* are metal ions or small organic molecules that must be present for an enzyme-catalyzed reaction to occur. The metal ions are usually magnesium, potassium, iron, or zinc.

26·16   Nucleic Acids

Nucleic acids *are polymers found primarily in cell nuclei.* They are indispensable components of every living thing. The kinds of nucleic acids found in cells are *d*eoxyribo*n*ucleic *a*cid (DNA) and *r*ibo*n*ucleic *a*cid (RNA). DNA stores the information needed to make proteins. It governs the reproduction and growth of cells and new organisms. RNA has a key role in the transmission of the information stored in DNA.

The monomers that make up DNA and RNA are called **nucleotides.** Nucleic acids are therefore polynucleotides. Each nucleotide consists of a phosphate group, a five-carbon sugar, and a nitrogen-containing compound called a nitrogen base.

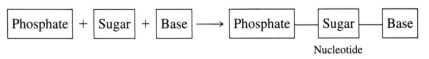

Figure 26·26
James Watson and Francis Crick are shown here with their original model of the DNA molecule. The model was based on chemical analyses and X-ray diffraction studies.

The sugar units in the nucleotides of DNA are the five-carbon monosaccharide ribose. The base may be one of four compounds. Adenine and guanine are each composed of a double ring. Thymine and cytosine are each composed of a single ring. These bases are abbreviated as A, G, T, and C (Figure 26·27). Deoxyribose, which has one less

Figure 26·27
The nucleotide monomers of DNA are linked together through their phosphate groups.

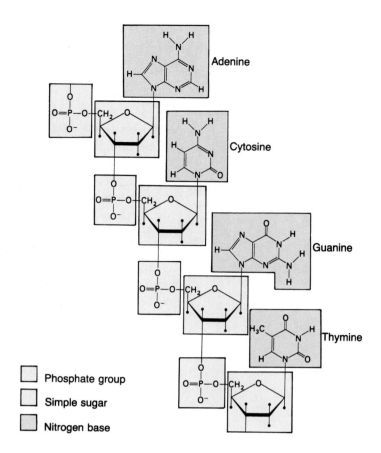

Phosphate group

Simple sugar

Nitrogen base

Adenine

Cytosine

Guanine

Thymine

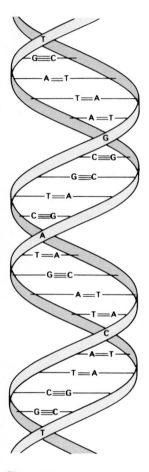

Figure 26·28
The DNA molecule is often referred to as a double helix. The nitrogen bases form hydrogen bonds to hold the two polynucleotide strands together.

DNA and RNA molecules, which carry the blueprint of life, are condensation polymers of nucleotide monomers.

oxygen than ribose, is the sugar in the nucleotide monomers of RNA. The base thymine is never found in RNA. Instead, it is replaced by a fifth base, uracil, abbreviated U.

Chemists studying nucleic acids have discovered that the amount of A in DNA is always equal to the amount T (A = T). Similarly, the amount of G is always equal to the amount of C (G = C). The significance of this fact was not apparent until 1953. At that time, James Watson and Francis Crick proposed that DNA molecules consist of two polynucleotide chains wrapped into a spiral shape (Figure 26·28). This is the famous double helix of DNA. In order for bases to fit neatly into the double helix, every double-ringed base must be matched with a single-ringed base on the opposing strand. The pairing of A with T and G with C provides the best possible fit. It also gives the maximum number of hydrogen bonds between the opposing bases. Thus, A—T and G—C makes the most stable arrangement in the double helix.

The molecular masses of DNA molecules reach into the millions and possibly billions. Even with only four bases, the number of possible sequences of nucleotides in a DNA chain is enormous. The order of the nitrogen bases A, T, G, and C in the DNA of an organism constitutes the genetic plan for that organism. Differences in the number and order of the bases in DNA ultimately are responsible for the diversity of living creatures.

Key Terms

addition reaction	26·6	halocarbon	26·2
alcohol	26·4	hydration reaction	26·6
aldehyde	26·8	hydrogenation	
alkyl halide	26·2	reaction	26·6
amino group	26·1	hydroxyl group	26·4
amino acid	26·16	ketone	26·8
aryl halide	26·2	lipid	26·14
Benedict's test	26·10	monomer	26·12
carbohydrate	26·13	monosaccharide	26·13
carbonyl group	26·8	nucleic acid	26·16
carboxyl group	26·9	nucleotide	26·16
carboxylic acid	26·9	peptide	26·15
dehydrogenation		peptide bond	26·15
reaction	26·10	polymer	26·12
denatured alcohol	26·5	polypeptide	26·15
disaccharide	26·13	polysaccharides	26·13
ester	26·11	protein	26·15
ether	26·7	saponification	26·14
fatty acid	26·9	substitution	26·3
Fehling's test	26·10	triglyceride	26·14
fermentation	26·5	wax	26·14
functional group	26·1	zwitterion	26·15

Chapter Summary

There are few useful reactions of saturated hydrocarbons. The chemical reactions of most organic compounds involve functional groups. A common functional group is the carbon–carbon double bond of an alkene. It undergoes the addition of water to form an alcohol. It can add a hydrogen halide or halogen to form a halocarbon, and it can add hydrogen to form an alkane. Alkenes also undergo addition polymerization to form useful materials such as polyethylene. The benzene ring usually undergoes substitution rather than addition.

Common functional groups containing oxygen include ethers, aldehydes, ketones, carboxylic acids, and esters. The latter four types of functional groups contain the carbon–oxygen double bond or carbonyl group. Alcohols may be oxidized to aldehydes or ketones. Aldehydes may be oxidized to carboxylic acids. Fehling's and Benedict's solutions can be used to detect the presence of aldehydes. Esters result from the combination of carboxylic acids and alcohols. Hydrolysis of an ester produces these components. Condensation polymerization of monomer units containing hydroxy and carboxyl groups in the same molecule gives polyesters.

Carbohydrates, lipids, proteins, and nucleic acids are the great classes of biological molecules. The carbohydrates are often found in nature as simple molecules containing one or a few sugar units. Condensation polymers containing hundreds or thousands of sugar units, as in starch and glycogen, are also found. Lipids are the substances of fats and oils. The simplest lipids are triglycerides, esters of long chain fatty acids and glycerol. Soaps are the alkali metal salts of fatty acids. Peptides and proteins are condensation polymers of amino acids. Likewise, the nucleic acids are condensation polymers of monomer units called nucleotides. These giant molecules carry the information needed for reproduction and growth of living organisms.

Practice Questions and Problems

12. Write a general structure for each of these types of compounds. *26·1*
  a. halocarbon   **c.** ester
  b. ketone   **d.** amide

13. Name the following compound *types*. *26·1*

a. $CH_3-\overset{\overset{\displaystyle O}{\|}}{C}-H$

b. $CH_3-CH_2-\overset{\overset{\displaystyle O}{\|}}{C}-CH_3$

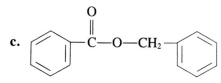

c.

d. CH_3—CH—OH
        |
       CH_3

14. Write a structural formula for each of the following compounds.   *26·2*
  a. 1,2,2-trichlorobutane
  b. 1,3,5-tribromobenzene
  c. 1,2-dichlorocyclohexane

15. Name the following halocarbons.   *26·2*

  a. CH_2=$CHCH_2Cl$

       CH_3 Cl
       | |
  b. $CH_3CHCH_2CHCH_2Cl$

  c.

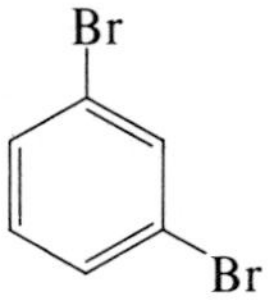

16. Write structural formulas and give IUPAC names for all the isomers of these compounds. *26·2*
  a. $C_3H_6Cl_2$
  b. C_4H_9Br

17. What organic products are formed in the following reactions?   *26·3*

  a. 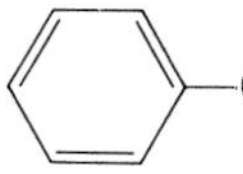 ⬡—ONa + CH_3Br ⟶ _____ + NaBr

  b. 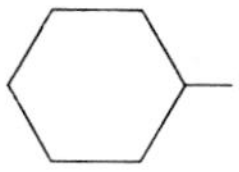 ⬡—Cl + NaOH ⟶ _____ + NaCl

  c. CH_3CHONa + CH_3CH_2Br ⟶ _____ + NaBr
       |
      CH_3

  d. 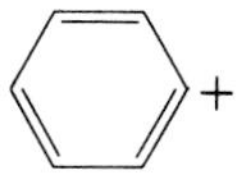 ⬡ + Br_2 $\xrightarrow{\text{catalyst}}$ _____ + HBr

18. Write the name (IUPAC, common, or both) for each of the following alcohols.   *26·4*

  a. $CH_3CH_2CHCH_3$ **c.** $CH_3CHCH_2CH_2OH$
         | |
        OH CH_3

                              CH_3
                              |
  b. CH_3CHCH_2OH **d.** $CH_3CH_2CCH_2CH_3$
        | |
       CH_3 OH

19. Identify each of the alcohols in Problem 18 as primary, secondary, or tertiary.   *26·4*

20. Explain why ethanol, CH_3CH_2OH, is soluble in water in all proportions whereas decanol, $CH_3(CH_2)_8CH_2OH$, is almost insoluble in water.   *26·5*

21. Show how hydrogen bonds form between molecules of these pairs of compounds.   *26·5*
  a. water–water
  b. water–methanol
  c. methanol–methanol

22. Write structures and names of the products obtained upon addition of each of the following reagents to ethene.   **a.** HBr **b.** Cl_2 **c.** H_2O
  d. H_2 **e.** HCl   *26·6*

23. Name the following ethers.   *26·7*

  a. $CH_3OCH_2CH_3$

  b. 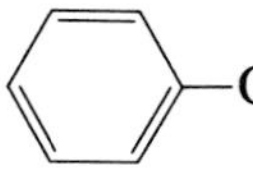 ⬡—O—CH_2CH_3

  c. $CH_3CHOCH_2CH_3$
            |
          CH_3

  d. $CH_3CHOCHCH_3$
           | |
         CH_3 CH_3

  e. CH_2=$CHOCH$=CH_2

24. Explain why diethyl ether is more soluble in water than is dihexyl ether. Would you expect propane to be more soluble than diethyl ether in water? Why?   *26·7*

25. What is a carbonyl group? Explain why a carbon–carbon double bond is nonpolar but a carbon–oxygen double bond is very polar.   *26·8*

26. Name these aldehydes and ketones.   *26·8*

              O
              ||
  a. CH_3CCH_3 **d.**

           CH_3
           |
  b. CH_3CHCH_2CHO **e.** CH_3CHO

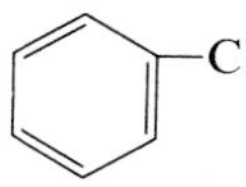

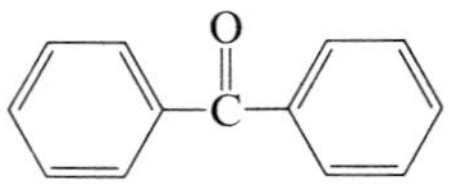

                             O
                             ||
  c. ⬡—CH_2CHO **f.** $CH_3CH_2CCH_2CH_2CH_3$

27. Propane $(CH_3CH_2CH_3)$ and acetaldehyde (CH_3CHO) have the same molecular mass, but propane boils at $-42°C$ whereas acetaldehyde boils at $20°C$. Why are the boiling points so different? *26·8*

28. Give common names for each of the following carboxylic acids. *26·9*
  a. $HCOOH$ **c.** CH_3CH_2COOH
  b. CH_3COOH **d.** $CH_3(CH_2)_{16}COOH$

29. What are the products of each of the following reactions? *26·9*
  a. $HCOOH + KOH \longrightarrow$
  b. $CH_3CH_2COOH + NaOH \longrightarrow$

30. Complete the reactions by writing the structure of the expected products. *26·10*

  a. $CH_3CH_2OH \xrightarrow{K_2Cr_2O_7}$

  b. $CH_3CH_2CHO \xrightarrow{K_2Cr_2O_7}$

  c. $CH_3CH_2\underset{\underset{CH_3}{|}}{C}HOH \xrightarrow{K_2Cr_2O_7}$

  d. (benzene ring)$-CH_2CHO \xrightarrow{K_2Cr_2O_7}$

  e. $CH_3CH_2\overset{\overset{O}{\|}}{C}CH_3 \xrightarrow{K_2Cr_2O_7}$

31. Give the names and structures of the expected oxidation products. *26·10*

  a. $CH_3CH_2\underset{\underset{CH_3}{|}}{\overset{\overset{OH}{|}}{C}}CH_2CH_3$

  b. $CH_3CH_2\underset{}{\overset{\overset{OH}{|}}{C}}HCH_2CH_3$

  c. (cyclohexane ring with OH)

  d. $CH_3\overset{\overset{CH_3}{|}}{C}HOH$

32. Write the name and structure for the alcohol that must be oxidized to make each of the following carbonyl compounds. *26·10*

  a. $HCHO$

  b. $CH_3\overset{\overset{O}{\|}}{C}HCH_3$

  c. $CH_3\overset{\overset{CH_3}{|}}{C}HCHO$

  d. (cyclohexane ring with $=O$)

33. Complete the following reactions by writing the structures of the expected products and by naming each of the reactants and products. *26·11*
  a. $CH_3COOCH_3 + H_2O \xrightarrow{HCl}$
  b. $CH_3CH_2CH_2COOCH_2CH_2CH_3 + H_2O \xrightarrow{NaOH}$
  c. $HCOOCH_2CH_3 + H_2O \xrightarrow{KOH}$

34. Write the structure and name of the ester that could be produced from each of the following reactions. *26·11*
  a. formic acid + methanol $\longrightarrow$
  b. butyric acid + ethanol $\longrightarrow$
  c. acetic acid + propanol $\longrightarrow$

35. What is the structure of the repeating units in a polymer in which the monomer is each compound?
  a. 1-butene   **b.** 1,2-dichloroethene   *26·12*

36. What is a disaccharide? *26·13*

37. Give a source and use for each.
  a. starch   **b.** cellulose   **c.** glycogen   *26·13*

38. A solution of glucose is treated with Benedict's solution. What would you expect to happen? Why? *26·13*

39. Name the two classes of organic compounds that are produced when waxes are hydrolyzed. *26·14*

40. Write the structure for glyceryl tristearate, a simple triglyceride. *26·14*

41. What is a soap? Give the name and formula of a typical soap molecule. *26·14*

42. The following compound is hydrolyzed by boiling with sodium hydroxide. What are the saponification products? *26·14*

$$CH_2-O-\overset{\overset{O}{\|}}{C}-(CH_2)_{14}CH_3$$
$$CH-O-\overset{\overset{O}{\|}}{C}-(CH_2)_{10}CH_3$$
$$CH_2-O-\overset{\overset{O}{\|}}{C}-(CH_2)_{16}CH_3$$

43. Write the structure and identify the R group for these amino acids.
  a. alanine   **b.** serine   **c.** phenylalanine   *26·15*

44. Define the term *zwitterion*. Draw the amino acid glycine as a zwitterion. *26·15*

45. What is the name given to the bond connecting two amino acids in a peptide chain?   26·15

46. Consider the tripeptide seryl-glycyl-phenylalanine. How many peptide bonds does this molecule have?   26·15

47. What is meant by the amino acid sequence of a protein?   26·15

48. Cells contain two types of nucleic acids. What are they called?   26·16

49. What is the structural difference between the sugar unit in RNA and the sugar unit in DNA?   26·16

50. What are the components of a nucleotide?   26·16

51. Explain the difference between a nucleotide and a nucleic acid.   26·16

52. What type of bonding holds a DNA double helix together?   26·16

53. Which of the following base pairs are found in a DNA molecule?   26·16
  a. A—A   **d.** G—C
  b. A—T   **e.** G—A
  c. C—G   **f.** A—U

Mastery Questions and Problems

54. Write the structures and give the names of the alcohols produced in the following reactions.   26·6

a. $CH_2{=}CH_2 + H_2O \xrightarrow{H^+}$

b. $CH_3CH{=}CHCH_3 + H_2O \xrightarrow[100°C]{H^+}$

c. $CH_3\overset{\underset{|}{CH_3}}{CH}{-}Br + NaOH \xrightarrow[100°C]{H_2O}$

d. $\overset{CH_3CH_2}{\underset{CH_3}{}}C{=}C\overset{CH_2CH_3}{\underset{CH_3}{}} + H_2O \xrightarrow[100°C]{H^+}$

55. Predict which of the following compounds has the highest boiling point. Formula masses are given in parentheses.   26·5
  a. CH_3CHO (44)
  b. CH_3CH_2OH (46)
  c. $CH_3CH_2CH_3$ (44)

56. Describe two typical ways of synthesizing alcohols.   26·6

57. Classify each of these compounds as an alcohol, a phenol, or an ether.   26·7

a. [naphthalen-2-ol structure with OH]

d. [phenol structure with OH]

b. [diphenyl ether structure with O]

e. $CH_3CH_2\overset{\underset{|}{CH_3}}{CH}OH$

c. [benzyl alcohol structure with CH₂OH]

58. Give the product of each of the following reactions. If there are none, write "no reaction."   26·10

a. $CH_3\overset{\underset{|}{OH}}{CH}CH(CH_3)_2 \xrightarrow[H_2SO_4]{K_2Cr_2O_7}$

b. $CH_3CH_2\overset{\underset{|}{CH_3}}{CH}CH_2OH \xrightarrow[H_2SO_4]{K_2Cr_2O_7}$

c. $CH_3\overset{\underset{|}{CH_3}}{CH}CH_2CHO \xrightarrow[\text{solution}]{\text{Benedict's}}$

59. Write the structural formulas for the products from these reactions.   26·6

a. $CH_3CH_2CH{=}CH_2 + Cl_2 \longrightarrow$

b. $CH_3CH_2CH{-}CH_2 + Br_2 \longrightarrow$

c. [cyclohexene structure] $+ HBR \longrightarrow$

d. $CH_3CH_2CH{=}C\overset{CH_3}{\underset{CH_3}{}} + H_2 \xrightarrow{\text{Pt or Pd}}$

60. Write the structure and name of the expected products for each of the following reactions.   26·11

a. $CH_3COOH + CH_3OH \xrightarrow{H^+}$
b. $CH_3CH_2CH_2COOCH_2CH_3 + H_2O \xrightarrow{NaOH}$
c. $CH_3CH_2OH \xrightarrow{K_2Cr_2O_7}$
d. $CH_3CH_2CH_2COOH + NaOH \longrightarrow$

Review Questions and Problems

61. A solution is made by diluting 250 mL of $0.210M$ $Ca(NO_3)_2$ solution with water to a final volume of 450 mL. Calculate the molarity of $Ca(NO_3)_2$ in the diluted solution.

62. A solution contains 24 g of K_2SO_4 in 150 mL of solution. What is the percent (mass/volume) of this solution?

63. In a saturated solution containing undissolved solute, the solute is continually dissolving, but the solution concentration remains constant. Explain.

64. What is the maximum number of orbitals in the p sublevel of an atom?   **a.** 1   **b.** 3   **c.** 5   **d.** 9

65. Using electron dot structures, illustrate the formation of F^- from a fluorine atom and a hydroxide ion from atoms of hydrogen and oxygen.

66. Calculate the mass, in grams, of one liter of SO_2 at standard temperature and pressure.

67. Name the following acids and bases.
  a. HNO_3 **d.** $Ca(OH)_2$
  b. H_2SO_3 **e.** $HClO_4$
  c. HNO_2 **f.** H_3PO_4

68. Give the oxidation numbers of the following atoms.
  a. Mn in $(MnO_4)^-$ **c.** C in $(C_2O_4)^{2-}$
  b. Cr in Cr_2O_3 **d.** P in PH_3

Challenging Questions and Problems

69. Cholesterol is a compound that is in our diet and is also synthesized in the liver. Sometimes it is deposited on the inner walls of blood vessels, causing hardening of the arteries. Describe the structural features and functional groups of this important molecule.

70. Hydrocarbons from petroleum are an important source of raw material for the chemical industry. Using reactions covered in this chapter and any required inorganic chemicals, propose a scheme for the manufacture of ethylene glycol, a major component of antifreeze, from petrochemical ethene.

Research Projects

1. How were the substances isolated by Pierre Pelletier and Joseph Caventou important to the pharmaceutical industry?

2. Devise a method to isolate the ester components of common fruits.

3. Make a diagram of an industrial-scale polymerization process.

4. Compare the saturations of various cooking oils.

5. Produce soaps from different fats and compare their properties.

6. Use paper chromatography to separate amino acids in a mixture. Identify each amino acid.

7. What are the structures for some common pesticides? How do these compounds operate? What problems are associated with their use?

8. Outline the steps involved in recombinant DNA technology. What are some of its products?

Readings and References

Baltimore, David. "The Brain of a Cell." *Science 84* (November 1984), pp. 149–151.

Eisner, Thomas. "Nature's Chemists." *Science Year* (1981), pp. 126–137.

Freidel, Robert. "The Plastics Man." *Science 84* (November 1984), pp. 49–51.

Hahn, James, and Lynn Hahn. *Plastics*. New York: Watts, 1974.

Milby, Robert V. *Plastics Technology*. New York: McGraw-Hill, 1973.

Yudkin, Michael, and Robin Offord. *A Guidebook to Biochemistry,* 4th ed. New York: Cambridge University Press, 1980.

Appendix A   Reference Tables

Table A·1   Some Properties of the Elements

Element	Symbol	Atomic number	Atomic mass	Melting point (°C)	Boiling point (°C)	Density (g/cm³) (gases at STP)	Major oxidation states
Actinium	Ac	89	(227.0482)	1050	3200	10.07	+3
Aluminum	Al	13	26.98154	660.37	2467	2.6989	+3
Americium	Am	95	243	994	2607	13.67	+3, +4, +5, +6
Antimony	Sb	51	121.75	630.74	1950	6.691	−3, +3, +5
Argon	Ar	18	39.948	−189.2	−185.7	.0017837	
Arsenic	As	33	74.9216	817	613	5.73	−3, +3, +5
Astatine	At	85	(210)	302	337	—	
Barium	Ba	56	137.33	725	1640	3.5	+2
Berkelium	Bk	97	(247)	986	—	14.78	
Beryllium	Be	4	9.01218	1278	2970	1.848	+2
Bismuth	Bi	83	208.9804	271.3	1560	9.747	+3, +5
Boron	B	5	10.81	2079	3675	2.34	+3
Bromine	Br	35	79.904	−7.2	58.78	3.12	−1, +1, +5
Cadmium	Cd	48	112.41	320.9	765	8.65	+2
Calcium	Ca	20	40.08	839	1484	1.55	+2
Californium	Cf	98	(251)	900	—	14	
Carbon	C	6	12.011	3550	4827	2.267	−4, +2, +4
Cerium	Ce	58	140.12	799	3426	6.657	+3, +4
Cesium	Cs	55	132.9054	28.40	669.3	1.873	+1
Chlorine	Cl	17	35.453	−100.98	−34.6	.003214	−1, +1, +5, +7
Chromium	Cr	24	51.996	1857	2672	7.18	+2, +3, +6
Cobalt	Co	27	58.9332	1495	2870	8.9	+2, +3
Copper	Cu	29	63.546	1083.4	2567	8.96	+1, +2
Curium	Cm	96	(247)	1340	—	13.51	+3
Dysprosium	Dy	66	162.50	1412	2562	8.550	+3
Einsteinium	Es	99	(252)	—	—	—	
Erbium	Er	68	167.26	159	2863	9.066	+3
Europium	Eu	63	151.96	822	1597	5.243	+2, +3
Fermium	Fm	100	(257)	—	—	—	
Fluorine	F	9	18.998403	−219.62	−188.54	.001696	−1
Francium	Fr	87	(223)	27	677	—	+1
Gadolinium	Gd	64	157.25	1313	3266	7.9004	+3
Gallium	Ga	31	69.72	29.78	2403	5.904	+3
Germanium	Ge	32	72.59	937.4	2830	5.323	+2, +4
Gold	Au	79	196.9665	1064.43	3080	19.3	+1, +3
Hafnium	Hf	72	178.49	2227	4602	13.31	+4
Helium	He	2	4.00260	−272.2	−268.934	.001785	
Holmium	Ho	67	164.9304	1474	2695	8.795	+3
Hydrogen	H	1	1.00794	−259.14	−252.87	.00008988	+1
Indium	In	49	114.82	156.61	2080	7.31	+1, +3
Iodine	I	53	126.9045	113.5	184.35	4.93	−1, +1, +5, +7
Iridium	Ir	77	192.22	2410	4130	22.42	+3, +4
Iron	Fe	26	55.847	1535	2750	7.874	+2, +3
Krypton	Kr	36	83.80	−156.6	−152.30	.003733	
Lanthanum	La	57	138.9055	921	3457	6.145	+3
Lawrencium	Lr	103	(260)	—	—	—	+3
Lead	Pb	82	207.2	327.502	1740	11.35	+2, +4
Lithium	Li	3	6.941	180.54	1342	0.534	+1
Lutetium	Lu	71	174.967	1663	3395	9.840	+3
Magnesium	Mg	12	24.305	648.8	1090	1.738	+2
Manganese	Mn	25	54.9380	1244	1962	7.32	+2, +3, +4, +7
Mendelevium	Md	101	257	—	—	—	+2, +3
Mercury	Hg	80	200.59	−38.842	356.58	13.546	+1, +2
Molybedenum	Mo	42	95.94	2617	4612	10.22	+6

Table A·1 Some Properties of the Elements (cont.)

Element	Symbol	Atomic number	Atomic mass	Melting point (°C)	Boiling point (°C)	Density (g/cm³) (gases at STP)	Major oxidation states
Neodymium	Nd	60	144.24	1021	3068	6.90	+3
Neon	Ne	10	20.179	−248.67	−246.048	.0008999	
Neptunium	Np	93	237.0482	640	3902	20.25	+3, +4, +5, +6
Nickel	Ni	28	58.69	1453	2732	8.902	+2, +3
Niobium	Nb	41	92.9064	2468	4742	8.57	+3, +5
Nitrogen	N	7	14.0067	−209.86	−195.8	.0012506	−3, +3, +5
Nobelium	No	102	(259)	—	—	—	+2, +3
Osmium	Os	76	190.2	3045	5027	22.57	+3, +4
Oxygen	O	8	15.9994	−218.4	−182.962	.001429	−2
Palladium	Pd	46	106.42	1554	2970	12.02	+2, +4
Phosphorus	P	15	30.97376	44.1	280	1.82	−3, +3, +5
Platinum	Pt	78	195.08	1772	3827	21.45	+2, +4
Plutonium	Pu	94	(244)	641	3232	19.84	+3, +4, +5, +6
Polonium	Po	84	(209)	254	962	9.32	+2, +4
Potassium	K	19	39.0982	63.25	760	.862	+1
Praseodymium	Pr	59	140.9077	931	3512	6.64	+3
Promethium	Pm	61	(145)	1168	2460	7.22	+3
Protactinium	Pa	91	231.0359	1560	4027	15.37	+4, +5
Radium	Ra	88	226.0254	700	1140	5.5	+2
Radon	Rn	86	(222)	−71	−61.8	.00973	
Rhenium	Re	75	186.207	3180	5627	21.02	+4, +6, +7
Rhodium	Rh	45	102.9055	1966	3727	12.41	+3
Rubidium	Rb	37	85.4678	38.89	686	1.532	+1
Ruthenium	Ru	44	101.07	2310	3900	12.41	+3
Samarium	Sm	62	150.36	1077	1791	7.520	+2, +3
Scandium	Sc	21	44.9559	1541	2831	2.989	+3
Selenium	Se	34	78.96	217	684.9	4.79	−2, +4, +6
Silicon	Si	14	28.0855	1410	2355	2.33	−4, +2, +4
Silver	Ag	47	107.8682	961.93	2212	10.50	+1
Sodium	Na	11	22.98977	97.81	882.9	0.971	+1
Strontium	Sr	38	87.62	769	1384	2.54	+2
Sulfur	S	16	32.06	112.8	444.7	2.07	−2, +4, +6
Tantalum	Ta	73	180.9479	2996	5425	16.654	+5
Technetium	Tc	43	(98)	2172	4877	11.50	+4, +6, +7
Tellurium	Te	52	127.60	449.5	989.8	6.24	−2, +4, +6
Terbium	Tb	65	158.9254	1356	3123	8.229	+3
Thallium	Tl	81	204.383	303.5	1457	11.85	+1, +3
Thorium	Th	90	232.0381	1750	4790	11.72	+4
Thulium	Tm	69	168.9342	1545	1947	9.321	+3
Tin	Sn	50	118.69	231.968	2270	7.31	+2, +4
Titanium	Ti	22	47.88	1660	3287	4.54	+2, +3, +4
Tungsten	W	74	183.85	3410	5660	19.3	+6
Uranium	U	92	238.0289	1132.3	3818	18.95	+3, +4, +5, +6
Vanadium	V	23	50.9415	1890	3380	6.11	+2, +3, +4, +5
Xenon	Xe	54	131.29	−111.9	−107.1	.005887	
Ytterbium	Yb	70	173.04	819	1194	6.965	+2, +3
Yttrium	Y	39	88.9059	1522	3338	4.469	+3
Zinc	Zn	30	65.38	419.58	907	7.133	+2
Zirconium	Zr	40	91.22	1852	4377	6.506	+4
Element 104	(Rf)	104					
Element 105	(Ha)	105					
Element 106		106					
Element 107		107					
Element 109		109					

Table A·2 Electron Configurations of the Elements

	Elements															Sublevels				
		$1s$	$2s$	$2p$	$3s$	$3p$	$3d$	$4s$	$4p$	$4d$	$4f$	$5s$	$5p$	$5d$	$5f$	$6s$	$6p$	$6d$	$6f$	$7s$
1	hydrogen	1																		
2	helium	2																		
3	lithium	2	1																	
4	beryllium	2	2																	
5	boron	2	2	1																
6	carbon	2	2	2																
7	nitrogen	2	2	3																
8	oxygen	2	2	4																
9	fluorine	2	2	5																
10	neon	2	2	6																
11	sodium	2	2	6	1															
12	magnesium	2	2	6	2															
13	aluminum	2	2	6	2	1														
14	silicon	2	2	6	2	2														
15	phosphorus	2	2	6	2	3														
16	sulfur	2	2	6	2	4														
17	chlorine	2	2	6	2	5														
18	argon	2	2	6	2	6														
19	potassium	2	2	6	2	6		1												
20	calcium	2	2	6	2	6		2												
21	scandium	2	2	6	2	6	1	2												
22	titanium	2	2	6	2	6	2	2												
23	vanadium	2	2	6	2	6	3	2												
24	chromium	2	2	6	2	6	5	1												
25	manganese	2	2	6	2	6	5	2												
26	iron	2	2	6	2	6	6	2												
27	cobalt	2	2	6	2	6	7	2												
28	nickel	2	2	6	2	6	8	2												
29	copper	2	2	6	2	6	10	1												
30	zinc	2	2	6	2	6	10	2												
31	gallium	2	2	6	2	6	10	2	1											
32	germanium	2	2	6	2	6	10	2	2											
33	arsenic	2	2	6	2	6	10	2	3											
34	selenium	2	2	6	2	6	10	2	4											
35	bromine	2	2	6	2	6	10	2	5											
36	krypton	2	2	6	2	6	10	2	6											
37	rubidium	2	2	6	2	6	10	2	6			1								
38	strontium	2	2	6	2	6	10	2	6			2								
39	yttrium	2	2	6	2	6	10	2	6	1		2								
40	zirconium	2	2	6	2	6	10	2	6	2		2								
41	niobium	2	2	6	2	6	10	2	6	4		1								
42	molybdenum	2	2	6	2	6	10	2	6	5		1								
43	technetium	2	2	6	2	6	10	2	6	5		2								
44	ruthenium	2	2	6	2	6	10	2	6	7		1								
45	rhodium	2	2	6	2	6	10	2	6	8		1								
46	palladium	2	2	6	2	6	10	2	6	10										
47	silver	2	2	6	2	6	10	2	6	10		1								
48	cadmium	2	2	6	2	6	10	2	6	10		2								
49	indium	2	2	6	2	6	10	2	6	10		2	1							
50	tin	2	2	6	2	6	10	2	6	10		2	2							
51	antimony	2	2	6	2	6	10	2	6	10		2	3							
52	tellurium	2	2	6	2	6	10	2	6	10		2	4							
53	iodine	2	2	6	2	6	10	2	6	10		2	5							
54	xenon	2	2	6	2	6	10	2	6	10		2	6							

Table A·2 Electron Configurations of the Elements (cont.)

	Elements	\	\	\	\	\	\	\	\	\	\	Sublevels	\	\	\	\	\	\	\	\
		1s	2s	2p	3s	3p	3d	4s	4p	4d	4f	5s	5p	5d	5f	6s	6p	6d	6f	7s
55	cesium	2	2	6	2	6	10	2	6	10		2	6			1				
56	barium	2	2	6	2	6	10	2	6	10		2	6			2				
57	lanthanum	2	2	6	2	6	10	2	6	10		2	6	1		2				
58	cerium	2	2	6	2	6	10	2	6	10	2	2	6			2				
59	praseodymium	2	2	6	2	6	10	2	6	10	3	2	6			2				
60	neodymium	2	2	6	2	6	10	2	6	10	4	2	6			2				
61	promethium	2	2	6	2	6	10	2	6	10	5	2	6			2				
62	samarium	2	2	6	2	6	10	2	6	10	6	2	6			2				
63	europium	2	2	6	2	6	10	2	6	10	7	2	6			2				
64	gadolinium	2	2	6	2	6	10	2	6	10	7	2	6	1		2				
65	terbium	2	2	6	2	6	10	2	6	10	9	2	6			2				
66	dysprosium	2	2	6	2	6	10	2	6	10	10	2	6			2				
67	holmium	2	2	6	2	6	10	2	6	10	11	2	6			2				
68	erbium	2	2	6	2	6	10	2	6	10	12	2	6			2				
69	thulium	2	2	6	2	6	10	2	6	10	13	2	6			2				
70	ytterbium	2	2	6	2	6	10	2	6	10	14	2	6			2				
71	lutetium	2	2	6	2	6	10	2	6	10	14	2	6	1		2				
72	hafnium	2	2	6	2	6	10	2	6	10	14	2	6	2		2				
73	tantalum	2	2	6	2	6	10	2	6	10	14	2	6	3		2				
74	tungsten	2	2	6	2	6	10	2	6	10	14	2	6	4		2				
75	rhenium	2	2	6	2	6	10	2	6	10	14	2	6	5		2				
76	osmium	2	2	6	2	6	10	2	6	10	14	2	6	6		2				
77	iridium	2	2	6	2	6	10	2	6	10	14	2	6	7		2				
78	platinum	2	2	6	2	6	10	2	6	10	14	2	6	9		1				
79	gold	2	2	6	2	6	10	2	6	10	14	2	6	10		1				
80	mercury	2	2	6	2	6	10	2	6	10	14	2	6	10		2				
81	thallium	2	2	6	2	6	10	2	6	10	14	2	6	10		2	1			
82	lead	2	2	6	2	6	10	2	6	10	14	2	6	10		2	2			
83	bismuth	2	2	6	2	6	10	2	6	10	14	2	6	10		2	3			
84	polonium	2	2	6	2	6	10	2	6	10	14	2	6	10		2	4			
85	astatine	2	2	6	2	6	10	2	6	10	14	2	6	10		2	5			
86	radon	2	2	6	2	6	10	2	6	10	14	2	6	10		2	6			
87	francium	2	2	6	2	6	10	2	6	10	14	2	6	10		2	6			1
88	radium	2	2	6	2	6	10	2	6	10	14	2	6	10		2	6			2
89	actinium	2	2	6	2	6	10	2	6	10	14	2	6	10		2	6	1		2
90	thorium	2	2	6	2	6	10	2	6	10	14	2	6	10		2	6	2		2
91	protactinium	2	2	6	2	6	10	2	6	10	14	2	6	10	2	2	6	1		2
92	uranium	2	2	6	2	6	10	2	6	10	14	2	6	10	3	2	6	1		2
93	neptunium	2	2	6	2	6	10	2	6	10	14	2	6	10	4	2	6	1		2
94	plutonium	2	2	6	2	6	10	2	6	10	14	2	6	10	6	2	6			2
95	americium	2	2	6	2	6	10	2	6	10	14	2	6	10	7	2	6			2
96	curium	2	2	6	2	6	10	2	6	10	14	2	6	10	7	2	6	1		2
97	berkelium	2	2	6	2	6	10	2	6	10	14	2	6	10	9	2	6			2
98	californium	2	2	6	2	6	10	2	6	10	14	2	6	10	10	2	6			2
99	einsteinium	2	2	6	2	6	10	2	6	10	14	2	6	10	11	2	6			2
100	fermium	2	2	6	2	6	10	2	6	10	14	2	6	10	12	2	6			2
101	mendelevium	2	2	6	2	6	10	2	6	10	14	2	6	10	13	2	6			2
102	nobelium	2	2	6	2	6	10	2	6	10	14	2	6	10	14	2	6			2
103	lawrencium	2	2	6	2	6	10	2	6	10	14	2	6	10	14	2	6	1		2
104	unnilquadium	2	2	6	2	6	10	2	6	10	14	2	6	10	14	2	6	2		2?
105	unnilpentium	2	2	6	2	6	10	2	6	10	14	2	6	10	14	2	6	3		2?
106	unnilhexium	2	2	6	2	6	10	2	6	10	14	2	6	10	14	2	6	4		2?
107	unnilseptium	2	2	6	2	6	10	2	6	10	14	2	6	10	14	2	6	5		2?
108	unniloctium	2	2	6	2	6	10	2	6	10	14	2	6	10	14	2	6	6		2?
109	unnilennium	2	2	6	2	6	10	2	6	10	14	2	6	10	14	2	6	7		2?

Table A·3 Symbols of Common Elements

Ag	silver	Cu	copper	O	oxygen
Al	aluminum	F	fluorine	P	phosphorus
As	arsenic	Fe	iron	Pb	lead
Au	gold	H	hydrogen	Pt	platinum
Ba	barium	Hg	mercury	S	sulfur
Bi	bismuth	I	iodine	Sb	antimony
Br	bromine	K	potassium	Sn	tin
C	carbon	Mg	magnesium	Sr	strontium
Ca	calcium	Mn	manganese	Ti	titanium
Cl	chlorine	N	nitrogen	U	uranium
Co	cobalt	Na	sodium	W	tungsten
Cr	chromium	Ni	nickel	Zn	zinc

Table A·4 Symbols of Common Polyatomic Ions

$C_2H_3O_2^-$	acetate	$Cr_2O_7^{2-}$	dichromate	NH_4^+	ammonium
ClO^-	hypochlorite	HCO_3^-	hydrogen carbonate	NO_3^-	nitrate
ClO_2^-	chlorite		bicarbonate	NO_2^-	nitrite
ClO_3^-	chlorate	H_3O^+	hydronium	O_2^{2-}	peroxide
ClO_4^-	perchlorate	HPO_4^{2-}	hydrogen phosphate	OH^-	hydroxide
CN^-	cyanide	HSO_3^-	hydrogen sulfite	PO_4^{3-}	phosphate
CO_3^{2-}	carbonate	HSO_4^-	hydrogen sulfate	SO_3^{2-}	sulfite
CrO_4^{2-}	chromate	MnO_4^-	permanganate	SO_4^{2-}	sulfate

Table A·5 Other Symbols and Abbreviations

α	alpha rays	gmm	gram molecular mass	m	mass
β	beta rays	H	enthalpy	m	molality
γ	gamma rays	H_f	heat of formation	mL	milliliter (*volume*)
Δ	change in	hr	hour	mm	millimeter (*length*)
δ^-, δ^+	partial atomic charge	h	Planck's constant	mol	mole (*amount*)
λ	wavelength	Hz	hertz (*frequency*)	mp	melting point
π	pi bond	J	joule (*energy*)	N	normality
σ	sigma bond	K	Kelvin (*temperature*)	n	neutron
ν	frequency	K_a	acid dissociation constant	n	number of moles
amu	atomic mass unit	K_b	base dissociation constant	n	principal quantum number
aq	aqueous solution	K_b	molal boiling point	P	pressure
atm	atmosphere (*pressure*)		elevation constant	p^+	proton
bp	boiling point	K_{eq}	equilibrium constant	Pa	pascal (*pressure*)
°C	degree Celsius (*temperature*)	K_f	molal freezing point	R	ideal gas constant
c	speed of light in a vacuum		depression constant	S	entropy
cm	centimeter (*length*)	K_w	ion product constant	s	second
D	density		for water	s	solid
E	energy	K_{sp}	solubility product constant	SI	International System
e^-	electron	kcal	kilocalorie (*energy*)		of Units
fp	freezing point	kg	kilogram (*mass*)	STP	standard temperature
G	Gibb's free energy	kPa	kilopascal (*pressure*)		and pressure
g	gram (*mass*)	L	liter (*volume*)	T	temperature
g	gas	*l*	liquid	$t_{1/2}$	half-life
gam	gram atomic mass	M	molarity	V	volume
gfm	gram formula mass	m	meter (*length*)	v	velocity

Table A·6 Physical Constants

Atomic mass unit	$1 \text{ amu} = 1.6605 \times 10^{-24} \text{ g}$
Avogadro's number	$N = 6.0221 \times 10^{23} \dfrac{\text{particles}}{\text{mol}}$
Gas constant	$R = 8.2056 \times 10^{-2} \dfrac{\text{L} \times \text{atm}}{\text{K} \times \text{mol}}$
Ideal gas molar volume	$V_m = 22.414 \dfrac{\text{L}}{\text{mol}}$
Masses of fundamental particles	
Electron (e^-)	$m_e = 0.0005486 \text{ amu}$
	$= 9.1096 \times 10^{-28} \text{ g}$
Proton (p^+)	$m_p = 1.007277 \text{ amu}$
	$= 1.67261 \times 10^{-24} \text{ g}$
Neutron (n)	$m_n = 1.008665 \text{ amu}$
	$= 1.67492 \times 10^{-24} \text{ g}$
Speed of light (in vacuum)	$c = 2.997925 \times 10^8 \dfrac{\text{m}}{\text{s}}$

Table A·7 Solubilities of Compounds at 25°C and 1 atm

	acetate	bromide	carbonate	chlorate	chloride	hydroxide	iodide	nitrate	oxide	perchlorate	phosphate	sulfate	sulfide
aluminum	S	S	—	S	S	I	S	S	I	S	I	S	d
ammonium	S	S	S	S	S	S	S	S	—	S	S	S	S
barium	S	S	I	S	S	S	S	S	sS	S	I	I	d
calcium	S	S	I	S	S	S	S	S	sS	S	I	sS	I
copper(II)	S	S	—	S	S	I	S	S	I	S	I	S	I
iron(II)	S	S	I	S	S	I	S	S	I	S	I	S	I
iron(III)	S	S	—	S	S	I	S	S	I	S	I	sS	d
lithium	S	S	sS	S	S	S	S	S	S	S	sS	S	S
magnesium	S	S	I	S	S	I	S	S	I	S	I	S	d
potassium	S	S	S	S	S	I	S	S	S	S	S	S	S
silver	sS	I	I	S	I	—	I	S	I	S	I	sS	I
sodium	S	S	S	S	S	S	S	S	S	S	S	S	S
strontium	S	S	I	S	S	S	S	S	S	S	I	I	I
zinc	S	S	I	S	S	I	S	S	I	S	I	S	I

Key: S = soluble
  sS = slightly soluble
  I = insoluble

d = decomposes in water
— = no such compound

B·1   Exponential (Scientific) Notation

Chemists often use very large and very small numbers. For example, the mass of a hydrogen atom is 0.000 000 000 000 000 000 000 001 67 g. The distance between two hydrogen atoms in a hydrogen molecule is 0.000 000 000 03 m. Even a relatively small quantity of hydrogen (2.0 g) is composed of 602 000 000 000 000 000 000 000 hydrogen molecules. Numbers this large and small are very inconvenient and even difficult to use, especially in calculations. When using very large and very small numbers it is helpful to write these numbers in *exponential form* or *scientific notation*.

In standard exponential form, a number is written as the product of two numbers: a *coefficient* and a *power of 10*. For example, the number 2300 written in exponential form is 2.3×10^3. The coefficient here is 2.3. A coefficient is a number greater than or equal to one and less than ten. The superscript here is 3. It is the *exponent* or power of 10. The exponent indicates how many times the coefficient 2.3 must be multiplied by 10 to equal the number 2300. The product of $2.3 \times 10 \times 10 \times 10$ (or 2.3×10^3) equals 2300. Some other examples are as follows.

$$12\ 000\ 000 = 1.2 \times 10^7$$

$$85\ 130 = 8.513 \times 10^4$$

When writing numbers greater than ten in exponential form, the exponent is equal to the number of places that the decimal point has been moved to the left.

$$\underbrace{12\ 000\ 000}_{7 \text{ places}} \qquad \underbrace{85\ 130}_{4 \text{ places}}$$

Numbers less than one have a negative exponent when written in exponential form. The number 0.000 72 written in exponential form is 7.2×10^{-4}. The negative exponent -4 indicates that the coefficient 7.2 must be divided four times by 10 to equal the number 0.000 72. Thus

$$7.2 \times 10^{-4} = \frac{7.2}{10 \times 10 \times 10 \times 10} = 0.000\ 72$$

Here are some other examples.

$$0.000\ 05 = 5 \times 10^{-5}$$

$$0.0342 = 3.42 \times 10^{-2}$$

When writing numbers less than one in exponential form, the value of the exponent equals the number of places the decimal has been moved to the right. The sign is negative.

$$\underset{5 \text{ places}}{0.000\ 05} \qquad \underset{2 \text{ places}}{0.0342}$$

Problem

1. Express these numbers in standard exponential form.

a. 20 000	**d.** 34.1	**g.** 40 230 000
b. 543.6	**e.** 0.000 55	**h.** 0.099
c. 0.000 005	**f.** 0.003 45	**i.** 628 000

When working problems, your calculated answer may not be in standard exponential form. Exponential numbers can be changed to standard form by using the rules just given.

$$504.2 \times 10^6 = 5.042 \times 10^8$$
2 places

$$0.15 \times 10^2 = 1.5 \times 10^1$$
1 place

$$42.2 \times 10^{-5} = 4.22 \times 10^{-4} \ (10^{-4} \text{ is larger than } 10^{-5})$$
1 place

$$0.0089 \times 10^{-2} = 8.9 \times 10^{-5}$$
3 places

Problem

2. Express these numbers in standard exponential form.

a. 34.5×10^5	**c.** 180×10^{-1}	**e.** 765×10^7
b. 0.004×10^2	**d.** 0.72×10^{-2}	**f.** 0.029×10^{-6}

Multiplication and Division

To multiply numbers written in exponential form, multiply the coefficients and add the exponents.

$$(3 \times 10^4) \times (2 \times 10^2) = (3 \times 2) \times 10^{4+2}$$
$$= 6 \times 10^6$$
$$(2.1 \times 10^3) \times (4.0 \times 10^{-7}) = (2.1 \times 4.0) \times 10^{3+(-7)}$$
$$= 8.4 \times 10^{-4}$$
$$(8.0 \times 10^{-2}) \times (7.0 \times 10^{-5}) = (8.0 \times 7.0) \times 10^{-2+(-5)}$$
$$= 56 \times 10^{-7}$$
$$= 5.6 \times 10^{-6} \text{ (standard form)}$$

Problem

3. Answer each problem in standard exponential form.

a. $(2 \times 10^9) \times (4 \times 10^3)$	**d.** $(3.4 \times 10^{-3}) \times (2.5 \times 10^{-5})$
b. $(6.2 \times 10^{-3}) \times (1.5 \times 10^1)$	**e.** $(0.10 \times 10^5) \times (4.9 \times 10^{-2})$
c. $10^{-4} \times 10^8 \times 10^{-2}$	**f.** $(88 \times 10^2) \times (0.15 \times 10^4)$

To divide numbers written in exponential form, divide the coefficients and subtract the exponent in the denominator from the exponent in the numerator.

$$\frac{3.0 \times 10^5}{6.0 \times 10^2} = \left(\frac{3.0}{6.0}\right) \times 10^{5-2} = 0.50 \times 10^3$$

$$= 5.0 \times 10^2 \text{ (standard form)}$$

$$\frac{8.4 \times 10^{-6}}{2.1 \times 10^2} = \left(\frac{8.4}{2.1}\right) \times 10^{-6-(+2)} = 4.0 \times 10^{-8}$$

$$\frac{4.56 \times 10^5}{2.93 \times 10^{-3}} = \left(\frac{4.56}{2.93}\right) \times 10^{5-(-3)} = 1.56 \times 10^8$$

Problem

4. a. 4.0×10^5
b. 4.0×10^9
c. 10^4
d. 1×10^2
e. 7.02×10^{-7}
f. $3.\overline{19} \times 10^{17}$
g. 1.70×10^{-3}
h. 2.52×10^{17}

4. Do each problem and express the answer in standard exponential form.

a. $\dfrac{8.8 \times 10^6}{2.2 \times 10^1}$

b. $\dfrac{5.2 \times 10^2}{1.3 \times 10^{-7}}$

c. $\dfrac{10^8 \times 10^{-3}}{10^{-4} \times 10^5}$

d. $\dfrac{1 \times 10^{-7}}{1 \times 10^{-9}}$

e. $\dfrac{0.40 \times 10^{-4}}{5.7 \times 10^1}$

f. $\dfrac{6.8 \times 10^{12}}{0.22 \times 10^{-4}}$

g. $\dfrac{13.6 \times 10^{12}}{8.00 \times 10^{15}}$

h. $\dfrac{753 \times 10^6}{0.300 \times 10^{-8}}$

Addition and Subtraction

Before numbers in exponential form are added or subtracted, the exponents must be the same. For example, what is the sum of 5.4×10^3 and 6.0×10^2? Rewrite the second number so that the exponent is a three, $6.0 \times 10^2 = 0.60 \times 10^3$. Now add the numbers.

$$(5.4 \times 10^3) + (0.60 \times 10^3) = (5.4 + 0.60) \times 10^3$$

$$= 6.0 \times 10^3$$

Similarly,

$$(3.42 \times 10^{-5}) - (2.5 \times 10^{-6}) = (3.42 \times 10^{-5}) - (0.25 \times 10^{-5})$$

$$= (3.42 - 0.25) \times 10^{-5}$$

$$= 3.17 \times 10^{-5}$$

Problem

5. a. 7.9×10^4
b. 7.3×10^{-2}
c. 6.2×10^{-8}
d. 6.4×10^{-2}
e. 2.435×10^6
f. 7.68×10^5
g. 1.028×10^5
h. 1.2×10^2

5. Do each problem and express the answer in standard exponential form.

a. $5.2 \times 10^4 + 2.7 \times 10^4$

b. $9.4 \times 10^{-2} - 2.1 \times 10^{-2}$

c. $6.6 \times 10^{-8} - 4.0 \times 10^{-9}$

d. $6.7 \times 10^{-2} - 3.0 \times 10^{-3}$

e. $23.4 \times 10^5 + 9.5 \times 10^4$

f. $568 \times 10^3 + 2 \times 10^5$

g. $3.75 \times 10^5 + 653 \times 10^3$

h. $0.0073 \times 10^5 - 61000 \times 10^{-2}$

B·2 Algebraic Equations

Many relationships in chemistry can be expressed by simple algebraic equations. Often an equation is not given in the form that is most useful for a particular problem. In such a case you must first solve the equation for the unknown quantity. Solving an equation means rearranging it so that the unknown quantity is on one side of the equation and all the known quantities are on the other side. For instance, consider the following equation.

$$K = {}^\circ C + 273$$

It states the relationship between the Kelvin and Celsius temperature scales (Chapter 2). Can this equation be used to find the Celsius temperature equivalent to 400 K? Yes, it can, if the equation is first solved for the unknown quantity, °C.

An equation is solved using the laws of equality. The **laws of equality** are summarized as follows. *If equals are added to, subtracted from, multiplied by, or divided by equals, the results are equal.* In other words, you can perform any of these mathematic operations on an equation and not destroy the equality, *as long as you do the same thing to both sides of the equation.* The laws of equality apply to any legitimate mathematic operation, including squaring, taking square roots, and taking the logarithm.

To solve the equation in the example for °C, subtract 273 from both sides of the equation.

$$K = {}^\circ C + 273$$

$$K - 273 = {}^\circ C + 273 - 273$$

$$^\circ C = K - 273$$

Once you have solved an equation, substitute in the known quantities and calculate the value of the unknown quantity. A temperature of 400 K is converted to °C as follows.

$$^\circ C = K - 273 = 400 - 273 = 127^\circ C$$

The relationship between the Fahrenheit and Celsius temperature scales is °F = (1.8)°C + 32. Use this relationship to find the Celsius temperature equivalent to 392°F.

To solve for °C, both the 1.8 and the 32 must be moved to the other side of the equation. Since the 32 is added to the quantity (1.8 times °C), first subtract 32 from both sides of the equation.

$$^\circ F = (1.8)^\circ C + 32$$

$$^\circ F - 32 = (1.8)^\circ C + \cancel{32} - \cancel{32}$$

$$^\circ F - 32 = (1.8)^\circ C$$

Now divide each side of the equation by 1.8.

$$\frac{^\circ F - 32}{1.8} = \frac{(\cancel{1.8})^\circ C}{\cancel{1.8}}$$

$$°C = \frac{°F - 32}{1.8}$$

Finally, substitute the given quantity.

$$°C = \frac{392 - 32}{1.8} = \frac{360}{1.8} = 200°C$$

An equation that shows how the volume of a gas changes with a change in temperature (Chapter 10) is as follows.

$$\frac{V_1}{T_1} = \frac{V_2}{T_2}$$

What is the value of T_2 when $V_1 = 5.0$ L, $V_2 = 15$ L, and $T_1 = 200$ K? Solve for T_2.

$$T_2 = \frac{V_2 T_1}{V_1}$$

Substitute the given quantities into the solved equation.

$$T_2 = \frac{(15\ \cancel{L})(200\ K)}{5.0\ \cancel{L}} = 600\ K$$

Problems

6. $T = \dfrac{P \times V}{n \times R}$

7. $V_1 = \dfrac{P_2 \times V_2 \times T_1}{T_2 \times P_1}$

8. $v = \sqrt{\dfrac{2E}{m}}$

9. $P_B = P_T - P_A - P_C$

10. a. $h = 20$
 b. $h = 26.25$
 c. $h = 0.16$
 d. $h = -11.7$

6. Solve for T: $P \times V = n \times R \times T$

7. Solve for V_1: $\dfrac{P_1 \times V_1}{T_1} = \dfrac{P_2 \times V_2}{T_2}$

8. Solve for v: $E = (m \times v^2)/2$

9. Solve for P_B: $P_T = P_A + P_B + P_C$.

10. Solve each of these equations for h. Calculate a value for h if $g = 12$, $k = 0.4$, and $m = 1.5$.

    a. $kh = \dfrac{g}{m}$ **c.** $gh - k = m$

    b. $\dfrac{g - m}{h} = k$ **d.** $\dfrac{mk}{g + h} = 2$

B·3 Percents

Percent means "parts of 100" or "parts per 100 parts." In slightly different terms, a percent is a part of a whole expressed in hundredths. The idea of a percent should be very familiar to you. Many times examination grades are expressed as a percent. What does a grade of 88% mean? Since the word percent (%) means "per 100 parts," 88% = 88/100, or 88 questions correct (the part) out of a possible 100 questions (the whole).

You are generally evaluated on exams that do not have 100 questions. Your grade can still be expressed as a percent. What is your grade

if you get 24 questions correct on a 30-question exam? The part over the whole, expressed as a percent is calculated as follows.

$$\frac{\text{Part}}{\text{Whole}} = \frac{\text{number correct}}{\text{number possible}} = \frac{24 \text{ questions correct}}{30 \text{ questions possible}} = 0.80 \text{ or } \frac{80}{100} \text{ or } 80\%$$

Based on the definition of percent, 0.80, 80/100, and 80% all express the same idea: eighty hundredths or 80 "per 100 parts." Mathematically, 0.80 can be shown to be equal to 80/100 because multiplying by 100/100 does not change the value of a number.

$$\frac{0.80}{1} \times \frac{100}{100} = \frac{80}{100}$$

An alternate way to calculate a percent is to multiply the ratio of the part over the whole by 100%.

$$\text{Percent} = \frac{\text{part}}{\text{whole}} \times 100\%$$

Problem

11. a. 73% correct
b. 82% correct
c. 57% correct

11. Calculate a percent grade for each exam.
   a. Eleven questions correctly answered on a 15-question exam.
   b. Forty-one questions correctly answered on a 50-question exam.
   c. Seventeen questions correctly answered on a 30-question exam.

A percent represents a relationship between two quantities and, as such, it can be used as a conversion factor (Chapter 3). For example, a friend tells you that she got a grade of 95% on a 40-question examination. How many questions did she answer correctly? A grade of 95% means 95 questions correct for each 100 questions possible.

$$40 \text{ questions possible} \times \frac{95 \text{ questions correct}}{100 \text{ questions possible}} = 38 \text{ questions correct}$$

As a final example of using a percent, six students are absent from class. If 80% of the students are present, what is the class enrollment? Since 80% of the class is present, the six students absent must represent 20% of the class. This absence rate of 20% means that 20 students are absent for each 100 students enrolled. Starting with the given, the number of students enrolled is calculated.

$$6 \text{ students absent} \times \frac{100 \text{ students enrolled}}{20 \text{ students absent}} = \frac{600}{20} = 30 \text{ students enrolled}$$

Problems

12. 23 g hydrogen peroxide
13. 55 mL alcohol

12. The antiseptic hydrogen peroxide is often sold as a 3.0% (by mass) solution, the rest being water. How many grams of hydrogen peroxide are in 750 g of this solution?

13. A nighttime cold medicine is 22% alcohol (by volume). How many mL of alcohol are in a 250 mL bottle of this medicine?

B·4 Graphing

The relationship between two variables in an experiment is often determined by graphing the experimental data. A graph is a "picture" of the data. Once a graph is constructed, additional information can be derived about the variables.

In constructing a graph we must first label the axes. The independent variable is plotted on the *x-axis* (*abscissa*). This is the horizontal axis. The independent variable is generally controlled by the experimenter. When the independent variable is changed, a corresponding change in the dependent variable is measured. The dependent variable is plotted on the *y-axis* (*ordinate*). This is the vertical axis. The label on each axis should include the unit of the quantity being graphed.

Before data can be plotted on a graph, each axis must be scaled. The scale must take into consideration the smallest and largest values of each quantity. Each interval (square on the graph paper) on the scale must represent the same amount. To make it easy to find numbers along the scale, the interval chosen is usually a multiple of 1, 2, 5, or 10. Although each scale can start at zero, this is not always practical.

Data is plotted by putting a point at the intersection of corresponding values of each pair of measurement. This is illustrated in the next example.

Once the data has been plotted, the points are connected by a smooth curve. This is not the same as "connecting-the-dots," which is an incorrect approach to drawing a line. A smooth curve comes as close as possible to all the plotted points. It may in fact not touch any of them.

Depending on the relationship between two variables the curve may or may not be a straight line. Two common curves are shown in graphs A and B.

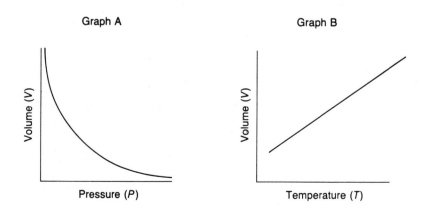

Graphs similar to these are found in Chapter 10 of the text. Graph A is typical of an inverse proportionality. As the independent variable (*P*) increases, the dependent variable (*V*) decreases. The product of the two variables at any point on the curve of an inverse proportionality is a constant. For graph A, $V \times P =$ constant.

The straight line in graph B is typical of a direct proportionality. As the independent variable (T) increases, there is a corresponding increase in the dependent variable (V). A straight line is represented by this general equation.

$$y = mx + b$$

Here y and x are the variables plotted on the vertical and horizontal axes respectively; m is the slope of the line; and b is the intercept on the y-axis.

The y intercept, b, is the value of y when x is zero. The slope, m, is the ratio of the change in y (Δy) for a corresponding change in x (Δx). This relationship is often symbolized in the following way.

$$m = \frac{\Delta y}{\Delta x}$$

As an example, consider this data about a bicyclist's trip. Assume that the bicyclist rode at a constant speed.

distance from home (km)	15	25	35	50	75
time (hours)	1	2	3	4.5	7

Let's graph this data using time as the independent variable, and then use the graph to answer the following questions.

a. How far from home was the bicyclist at the start of the trip?

b. How many hours did it take the bicyclist to get 40 km from home?

c. What was the bicyclist's average speed, in kilometers per hour, on the trip?

The plotted points are shown in Figure 1. Each point was plotted by finding the value of time on the x-axis, then moving up vertically to the value of the other variable (distance). A smooth curve, which in this case happens to be a straight line, has been drawn through the points.

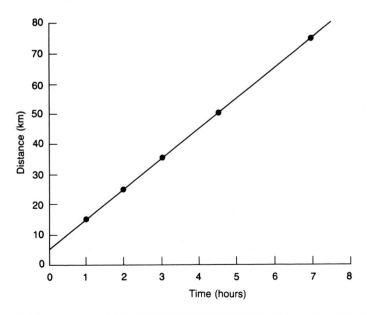

a. The graph in Figure 2 shows that the bicyclist started the trip 5 km from home. This is the value of the vertical axis (distance) when the time elapsed is zero (point *a* on the graph).

b. Find the given value, 40 km, on the vertical axis in Figure 2. Move to the right (horizontally) in the graph until you reach the line. Drop down vertically and read the value of time at this point (point *b*). It takes the bicyclist 3.5 hr to get 40 km from home. As another, similar example, how far is the bicyclist from home after riding 5 hr? Using the graph in Figure 2, start at 5 hr and go up to the line. Then move horizontally to the left. The distance, point *c*, is 55 km.

c. Speed is distance/time. The average speed of the bicyclist is the slope of the line. Calculate the slope using the data points from the previous part of this problem.

$$m = \frac{\Delta y}{\Delta x} = \frac{55 \text{ km} - 40 \text{ km}}{5 \text{ hr} - 3.5 \text{ hr}} = \frac{15 \text{ km}}{1.5 \text{ hr}} = 10 \text{ km/hr}$$

The equation for this line shows the relationship between time and distance traveled by the bicyclist.

$$\text{Distance} = (10 \text{ km/hr})(\text{time}) + 5 \text{ km}$$

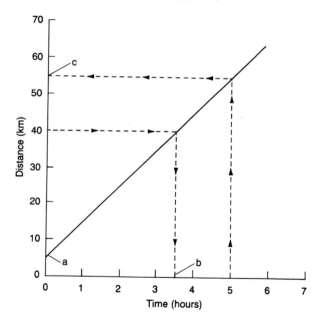

Problems

14. Use the data in the following table to draw a graph that shows the relationship between the Fahrenheit and Celsius temperature scales. Make degrees Fahrenheit the dependent variable. Use the graph to derive an equation between °F and °C. Then use the graph or the equation to complete the data table.

°F	50	212	356	−4	—	70	400
°C	10	100	180	−20	70	—	—

14.

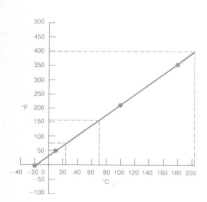

°F = (1.8 × °C) + 32
... 158 70 400
... 70   21 204

15. a.

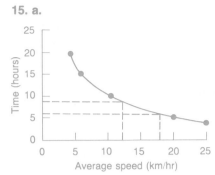

b. inverse
c. ~8.3 km/hr
d. 5.5 hours

16. a.

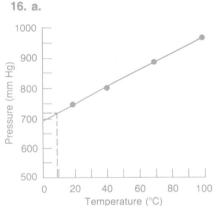

b. direct
c. ~9°C
d. ~700 mm Hg
e. m = 2.6
f. $P = 2.6T + 700$

15. A bicyclist wants to ride 100 kilometers. The data below show the time required to ride 100 kilometers at different average speeds.

Time (hours)	4	5	8	10	15	20
Average speed (km/hr)	25	20	12.5	10	6.6	5

a. Graph the data, using average speed as the independent variable.
b. Is this a direct or inverse proportionality?
c. Use the graph to determine what average speed must be maintained to complete the ride in 12 hours.
d. If a bicyclist maintains an average speed of 18 km/hr, how many hours does it take to ride 100 km?

16. The pressure of a fixed volume of gas varies with the temperature. A student collected the following data.

Temperature (°C)	10	20	40	70	100
sure (mm Hg)	726	750	800	880	960

a. Graph the data, using pressure as the dependent variable.
b. Is this a direct or inverse proportionality?
c. At what temperature is the gas pressure 722 mm Hg?
d. What is the pressure of this gas at a temperature of 0°C?
e. How does the pressure change with a change in temperature? That is, what is the slope of the line?
f. Write an equation relating pressure and temperature for this gas.

B·5   Logarithms

A logarithm is the exponent to which a fixed number (base) must be raised in order to produce a given number. Common logarithms use 10 as the base. A logarithm to the base 10 of a number is the exponent to which 10 must be raised to obtain the number. If $x = 10^y$, then log $x = y$. Here x is the number and y is the logarithm of x to the base 10.

Common logarithms must not be confused with natural logarithms which use base e, where $e = 2.71828$. When base 10 is used, logarithm is abbreviated $\log_{10}$, or often simply log. When the base e is used, logarithm is abbreviated ln.

The logarithm of a number has two parts, the characteristic, or whole-number part, and the mantissa, or decimal part. In the example log $421.6 = 2.6249$, the characteristic is 2 and the mantissa is 0.6249.

For numbers written in standard exponential form, the characteristic corresponds to the exponent of 10.

$$\log 10^1 = 1, \log 10^2 = 2, \log 10^3 = 3, \log 10^{-2} = -2.$$

The mantissa is the decimal part of a logarithm and can be looked up in a "log table." The number of significant figures in a logarithm is the number of figures in the mantissa.

As an example, the logarithm of 176 is found as follows.

1. Write 176 in exponential notation as 1.76×10^2.

2. Locate the number 1.7 in the column labeled N; then under the column headed 6 read the mantissa as 0.2455.

3. Because 1.76×10^2 contains only three significant figures, the mantissa is rounded off to three digits. Thus the mantissa is 0.246.

4. The characteristic is the exponent, 2.

5. The logarithm of 176 is 2.246 or log 176 = 2.246.

Logarithms can also be found using the log key of a calculator. Simply enter the number and press the key labeled "log".

Problem

17. a. 0.5378   **d.** −4.5072
   b. −2.0605   **e.** 9.1703
   c. 2.6590

17. Write the logarithms of the following numbers.
    a. 3.45   **b.** 0.0087   **c.** 456   **d.** 3.11×10^{-5} **e.** 1.48×10^9

The reverse process of converting a logarithm into a number is referred to as obtaining the antilogarithm. The antilogarithm of the logarithm of a number is the number itself. Here x represents any number.

$$\text{antilog } (\log x) = x$$

Antilogarithms can be obtained from a table of common logarithms. They can also be obtained with a calculator by using the "antilog" key, the "10^x" key, or the "inverse" key in conjuction with the "log" key.

For example, what is the antilog of the logarithm 4.618? Look in the body of the log table for the mantissa, 0.618. This value is found in the row with an N of 4.1 and in the column labeled 5. Thus the antilog of 0.618 is 4.15. The characteristic is 4. This corresponds to an exponential term of 10^4. The number whose log is 4.618 is 4.15×10^4.

Problem

18. a. 3.63×10^2 **d.** 1.07×10^1
   b. 1.29×10^6 **e.** 9.16
   c. 2.82×10^{-4}

18. Use a log table or a calculator to find the numbers (antilogarithms) which have the following logarithms.
    a. 2.56   **b.** 6.11   **c.** −3.55   **d.** 1.03   **e.** 0.962

There are rules based on the laws of exponents that must be followed when using logarithms for calculations. The logarithm of the product of two numbers is the sum of the number's logs.

$$\log(a \times b) = \log a + \log b$$

The log of the ratio of two numbers is the difference between the log of the denominator subtracted from the log of the numerator.

$$\log(a/b) = \log a - \log b.$$

Table B·5 Common Logarithms

x	0	1	2	3	4	5	6	7	8	9
1.0	.0000	.0043	.0086	.0128	.0170	.0212	.0253	.0294	.0334	.0374
1.1	.0414	.0453	.0492	.0531	.0569	.0607	.0645	.0682	.0719	.0755
1.2	.0792	.0828	.0864	.0899	.0934	.0969	.1004	.1038	.1072	.1106
1.3	.1139	.1173	.1206	.1239	.1271	.1303	.1335	.1367	.1399	.1430
1.4	.1461	.1492	.1523	.1553	.1584	.1614	.1644	.1673	.1703	.1732
1.5	.1761	.1790	.1818	.1847	.1875	.1903	.1931	.1959	.1987	.2014
1.6	.2041	.2068	.2095	.2122	.2148	.2175	.2201	.2227	.2253	.2279
1.7	.2304	.2330	.2355	.2380	.2405	.2430	.2455	.2480	.2504	.2529
1.8	.2553	.2577	.2601	.2625	.2648	.2672	.2695	.2718	.2742	.2765
1.9	.2788	.2810	.2833	.2856	.2878	.2900	.2923	.2945	.2967	.2989
2.0	.3010	.3032	.3054	.3075	.3096	.3118	.3139	.3160	.3181	.3201
2.1	.3222	.3243	.3263	.3284	.3304	.3324	.3345	.3365	.3385	.3404
2.2	.3424	.3444	.3464	.3483	.3502	.3522	.3541	.3560	.3579	.3598
2.3	.3617	.3636	.3655	.3674	.3692	.3711	.3729	.3747	.3766	.3784
2.4	.3802	.3820	.3838	.3856	.3874	.3892	.3909	.3927	.3945	.3962
2.5	.3979	.3997	.4014	.4031	.4048	.4065	.4082	.4099	.4116	.4133
2.6	.4150	.4166	.4183	.4200	.4216	.4232	.4249	.4265	.4281	.4298
2.7	.4314	.4330	.4346	.4362	.4378	.4393	.4409	.4425	.4440	.4456
2.8	.4472	.4487	.4502	.4518	.4533	.4548	.4564	.4579	.4594	.4609
2.9	.4624	.4639	.4654	.4669	.4683	.4698	.4713	.4728	.4742	.4757
3.0	.4771	.4786	.4800	.4814	.4829	.4843	.4857	.4871	.4886	.4900
3.1	.4914	.4928	.4942	.4955	.4969	.4983	.4997	.5011	.5024	.5038
3.2	.5051	.5065	.5079	.5092	.5105	.5119	.5132	.5145	.5159	.5172
3.3	.5185	.5198	.5211	.5224	.5237	.5250	.5263	.5276	.5289	.5307
3.4	.5315	.5328	.5340	.5353	.5366	.5378	.5391	.5403	.5416	.5428
3.5	.5441	.5453	.5465	.5478	.5490	.5502	.5514	.5527	.5539	.5551
3.6	.5563	.5575	.5587	.5599	.5611	.5623	.5635	.5647	.5658	.5670
3.7	.5682	.5694	.5705	.5717	.5729	.5740	.5752	.5763	.5775	.5786
3.8	.5798	.5809	.5821	.5832	.5843	.5855	.5866	.5877	.5888	.5899
3.9	.5911	.5922	.5933	.5944	.5955	.5966	.5977	.5988	.5999	.6010
4.0	.6021	.6031	.6042	.6053	.6064	.6075	.6085	.6096	.6107	.6117
4.1	.6128	.6138	.6149	.6160	.6170	.6180	.6191	.6201	.6212	.6222
4.2	.6232	.6243	.6253	.6263	.6274	.6284	.6294	.6304	.6314	.6325
4.3	.6335	.6345	.6355	.6365	.6375	.6385	.6395	.6405	.6415	.6425
4.4	.6435	.6444	.6454	.6464	.6474	.6484	.6493	.6503	.6513	.6522
4.5	.6532	.6542	.6551	.6561	.6571	.6580	.6590	.6599	.6609	.6618
4.6	.6628	.6637	.6646	.6656	.6665	.6675	.6684	.6693	.6702	.6712
4.7	.6721	.6730	.6739	.6749	.6758	.6767	.6776	.6785	.6794	.6803
4.8	.6812	.6821	.6830	.6839	.6848	.6857	.6866	.6875	.6884	.6893
4.9	.6902	.6911	.6920	.6928	.6937	.6946	.6955	.6964	.6972	.6981
5.0	.6990	.6998	.7007	.7016	.7024	.7033	.7042	.7050	.7059	.7067
5.1	.7076	.7084	.7093	.7101	.7110	.7118	.7126	.7135	.7143	.7152
5.2	.7160	.7168	.7177	.7185	.7193	.7202	.7210	.7218	.7226	.7235
5.3	.7243	.7251	.7259	.7267	.7275	.7284	.7292	.7300	.7308	.7316
5.4	.7324	.7332	.7340	.7348	.7356	.7364	.7372	.7380	.7388	.7396

Table B-5 Common Logarithms (cont.)

x	0	1	2	3	4	5	6	7	8	9
5.5	.7404	.7412	.7419	.7427	.7435	.7443	.7451	.7459	.7466	.7474
5.6	.7482	.7490	.7497	.7505	.7513	.7520	.7528	.7536	.7543	.7551
5.7	.7559	.7566	.7574	.7582	.7589	.7597	.7604	.7612	.7619	.7627
5.8	.7634	.7642	.7649	.7657	.7664	.7672	.7679	.7686	.7694	.7701
5.9	.7709	.7716	.7723	.7731	.7738	.7745	.7752	.7760	.7767	.7774
6.0	.7782	.7789	.7796	.7803	.7810	.7818	.7825	.7832	.7839	.7846
6.1	.7853	.7860	.7868	.7875	.7882	.7889	.7896	.7903	.7910	.7917
6.2	.7924	.7931	.7938	.7945	.7952	.7959	.7966	.7973	.7980	.7987
6.3	.7993	.8000	.8007	.8014	.8021	.8028	.8035	.8041	.8048	.8055
6.4	.8062	.8069	.8075	.8082	.8089	.8096	.8102	.8109	.8116	.8122
6.5	.8129	.8136	.8142	.8149	.8156	.8162	.8169	.8176	.8182	.8189
6.6	.8195	.8202	.8209	.8215	.8222	.8228	.8235	.8241	.8248	.8254
6.7	.8261	.8267	.8274	.8280	.8287	.8293	.8299	.8306	.8312	.8319
6.8	.8325	.8331	.8338	.8344	.8351	.8357	.8363	.8370	.8376	.8382
6.9	.8388	.8395	.8401	.8407	.8414	.8420	.8426	.8432	.8439	.8445
7.0	.8451	.8457	.8463	.8470	.8476	.8482	.8488	.8494	.8500	.8506
7.1	.8513	.8519	.8525	.8531	.8537	8543	.8549	.8555	.8561	.8567
7.2	.8573	.8579	.8585	.8591	.8597	.8603	.8609	.8615	.8621	.8627
7.3	.8633	.8639	.8645	.8651	.8657	.8663	.8669	.8675	.8681	.8686
7.4	.8692	.8698	.8704	.8710	.8716	.8722	.8727	.8733	.8739	.8745
7.5	.8751	.8756	.8762	.8768	.8774	.8779	.8785	.8791	.8797	.8802
7.6	.8808	.8814	.8820	.8825	.8831	.8837	.8842	.8848	.8854	.8859
7.7	.8865	.8871	.8876	.8882	.8887	.8893	.8899	.8904	.8910	.8915
7.8	.8921	.8927	.8932	.8938	.8943	.8949	.8954	.8960	.8965	.8971
7.9	.8976	.8982	.8987	.8993	.8998	.9004	.9009	.9015	.9020	.9025
8.0	.9031	.9036	.9042	.9047	.9053	.9058	.9063	.9069	.9074	.9079
8.1	.9085	.9090	.9096	.9101	.9106	.9112	.9117	.9122	.9128	.9133
8.2	.9138	.9143	.9149	.9154	.9159	.9165	.9170	.9175	.9180	.9186
8.3	.9191	.9196	.9201	.9206	.9212	.9217	.9222	.9227	.9232	.9238
8.4	.9243	.9248	.9253	.9258	.9263	.9269	.9274	.9279	.9284	.9289
8.5	.9294	.9299	.9304	.9309	.9315	.9320	.9325	.9330	.9335	.9340
8.6	.9345	.9350	.9555	.9360	.9365	.9370	.9375	.9380	.9385	.9390
8.7	.9395	.9400	.9405	.9410	.9415	.9420	.9425	.9430	.9435	.9440
8.8	.9445	.9450	.9455	.9460	.9465	.9469	.9474	.9479	.9484	.9489
8.9	.9494	.9499	.9504	.9509	.9513	.9518	.9523	.9528	.9533	.9538
9.0	.9542	.9547	.9552	.9557	.9562	.9566	.9571	.9576	.9581	.9586
9.1	.9590	.9595	.9600	.9605	.9609	.9614	.9619	.9624	.9628	.9633
9.2	.9638	.9643	.9647	.9652	.9657	.9661	.9666	.9671	.9675	.9680
9.3	.9685	.9689	.9694	.9699	.9703	.9708	.9713	.9717	.9722	.9727
9.4	.9731	.9736	.9741	.9745	.9750	.9754	.9759	.9763	.9768	.9773
9.5	.9777	.9782	.9786	.9791	.9795	.9800	.9805	.9809	.9914	.9818
9.6	.9823	.9827	.9832	.9836	.9841	.9845	.9850	.9854	.9859	.9863
9.7	.9868	.9872	.9877	.9881	.9886	.9890	.9894	.9899	.9903	.9908
9.8	.9912	.9917	.9921	.9926	.9930	.9934	.9939	.9943	.9948	.9952
9.9	.9956	.9961	.9965	.9969	.9974	.9978	.9983	.9987	.9991	.9996

Chapter 1

1. **a.** hypothesis (Further testing with improved experiments would prove that this is a faulty hypothesis (Section 1·12).) **b.** law **c.** experiment **d.** theory (Chapter 4)
2. **a.** solid **b.** liquid **c.** gas **d.** solid **e.** liquid
3. **a.** heterogeneous **b.** heterogeneous **c.** homogeneous **d.** homogeneous **e.** homogeneous
4. It is a mixture. The original liquid was a solution of a solid dissolved in a liquid. The components were separated by physical means.
5. **a.** tin **b.** copper **c.** nitrogen **d.** cadmium **e.** phosphorus **f.** chlorine
6. **a.** element **b.** compound **c.** mixture **d.** mixture **e.** element
7. Radiant energy (sun) to chemical energy (plants) to mechanical energy (person) to mechanical energy (bike) to kinetic energy (moving wheel) to mechanical energy (generator) to electrical energy (generator) to light energy (light bulb).
8. **a.** chemical **b.** physical **c.** chemical **d.** chemical **e.** physical **f.** chemical **g.** physical **h.** physical

Chapter 2

1. **a.** 4 **b.** 4 **c.** 2 **d.** 5 **e.** 1 **f.** 2 **g.** 3 **h.** 5
2. **a.** 8.71×10^1 m, 9×10^1 m **b.** 4.36×10^8 m, 4×10^8 m **c.** 1.55×10^{-2} m, 2×10^{-2} m **d.** 9.01×10^3 m, 9×10^3 m **e.** 1.78×10^{-3} m, 2×10^{-3} **f.** 6.30×10^2 m, 6×10^2 m
3. **a.** 79.15 m = 79.2 m **b.** 7.329 m = 7.33 m **c.** 11.53 m **d.** 17.31 m = 17.3 m
4. **a.** $10.126 = 1.0 \times 10^1$ m^2
   b. $5.22 \times 10^{-5} = 5.2 \times 10^{-5}$ m^2
   c. 674.56 = 675 m
   d. 0.20784 = 0.21 m
5. **a.** 2mm **b.** 16.4 cm **c.** 25.3 cm **d.** 1.9 cm
6. Density $= \dfrac{\text{mass}}{\text{volume}} = \dfrac{612 \text{ g}}{245 \text{ cm}^3} = 2.50$ g/cm^3
   Aluminum has a density of 2.70 g/cm^3. The metal is not aluminum.
7. Density $= \dfrac{\text{mass}}{\text{volume}} = \dfrac{15.8 \text{ g}}{19.7 \text{ cm}^3} = 0.802$ g/cm^3
   The ball will sink because its density is greater than the density of gasoline (0.70 g/cm^3).
8. The mass of an object does not change with a change in the force of gravity. Therefore the density of a person is the same regardless of location.
9. **a.** 2.70 **b.** 13.5 **c.** 0.917
10. K = 170 + 273 = 443 K
11. °C = 87 − 273 = − 186°C
12. The increase in temperature is 55°C. To increase the temperature of 1 gram of water by this amount would require 55 cal of heat energy. The energy required for 32.0 grams is: 32.0 g × 55 cal/g = 1760 cal.
13. Specific heat $= \dfrac{435 \text{ J}}{3.4 \text{ g} \times 64°\text{C}} = \dfrac{2.0 \text{ J}}{\text{g} \times °\text{C}}$

Chapter 3

1. **a.** Mass = volume × density
   $$= 0.87 \text{ cm}^3 \times \frac{19.2 \text{ g}}{1 \text{ cm}^3} = 17 \text{ g}$$
   b. $17 \text{ g} \times \dfrac{\$12}{1 \text{ g}} = = \$204$
2. Heat(J) = mass × ΔT × specific heat
   $$J = 10.0 \text{ g} \times 15.0°\text{C} \times \frac{4.18 \text{ J}}{\text{g} \times °\text{C}} = 627 \text{ J}$$
3. $\Delta T = \dfrac{\text{heat(cal)}}{\text{mass} \times \text{specific heat}} = \dfrac{8.5 \times 10^2 \text{cal}}{140 \text{ g} \times \dfrac{0.12 \text{ cal}}{\text{g} \times °\text{C}}} = 51°\text{C}$
   $T_{\text{final}} = T_{\text{inital}} + \Delta T = 21°\text{C} + 51°\text{C} = 72°\text{C}$
4. Find the mass of the added mercury using the density.
   $$\text{Mass} = \text{volume} \times \text{density} = 15.0 \text{ mL} \times \frac{13.5 \text{ g}}{1.0 \text{ mL}}$$
   $$= 203 \text{ g Hg}$$
   Add the mass of the mercury to the mass of the beaker.
   203 g + 56.7 g = 259.7 = 2.60×10^2 g
5. The density of silicon is 2.33 g/cm^3.
   $$\text{Volume} = \frac{\text{mass}}{\text{density}} = \frac{62.9 \text{ g}}{2.33 \text{ g/cm}^3} = 62.9 \text{ g} \times \frac{1 \text{ cm}^3}{2.33 \text{ g}}$$
   $$= 27.0 \text{ cm}^3$$
6. **a.** $\dfrac{1 \text{ m}}{10^6 \ \mu\text{m}}$ and $\dfrac{10^6 \ \mu\text{m}}{1 \text{ m}}$ **b.** $\dfrac{1 \text{ g}}{10^2 \text{ cg}}$ and $\dfrac{10^2 \text{ cg}}{1 \text{ g}}$
   c. $\dfrac{1 \text{ g H}_2\text{O}}{1 \text{ mL H}_2\text{O}}$ and $\dfrac{1 \text{ mL H}_2\text{O}}{1 \text{ g H}_2\text{O}}$ **d.** $\dfrac{10^3 \text{ J}}{1 \text{ kJ}}$ and $\dfrac{1 \text{ kJ}}{10^3 \text{ J}}$
7. $\dfrac{1 \text{ g}}{100 \text{ cg}}, \dfrac{100 \text{ cg}}{1 \text{ g}}, \dfrac{1 \text{ g}}{10^6 \ \mu\text{g}}, \dfrac{10^6 \ \mu\text{g}}{1 \text{ g}}, \dfrac{100 \text{ cg}}{10^6 \ \mu\text{g}}$, and $\dfrac{10^6 \ \mu\text{g}}{100 \text{ cg}}$
8. $85.4°\text{F temp. drop} \times 1 \dfrac{°\text{C temp. drop}}{1.8°\text{F temp. drop}} = 47.4°\text{C}$
9. There is 26.0 g of silver in 40.0 g of the amalgam.
   $$15.0 \text{ g amalgam} \times \frac{26.0 \text{ g silver}}{40.0 \text{ g amalgam}} = 9.75 \text{ g silver}$$
10. **a.** $0.73 \text{ km} \times \dfrac{10^3 \text{ m}}{1 \text{ km}} = 0.73 \times 10^3 \text{ m} = 7.3 \times 10^2 \text{ m}$
    b. $1.75 \text{ g} \times \dfrac{10^3 \text{ mg}}{1 \text{ g}} = 1.75 \times 10^3 \text{ mg}$
    c. $4.7 \text{ nm} \times \dfrac{1 \text{ m}}{10^9 \text{ nm}} = 4.7 \times 10^{-9} \text{ m}$
    d. $0.072 \text{ m} \times \dfrac{10^2 \text{ cm}}{1 \text{ m}} = 7.2 \text{ cm}$
    e. $53 \text{ cm}^3 \times \dfrac{1 \text{ dm}^3}{10^3 \text{ cm}^3} = 5.3 \times 10^{-2} \text{ dm}^3$
    f. $8.34 \text{ J} \times \dfrac{1 \text{ kJ}}{10^3 \text{ J}} = 8.34 \times 10^{-3} \text{ kJ}$
    g. $6.7 \text{ ms} \times \dfrac{1 \text{ s}}{10^3 \text{ ms}} = 6.7 \times 10^{-3} \text{ s}$
    h. $45.3 \text{ kcal} \times \dfrac{10^3 \text{cal}}{1 \text{ kcal}} = 4.53 \times 10^4 \text{ cal}$

11. a. $23.6 \text{ g B} \times \dfrac{1 \text{ cm}^3 \text{ B}}{2.34 \text{ g B}} = 10.1 \text{ cm}^3 \text{ B}$

b. $1.4 \text{ L Ar} \times \dfrac{1.78 \text{ g Ar}}{1 \text{ L Ar}} = 2.5 \text{ g Ar}$

c. $8.96 \text{ g Hg} \times \dfrac{1 \text{ cm}^3 \text{ Hg}}{13.5 \text{ g Hg}} = 0.664 \text{ cm}^3 \text{ Hg}$

12. a. $0.57 \ \mu\text{g} \times \dfrac{1 \text{ g}}{10^6 \ \mu\text{g}} \times \dfrac{10^2 \text{ cg}}{1 \text{ g}} = 0.57 \times 10^{-4}$
$= 5.7 \times 10^{-5} \text{ cg}$

b. $27.6 \ \mu\text{L} \times \dfrac{1 \text{ L}}{10^6 \ \mu\text{L}} \times \dfrac{10^3 \text{ mL}}{1 \text{ L}} = 27.6 \times 10^{-3}$
$= 2.76 \times 10^{-2} \text{ mL}$

c. $583 \text{ nm} \times \dfrac{1 \text{ m}}{10^9 \text{ nm}} \times \dfrac{10^3 \text{ mm}}{1 \text{ m}} = 583 \times 10^{-6}$
$= 5.83 \times 10^{-4} \text{ mm}$

d. $0.0023 \text{ kcal} \times \dfrac{10^3 \text{ cal}}{1 \text{ kcal}} \times \dfrac{10^1 \text{ dcal}}{1 \text{ cal}} = 0.0023 \times 10^4$
$= 2.3 \times 10^1 \text{ dcal}$

e. $678 \text{ eJ} \times \dfrac{1 \text{ J}}{10^2 \text{ eJ}} \times \dfrac{1 \text{ kJ}}{10^3 \text{ J}} = 678 \times 10^{-5}$
$= 6.78 \times 10^{-3} \text{ kJ}$

f. $5.75 \times 10^5 \text{ cg} \times \dfrac{1 \text{ g}}{10^2 \text{ cg}} \times \dfrac{10^9 \text{ ng}}{1 \text{ g}} = 5.75 \times 10^{12} \text{ ng}$

13. a. $\text{Mass} = \dfrac{\text{cal}}{(\Delta T) (\text{specific heat})}$
$7.5 \text{ kcal} = 7.5 \times 10^3 \text{ cal}$
$\text{Mass} = \dfrac{7.5 \times 10^3 \text{ cal}}{25^\circ\text{C} \times 1.00 \text{ cal}/(\text{g} \times ^\circ\text{C})} = 3.0 \times 10^2 \text{ g}$

b. $3.0 \times 10^2 \text{ g} \times \dfrac{1 \text{ kg}}{10^3 \text{ g}} = 3.0 \times 10^{-1} \text{ kg}$

14. a. $\dfrac{4.65 \text{ kg}}{1 \text{ L}} \times \dfrac{10^3 \text{ g}}{1 \text{ kg}} \times \dfrac{1 \text{ L}}{10^3 \text{ cm}^3} = 4.65 \text{ g/cm}^3$

b. $\dfrac{0.74 \text{ kcal}}{1 \text{ min}} \times \dfrac{10^3 \text{ cal}}{1 \text{ kcal}} \times \dfrac{1 \text{ min}}{60 \text{ s}} = 12 \text{ cal/s}$

c. $10 \text{ mm} = 1 \text{cm}; \ 10^2 \text{ mm}^2 = 1 \text{ cm}^2$
$\dfrac{1.42 \text{ g}}{1 \text{ cm}^2} \times \dfrac{10^3 \text{ mg}}{1 \text{ g}} \times \dfrac{1 \text{ cm}^2}{10^2 \text{ mm}^2} = 1.42 \times 10^1 \text{ mg/mm}^2$

Chapter 4

1. Six protons and six electrons.
2. Sodium.
3.

Atomic number	Mass number	Protons	Neutrons	Electrons	Symbol
7	14	7	7	7	N
9	19	9	10	9	F
19	39	19	20	19	K
27	59	27	32	27	Co

4. Oxygen-16: $^{16}_{8}\text{O}$; oxygen-18: $^{18}_{8}\text{O}$.
5. **a.** 6 **b.** 8 **c.** 138
6. Calculate the weighted average by multiplying the percent abundance of each isotope by that isotope's mass.

$$^{63}\text{Cu: } 63 \text{ amu} \times \dfrac{69.1}{100} = 43.5 \text{ amu}$$

$$^{65}\text{Cu: } 65 \text{ amu} \times \dfrac{30.9}{100} = \dfrac{20.1 \text{ amu}}{63.6 \text{ amu}}$$

Chapter 5

1. **a.** metal **b.** nonmetal **c.** metal **d.** nonmetal **e.** metal
2. Potassium, boron, and iodine.
3. **a.** Ca^{2+}, calcium ion **b.** one electron gained, fluoride ion **c.** Al, 3 electrons lost, aluminum ion **d.** Se^{2-}, selenide ion
4. Find the lead-to-oxygen mass ratio for each compound.

$$\dfrac{2.98 \text{ g Pb}}{0.461 \text{ g O}} = \dfrac{6.46 \text{ g Pb}}{1 \text{ g O}} \qquad \dfrac{9.89 \text{ g Pb}}{0.763 \text{ g O}} = \dfrac{12.96 \text{ g Pb}}{1 \text{ g O}}$$

Calculate the mass ratio of lead to 1 g of oxygen.

$$\dfrac{12.96 \text{ g Pb (compound 2)}}{6.46 \text{ g Pb (compound 1)}} = \dfrac{2}{1}$$

5. **a.** I^- **b.** Hg^{2+} **c.** P^{3-} **d.** Ba^{2+} **e.** Sn^{4+} **f.** Ag^+
6. **a.** copper(II) or cupric ion **b.** oxide ion **c.** lithium ion **d.** lead(II) or plumbous ion **e.** fluoride ion **f.** hydrogen ion
7. **a.** Li_2S **b.** SnO_2 **c.** HCl **d.** Mg_3N_2
8. **a.** aluminum iodide **b.** iron(II) oxide or ferrous oxide **c.** copper(I) sulfide or cuprous sulfide **d.** calcium selenide
9. **a.** BaSO_4 **b.** $\text{Al(HCO}_3)_3$ **c.** NaClO **d.** $\text{Pb(CrO}_4)_2$
10. **a.** chromium(II) nitrate or chromous nitrate **b.** magnesium phosphate **c.** copper(I) hydrogen phosphate or cuprous hydrogen phosphate **d.** lithium chromate
11. **a.** Al(OH)_3 **b.** potassium silicate **c.** lithium fluoride **d.** KClO_2 **e.** tin(II) phosphate or stannous phosphate **f.** $\text{Zn(HSO}_4)_2$
12. **a.** carbon tetrabromide **b.** dichlorine heptoxide **c.** dinitrogen pentoxide **d.** boron trichloride **e.** chromium(III) chloride
13. **a.** CS_2 **b.** N_2H_4 **c.** CCl_4 **d.** P_2O_3
14. **a.** hydrofluoric acid **b.** acetic acid **c.** sulfuric acid **d.** nitrous acid
15. **a.** H_2CrO_4 **b.** HI **c.** HClO_2 **d.** HClO_4
16. **a.** calcium carbonate **b.** potassium permanganate **c.** lead(II) chromate **d.** calcium hydrogen phosphate **e.** tin(II) dichromate **f.** magnesium phosphide **g.** ammonium sulfate **h.** diiodine dichloride **i.** nitrous acid **j.** strontium bromide
17. **a.** Sn(OH)_2 **b.** BaF_2 **c.** I_4O_9 **d.** $\text{Fe}_2\text{(C}_2\text{O}_4)_3$ **e.** H_2S **f.** $\text{Al(HCO}_3)_3$ **g.** Na_3PO_4 **h.** KClO_4 **i.** S_2O_3 **j.** $\text{Mg(NO}_3)_2$

Chapter 6

1. $1.20 \times 10^{25} \text{ atoms P} \times \dfrac{1.00 \text{ mol P}}{6.02 \times 10^{23} \text{ atoms P}}$
$= 0.199 \times 10^2 \text{ mol P} = 1.99 \times 10^1 \text{ mol P}$

2. $0.750 \text{ mol Zn} \times \dfrac{6.02 \times 10^{23} \text{ atoms Zn}}{1 \text{ mol Zn}}$
$= 4.52 \times 10^{23} \text{ atoms Zn}$

3. $0.400 \text{ mol N}_2\text{O}_5 \times \dfrac{6.02 \times 10^{23} \text{ molecules N}_2\text{O}_5}{1 \text{ mol N}_2\text{O}_5}$
$= 2.41 \times 10^{23} \text{ molecules N}_2\text{O}_5$

4. $1.20 \times 10^{24} \text{ molecules CO}_2 \times$
$\dfrac{1 \text{ mol CO}_2}{6.02 \times 10^{23} \text{ molecules CO}_2} = 1.99 \text{ mol CO}_2$

5. $0.036 \text{ mol (NH}_4)_3\text{PO}_4 \times \dfrac{6.02 \times 10^{23} \text{ formula units}}{1 \text{ mol (NH}_4)_3\text{PO}_4}$
$\times \dfrac{3 \text{NH}_4^+ \text{ ions}}{1 \text{ formula unit}} = 6.50 \times 10^{22} \text{ NH}_4^+ \text{ ions}$

6. Add the number of carbon atoms in each compound.

$$3.00 \text{ mol } C_2H_2 \times \frac{6.02 \times 10^{23} \text{ molecules } C_2H_2}{1 \text{ mol } C_2H_2} \times$$

$$\frac{2 \text{ atoms } C}{1 \text{ molecule } C_2H_2} = 36.1 \times 10^{23} \text{ atoms } C$$

$$= 3.61 \times 10^{24} \text{ atoms } C$$

$$0.700 \text{ mol CO} \times \frac{6.02 \times 10^{23} \text{ molecules CO}}{1 \text{ mol CO}} \times$$

$$\frac{1 \text{ atom } C}{1 \text{ molecule CO}} = 4.21 \times 10^{23} \text{ atoms } C$$

Total number carbon atoms $= 36.1 \times 10^{23} + 4.21 \times 10^{23}$

$$= 40.3 \times 10^{23}$$

$$= 4.03 \times 10^{24} \text{ atoms } C$$

7. Round off the gram atomic mass to tenths.
   a. 23.0 g
   b. 74.9 g
   c. 238.0 g

8. a. $1 \text{ mol } C \times \dfrac{12.0 \text{ g } C}{1 \text{ mol } C} = 12.0 \text{ g}$

$$4 \text{ mol } Cl \times \frac{35.5 \text{ g Cl}}{1 \text{ mol } Cl} = 142.0 \text{ g}$$

$$\text{gfm } CCl_4 = 154.0 \text{ g}$$

b. $1 \text{ mol } P \times \dfrac{31.0 \text{ g } P}{1 \text{ mol } P} = 31.0 \text{ g}$

$$3 \text{ mol } Cl \times \frac{35.5 \text{ g Cl}}{1 \text{ mol } Cl} = 106.5 \text{ g}$$

$$\text{gfm } PCl_3 = 137.5 \text{ g}$$

c. $8 \text{ mol } C \times \dfrac{12.0 \text{ g } C}{1 \text{ mol } C} = 96.0 \text{ g}$

$$18 \text{ mol } H \times \frac{1.0 \text{ g H}}{1 \text{ mol } H} = 18.0 \text{ g}$$

$$\text{gfm } C_8H_{18} = 114.0 \text{ g}$$

d. $2 \text{ mol } N \times \dfrac{14.0 \text{ g } N}{1 \text{ mol } N} = 28.0 \text{ g}$

$$5 \text{ mol } O \times \frac{16.0 \text{ g O}}{1 \text{ mol } O} = 80.0 \text{ g}$$

$$\text{gfm } N_2O_5 = 108.0 \text{ g}$$

9. a. $1 \text{ mol } Sr \times \dfrac{87.6 \text{ g Sr}}{1 \text{ mol } Sr} = 87.6 \text{ g}$

$$2 \text{ mol } Cl \times \frac{35.5 \text{ g Cl}}{1 \text{ mol } Cl} = 71.0 \text{ g}$$

$$\text{gfm } SrCl_2 = 158.6 \text{ g}$$

b. $2 \text{ mol } Na \times \dfrac{23.0 \text{ g Na}}{1 \text{ mol Na}} = 46.0 \text{ g}$

$$1 \text{ mol } C \times \frac{12.0 \text{ g } C}{1 \text{ mol } C} = 12.0 \text{ g}$$

$$3 \text{ mol } O \times \frac{16.0 \text{ g O}}{1 \text{ mol } O} = 48.0 \text{ g}$$

$$\text{gfm } Na_2CO_3 = 106.0 \text{ g}$$

c. $2 \text{ mol } Al \times \dfrac{27.0 \text{ g Al}}{1 \text{ mol } Al} = 54.0 \text{ g}$

$$3 \text{ mol } S \times \frac{32.1 \text{ g } S}{1 \text{ mol } S} = 96.3 \text{ g}$$

$$12 \text{ mol } O \times \frac{16.0 \text{ g O}}{1 \text{ mol } O} = 192.0 \text{ g}$$

$$\text{gfm } Al_2(SO_4)_3 = 342.3 \text{ g}$$

d. $1 \text{ mol } Ca \times \dfrac{40.1 \text{ g Ca}}{1 \text{ mol } Ca} = 40.1 \text{ g}$

$$2 \text{ mol } C \times \frac{12.0 \text{ g } C}{1 \text{ mol } C} = 24.0 \text{ g}$$

$$2 \text{ mol } N \times \frac{14.0 \text{ g } N}{1 \text{ mol } N} = 28.0 \text{ g}$$

$$\text{gfm } Ca(CN)_2 = 92.1 \text{ g}$$

10. a. $10.0 \text{ mol } Cr \times \dfrac{52.0 \text{ g Cr}}{1 \text{ mol } Cr} = 520 = 5.20 \times 10^2 \text{ g Cr}$

b. $3.32 \text{ mol } K \times \dfrac{39.1 \text{ g K}}{1 \text{ mol } K} = 129.8 = 1.30 \times 10^2 \text{ g K}$

c. $2.20 \times 10^{-3} \text{ mol } Sn \times \dfrac{118.7 \text{ g Sn}}{1 \text{ mol } Sn} = 0.261 \text{ g Sn}$

d. $0.720 \text{ mol } Be \times \dfrac{9.01 \text{ g Be}}{1 \text{ mol } Be} = 6.49 \text{ g Be}$

e. $2.40 \text{ mol } N_2 \times \dfrac{28.0 \text{ g } N_2}{1 \text{ mol } N_2} = 67.2 \text{ g } N_2$

f. $0.160 \text{ mol } H_2O_2 \times \dfrac{34.0 \text{ g } H_2O_2}{1 \text{ mol } H_2O_2} = 5.44 \text{ g } H_2O_2$

g. $5.08 \text{ mol } Ca(NO_3)_2 \times \dfrac{164.1 \text{ g } Ca(NO_3)_2}{1 \text{ mol } Ca(NO_3)_2} =$

$$8.34 \times 10^2 \text{ g } Ca(NO_3)_2$$

h. $15.0 \text{ mol } H_2SO_4 \times \dfrac{98.1 \text{ g } H_2SO_4}{1 \text{ mol } H_2SO_4} =$

$$1.47 \times 10^3 \text{ g } H_2SO_4$$

i. $4.52 \times 10^{-3} \text{ mol } C_{20}H_{42} \times \dfrac{282 \text{ g } C_{20}H_{42}}{1 \text{ mol } C_{20}H_{42}} =$

$$1.27 \text{ g } C_{20}H_{42}$$

j. $0.0112 \text{ mol } K_2CO_3 \times \dfrac{138.2 \text{ g } K_2CO_3}{1 \text{ mol } K_2CO_3} = 1.55 \text{ g } K_2CO_3$

11. a. $72.0 \text{ g Ar} \times \dfrac{1 \text{ mol Ar}}{39.9 \text{ g Ar}} = 1.80 \text{ mol Ar}$

b. $3.70 \times 10^{-1} \text{ g B} \times \dfrac{1 \text{ mol B}}{10.8 \text{ g B}} = 3.43 \times 10^{-2} \text{ mol B}$

c. $187 \text{ g Al} \times \dfrac{1 \text{ mol Al}}{27.0 \text{ g Al}} = 6.93 \text{ mol Al}$

d. $333 \text{ g } SnF_2 \times \dfrac{1 \text{ mol } SnF_2}{156.7 \text{ g } SnF_2} = 2.13 \text{ mol } SnF_2$

e. $7.21 \times 10^{-2} \text{ g He} \times \dfrac{1 \text{ mol He}}{4 \text{ g He}} = 1.80 \times 10^{-2} \text{ mol He}$

f. $27.4 \text{ g } TiO_2 \times \dfrac{1 \text{ mol } TiO_2}{79.9 \text{ g } TiO_2} = 0.343 \text{ mol } TiO_2$

g. $5.00 \text{ g } H_2 \times \dfrac{1 \text{ mol } H_2}{2.0 \text{ g } H_2} = 2.5 \text{ mol } H_2$

h. $0.000\ 264 \text{ g } Li_2HPO_4 \times \dfrac{1 \text{ mol } Li_2HPO_4}{109.8 \text{ g } Li_2HPO_4} =$

$$2.40 \times 10^{-6} \text{ mol } Li_2HPO_4$$

i. $11.0 \text{ g } CH_4 \times \dfrac{1 \text{ mol } CH_4}{16.0 \text{ g } CH_4} = 0.688 \text{ mol } CH_4$

j. $847 \text{ g } (NH_4)_2CO_3 \times \dfrac{1 \text{ mol } (NH_4)_2CO_3}{96.0 \text{ g } (NH_4)_2CO_3} =$

$$8.82 \text{ mol } (NH_4)_2CO_3$$

12. a. $5.40 \text{ mol O}_2 \times \dfrac{22.4 \text{ L O}_2}{1 \text{ mol O}_2} = 121 \text{ L O}_2$

b. $3.20 \times 10^{-2} \text{ mol CO}_2 \times \dfrac{22.4 \text{ L CO}_2}{1 \text{ mol CO}_2} = 0.717 \text{ L CO}_2$

c. $0.960 \text{ mol CH}_4 \times \dfrac{22.4 \text{ L CH}_4}{1 \text{ mol CH}_4} = 21.5 \text{ L CH}_4$

13. a. $89.6 \text{ L SO}_2 \times \dfrac{1 \text{ mol SO}_2}{22.4 \text{ L SO}_2} = 4.00 \text{ mol SO}_2$

b. $1.00 \times 10^3 \text{ L C}_2\text{H}_6 \times \dfrac{1 \text{ mol C}_2\text{H}_6}{22.4 \text{ L C}_2\text{H}_6} = 44.6 \text{ mol C}_2\text{H}_6$

c. $5.42 \times 10^{-1} \text{ mL Ne} \times \dfrac{1 \text{ L Ne}}{10^3 \text{ mL Ne}} \times \dfrac{1 \text{ mol Ne}}{22.4 \text{ L N}} =$
$\qquad\qquad\qquad\qquad\qquad\qquad 2.42 \times 10^{-5} \text{ mol Ne}$

14. At STP the gfm of any gas occupies a volume of 22.4 L.

a. gas A: $22.4 \text{ L} \times \dfrac{1.25 \text{ g}}{1 \text{ L}} = 28.0 \text{ g (nitrogen)}$

b. gas B: $22.4 \text{ L} \times \dfrac{2.86 \text{ g}}{1 \text{ L}} = 64.1 \text{ g (sulfur dioxide)}$

c. gas C: $22.4 \text{ L} \times \dfrac{0.714 \text{ g}}{1 \text{ L}} = 16.0 \text{ g (methane)}$

15. $1 \text{ atom Ni} \times \dfrac{1.00 \text{ mol Ni}}{6.02 \times 10^{23} \text{ atoms Ni}} \times \dfrac{58.7 \text{ g Ni}}{1.00 \text{ mol Ni}} =$
$\qquad\qquad\qquad\qquad\qquad\qquad 9.75 \times 10^{-23} \text{ g Ni}$

16. $6.00 \text{ L CO}_2 \times \dfrac{1.00 \text{ mol CO}_2}{22.4 \text{ L CO}_2} \times \dfrac{6.02 \times 10^{23} \text{ molec. CO}_2}{1 \text{ mol CO}_2} =$
1.61×10^{23} molecules of CO_2 or of any gas at STP.

17. a. Total mass = 29.0 g Ag + 4.30 g S = 33.3 g

$\%\text{Ag} = \dfrac{29.0 \text{ g}}{33.3 \text{ g}} \times 100\% = 87.1\%$

$\%\text{S} = \dfrac{4.30 \text{ g}}{33.3 \text{ g}} \times 100\% = 12.9\%$

b. 9.03 g Mg + 3.48 g N = 12.51 g total

$\%\text{Mg} = \dfrac{9.03 \text{ g}}{12.51 \text{ g}} \times 100\% = 72.2\%$

$\%\text{N} = \dfrac{3.48 \text{ g}}{12.51 \text{ g}} \times 100\% = 27.8\%$

c. 222.6 g Na + 77.4 g O = 300.0 g total

$\%\text{Na} = \dfrac{222.6 \text{ g}}{300.0 \text{ g}} \times 100\% = 74.2\%$

$\%\text{O} = \dfrac{77.4 \text{ g}}{300.0 \text{ g}} \times 100\% = 25.8\%$

18. a. gfm C_3H_8 = 44.0 g

$\%\text{C} = \dfrac{36.0 \text{ g}}{44.0 \text{ g}} \times 100\% = 81.8\%$

$\%\text{H} = \dfrac{8.0 \text{ g}}{44.0 \text{ g}} \times 100\% = 18.2\%$

b. gfm $NaHSO_4$ = 120.1 g

$\%\text{Na} = \dfrac{23.0 \text{ g}}{120.1 \text{ g}} \times 100\% = 19.2\%$

$\%\text{H} = \dfrac{1.0 \text{ g}}{120.1 \text{ g}} \times 100\% = 0.83\%$

$\%\text{S} = \dfrac{32.1 \text{ g}}{120.1 \text{ g}} \times 100\% = 26.7\%$

$\%\text{O} = \dfrac{64.0 \text{ g}}{120.1 \text{ g}} \times 100\% = 53.3\%$

c. gfm $Ca(C_2H_3O_2)_2$ = 158.1 g

$\%\text{Ca} = \dfrac{40.1 \text{ g}}{158.1 \text{ g}} \times 100\% = 25.4\%$

$\%\text{C} = \dfrac{48.0 \text{ g}}{158.1 \text{ g}} \times 100\% = 30.4\%$

$\%\text{H} = \dfrac{6.0 \text{ g}}{158.1 \text{ g}} \times 100\% = 3.8\%$

$\%\text{O} = \dfrac{64.0 \text{ g}}{158.1 \text{ g}} \times 100\% = 40.5\%$

d. gfm HCN = 27.0 g

$\%\text{H} = \dfrac{1.0 \text{ g}}{27.0 \text{ g}} \times 100\% = 3.7\%$

$\%\text{C} = \dfrac{12.0 \text{ g}}{27.0 \text{ g}} \times 100\% = 44.4\%$

$\%\text{N} = \dfrac{14.0 \text{ g}}{27.0 \text{ g}} \times 100\% = 51.9\%$

19. a. Percent of H in C_3H_8 is 18.2%, or 18.2 g H/100 g C_3H_8.

$350 \text{ g C}_3\text{H}_8 \times \dfrac{18.2 \text{ g H}}{100 \text{ g C}_3\text{H}_8} = 63.7 \text{ g H}$

b. $20.2 \text{ g NaHSO}_4 \times \dfrac{0.83 \text{ g H}}{100 \text{ g NaHSO}_4} = 0.17 \text{ g H}$

c. $124 \text{ g Ca(C}_2\text{H}_3\text{O}_2)_2 \times \dfrac{3.8 \text{ g H}}{100 \text{ g Ca(C}_2\text{H}_3\text{O}_2)_2} = 4.71 \text{ g H}$

d. $378 \text{ g HCN} \times \dfrac{3.7 \text{ g H}}{100 \text{ g HCN}} = 14 \text{ g H}$

20. a. Calculate the lowest whole-number ratio of moles.

$79.9 \text{ g C} \times \dfrac{1.00 \text{ mol C}}{12.0 \text{ g C}} = 6.66 \text{ mol C}$

$\dfrac{6.66 \text{ mol C}}{6.66} = 1 \text{ mol C}$

$20.1 \text{ g H} \times \dfrac{1.00 \text{ mol H}}{1.00 \text{ g H}} = 20.1 \text{ mol H}$

$\dfrac{20.1 \text{ mol H}}{6.66} = 3 \text{ mol H}$

Empirical formula = CH_3

b. $67.6 \text{ g Hg} \times \dfrac{1.00 \text{ mol Hg}}{200.6 \text{ g Hg}} = 0.337 \text{ mol Hg}$

$\dfrac{0.337 \text{ mol Hg}}{0.336} = 1 \text{ mol Hg}$

$10.8 \text{ g S} \times \dfrac{1.00 \text{ mol S}}{32.1 \text{ g S}} = 0.336 \text{ mol S}$

$\dfrac{0.336 \text{ mol S}}{0.336} = 1 \text{ mol S}$

$21.6 \text{ g O} \times \dfrac{1.00 \text{ mol O}}{16.0 \text{ g O}} = 1.35 \text{ mol O}$

$\dfrac{1.35 \text{ mol O}}{0.336} = 4 \text{ mol O} \quad$ Empirical formula = $HgSO_4$

c. $94.1 \text{ g O} \times \dfrac{1.00 \text{ mol O}}{16.0 \text{ g O}} = 5.88 \text{ mol O}$

$\dfrac{5.88 \text{ mol O}}{5.88} = 1 \text{ mol O}$

$5.9 \text{ g H} \times \dfrac{1.00 \text{ mol H}}{1.0 \text{ g H}} = 5.9 \text{ mol H}$

$\dfrac{5.9 \text{ mol H}}{5.88} = 1 \text{ mol H} \qquad$ Empirical formula = HO

d. $17.6 \text{ g Na} \times \dfrac{1.00 \text{ mol Na}}{23.0 \text{ g Na}} = 0.765 \text{ mol Na}$

$\dfrac{0.765 \text{ mol Na}}{0.763} = 1 \text{ mol Na}$

$39.7 \text{ g Cr} \times \dfrac{1.00 \text{ mol Cr}}{52.0 \text{ g Cr}} = 0.763 \text{ mol Cr}$

$\dfrac{0.763 \text{ mol Cr}}{0.763} = 1 \text{ mol Cr}$

$42.7 \text{ g O} \times \dfrac{1.00 \text{ mol O}}{16.0 \text{ g O}} = 2.67 \text{ mol O}$

$\dfrac{2.67 \text{ mol O}}{0.763} = 3.50 \text{ mol O}$

The result is $Na_1Cr_1O_{3.5}$. To get the lowest whole-number ratio, multiply through by 2. The empirical formula is $Na_2Cr_2O_7$.

e. $27.59 \text{ g C} \times \dfrac{1.00 \text{ mol C}}{12.0 \text{ g C}} = 2.30 \text{ mol C}$

$\dfrac{2.30 \text{ mol C}}{1.15} = 2 \text{ mol C}$

$1.15 \text{ g H} \times \dfrac{1.00 \text{ mol H}}{1.00 \text{ g H}} = 1.15 \text{ mol H}$

$\dfrac{1.15 \text{ mol H}}{1.15} = 1 \text{ mol H}$

$16.09 \text{ g N} \times \dfrac{1.00 \text{ mol N}}{14.0 \text{ g N}} = 1.15 \text{ mol N}$

$\dfrac{1.15 \text{ mol N}}{1.15} = 1 \text{ mol N}$

$55.17 \text{ g O} \times \dfrac{1.00 \text{ mol O}}{16.0 \text{ g O}} = 3.45 \text{ mol O}$

$\dfrac{3.45 \text{ mol O}}{1.15} = 3 \text{ mol O}$

Empirical formula = C_2HNO_3

21. Calculate the relative number of moles from the given masses.

a. $29.0 \text{ g Ag} \times \dfrac{1.00 \text{ mol Ag}}{107.9 \text{ g Ag}} = 0.269 \text{ mol Ag}$

$\dfrac{0.269 \text{ mol Ag}}{0.134} = 2 \text{ mol Ag}$

$4.30 \text{ g S} \times \dfrac{1.00 \text{ mol S}}{32.1 \text{ g S}} = 0.134 \text{ mol S}$

$\dfrac{0.134 \text{ mol S}}{0.134} = 1 \text{ mol S}$

Empirical formula = Ag_2S

b. $9.03 \text{ g Mg} \times \dfrac{1.00 \text{ mol Mg}}{24.3 \text{ g Mg}} = 0.372 \text{ mol Mg}$

$\dfrac{0.372 \text{ mol Mg}}{0.249} = 1.5 \text{ mol Mg}$

$3.48 \text{ g N} \times \dfrac{1.00 \text{ mol N}}{14.0 \text{ g N}} = 0.249 \text{ mol N}$

$\dfrac{0.249 \text{ mol N}}{0.249} = 1 \text{ mol N}$

The result is $Mg_{1.5}N_1$. Multiply through by 2. Empirical formula = Mg_3N_2

c. $222.6 \text{ g Na} \times \dfrac{1.00 \text{ mol Na}}{23.0 \text{ g Na}} = 9.68 \text{ mol Na}$

$\dfrac{9.68 \text{ mol Na}}{4.84} = 2 \text{ mol Na}$

$77.4 \text{ g O} \times \dfrac{1.00 \text{ mol O}}{16.0 \text{ g O}} = 4.84 \text{ mol O}$

$\dfrac{4.84 \text{ mol O}}{4.84} = 1 \text{ mol O}$

Empirical formula = Na_2O

22. Calculate the empirical formula.

$58.8 \text{ g C} \times \dfrac{1.00 \text{ mol C}}{12.0 \text{ g C}} = 4.90 \text{ mol C}$

$\dfrac{4.90 \text{ mol C}}{1.96} = 2.50 \text{ mol C}$

$9.8 \text{ g H} \times \dfrac{1.00 \text{ mol H}}{1.00 \text{ g H}} = 9.8 \text{ mol H}$

$\dfrac{9.80 \text{ mol H}}{1.96} = 5.00 \text{ mol H}$

$31.4 \text{ g O} \times \dfrac{1.00 \text{ mol O}}{16.0 \text{ g O}} = 1.96 \text{ mol O}$

$\dfrac{1.96 \text{ mol O}}{1.96} = 1 \text{ mol O}$

The result is $C_{2.5}H_5O_1$. Multiply through by 2. The empirical formula is $C_5H_{10}O_2$. This is also the molecular formula since the gfm of $C_5H_{10}O_2$ is 102 g, which is the gmm of the compound.

23. Calculate the empirical formula. The mass of hydrogen is: $7.36 \text{ g} - 6.93 \text{ g} = 0.43 \text{ g H}$

$6.93 \text{ g O} \times \dfrac{1.00 \text{ mol O}}{16.0 \text{ g O}} = 0.433 \text{ mol O}$

$\dfrac{0.433 \text{ mol O}}{0.43} = 1 \text{ mol O}$

$0.43 \text{ g H} \times \dfrac{1.0 \text{ mol H}}{1.0 \text{ g H}} = 0.43 \text{ mol H}$

$\dfrac{0.43 \text{ mol H}}{0.43} = 1 \text{ mol H}$

The empirical formula is HO. The gfm of HO is 17 g; the gmm of the compound is 34.0. It takes 34 g/17 g, or 2 empirical formula units to make the molecular formula. The molecular formula is H_2O_2.

Chapter 7

1. a. $Al(s) + O_2(g) \longrightarrow Al_2O_3(s)$
   b. $HgS(s) + O_2(g) \longrightarrow Hg(l) + SO_2(g)$
   c. $KClO_3(s) \xrightarrow{MnO_2} KCl(s) + O_2(g)$
2. a. Aqueous solutions of barium chloride and sulfuric acid when mixed produce a precipitate of barium sulfate and aqueous hydrochloric acid. **b.** Gaseous ammonia and oxygen react in the presence of platinum to produce mononitrogen monoxide gas and water vapor. **c.** The gas dinitrogen trioxide reacts with water to produce an aqueous solution of nitrous acid.
3. a. $2Al + N_2 \longrightarrow 2AlN$
   b. $2NaCl + H_2SO_4 \longrightarrow Na_2SO_4 + 2HCl$
   c. $2Al + 3CuSO_4 \longrightarrow Al_2(SO_4)_3 + 3Cu$
   d. $4P + 5O_2 \longrightarrow 2P_2O_5$
   e. $2Fe(OH)_3 \longrightarrow Fe_2O_3 + 3H_2O$

4. a. $2Na + 2H_2O \longrightarrow 2NaOH + H_2$
b. $H_2 + S \longrightarrow H_2S$
c. $2FeCl_3 + 3Ca(OH)_2 \longrightarrow 2Fe(OH)_3 + 3CaCl_2$
d. $2C + O_2 \longrightarrow 2CO$
e. $2KNO_3 \longrightarrow 2KNO_2 + O_2$
5. a. $Ca + S \longrightarrow CaS$
b. $2Fe + O_2 \longrightarrow 2FeO$
c. $4P + 5O_2 \longrightarrow 2P_2O_5$
d. $N_2O_5 + H_2O \longrightarrow 2HNO_3$
e. $Na_2O + H_2O \longrightarrow 2NaOH$
f. $2Mg + O_2 \longrightarrow 2MgO$
6. a. $NiCO_3 \longrightarrow NiO + CO_2$
b. $2Ag_2O \longrightarrow 4Ag + O_2$
c. $NH_4NO_3 \longrightarrow N_2O + 2H_2O$
7. a. $2Al + 3H_2SO_4 \longrightarrow Al_2(SO_4)_3 + 3H_2$
b. $Cl_2 + 2KI \longrightarrow 2KCl + I_2$
c. $Cu + FeSO_4 \longrightarrow$ no reaction
d. $2Li + 2H_2O \longrightarrow 2LiOH + H_2$
8. a. $3H_2SO_4 + 2Al(OH)_3 \longrightarrow Al_2(SO_4)_3 + 6H_2O$
b. $3KOH + H_3PO_4 \longrightarrow K_3PO_4 + 3H_2O$
c. $SrBr_2 + (NH_4)_2CO_3 \longrightarrow SrCO_3 + 2NH_4Br$
9. a. $C_6H_{12}O_6 + 6O_2 \longrightarrow 6CO_2 + 6H_2O$
b. $2C_8H_{18} + 25O_2 \longrightarrow 16CO_2 + 18H_2O$
10. a. $Mg + H_2SO_4 \longrightarrow MgSO_4 + H_2$ (single-replacement)
b. $3Fe + 2O_2 \longrightarrow Fe_3O_4$ (combination)
c. $2Pb(NO_3)_2 \longrightarrow 2PbO + 4NO_2 + O_2$ (decomposition)
d. $2C_2H_6 + 7O_2 \longrightarrow 4CO_2 + 6H_2O$ (combustion)
e. $Pb(NO_3)_2 + 2NaI \longrightarrow PbI_2 + 2NaNO_3$
(double-replacement)
f. $(NH_4)_2SO_4 + 2NaOH \longrightarrow 2NH_3 + 2H_2O + Na_2SO_4$
(double-replacement, then decomposition of NH_4OH)

Chapter 8
1. a. $2CO(g) + O_2(g) \longrightarrow 2CO_2(g)$
2 molecules CO + 1 molecule $O_2 \longrightarrow$ 2 molecules CO_2
2 mol CO + 1 mol $O_2 \longrightarrow$ 2 mol CO_2
$(2 \times 28\ g) + 32\ g = 2 \times 44\ g$
88 g = 88 g (law of conservation of mass)
44.8 L CO + 22.4 L $O_2 \longrightarrow$ 44.8 L CO_2
b. $2Na(s) + 2H_2O(l) \longrightarrow 2NaOH(aq) + H_2(g)$
2 atoms Na + 2 molecules $H_2O \longrightarrow$
2 formula units NaOH + 1 molecule H_2
2 mol Na + 2 mol $H_2O \longrightarrow$ 2 mol NaOH + 1 mol H_2
$(2 \times 23\ g) + (2 \times 18\ g) = (2 \times 40\ g) + 2\ g$
82 g = 82 g (law of conservation of mass)
c. $2C_2H_2(g) + 5O_2(g) \longrightarrow 4CO_2(g) + 2H_2O(g)$
2 molecules C_2H_2 + 5 molecules $O_2 \longrightarrow$
4 molecules CO_2 + 2 molecules H_2O
2 mol C_2H_2 + 5 mol $O_2 \longrightarrow$ 4 mol CO_2 + 2 mol H_2O
$(2 \times 26\ g) + (5 \times 32\ g) = (4 \times 44\ g) + (2 \times 18\ g)$
212 g = 212 g (law of conservation of mass)
$44.8\ L + 112\ L \longrightarrow 89.6\ L + 44.8\ L$

2. a. $\dfrac{4\ mol\ Al}{3\ mol\ O_2} \quad \dfrac{3\ mol\ O_2}{4\ mol\ Al} \quad \dfrac{4\ mol\ Al}{2\ mol\ Al_2O_3} \quad \dfrac{2\ mol\ Al_2O_3}{4\ mol\ Al}$

$\dfrac{3\ mol\ O_2}{2\ mol\ Al_2O_3} \quad \dfrac{2\ mol\ Al_2O_3}{3\ mol\ O_2}$

b. $2.3\ \text{mol Al}_2\text{O}_3 \times \dfrac{4\ mol\ Al}{2\ mol\ Al_2O_3} = 4.6\ mol\ Al$

c. $0.84\ \text{mol Al} \times \dfrac{3\ mol\ O_2}{4\ mol\ Al} = 0.63\ mol\ O_2$

d. $17.2\ \text{mol O}_2 \times \dfrac{2\ mol\ Al_2O_3}{3\ mol\ O_2} = 11.5\ mol\ Al_2O_3$

3. a. $13.0\ \text{g C}_2\text{H}_2 \times \dfrac{1\ mol\ C_2H_2}{26.0\ \text{g C}_2\text{H}_2} \times \dfrac{5\ mol\ O_2}{2\ \text{mol C}_2\text{H}_2} \times$
$\dfrac{32.0\ g\ O_2}{1\ \text{mol O}_2} = 40.0\ g\ O_2$

b. $13.0\ \text{g C}_2\text{H}_2 \times \dfrac{1\ mol\ C_2H_2}{26.0\ \text{g C}_2\text{H}_2} \times \dfrac{4\ \text{mol CO}_2}{2\ \text{mol C}_2\text{H}_2} \times$
$\dfrac{44.0\ g\ CO_2}{1\ \text{mol CO}_2} = 44.0\ g\ CO_2$

$13.0\ \text{g C}_2\text{H}_2 \times \dfrac{1\ mol\ C_2H_2}{26.0\ \text{g C}_2\text{H}_2} \times \dfrac{2\ \text{mol H}_2\text{O}}{2\ \text{mol C}_2\text{H}_2} \times$
$\dfrac{18.0\ g\ H_2O}{1\ \text{mol H}_2\text{O}} = 9.0\ g\ H_2O$

c. Mass reactants = mass products
$13.0\ g + 40.0\ g = 44.0\ g + 9.0\ g$
$53.0\ g = 53.0\ g$

4. a. $5.00\ \text{g CaC}_2 \times \dfrac{1\ \text{mol CaC}_2}{64.1\ \text{g CaC}_2} \times \dfrac{1\ \text{mol C}_2\text{H}_2}{1\ \text{mol CaC}_2} \times$
$\dfrac{26.0\ g\ C_2H_2}{1\ \text{mol C}_2\text{H}_2} = 2.03\ g\ C_2H_2$

b. $98.0\ \text{g H}_2\text{O} \times \dfrac{1\ mol\ H_2O}{18.0\ \text{g H}_2\text{O}} \times \dfrac{1\ mol\ CaC_2}{2\ \text{mol H}_2\text{O}} =$
$2.72\ mol\ CaC_2$

c. $5.34\ \text{mol C}_2\text{H}_2 \times \dfrac{1\ \text{mol Ca(OH)}_2}{1\ \text{mol C}_2\text{H}_2} \times \dfrac{74.1\ g\ Ca(OH)_2}{1\ \text{mol Ca(OH)}_2} =$
$396\ g\ Ca(OH)_2$

5. a. $\text{vol } G\ (L) \times \dfrac{1\ mol\ G}{22.4\ L\ G} \times \dfrac{b\ mol\ W}{a\ mol\ G} \times \dfrac{gfm\ W}{1\ mol\ W}$
$\longrightarrow$ mass of W

b. $\dfrac{\text{representative}}{\text{particles } G} \times \dfrac{1\ mol\ G}{6.02 \times 10^{23}} \times \dfrac{b\ mol\ W}{a\ mol\ G} \longrightarrow$ mol W

c. $\text{mass of } G \times \dfrac{1\ mol\ G}{gfm\ G} \times \dfrac{b\ mol\ W}{a\ mol\ G} \times$
$\dfrac{6.02 \times 10^{23}\ particles\ W}{1\ mol\ W} \longrightarrow$ particles W

6. a. $7.42 \times 10^{24}\ \text{molecules HF} \times \dfrac{1\ mol\ HF}{6.02 \times 10^{23}\ \text{molecules HF}} \times$
$\dfrac{1\ \text{mol SnF}_2}{2\ mol\ HF} \times \dfrac{156.7\ g\ SnF_2}{1\ \text{mol SnF}_2} = 9.66 \times 10^2\ g\ SnF_2$

b. $23.4\ \text{g Sn} \times \dfrac{1\ mol\ Sn}{118.7\ \text{g Sn}} \times \dfrac{1\ mol\ H_2}{1\ \text{mol Sn}} \times \dfrac{22.4\ L\ H_2}{1\ \text{mol H}_2} =$
$4.42\ L\ H_2$

c. $14.2\ \text{L H}_2 \times \dfrac{2\ L\ HF}{1\ \text{L H}_2} = 28.4\ L\ HF$

d. $80.0\ \text{L HF} \times \dfrac{1\ mol\ HF}{22.4\ \text{L HF}} \times \dfrac{1\ \text{mol H}_2}{2\ mol\ HF} \times$
$\dfrac{6.02 \times 10^{23}\ molecules\ H_2}{1\ \text{mol H}_2} = 1.08 \times 10^{24}\ molecules\ H_2$

7. 1. Complete combustion:

a. $2.70 \text{ mol } C_2H_4 \times \dfrac{3 \text{ mol } O_2}{1 \text{ mol } C_2H_4} = 8.10 \text{ mol } O_2$ required; O_2 is limiting

b. $6.30 \text{ mol } O_2 \times \dfrac{2 \text{ mol } H_2O}{3 \text{ mol } O_2} = 4.20 \text{ mol } H_2O$

c. Calculate the moles of C_2H_4 that react with 6.30 mol O_2.

$6.30 \text{ mol } O_2 \times \dfrac{1 \text{ mol } C_2H_4}{3 \text{ mol } O_2} = 2.10 \text{ mol } C_2H_4$ used;

excess $C_2H_4 = 2.70 - 2.10 = 0.60 \text{ mol } C_2H_4$

2. Incomplete combustion:

a. $2.70 \text{ mol } C_2H_4 \times \dfrac{2 \text{ mol } O_2}{1 \text{ mol } C_2H_4} = 5.40 \text{ mol } O_2$ required; O_2 is excess, C_2H_2 is limiting

b. $2.70 \text{ mol } C_2H_4 \times \dfrac{2 \text{ mol } H_2O}{1 \text{ mol } C_2H_4} = 5.40 \text{ mol } H_2O$

c. excess $O_2 = 6.30 - 5.40 = 0.90 \text{ mol } O_2$

8. a. Calculate the moles of each reactant.

$4.00 \text{ g HCl} \times \dfrac{1 \text{ mol HCl}}{36.5 \text{ g HCl}} = 0.110 \text{ mol HCl}$

$3.00 \text{ g Mg} \times \dfrac{1 \text{ mol Mg}}{24.3 \text{ g Mg}} = 0.123 \text{ mol Mg}$

HCl is limiting since the equation shows that twice as many moles of HCl are needed per mole of Mg.

$0.110 \text{ mol HCl} \times \dfrac{1 \text{ mol } H_2}{2 \text{ mol HCl}} \times \dfrac{2.0 \text{ g } H_2}{1 \text{ mol } H_2} = 0.110 \text{ g } H_2$

b. $0.110 \text{ g } H_2 \times \dfrac{1 \text{ mol } H_2}{2.0 \text{ g } H_2} \times \dfrac{22.4 \text{ L } H_2}{1 \text{ mol } H_2} = 1.23 \text{ L } H_2$

9. $1.87 \text{ g Al} \times \dfrac{1 \text{ mol Al}}{27.0 \text{ g Al}} \times \dfrac{3 \text{ mol Cu}}{2 \text{ mol Al}} \times \dfrac{63.5 \text{ g Cu}}{1 \text{ mol Cu}} =$

$6.60 \text{ g Cu (theoretical yield)}$

Percent yield $= \dfrac{3.74 \text{ g}}{6.60 \text{ g}} \times 100 = 56.7\%$

10. a. $583 \text{ g } SO_3 \times \dfrac{1 \text{ mol } SO_3}{80.1 \text{ g } SO_3} \times \dfrac{126.9 \text{ kJ}}{1 \text{ mol } SO_3} = 924 \text{ kJ}$

b. $924 \text{ kJ} \times \dfrac{1.00 \text{ kcal}}{4.18 \text{ kJ}} = 221 \text{ kcal}$

11. $22.2 \text{ kJ} \times \dfrac{2 \text{ mol } CO_2}{43.9 \text{ kJ}} \times \dfrac{6.02 \times 10^{23} \text{ molecules } CO_2}{1 \text{ mol } CO_2}$

$= 6.09 \times 10^{23} \text{ molecules } CO_2$

12. $\dfrac{44.0 \text{ kJ}}{1 \text{ mol } H_2O} \times \dfrac{1 \text{ mol } H_2O}{18.0 \text{ g } H_2O} \times \dfrac{1.00 \text{ kcal}}{4.18 \text{ kJ}} \times \dfrac{10^3 \text{ cal}}{1 \text{ kcal}} =$

$585 \dfrac{\text{cal}}{\text{g } H_2O}$

13. $\Delta H = H_f^\circ(\text{products}) - H_f^\circ(\text{reactants})$

a. $\Delta H = -393.5 \text{ kJ} + (2 \text{ mol})(-285.8 \text{ kJ/mol}) -$
(-74.86 kJ)
$= -393.5 \text{ kJ} - 571.6 \text{ kJ} + 74.86 \text{ kJ}$
$= -890.2 \text{ kJ}$

b. $\Delta H = (2 \text{ mol})(-393.5 \text{ kJ/mol}) -$
$(2 \text{ mol})(-110.5 \text{ kJ/mol})$
$= -787 \text{ kJ} \times (-221 \text{ kJ})$
$= -566 \text{ kJ}$

Chapter 9

1. If the temperature does not change, the average kinetic energy is unaffected.

2. At the same temperature, the average kinetic energies of the particles in any two samples of matter are the same.

3. An increase in the temperature causes an increase in the average kinetic energy of the gas particles.

4. If the absolute temperature is tripled, the average kinetic energy is tripled.

5. $190 \text{ mm Hg} \times \dfrac{1 \text{ atm}}{760 \text{ mm Hg}} = 0.25 \text{ atm}$

6. $253 \text{ mm Hg} \times \dfrac{1 \text{ atm}}{760 \text{ mm Hg}} = 0.333 \text{ atm}$

7. One mole of any gas at STP occupies a volume of 22.4 L. One mole of any substance contains 6.02×10^{23} particles.

$11.2 \text{ L } H_2 \times \dfrac{1 \text{ mol } H_2}{22.4 \text{ L } H_2} = \dfrac{11.2}{22.4} = 0.500 \text{ mol } H_2$

$0.500 \text{ mol } H_2 \times \dfrac{6.02 \times 10^{23} \text{ molecules } H_2}{1 \text{ mol } H_2} =$
$3.01 \times 10^{23} \text{ molecules } H_2$

8. $0.25 \text{ mol} \times \dfrac{22.4 \text{ L}}{1 \text{ mol}} = 5.6 \text{ L}$

9. The balanced equation shows that 2 mol of hydrogen reacts with 1 mol of oxygen.

Moles $H_2 \longrightarrow$ moles $O_2 \longrightarrow$ liters O_2

$1.0 \text{ mol } H_2 \times \dfrac{1 \text{ mol } O_2}{2 \text{ mol } H_2} \times \dfrac{22.4 \text{ L } O_2}{1 \text{ mol } O_2} = 11.2 \text{ L } O_2$

10. Change the given mass to moles, then to volume in liters.

Mass $\longrightarrow$ moles $\longrightarrow$ volume

$8.8 \text{ g } CO_2 \times \dfrac{1 \text{ mol } CO_2}{44.0 \text{ g } CO_2} \times \dfrac{22.4 \text{ L } CO_2}{1 \text{ mol } CO_2} = 4.5 \text{ L } CO_2$

Chapter 10

1. If the amount of gas is to be doubled while the pressure is kept the same, the volume of the container must be doubled.

2. A balloon shrinks when the temperature of the gas inside decreases. The pressure inside the balloon decreases because the average kinetic energy of the gas particles inside the balloon is lower at the lower temperature. The reduced kinetic energy results in fewer and less forceful collisions with the inside walls of the balloon.

3. The total pressure of a mixture of gases is equal to the sum of the partial pressure of each gas in the mixture.
$P_T = P_{O_2} + P_{N_2} + P_{He}$
$= 150 \text{ mm Hg} + 350 \text{ mm Hg} + 200 \text{ mm Hg}$
$= 700 \text{ mm Hg}$
Since 760 mm Hg equals 1.0 atm, we have:
$P_T = 700 \text{ mm Hg} \times \dfrac{1 \text{ atm}}{760 \text{ mm Hg}} = 0.92 \text{ atm}$

4. $P_1 \times V_1 = P_2 \times V_2$ (Boyle's law)
$V_2 = \dfrac{P_1 \times V_1}{P_2} = \dfrac{760 \text{ mm Hg} \times 2.50 \text{ L}}{304 \text{ mm Hg}} = 6.25 \text{ L}$
check: Because the pressure decreases, the volume should increase.

5. $\dfrac{V_1}{T_1} = \dfrac{V_2}{T_2}$ (Charles' law)

$$V_2 = \frac{V_1 \times T_1}{T_1} = \frac{6.8 \text{ L} \times 300\cancel{K}}{600\cancel{K}} = 3.4 \text{ L}$$

with annotations: $27°C + 273$ (pointing to $300\,K$), $327°C + 273$ (pointing to $600\,K$)

check: Because the temperature decreases, the volume should decrease.

6. $\dfrac{P_1}{T_1} = \dfrac{P_2}{T_2}$ (Gay-Lussac's law)

$$P_2 = \frac{P_1 \times T_2}{T_1} = \frac{50.0 \text{ mm Hg} \times 200\cancel{K}}{540\cancel{K}} = 18.5 \text{ mm Hg}$$

check: Because the temperature decreases, the pressure should decrease.

7. $\dfrac{P_1 \times V_1}{T_1} = \dfrac{P_2 \times V_2}{T_2}$ To use Charles' law, hold the pressure constant.

$$\frac{V_1}{T_1} = \frac{V_2 \times P_2}{T_2 \times P_1}$$

P_1 and P_2 cancel. Thus $\dfrac{V_1}{T_1} = \dfrac{V_2}{T_2}$ (Charles' law).

8. $\dfrac{P_1 \times V_1}{T_1} = \dfrac{P_2 \times V_2}{T_2}$

To use Gay-Lussac's law, hold the volume constant.

$$\frac{P_1}{T_1} = \frac{P_2 \times \cancel{V_2}}{T_2 \times \cancel{V_1}}$$

V_1 and V_2 cancel, and $\dfrac{P_1}{T_1} = \dfrac{P_2}{T_2}$ (Gay-Lussac's law).

9. $\dfrac{P_1 \times V_1}{T_1} = \dfrac{P_2 \times V_2}{T_2}$ (Combined gas law)

$$V_2 = \frac{P_1 \times V_1 \times T_2}{P_2 \times T_1} = \frac{1.5 \cancel{\text{atm}} \times 1.0 \text{ L} \times 373\cancel{K}}{6.0 \cancel{\text{atm}} \times 298\cancel{K}}$$

with annotations: $100°C + 273$ (pointing to $373\,K$), $25°C + 273$ (pointing to $298\,K$)

$$= 0.31 \text{ L}$$

check: The pressure increase (volume decrease) has a greater effect than the temperature increase (volume increase).

10. $P \times V = n \times R \times T$

$$n = \frac{P \times V}{R \times T} = \frac{18 \cancel{\text{atm}} \times 680 \text{ L}}{0.082 \dfrac{\cancel{L} \times \cancel{\text{atm}}}{\cancel{K} \times \cancel{\text{mol}}} 600\cancel{K}} = 2.5 \times 10^2 \text{ mol}$$

11. $P \times V = n \times R \times T$

$$n = \frac{P \times V}{R \times T} = \frac{1 \cancel{\text{atm}} \times 2.2\cancel{L}}{0.082 \dfrac{\cancel{L} \times \cancel{\text{atm}}}{K \times \text{mol}} 310\cancel{K}} = 0.087 \text{ mol air}$$

with annotation: $37°C + 273$ (pointing to $310\,K$)

$$0.087 \cancel{\text{mol air}} \times \frac{29 \text{ g air}}{1 \cancel{\text{mol air}}} = 2.5 \text{ g air}$$

12. The molar volume of an *ideal* gas is 22.41 L at STP. The molar volume of a *real* gas is less than 22.41 L. Intermolecular forces hold the gas particles together and reduce the volume. The decrease in volume depends upon the strength of the intermolecular attractive forces. Nonpolar O_2 and N_2 molecules behave like ideal gases. Their attractive forces are insignificant and their molar volumes are 22.41 L. The bonds in CH_4 are weakly polar but the molecule is nonpolar. Very weak intermolecular attractive forces reduce the molar volume to 22.38 L. The bonds in

CO_2 are moderately polar. The attractive forces between CO_2 molecules decrease the molar volume to 22.26 L. Ammonia molecules are polar and also form intermolecular hydrogen bonds. The strong attractive forces between the molecules reduce the molar volume to 22.06 L.

13. $\dfrac{\text{Rate H}_2}{\text{Rate Cl}_2} = \dfrac{\sqrt{\text{formula mass}_{Cl_2}}}{\sqrt{\text{formula mass}_{H_2}}} = \dfrac{\sqrt{71}}{\sqrt{2}} = \dfrac{8.4}{1.4} = 6.0$

Hydrogen diffuses six times faster than chlorine.

Chapter 11

1. a. 3 **b.** 1 **c.** 7 **d.** 3 **e.** 5 **f.** 9
2. $3d$, $4s$, $3p$, $3s$, $2p$
3. a. Boron has an atomic number of 5, an electron configuration of $1s^2 2s^2 2p^1$, and one unpaired electron. **b.** Fluorine has an atomic number of 9, an electron configuration of $1s^2 2s^2 2p^5$, and one unpaired electron.
4. a. Barium has an atomic number of 56. Its electron configuration is $1s^2 2s^2 2p^6 3s^2 3p^6 3d^{10} 4s^2 4p^6 4d^{10} 5s^2 5p^6 6s^2$. It has two electrons in its highest occupied energy level. **b.** Sodium has an atomic number of 11. Its electron configuration is $1s^2 2s^2 2p^6 3s^1$. It has one electron in its highest occupied energy level. **c.** Aluminum has an atomic number of 13. Its electron configuration is $1s^2 2s^2 2p^6 3s^2 3p^1$. It has three electrons in its highest occupied energy level. **d.** Oxygen has an atomic number of 8. Its electron configuration is $1s^2 2s^2 2p^4$. It has six electrons in its highest occupied energy level.
5. $\nu = \dfrac{c}{\lambda} = \dfrac{3.00 \times 10^{10} \cancel{\text{cm}} \text{ s}^{-1}}{5.00 \times 10^{-6} \cancel{\text{cm}}}$

$= 6.00 \times 10^{15} \text{ s}^{-1}$ (ultraviolet)
6. $\nu = \dfrac{c}{\lambda} = \dfrac{3.00 \times 10^{10} \cancel{\text{cm}} \text{ s}^{-1}}{6.56 \times 10^{-5} \cancel{\text{cm}}}$

$= 4.57 \times 10^{14} \text{ s}^{-1}$ (visible, orange-red)
7. Classical physics views energy changes as continuous. In the quantum concept energy changes occur in discrete units called quanta.
8. $E = h \times \nu$

$= 6.62 \times 10^{-34} \text{ J} \cancel{\text{s}} \times 3.20 \times 10^{11} \cancel{\text{s}^{-1}}$

$= 2.12 \times 10^{-22} \text{ J}$
9. The electron of the hydrogen atom is raised (excited) to the next highest energy level.

Chapter 12

1. a. Boron has 5 electrons. Reading the periodic table from left to right we have the first period, $1s^2$, and the second period, $2s^2\, 2p^1$. There is one electron in the $2p$ sublevel because boron is the third element in the p block. **b.** Magnesium has 12 electrons. The first two periods are $1s^2 2s^2 2p^6$. Next we have $3s^2$, which completes the electron configuration. **c.** Vanadium has 26 electrons. We go through the first three periods, $1s^2 2s^2 2p^6 3s^2 3p^6$, then $4s^2$ and finally $3d^3$. Vanadium is the third element in the d block, and the complete electron configuration is $1s^2 2s^2 2p^6 3s^2 3p^6 3d^3 4s^2$. **d.** Strontium, with 38 electrons, is in the fifth period. To get to strontium we pass through $1s^2 2s^2 2p^6 3s^2 3p^6 4s^2 3d^{10} 4p^6$, and finally $5s^2$. The electron configuration for strontium is $1s^2 2s^2 2p^6 3s^2 3p^6 3d^{10} 4s^2 4p^6 5s^2$.

2. a. The inert gas in period three is argon: $1s^2 2s^2 2p^6 3s^2 3p^6$.
b. The element in group 4A, period 4 is germanium with 32 electrons, $1s^2 2s^2 2p^6 3s^2 3p^6 3d^{10} 4s^2 4p^2$. **c.** Group 2A, period 6 is barium with 56 electrons, $1s^2 2s^2 2p^6 3s^2 3p^6 3d^{10} 4s^2 4p^6 4d^{10} 5s^2 5p^6 6s^2$.

3. Fluorine has nine protons and nine electrons, $1s^2 2s^2 2p^5$, and oxygen has eight protons and eight electrons, $1s^2 2s^2 2p^4$. In each element the outer electrons are shielded from the nucleus by two $1s$ electrons. The effect of the increased nuclear charge on fluorine pulls the outer electrons tighter than in oxygen, and the atomic radius decreases. Chlorine, with 17 protons and electrons, $1s^2 2s^2 2p^6 3s^2 3p^5$, has its outer electrons shielded from the nucleus by a layer of electrons in the second energy level. The third energy level of electrons experiences less nuclear attraction and is consequently larger. Therefore chlorine has a larger atomic radius than fluorine.

4. Electron affinities of nonmetals such as the halogens are large negative numbers. This is because these elements acquire noble gas configurations by gaining one or more electrons.

5. a. sodium **b.** phosphorus
6. a. Ge, germanium **b.** Mg, magnesium **c.** Nb, niobium **d.** P, phosphorus **e.** Ti, titanium **f.** F, fluorine

Chapter 13

1. a. 1 **b.** 4 **c.** 2 **d.** 6
2. Cu^+: $1s^2\ 2s^2\ 2p^6\ 3s^2\ 3p^6\ 3d^{10}$
Au^+: $1s^2\ 2s^2\ 2p^6\ 3s^2\ 3p^6\ 3d^{10}\ 4s^2\ 4p^6\ 4d^{10}\ 4f^{14}\ 5s^2\ 5p^6\ 5d^{10}$
Cd^{2+}: $1s^2\ 2s^2\ 2p^6\ 3s^2\ 3p^6\ 3d^{10}\ 4s^2\ 4p^6\ 4d^{10}$
Hg^{2+}: $1s^2\ 2s^2\ 2p^6\ 3s^2\ 3p^6\ 3d^{10}\ 4s^2\ 4p^6\ 4d^{10}\ 4f^{14}\ 5s^2\ 5p^6\ 5d^{10}$

3. a. lose 2 **b.** gain 1 **c.** lose 3 **d.** gain 2
4. a. S^{2-} **b.** Na^+ **c.** F^- **d.** Ba^{2+}
5. a. $K^+ \,[\ddot{\underset{\cdot\cdot}{I}}:]^-$, KI **b.** $Ca^{2+} \,[\ddot{\underset{\cdot\cdot}{S}}:]^{2-}$, CaS

c. Al^{3+} $[\ddot{\underset{\cdot\cdot}{O}}:]^{2-}$
Al^{3+} $[\ddot{\underset{\cdot\cdot}{O}}:]^{2-}$
$[\ddot{\underset{\cdot\cdot}{O}}:]^{2-}$, Al_2O_3

d. Na^+
$Na^+ \,[\ddot{\underset{\cdot\cdot}{P}}:]^{3-}$, Na_3P
Na^+

6. a. potassium iodide **b.** calcium sulfide **c.** aluminum oxide **d.** sodium phosphide
7. a. K^+I^- **b.** $Ca^{2+}S^{2-}$ **c.** $Al^{3+}O^{2-}$ **d.** Na^+P^{3-}
   KI   CaS Al_2O_3 Na_3P

Chapter 14

1. a. $:\!\ddot{C}l\!:\!\ddot{C}l\!:$ **b.** $:\!\ddot{B}r\!:\!\ddot{B}r\!:$ **c.** $:\!\ddot{I}\!:\!\ddot{I}\!:$

2. a. $H\!:\!\ddot{S}\!:\!H$ **b.** $H\!:\!\ddot{P}\!:\!H$ **c.** $:\!\ddot{C}l\!:\!\ddot{F}\!:$
   H

3. $\left[:\!\ddot{O}\!: \atop :\!\ddot{O}\!:\!S\!:\!\ddot{O}\!: \atop :\!\ddot{O}\!: \right]^{2-}$ $\left[:\!\ddot{O}\!: \atop :\!\ddot{O}\!:\!C\!:\!\ddot{O}\!: \right]^{2-}$

4. A sigma bond is formed by the overlap of two s orbitals, the overlap of an s orbital with a p orbital, or end-to-end overlap of two p orbitals.

$$\text{1 } s \text{ orbital} \quad + \quad \text{1}s \text{ orbital} \quad \longrightarrow \quad \text{sigma bond}$$

5. The boron in BF_3 shares only six valence electrons with the fluorines. An additional F^- can form a coordinate covalent bond with the BF_3. The geometry of the ion BF_4^- would be tetrahedral according to VSEPR theory, since this keeps the fluorines the maximum distance apart.

6.

Elements (electronegativities)	Electronegativity difference	Type of bond
a. H(2.1), Br(2.8)	0.7	Covalent (moderately polar)
b. K(0.8), Cl(3.0)	2.2	Ionic
c. C(2.5), O(3.5)	1.0	Covalent (very polar)
d. Cl(3.0), F(4.0)	1.0	Covalent (very polar)
e. Li(1.0), O(3.5)	2.5	Ionic
f. Br(2.8), Br(2.8)	0.0	Covalent (nonpolar)

7. The most polar bond will have the greatest electronegativity difference between the interacting atoms. In order of increasing polarity:

Elements	Electronegativity difference
e. F(4.0), F(4.0)	0.0
c. H(2.1), S(2.5)	0.4
d. H(2.1), C(2.5)	0.4
b. H(2.1), Br(2.8)	0.7
a. H(2.1), Cl(3.0)	0.9

8. From Table 14·4, the bond dissociation energy of a C—H bond is 393 kilojoules/mole.

$$\frac{393\text{ kJ}}{\text{mole C—H}} \times \frac{4\text{ mole C—H}}{\text{mole C—H}_4} \times 0.1\text{ mole CH}_4 = 157\text{ kJ}$$

9.

Chapter 15

1. Hydrogen-bonding between ammonia molecules occurs because ammonia is a polar molecule.

$$\underset{\text{H}\quad\text{H}\quad\text{H}}{\overset{\text{N}}{\diagup\;|\;\diagdown}}$$

Methane is a nonpolar molecule. It can have no hydrogen-bonding. Substances whose molecules form intermolecular hydrogen bonds tend to have higher boiling points.

2. Water is a polar solvent. Solutes that are ionic or polar generally dissolve in water. **a.** HCl is polar and will dissolve. **b.** NaI is ionic and will dissolve. **c.** NH_3 is polar and will dissolve. **d.** $MgSO_4$ is ionic and will dissolve. **e.** CH_4 is nonpolar and will not dissolve. **f.** $CaCO_3$ is ionic but will not dissolve. Some ionic compounds are insoluble in water because of the strong attractive forces within the solid crystal. **g.** Gasoline is nonpolar and will not dissolve.

3. First calculate the gram formula mass of the hydrate and of the attached water. Then calculate the percent of water
   Cu: $1 \times 63.5 = 63.5$
   S: $1 \times 32.1 = 32.1$
   O: $4 \times 16.0 = 64.0$
   H_2O: $5 \times 18.0 = \underline{90.0}$
   249.6 g/mol

$$\text{Percent H}_2\text{O} = \frac{\text{mass of H}_2\text{O}}{\text{mass of hydrate}} = \frac{90.0\text{ g}}{249.6\text{ g}} = 36.1\%$$

Chapter 16

1. The solubility of NaCl is 36.2 g NaCl per 100 mL of solution at 25°C.

$$750 \text{ mL} \times \frac{36.2 \text{ g NaCl}}{100 \text{ mL solution}} = 271.5 = 272 \text{ g NaCl}$$

2. Henry's law relates the solubility of a gas to the pressure of the gas above the liquid.

$$\frac{S_1}{P_1} = \frac{S_2}{P_2}$$

$$P_2 = \frac{S_2 P_1}{S_1}$$

(This is like solving Charles's law for T_2.)

$$P_2 = \frac{(9.5 \text{ g/L})(1.0 \text{ atm})}{(3.6 \text{ g/L})} = 2.6 \text{ atm}$$

This answer makes sense. To increase the solubility of a gas, the pressure of the gas above the liquid should be increased.

3. Molarity $(M) = \dfrac{\text{number of moles of solute}}{\text{number of liters of solution}}$

Change the given volume to the unit liters:

$$250 \text{ mL} \times \frac{1 \text{ L}}{1000 \text{ mL}} = 0.25 \text{ L}$$

$$\text{Molarity} = \frac{0.70 \text{ mol}}{0.25 \text{ L}} = 2.8 M$$

4. Moles glucose $= \dfrac{36.0 \text{ g}}{180 \text{ g/mol}} = 0.20 \text{ mol}$

$$\text{Molarity} = \frac{0.20 \text{ mol}}{2.0 \text{ L}} = 0.1 M$$

5. $2.0 M$ $CaCl_2$ means 2.0 mol $CaCl_2$ per 1.0 L.

$$250 \text{ mL} \times \frac{1.0 \text{ L}}{1000 \text{ mL}} \times \frac{2.0 \text{ mol } CaCl_2}{1.0 \text{ L}} = 0.50 \text{ mol } CaCl_2$$

To find the mass of $CaCl_2$, you need its gram formula mass (gfm).

Ca: $1 \times 40.1 = 40.1$ g
Cl: $2 \times 35.5 = 71.0$ g
$\qquad\qquad\qquad 111.1$ g/mol

$$\text{Mass of } CaCl_2 = 0.50 \text{ mol } CaCl_2 \times \frac{111.1 \text{ g } CaCl_2}{1 \text{ mol } CaCl_2}$$

$$= 55.5 = 56 \text{ g } CaCl_2$$

6. For dilution problems: $M_1 \times V_1 = M_2 \times V_2$

The volume of stock solution needed is

$$V_1 = \frac{M_2 \times V_2}{M_1} = \frac{(0.2 M \times 250 \text{ mL})}{1.0 M} = 50 \text{ mL}$$

Use a pipet to transfer 50 mL of the $1.0 M$ solution to a 250-mL volumetric flask. Then add distilled water up to the mark.

7. Percent by volume $= \dfrac{\text{volume of solute}}{\text{volume of solution}} \times 100\%$

$$= \frac{10 \text{ mL}}{200 \text{ mL}} \times 100\% = 5.0\% \text{ (v/v)}$$

8. 1.6% $MgSO_4$ (m/v) means that there is 1.6 g $MgSO_4$ in 100 of mL solution.

$$250 \text{ mL} \times \frac{1.6 \text{ g } MgSO_4}{100 \text{ mL}} = 4.0 \text{ g } MgSO_4$$

9. Percent (m/v) $= \dfrac{\text{mass of solute (g)}}{\text{volume of solution (mL)}} \times 100\%$

$$= \frac{2.7 \text{ g}}{75 \text{ mL}} \times 100\% = 3.6\% \text{ } CuSO_4 \text{ (m/v)}$$

10. Molality $= \dfrac{\text{moles of solute}}{1000 \text{ g of solvent}}$

Use a conversion factor to convert 10.0 g NaCl in 600 g H_2O to grams of NaCl in 1000 g H_2O.

$$1000 \text{ g } H_2O \times \frac{10.0 \text{ g NaCl}}{600 \text{ g } H_2O} = 16.7 \text{ g NaCl}$$

Convert 16.7 g NaCl to moles.
gfm NaCl $= 23.0 + 35.5 = 58.5$ g

$$16.7 \text{ g NaCl} \times \frac{1 \text{ mol NaCl}}{58.5 \text{ g NaCl}} = 0.285 \text{ mol NaCl}$$

When 10.0 g NaCl is dissolved in 600 g H_2O, the resulting solution is 0.285 molal NaCl.

11. Convert 300 g C_6H_5OH to moles.
gfm $C_2H_5OH = 24.0 + 5.0 + 16.0 + 1.0 = 46.0$ g

$$300 \text{ g } C_2H_5OH \times \frac{1 \text{ mol } C_2H_5OH}{46.0 \text{ g } C_2H_5OH} = 6.45 \text{ mol } C_2H_5OH$$

Convert 500 g H_2O to moles.
gfm $H_2O = 2.0 + 16.0 = 18.0$ g

$$500 \text{ g } H_2O \times \frac{1 \text{ mol } H_2O}{18.0 \text{ g } H_2O} = 27.8 \text{ mol } H_2O$$

The mole fraction of ethanol, X_E, in the solution is the number of moles of ethanol divided by the total number of moles in solution.

$$X_E = \frac{n_E}{n_E + n_{H_2O}} = \frac{6.45 \text{ mol}}{6.45 \text{ mol} + 27.8 \text{ mol}} = 0.188$$

The mole fraction of water, X_{H_2O}, is the number of moles of water divided by the total number of moles in solution.

$$X_{H_2O} = \frac{n_{H_2O}}{n_{H_2O} + n_E} = \frac{27.8 \text{ mol}}{27.8 \text{ mol} + 6.45 \text{ mol}} = 0.812$$

Total $= 1.000$

12. The solution contains 0.150 moles of NaCl in 1000 g H_2O. Use a conversion factor to convert 1000 g H_2O to moles of H_2O.
gfm $H_2O = 2.0 + 16.0 = 18.0$ g

$$1000 \text{ g } H_2O \times \frac{1 \text{ mol } H_2O}{18.0 \text{ g } H_2O} = 55.6 \text{ mol } H_2O$$

The mol fraction of sodium chloride, X_{NaCl}, is the number of moles of NaCl divided by the total number of moles in solution.

$$X_{NaCl} = \frac{n_{NaCl}}{n_{NaCl} + n_{H_2O}} = \frac{0.150}{0.150 + 55.6} = 0.00269$$

The mol fraction of water, X_{H_2O}, is the number of moles of H_2O divided by the total number of moles in solution.

$$X_{H_2O} = \frac{n_{H_2O}}{n_{H_2O} + n_{NaCl}} = \frac{55.6}{55.6 + 0.150} = 0.99731$$

Total $= 1.00000$

13. $X_{CH_3OH} = 0.40 = \dfrac{n_{CH_3OH}}{n_{CH_3OH} + n_{H_2O}}$

$$X_{H_2O} = 0.60 = \frac{n_{H_2O}}{n_{H_2O} + n_{CH_3OH}}$$

$$X_{CH_3OH} = \frac{0.6}{0.4} X_{H_2O} = 1.5 \times X_{H_2O}$$

Therefore: $n_{H_2O} = 1.5 \text{ } n_{CH_3OH}$
Substitute in first two equations to check:
$n_{H_2O} = 1.5$; $n_{CH_3OH} = 1.0$

$$X_{CH_3OH} = \frac{1}{1 + 1.5} = \frac{1}{2.5} = 0.4$$

$$X_{H_2O} = \frac{1.5}{1.5 + 1} = \frac{1.5}{2.5} = 0.6$$

To make a solution 0.40 mole fraction in CH_3OH we need a ratio of 1.5 mol H_2O to 1.0 mol CH_3OH.

gfm H_2O = 2.0 + 16.0 = 18.0 g

gfm CH_3OH = 12.0 + 3.0 + 16.0 + 1.0 = 32.0 g

Add 1.5 × 18.0 g = 27.0 g H_2O to 32.0 g CH_3OH to give an aqueous solution of methanol in which the mole fraction of methanol is 0.40.

14. Determine the molality of the solution.

$$\frac{\text{mol } CaCl_2}{1000 \text{ g } H_2O} = \frac{1.25 \text{ mol } CaCl_2}{1400 \text{ g } H_2O} \times \frac{1000 \text{ g } H_2O}{1 \text{ kg } H_2O}$$
$$= 0.893 \ m$$

One mol of $CaCl_2$ in water gives 3 mol of particles.

$CaCl_2(s) \rightarrow Ca^{2+}(aq) + 2 \ Cl^-(aq)$

The molality of *total* particles is:

3 × 0.893 m = 2.68 m

The boiling elevation is:

$\Delta T_b = K_b m = 0.512 \ °C/m \times 2.68 \ m$
$= 1.37 \ °C$

The boiling point of this solution is:

100°C + 1.37°C = 101.37°C

15. a. Determine the molality of the solution.

$$\frac{\text{mol } Na_2SO_4}{1000 \text{ g } H_2O} = \frac{1.40 \text{ mol } Na_2SO_4}{1750 \text{ g } H_2O} \times \frac{1000 \text{ g } H_2O}{1 \text{ kg } H_2O}$$
$$= 0.800 \ m$$

One mol of Na_2SO_4 in water gives 3 mol of particles.

$Na_2SO_4 \ (s) \rightarrow 2 \ Na^+(aq) + SO_4^{2-} \ (aq)$

The molality of *total* particles is:

3 × 0.800 m = 2.40 m

The freezing point depression is:

$\Delta T_f = K_f m = 1.86 \ °C/m \times 2.40 \ m$
$= 4.46 \ °C$

The freezing point of this solution is:

0 °C − 4.46 °C = −4.46 °C

b. The molality of the solution is:

$$\frac{\text{mol } MgSO_4}{1000 \text{ g } H_2O} = \frac{0.60 \text{ mol } MgSO_4}{1300 \text{ g } H_2O} \times \frac{1000 \text{ g } H_2O}{1 \text{ kg } H_2O}$$
$$= 0.46 \ m$$

One mole of $MgSO_4$ gives 2 mol of particles.

$MgSO_4(s) \rightarrow Mg^{2+}(aq) + SO_4^{2-}(aq)$

The molality of total particles is:

2 × 0.46 m = 0.92 m

The freezing point depression is:

$\Delta T_f = K_f m = 1.86 \ °C/m \times 0.92 \ m$
$= 1.71 \ °C$

The freezing point of this solution is:

0 °C − 1.71 °C = −1.71 °C

16. The boiling point elevation (4 × 0.52°C = 2.08°C) and freezing point depression (4 × −1.86 = −7.44°C) both show that the compound gave 4 mol of particles in solution. The formula must be $FeCl_3$.

17. The molal freezing point content for H_2O is:

$$K_f = 1.86 \ \frac{°C \text{ kg of } H_2O}{\text{mol of solute}}$$

The observed freezing point depression is:

$\Delta T_f = 0.390 \ °C$

First calculate the molarity of the solution.

$\Delta T_f = K_f \times m$

$$m = \frac{\Delta T_f}{K_f} = \frac{0.390 \ °C}{1.86 \ °C \text{ kg of } H_2O} = 0.210 \ \frac{\text{mol of solute}}{\text{kg of } H_2O}$$
$$\overline{\qquad \text{mol of solute} \qquad}$$

Now calculate moles of solute in solution.

$$0.210 \ \frac{\text{mol of solute}}{\text{kg of } H_2O} \times 475 \text{ g } H_2O \times \frac{1 \text{ kg of } H_2O}{1000 \text{ g } H_2O}$$
$$= 0.0998 \text{ mol solute}$$

Finally, use number of moles of solute and its mass to determine the molecular mass of the solute.

$$\text{Molecular mass of solute} = \frac{\text{mass of solute}}{\text{moles of solute}}$$
$$= \frac{3.90 \text{ g}}{0.0998 \text{ mol}}$$
$$= 39.1 \text{ g/mol}$$

Chapter 17

1. Reactions conducted by bacteria in food lead to spoilage. These reactions are faster at room temperature than in the cold. Bacteria also multiply faster in a warm environment.

2. At least four factors contribute to reaction rates: temperature (heating enables more reactant molecules to cross the activation energy barrier); concentration (more reactants in a given volume increase the chance for productive collisions); particle size (the smaller the particles, the more surface of reactant is exposed to reaction); and catalysis (catalysts provide a path of lower activation energy).

3. For a reaction first-order in species A:

   Rate = k[A]

   The rate is in units of concentration per unit of time (e.g. moles per liter per second), [A] is in moles per liter.

   Thus: Units of k = rate/[A]
   = moles per liter/time × liters per mole
   = 1/time[1]

4. Since the rate of a first-order reaction is directly proportional to the concentration of one reactant, the rate will be 0.25 mol/L × s when one-half the starting material remains, and 0.125 mol/L × s when one-fourth of the starting material remains.

5. For the hypothetical second-order reaction:

   A + B → C

   Rate = k[A][B]

   Units of k = rate/[A][B]
   $$= \frac{\text{mol}}{L \times s} \times \frac{L}{\text{mol}} \times \frac{L}{\text{mol}} = L/(\text{mol} \times s)$$

6. When NO_2^- is doubled with NH_4^+ held constant, the rate doubles. The reaction is first-order in NO_2^-. When NH_4^+ is doubled with NO_2^- held constant, the rate also doubles. The reaction is also first-order with respect to NH_4^+, and the overall reaction is second-order.

7. **a.** playing cards in use   **c.** a cup of water at 50°C
   b. a dissolved sugar cube   **d.** 1 g of powdered salt

8. $\Delta S^O = S^O(\text{products}) - S^O(\text{reactants})$

   Values of S^O for products and reactants are from Table 17·1. Units are J/K × mol.

   a. (39.75 + 213.6) − (88.7) = 165
   b. (2 × 69.94) − ((2 × 130.6) + 205.0) = −326.3
   c. (2 × 186.7) − (130.6 + 23) = 9.8

9. Calculate ΔG^O to determine if it is negative (spontaneous reaction) or positive (nonspontaneous reaction). Use the ΔG_f of Table 17·4. All units are kJ/mol.

   $\Delta G^O = \Delta G_f(\text{products}) - \Delta G_f(\text{reactants})$
   a. (2 × −384.03) − (2 × 0.00 + 0.00) = −768.06
   b. (2 × −1576.4) − (4 × 0.00 + 3 × 0.00) = −3152.8
   The reactions are spontaneous.

10. Recall that:
$$\Delta G^\circ = \Delta H^\circ - T\Delta S^\circ$$
From Table 17·1:
$$\Delta S^\circ = (2 \times 192.5) \times (3 \times 130.6 + 191.5)$$
$$= -198.3 \text{ J/K} \times \text{mol}$$
$$= -0.198 \text{ kJ/K} \times \text{mol}$$
$$\Delta H^\circ = \Delta G^\circ + T\Delta S^\circ$$
At 298 K:
$$\Delta H^\circ = -16.64 + (298 \times -0.198)$$
$$= -75.2 \text{ kJ/mol}$$

11. $K_{eq} = \dfrac{[NH_3]^2}{[H_2]^3 \times [N_2]}$

12. $K_{eq} = \dfrac{[0.10]}{[0.15]^3 \times [0.25]}$
$$= 12 \text{ (to two significant figures)}$$

13. $K_{eq} = \dfrac{[H_2] \times [I_2]}{[HI]^2}$

14. From problem 13:
$$K_{eq} = \dfrac{[H_2] \times [I_2]}{[HI]^2}$$
If $[H_2] = 0.50$ mol, $[I_2]$ must $= 0.50$ mol according to the balanced equation.
$$[HI]^2 = \dfrac{[0.50] \times [0.50]}{0.20}$$
$$= 1.25$$
$$[HI] = \sqrt{1.25}$$
$$= 1.1 \text{ (to two significant figures)}$$

15. For K_{eq} greater than 1.0, the products are usually favored.
 a. products **b.** reactants
 c. products **d.** reactants

16. a. Removing heat shifts equilibrium position toward reactants. (Heat is needed to make the reaction go.)
 b. Increasing pressure pushes equilibrium toward reactants.
 c. Removing H_2 draws equilibrium toward products.

Chapter 18

1. $[H^+] = \dfrac{K_w}{[OH^-]} = \dfrac{1 \times 10^{-14}}{1.0 \times 10^{-3}} = 1 \times 10^{-11}$ mol/L
Since $[OH^-]$ is greater than $[H^+]$, the solution is basic.

2. By definition, pH $= -\log[H^+]$,
 a. pH $= -\log(1 \times 10^{-10}) = -(0.0 - 10) = 10.0$
 b. pH $= -\log(1 \times 10^{-3}) = (0.0 - 3) = 3.0$
If the $[OH^-]$ concentration is given, first find the $[H^+]$ using K_w; then find the pH.

 c. $[H^+] = \dfrac{K_w}{[OH^-]} = \dfrac{1 \times 10^{-14}}{1 \times 10^{-2}} = 1 \times 10^{-12}$ mol/L
pH $= -\log(1 \times 10^{-12}) = -(0.0 - 12) = 12.0$

 d. $[H^+] = \dfrac{K_w}{[OH^-]} = \dfrac{1 \times 10^{-14}}{1 \times 10^{-11}} = 1 \times 10^{-3}$ mol/L
pH $= -\log(1 \times 10^{-2}) = -(0.0 - 12) = 12.0$

3. The pH of a solution with a hydrogen-ion concentration of $1 \times 10^{-x}M$ is x. **a.** pH $= 4.0$, $[H^+] = 1 \times 10^{-4}M$
 b. pH $= 11.0$, $[H^+] = 1 \times 10^{-11}M$ **c.** pH $= 8.0$, $[H^+] = 1 \times 10^{-8}M$

4. First find the $[H^+]$ as in the previous example. Then use K_w to find $[OH^-]$.
 a. pH $= 6.0$, $[H^+] = 1 \times 10^{-6}$
$$[OH^-] = \dfrac{1 \times 10^{-14}}{1 \times 10^{-6}} = 1 \times 10^{-8}M$$

 b. pH $= 9.0$, $[H^+] = 1 \times 10^{-9}$
$$[OH^-] = \dfrac{1 \times 10^{-14}}{1 \times 10^{-9}} = 1 \times 10^{-5}M$$
 c. pH $= 12.0$, $[H^+] = 1 \times 10^{-12}$
$$[OH^-] = \dfrac{1 \times 10^{-14}}{1 \times 10^{-12}} = 1 \times 10^{-2}M$$

5. a. 4.0 **b.** 3.0 **c.** 9.0 **d.** 10.0

6. a. $[H^+] = 5.0 \times 10^{-6}$
pH $= -\log(5.0) - \log(10^{-6})$
$= -(0.70) - (-6)$
$= 5.30$
 b. $[H^+] = 8.3 \times 10^{-10}$
pH $= -\log(8.3) - \log(10^{-10})$
$= -(0.92) - (-10)$
$= 9.08$
 c. $[H^+] = \dfrac{1 \times 10^{-14}}{2.0 \times 10^{-5}} = 5 \times 10^{-10}$
pH $= -\log(5.0) - \log(10^{-10})$
$= -(0.70) - (-10)$
$= 9.30$
 d. $[H^+] = \dfrac{1 \times 10^{-14}}{4.5 \times 10^{-11}} = 2.2 \times 10^{-4}$
pH $= -\log(2.2) - \log(10^{-4})$
$= -(0.34) - (-4)$
$= 3.66$

7. a. $[H^+] = 1 \times 10^{-5}M$
 b. pH $= 5.80$
$[H^+] = (10^{0.20})(10^{-6}) = 1.6 \times 10^{-6}M$
 c. pH $= 12.20$
$[H^+] = (10^{0.80})(10^{-13}) = 6.3 \times 10^{-13}M$
 d. pH $= 2.64$
$[H^+] = (10^{0.36})(10^{-3}) = 2.3 \times 10^{-3}M$

8. a. diprotic **b.** triprotic **c.** monoprotic

9. a. $2K + 2H_2O \rightarrow 2KOH + H_2$
 b. $Ca + 2H_2O \rightarrow Ca(OH)_2 + H_2$

10. a. $KOH \rightarrow K^+ + OH^-$
 b. $Mg(OH)_2 \rightarrow Mg^{2+} + 2OH^-$

11. $\underset{\substack{\text{acid} \\ \text{(hydrogen-} \\ \text{ion donor)}}}{HNO_3} + \underset{\substack{\text{base} \\ \text{(hydrogen-} \\ \text{ion acceptor)}}}{H_2O} \rightleftharpoons \underset{\substack{\text{conjugate} \\ \text{acid}}}{H_3O^+} + \underset{\substack{\text{conjugate} \\ \text{base}}}{NO_3^-}$

$\underset{\substack{\text{base} \\ \text{(hydrogen-} \\ \text{ion acceptor)}}}{CO_3^{2-}} + \underset{\substack{\text{acid} \\ \text{(hydrogen-} \\ \text{ion donor)}}}{H_2O} \rightleftharpoons \underset{\substack{\text{conjugate} \\ \text{acid}}}{HCO_3^-} + \underset{\substack{\text{conjugate} \\ \text{base}}}{OH^-}$

12. a. H^+ is the Lewis acid; H_2O is the Lewis base.
 b. $AlCl_3$ is the Lewis acid; Cl^- is the Lewis base.

13. Boric acid; weakest acid has lowest K_a.

14. The strongest acid is oxalic acid. The weakest acid is carbonic acid.

15. Ammonia is a weak base because it has a small K_b. Sodium hydroxide is a strong base because it has a large K_b.

16. a. pH $= -\log[H^+] = -\log(9.86) - \log(10^{-4})$
$= -(0.994) - (-4)$
$= 3.006$

 b. $K_a = \dfrac{[H^+][X^+]}{[HX]}$
$= \dfrac{(9.86 \times 10^{-4})(9.86 \times 10^{-4})}{0.199}$
$= 4.88 \times 10^{-6}$

Chapter 19

1. a. $HNO_3 + KOH \rightarrow KNO_3 + H_2O$
b. $2HCl + Mg(OH)_2 \rightarrow MgCl_2 + 2H_2O$
c. $H_3PO_4 + 3NH_4OH \rightarrow (NH_4)_3PO_4 + 3H_2O$

2. Write the equation for the neutralization.
$3NaOH + H_3PO_4 \rightarrow Na_3PO_4 + 3H_2O$

$$0.20 \text{ mol } H_3PO_4 \times \frac{3 \text{ mol NaOH}}{1 \text{ mol } H_3PO_4} = 0.60 \text{ mol NaOH}$$

3. Write the equation for the neutralization.
$HCl + KOH \rightarrow KCl + H_2O$

$$0.025 \text{ L KOH} \times \frac{1 \text{ mol KOH}}{1 \text{ L KOH}} \times \frac{1 \text{ mol HCl}}{1 \text{ mol KOH}}$$
$$\times \frac{1 \text{ L HCl}}{0.45 \text{ mol HCl}} \times \frac{10^3 \text{ mL HCl}}{1 \text{ L HCl}} = 56 \text{ mL HCl}$$

4. Write the equation for the neutralization.
$H_3PO_4 + 3NaOH \rightarrow Na_3PO_4 + 3H_2O$

$$0.0385 \text{ L NaOH} \times \frac{0.15 \text{ mol NaOH}}{1 \text{ L NaOH}} \times \frac{1 \text{ mol } H_3PO_4}{3 \text{ mol NaOH}}$$
$$= 0.00193 \text{ mol } H_3PO_4$$

$$\text{Molarity} = \frac{\text{mole}}{L} = \frac{0.00193 \text{ mol}}{0.015 \text{ L}} = 0.129M$$

5. Divide the gram equivalent mass by the number of equivalents per mol.

a. 1 Gram equiv mass KOH $= \dfrac{56.1 \text{ g}}{1} = 56.1$ g

(1 equivalent per mol)

b. 1 Gram equiv mass HCl $= \dfrac{36.5 \text{ g}}{1} = 56.1$ g

(1 equivalent per mol)

c. 1 Gram equiv mass $H_2SO_4 = \dfrac{98.0 \text{ g}}{2} = 49.0$ g

(2 equivalents per mol)

6. Equiv $= \dfrac{\text{gram molecular mass}}{\text{gram equivalent mass}}$

a. Gram equiv mass $Ca(OH)_2 = \dfrac{74.0 \text{ g}}{2} = 37.0$ g

Equiv $Ca(OH)_2 = \dfrac{3.7 \text{ g}}{37.0 \text{ g/equiv}} = 0.10$ equiv

b. Gram equiv mass $H_2SO_4 = \dfrac{98.0 \text{ g}}{2} = 49.0$ g

Equiv $H_2SO_4 = \dfrac{189 \text{ g}}{49.0 \text{ g/equiv}} = 3.86$ equiv

c. Gram equiv mass $H_3PO_4 = \dfrac{98.0 \text{ g}}{3} = 32.7$ g

Equiv $H_3PO_4 = \dfrac{9.8 \text{ g}}{37.2 \text{ g/equiv}} = 0.26$ equiv

7. Normality = molarity × number ionizable hydrogens
a. $2M$ HCl $= 2N$ HCl
b. $0.1M$ $CH_3COOH = 0.1N$ CH_3COOH
c. $0.3M$ $H_3PO_4 = 0.9N$ H_3PO_4
(three ionizable hydrogens)
d. $0.25M$ $H_2SO_4 = 0.50N$ H_2SO_4
(two ionizable hydrogens)

8. Normality = equivalents/liter

a. $20 \text{ g NaOH} \times \dfrac{1 \text{ equiv NaOH}}{40 \text{ g NaOH}} = 0.50$ equiv NaOH

$$N = \frac{0.50 \text{ equiv NaOH}}{1 \text{ L}} = 0.50N$$

b. $4.9 \text{ g } H_2SO_4 \times \dfrac{1 \text{ equiv } H_2SO_4}{49.0 \text{ g } H_2SO_4} = 0.10$ equiv H_2SO_4

$$N = \frac{0.10 \text{ equiv}}{0.50 \text{ L}} = 0.20N$$

9. Find the number of equivalents by multiplying the volume of the solution by the normality of the solution.

a. $0.55 \text{ L} \times \dfrac{1.8 \text{ equiv}}{1 \text{ L}} = 0.99$ equiv

b. $1.6 \text{ L} \times \dfrac{0.50 \text{ equiv}}{1 \text{ L}} = 0.80$ equiv

c. $0.25 \text{ L} \times \dfrac{0.28 \text{ equiv}}{1 \text{ L}} = 0.070$ equiv

10. The number of equivalents must be equal before and after dilution.
$N_1 \times V_1 = N_2 \times V_2$

$$V_1 = \frac{N_2 \times V_2}{N_1} = \frac{500 \text{ mL} \times 0.20N}{4.0N} = 25 \text{ mL}$$

Dilute 25 mL of $4.0N$ H_2SO_4 to 500 mL.

11. At the neutralization point, $N_A \times V_A = N_B \times V_B$.

$$V_B = \frac{N_A \times V_A}{N_B} = \frac{0.050N \times 75 \text{ mL}}{0.20N} = 19 \text{ mL}$$

12. At the equivalence point, the number of equivalents of acid and base are equal.
$N_A \times V_A = N_B \times V_B$

$$N_B = \frac{N_A \times V_A}{V_B} = \frac{0.40N \times 75 \text{ mL}}{25 \text{ mL}} = 1.2N \text{ base}$$

13 a. $HPO_4^{2-} + H^+ \rightarrow H_2PO_4^-$
b. $H_2PO_4^- + OH^- \rightarrow HPO_4^{2-} + H_2O$

14 a. $CH_3COO^- + H^+ \rightarrow CH_3COOH$
b. $NH_3 + H^+ \rightarrow NH_4^+$

15. Write the equation for the dissociation.
$PbS \rightleftharpoons Pb^{2+} + S^{2-}$
$K_{sp} = [Pb^{2+}] \times [S^{2-}] = 3 \times 10^{-28}$
At equilibrium, $[Pb^{2+}] = [S^{2-}]$,
Therefore: $[Pb^{2+}]^2 = 3 \times 10^{-28}$
$[Pb^{2+}] = 2 \times 10^{-14}M$

16. a. Write the equation for the dissociation.
$Ag_2S \rightleftharpoons 2Ag^+ + S^{2-}$
$K_{sp} = [Ag^+]^2 \times [S^{2-}] = 8 \times 10^{-51}$
When $[S^{2-}]$ is x, then $[Ag^+] = 2x$.
Substitute into the equation for K_{sp}.
$K_{sp} = (2x)^2(x) = 8 \times 10^{-51}$
$4x^3 = 8 \times 10^{-51}$
$x^3 = 2 \times 10^{-51}$
$x = 1 \times 10^{-17}$
$[Ag^+] = 2x = 2 \times 10^{-17}M$
b. $[S^{2-}] = x = 1 \times 10^{-17}M$

17. $SrSO_4 \rightleftharpoons Sr^{2+} + SO_4^{2-}$
$K_{sp} = [Sr^{2+}] \times [SO_4^{2-}] = 3.2 \times 10^{-7}$
At equilibrium, $[SO_4^{2-}] = x$ and
$[Sr^{2+}] = x + 0.10 \approx 0.10$.
$K_{sp} = 0.10 \times x = 3.2 \times 10^{-7}$
$x = 3.2 \times 10^{-6}M$

18. Calculate the solubility product of $PbCl_2$.
$K_{sp} = [Pb^{2+}] \times [Cl^-]^2$
$= 0.015 \times (0.025)^2 = 9.4 \times 10^{-6}$
Since the calculated solubility product does not exceed the K_{sp} for the saturated solution (K_{sp} of $PbCl_2 = 1 \times 10^{-5}$), precipitation will not occur.

Chapter 20

1. a. Write the equation to show the ions.

$2Na + S \rightarrow 2Na^+ + S^{2-}$

There has been a transfer of one electron from each of two sodium atoms.

The oxidation process is:

$2Na \rightarrow 2Na + 2e^-$ (loss of electrons)

The reduction process is:

$S + 2e^- \rightarrow S^{2-}$ (gain of electrons)

Na loses electrons and is oxidized; S gains electrons and is reduced. Therefore, Na is the reducing agent and S is the oxidizing agent.

b. Write the equation to show the ions.

$2K + Cl_2 \rightarrow 2K^+ + 2Cl^-$

There is a transfer of electrons from K to Cl_2.

Oxidation: $2K \rightarrow 2K^+ + 2e^-$ (loss of electrons)

Reduction: $Cl_2 + 2e \rightarrow 2Cl^-$ (gain of electrons)

K loses electrons and is oxidized; Cl_2 gains electrons and is reduced. K is the reducing agent; Cl_2 is the oxidizing agent.

c. Write the equation to show the ions.

$4Al + 3O_2 \rightarrow 4Al^{3+} + 6O^{2-}$

There is a transfer of electrons from Al to O_2.

Oxidation: $4Al \rightarrow 4Al^{3+} + 12e^-$ (loss of electrons)

Reduction: $3O_2 + 12e^- \rightarrow 6O^{2-}$ (gain of electrons)

Al loses electrons and is oxidized; O_2 gains electrons and is reduced. Al is the reducing agent; O_2 is the oxidizing agent.

2. a. Since chlorine is more electronegative than hydrogen, the electrons in the H—Cl bond will be shifted toward Cl and away from H. Therefore H_2 is oxidized and Cl_2 is reduced; H_2 is the reducing agent and Cl_2 is the oxidizing agent. **b.** Nitrogen is more electronegative than hydrogen. The electrons in the N—H bonds in NH_3 are shifted toward N and away from H. Therefore H_2 is oxidized and N_2 is reduced; H_2 is the reducing agent and N_2 is the oxidizing agent. **c.** Chlorine is more electronegative than sulfur. The electrons in the S—Cl bonds in SCl_2 are shifted toward Cl and away from S. Therefore S is oxidized and Cl_2 is reduced; S is the reducing agent and Cl_2 is the oxidizing agent. **d.** Oxygen is more electronegative than nitrogen. The electrons in the N—O bonds in NO_2 are shifted toward oxygen and away from nitrogen. Therefore N_2 is oxidized and O_2 is reduced; N_2 is the reducing agent and O_2 is the oxidizing agent. **e.** Fluorine is more electronegative than lithium. The electrons in LiF are completely transferred from Li to F_2 (LiF is an ionic compound). Therefore Li is oxidized and F_2 is reduced: Li is the reducing agent and F_2 is the oxidizing agent. **f.** Sulfur is more electronegative than hydrogen. The electrons in the H—S bonds in H_2S are shifted toward the sulfur and away from the hydrogen. Therefore hydrogen is oxidized and sulfur is reduced. Hydrogen is the reducing agent and sulfur is the oxidizing agent.

3. a. The oxidation number of oxygen is -2. Since there are five oxygen atoms and the sum of the oxidation numbers must be zero, the oxidation number of phosphorus must be $+5$.

$\overset{+5\ -2}{P_2O_5}$

check: $(2)(+5) + (5)(-2) = 0$.

b. The oxidation number of hydrogen is $+1$. The sum of the oxidation numbers of the nitrogen and hydrogen must equal the ionic charge, $1+$. The oxidation number of nitrogen is -3.

$\overset{-3\ +1}{NH_4^+}$

check: $(-3) + (4)(+1) = +1$.

c. The oxidation number of sodium is $+1$ and the oxidation number of oxygen is -2. The oxidation number of chromium is $+6$.

$\overset{+1\ \ +6\ -2}{Na_2Cr_2O_7}$

check: $(2)(+1) + (2)(+6) + (7)(-2) = 0$.

d. The oxidation number of hydrogen is $+1$ and the oxidation number of oxygen is -2. The oxidation number of calcium is $+2$.

$\overset{+2\ \ -2\ +1}{Ca(OH)_2}$

check: $(+2) + (2)(-2) + (2)(+1) = 0$.

4. Assign oxidation numbers to each element. An oxidation number decrease indicates reduction; an increase indicates oxidation.

a. $\overset{0}{2Na} + \overset{0}{Cl_2} \rightarrow \overset{+1\ -1}{2NaCl}$

Sodium is oxidized ($0 \rightarrow +1$). Chlorine is reduced ($0 \rightarrow -1$). Sodium (as Na) is the reducing agent; chlorine (as Cl_2) is the oxidizing agent.

b. $\overset{+1+5-2}{2HNO_3} + \overset{+1-1}{6HI} \rightarrow \overset{+2-2}{2NO} + \overset{0}{3I_2} + \overset{+1\ -2}{4H_2O}$

Nitrogen is reduced ($+5 \rightarrow +2$). Iodine is oxidized ($-1 \rightarrow 0$). Iodine (as HI) is the reducing agent; nitrogen (as HNO_3) is the oxidizing agent.

c. $\overset{+1\ -2}{3H_2S} + \overset{+1+5-2}{2HNO_3} \rightarrow \overset{0}{3S} + \overset{+2-2}{2NO} + \overset{+1\ -2}{4H_2O}$

Nitrogen is reduced ($+5 \rightarrow +2$). Sulfur is oxidized ($-2 \rightarrow 0$). Sulfur (as H_2S) is the reducing agent; nitrogen (as HNO_3) is the oxidizing agent.

d. $\overset{+2+6-2}{2PbSO_4} + \overset{+1-2}{2H_2O} \rightarrow \overset{0}{Pb} + \overset{+4-2}{PbO_2} + \overset{+1+6-2}{2H_2SO_4}$

Lead is oxidized ($+2 \rightarrow +4$). Lead is reduced ($+2 \rightarrow 0$). Lead (as $PbSO_4$) is both the reducing agent and the oxidizing agent.

5. *Step 1:* Assign oxidation numbers to all the atoms in the equation.

Step 2: Identify which atoms are oxidized and which are reduced.

Step 3: Use a line to connect the atoms that undergo oxidation. Use a separate line to connect the atoms that undergo reduction.

Step 4: Use appropriate coefficients to make the total increase in oxidation number equal to the total decrease in oxidation number.

Step 5: Do a final check to ensure the equation is balanced for both atoms and charge.

a. increase $(0 \rightarrow +3)$

oxidation

$\overset{0}{Al} + \overset{0}{Cl_2} \rightarrow \overset{+3\ -1}{AlCl_3}$

reduction

decrease $(0 \rightarrow -1)$

To balance the increase (+3) and the decrease (−1) in oxidation numbers, three chlorine atoms must be reduced (−3 decrease) for each aluminum atom that is oxidized (+3 increase). To get 3Cl on the left-hand side of the equation, put a coefficient of $\frac{3}{2}$ in front of Cl_2.

$$(1)(+3) = +3$$
$$Al + \tfrac{3}{2} Cl_2 \rightarrow AlCl_3$$
$$(3)(-1) = -3$$

The fractional coefficient can be removed by multiplying each term in the equation by 2.
$$2Al(s) + 3Cl_2(g) \rightarrow 2AlCl_3(s)$$
This equation is now balanced.

b. decrease $(+5 \rightarrow -1)$

$$\boxed{\text{reduction}}$$
$$\overset{+1+5-2}{KClO_3} \rightarrow \overset{+1-1}{KCl} + \overset{0}{O_2}$$
$$\boxed{\text{oxidation}}$$
increase $(-2 \rightarrow 0)$

To balance the increase (+2) and the decrease (−6) in oxidation number, three oxygen atoms must be oxidized (+6 increase) for each chlorine that is reduced (−6 decrease). To get 3 O on the right-hand side, put a coefficient of $\frac{3}{2}$ in front of O_2.

$$(1)(-6) = -6$$
$$KClO_3 \rightarrow KCl + \tfrac{3}{2}O_2$$
$$(3)(+2) = +6$$

The fractional coefficient can be removed by multiplying each term in the equation by 2.
$$2KClO_3(s) \rightarrow 2KCl(s) + 3O_2(g)$$
This equation is now balanced.

c. increase $(-3 \rightarrow +1)$

$$\boxed{\text{oxidation}}$$
$$\overset{-3+1}{PH_3} + \overset{0}{I_2} + \overset{+1-2}{H_2O} \rightarrow \overset{+1+1-2}{H_3PO_2} + \overset{+1-1}{HI}$$
$$\boxed{\text{reduction}}$$
decrease $(0 \rightarrow -1)$

To balance the increase (+4) and the decrease (−1) in oxidation numbers, one phosphorus atom must be oxidized (+4 increase) for every four iodine atoms that are reduced (−4 decrease). To get 4 I on the left-hand side, put a coefficient of 2 in front of I_2; then put a coefficient of 4 in front of HI.

$$(1)(+4) = +4$$
$$PH_3 + 2I_2 + H_2O \rightarrow H_3PO_2 + 4HI$$
$$(4)(-1) = -4$$

To balance the oxygen and hydrogen (the spectator atoms), put a coefficient of 2 in front of H_2O.
$$PH_3(g) + 2I_2(s) + 2H_2O(l) \rightarrow H_3PO_2(aq) + 4HI(aq)$$
This equation is now balanced.

d. increase $(0 \rightarrow +5)$

$$\boxed{\text{oxidation}}$$
$$\overset{0}{Cl_2} + \overset{+1-2+1}{KOH} \rightarrow \overset{+1+5-2}{KClO_3} + \overset{+1-1}{KCl} + \overset{+1-2}{H_2O}$$
$$\boxed{\text{reduction}}$$
decrease $(0 \rightarrow -1)$

To balance the increase (+5) and the decrease (−1) in oxidation numbers, one chlorine atom must be oxidized (+5 increase) for every five chlorine atoms that are reduced (−5 decrease). To get a total of 6 Cl on the left-hand side, put a coefficient of 3 in front of Cl_2; then put a coefficient of 5 in front of KCl.

$$(1)(+5) = +5$$
$$3Cl_2 + KOH \rightarrow KClO_3 + 5KCl + H_2O$$
$$(5)(-1) = -5$$

Finally, K, O, and H are balanced by inspection.
$$3Cl_2(g) + 6KOH(aq) \rightarrow$$
$$KClO_3(aq) + 5KCl(aq) + 3H_2O(l)$$
This equation is balanced.

e. decrease $(+5 \rightarrow +2)$

$$\boxed{\text{reduction}}$$
$$\overset{+5}{HNO_3} + \overset{-2}{H_2S} \rightarrow \overset{0}{S} + \overset{+2}{NO} + H_2O$$
$$\boxed{\text{oxidation}}$$
increase $(-2 \rightarrow 0)$

To balance the increase (+2) and the decrease (−3) in oxidation numbers, two nitrogen atoms must be reduced (−6 decrease) for every three sulfur atoms that are oxidized (+6 increase). Put coefficients of 2 in front of HNO_3 and NO to balance the nitrogen atoms. Put coefficients of 3 in front of H_2S and S.

$$(2)(-3) = -6$$
$$2HNO_3 + 3H_2S \rightarrow 3S + 2NO + H_2O$$
$$(3)(+2) = +6$$

Finally, H and O are balanced by inspection.
$$2HNO_3(aq) + 3H_2S(aq) \rightarrow 3S(s) + 2NO(g) + 4H_2O(l)$$
This equation is balanced.

f. decrease $(+7 \rightarrow 0)$

$$\boxed{\text{reduction}}$$
$$\overset{+1+7-2}{KIO_4} + \overset{+1-1}{KI} + \overset{+1-1}{HCl} \rightarrow \overset{+1-1}{KCl} + \overset{0}{I_2} + \overset{+1-2}{H_2O}$$
$$\boxed{\text{oxidation}}$$
increase $(-1 \rightarrow 0)$

To balance the decrease (−7) and the increase (+1) in oxidation numbers, one iodine atom (in KIO_4) must be reduced (−7 decrease) for every seven iodine atoms (in KI) that are oxidized (+7 increase). Put a coefficient of 7 in front of KI and a coefficient of 4 in front of I_2.

$$(1)(-7) = -7$$
$$KIO_4 + 7KI + HCl \rightarrow KCl + 4I_2 + H_2O$$
$$(7)(+1) = +7$$

Finally, balance K, H, O, and Cl by inspection.
$$KIO_4(aq) + 7KI(aq) + 8HCl(aq) \rightarrow$$
$$8KCl(aq) + 4I_2(s) + 4H_2O(l)$$
The equation is balanced.

6. a. This is a double-replacement reaction. There is no change in oxidation numbers, so this is not a redox reaction.
b. This is a decomposition reaction. There is no change in oxidation numbers.

c.
$$\overset{0}{Mg} + \overset{0}{Br_2} \rightarrow \overset{2+ \; 1-}{MgBr_2}$$
This is a redox combination reaction. Magnesium is oxidized. It is the reducing agent. Bromine is reduced. Bromine is the oxidizing agent.

d.
$$\overset{-3+1+3-2}{NH_4NO_2} \rightarrow \overset{0}{N_2} + \overset{+1 \; -2}{2H_2O}$$
This is a redox decomposition reaction. Nitrogen (in NO_2^-) is reduced. It is the oxidizing agent. Nitrogen (in NH_4^+) is oxidized. It is the reducing agent.

e.
$$\overset{+1 +5 -2}{2KClO_3} \rightarrow \overset{+1 -1}{2KCl} + \overset{0}{3O_2}$$
This is a redox decomposition reaction. Chlorine is reduced. It is the oxidizing agent. Oxygen is oxidized. It is the reducing agent.

f. This is a double-replacement reaction followed by a decomposition reaction (of H_2CO_3). There is no change in oxidation numbers.

g.
$$\overset{+2 -2}{CuO} + \overset{0}{H_2} \rightarrow \overset{0}{Cu} + \overset{+1 -2}{H_2O}$$
This is a redox reaction. Copper is reduced. It is the oxidizing agent. Hydrogen is oxidized. It is the reducing agent.

h. This is a decomposition reaction. There is no change in oxidation numbers.

i.
$$\overset{0}{Sb} + \overset{+1+5-2}{HNO_3} \rightarrow \overset{+5 \; -2}{Sb_2O_5} + \overset{+2-2}{NO} + \overset{+1 \; -2}{H_2O}$$
This is a redox reaction. Antimony is oxidized. It is the reducing agent. Nitrogen is reduced. It is the oxidizing agent.

7. a. *Step 1:* Write the equation in ionic form.
Step 2: Write the oxidation and reduction half-reactions.
Step 3: Balance the half-reactions, using H_2O, H^+, or OH^- as needed.
Step 4: Add electrons to one side of each half-reaction to balance the charges.
Step 5: Multiply each half-reaction to make the electron changes equal.
Step 6: Add the half-reactions and subtract terms that are on both sides.
Step 7: Balance the spectator ions by inspection if they are included.

a. $ClO_3^- + I^- \rightarrow Cl^- + I_2$ (acid solution)
Oxidation: $I^- \rightarrow I_2$
Reduction: $ClO_3^- \rightarrow Cl^-$

Balance:

Oxidation: $2I^- \rightarrow I_2$
Reduction: $ClO_3^- + 6H^+ \rightarrow Cl^- + 3H_2O$

Add electrons.

Oxidation: $2I^- \rightarrow I_2 + 2e^-$
Reduction: $ClO_3^- + 6H^+ + 6e^- \rightarrow Cl^- + 3H_2O$

Multiply oxidation half-reaction by 3.

Oxidation: $6I^- \rightarrow 3I_2 + 6e^-$
Reduction: $ClO_3^- + 6H^+ + 6e^- \rightarrow Cl^- + 3H_2O$

Add the half-reactions and subtract terms.
$$ClO_3^- + 6I^- + 6H^+ + \cancel{6e^-} \rightarrow$$
$$Cl^- + 3I_2 + 3H_2O + \cancel{6e^-}$$

The balanced equation is:
$$ClO_3^-(aq) + 6I^-(aq) + 6H^+(aq) \rightarrow$$
$$Cl^-(aq) + 3I_2(s) + 3H_2O(l)$$

b. $C_2O_4^{2-} + MnO_4^- \rightarrow Mn^{2+} + CO_2$ (acid solution)
Oxidation: $C_2O_4^{2-} \rightarrow CO_2$
Reduction: $MnO_4^- \rightarrow Mn^{2+}$

Balance:

Oxidation: $C_2O_4^{2-} \rightarrow 2CO_2$
Reduction: $MnO_4^- + 8H^+ \rightarrow Mn^{2+} + 4H_2O$

Add electrons.

Oxidation: $C_2O_4^{2-} \rightarrow 2CO_2 + 2e^-$
Reduction: $MnO_4^- + 8H^+ + 5e^- \rightarrow Mn^{2+} + 4H_2O$

Multiply oxidation half-reaction by 5 and reduction half-reaction by 2.

Oxidation: $5C_2O_4^{2-} \rightarrow 10CO_2 + 10e^-$
Reduction: $2MnO_4^- + 16H^+ + 10e^- \rightarrow 2Mn^{2+} + 8H_2O$

Add the half-reactions and subtract terms:
$$5C_2O_4^{2-} + 2MnO_4^- + 16H^+ + \cancel{10e^-} \rightarrow$$
$$2Mn^{2+} + 10CO_2 + 8H_2O + \cancel{10e^-}$$

The balanced equation is:
$$5C_2O_4^{2-}(aq) + 2MnO_4^-(aq) + 16H^+(aq) \rightarrow$$
$$2Mn^{2+}(aq) + 10CO_2(g) + 8H_2O(l)$$

c. $Br_2 + SO_2 \rightarrow Br^- + SO_4^{2-}$ (acid solution)
Oxidation: $SO_2 \rightarrow SO_4^{2-}$
Reduction: $Br_2 \rightarrow Br^-$

Balance:

Oxidation: $SO_2 + 2H_2O \rightarrow SO_4^{2-} + 4H^+$
Reduction: $Br_2 \rightarrow 2Br^-$

Add electrons.

Oxidation: $SO_2 + 2H_2O \rightarrow SO_4^{2-} + 4H^+ + 2e^-$
Reduction: $Br_2 + 2e^- \rightarrow 2Br^-$

Since the electron changes are equal, add the half-reactions and cancel terms.
$$Br_2 + SO_2 + 2H_2O + \cancel{2e^-} \rightarrow$$
$$2Br^- + SO_4^{2-} + 4H^+ + \cancel{2e^-}$$

The balanced equation is:
$$Br_2(l) + SO_2(g) + 2H_2O(l) \rightarrow$$
$$2Br^-(aq) + SO_4^{2-}(aq) + 4H^+(aq)$$

d. $MnO_2 + H^+ + NO_2^- \rightarrow NO_3^- + Mn^{2+} + 2H_2O$
Oxidation: $NO_2^- \rightarrow NO_3^-$
Reduction: $MnO_2 \rightarrow Mn^{2+}$

Balance:

Oxidation: $NO_2^- + H_2O \rightarrow NO_3^- + 2H^+$
Reduction: $MnO_2 + 4H^+ \rightarrow Mn^{2+} + 2H_2O$

Add electrons.

Oxidation: $NO_2^- + H_2O \rightarrow NO_3^- + 2H^+ + 2e^-$
Reduction: $MnO_2 + 4H^+ + 2e^- \rightarrow Mn^{2+} + 2H_2O$

Since the electron changes are equal, add the half-reactions and cancel terms.
$$MnO_2 + \overset{2}{\cancel{4H^+}} + NO_2^- + \cancel{H_2O} + \cancel{2e^-} \rightarrow$$
$$NO_3^- + Mn^{2+} + \cancel{2e^-} + 2H^+ + \overset{1}{\cancel{2H_2O}}$$
The balanced equation is:
$$MnO_2(s) + 2H^+(aq) + NO_2^-(aq) \rightarrow$$
$$NO_3^-(aq) + Mn^{2+}(aq) + H_2O(l)$$

e. $MnO_4^- + NO_2^- \rightarrow MnO_2 + NO_3^-$ (basic solution)

Oxidation: $NO_2^- \rightarrow NO_3^-$

Reduction: $MnO_4^- \rightarrow MnO_2$

Balance:

Oxidation: $NO_2^- + 2OH^- \rightarrow NO_3^- + H_2O$

Reduction: $MnO_4^- + 2H_2O \rightarrow MnO_2 + 4OH^-$

Add electrons.

Oxidation: $NO_2^- + 2OH^- \rightarrow NO_3^- + H_2O + 2e^-$

Reduction: $MnO_4^- + 2H_2O + 3e^- \rightarrow MnO_2 + 4OH^-$

Multiply the oxidation half-reaction by 3 and the reduction half-reaction by 2.

Oxidation: $3NO_2^- + 6OH^- \rightarrow 3NO_3^- + 3H_2O + 6e^-$

Reduction: $2MnO_4^- + 4H_2O + 6e^- \rightarrow 2MnO_2 + 8OH^-$

Add the half-reactions and cancel terms.

$$MnO_4^- + 3NO_2^- + \overset{1}{\cancel{4H_2O}} + \cancel{6OH^-} + \cancel{6e^-} \rightarrow$$
$$2MnO_2 + 3NO_3^- + \overset{2}{\cancel{3H_2O}} + \cancel{8OH^-} + \cancel{6e^-}$$

The balanced equation is:

$2MnO_4^-(aq) + 3NO_2^-(aq) + H_2O(l) \rightarrow$
$\qquad 2MnO_2(s) + 3NO_3^-(aq) + 2OH^-(aq)$

f. $Cl_2 \rightarrow ClO_3 + Cl$ (basic solution)

Oxidation: $Cl_2 \rightarrow ClO_3^-$

Reduction: $Cl_2 \rightarrow Cl^-$

Balance:

Oxidation: $Cl_2 + 12OH^- \rightarrow 2ClO_3^- + 6H_2O$

Reduction: $Cl_2 \rightarrow 2Cl^-$

Add electrons.

Oxidation: $Cl_2 + 12OH^- \rightarrow 2ClO_3^- + 6H_2O + 10e^-$

Reduction: $Cl_2 + 2e^- \rightarrow 2Cl^-$

Multiply the reduction half-reaction by 5.

Oxidation: $Cl_2 + 12OH^- \rightarrow 2ClO_3^- + 6H_2O + 10e^-$

Reduction: $5Cl_2 + 10e^- \rightarrow 10Cl^-$

Add the half-reactions and cancel terms.

$$\overbrace{5Cl_2 + Cl_2}^{6Cl_2} + 12OH^- + \cancel{10e^-} \rightarrow$$
$$2ClO_3^- + 10Cl^- + 6H_2O + \cancel{10e^-}$$

The balanced equation is:

$6Cl_2(g) + 12OH^-(aq) \rightarrow$
$\qquad 2ClO_3^-(aq) + 10Cl^- + 6H_2O(l)$

Chapter 21

1. The half-cell with the more positive reduction potential occurs as a reduction. In this cell Cu^{2+} is reduced and Al is oxidized. Because reduction takes place at the Cu^{2+} half-cell, this half-cell is the cathode.

The half-cell reactions are:

Oxidation: $Al(s) \rightarrow Al^{3+}(aq) + 3e^-$ (anode)

Reduction: $Cu^{2+}(aq) + 2e^- \rightarrow Cu(s)$ (cathode)

Before the reactions are added to give the overall cell reaction the electrons must cancel. Multiply each equation by a coefficient to give equal numbers of electrons.

$$2[Al(s) \rightarrow Al^{3+}(aq) + 3e^-]$$
$$3[Cu^{2+}(aq) + 2e^- \rightarrow Cu(s)]$$
$$\overline{2Al(s) + 3Cu^{2+}(aq) \rightarrow 2Al^{3+}(aq) + 3Cu(s)}$$

The standard cell potential can now be calculated.

$$E_{cell}^\circ = E_{red}^\circ - E_{oxid}^\circ$$

$$= E_{Cu^{2+}}^\circ - E_{Al^{3+}}^\circ$$
$$= +0.34V - (-1.66V)$$
$$= +2.00V$$

2. In this cell Ag^+ is reduced and Cu is oxidized. The Ag^+ half-cell is the cathode.

The half-cell reactions are:

Oxidation: $Cu(s) \rightarrow Cu^{2+}(aq) + 2e^-$ (anode)

Reduction: $Ag^+(aq) + e^- \rightarrow Ag(s)$ (cathode)

Before the reactions are added the electrons must cancel.

$$Cu(s) \rightarrow Cu^{2+}(aq) + 2e^-$$
$$2[Ag^+(aq) + e^- \rightarrow Ag(s)]$$
$$\overline{Cu(s) + 2Ag^+(aq) \rightarrow Cu^{2+}(aq) + 2Ag(s)}$$

The standard cell potential can now be calculated.

$$E_{cell}^\circ = E_{red}^\circ - E_{oxid}^\circ$$
$$E_{cell}^\circ = E_{Ag^+}^\circ - E_{Cu^{2+}}^\circ$$
$$= +0.80V - (+0.34V)$$
$$= +0.46V$$

3. Because the reaction is spontaneous as written Co^{2+} is reduced and Fe is oxidized.

The half-cell reactions are:

Oxidation: $Fe(s) \rightarrow Fe^{2+}(aq) + 2e^-$ (anode)

Reduction: $Co^{2+}(aq) + 2e^- \rightarrow Co(s)$ (cathode)

The standard cell potential can now be calculated.

$$E_{cell}^\circ = E_{red}^\circ - E_{oxid}^\circ$$
$$= E_{Co^{2+}}^\circ - E_{Fe^{2+}}^\circ$$

Substitute standard reduction potentials from Table 21·3.

$$= -0.28V - (-0.44V)$$
$$= +0.16V$$

4. **a.** The half-reactions are:

Oxidation: $Cu(s) \rightarrow Cu^{2+}(aq) + 2e^-$

Reduction: $2H^+(aq) + 2e^- \rightarrow H_2(g)$

The standard reduction potentials are found in Table 21·3.

$$E_{Cu^{2+}}^\circ = +0.34V$$
$$E_{H^+}^\circ = 0.00V$$

The standard cell potential is the difference of the potentials of the two cells.

$$E_{cell}^\circ = E_{red}^\circ - E_{oxid}^\circ$$
$$= E_{H^+}^\circ - E_{Cu^{2+}}^\circ$$
$$= 0.00V - (+0.34V)$$
$$= 0.34V$$

Since the standard cell potential is a negative number, the redox reaction is nonspontaneous as written.

b. The half-reactions are:

Oxidation: $Ag(s) \rightarrow Ag^+(aq) + e^-$

Reduction: $Fe^{2+}(aq) + 2e^- \rightarrow Fe(s)$

The standard reduction potentials are found in Table 21·3.

$$E_{Ag^+}^\circ = +0.80V$$
$$E_{Fe^{2+}}^\circ = -0.44V$$

The standard cell potential is the difference of the potentials of the two cells.

$$E_{cell}^\circ = E_{red}^\circ - E_{oxid}^\circ$$
$$= E_{Fe^{2+}}^\circ - E_{Ag^+}^\circ$$
$$= -0.44V - (+0.80V)$$
$$= -1.24V$$

Since the standard cell potential is a negative number, the redox reaction is nonspontaneous as written.

c. The half-reactions are:

Oxidation: $Cr(s) \rightarrow Cr^{3+}(aq) + 3e^-$

Reduction: $Zn^{2+}(aq) + 2e^- \rightarrow Zn(s)$

The standard reduction potentials are found in Table 21·3.

$$E°_{Cr^{3+}} = -0.74V$$
$$E°_{Zn^{2+}} = -0.76V$$

The standard cell potential is the difference of the potentials of the two cells.

$$E°_{cell} = E°_{red} - E°_{oxid}$$
$$= E°_{Zn^{2+}} - E°_{Cr^{3+}}$$
$$= -0.76V - (-0.74V)$$
$$= -0.02V$$

Since the standard cell potential is a negative number, the redox reaction is nonspontaneous as written.

Chapter 22

1. $2 K + 2 H_2O \rightarrow 2 KOH + H_2$

2. $MgO + CO_2 \rightarrow MgCO_3$

Chapter 24

1. The reactant is radium-226 ($^{226}_{88}Ra$). The products are an alpha particle and radon, with an atomic number of 86 and a mass number 222 (226 − 4).

$$^{226}_{88}Ra \rightarrow ^{222}_{86}Rn + ^4_2He$$

2. In beta decay a neutron decomposes to give a proton and an electron (beta radiation). This means that the mass numbers of the reactant and product are equal, but the atomic number increases by 1.

$$\overset{\text{same}}{^{210}_{82}Pb} \longrightarrow \underset{\text{increased by 1}}{^{210}_{83}Bi} + _{-1}^{0}e$$

3. The types of radiation in order of increasing penetrating power are: alpha radiation, beta radiation, and gamma radiation.

4.

Number of half-lives	Elapsed time (hr)	Mass of ^{56}Mn
0	0	1.00 mg
1	2.6	0.50 mg
2	5.2	0.25 mg
3	7.8	0.125 mg
4	10.4	0.0625 mg

After four half-lives there is 0.0625 mg of manganese-56 left.

5. A Geiger counter does not detect alpha particles; it is a beta radiation detector. Your hands may be contaminated.

Chapter 25

1.

```
    H  H  H  H  H
    |  |  |  |  |
H — C — C — C — C — C — H
    |  |  |  |  |
    H  H  H  H  H
```

```
    H  H  H  H  H  H
    |  |  |  |  |  |
H — C — C — C — C — C — C — H
    |  |  |  |  |  |
    H  H  H  H  H  H
```

2. $CH_3CH_2CH_2CH_2CH_3$, pentane

$CH_3CH_2CH_2CH_2CH_2CH_3$, hexane

3. a. propane
b. pentane
c. hexane

4. a. 2-methylbutane
b. 3-methylpentane
c. 3-ethylhexane

5. a. $CH_3CHCHCH_2CH_2CH_3$
with CH_3 substituents
2, 3-dimethylhexane

b. $CH_3CH_2CHCH_2CH_2CH_2CH_3$
with CH_2CH_3 substituent
3-ethylheptane

c. $CH_3CHCHCH_2CH_2CH_2CH_3$
with CH_3, CH_3, and CH_2CH_3 substituents
3-ethyl-2,4-dimethyloctane

6. Five structural isomers of molecular formula C_6H_{14} exist.

C—C—C—C—C—C
hexane

```
    C
    |
C—C—C—C—C
2-methylpentane
```

```
    C  C
    |  |
C—C—C—C
2,3-dimethylbutane
```

```
      C
      |
C—C—C—C—C
3-methylpentane
```

```
    C
    |
C—C—C—C
    |
    C
2,2-dimethylbutane
```

7. a. $CH_2{=}CHCH_2CH_2CH_3$,
1-pentene

b. cis-2-hexene (H, H, CH_3, $CH_2CH_2CH_3$)

trans-2-hexene (H, $CH_2CH_2CH_3$, CH_3, H)

c. 2-methyl-2-hexene (CH_3, CH_3)C=CHCH_2CH_2CH_3$

d. 2,3-dimethylbutene (CH_3, CH_3)C=C(CH_3, CH_3)

8. Nonsuperimposable mirror images are **a, d, e,** and **f.**

9. The asymmetric carbon (circled) is found in **c.** and **d.**

c. $CH_3{-}\overset{H}{\underset{Cl}{C}}{-}OH$

d. $CH_3{-}\overset{H}{\underset{CH_2CH_3}{C}}{-}CHO$

10. a. 1-phenylpropane
b. 2-phenylpropane
c. 2,5-dimethyl-3-phenylhexane

Chapter 26

1. **a.** —OH, hydroxyl **b.** —COOH, carboxyl
   c. —NH$_2$, amino
2. **a.** bromobenzene **b.** chloroethane **c.** 3-chloro-1-butene
3. **a.**

$$CH_3-\underset{\underset{H}{|}}{\overset{\overset{CH_3}{|}}{C}}-Cl$$

   c.

   b. ICH$_2$CCH$_2$CH$_2$CH$_3$ with CH$_3$ substituents

$$ICH_2\underset{\underset{CH_3}{|}}{\overset{\overset{CH_3}{|}}{C}}CH_2CH_2CH_3$$

4. **a.** butanol **b.** 2-propanol **c.** 2-methyl-1-butanol
5. **a.** primary **b.** secondary **c.** primary
6. **a.**

$$\underset{\underset{}{}}{\overset{\overset{Br\ \ Br}{|\ \ \ |}}{CH_2CHCH_2CH_3}}$$

   b.

$$\overset{\overset{I\ \ \ I}{|\ \ \ |}}{CH_3CHCHCH_3}$$

   c.

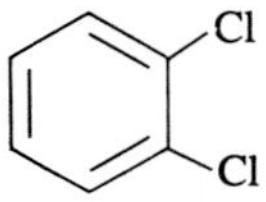

   d.

$$\overset{\overset{H\ \ H}{|\ \ \ |}}{CH_3CHCHCH_3}$$

7. **a.**

$$H-\underset{\underset{H}{|}}{\overset{\overset{CH_3}{|}}{C}}-\underset{\underset{Br}{|}}{\overset{\overset{CH_3}{|}}{C}}-H$$

   b.

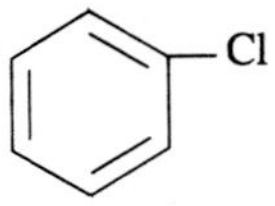

   c.

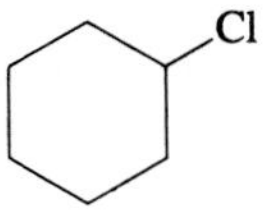

8. **a.** propanol **b.** 3-hexanone **c.** 3-methylpentanal
   d. butanone
9. **a.** CH$_3$CH$_2$CH$_2$COOH
   b. no reaction
   c.

$$CH_3CH_2\overset{\overset{O}{\|}}{C}CH_3$$

   d.

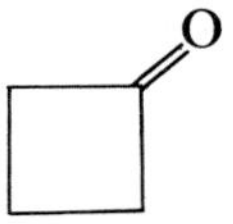

10. **a.** propanol, CH$_3$CH$_2$CH$_2$OH
    b. 2-butanol, CH$_3$CH$_2\overset{\overset{OH}{|}}{C}HCH_3$
    c. 2-methyl-1-butanol, CH$_3$CH$_2\overset{\overset{CH_3}{|}}{C}HCH_2OH$

11. **a.** CH$_3$CH$_2$COOH, CH$_3$CH$_2$OH;
    b. CH$_3$COOH,

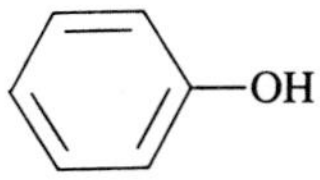

    c. CH$_3$CH$_2$COOH, CH$_3\overset{\overset{}{}}{C}HCH_2OH$ with CH$_3$

$$CH_3\underset{\underset{CH_3}{|}}{C}HCH_2OH$$

12. **a.** secondary **b.** tertiary **c.** primary **d.** primary
13. **a.** (CH$_3$)$_2$$\overset{\overset{H}{|}}{N^+}$—H + Cl$^-$
    b.

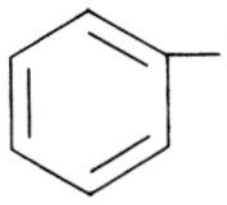

    c. CH$_3^+$NH$_3$ + NO$_3^-$
    d. CH$_3$CH$_2^+$NH$_3$ + H$_2$PO$_4^-$

absolute zero the zero point on the Kelvin temperature scale, equivalent to −273°C; all molecular motion theoretically stops at this temperature. *2·11*

accuracy the closeness of a measurement to the true value of what is being measured. *2·2*

acid a compound containing hydrogen that ionizes to yield hydrogen ions (H^+) in water. *5·13*

acid dissociation constant (K_a) the ratio of the concentration of the dissociated form of an acid to the undissociated form; stronger acids have larger K_a values than weaker acids. *18·8*

acidic solution any solution in which the hydrogen-ion concentration is greater than the hydroxide-ion concentration. *18·2*

activated complex an unstable arrangement of atoms that exists momentarily at the peak of the activation energy barrier; it represents an intermediate or transitional structure formed during the course of a reaction. *17·1*

activation energy the minimum energy colliding particles must have in order to react. *17·1*

activity series of metals a table listing metals in order of decreasing activity. *7·5*

actual yield the amount of product that forms when a reaction is carried out in the laboratory. *8·6*

addition polymerization the process that occurs when unsaturated monomers add to each other, forming a polymer. *26·12*

addition reaction a reaction in which a substance is added at the double bond of an alkene or at the triple bond of an alkyne. *26·6*

alcohol an organic compound having an −OH (hydroxyl) group; the general structure is R—OH. *26·4*

aldehyde an organic compound in which the carbon of the carbonyl group is joined to at least one hydrogen; the general formula is RCHO. *26·8*

aliphatic compound a hydrocarbon compound that does not contain a ring structure. *25·8*

alkali metal any metal in Group 1A of the periodic table. *12·10*

alkaline earth metal any metal in Group 2A of the periodic table. *12·10*

alkaline solution a basic solution. *18·2*

alkane a hydrocarbon containing only single covalent bonds; alkanes are saturated hydrocarbons. *25·1*

alkene a hydrocarbon containing one or more carbon-carbon double bonds; alkenes are unsaturated hydrocarbons. *25·5*

alkyl group a hydrocarbon substituent; methyl (CH_3) is an alkyl group. *25·3*

alkyl halide a halocarbon in which one or more halogen atoms are attached to the carbon atoms of an aliphatic chain. *26·2*

alkyne a hydrocarbon containing a carbon-carbon triple bond; alkynes are unsaturated hydrocarbons. *25·5*

allotrope a molecular form of an element that exists in two or more different forms in the same physical state; oxygen, O_2, and ozone, O_3, are allotropes of the element oxygen. *23·2*

alpha particle a positively charged particle emitted from certain radioactive nuclei; it consists of two protons and two neutrons and is identical to the nucleus of a helium atom. *24·2*

alpha radiation alpha particles emitted from a radioactive source. *24·2*

amide an organic compound having a nitrogen atom attached to the carbon of a carbonyl group; the general structures are

26·13

amine an organic derivative of ammonia; the general structures are

26·13

amino acid an organic compound having amino ($-NH_2$) and carboxylic acid ($-COOH$) groups in the same molecule; proteins are made up of the 20 naturally occurring amino acids. *26·16*

amphoteric a substance that can act both as an acid and a base; water is amphoteric. *18·6*

amplitude the height of a wave from the origin to the crest. *11·6*

amorphous a term used to describe a solid that lacks an ordered internal structure; denotes a random arrangement of atoms. *9·8*

analytical chemistry the study of the composition of substances. *1·1*

anion any atom or group of atoms with a negative charge. *5·2*

anode the electrode at which oxidation occurs. *21·2*

antibonding orbital a molecular orbital whose energy is higher than that of the atomic orbitals from which it is formed. *14·7*

aqueous solution (aq) a solution in which the solvent is water. *15·6*

arene any member of a special group of unsaturated cyclic hydrocarbons. *25·8*

aromatic compound a name originally given to the arenes because many of them have pleasant odors. *25·8*

aryl halide a halocarbon in which one or more halogens are attached to the carbon atoms of an arene ring. *26·2*

asymmetric carbon a carbon atom that has four different groups attached. *25·7*

atom the smallest particle of an element that retains the properties of that element. *4·1*

atomic emission spectrum the pattern of frequencies obtained by passing light emitted by atoms of an element in the gaseous state through a prism; the emission spectrum of each element is unique to that element. *11·6*

atomic mass the weighted average of the masses of the isotopes of an element. *4·7*

atomic mass unit a unit of mass equal to one-twelfth the mass of a carbon-12 atom. *4·5*

atomic number the number of protons in the nucleus of an atom of an element. *4·4*

atomic orbital a region in space around the nucleus of an atom where there is a high probability of finding an electron. *11·3*

atmospheric pressure the pressure exerted by air molecules in the atmosphere ·surrounding the earth, resulting from collisions of air molecules with objects. *9·3*

Aufbau principle electrons enter orbitals of lowest energy first. *11·4*

Avogadro's hypothesis equal volumes of gases at the same temperature and pressure contain equal numbers of particles. *9·4*

Avogadro's number the number of representative particles contained in one mole of a substance; equal to 6.02×10^{23} particles. *6·2*

balanced equation a chemical equation in which mass is conserved; each side of the equation has the same number of atoms of each element. *7·2*

band of stability the location of stable nuclei on a neutron-vs-proton plot. *24·3*

barometer an instrument used to measure atmospheric pressure. *9·3*

base a compound that ionizes to yield hydroxide ions (OH^-) in water. *5·7*

base dissociation constant (K_b) the ratio of the concentration of the dissociated form of a base to the undissociated form. *18·8*

basic oxygen process the process by which most of today's high quality steel is made; pressurized oxygen and lime are used to remove impurities in pig iron. *22·10*

basic solution any solution in which the hydroxide-ion concentration is greater than the hydrogen-ion concentration. *18·2*

battery a group of voltaic cells that are connected together. *21·4*

Benedict's test a test commonly used to detect the presence of aldehydes. *26·10*

Bessemer process one of the first methods used for making steel; a blast of hot air is bubbled through molten pig iron in a huge egg-shaped converter. *22·10*

beta particles a fast-moving electron emitted from certain radioactive nuclei, it is formed when a neutron decomposes. *24·2*

beta radiation fast-moving electrons (beta particles) emitted from a radioactive source. *24·2*

binary compound a compound composed of two elements; $NaCl$ and Al_2O_3 are binary compounds. *5·9*

biochemistry the study of the composition and changes in composition of living organisms. *1·1*

blast furnace a towerlike furnace in which carbon is used to reduce iron ore to metallic iron. *22·9*

boiling point (bp) the temperature at which the vapor pressure of a liquid is just equal to the external pressure on the liquid. *9·7*

boiling point elevation the difference in temperature between the boiling points of a solution and of the pure solvent. *16·7*

bond dissociation energy the amount of energy required to break a bond between atoms; it is usually expressed in kJ per mol of substance. *14·12*

bonding orbital a molecular orbital whose energy is lower than that of the atomic orbitals from which it is formed. *14·7*

Boyle's law for a fixed mass of gas at constant temperature, the volume of the gas varies inversely with pressure. *10·6*

branched-chain alkane an alkane with one or more alkyl groups attached. *25·3*

bronze an alloy chiefly composed of copper and tin; zinc, lead or other metals may be added to give it special properties. *22·4*

Brownian motion the chaotic movement of colloidal particles, caused by collision with water molecules of the medium in which they are dispersed. *15·10*

buffer a solution in which the pH remains relatively constant when small amounts of acid or base are added; it consists of a solution of a weak acid and the salt of a weak acid (or a solution of a weak base with the salt of a weak base.) *19·6*

buffer capacity a measure of the amount of acid or base that may be added to a buffer solution before a significant change in pH occurs. *19·6*

calorie (cal) the quantity of heat that raises the temperature of 1 g of pure water 1°C. *2·12*

carbohydrate the name given to a group of monomers and polymers of aldehydes and ketones that have numerous hydroxyl groups attached; sugars and starches are carbohydrates. *26·14*

carbonyl group a functional group having a carbon atom and an oxygen atom joined by a double bond;

$$\overset{\displaystyle O}{\underset{\displaystyle (-C-)}{\parallel}}$$

it is found in aldehydes, ketones, esters, and amides. *26·8*

carboxyl group a functional group consisting of a carbonyl group attached to a hydroxyl group;

$$\overset{\displaystyle O}{\underset{\displaystyle (-C-OH)}{\parallel}}$$

it is found in carboxylic acids. *26·9*

carboxylic acid an organic acid containing a carboxyl group; the general formula is RCOOH. *26·9*

cast iron the product formed when pig iron is melted with scrap iron. *22·10*

catalyst a substance that speeds up a reaction without being used up. *7·1*

cathode the electrode at which reduction occurs. *21·2*

cathode ray a stream of electrons produced at the negative electrode (cathode) of a tube containing a gas at low pressure. *4·2*

cation any atom or group of atoms with a positive charge. *5·2*

cell potential the difference between the reduction potentials of two half-cells. *21·6*

Celsius temperature scale the temperature scale on which the freezing point of water is 0° and the boiling point is 100°. *2·11*

charge the load of raw materials added to a blast furnace. *22·9*

Charles's Law the volume of a fixed mass of gas is directly proportional to its Kelvin temperature if the pressure is kept constant. *10·7*

chemical equation an expression representing a chemical reaction; the formulas of the reactants (on the left) are connected by an arrow with the formulas for the products (on the right). *7·1*

chemical equilibrium a state of balance in which forward and reverse reactions are taking place at the same rate; no net change in the amounts of reactants and products occurs in the chemical system. *17·10*

chemical formula a shorthand method used to show the number and type of atoms present in the smallest representative unit of a substance; the chemical formula of ammonia, with one nitrogen and three hydrogens, is NH_3. *5·4*

chemical property the ability of a substance to undergo chemical reactions and to form new substances. *1·11*

chemical reaction the changing of substances to other substances by the breaking of old bonds and the formation of new bonds. *1·11*

chemical symbol a one or two letter representation of an element. *1·8*

chemistry the study of the structure, properties, and composition of substances, and the changes that substances undergo. *1·1*

cis configuration a term applied to geometric isomers; it denotes an arrangement in which the substituted groups are on the same side of the double bond. *25·6*

coefficient a small whole number that appears in front of a formula in a balanced chemical equation. *7·2*

colligative property a property of a solution that depends on the concentration of the solute particles but is independent of the nature of the particles; boiling point elevation, freezing point depression, and vapor pressure lowering are colligative properties. *16·7*

colloid a liquid mixture containing particles that are intermediate in size between those of a suspension and a true solution; these particles are evenly distributed throughout the liquid and do not settle out with time. *15·10*

combination reaction a chemical change in which two or more substances react to form a single new substance; also called a synthesis reaction. *7·3*

combined gas law a relationship describing the behavior of gases that combines Boyle's law, Charles' law, and Gay-Lussac's law. *10·9*

combustion reaction a chemical change in which oxygen reacts with another substance, often producing energy in the form of heat and light. *7·7*

common ion an ion that is common to both salts in a solution; in a solution of silver nitrate and silver chloride, Ag^+ would be a common ion. *19·8*

common ion effect a decrease in the solubility of a substance caused by the addition of a common ion. *19·8*

compound a substance that can be separated into simpler substances (elements or other compounds) only by chemical reactions. *1·7*

concentrated solution a solution containing a large amount of solute. *16·4*

concentration a measurement of the amount of solute that is dissolved in a given quantity of solvent; usually expressed as mol/L. *16·4*

condensed structural formula a structural formula that leaves out some bonds and/or atoms; the presence of these atoms or bonds is understood. *25·2*

conjugate acid the particle formed when a base gains a hydrogen ion; NH_4^+ is the conjugate acid of the base NH_3. *18·6*

conjugate acid-base pair two substances that are related by the loss or gain of a single hydrogen ion. Ammonia (NH_3) and the ammonium ion (NH_4^+) are a conjugate acid-base pair. *18·6*

conjugate base the particle that remains when an acid has donated a hydrogen ion; OH^- is the conjugate base of the acid water. *18·6*

continuous-chain alkane a hydrocarbon that contains any number of carbon atoms in a straight chain. *25·2*

conversion factor a ratio of equivalent units used to express the relationship between quantities expressed in different units. *3·3*

coordinate covalent bond a covalent bond formed when one atom contributes both bonding electrons. *14·4*

coordination number the number of ions of opposite charge that surround each ion in a crystal. *13·5*

covalent atomic radius half of the distance between the nuclei of two atoms in a hominuclear diatomic molecule. *12·4*

cracking the controlled process by which hydrocarbons are broken down or rearranged into smaller, more useful molecules. *25·9*

cyclic hydrocarbon an organic compound that contains a hydrocarbon ring. *25·8*

crystal a substance in which the atoms, ions, or molecules are arranged in an orderly, repeating, three-dimensional pattern called a crystal lattice. *9·8*

Dalton's atomic theory the first theory to relate chemical changes to events at the atomic level. *4·1*

Dalton's law of partial pressures at constant volume and temperature, the total pressure of a mixture of gases is the sum of the partial pressures of all the gases present. *10·5*

data the observations that are recorded during an experiment. *1·2*

de Broglie's equation an equation that describes the wavelength of a moving particle; it predicts that all matter exhibits wavelike motions. *11·10*

decomposition reaction a chemical change in which a single compound is broken down into two or more simpler products. *7·4*

dehydrogenation reaction a reaction in which hydrogen is lost. *26·10*

deliquescent a term describing a substance that removes sufficient water from the air to form a solution; the process occurs when the solution formed has a lower vapor pressure than that of the water in the air. *15·8*

denatured alcohol ethanol to which a poisonous substance has been added to make it unfit to drink. *26·5*

density the ratio of the mass of an object to its volume. *2·9*

dessicant a hygroscopic substance used as a drying agent. *15·8*

diffusion the tendency of molecules and ions to move toward areas of lower concentration until the concentration is uniform throughout the system. *10·12*

dilute solution a solution containing a small amount of solute. *16·4*

dimensional analysis a technique of problem-solving that uses the units that are part of a measurement to help solve the problem. *3·4*

dipole a molecule that has two electrically charged regions, or poles. *14·11*

dipole interaction a weak intermolecular force resulting from the attraction of oppositely charged regions of polar molecules. *14·13*

disaccharide a carbohydrate formed from two monosaccharide units; common table sugar (sucrose) is a disaccharide. *26·14*

diprotic acid any acid that contains two ionizable protons (hydrogen ions); sulfuric acid (H_2SO_4) is a diprotic acid. *18·5*

dispersion force the weakest kind of intermolecular attraction; thought to be caused by the motion of electrons. *14·12*

distillation a purification process in which a liquid is evaporated and then condensed again to a liquid; used to separate dissolved solids from liquids or liquids from liquids according to boiling point. *1·6*

double covalent bond a covalent bond in which two pairs of electrons are shared by two atoms. *14·2*

double-replacement reaction a chemical change that involves an exchange of positive ions between two compounds. *7·6*

dry cell a commercial voltaic cell in which the electrolyte is a moist paste. *21·3*

effloresce to lose water of hydration; the process occurs when the hydrate has a vapor pressure higher than that of water vapor in the air. *15·8*

effusion a process that occurs when a gas escapes through a tiny hole in its container. *10·12*

electrical potential the ability of a voltaic cell to produce an electric current. *21·6*

electrochemical cell any device that converts chemical energy into electrical energy or electrical energy into chemical energy. *21·1*

electrochemical process the conversion of chemical energy into electrical energy or electrical energy into chemical energy; in an electrochemical cell, all electrochemical processes involve redox reactions. *21·1*

electrode a conductor in a circuit that carries electrons to or from a substance other than a metal. *21·2*

electrolysis a process in which electrical energy is used to bring about a chemical change. *21·9*

electrolyte a compound that conducts an electric current in aqueous solution or in the molten state; all ionic compounds are electrolytes, but most covalent compounds are not. *15·9*

electrolytic cell an electrochemical cell used to cause a chemical change through the application of electrical energy. *21·9*

electromagnetic radiation a series of energy waves that travel in a vacuum at a speed of 3.0×10^{10} cm/s; includes radio waves, microwaves, visible light, infrared and ultraviolet light, x-rays, and gamma rays. *11·6*

electron a negatively charged subatomic particle. *4·2*

electron affinity the energy that accompanies the addition of an electron to a gaseous atom. *12·6*

electron configuration the arrangement of electrons around the nucleus of an atom in its ground state. *11·4*

electron dot structures a notation that depicts valence electrons as dots around the atomic symbol of the element; the symbol represents the inner electrons and atomic nucleus; also called Lewis dot structures. *13·1*

electronegativity the tendency for an atom to attract electrons to itself when it is chemically combined with another element. *12·8*

element a substance that cannot be changed into a simpler substance under normal laboratory conditions. *1·7*

elementary reaction a reaction in which reactants are converted to products in a single step. *17·4*

empirical formula a formula with the lowest whole-number ratio of elements in a compound; the empirical formula of hydrogen peroxide, H_2O_2, is HO. *6·10*

emulsion the colloidal dispersion of one liquid in another. *15·10*

endergonic a nonspontaneous chemical reaction that proceeds with the absorption of free energy; work must be done to make the reaction proceed. *17·8*

endothermic reaction a chemical change in which energy is absorbed; the energy content of the products is higher than the energy content of the reactants. *8·7*

end point the point in a titration at which neutralization is just achieved. *19·2*

energy the capacity for doing work; it exists in several forms, including chemical, nuclear, electrical, radiant, mechanical, and thermal energies. *1·9*

energy level a region around the nucleus of an atom where an electron is likely to be moving. *11·1*

enthalpy (*H*) the amount of heat that a substance has at a given temperature and pressure. *8·8*

entropy (*S*) a measure of the disorder of a system; systems tend to go from a state of order (low entropy) to a state of maximum disorder (high entropy). *17·5*

equilibrium constant (K_{eq}) the ratio of product concentrations to reactant concentrations with each raised to a power given by the number of moles of the substance in the balanced chemical equation. *17·11*

equilibrium position the relative concentrations of reactants and products of a reaction that has reached equilibrium; it indicates whether the reactants or products are favored in the reversible reaction. *17·10*

equivalence point the point in a titration at which the number of equivalents of acid and base are equal. *19·4*

equivalent (equiv.) one equivalent is the amount of an acid (or base) that can give one mole of hydrogen (or hydroxide) ions. *19·3*

ester a derivative of a carboxylic acid in which the —OH of the carbonyl group has been replaced by an —OR from an alcohol; the general formula is RCOOR. *26·11*

ether an organic compound in which oxygen is bonded to two carbon groups; the general formula is R—O—R. *26·7*

evaporation the vaporization of a liquid in an open container. *9·6*

excess reagent a reagent present in a quantity that is more than sufficient to react with a limiting reagent; any reactant that remains after the limiting reagent is used up in a chemical reaction. *8.5*

exergonic a spontaneous reaction that releases free energy. *17·8*

exothermic reaction a chemical change in which energy is released in the form of heat; the energy content of the products is less than the energy content of the reactants. *8·7*

experiment a carefully controlled, repeatable procedure for gathering data to test a hypothesis. *1·2*

fatty acid the name originally given to continuous chain carboxylic acids first isolated from fats. *26·9*

Fehling's test a test used to detect aldehydes. *26·10*

fermentation the production of ethanol from sugars by the action of yeast or bacteria. *26·5*

film badge a small radiation detector worn by persons who work near radiation sources; it consists of several layers of photographic film covered with black light-proof paper. *24·8*

first order reaction a reaction in which the reaction rate is proportional to the concentration of only one reactant. *17·3*

fission the splitting of a nucleus into smaller fragments, accompanied by the release of neutrons and a large amount of energy. *24·6*

flux a material, usually lime, added during smelting to combine with undesirable material in an ore. *22·8*

formula unit the lowest whole-number ratio of ions in an ionic compound; in magnesium chloride, the ratio of magnesium ions to chloride ions is 1·2 and the formula unit is $MgCl_2$. *5·4*

free energy the potential energy contained in a reaction system; the energy available to do work. *17·8*

freezing point depression the difference in temperature between the freezing points of a solution and of the pure solvent. *16·7*

frequency (ν) the number of wave cycles that pass a given point per unit of time. *11·6*

froth flotation a method commonly used to enrich sulfide ores of copper and lead by separating ore from gangue. *22·8*

fuel cell a voltaic cell in which a fuel substance undergoes oxidation to produce electrical energy. *21·5*

functional group a specific arrangement of atoms in an organic compound that is capable of characteristic chemical reactions; the chemistry of an organic compound is determined by its functional groups. *26·1*

fusion a reaction in which two light nuclei combine to produce a nucleus of heavier mass, accompanied by the release of a large amount of energy. *24·7*

gamma radiation high energy electromagnetic radiation emitted by certain radioactive nuclei; gamma rays have no mass or electrical charge. *24·2*

gangue the worthless sand and rock contained in freshly mined ore. *22·8*

gas matter that has no definite shape or volume; it adopts the shape and volume of its container. *1·4*

gas pressure a force resulting from the simultaneous collisions of billions of gas particles on an object. *9·3*

Gay-Lussac's law the pressure of a fixed mass of gas is directly proportional to the Kelvin temperature if the volume is kept constant. *10·8*

Geiger counter a gas-filled metal tube used to detect the presence of beta radiation. *24·8*

geometric isomer an organic compound that differs from another compound only in the geometry of their substituted groups. *25·6*

Gibbs free energy change (ΔG) the maximum amount of energy that can be coupled to another process to do useful work. *17·9*

Graham's laws of effusion the rate of effusion of a gas is inversely proportional to the square root of its formula mass; this relationship is also true for the diffusion of gases. *10·12*

gram a metric mass unit equal to the mass of 1 cm^3 of water at 4°C. *2·8*

gram atomic mass (gam) the mass, in grams of one mole of atoms in a monatomic element; it is numerically equal to the atomic mass in amu. *6·3*

gram equivalent mass of an acid the mass of one equivalent of an acid expressed in grams. *19·3*

gram equivalent mass of a base the mass of one equivalent of a base expressed in grams. *19·3*

gram formula mass (gfm) the mass of one mole of an ionic compound, equal to the formula mass expressed in grams; the expression may be used in broader sense to refer to a mole of any element, molecular compound, or ionic compound. *6·3*

gram molecular mass (gmm) the mass of one mole of a molecular substance; it is equal to the formula mass expressed in grams. *6·3*

ground state the lowest energy level occupied by an electron when an atom is in its most stable energy state. *11·9*

group a vertical column of elements in the periodic table; the constituent elements of a group have similar chemical and physical properties. *5·1*

half-cell the part of a voltaic cell in which either oxidation or reduction occurs; it consists of a single electrode immersed in a solution of its ions. *21·2*

half-life ($t_{1/2}$ the time required for one-half of the atoms of a radioisotope to emit radiation and decay to products. *24·4*

half-reaction an equation showing either the reduction or the oxidation of a species in an oxidation-reduction reaction. *20·7*

half-reaction method a method of balancing a redox equation by balancing the oxidation and reduction half-reactions. *20·7*

halide ions a negative ion formed when a halogen atom gains an electron. *13·3*

halocarbon any member of a class of organic compounds containing covalently bonded fluorine, chlorine, bromine, or iodine.   *26·2*

halogen any member of the nonmetallic elements in Group 7A of the periodic table.   *12·15*

heat the energy that is transferred from one body to another because of a temperature difference.   *1·9*

heat capacity the quantity of heat required to change an object's temperature by exactly 1°C.   *2·13*

heat of combustion the heat absorbed or released during a chemical reaction in which one mole of a substance is completely burned.   *8·8*

heat of condensation the heat, in calories, released when one gram of a gas condenses to a liquid at the liquid's boiling point.   *9·10*

heat of fusion the heat, in calories, required to melt one gram of a solid at its melting point.   *9·10*

heat of reaction the heat relaeased or absorbed during a chemical reaction; equivalent to *H,* the change in enthalpy.   *8·8*

heat of solidification the heat, in calories, given up as one gram of a liquid changes to a solid at the solid's melting point.   *9·10*

heat of vaporization the heat, in calories, required to change one gram of a liquid to a gas at the liquid's boiling point (at atmospheric pressure).   *9·10*

heat transfer the process in which heat moves from a warm object to a cooler object.   *2·11*

Heisenberg uncertainty principle it is impossible to know both the velocity and the position of a particle at the same time.   *11·10*

Henry's law at a given temperature the solubility of a gas in a liquid is directly proportional to the pressure of the gas above the liquid.   *16·3*

hertz (Hz) the SI unit of frequency, equal to one cycle per second.   *11·6*

heterogeneous mixture a mixture that is not uniform in composition; its components are readily distinguished.   *1·6*

heterogeneous reactions a reaction carried out with a heterogeneous mixture of reactants.   *17·2*

homogeneous mixture a mixture that is completely uniform in composition; its components are not distinguishable.   *1·6*

homologous series a series formed by a group of compounds in which there is a constant increment of change in molecular structure from one compound in the series to the next.   *25·2*

Hund's rule when electrons occupy orbitals of equal energy, one electron enters each orbital until all orbitals contain one electron with their spins parallel.   *11·4*

hybridization a process in which several atomic orbitals (such as *s* and *p* orbitals) mix to form the same number of equivalent hybrid orbitals.   *14·9*

hydration reaction a reaction in which water is added to an alkene.   *26·6*

hydrocarbon an organic compound that contains only carbon and hydrogen.   *25·0*

hydrogenation a process used to make solid shortenings and margarine; it involves adding hydrogen to an oil at high temperature and pressure in the presence of a catalyst.   *23·1*

hydrogenation reaction a reaction in which hydrogen is added to a carbon-carbon double bond to give an alkane.   *26·6*

hydrogen bond a relatively strong intermolecular force in which a hydrogen atom that is covalently bonded to a very electronegative atom is also weakly bonded to an unshared electron pair of an electronegative atom in the same molecule or one nearby.   *14·13*

hydrogen-ion acceptor a base, according to the Brønsted-Lowry theory.   *18·6*

hydrogen-ion donor an acid, according to the Brønsted-Lowry theory.   *18·6*

hydrometer a device used to measure the specific gravity of a liquid.   *2·10*

hydronium ion (H_3O^+) the positive ion formed when a water molecule gains a hydrogen ion; all hydrogen ions in aqueous solution are present as hydronium ions.   *18·2*

hydroxide ion (OH^-) the negative ion formed when a water molecule loses a hydrogen ion.   *18·2*

hydroxyl group the —OH functional group present in alcohols.   *26·4*

hygroscopic a term describing salts and other compounds that remove moisture from the air.   *15·8*

hypothesis a descriptive model used to explain observations.   *1·2*

ideal gas constant (R) a term in the ideal gas law, which has the value 0.0821 (L × atm)/(K × mol).   *10·10*

ideal gas law the relationship $P \times V = n \times R \times T,$ which describes the behavior of an ideal gas.   *10·10*

immiscible liquids that are insoluble in one another; oil and water are immiscible.   *16·2*

inhibitor a substance that interferes with catalysis.   *17·2*

inorganic chemistry the study of substances that do not contain carbon.   *1·1*

intermediate a product of a reaction that immediately becomes a reactant of another reaction.   *17·4*

International System of Units (SI) the revised version of the metric system, adopted by international agreement in 1960.   *2·5*

ion an atom or group of atoms that has a positive or negative charge; cations are ions with a positive charge, and anions are ions with a negative charge.   *5·2*

ionic bond the electrostatic attraction that binds oppositely charged ions together.   *13·4*

ionic compound a compound composed of positive and negative ions.   *5·3*

ionization energy the energy required to remove an electron from a gaseous atom.   *12·5*

ionizing radiation radiation which has enough energy to produce ions by knocking electrons off some of the atoms it strikes.   *24·8*

ion product constant for water (K_w) the product of the hydrogen ion and hydroxide ion concentrations of water; it is 1×10^{-14} at 25°C.   *18·2*

isotopes atoms of the same element that have the same atomic number but different atomic masses due to a different number of neutrons.   *4·6*

IUPAC system an internationally accepted system of naming compounds proposed by the International Union of Pure and Applied Chemistry (IUPAC). *25·2*

joule (j) the SI unit of energy; 4.184 joules equal 1.000 calorie. *2·12*

Kelvin temperature scale the temperature scale in which the freezing point of water is 273 K and the boiling point is 373 K; 0 K is absolute zero. *2·11*

ketone an organic compound in which the carbon of the carbonyl group is joined to two other carbons; the general formula is RCOR. *26·8*

kilogram (kg) the mass of 1 L of water at 4°C; it is the base unit of mass in the metric system. *2·8*

kinetic energy the energy an object has because of its motion. *1·9*

kinetic theory a theory explaining the states of matter, based on the concept that the particles in all forms of matter are in constant motion. *9·1*

law of conservation of energy energy is neither created nor destroyed in an ordinary chemical or physical process. *1·10*

law of conservation of mass mass can be neither created nor destroyed in an ordinary chemical or physical process. *1·12*

law of definite proportions in any chemical compound, the elements are always combined in the same proportion by mass. *5·3*

law of disorder it is a natural tendency of systems to move in the direction of maximum chaos or disorder. *17·5*

law of multiple proportions whenever two elements form more than one compound, the different masses of one element that combine with the same mass of the other element are in the ratio of small whole numbers. *5·5*

Le Châtelier's principle when stress is applied to a system at equilibrium, the system changes to relieve the stress. *17·12*

Lewis acid any substance that can accept a pair of electrons to form a covalent bond. *18·7*

Lewis base any substance that can donate a pair of electrons to form a covalent bond. *18·7*

limiting reagent any reactant that is used up first in a chemical reaction; it determines the amount of product that can be formed in the reaction. *8·5*

lime calcium oxide, CaO; it is sometimes called quicklime. *22·2*

lipid a member of a large class of relatively water-insoluble organic compounds; fats, oils, and waxes are lipids. *26·15*

liquid a form of matter that flows, has a fixed volume, and takes the shape of its container. *1·4*

liter (L) the volume of a cube measuring 10 centimeters on each edge (1000 cm³); it is the common unprefixed unit of volume in the metric system. *2·7*

mass the amount of matter that an object contains; the SI base unit of mass is the kilogram. *1·3*

mass number the total number of protons and neutrons in the nucleus of an atom. *4·5*

matter anything that takes up space and has mass. *1·3*

melting point (mp) the temperature at which a substance changes from solid to a liquid; the melting point of water is 0°C. *9·8*

metal one of a class of elements that includes a large majority of the known elements; metals are characteristically lustrous, malleable, ductile, and good conductors of heat and electricity. *5·1*

metallic bond the force of attraction that holds metals together; it consists of the attraction of free-floating valence electrons for positively charged metal ions. *13·6*

metalloid one of a class of elements having properties of both metals and nonmetals. *5·1*

metallurgy the various procedures used to separate metals from their ores. *22·8*

meter the base unit of length in the metric and SI measurement systems. *2·6*

metric system the standards of measurement based on units of 10. *2·5*

millimeter of mercury (mm Hg) a unit of pressure; it is the pressure needed to support a column of mercury one millimeter high. *9·3*

miscible liquids that will dissolve in each other. *16·2*

mixture a combination of two or more substances that are not chemically combined. *1·6*

molal boiling point elevation constant (K_b) the change in boiling point for a 1 molal solution of a nonvolatile molecular solute. *16·10*

molal freezing point depression constant (K_f) the change in freezing point for a 1 molal solution of a nonvolatile molecular solute. *16·10*

molality (m) the concentration of solute in a solution expressed as the number of moles of solute dissolved in 1 kilogram (1,000 g) of solvent. *16·8*

molar mass an expression sometimes used in place of gram formula mass to refer to the mass of a mole of any element or compound. *6·4*

molar volume the volume occupied by one mole of a gas at standard temperature and pressure (STP); 22.4 L. *6·6*

molarity (M) the concentration of solute in a solution expressed as the number of moles of solute dissolved in 1 L of solution. *16·4*

mole (mol) the amount of a substance that contains 6.02×10^{23} representative particles of that substance; a gram formula mass of any substance. *6·2*

molecule a neutral chemically bonded group of atoms that act as a unit. *5·3*

molecular compound a compound that is composed of molecules. *5·3*

molecular formula a chemical formula that shows the actual number and kinds of atoms present in a molecule of a compound. *5·4*

molecular orbital an orbital resulting from the overlapping of atomic orbitals when two atoms combine. *14·7*

mole fraction the ratio of the moles of solute in solution to the total number of moles of both solvent and solute. *16·8*

Monel metal a strong, corrosion-resistant alloy of nickel and cobalt. *22·6*

monomer a simple molecule that combines to form the repeating unit of a polymer. *26·12*

monoprotic acid any acid that contains one ionizable proton (hydrogen ion); nitric acid (HNO_3) is a monoprotic acid. *18·5*

monosaccharide a carbohydrate consisting of one sugar unit; it is also called a simple sugar. *26·14*

network solid a substance in which all of the atoms are covalently bonded to each other. *14·14*

neutralization reaction a reaction in which an acid and a base react in an aqueous solution to produce a salt and water. *19·1*

neutral solution an aqueous solution in which the concentrations of hydrogen and hydroxide ions are 1.0×10^{-7} mol/L; it has a pH of 7.0. *18·2*

neutron a subatomic particle with no charge and a mass of one amu found in the nucleus of the atom. *4·2*

neutron absorption a process used in a nuclear reactor to slow down the chain reaction by decreasing the number of moving neutrons; this is done with control rods made of a material like cadmium that absorbs neutrons. *24·6*

neutron moderation a process used in a nuclear reactor to slow down the neutrons so they can be captured by the reactor fuel to continue the chain reaction; water and carbon are good moderators. *24·6*

noble gas any member of a group of gaseous elements in Group 0 of the periodic table; the *s* and *p* sublevels of their outermost energy level are filled. *12·3*

nonelectrolyte a compound that does not conduct an electric current in aqueous solution or in the molten state. *15·9*

nonmetal one of a class of elements that are not lustrous and are generally poor conductors of heat and electricity; nonmetals are grouped on the right side of the periodic table. *5·1*

nonpolar covalent bond a bond formed when the atoms in a molecule are alike and the bonding electrons are shared equally. *14·10*

nonspontaneous reaction a reaction that does not give products under the specified conditions. *17·7*

normal boiling point the boiling point of a liquid at a pressure of one atmosphere. *9·7*

normality (*N*) the concentration of a solution expressed as the number of equivalents of solute in 1 L of solution. *19·4*

nucleic acid a polymer of ribonucleotides (RNA) or deoxyribonucleotides (DNA) found primarily in cell nuclei; nucleic acids play an important role in the transmission of hereditary characteristics, protein synthesis, and the control of cell activities. *26·17*

nucleotide one of the monomers that make up DNA and RNA; it consists of a nitrogen-containing base (a purine or pyrimidine), a sugar (ribose or deoxyribose), and a phosphate. *26·17*

nucleus the dense central portion of an atom, composed of protons and neutrons. *4·3*

observation the noting and recording of facts and events. *1·2*

octet rule atoms react by gaining or losing electrons so as to acquire the stable electron structure of a noble gas, usually eight valence electrons, *13·2*

open-hearth method a process in which pig iron is converted to high quality steel in a shallow vessel, or hearth. *22·10*

ore a mineral used for commercial production of a metal. *22·8*

organic chemistry the study of compounds that contain the element carbon. *1·1*

oxidation a process that involves a complete or partial loss of electrons or a gain of oxygen; it results in an increase in the oxidation number of an atom. *20·1*

oxidation number a positive or negative number assigned to a combined atom according to a set of arbitrary rules; generally it is the charge an atom would have if the electrons in each bond were assigned to the atoms of the more electronegative element. *20·3*

oxidation number change method a method of balancing a redox equation by comparing the increases and decreases in oxidation numbers. *20·5*

oxidation–reduction reaction a reaction that involves the transfer of electrons between reactants during a chemical change. *20·0*

oxidizing agent the substance in a redox reaction that accepts electrons; in the reaction, the oxidizing agent is reduced. *20·2*

paramagnetic a term used to describe a substance that shows a relatively strong attraction to an external magnetic field; these substances have molecules containing one or more unpaired electrons. *14·6*

partial pressure the pressure exerted by each gas in a gaseous mixture. *10·5*

pascal (Pa) the SI unit of pressure. *9·3*

Pauli exclusion principle no more than two electrons can occupy an atomic orbital; these electrons must have opposite spins. *11·4*

peptide an organic compound formed by a combination of amino acids in which the amino group of one acid is united with the carboxylic group of another through an amide bond. *26·16*

peptide bond the bond between the carbonyl group of one amino acid and the nitrogen of the next amino acid in the peptide chain; the structure is

$$\begin{array}{cc} O & H \\ \parallel & \mid \\ -C & -N- \end{array} \qquad 26\cdot16$$

percent composition the percent by mass of each element in a compound. *6·9*

percent yield the ratio of the actual yield to the theoretical yield for a chemical reaction expressed as a percentage; a measure of the efficiency of a reaction. *8·6*

period a horizontal row of elements in the periodic table. *12·2*

periodic law when the elements are arranged in order of increasing atomic number, there is a periodic repetition of their physical and chemical properties. *12·2*

periodic table an arrangement of elements into rows and columns according to similarities in their properties. *5·1*

pH a number used to denote the hydrogen-ion concentration, or acidity, of a solution; it is the negative logarithm of the hydrogen ion concentration of a solution. *18·3*

phase any part of a system with uniform composition and properties. *1·6*

phase change a change in the physical state of a substance. *9·9*

photoelectric effect a process in which electrons are ejected by certain metals when light of sufficient frequency shines on them. *11·8*

photon a quantum of light; a discrete bundle of electromagnetic energy that behaves as a particle. *11·8*

physical change an alteration of a substance that does not affect its chemical composition. *1·5*

physical chemistry the study of the theoretical basis of chemical behavior, relying on mathematics and physics. *1·1*

physical property a quality of a substance that can be observed or measured without changing the substance's chemical composition. *1·3*

pi bond (π bond) a bond in which the bonding electrons are most likely to be found in the sausage-shaped regions above and below the nuclei of the bonded atoms. *14·7*

pig iron the form of iron obtained from a blast furnace; it contains impurities and undergoes further treatment to produce steel. *22·9*

Planck's constant (h) a number used to calculate the radiant energy, E, absorbed or emitted by a body from the frequency of the radiation. *11·7*

polar bond a bond formed when two different atoms are joined by a covalent bond and the bonding electrons are shared unequally. *14·10*

polar covalent bond see polar bond. *14·10*

polar molecule a molecule in which one or more atoms is slightly negative, and one or more is slightly positive in such a way that the polarities do not cancel; water is a polar molecule. *14·10*

polyatomic ion a tightly bound group of atoms that behaves as a unit and carries a charge. *5·7*

polymer a very large molecule formed by the covalent bonding of repeating small molecules, known as monomers. *26·12*

polypeptide a peptide with more than 10 amino acid residues. *26·16*

polysaccharides a complex carbohydrate polymer formed by the linkage of many monosaccharide monomers; starch, glycogen, and cellulose are polysaccharides. *26·14*

positron a particle which has the same mass as an electron but has a positive charge. *24·3*

potential energy the energy stored in an object as a result of its position or composition. *1·9*

precision the reproducibility, under the same conditions, of a measurement. *2·2*

product a substance formed in a chemical reaction. *1·11*

protein any peptide with more than 100 amino acid residues. *26·16*

proton a positively charged subatomic particle found in the nucleus of an atom. *4·2*

qualitative measurement a measurement which gives descriptive, nonnumeric results. *2·1*

quantitative measurement a measurement which gives definite, usually numeric results. *2·1*

quantum a small package, or unit, of electromagnetic energy: the amount of energy required to move an electron from its present energy level to the next higher one. *11·1*

quantum mechanical model the modern description, primarily mathematical, of the behavior of electrons in atoms. *11·2*

radiation the penetrating rays emitted by a radioactive source; also, the giving off of energy in various forms such as heat, light, or radiowaves. *24·1*

radioactive decay the process in which an unstable nucleus loses energy by emitting radiation. *24·1*

radioactivity the property by which an atomic nucleus gives off alpha, beta, or gamma radiation. *24·1*

radioisotopes isotopes that have unstable nuclei and undergo radioactive decay. *24·1*

rate law an expression relating the rate of a reaction to the concentration of the reactants. *17·3*

reactant a starting substance in a chemical reaction. *1·11*

reaction mechanism a series of elementary reactions that take place during the course of a complex reaction. *17·4*

reaction rate a measure of the number of atoms, ions, or molecules that react to form products in a specified time. *17·1*

redox reaction another name for an oxidation-reduction reaction. *20·0*

reducing agent the substance in a redox reaction that donates electrons; in the reaction, the reducing agent is oxidized. *20·2*

reduction a process that involves a complete or partial gain of electrons or the loss of oxygen; it results in a decrease in the oxidation number of an atom. *20·1*

reduction potential a measure of the tendency of a given half-reaction to occur as a reduction (gain of electrons) in an electrochemical cell. *21·6*

representative element an element that belongs to an A group in the periodic table; they are called representative elements because they illustrate the entire range of chemical properties. *5·1*

representative particle the smallest unit into which a substance can be broken down without a change in composition; the term refers to whether a substance commonly exists as atoms, ions, or molecules. *6·2*

resonance a phenomenon that occurs when two or more equally valid electron dot structures can be written for a molecule; the actual bonding is believed to be a hybrid or mixture of the extremes represented by the resonance forms. *14·5*

reversible reaction a reaction in which the conversion of reactants into products and the conversion of products into reactants occur simultaneously. *17·10*

roasting a process used to purify sulfide ores by heating the ore with air. *22·8*

salt bridge a tube containing a conducting solution used to connect half-cells in a voltaic cell; it allows the passage of ions from one compartment to another but prevents the solutions from mixing completely. *21·2*

salt hydrolysis a process in which the cations or anions of a dissociated salt accept hydrogen ions from water or donate hydrogen ions to water; solutions containing hydrolyzed salts may be either acidic or basic. *19·5*

saponification the process used to make soap; it involves the hydrolysis of fats or oils by hot aqueous sodium hydroxide. *26·15*

saturated compound an organic compound in which all carbon atoms are joined by single covalent bonds; it contains the maximum number of hydrogen atoms. *25·5*

saturated solution a solution containing the maximum amount of solute for a given amount of solvent at a constant temperature and pressure; in a saturated solution, the dissolved and undissolved solute are in dynamic equilibrium. *16·2*

scientific law a concise statement that summarizes the results of a broad variety of observations and experiments. *1·2*

scientific method a method of inquiry that involves observations, hypotheses, and experiments to formulate theories. *1·2*

scintillation counter a device that uses a specially coated surface called a phosphor to detect radiation; ionizing radiation striking this surface produces bright flashes of light (scintillations). *24·8*

self-ionization a term describing the reaction in which two water molecules react to give ions. *18·2*

semimetal a metalloid. *5·1*

sigma bond (σ bond) a bond formed when two atomic orbitals combine to form a molecular orbital that is symmetrical along the axis connecting the two atomic nuclei. *14·7*

significant figures all the digits that can be known accurately in a measurement, plus a last estimated digit. *2·3*

single covalent bond a bond formed when a pair of electrons is shared between two atoms. *14·1*

single-replacement reaction a chemical change in which atoms of an element replace atoms of a second element in a compound; also called a displacement reaction. *7·5*

skeleton equation a chemical equation that does not indicate the relative amounts of reactants and products. *7·1*

slag the fused waste material from a smelting process; it is usually composed of silicates. *22·8*

slaked lime calcium hydroxide, $Ca(OH)_2$. *22·2*

smelting a process in which impurities are removed from an ore by melting. *22·8*

solid matter which has a definite shape and volume. *1·4*

solubility the amount of a substance that dissolves in a given quantity of solvent at specified conditions of temperature and pressure to produce a saturated solution. *16·2*

solubility product constant (K_{sp}) an equilibrium constant that can be applied to the solubility of electrolytes; it is equal to the product of the concentration terms each raised to the power of the coefficient of the substance in the dissociation equation. *19·7*

solute dissolved particles in a solution. *15·6*

solution a homogenous mixture. *1·6*

solvation a process that occurs when an ionic solute dissolves; in solution, the ions are surrounded by solvent molecules. *15·7*

solvent the dissolving medium in a solution. *15·6*

specific gravity the ratio of the density of a substance to that of a standard substance (usually water). *2·10*

specific heat the quantity of heat required to raise the temperature of 1 g of a substance by 1°C. *2·13*

specific rate constant a proportionality constant relating the concentrations of reactants to the rate of the reaction. *17·3*

spectator ion an ion that does not change oxidation number or composition during a reaction. *20·7*

spectrum the range of wavelengths and frequencies making up light; the wavelengths are separated when a beam of white light passes through a prism. *11·6*

spontaneous reaction a reaction known to give the products as written in a balanced equation. *17·7*

standard atmosphere (atm) a unit of pressure; it is the pressure required to support 760 mm of mercury in a mercury barometer at 25°C; this is the average atmospheric pressure at sea level. *9·3*

standard cell potential the measured cell potential when the ion concentrations in the half-cells are 1.00 M, at 1 atm of pressure and 25°C. *21·6*

standard entropy (S^0) the entropy of a substance in its stable state at 25°C and 1 atm. *17·6*

standard heat of formation (H_f^0) the change in enthalpy (H) for a reaction in which one mole of a compound is formed from its constituent elements. *8·8*

standard hydrogen electrode an arbitrary reference electrode (half-cell) used with another electrode (half-cell) to measure the standard reduction potential of that cell; the standard reduction potential of the hydrogen electrode is assigned a value of 0.00 V. *21·6*

standard solution a solution of known concentration used in carrying out a titration. *19·2*

standard temperature and pressure (STP) the conditions under which the volume of a gas is usually measured; standard temperature is 0°C and standard pressure is 1 atmosphere (atm). *6·6*

stereoisomers an organic molecule having the same molecular structure as another molecule, but differing in the arrangement of the atoms in space. *25·7*

stoichiometry that portion of chemistry dealing with numerical relationships in chemical reactions; the calculation of quantities of substances involved in chemical equations. *8·0*

strong acid an acid that is completely (or almost completely) ionized in aqueous solution. *18·8*

strong base a base that completely dissociates into metal ions and hydroxide ions in aqueous solution. *18·8*

strong electrolyte a solution in which a large portion of the solute exists as ions. *15·9*

structural formula a chemical formula that shows the arrangement of atoms in a molecule or a polyatomic ion; each dash between two atoms indicates a pair of shared electrons. *14·1*

structural isomer a compound that has the same molecular formula as another compound but has a different molecular structure. *25·4*

sublimation the conversion of a solid to a gas without passing through the liquid state. *9·9*

substance a sample of matter having a uniform and definite composition; it can be either an element or a compound. *1·3*

substituent an atom or group of atoms that can take the place of a hydrogen atom on a parent hydrocarbon molecule. *25·3*

substitution the replacement of an atom or group of atoms by another atom or group of atoms. *26·3*

supercooled liquid a term sometimes used to describe glasses, transparent materials produced when an inorganic substance cools to a rigid state without crystallizing; their internal structure is intermediate between that of a crystalline solid and free-flowing liquid. *9·8*

supersaturated solution a solution that contains more solute that it can theoretically hold at a given temperature. *16·3*

surface tension an inward force that tends to minimize the surface area of a liquid; it causes the surface to behave as if it were covered by a thin skin. *15·2*

surfactant a surface active agent; any substance whose molecules interface with the hydrogen bonding between water molecules, reducing surface tension; soaps and detergents are surfactants. *15·2*

suspension a mixture from which some of the particles settle out slowly upon standing. *15·10*

temperature the degree of hotness or coldness of an object, which is a measure of the average kinetic energy of the molecules of the object. *2·11*

ternary compound a compound containing atoms of three different elements, with one or more polyatomic ions usually present; Na_2CO_3 and $Mg(OH)_2$ are ternary ionic compounds. *5·11*

tetrahedral angle a bond angle of 109.5° created when a central atom forms four bonds directed toward the corners of a regular tetrahedron. *14·8*

theoretical yield the amount of product that could form during a reaction calculated from a balanced chemical equation; it represents the maximum amount of product that could be formed from a given amount of reactant. *8·6*

theory a thoroughly tested model that explains why experiments give certain results. *1·2*

thermochemical equation a chemical equation that includes the amount of heat produced or absorbed during the reaction. *8·7*

titration a method of reacting a solution of unknown concentration with one of known concentration; this procedure is often used to determine the concentrations of acids and bases. *19·2*

trans **configuration** a term applied to geometric isomers; it denotes an arrangement in which the substituted groups are on opposite sides of the double bond. *25·6*

transition metal an element found in one of the B groups in the periodic table. *5·1*

transition state a term sometimes used to refer to the activated complex. *17·1*

transmutation the conversion of an atom of one element into an atom of another element by the emission of radiation. *24·5*

transuranium element an element in the periodic table whose atomic number is above 92. *24·5*

triglyceride an ester in which all three hydroxyl groups on a glycogen molecule have been replaced by long-chain fatty acids; fats are triglycerides. *26·15*

triple covalent bond a covalent bond in which three pairs of electrons are shared by two atoms. *14·2*

triprotic acid any acid that contains three ionizable protons (hydrogen ions); phosphoric acid (H_3PO_4) is a triprotic acid. *18·5*

Tyndall effect the visible path produced by a beam of light passing through a colloidal dispersion or suspension; the phenomenon is caused by the scattering of light by the colloidal and suspended particles. *15·10*

unit cell the smallest group of particles within a crystal that retains the geometric shape of the crystal. *9·8*

unsaturated a solution that contains less solute than a saturated solution at a given temperature and pressure. *16·2*

unsaturated compound an organic compound with one or more double or triple carbon–carbon bonds. *25·5*

unshared pair a pair of valence electrons that is not involved in bonding. *14·1*

valence electron an electron in the highest occupied energy level of an atom. *13·1*

van der Waals force a term used to describe the weakest intermolecular attractions; these include dispersion forces and dipole interactions. *14·13*

vapor a substance in the gaseous state that is ordinarily (at room temperature) a liquid or solid. *1·4*

vapor pressure the pressure produced when vaporized particles above the liquid in a sealed container collide with the container walls; when the container is saturated with vapor, a dynamic equilibrium exists between the gas and the liquid. *9·6*

vaporization the conversion of a liquid to a gas at a temperature below its boiling point. *9·6*

voltaic cell an electrochemical cell used to convert chemical energy into electrical energy; the energy is produced by a spontaneous redox reaction. *21·2*

volume the space occupied by matter. *2·7*

VSEPR theory valence-shell electron-pair repulsion theory; because electron pairs repel, molecules adjust their shapes so that valence-electron pairs are as far apart as possible. *14·8*

water of hydration water molecules that are an integral part of a crystal structure. *15·8*

wavelength (λ) the distance between two adjacent crests of a wave. *11·6*

wax an ester of a long-chain fatty acid and a long-chain alcohol. *26·15*

weak acid an acid that is only slightly ionized in aqueous solution. *18·8*

weak base a base that does not dissociate completely in aqueous solution. *18·8*

weak electrolyte a solution in which only a fraction of the solute exists as ions. *15·9*

weight a measure of the force of attraction between the earth and an object. *2·8*

zwitterion an internal salt of an amino acid. *26·16*

Index

Acknowledgments

Photographs

Chapter 1 1 Ken Sakamoto/Black Star; 2 TL Andree Abecassis*; 2 TR John Blaustein/Woodfin Camp & Associates; 4 Culver Pictures; 5 Culver Pictures; 8 B Ed Rescher/Peter Arnold Inc.; 12 Culver Pictures; 18 Fritz Goro/Life Magazine © 1949, Time Inc.

Chapter 2 22 B Culver Pictures; 24 Dick Durrance II/Woodfin Camp & Associates; 33 NASA; 40 T Bob Hahn/Taurus Photos; 43 Mark S. Carlson/Tom Stack & Associates

Chapter 3 51 Mark Tushman*; 52 © Richard Pasley 1984/Stock, Boston; 58 Dan McCoy/Rainbow; 62 L David Madison/Bruce Coleman Inc.

Chapter 4 66 Dan McCoy/Rainbow; 68 Michael Isaacson/Cornell University; 69 The Bettmann Archive Inc.; 73 John S. Flanner/Bruce Coleman Inc.

Chapter 5 89 Mike Price/Bruce Coleman Inc.; 98 The Bettmann Archive Inc.; 99 George B. Fry III*; 100 Spencer Swanger/Tom Stack & Associates; 102 Joy Spurr/Bruce Coleman Inc.; 104 L Pam Hasegawa/Taurus Photos; 109 Martin M. Rotker/Taurus Photos

Chapter 6 136 © Tom Tracy

Chapter 7 150 Fisk Library, Special Collections; 162 Gary Benson/Black Star; 163 Chuck O'Rear/West Light

Chapter 8 168 Allen B. Smith/Tom Stack & Associates; 171 Michael Freeman/Bruce Coleman Inc.; 173 Larry Lee/Unocal; 175 NASA; 179 Peter Arnold Inc.; 180 Stacy Pick/Stock, Boston; 184 Craig Aurness/West Light

Chapter 9 198 Larry R. Ditto/Bruce Coleman Inc.; 200 T Hank Morgan/Rainbow; 208 Martin M. Rotker/Taurus Photos; 212 Mark Tushman*; 215 Bob & Clara Calhoun/Bruce Coleman Inc.

Chapter 10 220 Gary Randall/Tom Stack & Associates; 226 Stouffer Enterprises/Bruce Coleman Inc.; 228 David L. Shogren/Tom Stack & Associates; 236 Ian Berry/Magnum Photos; 237 The Bettmann Archive Inc.

Chapter 11 246 The Bettmann Archive Inc.; 250 T Richard Pasley/Stock, Boston; 253 Ullstein Bilderdienst; 254 Kodansha/The Image Bank West; 257 Kodansha/The Image Bank West; 258 Kodansha/The Image Bank West; 260 Charles Brett/Bruce Coleman Inc. 261 The Bettmann Archive Inc.; 264 James H. Karolas/Peter Arnold Inc.

Chapter 12 272 The Granger Collection; 273 The Bettmann Archive Inc.; 287 T Dave Woodward/Taurus Photos; 287 B Argonne National Lab; 288 R Runk-Schoenberger/Grant Heilman Photography; 289 B Chuck O'Rear/West Light; 290 Dave Davidson/Tom Stack & Associates; 293 T Peter Arnold/Peter Arnold Inc.; 293 B Cary Wolinsky/Stock, Boston; 294 © 1959 by California Institute of Technology

Chapter 13 301 University of California Archives, The Bancroft Library; 306 Griffith Laboratories; 307 T Gilles Peress/Magnum Photos; 307 B Hans Pfletschinger/Peter Arnold Inc.; 308 Runk-Schoenberger/Grant Heilman Photography; 309 Paul Tishman Collection; 310 Robert M. Holt

Chapter 14 331 Dan McCoy/Rainbow; 340 John Shaw/Tom Stack & Associates

Chapter 15 348 Robert Landau/West Light; 350 T Ron Watts/Black Star; 351 Raymond Mendez/Animals, Animals; 352 Dennis Stock/Magnum Photos; 354 T John Shaw/Tom Stack & Associates; 356 Antony C. Wilbraham; 364 T Tom Stack/Tom Stack & Associates; 364 C Brian Parker/Tom Stack & Associates; 364 B Tom Stack/Tom Stack & Associates

Chapter 16 370 Randall Hyman/Stock, Boston; 375 Ed Robinson/Tom Stack & Associates; 376 E. Degginger/Bruce Coleman Inc.; 381 Columbiana Collection/Columbia University

Chapter 17 398 The Bettmann Archive Inc.; 406 Ralph Oberlander/Stock, Boston; 410 Sharon Klein/Taurus Photos; 413 Paul Agich/Tom Stack & Associates; 417 © Tom Tracy; 421 Tom Stack/Tom Stack & Associates

Chapter 18 439 Culver Pictures; 441 E. Sherman/Bruce Coleman Inc.

Chapter 19 468 Richard Pasley/Stock, Boston; 471 Martin M. Rotker/Taurus Photo

Chapter 20 478 Harvey Lloyd/Peter Arnold Inc.; 482 Michael Collier/Stock, Boston; 484 L E. Herwig/The Image Bank West; 485 Craig Aurness/West Light; 492 NASA

Chapter 21 505 The Bettmann Archive Inc.; 517 Courtesy, Occidental Chemical; 520 Ellis Herwig/Stock, Boston

Chapter 22 526 Liane Enzelis/Stock, Boston; 532 B Stacy Pick/Stock, Boston; 535 L Tom Flynn/Taurus Photos; 535 R © Tom Tracy; 536 L. Stepanowicz/Bruce Coleman Inc.; 538 T John Running/Stock, Boston; 538 B Kennecott; 539 © Tom Tracy

Chapter 23 549 The Bettmann Archive Inc.; 551 Brad Hess/Black Star; 553 Emery Chemicals; 555 Bill Pierce/Rainbow; 559 L Grant Heilman Photography; 559 R Suzi Barnes/Tom Stack & Associates

Chapter 24 568 © Tom Tracy; 576 Harvey Lloyd/Peter Arnold Inc.; 578 Argonne National Lab; 579 Dan McCoy/Rainbow; 582 T NASA; 582 B Courtesy of JET Joint Undertaking; 583 Dan McCoy/Rainbow; 584 Culver Pictures; 585 T Dan McCoy/Rainbow

Chapter 25 590 Larry Lee/West Light; 592 Historical Pictures Service; 595 W. B. Finch/Stock, Boston; 599 T George D. Lepp/Bruce Coleman Inc.; 601 Steve Dunwell/The Image Bank West

Chapter 26 619 Kenneth Garrett/West Light; 623 U.S. Industrial Chemicals Co.; 624 Wide World Photos; 627 Bob Hahn/Taurus Photos; 628 Joy Spurr/Bruce Coleman Inc.; 631 © Tom Pantages; 638 Frank Siteman/Stock, Boston; 640 Jane Burton/Bruce Coleman Inc.; 645 T Irving Geis; 645 B The Bettmann Archive Inc.

*Photographs taken expressly for Addison-Wesley.

Stephen Frisch*: 2B, 7, 11, 20, 22TL, 22TR, 34, 39, 40B 48, 50, 55T, 57, 62R, 86, 97, 114, 127, 137, 142, 145, 155, 157, 159, 176, 178, 185, 187B, 189, 200B, 204, 213, 234, 239, 251B, 265, 286, 288L, 289T, 326, 335, 342, 354B, 358L, 377, 380, 384, 397, 418, 432, 442, 446, 456, 459, 461, 462, 472, 480, 484R, 491, 495, 496, 506, 529, 531, 546, 550, 558, 562, 563, 569, 585B, 609B, 614, 621, 622, 625, 636, 637.

Wayland Lee/Addison-Wesley Staff: 8T, 9T, 10, 13, 15, 23, 28, 32, 35, 37, 38, 42, 55B, 60T, 84, 87, 92, 93, 95, 101, 104R, 116, 118, 119, 121, 123, 129, 132, 133, 144, 149, 151, 156, 183, 187T, 205, 210, 225, 230, 291, 292, 323, 350B, 355, 359, 361, 363, 372, 373, 379, 433, 434, 436, 445, 449, 451, 465, 466, 467, 469, 473, 481, 487, 489, 490, 497, 504, 528, 532T, 534, 537, 548, 554, 556, 596, 597, 607, 609T, 634, 635, 639.

Special thanks to Biosearch Inc.; Chemistry Department, College of Marin, Kentfield; Etel Inc., San Raphael, California; Joel J. Kudler, D. D. S., Sausalito, California; Low Temperature Lab, University of California, Berkeley; Pilgrim Plating, San Raphael, California; Penelope Comfort Starr, Architectural Stain Glass, San Anselmo, California; Michael Stinson, College of Marin, Kentfield, California; Whitehead & Zimmerman, San Francisco, California.

Illustrations

Shirley Bortoli: Fig. 1.7, 1.12, 1.18, 2.5, 2.6, 2.9, 2.12, 2.15, 4.11, 4.14, 6.11, 7.20, 8.21, 9.6, 9.10, 9.12, 9.16, 11.13, 13.11, 13.13a, 14.14, 14.28, 14.29, 15.12, 15.15, 16.11, 16.16, 16.18, 17.7, 22.8, 22.15, 22.17, 24.3, 24.6, 25.14

Debby Morse: Fig. 4.6, 4.7, 4.8, 4.9, 5.9, 5.10, 5.13, 9.17, 11.3, 11.5, 11.6, 12.6, 12.9, 13.15, 14.2, 14.4, 14.5, 14.6, 14.7, 14.8, 14.9, 14.10, 14.13, 14.15, 14.16, 14.17, 14.18, 14.19a&b, 14.20, 14.21, 14.22, 14.23, 14.24, 14.25, 14.27, 14.32, 15.3 left, 15.7a&b, 18.4, 18.9, 18.12, 18.13, 19.2, 23.14, 23.15, 25.3, 25.9, 25.10, 25.13, 25.15

Masami Miyamoto: Fig. 10.4, 10.5, 10.6, 10.13, 10.17, 10.18, 10.23, 21.9, 21.10, 21.12, 21.15, 22.11, 22.21, 22.22, 22.23, 23.8, 23.12, 23.17, 23.22, 25.18, 25.19